# MATHEMATICAL
# TABLES

## FROM HANDBOOK OF CHEMISTRY AND PHYSICS

### ELEVENTH EDITION

*Editor in Chief*

**Charles D. Hodgman, M.S.**
Professor Emeritus, Case Institute of Technology

*Associate Editor in Charge of Mathematics*
**Samuel M. Selby, Ph.D.**
Chairman, Mathematics Department at University of Akron

*Associate Editor in Charge of Chemistry*
**Robert C. Weast, Ph.D.**
Professor of Chemistry at Case Institute of Technology

▼

## CHEMICAL RUBBER PUBLISHING CO.
2310 Superior Ave. N.E., CLEVELAND, OHIO

**Mathematical Tables
from the Handbook of Chemistry and Physics**

Copyrighted in the United States of America
1931, 1932, 1933, 1934, 1936, 1938, 1941,
1946, 1947, 1949, 1951, 1952, 1954, 1959

By

THE CHEMICAL RUBBER PUBLISHING COMPANY
CLEVELAND, OHIO

The Chemical Rubber Publishing Company, 1959
Printed in the United States of America.

Library of Congress Card No. 30-4052

*©Notice of copyright in compliance with
above copyright laws and conventions.

First printing, December, 1959
Second printing, September, 1960
Third printing, September, 1961
**Fourth printing, June, 1962**
**Fifth printing, February 1963**

# *Preface*

The collection of mathematical tables and formulae, originally published in the Handbook of Chemistry and Physics was intended to provide tables of logarithms, trigonometric functions, numerical constants and mathematical formulae and equations adequate for the ordinary computations of chemistry and physics. The convenience of form and completeness of the collection led to many requests for a separate publication, which would make the tables more readily available for general computation and reference or for use by students of mathematics.

Since the first publication of the separate Mathematical Tables extensive additions and revisions have been made, the current editions presenting more than twice the material of the original volume.

Every precaution has been used to insure accuracy in the numerical values, the proofs having been read repeatedly and against several sources where possible. A large portion of the material has been computed especially for this volume. Notice of any errors which may be discovered will be sincerely appreciated.

In addition to suggestions and contributions from a large number of users of the book we wish especially to acknowledge the valuable collaboration of the following persons:

Albert A. Bennett, Brown University
* W. Bruce Ross, McGill University
* Deceased.

B. H. Brown, Dartmouth College
James W. Glover, University of Michigan
D. A. Hill,
THE CHEMICAL RUBBER PUBLISHING CO.
Cleveland, Ohio.

# *Preface to the Eleventh Edition*

Mathematical tables and formulas in this Eleventh Edition are similar in content and arrangement to the Mathematical Section of the 44th Edition of the Handbook of Chemistry and Physics.

Frequent revision and expansion of these mathematical tables are necessary to assist students and professional personnel with the mathematics important in present day and future scientific studies.

Among the new contents in the present edition will be found thirteen added pages of differential equations to increase significantly the usefulness of that portion of the book. The section of the book concerned with Fourier Series has been enlarged by inclusion of special power series, Bernoulii Numbers, and tables for finite sine and cosine transforms. Inclusion of a table of natural trigonometric functions of decimal multiples of $\pi$ radians should be of aid to persons concerned with wave mechanics. The table giving the sums of powers of natural numbers should be helpful. It is hoped that the several new pages of explanation concerning use of certain tables, addition of Napier's Rules for Right Spherical Triangles and inclusion of graphs of certain trigonometric functions will find wide use.

We wish to thank all who have contributed suggestions for material to be added to our book. Likewise we appreciate the advice regarding revision of certain existing tables. Without such help it would not be possible to improve this book.

THE EDITORS

January 1, 1963.

# CONTENTS

## MATHEMATICAL TABLES

vii

## CONTENTS

## CONTENTS

# USE OF MATHEMATICAL TABLES

For a complete discussion of the principles and use of mathematical tables, textbooks on the subject should be consulted. The following brief statements are intended to give only sufficient information to make possible the intelligent use of the tables, omitting for the most part any attempt at treating the theory and principles.

**Exponential Method of Expressing Numbers**—For convenience in writing and manipulation, numbers are often expressed as factors of appropriate powers of 10. The following examples will illustrate:

| | | |
|---|---|---|
| 2,380,000,000. | may be written | $2.38 \times 10^9$ |
| 238. | may be written | $2.38 \times 10^2$ |
| .238 | may be written | $2.38 \times 10^{-1}$ |
| .000000238 | may be written | $2.38 \times 10^{-7}$ |

**Logarithms**—The logarithm of a number is the exponent of that power to which another number, the base, must be raised to give the number first named. Any positive number greater than 1 might serve as a base. Two have been selected, yielding two systems of logarithms. One base, 2.718 . . . . usually indicated by the letter $e$, gives rise to a system of logarithms convenient in higher mathematics. These are called natural, Napierian, or hyperbolic logarithms. Reference will be made to their use in a subsequent paragraph.

The other base used is 10, giving logarithms particularly adapted to use in computation, called common or Briggsian logarithms. Tables of logarithms given without designation are invariably of this latter type.

Since most numbers are irrational powers of ten, a common logarithm, in general, consists of an integer which is called the characteristic and an endless decimal, the mantissa.

It is to be observed that the common logarithms of all numbers expressed by the same figures in the same order with the decimal point in different positions have different characteristics but the same mantissa. To illustrate:—if the decimal point stand after the first figure of a number, counting from the left, the characteristic is 0; if after two figures, it is 1; if after three figures, it is 2, and so forth. If the decimal point stand before the first significant figure the characteristic is $-1$, usually written $\bar{1}$; if there is one zero between the decimal point and the first significant figure it is 2 and so on. For example: log 256 = 2.40824, log 2.56 = 0.40824, log 0.256 = $\bar{1}$.40824, log 0.00256 = $\bar{3}$.40824. The two latter are often written log 0.256 = 9.40824 $-10$, log 0.00256 = 7.40824 $-10$.

A method of determining characteristics of logarithms is to write the number with one figure to the left of the decimal point multiplied by the appropriate power of 10. The characteristic is then the exponent used. For example:

$$256,000,000 = 2.56 \times 10^8 \quad \log = 8.40824$$
$$0.000000256 = 2.56 \times 10^{-7} \quad \log = \overline{7}.40824 \text{ or } 3.40824 - 10$$

Inasmuch as the characteristic may be determined by inspection the mantissas only are given in tables of common logarithms.

To find the logarithm of a number:

For a number of four figures, take out the tabular mantissa on a line with the first three figures of the number and under its fourth figure. The characteristic is determined as previously explained.

For a number of less than four figures, supply zeros to make a four figure number and take the value of the mantissa from the tables as before. For example: $\log 2 = \log 2.000 = 0.30103$.

For a number of more than four figures, take the tabular value of the mantissa for the first four figures; find the difference between this mantissa and the next greater tabular mantissa and multiply the difference so found by the remaining figures of the number as a decimal and add the product to the mantissa of the first four figures. For example: to find log 46.762.

$$\log 46.76 = 1.66987$$

Tabular difference between this mantissa and that for 4677 is .00010.

$$\therefore \log 46.762 = 1.66987 + .2 \times .00010$$
$$= 1.66987 + .00002$$
$$= 1.66989$$

To find the number corresponding to a given logarithm:

If the mantissa is found exactly in the table, join the figure at the top which is directly above the given mantissa to the three figures on the line at the left and place the decimal point according to the characteristic of the logarithm. For example, $\log^{-1}$ (antilogarithm) $3.39967 = 2510$.

If the mantissa is not found exactly in the table it is necessary to interpolate. For example, $\log^{-1} 3.40028 = 2513. + \frac{9}{18} = 2513.5$.

The column of proportional parts at the right of each page of the table shows, under the heading of the various tabular differences, the parts of these differences which correspond to the digits from 1 to 9 in the fifth place. This makes it possible to take out a logarithm for a five figure number or to find an antilogarithm of the same number of significant figures with increased facility, usually by inspection.

2

The following formulae express the relations on which the use of logarithms is based:

$$\log ab = \log a + \log b$$

$$\log \frac{a}{b} = \log a - \log b$$

$$\log a^n = n \times \log a$$

$$\log \sqrt[n]{a} = \frac{\log a}{n}.$$

The following examples will serve as illustrations:

1. $52600 \times 0.00381 \times 2.74 = 549.1$

$$\log 52600 = 4.72099$$
$$\log 0.00381 = \bar{3}.58092$$
$$\log 2.74 = 0.43775$$

$$\text{Sum:} = 2.73966$$
$$\text{Antilogarithm} = 549.1$$

The sum is the logarithm of the product, the mantissa of which is 73966. On looking up this mantissa in the logarithm tables we see that it corresponds to the digits 5491. The characteristic is 2, hence there are three figures before the decimal point. The number corresponding to the logarithm, called the antilogarithm, is 549.1.

2. $0.00123 \div 52.7 = 0.00002334$     An Alternative method:

$$\log 0.00123 = \bar{3}.08991 \qquad \log 0.00123 = 7.08991 - 10$$
$$\log \quad 52.7 = 1.72181 \qquad \log \quad 52.7 = 1.72181$$

Subtracting    $\bar{5}.36810$              $5.36810 - 10$

Antilog       $0.00002334$

The characteristic $\bar{5}$ (5. $-10$) shows four zeros after the decimal point before the first significant figure.

3. $\dfrac{273 \times 780}{292 \times 760} \times 15 \times 0.09 = 1.295$

$$\log \quad 273 = 2.43616 \qquad\qquad \log 292 = 2.46538$$
$$\log \quad 780 = 2.89209 \qquad\qquad \log 760 = 2.88081$$
$$\log \quad 15 = 1.17609$$
$$\log 0.09 = \bar{2}.95424 \qquad\qquad \text{log denominator} = 5.34619$$

$$\log \text{sum} = 5.45858$$

$$\begin{aligned}\log \text{numerator} &= 5.45858 \\ \log \text{denominator} &= 5.34619\end{aligned}$$

$$\begin{aligned}\text{subtracting} &= 0.11239 \\ \text{antilogarithm} &= 1.295\end{aligned}$$

3

As division may be accomplished by multiplying by the reciprocal of a number, the above may be considerably simplified. The logarithm of the reciprocal of a number, called the cologarithm, is readily obtained from the table by subtracting the logarithm of the number from zero. This may readily be read off from the table of mantissas. Change the sign of the characteristic algebraically adding to it −1, then mentally subtract each figure of the mantissa from 9 proceeding from left to right, the last figure being subtracted from 10. The example then is:

$$\begin{array}{lll}
\log & 273 & = 2.43616 \\
\log & 780 & = 2.89209 \\
\log & 15 & = 1.17609 \\
\log & 0.09 & = \bar{2}.95424 \\
\text{colog } 292 & & = \bar{3}.53462 \\
\text{colog } 760 & & = \bar{3}.11919 \\
\hline
& & 0.11239
\end{array}$$

4. $(0.00098)^4 = 9.224 \times 10^{-13}$    An alternative method:

$$\log 0.00098 = \bar{4}.99123 \qquad \log 0.00098 = 6.99123 - 10$$

$$\underline{\phantom{xxx}4\phantom{xxx}} \qquad\qquad\qquad \underline{\phantom{xxxxx}4}$$

$$\begin{array}{ll}
& 3.96492\text{(a)} \\
\bar{4} \times 4 \quad & \overline{16.} \qquad \text{(b)} \\
\hline
\log (0.00098)^4 = & \bar{13}.96492\text{(c)}
\end{array} \qquad \begin{array}{l}
27.96492 - 40 \\
\text{or } 7.96492 - 20 \\
\text{or } \bar{13}.96492
\end{array}$$

antilog $= 9.224 \times 10^{-13}$ \qquad antilog $= 9.224 \times 10^{-13}$

In the above it will be noted that the mantissa is always positive hence the multiplication of the mantissa shown at (a) while (b) shows the multiplication of the characteristic. (c) is the algebraic sum.

5. $\sqrt[5]{492} = 3.455$

$\log 492 = 2.69197$

Dividing the logarithm by 5 gives as the logarithm of the root 0.53839 the antilogarithm of which is 3.455 both characteristic and mantissa being positive. When the characteristic is negative and not evenly divisible by the root to be taken a modification of the logarithm is necessary.

6. $\sqrt[3]{0.000372} =$

$$\begin{array}{ll}
\log 3.72 \times 10^{-4} = & \bar{4}.57054 \qquad \text{(a)} \\
= & 26.57054 - 30 \quad \text{(b)}
\end{array}$$

dividing (b) by 3 gives $8.85685 - 10$ which may be written

4

$\overline{2}.85685$ and is the logarithm of the root sought, the antilogarithm of which is 0.07192.

| 7. | $0.000372^{1.2} = 0.000076674$ | 8. | $(0.000372)^{-1.32} = 33642$ |
|---|---|---|---|
| | log 0.000372 $= \overline{4}.57054$ | | colog 0.000372 $= 3.42946$ |
| | or $6.57054 - 10$ | | 1.32 |
| | 1.2 | | |
| | | | 4.52689 |
| | $7.88465 - 12$ | | antilogarithm 33642 |
| | antilogarithm 0.000076674 | | |

**Four-Place Logarithms**—This short table on two facing pages makes possible logarithmic computation precise to four significant figures, (three without interpolation). The mantissa is given complete and the proportional parts indicated for each line.

**Four-Place Antilogarithms**—Some computers prefer to use separate tables for determining antilogarithms; the table being entered from the margins with the logarithm and the number being found in the body of the table. Such a table is given to accompany the four-place logarithms.

**Five-Place Logarithms**—For computation involving five significant figures, (four without interpolation) the five-place table will be adequate. Since the first two figures will be the same for several lines of the table they are given in the first line only. The point at which these first two figures change is indicated by an asterisk. While space does not permit the proportional parts for each line, tables will be found for each tabular difference.

The supplementary table following the five-place logarithms, giving seven-place logarithms for numbers of five significant figures from 10,000 to 12,000 will be found convenient to increase precision and avoid the inconvenience of interpolation where the differences are large.

**Logarithms of the Trigonometric Functions**—Logarithms of the functions are given for each minute from 0–360°.

The quantity $-10$ is to be appended to all logarithms of the sine and cosine, to logarithms of the tangent from 0–45° and of the cotangent from 45–90°.

With degrees indicated at either side of the top of the page use the column headings at the top. With degrees stated at the bottom of the page use the column designations at the bottom.

With degrees at the left (top or bottom) use the minute column at the left, and with degrees on the right side of the page use the minute column at the right.

To illustrate the proper employment of headings for angles in the four quadrants—

| | |
|---|---|
| log sin    6° 24′ = 9.04715 − 10 | log sin 186° 24′ = 9.04715 − 10 |
| log sin   83° 15′ = 9.99698 − 10 | log sin 263° 15′ = 9.99698 − 10 |
| log cos   96° 41′ = 9.06589 − 10 | log cos 276° 41′ = 9.06589 − 10 |
| log cos 173° 49′ = 9.99747 − 10 | log cos 353° 49′ = 9.99747 − 10 |

For the accurate determination of values where the tabular differences are large, the values of CS and CT are given. The following equations indicate their use.

To find the logarithm of the functions of an angle:

| For angles 0–3° | For angles 87–90° |
|---|---|
| $\log \sin \theta = \log \theta'' - CS$ | $\log \cos \theta = \log (90° - \theta)'' - CS$ |
| $\log \tan \theta = \log \theta'' - CT$ | $\log \cot \theta = \log (90° - \theta)'' - CT$ |
| $\log \cot \theta = \text{colog} \tan \theta$ | $\log \tan \theta = \text{colog} \cot \theta$ |

To find the angle:

| For angles 0–3° | For angles 87–90° |
|---|---|
| $\log \theta'' = \log \sin \theta + CS$ | $\log (90° - \theta)'' = \log \cos \theta + CS$ |
| $\log \theta'' = \log \tan \theta + CT$ | $\log (90° - \theta)'' = \log \cot \theta + CT$ |

In the above expressions, $\theta''$ and $(90° - \theta)''$ are used to indicate the value of the angles expressed in seconds. The values in the body of the table are the cologarithms and should be used as indicated above.

The values of the logarithms S and T are also given in a separate table. For these the following relations hold:

To find the functions of an angle.

| | |
|---|---|
| $\log \sin \theta = \log \theta'' + S$ | $\log \cos \theta = \log (90° - \theta)'' + S$ |
| $\log \tan \theta = \log \theta'' + T$ | $\log \cot \theta = \log (90° - \theta)'' + T$ |

To find the angle.

| | |
|---|---|
| $\log \theta'' = \log \sin \theta - S$ | $\log (90° - \theta)'' = \log \cos \theta - S$ |
| $\log \theta'' = \log \tan \theta - T$ | $\log (90° - \theta)'' = \log \cot \theta - T$ |

Where the values of CS and CT are given, the angles expressed in seconds are given in the supplementary column at the left.

The tabular differences are given under the headings "d" and "c.d.", the latter referring to the common difference for the tangent and cotangent. Tables of proportional parts ("P.P.") facilitate interpolation. At the bottom of each column will be found special proportional parts between the tabular differences for the tangent or cotangent and those for the sine or cosine. These are useful when one function is to be obtained directly from the other without determining the angle.

For example, suppose log tan $\theta$ is given as 9.67644 and log cos $\theta$ is required. The difference between the given logarithm and that given in the table, 9.67622 (opposite 25° 23′), is 22.

The tabular differences of the two logarithmic functions at this place are 32 and 6. In the proportional table for $\frac{6}{32}$, 22 corresponds to 4; this, subtracted from the tabular logarithmic cosine 9.95591, gives the required log cos $\theta$ = 9.95587.

The symbols $\bar{5}$ and $\dot{5}$ are used to indicate how the terminal 5 has been derived. For example, the logarithm 8.83075 is more fully given as 8.8307495 while the value 9.40825 is derived from 9.4082539. Thus, in rounding off to four places, a number ending in $\bar{5}$ should be decreased but a number ending in $\dot{5}$ should be increased.

**Natural Trigonometric Functions**—Values of the natural trigonometric functions of angles are given for each minute from 0–360°.

For degrees indicated at the top of the page use the column headings at the top. For degrees indicated at the bottom use the column indications at the bottom.

With degrees at the left of each block (top or bottom), use the minute column at the left and with degrees at the right of each block use the minute column at the right.

**Natural Functions and their Logarithms** are given for angles in degrees and tenths from 0 to 90 degrees.

**Natural Functions and their Logarithms** are given for angles in radians and hundredths, from 0 to 2 radians.

**Haversines**—Values of $(1 - \cos \theta)/2$ for angles between 0 and 180° are given to four significant figures. The four-place mantissas of the logarithms of the haversines are also given. The correct characteristic must be provided in each case.

The listed values of the haversines were derived from values which were computed to seven significant figures. The logarithms were independently derived from the more exact values of the haversines and are, therefore, in many cases not the exact value of the logarithm of the haversine as listed. This is notably true at the beginning of the table where the logarithm can be given with more exactness than the function.

**Natural Logarithms**—The natural logarithms of numbers from 0.000 to 999. are given in a group of four tables. The method of finding logarithms of numbers not included in the tables is indicated at the beginning of the third page. A convenient table of constants occurs at the top of the fourth page.

The first page gives the natural logarithms of numbers from 0.000 to 0.499. Since the characteristics change rapidly for the smaller numbers, they are indicated *above* the mantissa in the first line. In the second and following lines the characteristics are given at the left only. For example, $\log_e 0.004 = -5.52146$; $\log_e 0.014 = -4.26870$.

The succeeding pages give the natural logarithms of numbers up to 999.

# USE OF MATHEMATICAL TABLES (Continued)

**Exponential Functions**—Values of $e^x$, log $e^x$ and $e^{-x}$ where $e$ is the base of the natural system of logarithms 2.71828 . . . and $x$ has values from 0 to 10. Facilitating the solution of exponential equations, these tables also serve as a table of natural or Naperian antilogarithms. For instance if the logarithm or exponent $x = 3.26$ the corresponding number or value of $e^x$ is 26.050. Its reciprocal $e^{-x}$ is .038388.

**Hyperbolic Functions**—The table gives the values and logarithms of the hyperbolic sine $x$, cosine $x$, tangent $x$ and cotangent $x$ for values of $x$ from 0 to 10.

**Degrees-Radians**—This table gives the value in radians to five significant figures; for each 10 minutes from $0°\,0'$ to $90°\,0'$; for each degree from 90 to 180; for each 10 degrees from 180 to 480. Values are also given for each minute from $0–60'$ and for each second from $0–60''$.

Tables are also provided to facilitate changing from degrees and decimal fractions to radians, from decimal fractions of a degree to minutes and seconds and the reverse operations.

**Numerical Tables**—The first section gives the reciprocals of numbers from 0 to 1000 and circumferences and areas of circles with diameters having these values. Reciprocals and circumferences for values not listed can be obtained by an appropriate shift of the decimal point.

The second section is devoted to squares, cubes and roots. The squares and cubes from 1 to 1000 are given exactly. The roots are given to seven significant figures. Since the square roots of $10n$ are given, values of the square roots from 1 to 10,000 may be found directly. For the square roots of numbers below and above this range, use may be made of the following relations: $\sqrt{100n} = 10\sqrt{n}$; $\sqrt{1000n} = 10\sqrt{10n}$; $\sqrt{\frac{1}{10}n} = \frac{1}{10}\sqrt{10n}$; $\sqrt{\frac{1}{100}n} = \frac{1}{10}\sqrt{n}$; $\sqrt{\frac{1}{1000}n} = \frac{1}{100}\sqrt{10n}$. For example, the square root of 0.268 may be found by using the form, $\sqrt{0.268} = \frac{1}{100}\sqrt{10 \times 268}$. The tabular value for the square root of $10n$ for 268 is 51.76872. Hence, the desired root is 0.5176872.

Values of cube roots for all numbers from 1 to 100,000 will be found directly in the table. Cube roots for numbers above or below this range will be found from the following relations: $\sqrt[3]{1000n} = 10\sqrt[3]{n}$; $\sqrt[3]{10,000n} = 10\sqrt[3]{10n}$; $\sqrt[3]{100,000n} = 10\sqrt[3]{100n}$; $\sqrt[3]{\frac{1}{10}n} = \frac{1}{10}\sqrt[3]{100n}$; $\sqrt[3]{\frac{1}{100}n} = \frac{1}{10}\sqrt[3]{10n}$; $\sqrt[3]{\frac{1}{1000}n} = \frac{1}{10}\sqrt[3]{n}$. For example, the cube root of 731,000 may be found by using the form, $\sqrt[3]{731,000} = 10\sqrt[3]{731}$. The tabular value of the root for 731 is 9.008223. The desired root is, therefore, 90.08223.

**Powers of Numbers**—This table is given to supplement the values of squares and cubes of numbers found in the preceding numerical table. The larger numbers are expressed exponentially to at least seven significant figures. The approximate value written as a whole number may be obtained by shifting the decimal point to the right by the number of places indicated in the exponent of 10 shown at the head of each group of values. For example: the approximate value of $33^8$ is found in the table as $14.064086 \times 10^{11}$. Written as a whole number it is 1,406,408,600,000.

**Factorials and their Logarithms**—The product $n \times (n-1) \times (n-2) \times \cdots \times 1$ is called factorial $n$, expressed as $n!$ or $\lfloor n$. For example: factorial $5 = 5 \times 4 \times 3 \times 2 \times 1 = 120$. Factorials are very often met with in series. For purposes of computation in such cases the table giving the values of the factorials and of their logarithms for numbers from 1 to 100 is provided. The values of the factorials are expressed exponentially to 5 significant figures.

A brief table of exact values and reciprocals of factorials is to be found on page 165.

**Factors for Computing Probable Errors**—The probable error of a series of $n$ measures $a_1, a_2, a_3 \ldots a_n$, the mean of which is $m$, is given by the expression,

$$e = \frac{0.6745}{\sqrt{n-1}} \sqrt{(m-a_1)^2 + (m-a_2)^2 + \cdots (m-a_n)^2}$$

The probable error of the mean is,

$$E = \frac{0.6745}{\sqrt{n(n-1)}} \sqrt{(m-a_1)^2 + (m-a_2)^2 + \cdots (m-a_n)^2}$$

The following approximate equations are convenient forms for computation,

$$e = 0.8453 \frac{\Sigma d}{\sqrt{n(n-1)}}$$

$$E = 0.8453 \frac{\Sigma d}{n\sqrt{n-1}}$$

The symbol $\Sigma d$ represents the arithmetical sum of the deviations.

For convenience in computing the probable error the value of several of the factors involved is given for values of $n$ from 2 to 100.

**Probability of Occurrence of Deviations**—The significance of deviations is indicated by this table. The probability of occurrence of deviations as great as or greater than any specific value is given for various ratios of deviation to probable error and also with respect to the standard deviation $\sigma$. The probability of occurrence is stated in per cent or chances in 100. The odds against occurrence are also stated. The probable error is $0.6745 \times (\sigma)$.

**Normal Curve of Error**—If, for a large number of observations, the frequency $y$, of the occurrence of an error of magnitude $t$ be plotted, a curve results whose equation may be written,

$$y = \frac{1}{\sqrt{2\pi}} e^{-t^2/2}$$

The area, ordinates and derivatives for this curve given in the table are useful in the treatment of observational data. A text on statistical methods should be consulted for a complete explanation.

**Factors and Primes**—The table presents the prime factors of *all* factorable numbers and the logarithms of all prime numbers from 1 to 2000.

## Conversion Tables

| Inches | Centimeters | Centimeters | Inches |
|---|---|---|---|
| 1 | 2.54 | 1 | 0.393701 |
| 2 | 5.08 | 2 | 0.787402 |
| 3 | 7.62 | 3 | 1.181103 |
| 4 | 10.16 | 4 | 1.574804 |
| 5 | 12.70 | 5 | 1.968505 |
| 6 | 15.24 | 6 | 2.362206 |
| 7 | 17.78 | 7 | 2.755907 |
| 8 | 20.32 | 8 | 3.149608 |
| 9 | 22.86 | 9 | 3.543309 |

| Feet | Meters | Meters | Feet |
|---|---|---|---|
| 1 | 0.3048 | 1 | 3.280840 |
| 2 | 0.6096 | 2 | 6.561680 |
| 3 | 0.9144 | 3 | 9.842520 |
| 4 | 1.2192 | 4 | 13.123360 |
| 5 | 1.5240 | 5 | 16.404200 |
| 6 | 1.8288 | 6 | 19.685040 |
| 7 | 2.1336 | 7 | 22.965880 |
| 8 | 2.4384 | 8 | 26.246720 |
| 9 | 2.7432 | 9 | 29.527560 |

| Yards | Meters | Meters | Yards |
|---|---|---|---|
| 1 | 0.9144 | 1 | 1.0936133 |
| 2 | 1.8288 | 2 | 2.1872266 |
| 3 | 2.7432 | 3 | 3.2808399 |
| 4 | 3.6576 | 4 | 4.3744532 |
| 5 | 4.5720 | 5 | 5.4680665 |
| 6 | 5.4864 | 6 | 6.5616798 |
| 7 | 6.4008 | 7 | 7.6552931 |
| 8 | 7.1352 | 8 | 8.7489064 |
| 9 | 8.2296 | 9 | 9.8425197 |

## Conversion Tables (Continued)

| Miles (Statute) | Kilometers | Kilometers | Miles |
|---|---|---|---|
| 1 | 1.609344 | 1 | 0.6213712 |
| 2 | 3.218688 | 2 | 1.2427424 |
| 3 | 4.828032 | 3 | 1.8641136 |
| 4 | 6.437376 | 4 | 2.4854848 |
| 5 | 8.046720 | 5 | 3.1068560 |
| 6 | 9.656064 | 6 | 3.7282272 |
| 7 | 11.265408 | 7 | 4.3495984 |
| 8 | 12.874752 | 8 | 4.9709696 |
| 9 | 14.484096 | 9 | 5.5923408 |
| Pounds (av) | Kilograms | Kilograms | Pounds (av) |
| 1 | 0.45359237 | 1 | 2.2046226 |
| 2 | 0.90718474 | 2 | 4.4092452 |
| 3 | 1.36077711 | 3 | 6.6138678 |
| 4 | 1.81436948 | 4 | 8.8184904 |
| 5 | 2.26796185 | 5 | 11.0231130 |
| 6 | 2.72155422 | 6 | 13.2277356 |
| 7 | 3.17514659 | 7 | 15.4323582 |
| 8 | 3.62873896 | 8 | 17.6369808 |
| 9 | 4.08233133 | 9 | 19.8416034 |

## Conversion Factors

### U. S. AND METRIC UNITS

Each unit in bold face type is followed by its equivalent in other units of the same quantity.

**Acre**—0.0015625 square mile (statute); 4.3560 × 10⁴ square feet; 0.40468564 hectare.

**Bushel—(U. S.)**—1.244456 cubic feet; 2150.42 cubic inches; 0.035239 cubic meter; 35.23808 liters.

**Centimeter**—0.0328084 foot; 0.393701 inch.

**Circular Mil**—7.853982 × 10⁻⁷ square inches; 5.067075 × 10⁻⁶ square centimeters.

**Cubic Centimeter**—0.061024 cubic inch; 0.270512 dram (U. S. fluid); 16.230664 minims (U. S.); 0.999972 milliliter.

**Cubic Foot**—0.803564 bushel (U. S.); 7.480520 gallons (U. S. liquid); 0.028317 cubic meter; 28.31605 liters.

**Cubic Inch**—16.387064 cubic centimeters.

**Cubic Meter**—35.314667 cubic feet; 264.17205 gallons (U. S. liquid).

**Foot**—0.3048 meter.

**Gallon (U. S. liquid)**—0.1336816 cubic foot; 0.832675 gallon (British); 231 cubic inches; 0.0037854 cubic meter; 3.785306 liters.

**Grain**—0.06479891 gram.

**Gram**—0.00220462 pound (avoirdupois); 0.035274 ounce (avoirdupois); 15.432358 grains.

**Hectare**—2.471054 acres; 1.07639 × 10⁵ square feet.

**Inch**—2.54 centimeters.

**Kilogram**—2.204623 pounds (avoirdupois).

**Kilometer**—0.621371 mile (statute).

**Liter**—0.264179 gallon (U. S. liquid); 0.0353157 cubic foot; 1.056718 quarts (U. S. liquid).

**Meter**—1.093613 yards; 3.280840 feet; 39.37008 inches.

**Mile (statute)**—1.609344 kilometers.

**Ounce (U. S. fluid)**—1.804688 cubic inches; 29.573730 cubic centimeters.

**Ounce (avoirdupois)**—28.349523 grams.

**Ounce (apothecary or troy)**—31.103486 grams.

**Pint (U. S. liquid)**—0.473163 liter; 473.17647 cubic centimeters.

**Pound (avoirdupois)**—0.453592 kilogram; 453.59237 grams.

**Pound (apothecary or troy)**—0.3732417 kilogram, 373.24172 grams.

**Quart (U. S. dry)**—1.10119 liters.

**Quart (liquid)**—0.946326 liter.

**Radian**—57.295779 degrees.

**Rod**—5.0292 meters.

**Square Centimeter**—0.155000 square inch.

**Square Foot**—0.09290304 square meter.

**Square Inch**—645.16 square millimeters.

**Square Meter**—10.763910 square feet.

**Square Yard**—0.836127 square meter.

**Ton (short)**—907.18474 kilograms.

**Yard**—0.9144 meter.

# NUMERICAL CONSTANTS

## Numbers Containing $\pi$

$\pi = 3.14159\ 26536$   $\log_{10} \pi = 0.49714\ 98727$   $\log_e \pi = 1.14472\ 98858$

| | Number | Logarithm | | Number | Logarithm |
|---|---|---|---|---|---|
| $\pi$ | 3.1415 927 | 0.4971 499 | $\pi^2$ | 9.8696 044 | 0.9942 997 |
| $2\pi$ | 6.2831 853 | 0.7981 799 | $2\pi^2$ | 19.7392 088 | 1.2953 297 |
| $3\pi$ | 9.4247 780 | 0.9742 711 | $4\pi^2$ | 39.4784 176 | 1.5963 597 |
| $4\pi$ | 12.5663 706 | 1.0992 099 | $1/\pi^2$ | 0.1013 212 | 9.0057 003 − 10 |
| $8\pi$ | 25.1327 412 | 1.4002 399 | $1/(2\pi^2)$ | 0.0506 606 | 8.7046 703 − 10 |
| $\pi/2$ | 1.5707 963 | 0.1961 199 | $1/(4\pi^2)$ | 0.0253 303 | 8.4036 403 − 10 |
| $\pi/3$ | 1.0471 976 | 0.0200 286 | $\sqrt{\pi}$ | 1.7724 539 | 0.2485 749 |
| $\pi/4$ | 0.7853 982 | 9.8950 899 − 10 | $\sqrt{\pi/4}$ or | 0.8862 269 | 9.9475 449 − 10 |
| $\pi/6$ | 0.5235 988 | 9.7189 986 − 10 | $\sqrt{\pi}/2$ | | |
| $\pi/8$ | 0.3926 991 | 9.5940 599 − 10 | $\sqrt{\pi/4}$ | 0.4431 135 | 9.6465 149 − 10 |
| $2\pi/3$ | 2.0943 951 | 0.3210 586 | $\sqrt{\pi/2}$ | 1.2533 141 | 0.0980 599 |
| $4\pi/3$ | 4.1887 902 | 0.6220 886 | $\sqrt{2/\pi}$ | 0.7978 846 | 9.9019 401 − 10 |
| $1/\pi$ | 0.3183 099 | 9.5028 501 − 10 | $\pi^3$ | 31.0062 767 | 1.4914 496 |
| $2/\pi$ | 0.6366 198 | 9.8038 801 − 10 | $\sqrt[3]{\pi}$ | 1.4645 919 | 0.1657 166 |
| $4/\pi$ | 1.2732 395 | 0.1049 101 | $1/\sqrt[3]{\pi}$ | 0.6827 841 | 9.8342 834 − 10 |
| $1/(2\pi)$ | 0.1591 549 | 9.2018 201 − 10 | $\sqrt[3]{\pi^2}$ | 2.1450 294 | 0.3314 332 |
| $1/(4\pi)$ | 0.0795 775 | 8.9007 901 − 10 | $1/\sqrt{\pi}$ | 0.5641 896 | 9.7514 251 − 10 |
| $1/(6\pi)$ | 0.0530 516 | 8.7246 989 − 10 | $1/\sqrt{2\pi}$ | 0.3989 423 | 9.6009 101 − 10 |
| $1/(8\pi)$ | 0.0397 887 | 8.5997 601 − 10 | $2/\sqrt{\pi}$ | 1.1283 792 | 0.0524 551 |
| $\pi/180$ | 0.0174 533 | 8.2418 774 − 10 | | | |
| $180/\pi$ | 57.2957 795 | 1.7581 226 | | | |

## Logarithmic Constants

$e = 2.71828\ 18284\ 59045$   $M = \log_{10} e = 0.43429\ 44819\ 03251\ 82765$
$1/e = 0.36787\ 94412$   $1/M = \log_e 10 = 2.30258\ 50929\ 94045\ 68402$
$\log_{10} M = \log_{10} \log_{10} e = 9.63778\ 43113 - 10$
$\log_e 2 = 0.69314\ 71806$   $\log_{10} 2 = 0.30102\ 99957$
$\log_e 3 = 1.09861\ 22887$   $\log_{10} 3 = 0.47712\ 12547$

## Change of Base

$$\log_a x = \log_b x / \log_b a$$
$$\log_{10} x = \log_e x / \log_e 10 \qquad \log_e x = \log_{10} x / \log_{10} e$$
$$\log_e x = 1/M \log_{10} x = 2.30258\ 50930 \log_{10} x$$
$$\log_{10} x = M \log_e x = 0.43429\ 44819 \log_e x$$

## Euler's Constant $\gamma = 0.57721\ 56649\ 01533$

# DECIMAL EQUIVALENTS OF COMMON FRACTIONS

| | | | | | | | |
|---|---|---|---|---|---|---|---|
| | 1/32 | 2/64 = | 0.03125 | | 17/32 | 34/64 = | 0.53125 |
| 1/16 | 2/32 | 4/64 = | .0625 | 9/16 | 18/32 | 36/64 = | .5625 |
| | 3/32 | 6/64 = | .09375 | | 19/32 | 38/64 = | .59375 |
| 1/8 | 4/32 | 8/64 = | .125 | 5/8 | 20/32 | 40/64 = | .625 |
| | 5/32 | 10/64 = | .15625 | | 21/32 | 42/64 = | .65625 |
| 3/16 | 6/32 | 12/64 = | .1875 | 11/16 | 22/32 | 44/64 = | .6875 |
| | 7/32 | 14/64 = | .21875 | | 23/32 | 46/64 = | .71875 |
| 1/4 | 8/32 | 16/64 = | .25 | 3/4 | 24/32 | 48/64 = | .75 |
| | 9/32 | 18/64 = | .28125 | | 25/32 | 50/64 = | .78125 |
| 5/16 | 10/32 | 20/64 = | .3125 | 13/16 | 26/32 | 52/64 = | .8125 |
| | 11/32 | 22/64 = | .34375 | | 27/32 | 54/64 = | .84375 |
| 3/8 | 12/32 | 24/64 = | .375 | 7/8 | 28/32 | 56/64 = | .875 |
| | 13/32 | 26/64 = | .40625 | | 29/32 | 58/64 = | .90625 |
| 7/16 | 14/32 | 28/64 = | .4375 | 15/16 | 30/32 | 60/64 = | .9375 |
| | 15/32 | 30/64 = | .46875 | | 31/32 | 62/64 = | .96875 |
| 1/2 | 16/32 | 32/64 = | .50 | | | | |

# MULTIPLES OF $\frac{\pi}{2}$

| n | $n\frac{\pi}{2}$ | | n | $n\frac{\pi}{2}$ | |
|---|---|---|---|---|---|
| 1 | 1.57079 | 63268 | 51 | 80.11061 | 26665 |
| 2 | 3.14159 | 26536 | 52 | 81.68140 | 89933 |
| 3 | 4.71238 | 89804 | 53 | 83.25220 | 53201 |
| 4 | 6.28318 | 53072 | 54 | 84.82300 | 16469 |
| 5 | 7.85398 | 16340 | 55 | 86.39379 | 79737 |
| 6 | 9.42477 | 79608 | 56 | 87.96459 | 43005 |
| 7 | 10.99557 | 42876 | 57 | 89.53539 | 06273 |
| 8 | 12.56637 | 06144 | 58 | 91.10618 | 69541 |
| 9 | 14.13716 | 69412 | 59 | 92.67698 | 32809 |
| 10 | 15.70796 | 32679 | 60 | 94.24777 | 96077 |
| 11 | 17.27875 | 95947 | 61 | 95.81857 | 59345 |
| 12 | 18.84955 | 59215 | 62 | 97.38937 | 22613 |
| 13 | 20.42035 | 22483 | 63 | 98.96016 | 85881 |
| 14 | 21.99114 | 85751 | 64 | 100.53096 | 49149 |
| 15 | 23.56194 | 49019 | 65 | 102.10176 | 12417 |
| 16 | 25.13274 | 12287 | 66 | 103.67255 | 75685 |
| 17 | 26.70353 | 75555 | 67 | 105.24335 | 38953 |
| 18 | 28.27433 | 38823 | 68 | 106.81415 | 02221 |
| 19 | 29.84513 | 02091 | 69 | 108.38494 | 65488 |
| 20 | 31.41592 | 65359 | 70 | 109.95574 | 28756 |
| 21 | 32.98672 | 28627 | 71 | 111.52653 | 92024 |
| 22 | 34.55751 | 91895 | 72 | 113.09733 | 55292 |
| 23 | 36.12831 | 55163 | 73 | 114.66813 | 18560 |
| 24 | 37.69911 | 18431 | 74 | 116.23892 | 81828 |
| 25 | 39.26990 | 81699 | 75 | 117.80972 | 45096 |
| 26 | 40.84070 | 44967 | 76 | 119.38052 | 08364 |
| 27 | 42.41150 | 08235 | 77 | 120.95131 | 71632 |
| 28 | 43.98229 | 71503 | 78 | 122.52211 | 34900 |
| 29 | 45.55309 | 34771 | 79 | 124.09290 | 98168 |
| 30 | 47.12388 | 98038 | 80 | 125.66370 | 61436 |
| 31 | 48.69468 | 61306 | 81 | 127.23450 | 24704 |
| 32 | 50.26548 | 24574 | 82 | 128.80529 | 87972 |
| 33 | 51.83627 | 87842 | 83 | 130.37609 | 51240 |
| 34 | 53.40707 | 51110 | 84 | 131.94689 | 14508 |
| 35 | 54.97787 | 14378 | 85 | 133.51768 | 77776 |
| 36 | 56.54866 | 77646 | 86 | 135.08848 | 41044 |
| 37 | 58.11946 | 40914 | 87 | 136.65928 | 04312 |
| 38 | 59.69026 | 04182 | 88 | 138.23007 | 67580 |
| 39 | 61.26105 | 67450 | 89 | 139.80087 | 30847 |
| 40 | 62.83185 | 30718 | 90 | 141.37166 | 94115 |
| 41 | 64.40264 | 93986 | 91 | 142.94246 | 57383 |
| 42 | 65.97344 | 57254 | 92 | 144.51326 | 20651 |
| 43 | 67.54424 | 20522 | 93 | 146.08405 | 83919 |
| 44 | 69.11503 | 83790 | 94 | 147.65485 | 47187 |
| 45 | 70.68583 | 47058 | 95 | 149.22565 | 10455 |
| 46 | 72.25663 | 10326 | 96 | 150.79644 | 73723 |
| 47 | 73.82742 | 73594 | 97 | 152.36724 | 36991 |
| 48 | 75.39822 | 36862 | 98 | 153.93804 | 00259 |
| 49 | 76.96902 | 00129 | 99 | 155.50883 | 63527 |
| 50 | 78.53981 | 63397 | 100 | 157.07963 | 26795 |

# MISCELLANEOUS CONSTANTS

Equatorial radius of the earth, 6378.388 km; 3963.34 miles (statute).

Polar radius of the earth, 6356.912 km; 3949.99 miles (statute).

1 degree of latitude at $40°$ = 69 miles.

1 international nautical mile = 1.15078 miles (statute) = 1852 meters = 6080 feet.

Mean density of the earth, 5.522 $gm/cm^3$, 344.7 $lb/ft^3$.

Constant of gravitation, $6.673 \pm 0.003 \times 10^{-8} cm^3/gm \times sec^2$.

Acceleration due to gravity at sea level, latitude $45°$, 980.621 $cm/sec^2$ = 32.1725 $ft/sec^2$.

Length of seconds pendulum at sea level, latitude $45°$, 99.3577 cm = 39.1171 in.

1 knot (international) = 101.269 ft/min. = 1.6878 ft/sec = 1.1508 miles (statute)/hr.

1 micron = $10^{-4}$ mm.

1 angstrom unit = $10^{-8}$ cm.

Mass of hydrogen atom $(1.67339 \pm 0.00031) \times 10^{-24}$ gram.

Avogadro's number (physical) $(6.02486 \pm 0.00016) \times 10^{23}$ per gram mole.

Avogadro's number (chemical) $(6.02322 \pm 0.00016) \times 10^{23}$ per gram mole.

Planck's constant $(6.62517 \pm 0.00023) \times 10^{-27}$ erg-sec.

Density of Mercury $0°C$ = 13.5955 $g/cm^3$.

Density of water, maximum at $3.98°C$ = 0.999973 $gm/cm^3$.

Density of air, $0°C$ and 760 mm = 1.2929 g/liter.

Velocity of sound in dry air, $0°C.$, 331.36 m/sec = 1087.1 ft/sec.

Velocity of light in vacuum = $(2.99793 \pm 0.000004) \times 10^{10}$ cm/sec.

Heat of fusion of water at $0°C$, 79.71 cal/g.

Heat of vaporization of water, $100°C$, 539.55 cal/g.

Electrochemical equivalent of silver, 0.001118 g/sec international ampere.

Absolute wave length of red cadmium light in air, $15°C$, 760 mm pressure, 6438.4696 angstrom units.

Wave length of orange-red line of krypton 86, 6057.802 Å.

## GREEK ALPHABET

| Greek letter | Greek name | English equivalent | Greek letter | Greek name | English equivalent |
|---|---|---|---|---|---|
| A α | Alpha | a | N ν | Nu | n |
| B β | Beta | b | Ξ ξ | Xi | x |
| Γ γ | Gamma | g | O o | Omicron | ŏ |
| Δ δ | Delta | d | Π π | Pi | p |
| E ε | Epsilon | ĕ | P ρ | Rho | r |
| Z ζ | Zeta | z | Σ σ s | Sigma | s |
| H η | Eta | ē | T τ | Tau | t |
| Θ θ ϑ | Theta | th | Υ υ | Upsilon | u |
| I ι | Iota | i | Φ φ | Phi | ph |
| K κ | Kappa | k | X χ | Chi | ch |
| Λ λ | Lambda | l | Ψ ψ | Psi | ps |
| M μ | Mu | m | Ω ω | Omega | ō |

| N | 0 | 1 | 2 | 3 | 4 | 5 | 6 | 7 | 8 | 9 | 1 | 2 | 3 | 4 | 5 | 6 | 7 | 8 | 9 |
|---|---|---|---|---|---|---|---|---|---|---|---|---|---|---|---|---|---|---|---|
| | | | | | | | | | | | | | | Proportional Parts | | | | | |
| 10 | 0000 | 0043 | 0086 | 0128 | 0170 | 0212 | 0253 | 0294 | 0334 | 0374 | *4 | 8 | 12 | 17 | 21 | 25 | 29 | 33 | 37 |
| 11 | 0414 | 0453 | 0492 | 0531 | 0569 | 0607 | 0645 | 0682 | 0719 | 0755 | 4 | 8 | 11 | 15 | 19 | 23 | 26 | 30 | 34 |
| 12 | 0792 | 0828 | 0864 | 0899 | 0934 | 0969 | 1004 | 1038 | 1072 | 1106 | 3 | 7 | 10 | 14 | 17 | 21 | 24 | 28 | 31 |
| 13 | 1139 | 1173 | 1206 | 1239 | 1271 | 1303 | 1335 | 1367 | 1399 | 1430 | 3 | 6 | 10 | 13 | 16 | 19 | 23 | 26 | 29 |
| 14 | 1461 | 1492 | 1523 | 1553 | 1584 | 1614 | 1644 | 1673 | 1703 | 1732 | 3 | 6 | 9 | 12 | 15 | 18 | 21 | 24 | 27 |
| 15 | 1761 | 1790 | 1818 | 1847 | 1875 | 1903 | 1931 | 1959 | 1987 | 2014 | *3 | 6 | 8 | 11 | 14 | 17 | 20 | 22 | 25 |
| 16 | 2041 | 2068 | 2095 | 2122 | 2148 | 2175 | 2201 | 2227 | 2253 | 2279 | 3 | 5 | 8 | 11 | 13 | 16 | 18 | 21 | 24 |
| 17 | 2304 | 2330 | 2355 | 2380 | 2405 | 2430 | 2455 | 2480 | 2504 | 2529 | 2 | 5 | 7 | 10 | 12 | 15 | 17 | 20 | 22 |
| 18 | 2553 | 2577 | 2601 | 2625 | 2648 | 2672 | 2695 | 2718 | 2742 | 2765 | 2 | 5 | 7 | 9 | 12 | 14 | 16 | 19 | 21 |
| 19 | 2788 | 2810 | 2833 | 2856 | 2878 | 2900 | 2923 | 2945 | 2967 | 2989 | 2 | 4 | 7 | 9 | 11 | 13 | 16 | 18 | 20 |
| 20 | 3010 | 3032 | 3054 | 3075 | 3096 | 3118 | 3139 | 3160 | 3181 | 3201 | 2 | 4 | 6 | 8 | 11 | 13 | 15 | 17 | 19 |
| 21 | 3222 | 3243 | 3263 | 3284 | 3304 | 3324 | 3345 | 3365 | 3385 | 3404 | 2 | 4 | 6 | 8 | 10 | 12 | 14 | 16 | 18 |
| 22 | 3424 | 3444 | 3464 | 3483 | 3502 | 3522 | 3541 | 3560 | 3579 | 3598 | 2 | 4 | 6 | 8 | 10 | 12 | 14 | 15 | 17 |
| 23 | 3617 | 3636 | 3655 | 3674 | 3692 | 3711 | 3729 | 3747 | 3766 | 3784 | 2 | 4 | 6 | 7 | 9 | 11 | 13 | 15 | 17 |
| 24 | 3802 | 3820 | 3838 | 3856 | 3874 | 3892 | 3909 | 3927 | 3945 | 3962 | 2 | 4 | 5 | 7 | 9 | 11 | 12 | 14 | 16 |
| 25 | 3979 | 3997 | 4014 | 4031 | 4048 | 4065 | 4082 | 4099 | 4116 | 4133 | 2 | 3 | 5 | 7 | 9 | 10 | 12 | 14 | 15 |
| 26 | 4150 | 4166 | 4183 | 4200 | 4216 | 4232 | 4249 | 4265 | 4281 | 4298 | 2 | 3 | 5 | 7 | 8 | 10 | 11 | 13 | 15 |
| 27 | 4314 | 4330 | 4346 | 4362 | 4378 | 4393 | 4409 | 4425 | 4440 | 4456 | 2 | 3 | 5 | 6 | 8 | 9 | 11 | 13 | 14 |
| 28 | 4472 | 4487 | 4502 | 4518 | 4533 | 4548 | 4564 | 4579 | 4594 | 4609 | 2 | 3 | 5 | 6 | 8 | 9 | 11 | 12 | 14 |
| 29 | 4624 | 4639 | 4654 | 4669 | 4683 | 4698 | 4713 | 4728 | 4742 | 4757 | 1 | 3 | 4 | 6 | 7 | 9 | 10 | 12 | 13 |
| 30 | 4771 | 4786 | 4800 | 4814 | 4829 | 4843 | 4857 | 4871 | 4886 | 4900 | 1 | 3 | 4 | 6 | 7 | 9 | 10 | 11 | 13 |
| 31 | 4914 | 4928 | 4942 | 4955 | 4969 | 4983 | 4997 | 5011 | 5024 | 5038 | 1 | 3 | 4 | 6 | 7 | 8 | 10 | 11 | 12 |
| 32 | 5051 | 5065 | 5079 | 5092 | 5105 | 5119 | 5132 | 5145 | 5159 | 5172 | 1 | 3 | 4 | 5 | 7 | 8 | 9 | 11 | 12 |
| 33 | 5185 | 5198 | 5211 | 5224 | 5237 | 5250 | 5263 | 5276 | 5289 | 5302 | 1 | 3 | 4 | 5 | 6 | 8 | 9 | 10 | 12 |
| 34 | 5315 | 5328 | 5340 | 5353 | 5366 | 5378 | 5391 | 5403 | 5416 | 5428 | 1 | 3 | 4 | 5 | 6 | 8 | 9 | 10 | 11 |
| 35 | 5441 | 5453 | 5465 | 5478 | 5490 | 5502 | 5514 | 5527 | 5539 | 5551 | 1 | 2 | 4 | 5 | 6 | 7 | 9 | 10 | 11 |
| 36 | 5563 | 5575 | 5587 | 5599 | 5611 | 5623 | 5635 | 5647 | 5658 | 5670 | 1 | 2 | 4 | 5 | 6 | 7 | 8 | 10 | 11 |
| 37 | 5682 | 5694 | 5705 | 5717 | 5729 | 5740 | 5752 | 5763 | 5775 | 5786 | 1 | 2 | 3 | 5 | 6 | 7 | 8 | 9 | 10 |
| 38 | 5798 | 5809 | 5821 | 5832 | 5843 | 5855 | 5866 | 5877 | 5888 | 5899 | 1 | 2 | 3 | 5 | 6 | 7 | 8 | 9 | 10 |
| 39 | 5911 | 5922 | 5933 | 5944 | 5955 | 5966 | 5977 | 5988 | 5999 | 6010 | 1 | 2 | 3 | 4 | 5 | 7 | 8 | 9 | 10 |
| 40 | 6021 | 6031 | 6042 | 6053 | 6064 | 6075 | 6085 | 6096 | 6107 | 6117 | 1 | 2 | 3 | 4 | 5 | 6 | 8 | 9 | 10 |
| 41 | 6128 | 6138 | 6149 | 6160 | 6170 | 6180 | 6191 | 6201 | 6212 | 6222 | 1 | 2 | 3 | 4 | 5 | 6 | 7 | 8 | 9 |
| 42 | 6232 | 6243 | 6253 | 6263 | 6274 | 6284 | 6294 | 6304 | 6314 | 6325 | 1 | 2 | 3 | 4 | 5 | 6 | 7 | 8 | 9 |
| 43 | 6335 | 6345 | 6355 | 6365 | 6375 | 6385 | 6395 | 6405 | 6415 | 6425 | 1 | 2 | 3 | 4 | 5 | 6 | 7 | 8 | 9 |
| 44 | 6435 | 6444 | 6454 | 6464 | 6474 | 6484 | 6493 | 6503 | 6513 | 6522 | 1 | 2 | 3 | 4 | 5 | 6 | 7 | 8 | 9 |
| 45 | 6532 | 6542 | 6551 | 6561 | 6571 | 6580 | 6590 | 6599 | 6609 | 6618 | 1 | 2 | 3 | 4 | 5 | 6 | 7 | 8 | 9 |
| 46 | 6628 | 6637 | 6646 | 6656 | 6665 | 6675 | 6684 | 6693 | 6702 | 6712 | 1 | 2 | 3 | 4 | 5 | 6 | 7 | 7 | 8 |
| 47 | 6721 | 6730 | 6739 | 6749 | 6758 | 6767 | 6776 | 6785 | 6794 | 6803 | 1 | 2 | 3 | 4 | 5 | 5 | 6 | 7 | 8 |
| 48 | 6812 | 6821 | 6830 | 6839 | 6848 | 6857 | 6866 | 6875 | 6884 | 6893 | 1 | 2 | 3 | 4 | 4 | 5 | 6 | 7 | 8 |
| 49 | 6902 | 6911 | 6920 | 6928 | 6937 | 6946 | 6955 | 6964 | 6972 | 6981 | 1 | 2 | 3 | 4 | 4 | 5 | 6 | 7 | 8 |
| 50 | 6990 | 6998 | 7007 | 7016 | 7024 | 7033 | 7042 | 7050 | 7059 | 7067 | 1 | 2 | 3 | 3 | 4 | 5 | 6 | 7 | 8 |
| 51 | 7076 | 7084 | 7093 | 7101 | 7110 | 7118 | 7126 | 7135 | 7143 | 7152 | 1 | 2 | 3 | 3 | 4 | 5 | 6 | 7 | 8 |
| 52 | 7160 | 7168 | 7177 | 7185 | 7193 | 7202 | 7210 | 7218 | 7226 | 7235 | 1 | 2 | 2 | 3 | 4 | 5 | 6 | 7 | 7 |
| 53 | 7243 | 7251 | 7259 | 7267 | 7275 | 7284 | 7292 | 7300 | 7308 | 7316 | 1 | 2 | 2 | 3 | 4 | 5 | 6 | 6 | 7 |
| 54 | 7324 | 7332 | 7340 | 7348 | 7356 | 7364 | 7372 | 7380 | 7388 | 7396 | 1 | 2 | 2 | 3 | 4 | 5 | 6 | 6 | 7 |
| N | 0 | 1 | 2 | 3 | 4 | 5 | 6 | 7 | 8 | 9 | 1 | 2 | 3 | 4 | 5 | 6 | 7 | 8 | 9 |

○ Interpolation in this section of the table is inaccurate

| N | 0 | 1 | 2 | 3 | 4 | 5 | 6 | 7 | 8 | 9 | 1 | 2 | 3 | 4 | 5 | 6 | 7 | 8 | 9 |
|---|---|---|---|---|---|---|---|---|---|---|---|---|---|---|---|---|---|---|---|
| | | | | | | | | | | | Proportional Parts | | | | | | | | |
| 55 | 7404 | 7412 | 7419 | 7427 | 7435 | 7443 | 7451 | 7459 | 7466 | 7474 | 1 | 2 | 2 | 3 | 4 | 5 | 5 | 6 | 7 |
| 56 | 7482 | 7490 | 7497 | 7505 | 7513 | 7520 | 7528 | 7536 | 7543 | 7551 | 1 | 2 | 2 | 3 | 4 | 5 | 5 | 6 | 7 |
| 57 | 7559 | 7566 | 7574 | 7582 | 7589 | 7597 | 7604 | 7612 | 7619 | 7627 | 1 | 2 | 2 | 3 | 4 | 5 | 5 | 6 | 7 |
| 58 | 7634 | 7642 | 7649 | 7657 | 7664 | 7672 | 7679 | 7686 | 7694 | 7701 | 1 | 1 | 2 | 3 | 4 | 4 | 5 | 6 | 7 |
| 59 | 7709 | 7716 | 7723 | 7731 | 7738 | 7745 | 7752 | 7760 | 7767 | 7774 | 1 | 1 | 2 | 3 | 4 | 4 | 5 | 6 | 7 |
| 60 | 7782 | 7789 | 7796 | 7803 | 7810 | 7818 | 7825 | 7832 | 7839 | 7846 | 1 | 1 | 2 | 3 | 4 | 4 | 5 | 6 | 6 |
| 61 | 7853 | 7860 | 7868 | 7875 | 7882 | 7889 | 7896 | 7903 | 7910 | 7917 | 1 | 1 | 2 | 3 | 4 | 4 | 5 | 6 | 6 |
| 62 | 7924 | 7931 | 7938 | 7945 | 7952 | 7959 | 7966 | 7973 | 7980 | 7987 | 1 | 1 | 2 | 3 | 3 | 4 | 5 | 6 | 6 |
| 63 | 7993 | 8000 | 8007 | 8014 | 8021 | 8028 | 8035 | 8041 | 8048 | 8055 | 1 | 1 | 2 | 3 | 3 | 4 | 5 | 5 | 6 |
| 64 | 8062 | 8069 | 8075 | 8082 | 8089 | 8096 | 8102 | 8109 | 8116 | 8122 | 1 | 1 | 2 | 3 | 3 | 4 | 5 | 5 | 6 |
| 65 | 8129 | 8136 | 8142 | 8149 | 8156 | 8162 | 8169 | 8176 | 8182 | 8189 | 1 | 1 | 2 | 3 | 3 | 4 | 5 | 5 | 6 |
| 66 | 8195 | 8202 | 8209 | 8215 | 8222 | 8228 | 8235 | 8241 | 8248 | 8254 | 1 | 1 | 2 | 3 | 3 | 4 | 5 | 5 | 6 |
| 67 | 8261 | 8267 | 8274 | 8280 | 8287 | 8293 | 8299 | 8306 | 8312 | 8319 | 1 | 1 | 2 | 3 | 3 | 4 | 5 | 5 | 6 |
| 68 | 8325 | 8331 | 8338 | 8344 | 8351 | 8357 | 8363 | 8370 | 8376 | 8382 | 1 | 1 | 2 | 3 | 3 | 4 | 4 | 5 | 6 |
| 69 | 8388 | 8395 | 8401 | 8407 | 8414 | 8420 | 8426 | 8432 | 8439 | 8445 | 1 | 1 | 2 | 2 | 3 | 4 | 4 | 5 | 6 |
| 70 | 8451 | 8457 | 8463 | 8470 | 8476 | 8482 | 8488 | 8494 | 8500 | 8506 | 1 | 1 | 2 | 2 | 3 | 4 | 4 | 5 | 6 |
| 71 | 8513 | 8519 | 8525 | 8531 | 8537 | 8543 | 8549 | 8555 | 8561 | 8567 | 1 | 1 | 2 | 2 | 3 | 4 | 4 | 5 | 5 |
| 72 | 8573 | 8579 | 8585 | 8591 | 8597 | 8603 | 8609 | 8615 | 8621 | 8627 | 1 | 1 | 2 | 2 | 3 | 4 | 4 | 5 | 5 |
| 73 | 8633 | 8639 | 8645 | 8651 | 8657 | 8663 | 8669 | 8675 | 8681 | 8686 | 1 | 1 | 2 | 2 | 3 | 4 | 4 | 5 | 5 |
| 74 | 8692 | 8698 | 8704 | 8710 | 8716 | 8722 | 8727 | 8733 | 8739 | 8745 | 1 | 1 | 2 | 2 | 3 | 4 | 4 | 5 | 5 |
| 75 | 8751 | 8756 | 8762 | 8768 | 8774 | 8779 | 8785 | 8791 | 8797 | 8802 | 1 | 1 | 2 | 2 | 3 | 3 | 4 | 5 | 5 |
| 76 | 8808 | 8814 | 8820 | 8825 | 8831 | 8837 | 8842 | 8848 | 8854 | 8859 | 1 | 1 | 2 | 2 | 3 | 3 | 4 | 5 | 5 |
| 77 | 8865 | 8871 | 8876 | 8882 | 8887 | 8893 | 8899 | 8904 | 8910 | 8915 | 1 | 1 | 2 | 2 | 3 | 3 | 4 | 4 | 5 |
| 78 | 8921 | 8927 | 8932 | 8938 | 8943 | 8949 | 8954 | 8960 | 8965 | 8971 | 1 | 1 | 2 | 2 | 3 | 3 | 4 | 4 | 5 |
| 79 | 8976 | 8982 | 8987 | 8993 | 8998 | 9004 | 9009 | 9015 | 9020 | 9025 | 1 | 1 | 2 | 2 | 3 | 3 | 4 | 4 | 5 |
| 80 | 9031 | 9036 | 9042 | 9047 | 9053 | 9058 | 9063 | 9069 | 9074 | 9079 | 1 | 1 | 2 | 2 | 3 | 3 | 4 | 4 | 5 |
| 81 | 9085 | 9090 | 9096 | 9101 | 9106 | 9112 | 9117 | 9122 | 9128 | 9133 | 1 | 1 | 2 | 2 | 3 | 3 | 4 | 4 | 5 |
| 82 | 9138 | 9143 | 9149 | 9154 | 9159 | 9165 | 9170 | 9175 | 9180 | 9186 | 1 | 1 | 2 | 2 | 3 | 3 | 4 | 4 | 5 |
| 83 | 9191 | 9196 | 9201 | 9206 | 9212 | 9217 | 9222 | 9227 | 9232 | 9238 | 1 | 1 | 2 | 2 | 3 | 3 | 4 | 4 | 5 |
| 84 | 9243 | 9248 | 9253 | 9258 | 9263 | 9269 | 9274 | 9279 | 9284 | 9289 | 1 | 1 | 2 | 2 | 3 | 3 | 4 | 4 | 5 |
| 85 | 9294 | 9299 | 9304 | 9309 | 9315 | 9320 | 9325 | 9330 | 9335 | 9340 | 1 | 1 | 2 | 2 | 3 | 3 | 4 | 4 | 5 |
| 86 | 9345 | 9350 | 9355 | 9360 | 9365 | 9370 | 9375 | 9380 | 9385 | 9390 | 1 | 1 | 2 | 2 | 3 | 3 | 4 | 4 | 5 |
| 87 | 9395 | 9400 | 9405 | 9410 | 9415 | 9420 | 9425 | 9430 | 9435 | 9440 | 0 | 1 | 1 | 2 | 2 | 3 | 3 | 4 | 4 |
| 88 | 9445 | 9450 | 9455 | 9460 | 9465 | 9469 | 9474 | 9479 | 9484 | 9489 | 0 | 1 | 1 | 2 | 2 | 3 | 3 | 4 | 4 |
| 89 | 9494 | 9499 | 9504 | 9509 | 9513 | 9518 | 9523 | 9528 | 9533 | 9538 | 0 | 1 | 1 | 2 | 2 | 3 | 3 | 4 | 4 |
| 90 | 9542 | 9547 | 9552 | 9557 | 9562 | 9566 | 9571 | 9576 | 9581 | 9586 | 0 | 1 | 1 | 2 | 2 | 3 | 3 | 4 | 4 |
| 91 | 9590 | 9595 | 9600 | 9605 | 9609 | 9614 | 9619 | 9624 | 9628 | 9633 | 0 | 1 | 1 | 2 | 2 | 3 | 3 | 4 | 4 |
| 92 | 9638 | 9643 | 9647 | 9652 | 9657 | 9661 | 9666 | 9671 | 9675 | 9680 | 0 | 1 | 1 | 2 | 2 | 3 | 3 | 4 | 4 |
| 93 | 9685 | 9689 | 9694 | 9699 | 9703 | 9708 | 9713 | 9717 | 9722 | 9727 | 0 | 1 | 1 | 2 | 2 | 3 | 3 | 4 | 4 |
| 94 | 9731 | 9736 | 9741 | 9745 | 9750 | 9754 | 9759 | 9763 | 9768 | 9773 | 0 | 1 | 1 | 2 | 2 | 3 | 3 | 4 | 4 |
| 95 | 9777 | 9782 | 9786 | 9791 | 9795 | 9800 | 9805 | 9809 | 9814 | 9818 | 0 | 1 | 1 | 2 | 2 | 3 | 3 | 4 | 4 |
| 96 | 9823 | 9827 | 9832 | 9836 | 9841 | 9845 | 9850 | 9854 | 9859 | 9863 | 0 | 1 | 1 | 2 | 2 | 3 | 3 | 4 | 4 |
| 97 | 9868 | 9872 | 9877 | 9881 | 9886 | 9890 | 9894 | 9899 | 9903 | 9908 | 0 | 1 | 1 | 2 | 2 | 3 | 3 | 4 | 4 |
| 98 | 9912 | 9917 | 9921 | 9926 | 9930 | 9934 | 9939 | 9943 | 9948 | 9952 | 0 | 1 | 1 | 2 | 2 | 3 | 3 | 4 | 4 |
| 99 | 9956 | 9961 | 9965 | 9969 | 9974 | 9978 | 9983 | 9987 | 9991 | 9996 | 0 | 1 | 1 | 2 | 2 | 3 | 3 | 3 | 4 |
| N | 0 | 1 | 2 | 3 | 4 | 5 | 6 | 7 | 8 | 9 | 1 | 2 | 3 | 4 | 5 | 6 | 7 | 8 | 9 |

| N | 0 | 1 | 2 | 3 | 4 | 5 | 6 | 7 | 8 | 9 |
|---|---|---|---|---|---|---|---|---|---|---|
| .10 | $-1.000$ | $-.9957$ | $-.9914$ | $-.9872$ | $-.9830$ | $-.9788$ | $-.9747$ | $-.9706$ | $-.9666$ | $-.9626$ |
| .11 | $-.9586$ | $-.9547$ | $-.9508$ | $-.9469$ | $-.9431$ | $-.9393$ | $-.9355$ | $-.9318$ | $-.9281$ | $-.9245$ |
| .12 | $-.9208$ | $-.9172$ | $-.9136$ | $-.9101$ | $-.9066$ | $-.9031$ | $-.8996$ | $-.8962$ | $-.8928$ | $-.8894$ |
| .13 | $-.8861$ | $-.8827$ | $-.8794$ | $-.8761$ | $-.8729$ | $-.8697$ | $-.8665$ | $-.8633$ | $-.8601$ | $-.8570$ |
| .14 | $-.8539$ | $-.8508$ | $-.8477$ | $-.8447$ | $-.8416$ | $-.8386$ | $-.8356$ | $-.8327$ | $-.8297$ | $-.8268$ |
| .15 | $-.8239$ | $-.8210$ | $-.8182$ | $-.8153$ | $-.8125$ | $-.8097$ | $-.8069$ | $-.8041$ | $-.8013$ | $-.7986$ |
| .16 | $-.7959$ | $-.7932$ | $-.7905$ | $-.7878$ | $-.7852$ | $-.7825$ | $-.7799$ | $-.7773$ | $-.7747$ | $-.7721$ |
| .17 | $-.7696$ | $.-7670$ | $-.7645$ | $-.7620$ | $-.7595$ | $-.7570$ | $-.7545$ | $-.7520$ | $-.7496$ | $-.7471$ |
| .18 | $-.7447$ | $-.7423$ | $-.7399$ | $-.7375$ | $-.7352$ | $-.7328$ | $-.7305$ | $-.7282$ | $-.7258$ | $-.7235$ |
| .19 | $-.7212$ | $-.7190$ | $-.7167$ | $-.7144$ | $-.7122$ | $-.7100$ | $-.7077$ | $-.7055$ | $-.7033$ | $-.7011$ |
| .20 | $-.6990$ | $-.6968$ | $-.6946$ | $-.6925$ | $-.6904$ | $-.6882$ | $-.6861$ | $-.6840$ | $-.6819$ | $-.6799$ |
| .21 | $-.6778$ | $-.6757$ | $-.6737$ | $-.6716$ | $-.6696$ | $-.6676$ | $-.6655$ | $-.6635$ | $-.6615$ | $-.6596$ |
| .22 | $-.6576$ | $-.6556$ | $-.6536$ | $-.6517$ | $-.6498$ | $-.6478$ | $-.6459$ | $-.6440$ | $-.6421$ | $-.6402$ |
| .23 | $-.6383$ | $-.6364$ | $-.6345$ | $-.6326$ | $-.6308$ | $-.6289$ | $-.6271$ | $-.6253$ | $-.6234$ | $-.6216$ |
| .24 | $-.6198$ | $-.6180$ | $-.6162$ | $-.6144$ | $-.6126$ | $-.6108$ | $-.6091$ | $-.6073$ | $-.6055$ | $-.6038$ |
| .25 | $-.6021$ | $-.6003$ | $-.5986$ | $-.5969$ | $-.5952$ | $-.5935$ | $-.5918$ | $-.5901$ | $-.5884$ | $-.5867$ |
| .26 | $-.5850$ | $-.5834$ | $-.5817$ | $-.5800$ | $-.5784$ | $-.5768$ | $-.5751$ | $-.5735$ | $-.5719$ | $-.5702$ |
| .27 | $-.5686$ | $-.5670$ | $-.5654$ | $-.5638$ | $-.5622$ | $-.5607$ | $-.5591$ | $-.5575$ | $-.5560$ | $-.5544$ |
| .28 | $-.5528$ | $-.5513$ | $-.5498$ | $-.5482$ | $-.5467$ | $-.5452$ | $-.5436$ | $-.5421$ | $-.5406$ | $-.5391$ |
| .29 | $-.5376$ | $-.5361$ | $-.5346$ | $-.5331$ | $-.5317$ | $-.5302$ | $-.5287$ | $-.5272$ | $-.5258$ | $-.5243$ |
| .30 | $-.5229$ | $-.5214$ | $-.5200$ | $-.5186$ | $-.5171$ | $-.5157$ | $-.5143$ | $-.5129$ | $-.5114$ | $-.5100$ |
| .31 | $-.5086$ | $-.5072$ | $-.5058$ | $-.5045$ | $-.5031$ | $-.5017$ | $-.5003$ | $-.4989$ | $-.4976$ | $-.4962$ |
| .32 | $-.4949$ | $-.4935$ | $-.4921$ | $-.4908$ | $-.4895$ | $-.4881$ | $-.4868$ | $-.4855$ | $-.4841$ | $-.4828$ |
| .33 | $-.4815$ | $-.4802$ | $-.4789$ | $-.4776$ | $-.4763$ | $-.4750$ | $-.4737$ | $-.4724$ | $-.4711$ | $-.4698$ |
| .34 | $-.4685$ | $-.4672$ | $-.4660$ | $-.4647$ | $-.4634$ | $-.4622$ | $-.4609$ | $-.4597$ | $-.4584$ | $-.4572$ |
| .35 | $-.4559$ | $-.4547$ | $-.4535$ | $-.4522$ | $-.4510$ | $-.4498$ | $-.4486$ | $-.4473$ | $-.4461$ | $-.4449$ |
| .36 | $-.4437$ | $-.4425$ | $-.4413$ | $-.4401$ | $-.4389$ | $-.4377$ | $-.4365$ | $-.4353$ | $-.4342$ | $-.4330$ |
| .37 | $-.4318$ | $-.4306$ | $-.4295$ | $-.4283$ | $-.4271$ | $-.4260$ | $-.4248$ | $-.4237$ | $-.4225$ | $-.4214$ |
| .38 | $-.4202$ | $-.4191$ | $-.4179$ | $-.4168$ | $-.4157$ | $-.4145$ | $-.4134$ | $-.4123$ | $-.4112$ | $-.4101$ |
| .39 | $-.4089$ | $-.4078$ | $-.4067$ | $-.4056$ | $-.4045$ | $-.4034$ | $-.4023$ | $-.4012$ | $-.4001$ | $-.3990$ |
| .40 | $-.3979$ | $-.3969$ | $-.3958$ | $-.3947$ | $-.3936$ | $-.3925$ | $-.3915$ | $-.3904$ | $-.3893$ | $-.3883$ |
| .41 | $-.3872$ | $-.3862$ | $-.3851$ | $-.3840$ | $-.3830$ | $-.3820$ | $-.3809$ | $-.3799$ | $-.3788$ | $-.3778$ |
| .42 | $-.3768$ | $-.3757$ | $-.3747$ | $-.3737$ | $-.3726$ | $-.3716$ | $-.3706$ | $-.3696$ | $-.3686$ | $-.3675$ |
| .43 | $-.3665$ | $-.3655$ | $-.3645$ | $-.3635$ | $-.3625$ | $-.3615$ | $-.3605$ | $-.3595$ | $-.3585$ | $-.3575$ |
| .44 | $-.3565$ | $-.3556$ | $-.3546$ | $-.3536$ | $-.3526$ | $-.3516$ | $-.3507$ | $-.3497$ | $-.3487$ | $-.3478$ |
| .45 | $-.3468$ | $-.3458$ | $-.3449$ | $-.3439$ | $-.3429$ | $-.3420$ | $-.3410$ | $-.3401$ | $-.3391$ | $-.3382$ |
| .46 | $-.3372$ | $-.3363$ | $-.3354$ | $-.3344$ | $-.3335$ | $-.3325$ | $-.3316$ | $-.3307$ | $-.3298$ | $-.3288$ |
| .47 | $-.3279$ | $-.3270$ | $-.3261$ | $-.3251$ | $-.3242$ | $-.3233$ | $-.3224$ | $-.3215$ | $-.3206$ | $-.3197$ |
| .48 | $-.3188$ | $-.3179$ | $-.3170$ | $-.3161$ | $-.3152$ | $-.3143$ | $-.3134$ | $-.3125$ | $-.3116$ | $-.3107$ |
| .49 | $-.3098$ | $-.3089$ | $-.3080$ | $-.3072$ | $-.3063$ | $-.3054$ | $-.3045$ | $-.3036$ | $-.3028$ | $-.3019$ |
| .50 | $-.3010$ | $-.3002$ | $-.2993$ | $-.2984$ | $-.2976$ | $-.2967$ | $-.2958$ | $-.2950$ | $-.2941$ | $-.2933$ |
| .51 | $-.2924$ | $-.2916$ | $-.2907$ | $-.2899$ | $-.2890$ | $-.2882$ | $-.2874$ | $-.2865$ | $-.2857$ | $-.2848$ |
| .52 | $-.2840$ | $-.2832$ | $-.2823$ | $-.2815$ | $-.2807$ | $-.2798$ | $-.2790$ | $-.2782$ | $-.2774$ | $-.2765$ |
| .53 | $-.2757$ | $-.2749$ | $-.2741$ | $-.2733$ | $-.2725$ | $-.2716$ | $-.2708$ | $-.2700$ | $-.2692$ | $-.2684$ |
| .54 | $-.2676$ | $-.2668$ | $-.2660$ | $-.2652$ | $-.2644$ | $-.2636$ | $-.2628$ | $-.2620$ | $-.2612$ | $-.2604$ |

* This table gives the logarithms of the decimal fractions which are negative numbers. For example $\log 0.61 = -0.2147 = 9.7853 - 10$. It should be noted that the entries as given can be used conveniently to find cologarithms of positive numbers. Every positive number $N = P \cdot (10)^k$, where $0 < P \leqq 1$. Since $\text{colog } N = -\log N$, it follows that $\text{colog } N = -\log P - k$.

For example $\text{colog } 0.61 = -\log 0.61 = 0.2147$; $\text{colog } 61 = 0.2147 - 2$; and $\text{colog } 0.00061 = 3.2147$.

# OF DECIMAL FRACTIONS

| N | 0 | 1 | 2 | 3 | 4 | 5 | 6 | 7 | 8 | 9 |
|---|---|---|---|---|---|---|---|---|---|---|
| .55 | −.2596 | −.2588 | −.2581 | −.2573 | −.2565 | −.2557 | −.2549 | −.2541 | −.2534 | −.2526 |
| .56 | −.2518 | −.2510 | −.2503 | −.2495 | −.2487 | −.2480 | −.2472 | −.2464 | −.2457 | −.2449 |
| .57 | −.2441 | −.2434 | −.2426 | −.2418 | −.2411 | −.2403 | −.2396 | −.2388 | −.2381 | −.2373 |
| .58 | −.2366 | −.2358 | −.2351 | −.2343 | −.2336 | −.2328 | −.2321 | −.2314 | −.2306 | −.2299 |
| .59 | −.2291 | −.2284 | −.2277 | −.2269 | −.2262 | −.2255 | −.2248 | −.2240 | −.2233 | −.2226 |
| .60 | −.2218 | −.2211 | −.2204 | −.2197 | −.2190 | −.2182 | −.2175 | −.2168 | −.2161 | −.2154 |
| .61 | −.2147 | −.2140 | −.2132 | −.2125 | −.2118 | −.2111 | −.2104 | −.2097 | −.2090 | −.2083 |
| .62 | −.2076 | −.2069 | −.2062 | −.2055 | −.2048 | −.2041 | −.2034 | −.2027 | −.2020 | −.2013 |
| .63 | −.2007 | −.2000 | −.1993 | −.1986 | −.1979 | −.1972 | −.1965 | −.1959 | −.1952 | −.1945 |
| .64 | −.1938 | −.1931 | −.1925 | −.1918 | −.1911 | −.1904 | −.1898 | −.1891 | −.1884 | −.1878 |
| .65 | −.1871 | −.1864 | −.1858 | −.1851 | −.1844 | −.1838 | −.1831 | −.1824 | −.1818 | −.1811 |
| .66 | −.1805 | −.1798 | −.1791 | −.1785 | −.1778 | −.1772 | −.1765 | −.1759 | −.1752 | −.1746 |
| .67 | −.1739 | −.1733 | −.1726 | −.1720 | −.1713 | −.1707 | −.1701 | −.1694 | −.1688 | −.1681 |
| .68 | −.1675 | −.1669 | −.1662 | −.1656 | −.1649 | −.1643 | −.1637 | −.1630 | −.1624 | −.1618 |
| .69 | −.1612 | −.1605 | −.1599 | −.1593 | −.1586 | −.1580 | −.1574 | −.1568 | −.1561 | −.1555 |
| .70 | −.1549 | −.1543 | −.1537 | −.1530 | −.1524 | −.1518 | −.1512 | −.1506 | −.1500 | −.1494 |
| .71 | −.1487 | −.1481 | −.1475 | −.1469 | −.1463 | −.1457 | −.1451 | −.1445 | −.1439 | −.1433 |
| .72 | −.1427 | −.1421 | −.1415 | −.1409 | −.1403 | −.1397 | −.1391 | −.1385 | −.1379 | −.1373 |
| .73 | −.1367 | −.1361 | −.1355 | −.1349 | −.1343 | −.1337 | −.1331 | −.1325 | −.1319 | −.1314 |
| .74 | −.1308 | −.1302 | −.1296 | −.1290 | −.1284 | −.1278 | −.1273 | −.1267 | −.1261 | −.1255 |
| .75 | −.1249 | −.1244 | −.1238 | −.1232 | −.1226 | −.1221 | −.1215 | −.1209 | −.1203 | −.1198 |
| .76 | −.1192 | −.1186 | −.1180 | −.1175 | −.1169 | −.1163 | −.1158 | −.1152 | −.1146 | −.1141 |
| .77 | −.1135 | −.1129 | −.1124 | −.1118 | −.1113 | −.1107 | −.1101 | −.1096 | −.1090 | −.1085 |
| .78 | −.1079 | −.1073 | −.1068 | −.1062 | −.1057 | −.1051 | −.1046 | −.1040 | −.1035 | −.1029 |
| .79 | −.1024 | −.1018 | −.1013 | −.1007 | −.1002 | −.0996 | −.0991 | −.0985 | −.0980 | −.0975 |
| .80 | −.0969 | −.0964 | −.0958 | −.0953 | −.0947 | −.0942 | −.0937 | −.0931 | −.0926 | −.0921 |
| .81 | −.0915 | −.0910 | −.0904 | −.0899 | −.0894 | −.0888 | −.0883 | −.0878 | −.0872 | −.0867 |
| .82 | −.0862 | −.0857 | −.0851 | −.0846 | −.0841 | −.0835 | −.0830 | −.0825 | −.0820 | −.0814 |
| .83 | −.0809 | −.0804 | −.0799 | −.0794 | −.0788 | −.0783 | −.0778 | −.0773 | −.0768 | −.0762 |
| .84 | −.0757 | −.0752 | −.0747 | −.0742 | −.0737 | −.0731 | −.0726 | −.0721 | −.0716 | −.0711 |
| .85 | −.0706 | −.0701 | −.0696 | −.0691 | −.0685 | −.0680 | −.0675 | −.0670 | −.0665 | −.0660 |
| .86 | −.0655 | −.0650 | −.0645 | −.0640 | −.0635 | −.0630 | −.0625 | −.0620 | −.0615 | −.0610 |
| .87 | −.0605 | −.0600 | −.0595 | −.0590 | −.0585 | −.0580 | −.0575 | −.0570 | −.0565 | −.0560 |
| .88 | −.0555 | −.0550 | −.0545 | −.0540 | −.0535 | −.0531 | −.0526 | −.0521 | −.0516 | −.0511 |
| .89 | −.0506 | −.0501 | −.0496 | −.0491 | −.0487 | −.0482 | −.0477 | −.0472 | −.0467 | −.0462 |
| .90 | −.0458 | −.0453 | −.0448 | −.0443 | −.0438 | −.0434 | −.0429 | −.0424 | −.0419 | −.0414 |
| .91 | −.0410 | −.0405 | −.0400 | −.0395 | −.0391 | −.0386 | −.0381 | −.0376 | −.0372 | −.0367 |
| .92 | −.0362 | −.0357 | −.0353 | −.0348 | −.0343 | −.0339 | −.0334 | −.0329 | −.0325 | −.0320 |
| .93 | −.0315 | −.0311 | −.0306 | −.0301 | −.0297 | −.0292 | −.0287 | −.0283 | −.0278 | −.0273 |
| .94 | −.0269 | −.0264 | −.0259 | −.0255 | −.0250 | −.0246 | −.0241 | −.0237 | −.0232 | −.0227 |
| .95 | −.0223 | −.0218 | −.0214 | −.0209 | −.0205 | −.0200 | −.0195 | −.0191 | −.0186 | −.0182 |
| .96 | −.0177 | −.0173 | −.0168 | −.0164 | −.0159 | −.0155 | −.0150 | −.0146 | −.0141 | −.0137 |
| .97 | −.0132 | −.0128 | −.0123 | −.0119 | −.0114 | −.0110 | −.0106 | −.0101 | −.0097 | −.0092 |
| .98 | −.0088 | −.0083 | −.0079 | −.0074 | −.0070 | −.0066 | −.0061 | −.0057 | −.0052 | −.0048 |
| .99 | −.0044 | −.0039 | −.0035 | −.0031 | −.0026 | −.0022 | −.0017 | −.0013 | −.0009 | −.0004 |

# ANTILOGARITHMS

| | 0 | 1 | 2 | 3 | 4 | 5 | 6 | 7 | 8 | 9 | Proportional Parts | | | | | | | | |
|---|---|---|---|---|---|---|---|---|---|---|---|---|---|---|---|---|---|---|---|
| | | | | | | | | | | | 1 | 2 | 3 | 4 | 5 | 6 | 7 | 8 | 9 |
| .00 | 1000 | 1002 | 1005 | 1007 | 1009 | 1012 | 1014 | 1016 | 1019 | 1021 | 0 | 0 | 1 | 1 | 1 | 1 | 2 | 2 | 2 |
| .01 | 1023 | 1026 | 1028 | 1030 | 1033 | 1035 | 1038 | 1040 | 1042 | 1045 | 0 | 0 | 1 | 1 | 1 | 1 | 2 | 2 | 2 |
| .02 | 1047 | 1050 | 1052 | 1054 | 1057 | 1059 | 1062 | 1064 | 1067 | 1069 | 0 | 0 | 1 | 1 | 1 | 1 | 2 | 2 | 2 |
| .03 | 1072 | 1074 | 1076 | 1079 | 1081 | 1084 | 1086 | 1089 | 1091 | 1094 | 0 | 0 | 1 | 1 | 1 | 1 | 2 | 2 | 2 |
| .04 | 1096 | 1099 | 1102 | 1104 | 1107 | 1109 | 1112 | 1114 | 1117 | 1119 | 0 | 1 | 1 | 1 | 1 | 2 | 2 | 2 | 2 |
| .05 | 1122 | 1125 | 1127 | 1130 | 1132 | 1135 | 1138 | 1140 | 1143 | 1146 | 0 | 1 | 1 | 1 | 1 | 2 | 2 | 2 | 2 |
| .06 | 1148 | 1151 | 1153 | 1156 | 1159 | 1161 | 1164 | 1167 | 1169 | 1172 | 0 | 1 | 1 | 1 | 1 | 2 | 2 | 2 | 2 |
| .07 | 1175 | 1178 | 1180 | 1183 | 1186 | 1189 | 1191 | 1194 | 1197 | 1199 | 0 | 1 | 1 | 1 | 1 | 2 | 2 | 2 | 2 |
| .08 | 1202 | 1205 | 1208 | 1211 | 1213 | 1216 | 1219 | 1222 | 1225 | 1227 | 0 | 1 | 1 | 1 | 1 | 2 | 2 | 2 | 3 |
| .09 | 1230 | 1233 | 1236 | 1239 | 1242 | 1245 | 1247 | 1250 | 1253 | 1256 | 0 | 1 | 1 | 1 | 1 | 2 | 2 | 2 | 3 |
| 10 | 1259 | 1262 | 1265 | 1268 | 1271 | 1274 | 1276 | 1279 | 1282 | 1285 | 0 | 1 | 1 | 1 | 1 | 2 | 2 | 2 | 3 |
| .11 | 1288 | 1291 | 1294 | 1297 | 1300 | 1303 | 1306 | 1309 | 1312 | 1315 | 0 | 1 | 1 | 1 | 2 | 2 | 2 | 3 | 3 |
| 12 | 1318 | 1321 | 1324 | 1327 | 1330 | 1334 | 1337 | 1340 | 1343 | 1346 | 0 | 1 | 1 | 1 | 2 | 2 | 2 | 3 | 3 |
| .13 | 1349 | 1352 | 1355 | 1358 | 1361 | 1365 | 1368 | 1371 | 1374 | 1377 | 0 | 1 | 1 | 1 | 2 | 2 | 2 | 3 | 3 |
| .14 | 1380 | 1384 | 1387 | 1390 | 1393 | 1396 | 1400 | 1403 | 1406 | 1409 | 0 | 1 | 1 | 1 | 2 | 2 | 2 | 3 | 3 |
| .15 | 1413 | 1416 | 1419 | 1422 | 1426 | 1429 | 1432 | 1435 | 1439 | 1442 | 0 | 1 | 1 | 1 | 2 | 2 | 2 | 3 | 3 |
| .16 | 1445 | 1449 | 1452 | 1455 | 1459 | 1462 | 1466 | 1469 | 1472 | 1476 | 0 | 1 | 1 | 1 | 2 | 2 | 2 | 3 | 3 |
| .17 | 1479 | 1483 | 1486 | 1489 | 1493 | 1496 | 1500 | 1503 | 1507 | 1510 | 0 | 1 | 1 | 1 | 2 | 2 | 2 | 3 | 3 |
| 18 | 1514 | 1517 | 1521 | 1524 | 1528 | 1531 | 1535 | 1538 | 1542 | 1545 | 0 | 1 | 1 | 1 | 2 | 2 | 2 | 3 | 3 |
| .19 | 1549 | 1552 | 1556 | 1560 | 1563 | 1567 | 1570 | 1574 | 1578 | 1581 | 0 | 1 | 1 | 1 | 2 | 2 | 3 | 3 | 3 |
| .20 | 1585 | 1589 | 1592 | 1596 | 1600 | 1603 | 1607 | 1611 | 1614 | 1618 | 0 | 1 | 1 | 1 | 2 | 2 | 3 | 3 | 3 |
| .21 | 1622 | 1626 | 1629 | 1633 | 1637 | 1641 | 1644 | 1648 | 1652 | 1656 | 0 | 1 | 1 | 2 | 2 | 2 | 3 | 3 | 3 |
| .22 | 1660 | 1663 | 1667 | 1671 | 1675 | 1679 | 1683 | 1687 | 1690 | 1694 | 0 | 1 | 1 | 2 | 2 | 2 | 3 | 3 | 3 |
| 23 | 1698 | 1702 | 1706 | 1710 | 1714 | 1718 | 1722 | 1726 | 1730 | 1734 | 0 | 1 | 1 | 2 | 2 | 2 | 3 | 3 | 4 |
| .24 | 1738 | 1742 | 1746 | 1750 | 1754 | 1758 | 1762 | 1766 | 1770 | 1774 | 0 | 1 | 1 | 2 | 2 | 2 | 3 | 3 | 4 |
| 25 | 1778 | 1782 | 1786 | 1791 | 1795 | 1799 | 1803 | 1807 | 1811 | 1816 | 0 | 1 | 1 | 2 | 2 | 2 | 3 | 3 | 4 |
| 26 | 1820 | 1824 | 1828 | 1832 | 1837 | 1841 | 1845 | 1849 | 1854 | 1858 | 0 | 1 | 1 | 2 | 2 | 3 | 3 | 3 | 4 |
| 27 | 1862 | 1866 | 1871 | 1875 | 1879 | 1884 | 1888 | 1892 | 1897 | 1901 | 0 | 1 | 1 | 2 | 2 | 3 | 3 | 3 | 4 |
| .28 | 1905 | 1910 | 1914 | 1919 | 1923 | 1928 | 1932 | 1936 | 1941 | 1945 | 0 | 1 | 1 | 2 | 2 | 3 | 3 | 4 | 4 |
| .29 | 1950 | 1954 | 1959 | 1963 | 1968 | 1972 | 1977 | 1982 | 1986 | 1991 | 0 | 1 | 1 | 2 | 2 | 3 | 3 | 4 | 4 |
| .30 | 1995 | 2000 | 2004 | 2009 | 2014 | 2018 | 2023 | 2028 | 2032 | 2037 | 0 | 1 | 1 | 2 | 2 | 3 | 3 | 4 | 4 |
| 31 | 2042 | 2046 | 2051 | 2056 | 2061 | 2065 | 2070 | 2075 | 2080 | 2084 | 0 | 1 | 1 | 2 | 2 | 3 | 3 | 4 | 4 |
| 32 | 2089 | 2094 | 2099 | 2104 | 2109 | 2113 | 2118 | 2123 | 2128 | 2133 | 0 | 1 | 1 | 2 | 2 | 3 | 3 | 4 | 4 |
| 33 | 2138 | 2143 | 2148 | 2153 | 2158 | 2163 | 2168 | 2173 | 2178 | 2183 | 0 | 1 | 1 | 2 | 2 | 3 | 3 | 4 | 4 |
| .34 | 2188 | 2193 | 2198 | 2203 | 2208 | 2213 | 2218 | 2223 | 2228 | 2234 | 1 | 1 | 2 | 2 | 3 | 3 | 4 | 4 | 5 |
| .35 | 2239 | 2244 | 2249 | 2254 | 2259 | 2265 | 2270 | 2275 | 2280 | 2286 | 1 | 1 | 2 | 2 | 3 | 3 | 4 | 4 | 5 |
| .36 | 2291 | 2296 | 2301 | 2307 | 2312 | 2317 | 2323 | 2328 | 2333 | 2339 | 1 | 1 | 2 | 2 | 3 | 3 | 4 | 4 | 5 |
| .37 | 2344 | 2350 | 2355 | 2360 | 2366 | 2371 | 2377 | 2382 | 2388 | 2393 | 1 | 1 | 2 | 2 | 3 | 3 | 4 | 4 | 5 |
| .38 | 2399 | 2404 | 2410 | 2415 | 2421 | 2427 | 2432 | 2438 | 2443 | 2449 | 1 | 1 | 2 | 2 | 3 | 3 | 4 | 5 | 5 |
| .39 | 2455 | 2460 | 2466 | 2472 | 2477 | 2483 | 2489 | 2495 | 2500 | 2506 | 1 | 1 | 2 | 2 | 3 | 3 | 4 | 5 | 5 |
| .40 | 2512 | 2518 | 2523 | 2529 | 2535 | 2541 | 2547 | 2553 | 2559 | 2564 | 1 | 1 | 2 | 2 | 3 | 4 | 4 | 5 | 5 |
| .41 | 2570 | 2576 | 2582 | 2588 | 2594 | 2600 | 2606 | 2612 | 2618 | 2624 | 1 | 1 | 2 | 2 | 3 | 4 | 4 | 5 | 5 |
| .42 | 2630 | 2636 | 2642 | 2649 | 2655 | 2661 | 2667 | 2673 | 2679 | 2685 | 1 | 1 | 2 | 2 | 3 | 4 | 4 | 5 | 6 |
| .43 | 2692 | 2698 | 2704 | 2710 | 2716 | 2723 | 2729 | 2735 | 2742 | 2748 | 1 | 1 | 2 | 3 | 3 | 4 | 4 | 5 | 6 |
| .44 | 2754 | 2761 | 2767 | 2773 | 2780 | 2786 | 2793 | 2799 | 2805 | 2812 | 1 | 1 | 2 | 3 | 3 | 4 | 4 | 5 | 6 |
| .45 | 2818 | 2825 | 2831 | 2838 | 2844 | 2851 | 2858 | 2864 | 2871 | 2877 | 1 | 1 | 2 | 3 | 3 | 4 | 5 | 5 | 6 |
| .46 | 2884 | 2891 | 2897 | 2904 | 2911 | 2917 | 2924 | 2931 | 2938 | 2944 | 1 | 1 | 2 | 3 | 3 | 4 | 5 | 5 | 6 |
| .47 | 2951 | 2958 | 2965 | 2972 | 2979 | 2985 | 2992 | 2999 | 3006 | 3013 | 1 | 1 | 2 | 3 | 3 | 4 | 5 | 5 | 6 |
| .48 | 3020 | 3027 | 3034 | 3041 | 3048 | 3055 | 3062 | 3069 | 3076 | 3083 | 1 | 1 | 2 | 3 | 4 | 4 | 5 | 6 | 6 |
| .49 | 3090 | 3097 | 3105 | 3112 | 3119 | 3126 | 3133 | 3141 | 3148 | 3155 | 1 | 1 | 2 | 3 | 4 | 4 | 5 | 6 | 6 |
| | 0 | 1 | 2 | 3 | 4 | 5 | 6 | 7 | 8 | 9 | 1 | 2 | 3 | 4 | 5 | 6 | 7 | 8 | 9 |

| | 0 | 1 | 2 | 3 | 4 | 5 | 6 | 7 | 8 | 9 | 1 | 2 | 3 | 4 | 5 | 6 | 7 | 8 | 9 |
|---|---|---|---|---|---|---|---|---|---|---|---|---|---|---|---|---|---|---|---|
| .50 | 3162 | 3170 | 3177 | 3184 | 3192 | 3199 | 3206 | 3214 | 3221 | 3228 | 1 | 1 | 2 | 3 | 4 | 4 | 5 | 6 | 7 |
| .51 | 3236 | 3243 | 3251 | 3258 | 3266 | 3273 | 3281 | 3289 | 3296 | 3304 | 1 | 2 | 2 | 3 | 4 | 5 | 5 | 6 | 7 |
| .52 | 3311 | 3319 | 3327 | 3334 | 3342 | 3350 | 3357 | 3365 | 3373 | 3381 | 1 | 2 | 2 | 3 | 4 | 5 | 5 | 6 | 7 |
| .53 | 3388 | 3396 | 3404 | 3412 | 3420 | 3428 | 3436 | 3443 | 3451 | 3459 | 1 | 2 | 2 | 3 | 4 | 5 | 5 | 6 | 7 |
| .54 | 3467 | 3475 | 3483 | 3491 | 3499 | 3508 | 3516 | 3524 | 3532 | 3540 | 1 | 2 | 2 | 3 | 4 | 5 | 6 | 6 | 7 |
| .55 | 3548 | 3556 | 3565 | 3573 | 3581 | 3589 | 3597 | 3606 | 3614 | 3622 | 1 | 2 | 2 | 3 | 4 | 5 | 6 | 7 | 7 |
| .56 | 3631 | 3639 | 3648 | 3656 | 3664 | 3673 | 3681 | 3690 | 3698 | 3707 | 1 | 2 | 3 | 3 | 4 | 5 | 6 | 7 | 8 |
| .57 | 3715 | 3724 | 3733 | 3741 | 3750 | 3758 | 3767 | 3776 | 3784 | 3793 | 1 | 2 | 3 | 3 | 4 | 5 | 6 | 7 | 8 |
| .58 | 3802 | 3811 | 3819 | 3828 | 3837 | 3846 | 3855 | 3864 | 3873 | 3882 | 1 | 2 | 3 | 4 | 4 | 5 | 6 | 7 | 8 |
| .59 | 3890 | 3899 | 3908 | 3917 | 3926 | 3936 | 3945 | 3954 | 3963 | 3972 | 1 | 2 | 3 | 4 | 5 | 5 | 6 | 7 | 8 |
| .60 | 3981 | 3990 | 3999 | 4009 | 4018 | 4027 | 4036 | 4046 | 4055 | 4064 | 1 | 2 | 3 | 4 | 5 | 6 | 6 | 7 | 8 |
| .61 | 4074 | 4083 | 4093 | 4102 | 4111 | 4121 | 4130 | 4140 | 4150 | 4159 | 1 | 2 | 3 | 4 | 5 | 6 | 7 | 8 | 9 |
| .62 | 4169 | 4178 | 4188 | 4198 | 4207 | 4217 | 4227 | 4236 | 4246 | 4256 | 1 | 2 | 3 | 4 | 5 | 6 | 7 | 8 | 9 |
| .63 | 4266 | 4276 | 4285 | 4295 | 4305 | 4315 | 4325 | 4335 | 4345 | 4355 | 1 | 2 | 3 | 4 | 5 | 6 | 7 | 8 | 9 |
| .64 | 4365 | 4375 | 4385 | 4395 | 4406 | 4416 | 4426 | 4436 | 4446 | 4457 | 1 | 2 | 3 | 4 | 5 | 6 | 7 | 8 | 9 |
| .65 | 4467 | 4477 | 4487 | 4498 | 4508 | 4519 | 4529 | 4539 | 4550 | 4560 | 1 | 2 | 3 | 4 | 5 | 6 | 7 | 8 | 9 |
| .66 | 4571 | 4581 | 4592 | 4603 | 4613 | 4624 | 4634 | 4645 | 4656 | 4667 | 1 | 2 | 3 | 4 | 5 | 6 | 7 | 9 | 10 |
| .67 | 4677 | 4688 | 4699 | 4710 | 4721 | 4732 | 4742 | 4753 | 4764 | 4775 | 1 | 2 | 3 | 4 | 5 | 7 | 8 | 9 | 10 |
| .68 | 4786 | 4797 | 4808 | 4819 | 4831 | 4842 | 4853 | 4864 | 4875 | 4887 | 1 | 2 | 3 | 4 | 5 | 7 | 8 | 9 | 10 |
| .69 | 4898 | 4909 | 4920 | 4932 | 4943 | 4955 | 4966 | 4977 | 4989 | 5000 | 1 | 2 | 3 | 5 | 6 | 7 | 8 | 9 | 10 |
| .70 | 5012 | 5023 | 5035 | 5047 | 5058 | 5070 | 5082 | 5093 | 5105 | 5117 | 1 | 2 | 4 | 5 | 6 | 7 | 8 | 9 | 11 |
| .71 | 5129 | 5140 | 5152 | 5164 | 5176 | 5188 | 5200 | 5212 | 5224 | 5236 | 1 | 2 | 4 | 5 | 6 | 7 | 8 | 10 | 11 |
| .72 | 5248 | 5260 | 5272 | 5284 | 5297 | 5309 | 5321 | 5333 | 5346 | 5358 | 1 | 2 | 4 | 5 | 6 | 7 | 9 | 10 | 11 |
| .73 | 5370 | 5383 | 5395 | 5408 | 5420 | 5433 | 5445 | 5458 | 5470 | 5483 | 1 | 3 | 4 | 5 | 6 | 8 | 9 | 10 | 11 |
| .74 | 5495 | 5508 | 5521 | 5534 | 5546 | 5559 | 5572 | 5585 | 5598 | 5610 | 1 | 3 | 4 | 5 | 6 | 8 | 9 | 10 | 12 |
| .75 | 5623 | 5636 | 5649 | 5662 | 5675 | 5689 | 5702 | 5715 | 5728 | 5741 | 1 | 3 | 4 | 5 | 7 | 8 | 9 | 10 | 12 |
| .76 | 5754 | 5768 | 5781 | 5794 | 5808 | 5821 | 5834 | 5848 | 5861 | 5875 | 1 | 3 | 4 | 5 | 7 | 8 | 9 | 11 | 12 |
| .77 | 5888 | 5902 | 5916 | 5929 | 5943 | 5957 | 5970 | 5984 | 5998 | 6012 | 1 | 3 | 4 | 5 | 7 | 8 | 10 | 11 | 12 |
| .78 | 6026 | 6039 | 6053 | 6067 | 6081 | 6095 | 6109 | 6124 | 6138 | 6152 | 1 | 3 | 4 | 6 | 7 | 8 | 10 | 11 | 13 |
| .79 | 6166 | 6180 | 6194 | 6209 | 6223 | 6237 | 6252 | 6266 | 6281 | 6295 | 1 | 3 | 4 | 6 | 7 | 9 | 10 | 11 | 13 |
| .80 | 6310 | 6324 | 6339 | 6353 | 6368 | 6383 | 6397 | 6412 | 6427 | 6442 | 1 | 3 | 4 | 6 | 7 | 9 | 10 | 12 | 13 |
| .81 | 6457 | 6471 | 6486 | 6501 | 6516 | 6531 | 6546 | 6561 | 6577 | 6592 | 2 | 3 | 5 | 6 | 8 | 9 | 11 | 12 | 14 |
| .82 | 6607 | 6622 | 6637 | 6653 | 6668 | 6683 | 6699 | 6714 | 6730 | 6745 | 2 | 3 | 5 | 6 | 8 | 9 | 11 | 12 | 14 |
| .83 | 6761 | 6776 | 6792 | 6808 | 6823 | 6839 | 6855 | 6871 | 6887 | 6902 | 2 | 3 | 5 | 6 | 8 | 9 | 11 | 13 | 14 |
| .84 | 6918 | 6934 | 6950 | 6966 | 6982 | 6998 | 7015 | 7031 | 7047 | 7063 | 2 | 3 | 5 | 6 | 8 | 10 | 11 | 13 | 15 |
| .85 | 7079 | 7096 | 7112 | 7129 | 7145 | 7161 | 7178 | 7194 | 7211 | 7228 | 2 | 3 | 5 | 7 | 8 | 10 | 12 | 13 | 15 |
| .86 | 7244 | 7261 | 7278 | 7295 | 7311 | 7328 | 7345 | 7362 | 7379 | 7396 | 2 | 3 | 5 | 7 | 8 | 10 | 12 | 13 | 15 |
| .87 | 7413 | 7430 | 7447 | 7464 | 7482 | 7499 | 7516 | 7534 | 7551 | 7568 | 2 | 3 | 5 | 7 | 9 | 10 | 12 | 14 | 16 |
| .88 | 7586 | 7603 | 7621 | 7638 | 7656 | 7674 | 7691 | 7709 | 7727 | 7745 | 2 | 4 | 5 | 7 | 9 | 11 | 12 | 14 | 16 |
| .89 | 7762 | 7780 | 7798 | 7816 | 7834 | 7852 | 7870 | 7889 | 7907 | 7925 | 2 | 4 | 5 | 7 | 9 | 11 | 13 | 14 | 16 |
| .90 | 7943 | 7962 | 7980 | 7998 | 8017 | 8035 | 8054 | 8072 | 8091 | 8110 | 2 | 4 | 6 | 7 | 9 | 11 | 13 | 15 | 17 |
| .91 | 8128 | 8147 | 8166 | 8185 | 8204 | 8222 | 8241 | 8260 | 8279 | 8299 | 2 | 4 | 6 | 8 | 9 | 11 | 13 | 15 | 17 |
| .92 | 8318 | 8337 | 8356 | 8375 | 8395 | 8414 | 8433 | 8453 | 8472 | 8492 | 2 | 4 | 6 | 8 | 10 | 12 | 14 | 15 | 17 |
| .93 | 8511 | 8531 | 8551 | 8570 | 8590 | 8610 | 8630 | 8650 | 8670 | 8690 | 2 | 4 | 6 | 8 | 10 | 12 | 14 | 16 | 18 |
| .94 | 8710 | 8730 | 8750 | 8770 | 8790 | 8810 | 8831 | 8851 | 8872 | 8892 | 2 | 4 | 6 | 8 | 10 | 12 | 14 | 16 | 18 |
| .95 | 8913 | 8933 | 8954 | 8974 | 8995 | 9016 | 9036 | 9057 | 9078 | 9099 | 2 | 4 | 6 | 8 | 10 | 12 | 15 | 17 | 19 |
| .96 | 9120 | 9141 | 9162 | 9183 | 9204 | 9226 | 9247 | 9268 | 9290 | 9311 | 2 | 4 | 6 | 8 | 11 | 13 | 15 | 17 | 19 |
| .97 | 9333 | 9354 | 9376 | 9397 | 9419 | 9441 | 9462 | 9484 | 9506 | 9528 | 2 | 4 | 7 | 9 | 11 | 13 | 15 | 17 | 20 |
| .98 | 9550 | 9572 | 9594 | 9616 | 9638 | 9661 | 9683 | 9705 | 9727 | 9750 | 2 | 4 | 7 | 9 | 11 | 13 | 16 | 18 | 20 |
| .99 | 9772 | 9795 | 9817 | 9840 | 9863 | 9886 | 9908 | 9931 | 9954 | 9977 | 2 | 5 | 7 | 9 | 11 | 14 | 16 | 18 | 20 |
| | 0 | 1 | 2 | 3 | 4 | 5 | 6 | 7 | 8 | 9 | 1 | 2 | 3 | 4 | 5 | 6 | 7 | 8 | 9 |

Proportional Parts

# FIVE-PLACE LOGARITHMS

| N. | 0 | 1 | 2 | 3 | 4 | 5 | 6 | 7 | 8 | 9 | Proportional parts |
|----|---|---|---|---|---|---|---|---|---|---|---|

|   |   |   |   |   |   |   |   |   |   |   | **44 43 42** |
|---|---|---|---|---|---|---|---|---|---|---|---|
| **100** | 00 000 | 043 | 087 | 130 | 173 | 217 | 260 | 303 | 346 | 389 | 1| 4,4  4,3  4,2 |
| **101** | | 432 | 475 | 518 | 561 | 604 | 647 | 689 | 732 | 775 | 817 | 2| 8,8  8,6  8,4 |
| **102** | | 860 | 903 | 945 | 988 | *030 | *072 | *115 | *157 | *199 | *242 | 3| 13,2 12,9 12,6 |
| **103** | 01 284 | 326 | 368 | 410 | 452 | 494 | 536 | 578 | 620 | 662 | 4| 17,6 17,2 16,8 |
| **104** | | 703 | 745 | 787 | 828 | 870 | 912 | 953 | 995 | *036 | *078 | 5| 22,0 21,5 21,0 |
| **105** | 02 119 | 160 | 202 | 243 | 284 | 325 | 366 | 407 | 449 | 490 | 6| 26,4 25,8 25,2 |
| **106** | | 531 | 572 | 612 | 653 | 694 | 735 | 776 | 816 | 857 | 898 | 7| 30,8 30,1 29,4 |
| **107** | | 938 | 979 | *019 | *060 | *100 | *141 | *181 | *222 | *262 | *302 | 8| 35,2 34,4 33,6 |
| **108** | 03 342 | 383 | 423 | 463 | 503 | 543 | 583 | 623 | 663 | 703 | 9| 39,6 38,7 37,8 |
| **109** | | 743 | 782 | 822 | 862 | 902 | 941 | 981 | *021 | *060 | *100 | |

|   |   |   |   |   |   |   |   |   |   |   | **41 40 39** |
|---|---|---|---|---|---|---|---|---|---|---|---|
| **110** | 04 139 | 179 | 218 | 258 | 297 | 336 | 376 | 415 | 454 | 493 | 1| 4,1  4,0  3,9 |
| **111** | | 532 | 571 | 610 | 650 | 689 | 727 | 766 | 805 | 844 | 883 | 2| 8,2  8,0  7,8 |
| **112** | | 922 | 961 | 999 | *038 | *077 | *115 | *154 | *192 | *231 | *269 | 3| 12,3 12,0 11,7 |
| **113** | 05 308 | 346 | 385 | 423 | 461 | 500 | 538 | 576 | 614 | 652 | 4| 16,4 16,0 15,6 |
| **114** | | 690 | 729 | 767 | 805 | 843 | 881 | 918 | 956 | 994 | *032 | 5| 20,5 20,0 19,5 |
| **115** | 06 070 | 108 | 145 | 183 | 221 | 258 | 296 | 333 | 371 | 408 | 6| 24,6 24,0 23,4 |
| **116** | | 446 | 483 | 521 | 558 | 595 | 633 | 670 | 707 | 744 | 781 | 7| 28,7 28,0 27,3 |
| **117** | | 819 | 856 | 893 | 930 | 967 | *004 | *041 | *078 | *115 | *151 | 8| 32,8 32,0 31,2 |
| **118** | 07 188 | 225 | 262 | 298 | 335 | 372 | 408 | 445 | 482 | 518 | 9| 36,9 36,0 35,1 |
| **119** | | 555 | 591 | 628 | 664 | 700 | 737 | 773 | 809 | 846 | 882 | |

|   |   |   |   |   |   |   |   |   |   |   | **38 37 36** |
|---|---|---|---|---|---|---|---|---|---|---|---|
| **120** | | 918 | 954 | 990 | *027 | *063 | *099 | *135 | *171 | *207 | *243 | 1| 3,8  3,7  3,6 |
| **121** | 08 279 | 314 | 350 | 386 | 422 | 458 | 493 | 529 | 565 | 600 | 2| 7,6  7,4  7,2 |
| **122** | | 636 | 672 | 707 | 743 | 778 | 814 | 849 | 884 | 920 | 955 | 3| 11,4 11,1 10,8 |
| **123** | | 991 | *026 | *061 | *096 | *132 | *167 | *202 | *237 | *272 | *307 | 4| 15,2 14,8 14,4 |
| **124** | 09 342 | 377 | 412 | 447 | 482 | 517 | 552 | 587 | 621 | 656 | 5| 19,0 18,5 18,0 |
| **125** | | 691 | 726 | 760 | 795 | 830 | 864 | 899 | 934 | 968 | *003 | 6| 22,8 22,2 21,6 |
| **126** | 10 037 | 072 | 106 | 140 | 175 | 209 | 243 | 278 | 312 | 346 | 7| 26,6 25,9 25,2 |
| **127** | | 380 | 415 | 449 | 483 | 517 | 551 | 585 | 619 | 653 | 687 | 8| 30,4 29,6 28,8 |
| **128** | | 721 | 755 | 789 | 823 | 857 | 890 | 924 | 958 | 992 | *025 | 9| 34,2 33,3 32,4 |
| **129** | 11 059 | 093 | 126 | 160 | 193 | 227 | 261 | 294 | 327 | 361 | |

|   |   |   |   |   |   |   |   |   |   |   | **35 34 33** |
|---|---|---|---|---|---|---|---|---|---|---|---|
| **130** | | 394 | 428 | 461 | 494 | 528 | 561 | 594 | 628 | 661 | 694 | 1| 3,5  3,4  3,3 |
| **131** | | 727 | 760 | 793 | 826 | 860 | 893 | 926 | 959 | 992 | *024 | 2| 7,0  6,8  6,6 |
| **132** | 12 057 | 090 | 123 | 156 | 189 | 222 | 254 | 287 | 320 | 352 | 3| 10,5 10,2  9,9 |
| **133** | | 385 | 418 | 450 | 483 | 516 | 548 | 581 | 613 | 646 | 678 | 4| 14,0 13,6 13,2 |
| **134** | | 710 | 743 | 775 | 808 | 840 | 872 | 905 | 937 | 969 | *001 | 5| 17,5 17,0 16,5 |
| **135** | 13 033 | 066 | 098 | 130 | 162 | 194 | 226 | 258 | 290 | 322 | 6| 21,0 20,4 19,8 |
| **136** | | 354 | 386 | 418 | 450 | 481 | 513 | 545 | 577 | 609 | 640 | 7| 24,5 23,8 23,1 |
| **137** | | 672 | 704 | 735 | 767 | 799 | 830 | 862 | 893 | 925 | 956 | 8| 28,0 27,2 26,4 |
| **138** | | 988 | *019 | *051 | *082 | *114 | *145 | *176 | *208 | *239 | *270 | 9| 31,5 30,6 29,7 |
| **139** | 14 301 | 333 | 364 | 395 | 426 | 457 | 489 | 520 | 551 | 582 | |

|   |   |   |   |   |   |   |   |   |   |   | **32 31 30** |
|---|---|---|---|---|---|---|---|---|---|---|---|
| **140** | | 613 | 644 | 675 | 706 | 737 | 768 | 799 | 829 | 860 | 891 | 1| 3,2  3,1  3,0 |
| **141** | | 922 | 953 | 983 | *014 | *045 | *076 | *106 | *137 | *168 | *198 | 2| 6,4  6,2  6,0 |
| **142** | 15 229 | 259 | 290 | 320 | 351 | 381 | 412 | 442 | 473 | 503 | 3| 9,6  9,3  9,0 |
| **143** | | 534 | 564 | 594 | 625 | 655 | 685 | 715 | 746 | 776 | 806 | 4| 12,8 12,4 12,0 |
| **144** | | 836 | 866 | 897 | 927 | 957 | 987 | *017 | *047 | *077 | *107 | 5| 16,0 15,5 15,0 |
| **145** | 16 137 | 167 | 197 | 227 | 256 | 286 | 316 | 346 | 376 | 406 | 6| 19,2 18,6 18,0 |
| **146** | | 435 | 465 | 495 | 524 | 554 | 584 | 613 | 643 | 673 | 702 | 7| 22,4 21,7 21,0 |
| **147** | | 732 | 761 | 791 | 820 | 850 | 879 | 909 | 938 | 967 | 997 | 8| 25,6 24,8 24,0 |
| **148** | 17 026 | 056 | 085 | 114 | 143 | 173 | 202 | 231 | 260 | 289 | 9| 28,8 27,9 27,0 |
| **149** | | 319 | 348 | 377 | 406 | 435 | 464 | 493 | 522 | 551 | 580 | |

| **150** | | 609 | 638 | 667 | 696 | 725 | 754 | 782 | 811 | 840 | 869 | |

| N. | 0 | 1 | 2 | 3 | 4 | 5 | 6 | 7 | 8 | 9 | Proportional parts |

| N. | 0 | 1 | 2 | 3 | 4 | 5 | 6 | 7 | 8 | 9 |
|---|---|---|---|---|---|---|---|---|---|---|
| **150** | 17 609 | 638 | 667 | 696 | 725 | 754 | 782 | 811 | 840 | 869 |
| 151 | 898 | 926 | 955 | 984 | *013 | *041 | *070 | *099 | *127 | *156 |
| 152 | 18 184 | 213 | 241 | 270 | 298 | 327 | 355 | 384 | 412 | 441 |
| 153 | 469 | 498 | 526 | 554 | 583 | 611 | 639 | 667 | 696 | 724 |
| 154 | 752 | 780 | 808 | 837 | 865 | 893 | 921 | 949 | 977 | *005 |
| 155 | 19 033 | 061 | 089 | 117 | 145 | 173 | 201 | 229 | 257 | 285 |
| 156 | 312 | 340 | 368 | 396 | 424 | 451 | 479 | 507 | 535 | 562 |
| 157 | 590 | 618 | 645 | 673 | 700 | 728 | 756 | 783 | 811 | 838 |
| 158 | 866 | 893 | 921 | 948 | 976 | *003 | *030 | *058 | *085 | *112 |
| 159 | 20 140 | 167 | 194 | 222 | 249 | 276 | 303 | 330 | 358 | 385 |
| **160** | 412 | 439 | 466 | 493 | 520 | 548 | 575 | 602 | 629 | 656 |
| 161 | 683 | 710 | 737 | 763 | 790 | 817 | 844 | 871 | 898 | 925 |
| 162 | 952 | 978 | *005 | *032 | *059 | *085 | *112 | *139 | *165 | *192 |
| 163 | 21 219 | 245 | 272 | 299 | 325 | 352 | 378 | 405 | 431 | 458 |
| 164 | 484 | 511 | 537 | 564 | 590 | 617 | 643 | 669 | 696 | 722 |
| 165 | 748 | 775 | 801 | 827 | 854 | 880 | 906 | 932 | 958 | 985 |
| 166 | 22 011 | 037 | 063 | 089 | 115 | 141 | 167 | 194 | 220 | 246 |
| 167 | 272 | 298 | 324 | 350 | 376 | 401 | 427 | 453 | 479 | 505 |
| 168 | 531 | 557 | 583 | 608 | 634 | 660 | 686 | 712 | 737 | 763 |
| 169 | 789 | 814 | 840 | 866 | 891 | 917 | 943 | 968 | 994 | *019 |
| **170** | 23 045 | 070 | 096 | 121 | 147 | 172 | 198 | 223 | 249 | 274 |
| 171 | 300 | 325 | 350 | 376 | 401 | 426 | 452 | 477 | 502 | 528 |
| 172 | 553 | 578 | 603 | 629 | 654 | 679 | 704 | 729 | 754 | 779 |
| 173 | 805 | 830 | 855 | 880 | 905 | 930 | 955 | 980 | *005 | *030 |
| 174 | 24 055 | 080 | 105 | 130 | 155 | 180 | 204 | 229 | 254 | 279 |
| 175 | 304 | 329 | 353 | 378 | 403 | 428 | 452 | 477 | 502 | 527 |
| 176 | 551 | 576 | 601 | 625 | 650 | 674 | 699 | 724 | 748 | 773 |
| 177 | 797 | 822 | 846 | 871 | 895 | 920 | 944 | 969 | 993 | *018 |
| 178 | 25 042 | 066 | 091 | 115 | 139 | 164 | 188 | 212 | 237 | 261 |
| 179 | 285 | 310 | 334 | 358 | 382 | 406 | 431 | 455 | 479 | 503 |
| **180** | 527 | 551 | 575 | 600 | 624 | 648 | 672 | 696 | 720 | 744 |
| 181 | 768 | 792 | 816 | 840 | 864 | 888 | 912 | 935 | 959 | 983 |
| 182 | 26 007 | 031 | 055 | 079 | 102 | 126 | 150 | 174 | 198 | 221 |
| 183 | 245 | 269 | 293 | 316 | 340 | 364 | 387 | 411 | 435 | 458 |
| 184 | 482 | 505 | 529 | 553 | 576 | 600 | 623 | 647 | 670 | 694 |
| 185 | 717 | 741 | 764 | 788 | 811 | 834 | 858 | 881 | 905 | 928 |
| 186 | 951 | 975 | 998 | *021 | *045 | *068 | *091 | *114 | *138 | *161 |
| 187 | 27 184 | 207 | 231 | 254 | 277 | 300 | 323 | 346 | 370 | 393 |
| 188 | 416 | 439 | 462 | 485 | 508 | 531 | 554 | 577 | 600 | 623 |
| 189 | 646 | 669 | 692 | 715 | 738 | 761 | 784 | 807 | 830 | 852 |
| **190** | 875 | 898 | 921 | 944 | 967 | 989 | *012 | *035 | *058 | *081 |
| 191 | 28 103 | 126 | 149 | 171 | 194 | 217 | 240 | 262 | 285 | 307 |
| 192 | 330 | 353 | 375 | 398 | 421 | 443 | 466 | 488 | 511 | 533 |
| 193 | 556 | 578 | 601 | 623 | 646 | 668 | 691 | 713 | 735 | 758 |
| 194 | 780 | 803 | 825 | 847 | 870 | 892 | 914 | 937 | 959 | 981 |
| 195 | 29 003 | 026 | 048 | 070 | 092 | 115 | 137 | 159 | 181 | 203 |
| 196 | 226 | 248 | 270 | 292 | 314 | 336 | 358 | 380 | 403 | 425 |
| 197 | 447 | 469 | 491 | 513 | 535 | 557 | 579 | 601 | 623 | 645 |
| 198 | 667 | 688 | 710 | 732 | 754 | 776 | 798 | 820 | 842 | 863 |
| 199 | 885 | 907 | 929 | 951 | 973 | 994 | *016 | *038 | *060 | *081 |
| **200** | 30 103 | 125 | 146 | 168 | 190 | 211 | 233 | 255 | 276 | 298 |

**Proportional parts**

| | 29 | 28 | | | 27 | 26 | | | 25 | | | 24 | 23 | | | 22 | 21 |
|---|---|---|---|---|---|---|---|---|---|---|---|---|---|---|---|---|---|
| 1 | 2,9 | 2,8 | | 1 | 2,7 | 2,6 | | 1 | 2,5 | | 1 | 2,4 | 2,3 | | 1 | 2,2 | 2,1 |
| 2 | 5,8 | 5,6 | | 2 | 5,4 | 5,2 | | 2 | 5,0 | | 2 | 4,8 | 4,6 | | 2 | 4,4 | 4,2 |
| 3 | 8,7 | 8,4 | | 3 | 8,1 | 7,8 | | 3 | 7,5 | | 3 | 7,2 | 6,9 | | 3 | 6,6 | 6,3 |
| 4 | 11,6 | 11,2 | | 4 | 10,8 | 10,4 | | 4 | 10,0 | | 4 | 9,6 | 9,2 | | 4 | 8,8 | 8,4 |
| 5 | 14,5 | 14,0 | | 5 | 13,5 | 13,0 | | 5 | 12,5 | | 5 | 12,0 | 11,5 | | 5 | 11,0 | 10,5 |
| 6 | 17,4 | 16,8 | | 6 | 16,2 | 15,6 | | 6 | 15,0 | | 6 | 14,4 | 13,8 | | 6 | 13,2 | 12,6 |
| 7 | 20,3 | 19,6 | | 7 | 18,9 | 18,2 | | 7 | 17,5 | | 7 | 16,8 | 16,1 | | 7 | 15,4 | 14,7 |
| 8 | 23,2 | 22,4 | | 8 | 21,6 | 20,8 | | 8 | 20,0 | | 8 | 19,2 | 18,4 | | 8 | 17,6 | 16,8 |
| 9 | 26,1 | 25,2 | | 9 | 24,3 | 23,4 | | 9 | 22,5 | | 9 | 21,6 | 20,7 | | 9 | 19,8 | 18,9 |

| N. | 0 | 1 | 2 | 3 | 4 | 5 | 6 | 7 | 8 | 9 | Proportional parts |
|---|---|---|---|---|---|---|---|---|---|---|---|

| N. | 0 | 1 | 2 | 3 | 4 | 5 | 6 | 7 | 8 | 9 |
|---|---|---|---|---|---|---|---|---|---|---|
| **200** | 30 103 | 125 | 146 | 168 | 190 | 211 | 233 | 255 | 276 | 298 |
| 201 | 320 | 341 | 363 | 384 | 406 | 428 | 449 | 471 | 492 | 514 |
| 202 | 535 | 557 | 578 | 600 | 621 | 643 | 664 | 685 | 707 | 728 |
| 203 | 750 | 771 | 792 | 814 | 835 | 856 | 878 | 899 | 920 | 942 |
| 204 | 963 | 984 | *006 | *027 | *048 | *069 | *091 | *112 | *133 | *154 |
| 205 | 31 175 | 197 | 218 | 239 | 260 | 281 | 302 | 323 | 345 | 366 |
| 206 | 387 | 408 | 429 | 450 | 471 | 492 | 513 | 534 | 555 | 576 |
| 207 | 597 | 618 | 639 | 660 | 681 | 702 | 723 | 744 | 765 | 785 |
| 208 | 806 | 827 | 848 | 869 | 890 | 911 | 931 | 952 | 973 | 994 |
| 209 | 32 015 | 035 | 056 | 077 | 098 | 118 | 139 | 160 | 181 | 201 |
| **210** | 222 | 243 | 263 | 284 | 305 | 325 | 346 | 366 | 387 | 408 |
| 211 | 428 | 449 | 469 | 490 | 510 | 531 | 552 | 572 | 593 | 613 |
| 212 | 634 | 654 | 675 | 695 | 715 | 736 | 756 | 777 | 797 | 818 |
| 213 | 838 | 858 | 879 | 899 | 919 | 940 | 960 | 980 | *001 | *021 |
| 214 | 33 041 | 062 | 082 | 102 | 122 | 143 | 163 | 183 | 203 | 224 |
| 215 | 244 | 264 | 284 | 304 | 325 | 345 | 365 | 385 | 405 | 425 |
| 216 | 445 | 465 | 486 | 506 | 526 | 546 | 566 | 586 | 606 | 626 |
| 217 | 646 | 666 | 686 | 706 | 726 | 746 | 766 | 786 | 806 | 826 |
| 218 | 846 | 866 | 885 | 905 | 925 | 945 | 965 | 985 | *005 | *025 |
| 219 | 34 044 | 064 | 084 | 104 | 124 | 143 | 163 | 183 | 203 | 223 |
| **220** | 242 | 262 | 282 | 301 | 321 | 341 | 361 | 380 | 400 | 420 |
| 221 | 439 | 459 | 479 | 498 | 518 | 537 | 557 | 577 | 596 | 616 |
| 222 | 635 | 655 | 674 | 694 | 713 | 733 | 753 | 772 | 792 | 811 |
| 223 | 830 | 850 | 869 | 889 | 908 | 928 | 947 | 967 | 986 | *005 |
| 224 | 35 025 | 044 | 064 | 083 | 102 | 122 | 141 | 160 | 180 | 199 |
| 225 | 218 | 238 | 257 | 276 | 295 | 315 | 334 | 353 | 372 | 392 |
| 226 | 411 | 430 | 449 | 468 | 488 | 507 | 526 | 545 | 564 | 583 |
| 227 | 603 | 622 | 641 | 660 | 679 | 698 | 717 | 736 | 755 | 774 |
| 228 | 793 | 813 | 832 | 851 | 870 | 889 | 908 | 927 | 946 | 965 |
| 229 | 984 | *003 | *021 | *040 | *059 | *078 | *097 | *116 | *135 | *154 |
| **230** | 36 173 | 192 | 211 | 229 | 248 | 267 | 286 | 305 | 324 | 342 |
| 231 | 361 | 380 | 399 | 418 | 436 | 455 | 474 | 493 | 511 | 530 |
| 232 | 549 | 568 | 586 | 605 | 624 | 642 | 661 | 680 | 698 | 717 |
| 233 | 736 | 754 | 773 | 791 | 810 | 829 | 847 | 866 | 884 | 903 |
| 234 | 922 | 940 | 959 | 977 | 996 | *014 | *033 | *051 | *070 | *088 |
| 235 | 37 107 | 125 | 144 | 162 | 181 | 199 | 218 | 236 | 254 | 273 |
| 236 | 291 | 310 | 328 | 346 | 365 | 383 | 401 | 420 | 438 | 457 |
| 237 | 475 | 493 | 511 | 530 | 548 | 566 | 585 | 603 | 621 | 639 |
| 238 | 658 | 676 | 694 | 712 | 731 | 749 | 767 | 785 | 803 | 822 |
| 239 | 840 | 858 | 876 | 894 | 912 | 931 | 949 | 967 | 985 | *003 |
| **240** | 38 021 | 039 | 057 | 075 | 093 | 112 | 130 | 148 | 166 | 184 |
| 241 | 202 | 220 | 238 | 256 | 274 | 292 | 310 | 328 | 346 | 364 |
| 242 | 382 | 399 | 417 | 435 | 453 | 471 | 489 | 507 | 525 | 543 |
| 243 | 561 | 578 | 596 | 614 | 632 | 650 | 668 | 686 | 703 | 721 |
| 244 | 739 | 757 | 775 | 792 | 810 | 828 | 846 | 863 | 881 | 899 |
| 245 | 917 | 934 | 952 | 970 | 987 | *005 | *023 | *041 | *058 | *076 |
| 246 | 39 094 | 111 | 129 | 146 | 164 | 182 | 199 | 217 | 235 | 252 |
| 247 | 270 | 287 | 305 | 322 | 340 | 358 | 375 | 393 | 410 | 428 |
| 248 | 445 | 463 | 480 | 498 | 515 | 533 | 550 | 568 | 585 | 602 |
| 249 | 620 | 637 | 655 | 672 | 690 | 707 | 724 | 742 | 759 | 777 |
| **250** | 794 | 811 | 829 | 846 | 863 | 881 | 898 | 915 | 933 | 950 |

**Proportional parts**

| | 22 | 21 |
|---|---|---|
| 1 | 2,2 | 2,1 |
| 2 | 4,4 | 4,2 |
| 3 | 6,6 | 6,3 |
| 4 | 8,8 | 8,4 |
| 5 | 11,0 | 10,5 |
| 6 | 13,2 | 12,6 |
| 7 | 15,4 | 14,7 |
| 8 | 17,6 | 16,8 |
| 9 | 19,8 | 18,9 |

| | 20 |
|---|---|
| 1 | 2,0 |
| 2 | 4,0 |
| 3 | 6,0 |
| 4 | 8,0 |
| 5 | 10,0 |
| 6 | 12,0 |
| 7 | 14,0 |
| 8 | 16,0 |
| 9 | 18,0 |

| | 19 |
|---|---|
| 1 | 1,9 |
| 2 | 3,8 |
| 3 | 5,7 |
| 4 | 7,6 |
| 5 | 9,5 |
| 6 | 11,4 |
| 7 | 13,3 |
| 8 | 15,2 |
| 9 | 17,1 |

| | 18 |
|---|---|
| 1 | 1,8 |
| 2 | 3,6 |
| 3 | 5,4 |
| 4 | 7,2 |
| 5 | 9,0 |
| 6 | 10,8 |
| 7 | 12,6 |
| 8 | 14,4 |
| 9 | 16,2 |

| | 17 |
|---|---|
| 1 | 1,7 |
| 2 | 3,4 |
| 3 | 5,1 |
| 4 | 6,8 |
| 5 | 8,5 |
| 6 | 10,2 |
| 7 | 11,9 |
| 8 | 13,6 |
| 9 | 15,3 |

| N. | 0 | 1 | 2 | 3 | 4 | 5 | 6 | 7 | 8 | 9 | Proportional parts |
|---|---|---|---|---|---|---|---|---|---|---|---|

| N. | 0 | 1 | 2 | 3 | 4 | 5 | 6 | 7 | 8 | 9 | Proportional parts | |
|---|---|---|---|---|---|---|---|---|---|---|---|---|
| 250 | 39 794 | 811 | 829 | 846 | 863 | 881 | 898 | 915 | 933 | 950 | | **18** |
| 251 | 967 | 985 | *002 | *019 | *037 | *054 | *071 | *088 | *106 | *123 | 1 | 1,8 |
| 252 | 40 140 | 157 | 175 | 192 | 209 | 226 | 243 | 261 | 278 | 295 | 2 | 3,6 |
| 253 | 312 | 329 | 346 | 364 | 381 | 398 | 415 | 432 | 449 | 466 | 3 | 5,4 |
| 254 | 483 | 500 | 518 | 535 | 552 | 569 | 586 | 603 | 620 | 637 | 4 | 7,2 |
| 255 | 654 | 671 | 688 | 705 | 722 | 739 | 756 | 773 | 790 | 807 | 5 | 9,0 |
| 256 | 824 | 841 | 858 | 875 | 892 | 909 | 926 | 943 | 960 | 976 | 6 | 10,8 |
| 257 | 993 | *010 | *027 | *044 | *061 | *078 | *095 | *111 | *128 | *145 | 7 | 12,6 |
| 258 | 41 162 | 179 | 196 | 212 | 229 | 246 | 263 | 280 | 296 | 313 | 8 | 14,4 |
| 259 | 330 | 347 | 363 | 380 | 397 | 414 | 430 | 447 | 464 | 481 | 9 | 16,2 |
| **260** | 497 | 514 | 531 | 547 | 564 | 581 | 597 | 614 | 631 | 647 | | **17** |
| 261 | 664 | 681 | 697 | 714 | 731 | 747 | 764 | 780 | 797 | 814 | 1 | 1,7 |
| 262 | 830 | 847 | 863 | 880 | 896 | 913 | 929 | 946 | 963 | 979 | 2 | 3,4 |
| 263 | 996 | *012 | *029 | *045 | *062 | *078 | *095 | *111 | *127 | *144 | 3 | 5,1 |
| 264 | 42 160 | 177 | 193 | 210 | 226 | 243 | 259 | 275 | 292 | 308 | 4 | 6,8 |
| 265 | 325 | 341 | 357 | 374 | 390 | 406 | 423 | 439 | 455 | 472 | 5 | 8,5 |
| 266 | 488 | 504 | 521 | 537 | 553 | 570 | 586 | 602 | 619 | 635 | 6 | 10,2 |
| 267 | 651 | 667 | 684 | 700 | 716 | 732 | 749 | 765 | 781 | 797 | 7 | 11,9 |
| 268 | 813 | 830 | 846 | 862 | 878 | 894 | 911 | 927 | 943 | 959 | 8 | 13,6 |
| 269 | 975 | 991 | *008 | *024 | *040 | *056 | *072 | *088 | *104 | *120 | 9 | 15,3 |
| **270** | 43 136 | 152 | 169 | 185 | 201 | 217 | 233 | 249 | 265 | 281 | | **16** |
| 271 | 297 | 313 | 329 | 345 | 361 | 377 | 393 | 409 | 425 | 441 | 1 | 1,6 |
| 272 | 457 | 473 | 489 | 505 | 521 | 537 | 553 | 569 | 584 | 600 | 2 | 3,2 |
| 273 | 616 | 632 | 648 | 664 | 680 | 696 | 712 | 727 | 743 | 759 | 3 | 4,8 |
| 274 | 775 | 791 | 807 | 823 | 838 | 854 | 870 | 886 | 902 | 917 | 4 | 6,4 |
| 275 | 933 | 949 | 965 | 981 | 996 | *012 | *028 | *044 | *059 | *075 | 5 | 8,0 |
| 276 | 44 091 | 107 | 122 | 138 | 154 | 170 | 185 | 201 | 217 | 232 | 6 | 9,6 |
| 277 | 248 | 264 | 279 | 295 | 311 | 326 | 342 | 358 | 373 | 389 | 7 | 11,2 |
| 278 | 404 | 420 | 436 | 451 | 467 | 483 | 498 | 514 | 529 | 545 | 8 | 12,8 |
| 279 | 560 | 576 | 592 | 607 | 623 | 638 | 654 | 669 | 685 | 700 | 9 | 14,4 |
| **280** | 716 | 731 | 747 | 762 | 778 | 793 | 809 | 824 | 840 | 855 | | **15** |
| 281 | 871 | 886 | 902 | 917 | 932 | 948 | 963 | 979 | 994 | *010 | 1 | 1,5 |
| 282 | 45 025 | 040 | 056 | 071 | 086 | 102 | 117 | 133 | 148 | 163 | 2 | 3,0 |
| 283 | 179 | 194 | 209 | 225 | 240 | 255 | 271 | 286 | 301 | 317 | 3 | 4,5 |
| 284 | 332 | 347 | 362 | 378 | 393 | 408 | 423 | 439 | 454 | 469 | 4 | 6,0 |
| 285 | 484 | 500 | 515 | 530 | 545 | 561 | 576 | 591 | 606 | 621 | 5 | 7,5 |
| 286 | 637 | 652 | 667 | 682 | 697 | 712 | 728 | 743 | 758 | 773 | 6 | 9,0 |
| 287 | 788 | 803 | 818 | 834 | 849 | 864 | 879 | 894 | 909 | 924 | 7 | 10,5 |
| 288 | 939 | 954 | 969 | 984 | *000 | *015 | *030 | *045 | *060 | *075 | 8 | 12,0 |
| 289 | 46 090 | 105 | 120 | 135 | 150 | 165 | 180 | 195 | 210 | 225 | 9 | 13,5 |
| **290** | 240 | 255 | 270 | 285 | 300 | 315 | 330 | 345 | 359 | 374 | | **14** |
| 291 | 389 | 404 | 419 | 434 | 449 | 464 | 479 | 494 | 509 | 523 | 1 | 1,4 |
| 292 | 538 | 553 | 568 | 583 | 598 | 613 | 627 | 642 | 657 | 672 | 2 | 2,8 |
| 293 | 687 | 702 | 716 | 731 | 746 | 761 | 776 | 790 | 805 | 820 | 3 | 4,2 |
| 294 | 835 | 850 | 864 | 879 | 894 | 909 | 923 | 938 | 953 | 967 | 4 | 5,6 |
| 295 | 982 | 997 | *012 | *026 | *041 | *056 | *070 | *085 | *100 | *114 | 5 | 7,0 |
| 296 | 47 129 | 144 | 159 | 173 | 188 | 202 | 217 | 232 | 246 | 261 | 6 | 8,4 |
| 297 | 276 | 290 | 305 | 319 | 334 | 349 | 363 | 378 | 392 | 407 | 7 | 9,8 |
| 298 | 422 | 436 | 451 | 465 | 480 | 494 | 509 | 524 | 538 | 553 | 8 | 11,2 |
| 299 | 567 | 582 | 596 | 611 | 625 | 640 | 654 | 669 | 683 | 698 | 9 | 12,6 |
| **300** | 712 | 727 | 741 | 756 | 770 | 784 | 799 | 813 | 828 | 842 | | |

| N. | 0 | 1 | 2 | 3 | 4 | 5 | 6 | 7 | 8 | 9 | Proportional parts |
|---|---|---|---|---|---|---|---|---|---|---|---|

| N. | 0 | 1 | 2 | 3 | 4 | 5 | 6 | 7 | 8 | 9 |
|---|---|---|---|---|---|---|---|---|---|---|
| **300** | 47 712 | 727 | 741 | 756 | 770 | 784 | 799 | 813 | 828 | 842 |
| 301 | 857 | 871 | 885 | 900 | 914 | 929 | 943 | 958 | 972 | 986 |
| 302 | 48 001 | 015 | 029 | 044 | 058 | 073 | 087 | 101 | 116 | 130 |
| 303 | 144 | 159 | 173 | 187 | 202 | 216 | 230 | 244 | 259 | 273 |
| 304 | 287 | 302 | 316 | 330 | 344 | 359 | 373 | 387 | 401 | 416 |
| 305 | 430 | 444 | 458 | 473 | 487 | 501 | 515 | 530 | 544 | 558 |
| 306 | 572 | 586 | 601 | 615 | 629 | 643 | 657 | 671 | 686 | 700 |
| 307 | 714 | 728 | 742 | 756 | 770 | 785 | 799 | 813 | 827 | 841 |
| 308 | 855 | 869 | 883 | 897 | 911 | 926 | 940 | 954 | 968 | 982 |
| 309 | 996 | *010 | *024 | *038 | *052 | *066 | *080 | *094 | *108 | *122 |
| **310** | 49 136 | 150 | 164 | 178 | 192 | 206 | 220 | 234 | 248 | 262 |
| 311 | 276 | 290 | 304 | 318 | 332 | 346 | 360 | 374 | 388 | 402 |
| 312 | 415 | 429 | 443 | 457 | 471 | 485 | 499 | 513 | 527 | 541 |
| 313 | 554 | 568 | 582 | 596 | 610 | 624 | 638 | 651 | 665 | 679 |
| 314 | 693 | 707 | 721 | 734 | 748 | 762 | 776 | 790 | 803 | 817 |
| 315 | 831 | 845 | 859 | 872 | 886 | 900 | 914 | 927 | 941 | 955 |
| 316 | 969 | 982 | 996 | *010 | *024 | *037 | *051 | *065 | *079 | *092 |
| 317 | 50 106 | 120 | 133 | 147 | 161 | 174 | 188 | 202 | 215 | 229 |
| 318 | 243 | 256 | 270 | 284 | 297 | 311 | 325 | 338 | 352 | 365 |
| 319 | 379 | 393 | 406 | 420 | 433 | 447 | 461 | 474 | 488 | 501 |
| **320** | 515 | 529 | 542 | 556 | 569 | 583 | 596 | 610 | 623 | 637 |
| 321 | 651 | 664 | 678 | 691 | 705 | 718 | 732 | 745 | 759 | 772 |
| 322 | 786 | 799 | 813 | 826 | 840 | 853 | 866 | 880 | 893 | 907 |
| 323 | 920 | 934 | 947 | 961 | 974 | 987 | *001 | *014 | *028 | *041 |
| 324 | 51 055 | 068 | 081 | 095 | 108 | 121 | 135 | 148 | 162 | 175 |
| 325 | 188 | 202 | 215 | 228 | 242 | 255 | 268 | 282 | 295 | 308 |
| 326 | 322 | 335 | 348 | 362 | 375 | 388 | 402 | 415 | 428 | 441 |
| 327 | 455 | 468 | 481 | 495 | 508 | 521 | 534 | 548 | 561 | 574 |
| 328 | 587 | 601 | 614 | 627 | 640 | 654 | 667 | 680 | 693 | 706 |
| 329 | 720 | 733 | 746 | 759 | 772 | 786 | 799 | 812 | 825 | 838 |
| **330** | 851 | 865 | 878 | 891 | 904 | 917 | 930 | 943 | 957 | 970 |
| 331 | 983 | 996 | *009 | *022 | *035 | *048 | *061 | *075 | *088 | *101 |
| 332 | 52 114 | 127 | 140 | 153 | 166 | 179 | 192 | 205 | 218 | 231 |
| 333 | 244 | 257 | 270 | 284 | 297 | 310 | 323 | 336 | 349 | 362 |
| 334 | 375 | 388 | 401 | 414 | 427 | 440 | 453 | 466 | 479 | 492 |
| 335 | 504 | 517 | 530 | 543 | 556 | 569 | 582 | 595 | 608 | 621 |
| 336 | 634 | 647 | 660 | 673 | 686 | 699 | 711 | 724 | 737 | 750 |
| 337 | 763 | 776 | 789 | 802 | 815 | 827 | 840 | 853 | 866 | 879 |
| 338 | 892 | 905 | 917 | 930 | 943 | 956 | 969 | 982 | 994 | *007 |
| 339 | 53 020 | 033 | 046 | 058 | 071 | 084 | 097 | 110 | 122 | 135 |
| **340** | 148 | 161 | 173 | 186 | 199 | 212 | 224 | 237 | 250 | 263 |
| 341 | 275 | 288 | 301 | 314 | 326 | 339 | 352 | 364 | 377 | 390 |
| 342 | 403 | 415 | 428 | 441 | 453 | 466 | 479 | 491 | 504 | 517 |
| 343 | 529 | 542 | 555 | 567 | 580 | 593 | 605 | 618 | 631 | 643 |
| 344 | 656 | 668 | 681 | 694 | 706 | 719 | 732 | 744 | 757 | 769 |
| 345 | 782 | 794 | 807 | 820 | 832 | 845 | 857 | 870 | 882 | 895 |
| 346 | 908 | 920 | 933 | 945 | 958 | 970 | 983 | 995 | *008 | *020 |
| 347 | 54 033 | 045 | 058 | 070 | 083 | 095 | 108 | 120 | 133 | 145 |
| 348 | 158 | 170 | 183 | 195 | 208 | 220 | 233 | 245 | 258 | 270 |
| 349 | 283 | 295 | 307 | 320 | 332 | 345 | 357 | 370 | 382 | 394 |
| **350** | 407 | 419 | 432 | 444 | 456 | 469 | 481 | 494 | 506 | 518 |
| N. | 0 | 1 | 2 | 3 | 4 | 5 | 6 | 7 | 8 | 9 |

**Proportional parts**

**15**
| | |
|---|---|
| 1 | 1,5 |
| 2 | 3,0 |
| 3 | 4,5 |
| 4 | 6,0 |
| 5 | 7,5 |
| 6 | 9,0 |
| 7 | 10,5 |
| 8 | 12,0 |
| 9 | 13,5 |

**14**
| | |
|---|---|
| 1 | 1,4 |
| 2 | 2,8 |
| 3 | 4,2 |
| 4 | 5,6 |
| 5 | 7,0 |
| 6 | 8,4 |
| 7 | 9,8 |
| 8 | 11,2 |
| 9 | 12,6 |

**13**
| | |
|---|---|
| 1 | 1,3 |
| 2 | 2,6 |
| 3 | 3,9 |
| 4 | 5,2 |
| 5 | 6,5 |
| 6 | 7,8 |
| 7 | 9,1 |
| 8 | 10,4 |
| 9 | 11,7 |

**12**
| | |
|---|---|
| 1 | 1,2 |
| 2 | 2,4 |
| 3 | 3,6 |
| 4 | 4,8 |
| 5 | 6,0 |
| 6 | 7,2 |
| 7 | 8,4 |
| 8 | 9,6 |
| 9 | 10,8 |

| N. | 0 | 1 | 2 | 3 | 4 | 5 | 6 | 7 | 8 | 9 | Proportional parts |
|---|---|---|---|---|---|---|---|---|---|---|---|
| 350 | 54 407 | 419 | 432 | 444 | 456 | 469 | 481 | 494 | 506 | 518 | |
| 351 | 531 | 543 | 555 | 568 | 580 | 593 | 605 | 617 | 630 | 642 | |
| 352 | 654 | 667 | 679 | 691 | 704 | 716 | 728 | 741 | 753 | 765 | |
| 353 | 777 | 790 | 802 | 814 | 827 | 839 | 851 | 864 | 876 | 888 | **13** |
| 354 | 900 | 913 | 925 | 937 | 949 | 962 | 974 | 986 | 998 | *011 | 1\| 1,3 |
| 355 | 55 023 | 035 | 047 | 060 | 072 | 084 | 096 | 108 | 121 | 133 | 2\| 2,6 |
| 356 | 145 | 157 | 169 | 182 | 194 | 206 | 218 | 230 | 242 | 255 | 3\| 3,9 |
| 357 | 267 | 279 | 291 | 303 | 315 | 328 | 340 | 352 | 364 | 376 | 4\| 5,2 |
| 358 | 388 | 400 | 413 | 425 | 437 | 449 | 461 | 473 | 485 | 497 | 5\| 6,5 |
| 359 | 509 | 522 | 534 | 546 | 558 | 570 | 582 | 594 | 606 | 618 | 6\| 7,8 |
| | | | | | | | | | | | 7\| 9,1 |
| 360 | 630 | 642 | 654 | 666 | 678 | 691 | 703 | 715 | 727 | 739 | 8\| 10,4 |
| 361 | 751 | 763 | 775 | 787 | 799 | 811 | 823 | 835 | 847 | 859 | 9\| 11,7 |
| 362 | 871 | 883 | 895 | 907 | 919 | 931 | 943 | 955 | 967 | 979 | |
| 363 | 991 | *003 | *015 | *027 | *038 | *050 | *062 | *074 | *086 | *098 | |
| 364 | 56 110 | 122 | 134 | 146 | 158 | 170 | 182 | 194 | 205 | 217 | **12** |
| 365 | 229 | 241 | 253 | 265 | 277 | 289 | 301 | 312 | 324 | 336 | 1\| 1,2 |
| 366 | 348 | 360 | 372 | 384 | 396 | 407 | 419 | 431 | 443 | 455 | 2\| 2,4 |
| 367 | 467 | 478 | 490 | 502 | 514 | 526 | 538 | 549 | 561 | 573 | 3\| 3,6 |
| 368 | 585 | 597 | 608 | 620 | 632 | 644 | 656 | 667 | 679 | 691 | 4\| 4,8 |
| 369 | 703 | 714 | 726 | 738 | 750 | 761 | 773 | 785 | 797 | 808 | 5\| 6,0 |
| 370 | 820 | 832 | 844 | 855 | 867 | 879 | 891 | 902 | 914 | 926 | 6\| 7,2 |
| 371 | 937 | 949 | 961 | 972 | 984 | 996 | *008 | *019 | *031 | *043 | 7\| 8,4 |
| 372 | 57 054 | 066 | 078 | 089 | 101 | 113 | 124 | 136 | 148 | 159 | 8\| 9,6 |
| 373 | 171 | 183 | 194 | 206 | 217 | 229 | 241 | 252 | 264 | 276 | 9\| 10,8 |
| 374 | 287 | 299 | 310 | 322 | 334 | 345 | 357 | 368 | 380 | 392 | |
| 375 | 403 | 415 | 426 | 438 | 449 | 461 | 473 | 484 | 496 | 507 | |
| 376 | 519 | 530 | 542 | 553 | 565 | 576 | 588 | 600 | 611 | 623 | |
| 377 | 634 | 646 | 657 | 669 | 680 | 692 | 703 | 715 | 726 | 738 | **11** |
| 378 | 749 | 761 | 772 | 784 | 795 | 807 | 818 | 830 | 841 | 852 | 1\| 1,1 |
| 379 | 864 | 875 | 887 | 898 | 910 | 921 | 933 | 944 | 955 | 967 | 2\| 2,2 |
| | | | | | | | | | | | 3\| 3,3 |
| 380 | 978 | 990 | *001 | *013 | *024 | *035 | *047 | *058 | *070 | *081 | 4\| 4,4 |
| 381 | 58 092 | 104 | 115 | 127 | 138 | 149 | 161 | 172 | 184 | 195 | 5\| 5,5 |
| 382 | 206 | 218 | 229 | 240 | 252 | 263 | 274 | 286 | 297 | 309 | 6\| 6,6 |
| 383 | 320 | 331 | 343 | 354 | 365 | 377 | 388 | 399 | 410 | 422 | 7\| 7,7 |
| 384 | 433 | 444 | 456 | 467 | 478 | 490 | 501 | 512 | 524 | 535 | 8\| 8,8 |
| 385 | 546 | 557 | 569 | 580 | 591 | 602 | 614 | 625 | 636 | 647 | 9\| 9,9 |
| 386 | 659 | 670 | 681 | 692 | 704 | 715 | 726 | 737 | 749 | 760 | |
| 387 | 771 | 782 | 794 | 805 | 816 | 827 | 838 | 850 | 861 | 872 | |
| 388 | 883 | 894 | 906 | 917 | 928 | 939 | 950 | 961 | 973 | 984 | **10** |
| 389 | 995 | *006 | *017 | *028 | *040 | *051 | *062 | *073 | *084 | *095 | 1\| 1,0 |
| | | | | | | | | | | | 2\| 2,0 |
| 390 | 59 106 | 118 | 129 | 140 | 151 | 162 | 173 | 184 | 195 | 207 | 3\| 3,0 |
| 391 | 218 | 229 | 240 | 251 | 262 | 273 | 284 | 295 | 306 | 318 | 4\| 4,0 |
| 392 | 329 | 340 | 351 | 362 | 373 | 384 | 395 | 406 | 417 | 428 | 5\| 5,0 |
| 393 | 439 | 450 | 461 | 472 | 483 | 494 | 506 | 517 | 528 | 539 | 6\| 6,0 |
| 394 | 550 | 561 | 572 | 583 | 594 | 605 | 616 | 627 | 638 | 649 | 7\| 7,0 |
| 395 | 660 | 671 | 682 | 693 | 704 | 715 | 726 | 737 | 748 | 759 | 8\| 8,0 |
| 396 | 770 | 780 | 791 | 802 | 813 | 824 | 835 | 846 | 857 | 868 | 9\| 9,0 |
| 397 | 879 | 890 | 901 | 912 | 923 | 934 | 945 | 956 | 966 | 977 | |
| 398 | 988 | 999 | *010 | *021 | *032 | *043 | *054 | *065 | *076 | *086 | |
| 399 | 60 097 | 108 | 119 | 130 | 141 | 152 | 163 | 173 | 184 | 195 | |
| 400 | 206 | 217 | 228 | 239 | 249 | 260 | 271 | 282 | 293 | 304 | |

| N. | 0 | 1 | 2 | 3 | 4 | 5 | 6 | 7 | 8 | 9 | Proportional parts |
|---|---|---|---|---|---|---|---|---|---|---|---|

| N. | 0 | 1 | 2 | 3 | 4 | 5 | 6 | 7 | 8 | 9 |
|---|---|---|---|---|---|---|---|---|---|---|
| **400** | 60 206 | 217 | 228 | 239 | 249 | 260 | 271 | 282 | 293 | 304 |
| 401 | 314 | 325 | 336 | 347 | 358 | 369 | 379 | 390 | 401 | 412 |
| 402 | 423 | 433 | 444 | 455 | 466 | 477 | 487 | 498 | 509 | 520 |
| 403 | 531 | 541 | 552 | 563 | 574 | 584 | 595 | 606 | 617 | 627 |
| 404 | 638 | 649 | 660 | 670 | 681 | 692 | 703 | 713 | 724 | 735 |
| 405 | 746 | 756 | 767 | 778 | 788 | 799 | 810 | 821 | 831 | 842 |
| 406 | 853 | 863 | 874 | 885 | 895 | 906 | 917 | 927 | 938 | 949 |
| 407 | 959 | 970 | 981 | 991 | *002 | *013 | *023 | *034 | *045 | *055 |
| 408 | 61 066 | 077 | 087 | 098 | 109 | 119 | 130 | 140 | 151 | 162 |
| 409 | 172 | 183 | 194 | 204 | 215 | 225 | 236 | 247 | 257 | 268 |
| **410** | 278 | 289 | 300 | 310 | 321 | 331 | 342 | 352 | 363 | 374 |
| 411 | 384 | 395 | 405 | 416 | 426 | 437 | 448 | 458 | 469 | 479 |
| 412 | 490 | 500 | 511 | 521 | 532 | 542 | 553 | 563 | 574 | 584 |
| 413 | 595 | 606 | 616 | 627 | 637 | 648 | 658 | 669 | 679 | 690 |
| 414 | 700 | 711 | 721 | 731 | 742 | 752 | 763 | 773 | 784 | 794 |
| 415 | 805 | 815 | 826 | 836 | 847 | 857 | 868 | 878 | 888 | 899 |
| 416 | 909 | 920 | 930 | 941 | 951 | 962 | 972 | 982 | 993 | *003 |
| 417 | 62 014 | 024 | 034 | 045 | 055 | 066 | 076 | 086 | 097 | 107 |
| 418 | 118 | 128 | 138 | 149 | 159 | 170 | 180 | 190 | 201 | 211 |
| 419 | 221 | 232 | 242 | 252 | 263 | 273 | 284 | 294 | 304 | 315 |
| **420** | 325 | 335 | 346 | 356 | 366 | 377 | 387 | 397 | 408 | 418 |
| 421 | 428 | 439 | 449 | 459 | 469 | 480 | 490 | 500 | 511 | 521 |
| 422 | 531 | 542 | 552 | 562 | 572 | 583 | 593 | 603 | 613 | 624 |
| 423 | 634 | 644 | 655 | 665 | 675 | 685 | 696 | 706 | 716 | 726 |
| 424 | 737 | 747 | 757 | 767 | 778 | 788 | 798 | 808 | 818 | 829 |
| 425 | 839 | 849 | 859 | 870 | 880 | 890 | 900 | 910 | 921 | 931 |
| 426 | 941 | 951 | 961 | 972 | 982 | 992 | *002 | *012 | *022 | *033 |
| 427 | 63 043 | 053 | 063 | 073 | 083 | 094 | 104 | 114 | 124 | 134 |
| 428 | 144 | 155 | 165 | 175 | 185 | 195 | 205 | 215 | 225 | 236 |
| 429 | 246 | 256 | 266 | 276 | 286 | 296 | 306 | 317 | 327 | 337 |
| **430** | 347 | 357 | 367 | 377 | 387 | 397 | 407 | 417 | 428 | 438 |
| 431 | 448 | 458 | 468 | 478 | 488 | 498 | 508 | 518 | 528 | 538 |
| 432 | 548 | 558 | 568 | 579 | 589 | 599 | 609 | 619 | 629 | 639 |
| 433 | 649 | 659 | 669 | 679 | 689 | 699 | 709 | 719 | 729 | 739 |
| 434 | 749 | 759 | 769 | 779 | 789 | 799 | 809 | 819 | 829 | 839 |
| 435 | 849 | 859 | 869 | 879 | 889 | 899 | 909 | 919 | 929 | 939 |
| 436 | 949 | 959 | 969 | 979 | 988 | 998 | *008 | *018 | *028 | *038 |
| 437 | 64 048 | 058 | 068 | 078 | 088 | 098 | 108 | 118 | 128 | 137 |
| 438 | 147 | 157 | 167 | 177 | 187 | 197 | 207 | 217 | 227 | 237 |
| 439 | 246 | 256 | 266 | 276 | 286 | 296 | 306 | 316 | 326 | 335 |
| **440** | 345 | 355 | 365 | 375 | 385 | 395 | 404 | 414 | 424 | 434 |
| 441 | 444 | 454 | 464 | 473 | 483 | 493 | 503 | 513 | 523 | 532 |
| 442 | 542 | 552 | 562 | 572 | 582 | 591 | 601 | 611 | 621 | 631 |
| 443 | 640 | 650 | 660 | 670 | 680 | 689 | 699 | 709 | 719 | 729 |
| 444 | 738 | 748 | 758 | 768 | 777 | 787 | 797 | 807 | 816 | 826 |
| 445 | 836 | 846 | 856 | 865 | 875 | 885 | 895 | 904 | 914 | 924 |
| 446 | 933 | 943 | 953 | 963 | 972 | 982 | 992 | *002 | *011 | *021 |
| 447 | 65 031 | 040 | 050 | 060 | 070 | 079 | 089 | 099 | 108 | 118 |
| 448 | 128 | 137 | 147 | 157 | 167 | 176 | 186 | 196 | 205 | 215 |
| 449 | 225 | 234 | 244 | 254 | 263 | 273 | 283 | 292 | 302 | 312 |
| **450** | 321 | 331 | 341 | 350 | 360 | 369 | 379 | 389 | 398 | 408 |

Proportional parts

**11**
1 1.1
2 2.2
3 3.3
4 4.4
5 5.5
6 6.6
7 7.7
8 8.8
9 9.9

**10**
1 1.0
2 2.0
3 3.0
4 4.0
5 5.0
6 6.0
7 7.0
8 8.0
9 9.0

**9**
1 0.9
2 1.8
3 2.7
4 3.6
5 4.5
6 5.4
7 6.3
8 7.2
9 8.1

| N. | 0 | 1 | 2 | 3 | 4 | 5 | 6 | 7 | 8 | 9 |
|---|---|---|---|---|---|---|---|---|---|---|
| **450** | 65 321 | 331 | 341 | 350 | 360 | 369 | 379 | 389 | 398 | 408 |
| 451 | 418 | 427 | 437 | 447 | 456 | 466 | 475 | 485 | 495 | 504 |
| 452 | 514 | 523 | 533 | 543 | 552 | 562 | 571 | 581 | 591 | 600 |
| 453 | 610 | 619 | 629 | 639 | 648 | 658 | 667 | 677 | 686 | 696 |
| 454 | 706 | 715 | 725 | 734 | 744 | 753 | 763 | 772 | 782 | 792 |
| 455 | 801 | 811 | 820 | 830 | 839 | 849 | 858 | 868 | 877 | 887 |
| 456 | 896 | 906 | 916 | 925 | 935 | 944 | 954 | 963 | 973 | 982 |
| 457 | 992 | *001 | *011 | *020 | *030 | *039 | *049 | *058 | *068 | *077 |
| 458 | 66 087 | 096 | 106 | 115 | 124 | 134 | 143 | 153 | 162 | 172 |
| 459 | 181 | 191 | 200 | 210 | 219 | 229 | 238 | 247 | 257 | 266 |
| **460** | 276 | 285 | 295 | 304 | 314 | 323 | 332 | 342 | 351 | 361 |
| 461 | 370 | 380 | 389 | 398 | 408 | 417 | 427 | 436 | 445 | 455 |
| 462 | 464 | 474 | 483 | 492 | 502 | 511 | 521 | 530 | 539 | 549 |
| 463 | 558 | 567 | 577 | 586 | 596 | 605 | 614 | 624 | 633 | 642 |
| 464 | 652 | 661 | 671 | 680 | 689 | 699 | 708 | 717 | 727 | 736 |
| 465 | 745 | 755 | 764 | 773 | 783 | 792 | 801 | 811 | 820 | 829 |
| 466 | 839 | 848 | 857 | 867 | 876 | 885 | 894 | 904 | 913 | 922 |
| 467 | 932 | 941 | 950 | 960 | 969 | 978 | 987 | 997 | *006 | *015 |
| 468 | 67 025 | 034 | 043 | 052 | 062 | 071 | 080 | 089 | 099 | 108 |
| 469 | 117 | 127 | 136 | 145 | 154 | 164 | 173 | 182 | 191 | 201 |
| **470** | 210 | 219 | 228 | 237 | 247 | 256 | 265 | 274 | 284 | 293 |
| 471 | 302 | 311 | 321 | 330 | 339 | 348 | 357 | 367 | 376 | 385 |
| 472 | 394 | 403 | 413 | 422 | 431 | 440 | 449 | 459 | 468 | 477 |
| 473 | 486 | 495 | 504 | 514 | 523 | 532 | 541 | 550 | 560 | 569 |
| 474 | 578 | 587 | 596 | 605 | 614 | 624 | 633 | 642 | 651 | 660 |
| 475 | 669 | 679 | 688 | 697 | 706 | 715 | 724 | 733 | 742 | 752 |
| 476 | 761 | 770 | 779 | 788 | 797 | 806 | 815 | 825 | 834 | 843 |
| 477 | 852 | 861 | 870 | 879 | 888 | 897 | 906 | 916 | 925 | 934 |
| 478 | 943 | 952 | 961 | 970 | 979 | 988 | 997 | *006 | *015 | *024 |
| 479 | 68 034 | 043 | 052 | 061 | 070 | 079 | 088 | 097 | 106 | 115 |
| **480** | 124 | 133 | 142 | 151 | 160 | 169 | 178 | 187 | 196 | 205 |
| 481 | 215 | 224 | 233 | 242 | 251 | 260 | 269 | 278 | 287 | 296 |
| 482 | 305 | 314 | 323 | 332 | 341 | 350 | 359 | 368 | 377 | 386 |
| 483 | 395 | 404 | 413 | 422 | 431 | 440 | 449 | 458 | 467 | 476 |
| 484 | 485 | 494 | 502 | 511 | 520 | 529 | 538 | 547 | 556 | 565 |
| 485 | 574 | 583 | 592 | 601 | 610 | 619 | 628 | 637 | 646 | 655 |
| 486 | 664 | 673 | 681 | 690 | 699 | 708 | 717 | 726 | 735 | 744 |
| 487 | 753 | 762 | 771 | 780 | 789 | 797 | 806 | 815 | 824 | 833 |
| 488 | 842 | 851 | 860 | 869 | 878 | 886 | 895 | 904 | 913 | 922 |
| 489 | 931 | 940 | 949 | 958 | 966 | 975 | 984 | 993 | *002 | *011 |
| **490** | 69 020 | 028 | 037 | 046 | 055 | 064 | 073 | 082 | 090 | 099 |
| 491 | 108 | 117 | 126 | 135 | 144 | 152 | 161 | 170 | 179 | 188 |
| 492 | 197 | 205 | 214 | 223 | 232 | 241 | 249 | 258 | 267 | 276 |
| 493 | 285 | 294 | 302 | 311 | 320 | 329 | 338 | 346 | 355 | 364 |
| 494 | 373 | 381 | 390 | 399 | 408 | 417 | 425 | 434 | 443 | 452 |
| 495 | 461 | 469 | 478 | 487 | 496 | 504 | 513 | 522 | 531 | 539 |
| 496 | 548 | 557 | 566 | 574 | 583 | 592 | 601 | 609 | 618 | 627 |
| 497 | 636 | 644 | 653 | 662 | 671 | 679 | 688 | 697 | 705 | 714 |
| 498 | 723 | 732 | 740 | 749 | 758 | 767 | 775 | 784 | 793 | 801 |
| 499 | 810 | 819 | 827 | 836 | 845 | 854 | 862 | 871 | 880 | 888 |
| **500** | 897 | 906 | 914 | 923 | 932 | 940 | 949 | 958 | 966 | 975 |

| N. | 0 | 1 | 2 | 3 | 4 | 5 | 6 | 7 | 8 | 9 |
|---|---|---|---|---|---|---|---|---|---|---|

Proportional parts

**10**

| 1 | 1.0 |
|---|---|
| 2 | 2.0 |
| 3 | 3.0 |
| 4 | 4.0 |
| 5 | 5.0 |
| 6 | 6.0 |
| 7 | 7.0 |
| 8 | 8.0 |
| 9 | 9.0 |

**9**

| 1 | 0.9 |
|---|---|
| 2 | 1.8 |
| 3 | 2.7 |
| 4 | 3.6 |
| 5 | 4.5 |
| 6 | 5.4 |
| 7 | 6.3 |
| 8 | 7.2 |
| 9 | 8.1 |

**8**

| 1 | 0.8 |
|---|---|
| 2 | 1.6 |
| 3 | 2.4 |
| 4 | 3.2 |
| 5 | 4.0 |
| 6 | 4.8 |
| 7 | 5.6 |
| 8 | 6.4 |
| 9 | 7.2 |

| N. | 0 | 1 | 2 | 3 | 4 | 5 | 6 | 7 | 8 | 9 | Proportional parts |
|---|---|---|---|---|---|---|---|---|---|---|---|
| **500** | 69 897 | 906 | 914 | 923 | 932 | 940 | 949 | 958 | 966 | 975 | |
| 501 | 984 | 992 | *001 | *010 | *018 | *027 | *036 | *044 | *053 | *062 | |
| 502 | 70 070 | 079 | 088 | 096 | 105 | 114 | 122 | 131 | 140 | 148 | |
| 503 | 157 | 165 | 174 | 183 | 191 | 200 | 209 | 217 | 226 | 234 | |
| 504 | 243 | 252 | 260 | 269 | 278 | 286 | 295 | 303 | 312 | 321 | |
| 505 | 329 | 338 | 346 | 355 | 364 | 372 | 381 | 389 | 398 | 406 | |
| 506 | 415 | 424 | 432 | 441 | 449 | 458 | 467 | 475 | 484 | 492 | |
| 507 | 501 | 509 | 518 | 526 | 535 | 544 | 552 | 561 | 569 | 578 | **9** |
| 508 | 586 | 595 | 603 | 612 | 621 | 629 | 638 | 646 | 655 | 663 | 1 \| 0,9 |
| 509 | 672 | 680 | 689 | 697 | 706 | 714 | 723 | 731 | 740 | 749 | 2 \| 1,8 |
| | | | | | | | | | | | 3 \| 2,7 |
| **510** | 757 | 766 | 774 | 783 | 791 | 800 | 808 | 817 | 825 | 834 | 4 \| 3,6 |
| 511 | 842 | 851 | 859 | 868 | 876 | 885 | 893 | 902 | 910 | 919 | 5 \| 4,5 |
| 512 | 927 | 935 | 944 | 952 | 961 | 969 | 978 | 986 | 995 | *003 | 6 \| 5,4 |
| 513 | 71 012 | 020 | 029 | 037 | 046 | 054 | 063 | 071 | 079 | 088 | 7 \| 6,3 |
| 514 | 096 | 105 | 113 | 122 | 130 | 139 | 147 | 155 | 164 | 172 | 8 \| 7,2 |
| 515 | 181 | 189 | 198 | 206 | 214 | 223 | 231 | 240 | 248 | 257 | 9 \| 8,1 |
| 516 | 265 | 273 | 282 | 290 | 299 | 307 | 315 | 324 | 332 | 341 | |
| 517 | 349 | 357 | 366 | 374 | 383 | 391 | 399 | 408 | 416 | 425 | |
| 518 | 433 | 441 | 450 | 458 | 466 | 475 | 483 | 492 | 500 | 508 | |
| 519 | 517 | 525 | 533 | 542 | 550 | 559 | 567 | 575 | 584 | 592 | |
| **520** | 600 | 609 | 617 | 625 | 634 | 642 | 650 | 659 | 667 | 675 | **8** |
| 521 | 684 | 692 | 700 | 709 | 717 | 725 | 734 | 742 | 750 | 759 | 1 \| 0,8 |
| 522 | 767 | 775 | 784 | 792 | 800 | 809 | 817 | 825 | 834 | 842 | 2 \| 1,6 |
| 523 | 850 | 858 | 867 | 875 | 883 | 892 | 900 | 908 | 917 | 925 | 3 \| 2,4 |
| 524 | 933 | 941 | 950 | 958 | 966 | 975 | 983 | 991 | 999 | *008 | 4 \| 3,2 |
| 525 | 72 016 | 024 | 032 | 041 | 049 | 057 | 066 | 074 | 082 | 090 | 5 \| 4,0 |
| 526 | 099 | 107 | 115 | 123 | 132 | 140 | 148 | 156 | 165 | 173 | 6 \| 4,8 |
| 527 | 181 | 189 | 198 | 206 | 214 | 222 | 230 | 239 | 247 | 255 | 7 \| 5,6 |
| 528 | 263 | 272 | 280 | 288 | 296 | 304 | 313 | 321 | 329 | 337 | 8 \| 6,4 |
| 529 | 346 | 354 | 362 | 370 | 378 | 387 | 395 | 403 | 411 | 419 | 9 \| 7,2 |
| **530** | 428 | 436 | 444 | 452 | 460 | 469 | 477 | 485 | 493 | 501 | |
| 531 | 509 | 518 | 526 | 534 | 542 | 550 | 558 | 567 | 575 | 583 | |
| 532 | 591 | 599 | 607 | 616 | 624 | 632 | 640 | 648 | 656 | 665 | |
| 533 | 673 | 681 | 689 | 697 | 705 | 713 | 722 | 730 | 738 | 746 | |
| 534 | 754 | 762 | 770 | 779 | 787 | 795 | 803 | 811 | 819 | 827 | |
| 535 | 835 | 843 | 852 | 860 | 868 | 876 | 884 | 892 | 900 | 908 | **7** |
| 536 | 916 | 925 | 933 | 941 | 949 | 957 | 965 | 973 | 981 | 989 | 1 \| 0,7 |
| 537 | 997 | *006 | *014 | *022 | *030 | *038 | *046 | *054 | *062 | *070 | 2 \| 1,4 |
| 538 | 73 078 | 086 | 094 | 102 | 111 | 119 | 127 | 135 | 143 | 151 | 3 \| 2,1 |
| 539 | 159 | 167 | 175 | 183 | 191 | 199 | 207 | 215 | 223 | 231 | 4 \| 2,8 |
| | | | | | | | | | | | 5 \| 3,5 |
| **540** | 239 | 247 | 255 | 263 | 272 | 280 | 288 | 296 | 304 | 312 | 6 \| 4,2 |
| 541 | 320 | 328 | 336 | 344 | 352 | 360 | 368 | 376 | 384 | 392 | 7 \| 4,9 |
| 542 | 400 | 408 | 416 | 424 | 432 | 440 | 448 | 456 | 464 | 472 | 8 \| 5,6 |
| 543 | 480 | 488 | 496 | 504 | 512 | 520 | 528 | 536 | 544 | 552 | 9 \| 6,3 |
| 544 | 560 | 568 | 576 | 584 | 592 | 600 | 608 | 616 | 624 | 632 | |
| 545 | 640 | 648 | 656 | 664 | 672 | 679 | 687 | 695 | 703 | 711 | |
| 546 | 719 | 727 | 735 | 743 | 751 | 759 | 767 | 775 | 783 | 791 | |
| 547 | 799 | 807 | 815 | 823 | 830 | 838 | 846 | 854 | 862 | 870 | |
| 548 | 878 | 886 | 894 | 902 | 910 | 918 | 926 | 933 | 941 | 949 | |
| 549 | 957 | 965 | 973 | 981 | 989 | 997 | *005 | *013 | *020 | *028 | |
| **550** | 74 036 | 044 | 052 | 060 | 068 | 076 | 084 | 092 | 099 | 107 | |
| N. | 0 | 1 | 2 | 3 | 4 | 5 | 6 | 7 | 8 | 9 | Proportional parts |

| N. | 0 | 1 | 2 | 3 | 4 | 5 | 6 | 7 | 8 | 9 | Proportional parts |
|---|---|---|---|---|---|---|---|---|---|---|---|
| **550** | 74 036 | 044 | 052 | 060 | 068 | 076 | 084 | 092 | 099 | 107 | |
| 551 | 115 | 123 | 131 | 139 | 147 | 155 | 162 | 170 | 178 | 186 | |
| 552 | 194 | 202 | 210 | 218 | 225 | 233 | 241 | 249 | 257 | 265 | |
| 553 | 273 | 280 | 288 | 296 | 304 | 312 | 320 | 327 | 335 | 343 | |
| 554 | 351 | 359 | 367 | 374 | 382 | 390 | 398 | 406 | 414 | 421 | |
| 555 | 429 | 437 | 445 | 453 | 461 | 468 | 476 | 484 | 492 | 500 | |
| 556 | 507 | 515 | 523 | 531 | 539 | 547 | 554 | 562 | 570 | 578 | |
| 557 | 586 | 593 | 601 | 609 | 617 | 624 | 632 | 640 | 648 | 656 | |
| 558 | 663 | 671 | 679 | 687 | 695 | 702 | 710 | 718 | 726 | 733 | |
| 559 | 741 | 749 | 757 | 764 | 772 | 780 | 788 | 796 | 803 | 811 | |
| **560** | 819 | 827 | 834 | 842 | 850 | 858 | 865 | 873 | 881 | 889 | **8** |
| 561 | 896 | 904 | 912 | 920 | 927 | 935 | 943 | 950 | 958 | 966 | 1 │ 0,8 |
| 562 | 974 | 981 | 989 | 997 | *005 | *012 | *020 | *028* | 035 | *043 | 2 │ 1,6 |
| 563 | 75 051 | 059 | 066 | 074 | 082 | 089 | 097 | 105 | 113 | 120 | 3 │ 2,4 |
| 564 | 128 | 136 | 143 | 151 | 159 | 166 | 174 | 182 | 189 | 197 | 4 │ 3,2 |
| 565 | 205 | 213 | 220 | 228 | 236 | 243 | 251 | 259 | 266 | 274 | 5 │ 4,0 |
| 566 | 282 | 289 | 297 | 305 | 312 | 320 | 328 | 335 | 343 | 351 | 6 │ 4,8 |
| 567 | 358 | 366 | 374 | 381 | 389 | 397 | 404 | 412 | 420 | 427 | 7 │ 5,6 |
| 568 | 435 | 442 | 450 | 458 | 465 | 473 | 481 | 488 | 496 | 504 | 8 │ 6,4 |
| 569 | 511 | 519 | 526 | 534 | 542 | 549 | 557 | 565 | 572 | 580 | 9 │ 7,2 |
| **570** | 587 | 595 | 603 | 610 | 618 | 626 | 633 | 641 | 648 | 656 | |
| 571 | 664 | 671 | 679 | 686 | 694 | 702 | 709 | 717 | 724 | 732 | |
| 572 | 740 | 747 | 755 | 762 | 770 | 778 | 785 | 793 | 800 | 808 | |
| 573 | 815 | 823 | 831 | 838 | 846 | 853 | 861 | 868 | 876 | 884 | |
| 574 | 891 | 899 | 906 | 914 | 921 | 929 | 937 | 944 | 952 | 959 | |
| 575 | 967 | 974 | 982 | 989 | 997 | *005 | *012 | *020 | *027 | *035 | |
| 576 | 76 042 | 050 | 057 | 065 | 072 | 080 | 087 | 095 | 103 | 110 | |
| 577 | 118 | 125 | 133 | 140 | 148 | 155 | 163 | 170 | 178 | 185 | |
| 578 | 193 | 200 | 208 | 215 | 223 | 230 | 238 | 245 | 253 | 260 | |
| 579 | 268 | 275 | 283 | 290 | 298 | 305 | 313 | 320 | 328 | 335 | |
| **580** | 343 | 350 | 358 | 365 | 373 | 380 | 388 | 395 | 403 | 410 | **7** |
| 581 | 418 | 425 | 433 | 440 | 448 | 455 | 462 | 470 | 477 | 485 | 1 │ 0,7 |
| 582 | 492 | 500 | 507 | 515 | 522 | 530 | 537 | 545 | 552 | 559 | 2 │ 1,4 |
| 583 | 567 | 574 | 582 | 589 | 597 | 604 | 612 | 619 | 626 | 634 | 3 │ 2,1 |
| 584 | 641 | 649 | 656 | 664 | 671 | 678 | 686 | 693 | 701 | 708 | 4 │ 2,8 |
| 585 | 716 | 723 | 730 | 738 | 745 | 753 | 760 | 768 | 775 | 782 | 5 │ 3,5 |
| 586 | 790 | 797 | 805 | 812 | 819 | 827 | 834 | 842 | 849 | 856 | 6 │ 4,2 |
| 587 | 864 | 871 | 879 | 886 | 893 | 901 | 908 | 916 | 923 | 930 | 7 │ 4,9 |
| 588 | 938 | 945 | 953 | 960 | 967 | 975 | 982 | 989 | 997 | *004 | 8 │ 5,6 |
| 589 | 77 012 | 019 | 026 | 034 | 041 | 048 | 056 | 063 | 070 | 078 | 9 │ 6,3 |
| **590** | 085 | 093 | 100 | 107 | 115 | 122 | 129 | 137 | 144 | 151 | |
| 591 | 159 | 166 | 173 | 181 | 188 | 195 | 203 | 210 | 217 | 225 | |
| 592 | 232 | 240 | 247 | 254 | 262 | 269 | 276 | 283 | 291 | 298 | |
| 593 | 305 | 313 | 320 | 327 | 335 | 342 | 349 | 357 | 364 | 371 | |
| 594 | 379 | 386 | 393 | 401 | 408 | 415 | 422 | 430 | 437 | 444 | |
| 595 | 452 | 459 | 466 | 474 | 481 | 488 | 495 | 503 | 510 | 517 | |
| 596 | 525 | 532 | 539 | 546 | 554 | 561 | 568 | 576 | 583 | 590 | |
| 597 | 597 | 605 | 612 | 619 | 627 | 634 | 641 | 648 | 656 | 663 | |
| 598 | 670 | 677 | 685 | 692 | 699 | 706 | 714 | 721 | 728 | 735 | |
| 599 | 743 | 750 | 757 | 764 | 772 | 779 | 786 | 793 | 801 | 808 | |
| **600** | 815 | 822 | 830 | 837 | 844 | 851 | 859 | 866 | 873 | 880 | |
| N. | 0 | 1 | 2 | 3 | 4 | 5 | 6 | 7 | 8 | 9 | Proportional parts |

# FIVE-PLACE LOGARITHMS (Continued)

| N. | 0 | 1 | 2 | 3 | 4 | 5 | 6 | 7 | 8 | 9 |
|---|---|---|---|---|---|---|---|---|---|---|
| **600** | 77 815 | 822 | 830 | 837 | 844 | 851 | 859 | 366 | 873 | 880 |
| 601 | 887 | 895 | 902 | 909 | 916 | 924 | 931 | 938 | 945 | 952 |
| 602 | 960 | 967 | 974 | 981 | 988 | 996 | *003 | *010 | *017 | *025 |
| 603 | 78 032 | 059 | 046 | 053 | 061 | 068 | 075 | 082 | 089 | 097 |
| 604 | 104 | 111 | 118 | 125 | 132 | 140 | 147 | 154 | 161 | 168 |
| 605 | 176 | 183 | 190 | 197 | 204 | 211 | 219 | 226 | 233 | 240 |
| 606 | 247 | 254 | 262 | 269 | 276 | 283 | 290 | 297 | 305 | 312 |
| 607 | 319 | 326 | 333 | 340 | 347 | 355 | 362 | 369 | 376 | 383 |
| 608 | 390 | 398 | 405 | 412 | 419 | 426 | 433 | 440 | 447 | 455 |
| 609 | 462 | 469 | 476 | 483 | 490 | 497 | 504 | 512 | 519 | 526 |
| **610** | 533 | 540 | 547 | 554 | 561 | 569 | 576 | 583 | 590 | 597 |
| 611 | 604 | 611 | 618 | 625 | 633 | 640 | 647 | 654 | 661 | 668 |
| 612 | 675 | 682 | 689 | 696 | 704 | 711 | 718 | 725 | 732 | 739 |
| 613 | 746 | 753 | 760 | 767 | 774 | 781 | 789 | 796 | 803 | 810 |
| 614 | 817 | 824 | 831 | 838 | 845 | 852 | 859 | 866 | 873 | 880 |
| 615 | 888 | 895 | 902 | 909 | 916 | 923 | 930 | 937 | 944 | 951 |
| 616 | 958 | 965 | 972 | 979 | 986 | 993 | *000 | *007 | *014 | *021 |
| 617 | 79 029 | 036 | 043 | 050 | 057 | 064 | 071 | 078 | 085 | 092 |
| 618 | 099 | 106 | 113 | 120 | 127 | 134 | 141 | 148 | 155 | 162 |
| 619 | 169 | 176 | 183 | 190 | 197 | 204 | 211 | 218 | 225 | 232 |
| **620** | 239 | 246 | 253 | 260 | 267 | 274 | 281 | 288 | 295 | 302 |
| 621 | 309 | 316 | 323 | 330 | 337 | 344 | 351 | 358 | 365 | 372 |
| 622 | 379 | 386 | 393 | 400 | 407 | 414 | 421 | 428 | 435 | 442 |
| 623 | 449 | 456 | 463 | 470 | 477 | 484 | 491 | 498 | 505 | 511 |
| 624 | 518 | 525 | 532 | 539 | 546 | 553 | 560 | 567 | 574 | 581 |
| 625 | 588 | 595 | 602 | 609 | 616 | 623 | 630 | 637 | 644 | 650 |
| 626 | 657 | 664 | 671 | 678 | 685 | 692 | 699 | 706 | 713 | 720 |
| 627 | 727 | 734 | 741 | 748 | 754 | 761 | 768 | 775 | 782 | 789 |
| 628 | 796 | 803 | 810 | 817 | 824 | 831 | 837 | 844 | 851 | 858 |
| 629 | 865 | 872 | 879 | 886 | 893 | 900 | 906 | 913 | 920 | 927 |
| **630** | 934 | 941 | 948 | 955 | 962 | 969 | 975 | 982 | 989 | 996 |
| 631 | 80 003 | 010 | 017 | 024 | 030 | 037 | 044 | 051 | 058 | 065 |
| 632 | 072 | 079 | 085 | 092 | 099 | 106 | 113 | 120 | 127 | 134 |
| 633 | 140 | 147 | 154 | 161 | 168 | 175 | 182 | 188 | 195 | 202 |
| 634 | 209 | 216 | 223 | 229 | 236 | 243 | 250 | 257 | 264 | 271 |
| 635 | 277 | 284 | 291 | 298 | 305 | 312 | 318 | 325 | 332 | 339 |
| 636 | 346 | 353 | 359 | 366 | 373 | 380 | 387 | 393 | 400 | 407 |
| 637 | 414 | 421 | 428 | 434 | 441 | 448 | 455 | 462 | 468 | 475 |
| 638 | 482 | 489 | 496 | 502 | 509 | 516 | 523 | 530 | 536 | 543 |
| 639 | 550 | 557 | 564 | 570 | 577 | 584 | 591 | 598 | 604 | 611 |
| **640** | 618 | 625 | 632 | 638 | 645 | 652 | 659 | 665 | 672 | 679 |
| 641 | 686 | 693 | 699 | 706 | 713 | 720 | 726 | 733 | 740 | 747 |
| 642 | 754 | 760 | 767 | 774 | 781 | 787 | 794 | 801 | 808 | 814 |
| 643 | 821 | 828 | 835 | 841 | 848 | 855 | 862 | 868 | 875 | 882 |
| 644 | 889 | 895 | 902 | 909 | 916 | 922 | 929 | 936 | 943 | 949 |
| 645 | 956 | 963 | 969 | 976 | 983 | 990 | 996 | *003 | *010 | *017 |
| 646 | 81 023 | 030 | 037 | 043 | 050 | 057 | 064 | 070 | 077 | 084 |
| 647 | 090 | 097 | 104 | 111 | 117 | 124 | 131 | 137 | 144 | 151 |
| 648 | 158 | 164 | 171 | 178 | 184 | 191 | 198 | 204 | 211 | 218 |
| 649 | 224 | 231 | 238 | 245 | 251 | 258 | 265 | 271 | 278 | 285 |
| **650** | 291 | 298 | 305 | 311 | 318 | 325 | 331 | 338 | 345 | 351 |

Proportional parts

**8**
1 | 0.8
2 | 1.6
3 | 2.4
4 | 3.2
5 | 4.0
6 | 4.8
7 | 5.6
8 | 6.4
9 | 7.2

**7**
1 | 0.7
2 | 1.4
3 | 2.1
4 | 2.8
5 | 3.5
6 | 4.2
7 | 4.9
8 | 5.6
9 | 6.3

**6**
1 | 0.6
2 | 1.2
3 | 1.8
4 | 2.4
5 | 3.0
6 | 3.6
7 | 4.2
8 | 4.8
9 | 5.4

| N. | 0 | 1 | 2 | 3 | 4 | 5 | 6 | 7 | 8 | 9 | Proportional parts |
|---|---|---|---|---|---|---|---|---|---|---|---|
| **650** | 81 291 | 298 | 305 | 311 | 318 | 325 | 331 | 338 | 345 | 351 | |
| 651 | 358 | 365 | 371 | 378 | 385 | 391 | 398 | 405 | 411 | 418 | |
| 652 | 425 | 431 | 438 | 445 | 451 | 458 | 465 | 471 | 478 | 485 | |
| 653 | 491 | 498 | 505 | 511 | 518 | 525 | 531 | 538 | 544 | 551 | |
| 654 | 558 | 564 | 571 | 578 | 584 | 591 | 598 | 604 | 611 | 617 | |
| 655 | 624 | 631 | 637 | 644 | 651 | 657 | 664 | 671 | 677 | 684 | |
| 656 | 690 | 697 | 704 | 710 | 717 | 723 | 730 | 737 | 743 | 750 | |
| 657 | 757 | 763 | 770 | 776 | 783 | 790 | 796 | 803 | 809 | 816 | |
| 658 | 823 | 829 | 836 | 842 | 849 | 856 | 862 | 869 | 875 | 882 | |
| 659 | 889 | 895 | 902 | 908 | 915 | 921 | 928 | 935 | 941 | 948 | |
| **660** | 954 | 961 | 968 | 974 | 981 | 987 | 994 | *000 | *007 | *014 | **7** |
| 661 | 82 0?0 | 027 | 033 | 040 | 046 | 053 | 060 | 066 | 073 | 079 | 1 \| 0.7 |
| 662 | 086 | 092 | 099 | 105 | 112 | 119 | 125 | 132 | 138 | 145 | 2 \| 1.4 |
| 663 | 151 | 158 | 164 | 171 | 178 | 184 | 191 | 197 | 204 | 210 | 3 \| 2.1 |
| 664 | 217 | 223 | 230 | 236 | 243 | 249 | 256 | 263 | 269 | 276 | 4 \| 2.8 |
| 665 | 282 | 289 | 295 | 302 | 308 | 315 | 321 | 328 | 334 | 341 | 5 \| 3.5 |
| 666 | 347 | 354 | 360 | 367 | 373 | 380 | 387 | 393 | 400 | 406 | 6 \| 4.2 |
| 667 | 413 | 419 | 426 | 432 | 439 | 445 | 452 | 458 | 465 | 471 | 7 \| 4.9 |
| 668 | 478 | 484 | 491 | 497 | 504 | 510 | 517 | 523 | 530 | 536 | 8 \| 5.6 |
| 669 | 543 | 549 | 556 | 562 | 569 | 575 | 582 | 588 | 595 | 601 | 9 \| 6.3 |
| **670** | 607 | 614 | 620 | 627 | 633 | 640 | 646 | 653 | 659 | 666 | |
| 671 | 672 | 679 | 685 | 692 | 698 | 705 | 711 | 718 | 724 | 730 | |
| 672 | 737 | 743 | 750 | 756 | 763 | 769 | 776 | 782 | 789 | 795 | |
| 673 | 802 | 808 | 814 | 821 | 827 | 834 | 840 | 847 | 853 | 860 | |
| 674 | 866 | 872 | 879 | 885 | 892 | 898 | 905 | 911 | 918 | 924 | |
| 675 | 930 | 937 | 943 | 950 | 956 | 963 | 969 | 975 | 982 | 988 | |
| 676 | 995 | *001 | *008 | *014 | *020 | *027 | *033 | *040 | *046 | *052 | |
| 677 | 83 059 | 065 | 072 | 078 | 085 | 091 | 097 | 104 | 110 | 117 | |
| 678 | 123 | 129 | 136 | 142 | 149 | 155 | 161 | 168 | 174 | 181 | |
| 679 | 187 | 193 | 200 | 206 | 213 | 219 | 225 | 232 | 238 | 245 | |
| **680** | 251 | 257 | 264 | 270 | 276 | 283 | 289 | 296 | 302 | 308 | **6** |
| 681 | 315 | 321 | 327 | 334 | 340 | 347 | 353 | 359 | 366 | 372 | 1 \| 0.6 |
| 682 | 378 | 385 | 391 | 398 | 404 | 410 | 417 | 423 | 429 | 436 | 2 \| 1.2 |
| 683 | 442 | 448 | 455 | 461 | 467 | 474 | 480 | 487 | 493 | 499 | 3 \| 1.8 |
| 684 | 506 | 512 | 518 | 525 | 531 | 537 | 544 | 550 | 556 | 563 | 4 \| 2.4 |
| 685 | 569 | 575 | 582 | 588 | 594 | 601 | 607 | 613 | 620 | 626 | 5 \| 3.0 |
| 686 | 632 | 639 | 645 | 651 | 658 | 664 | 670 | 677 | 683 | 689 | 6 \| 3.6 |
| 687 | 696 | 702 | 708 | 715 | 721 | 727 | 734 | 740 | 746 | 753 | 7 \| 4.2 |
| 688 | 759 | 765 | 771 | 778 | 784 | 790 | 797 | 803 | 809 | 816 | 8 \| 4.8 |
| 689 | 822 | 828 | 835 | 841 | 847 | 853 | 860 | 866 | 872 | 879 | 9 \| 5.4 |
| **690** | 885 | 891 | 897 | 904 | 910 | 916 | 923 | 929 | 935 | 942 | |
| 691 | 948 | 954 | 960 | 967 | 973 | 979 | 985 | 992 | 998 | *004 | |
| 692 | 84 011 | 017 | 023 | 029 | 036 | 042 | 048 | 055 | 061 | 067 | |
| 693 | 073 | 080 | 086 | 092 | 098 | 105 | 111 | 117 | 123 | 130 | |
| 694 | 136 | 142 | 148 | 155 | 161 | 167 | 173 | 180 | 186 | 192 | |
| 695 | 198 | 205 | 211 | 217 | 223 | 230 | 236 | 242 | 248 | 255 | |
| 696 | 261 | 267 | 273 | 280 | 286 | 292 | 298 | 305 | 311 | 317 | |
| 697 | 323 | 330 | 336 | 342 | 348 | 354 | 361 | 367 | 373 | 379 | |
| 698 | 386 | 392 | 398 | 404 | 410 | 417 | 423 | 429 | 435 | 442 | |
| 699 | 448 | 454 | 460 | 466 | 473 | 479 | 485 | 491 | 497 | 504 | |
| **700** | 510 | 516 | 522 | 528 | 535 | 541 | 547 | 553 | 559 | 566 | |
| N. | 0 | 1 | 2 | 3 | 4 | 5 | 6 | 7 | 8 | 9 | Proportional parts |

| N. | 0 | 1 | 2 | 3 | 4 | 5 | 6 | 7 | 8 | 9 | Proportional parts |
|---|---|---|---|---|---|---|---|---|---|---|---|
| **700** | 84 510 | 516 | 522 | 528 | 535 | 541 | 547 | 553 | 559 | 566 | |
| 701 | 572 | 578 | 584 | 590 | 597 | 603 | 609 | 615 | 621 | 628 | |
| 702 | 634 | 640 | 646 | 652 | 658 | 665 | 671 | 677 | 683 | 689 | |
| 703 | 696 | 702 | 708 | 714 | 720 | 726 | 733 | 739 | 745 | 751 | |
| 704 | 757 | 763 | 770 | 776 | 782 | 788 | 794 | 800 | 807 | 813 | |
| 705 | 819 | 825 | 831 | 837 | 844 | 850 | 856 | 862 | 868 | 874 | |
| 706 | 880 | 887 | 893 | 899 | 905 | 911 | 917 | 924 | 930 | 936 | **7** |
| 707 | 942 | 948 | 954 | 960 | 967 | 973 | 979 | 985 | 991 | 997 | 1 \| 0.7 |
| 708 | 85 003 | 009 | 016 | 022 | 028 | 034 | 040 | 046 | 052 | 058 | 2 \| 1.4 |
| 709 | 065 | 071 | 077 | 083 | 089 | 095 | 101 | 107 | 114 | 120 | 3 \| 2.1 |
| **710** | 126 | 132 | 138 | 144 | 150 | 156 | 163 | 169 | 175 | 181 | 4 \| 2.8 |
| 711 | 187 | 193 | 199 | 205 | 211 | 217 | 224 | 230 | 236 | 242 | 5 \| 3.5 |
| 712 | 248 | 254 | 260 | 266 | 272 | 278 | 285 | 291 | 297 | 303 | 6 \| 4.2 |
| 713 | 309 | 315 | 321 | 327 | 333 | 339 | 345 | 352 | 358 | 364 | 7 \| 4.9 |
| 714 | 370 | 376 | 382 | 388 | 394 | 400 | 406 | 412 | 418 | 425 | 8 \| 5.6 |
| 715 | 431 | 437 | 443 | 449 | 455 | 461 | 467 | 473 | 479 | 485 | 9 \| 6.3 |
| 716 | 491 | 497 | 503 | 509 | 516 | 522 | 528 | 534 | 540 | 546 | |
| 717 | 552 | 558 | 564 | 570 | 576 | 582 | 588 | 594 | 600 | 606 | |
| 718 | 612 | 618 | 625 | 631 | 637 | 643 | 649 | 655 | 661 | 667 | |
| 719 | 673 | 679 | 685 | 691 | 697 | 703 | 709 | 715 | 721 | 727 | |
| **720** | 733 | 739 | 745 | 751 | 757 | 763 | 769 | 775 | 781 | 788 | |
| 721 | 794 | 800 | 806 | 812 | 818 | 824 | 830 | 836 | 842 | 848 | **6** |
| 722 | 854 | 860 | 866 | 872 | 878 | 884 | 890 | 896 | 902 | 908 | 1 \| 0.6 |
| 723 | 914 | 920 | 926 | 932 | 938 | 944 | 950 | 956 | 962 | 968 | 2 \| 1.2 |
| 724 | 974 | 980 | 986 | 992 | 998 | *004 | *010 | *016 | *022 | *028 | 3 \| 1.8 |
| 725 | 86 034 | 040 | 046 | 052 | 058 | 064 | 070 | 076 | 082 | 088 | 4 \| 2.4 |
| 726 | 094 | 100 | 106 | 112 | 118 | 124 | 130 | 136 | 141 | 147 | 5 \| 3.0 |
| 727 | 153 | 159 | 165 | 171 | 177 | 183 | 189 | 195 | 201 | 207 | 6 \| 3.6 |
| 728 | 213 | 219 | 225 | 231 | 237 | 243 | 249 | 255 | 261 | 267 | 7 \| 4.2 |
| 729 | 273 | 279 | 285 | 291 | 297 | 303 | 308 | 314 | 320 | 326 | 8 \| 4.8 |
| **730** | 332 | 338 | 344 | 350 | 356 | 362 | 368 | 374 | 380 | 386 | 9 \| 5.4 |
| 731 | 392 | 398 | 404 | 410 | 415 | 421 | 427 | 433 | 439 | 445 | |
| 732 | 451 | 457 | 463 | 469 | 475 | 481 | 487 | 493 | 499 | 504 | |
| 733 | 510 | 516 | 522 | 528 | 534 | 540 | 546 | 552 | 558 | 564 | |
| 734 | 570 | 576 | 581 | 587 | 593 | 599 | 605 | 611 | 617 | 623 | |
| 735 | 629 | 635 | 641 | 646 | 652 | 658 | 664 | 670 | 676 | 682 | **5** |
| 736 | 688 | 694 | 700 | 705 | 711 | 717 | 723 | 729 | 735 | 741 | 1 \| 0.5 |
| 737 | 747 | 753 | 759 | 764 | 770 | 776 | 782 | 788 | 794 | 800 | 2 \| 1.0 |
| 738 | 806 | 812 | 817 | 823 | 829 | 835 | 841 | 847 | 853 | 859 | 3 \| 1.5 |
| 739 | 864 | 870 | 876 | 882 | 888 | 894 | 900 | 906 | 911 | 917 | 4 \| 2.0 |
| **740** | 923 | 929 | 935 | 941 | 947 | 953 | 958 | 964 | 970 | 976 | 5 \| 2.5 |
| 741 | 982 | 988 | 994 | 999 | *005 | *011 | *017 | *023 | *029 | *035 | 6 \| 3.0 |
| 742 | 87 040 | 046 | 052 | 058 | 064 | 070 | 075 | 081 | 087 | 093 | 7 \| 3.5 |
| 743 | 099 | 105 | 111 | 116 | 122 | 128 | 134 | 140 | 146 | 151 | 8 \| 4.0 |
| 744 | 157 | 163 | 169 | 175 | 181 | 186 | 192 | 198 | 204 | 210 | 9 \| 4.5 |
| 745 | 216 | 221 | 227 | 233 | 239 | 245 | 251 | 256 | 262 | 268 | |
| 746 | 274 | 280 | 286 | 291 | 297 | 303 | 309 | 315 | 320 | 326 | |
| 747 | 332 | 338 | 344 | 349 | 355 | 361 | 367 | 373 | 379 | 384 | |
| 748 | 390 | 396 | 402 | 408 | 413 | 419 | 425 | 431 | 437 | 442 | |
| 749 | 448 | 454 | 460 | 466 | 471 | 477 | 483 | 489 | 495 | 500 | |
| **750** | 506 | 512 | 518 | 523 | 529 | 535 | 541 | 547 | 552 | 558 | |
| N. | 0 | 1 | 2 | 3 | 4 | 5 | 6 | 7 | 8 | 9 | Proportional parts |

| N. | 0 | 1 | 2 | 3 | 4 | 5 | 6 | 7 | 8 | 9 | Proportional parts |
|---|---|---|---|---|---|---|---|---|---|---|---|
| **750** | 87 506 | 512 | 518 | 523 | 529 | 535 | 541 | 547 | 552 | 558 | |
| 751 | 564 | 570 | 576 | 581 | 587 | 593 | 599 | 604 | 610 | 616 | |
| 752 | 622 | 628 | 633 | 639 | 645 | 651 | 656 | 662 | 668 | 674 | |
| 753 | 679 | 685 | 691 | 697 | 703 | 708 | 714 | 720 | 726 | 731 | |
| 754 | 737 | 743 | 749 | 754 | 760 | 766 | 772 | 777 | 783 | 789 | |
| 755 | 795 | 800 | 806 | 812 | 818 | 823 | 829 | 835 | 841 | 846 | |
| 756 | 852 | 858 | 864 | 869 | 875 | 881 | 887 | 892 | 898 | 904 | |
| 757 | 910 | 915 | 921 | 927 | 933 | 938 | 944 | 950 | 955 | 961 | |
| 758 | 967 | 973 | 978 | 984 | 990 | 996 | *001 | *007 | *013 | *018 | |
| 759 | 88 024 | 030 | 036 | 041 | 047 | 053 | 058 | 064 | 070 | 076 | |
| **760** | 081 | 087 | 093 | 098 | 104 | 110 | 116 | 121 | 127 | 133 | **6** |
| 761 | 138 | 144 | 150 | 156 | 161 | 167 | 173 | 178 | 184 | 190 | 1 \| 0.6 |
| 762 | 195 | 201 | 207 | 213 | 218 | 224 | 230 | 235 | 241 | 247 | 2 \| 1.2 |
| 763 | 252 | 258 | 264 | 270 | 275 | 281 | 287 | 292 | 298 | 304 | 3 \| 1.8 |
| 764 | 309 | 315 | 321 | 326 | 332 | 338 | 343 | 349 | 355 | 360 | 4 \| 2.4 |
| 765 | 366 | 372 | 377 | 383 | 389 | 395 | 400 | 406 | 412 | 417 | 5 \| 3.0 |
| 766 | 423 | 429 | 434 | 440 | 446 | 451 | 457 | 463 | 468 | 474 | 6 \| 3.6 |
| 767 | 480 | 485 | 491 | 497 | 502 | 508 | 513 | 519 | 525 | 530 | 7 \| 4.2 |
| 768 | 536 | 542 | 547 | 553 | 559 | 564 | 570 | 576 | 581 | 587 | 8 \| 4.8 |
| 769 | 593 | 598 | 604 | 610 | 615 | 621 | 627 | 632 | 638 | 643 | 9 \| 5.4 |
| **770** | 649 | 655 | 660 | 666 | 672 | 677 | 683 | 689 | 694 | 700 | |
| 771 | 705 | 711 | 717 | 722 | 728 | 734 | 739 | 745 | 750 | 756 | |
| 772 | 762 | 767 | 773 | 779 | 784 | 790 | 795 | 801 | 807 | 812 | |
| 773 | 818 | 824 | 829 | 835 | 840 | 846 | 852 | 857 | 863 | 868 | |
| 774 | 874 | 880 | 885 | 891 | 897 | 902 | 908 | 913 | 919 | 925 | |
| 775 | 930 | 936 | 941 | 947 | 953 | 958 | 964 | 969 | 975 | 981 | |
| 776 | 986 | 992 | 997 | *003 | *009 | *014 | *020 | *025 | *031 | *037 | |
| 777 | 89 042 | 048 | 053 | 059 | 064 | 070 | 076 | 081 | 087 | 092 | |
| 778 | 098 | 104 | 109 | 115 | 120 | 126 | 131 | 137 | 143 | 148 | |
| 779 | 154 | 159 | 165 | 170 | 176 | 182 | 187 | 193 | 198 | 204 | |
| **780** | 209 | 215 | 221 | 226 | 232 | 237 | 243 | 248 | 254 | 260 | **5** |
| 781 | 265 | 271 | 276 | 282 | 287 | 293 | 298 | 304 | 310 | 315 | 1 \| 0.5 |
| 782 | 321 | 326 | 332 | 337 | 343 | 348 | 354 | 360 | 365 | 371 | 2 \| 1.0 |
| 783 | 376 | 382 | 387 | 393 | 398 | 404 | 409 | 415 | 421 | 426 | 3 \| 1.5 |
| 784 | 432 | 437 | 443 | 448 | 454 | 459 | 465 | 470 | 476 | 481 | 4 \| 2.0 |
| 785 | 487 | 492 | 498 | 504 | 509 | 515 | 520 | 526 | 531 | 537 | 5 \| 2.5 |
| 786 | 542 | 548 | 553 | 559 | 564 | 570 | 575 | 581 | 586 | 592 | 6 \| 3.0 |
| 787 | 597 | 603 | 609 | 614 | 620 | 625 | 631 | 636 | 642 | 647 | 7 \| 3.5 |
| 788 | 653 | 658 | 664 | 669 | 675 | 680 | 686 | 691 | 697 | 702 | 8 \| 4.0 |
| 789 | 708 | 713 | 719 | 724 | 730 | 735 | 741 | 746 | 752 | 757 | 9 \| 4.5 |
| **790** | 763 | 768 | 774 | 779 | 785 | 790 | 796 | 801 | 807 | 812 | |
| 791 | 818 | 823 | 829 | 834 | 840 | 845 | 851 | 856 | 862 | 867 | |
| 792 | 873 | 878 | 883 | 889 | 894 | 900 | 905 | 911 | 916 | 922 | |
| 793 | 927 | 933 | 938 | 944 | 949 | 955 | 960 | 966 | 971 | 977 | |
| 794 | 982 | 988 | 993 | 998 | *004 | *009 | *015 | *020 | *026 | *031 | |
| 795 | 90 037 | 042 | 048 | 053 | 059 | 064 | 069 | 075 | 080 | 086 | |
| 796 | 091 | 097 | 102 | 108 | 113 | 119 | 124 | 129 | 135 | 140 | |
| 797 | 146 | 151 | 157 | 162 | 168 | 173 | 179 | 184 | 189 | 195 | |
| 798 | 200 | 206 | 211 | 217 | 222 | 227 | 233 | 238 | 244 | 249 | |
| 799 | 255 | 260 | 266 | 271 | 276 | 282 | 287 | 293 | 298 | 304 | |
| **800** | 309 | 314 | 320 | 325 | 331 | 336 | 342 | 347 | 352 | 358 | |
| N. | 0 | 1 | 2 | 3 | 4 | 5 | 6 | 7 | 8 | 9 | Proportional parts |

| N. | 0 | 1 | 2 | 3 | 4 | 5 | 6 | 7 | 8 | 9 | Proportional parts |
|----|---|---|---|---|---|---|---|---|---|---|---|
| **800** | 90 309 | 314 | 320 | 325 | 331 | 336 | 342 | 347 | 352 | 358 | |
| 801 | 363 | 369 | 374 | 380 | 385 | 390 | 396 | 401 | 407 | 412 | |
| 802 | 417 | 423 | 428 | 434 | 439 | 445 | 450 | 455 | 461 | 466 | |
| 803 | 472 | 477 | 482 | 488 | 493 | 499 | 504 | 509 | 515 | 520 | |
| 804 | 526 | 531 | 536 | 542 | 547 | 553 | 558 | 563 | 569 | 574 | |
| 805 | 580 | 585 | 590 | 596 | 601 | 607 | 612 | 617 | 623 | 628 | |
| 806 | 634 | 639 | 644 | 650 | 655 | 660 | 666 | 671 | 677 | 682 | |
| 807 | 687 | 693 | 698 | 703 | 709 | 714 | 720 | 725 | 730 | 736 | |
| 808 | 741 | 747 | 752 | 757 | 763 | 768 | 773 | 779 | 784 | 789 | |
| 809 | 795 | 800 | 806 | 811 | 816 | 822 | 827 | 832 | 838 | 843 | |
| **810** | 849 | 854 | 859 | 865 | 870 | 875 | 881 | 886 | 891 | 897 | **6** |
| 811 | 902 | 907 | 913 | 918 | 924 | 929 | 934 | 940 | 945 | 950 | 1 \| 0.6 |
| 812 | 956 | 961 | 966 | 972 | 977 | 982 | 988 | 993 | 998 | *004 | 2 \| 1.2 |
| 813 | 91 009 | 014 | 020 | 025 | 030 | 036 | 041 | 046 | 052 | 057 | 3 \| 1.8 |
| 814 | 062 | 068 | 073 | 078 | 084 | 089 | 094 | 100 | 105 | 110 | 4 \| 2.4 |
| 815 | 116 | 121 | 126 | 132 | 137 | 142 | 148 | 153 | 158 | 164 | 5 \| 3.0 |
| 816 | 169 | 174 | 180 | 185 | 190 | 196 | 201 | 206 | 212 | 217 | 6 \| 3.6 |
| 817 | 222 | 228 | 233 | 238 | 243 | 249 | 254 | 259 | 265 | 270 | 7 \| 4.2 |
| 818 | 275 | 281 | 286 | 291 | 297 | 302 | 307 | 312 | 318 | 323 | 8 \| 4.8 |
| 819 | 328 | 334 | 339 | 344 | 350 | 355 | 360 | 365 | 371 | 376 | 9 \| 5.4 |
| **820** | 381 | 387 | 392 | 397 | 403 | 408 | 413 | 418 | 424 | 429 | |
| 821 | 434 | 440 | 445 | 450 | 455 | 461 | 466 | 471 | 477 | 482 | |
| 822 | 487 | 492 | 498 | 503 | 508 | 514 | 519 | 524 | 529 | 535 | |
| 823 | 540 | 545 | 551 | 556 | 561 | 566 | 572 | 577 | 582 | 587 | |
| 824 | 593 | 598 | 603 | 609 | 614 | 619 | 624 | 630 | 635 | 640 | |
| 825 | 645 | 651 | 656 | 661 | 666 | 672 | 677 | 682 | 687 | 693 | |
| 826 | 698 | 703 | 709 | 714 | 719 | 724 | 730 | 735 | 740 | 745 | |
| 827 | 751 | 756 | 761 | 766 | 772 | 777 | 782 | 787 | 793 | 798 | |
| 828 | 803 | 808 | 814 | 819 | 824 | 829 | 834 | 840 | 845 | 850 | |
| 829 | 855 | 861 | 866 | 871 | 876 | 882 | 887 | 892 | 897 | 903 | |
| **830** | 908 | 913 | 918 | 924 | 929 | 934 | 939 | 944 | 950 | 955 | **5** |
| 831 | 960 | 965 | 971 | 976 | 981 | 986 | 991 | 997 | *002 | *007 | 1 \| 0.5 |
| 832 | 92 012 | 018 | 023 | 028 | 033 | 038 | 044 | 049 | 054 | 059 | 2 \| 1.0 |
| 833 | 065 | 070 | 075 | 080 | 085 | 091 | 096 | 101 | 106 | 111 | 3 \| 1.5 |
| 834 | 117 | 122 | 127 | 132 | 137 | 143 | 148 | 153 | 158 | 163 | 4 \| 2.0 |
| 835 | 169 | 174 | 179 | 184 | 189 | 195 | 200 | 205 | 210 | 215 | 5 \| 2.5 |
| 836 | 221 | 226 | 231 | 236 | 241 | 247 | 252 | 257 | 262 | 267 | 6 \| 3.0 |
| 837 | 273 | 278 | 283 | 288 | 293 | 298 | 304 | 309 | 314 | 319 | 7 \| 3.5 |
| 838 | 324 | 330 | 335 | 340 | 345 | 350 | 355 | 361 | 366 | 371 | 8 \| 4.0 |
| 839 | 376 | 381 | 387 | 392 | 397 | 402 | 407 | 412 | 418 | 423 | 9 \| 4.5 |
| **840** | 428 | 433 | 438 | 443 | 449 | 454 | 459 | 464 | 469 | 474 | |
| 841 | 480 | 485 | 490 | 495 | 500 | 505 | 511 | 516 | 521 | 526 | |
| 842 | 531 | 536 | 542 | 547 | 552 | 557 | 562 | 567 | 572 | 578 | |
| 843 | 583 | 588 | 593 | 598 | 603 | 609 | 614 | 619 | 624 | 629 | |
| 844 | 634 | 639 | 645 | 650 | 655 | 660 | 665 | 670 | 675 | 681 | |
| 845 | 686 | 691 | 696 | 701 | 706 | 711 | 716 | 722 | 727 | 732 | |
| 846 | 737 | 742 | 747 | 752 | 758 | 763 | 768 | 773 | 778 | 783 | |
| 847 | 788 | 793 | 799 | 804 | 809 | 814 | 819 | 824 | 829 | 834 | |
| 848 | 840 | 845 | 850 | 855 | 860 | 865 | 870 | 875 | 881 | 886 | |
| 849 | 891 | 896 | 901 | 906 | 911 | 916 | 921 | 927 | 932 | 937 | |
| **850** | 942 | 947 | 952 | 957 | 962 | 967 | 973 | 978 | 983 | 988 | |

| N. | 0 | 1 | 2 | 3 | 4 | 5 | 6 | 7 | 8 | 9 | Proportional parts |
|----|---|---|---|---|---|---|---|---|---|---|---|

| N. | 0 | 1 | 2 | 3 | 4 | 5 | 6 | 7 | 8 | 9 | Proportional parts |
|---|---|---|---|---|---|---|---|---|---|---|---|
| **850** | 92 942 | 947 | 952 | 957 | 962 | 967 | 973 | 978 | 983 | 988 | |
| 851 | 993 | 998 | *003 | *008 | *013 | *018 | *024 | *029 | *034 | *039 | |
| 852 | 93 044 | 049 | 054 | 059 | 064 | 069 | 075 | 080 | 085 | 090 | |
| 853 | 095 | 100 | 105 | 110 | 115 | 120 | 125 | 131 | 136 | 141 | |
| 854 | 146 | 151 | 156 | 161 | 166 | 171 | 176 | 181 | 186 | 192 | |
| 855 | 197 | 202 | 207 | 212 | 217 | 222 | 227 | 232 | 237 | 242 | **6** |
| 856 | 247 | 252 | 258 | 263 | 268 | 273 | 278 | 283 | 288 | 293 | |
| 857 | 298 | 303 | 308 | 313 | 318 | 323 | 328 | 334 | 339 | 344 | 1 0.6 |
| 858 | 349 | 354 | 359 | 364 | 369 | 374 | 379 | 384 | 389 | 394 | 2 1.2 |
| 859 | 399 | 404 | 409 | 414 | 420 | 425 | 430 | 435 | 440 | 445 | 3 1.8 |
| | | | | | | | | | | | 4 2.4 |
| **860** | 450 | 455 | 460 | 465 | 470 | 475 | 480 | 485 | 490 | 495 | 5 3.0 |
| 861 | 500 | 505 | 510 | 515 | 520 | 526 | 531 | 536 | 541 | 546 | 6 3.6 |
| 862 | 551 | 556 | 561 | 566 | 571 | 576 | 581 | 586 | 591 | 596 | 7 4.2 |
| 863 | 601 | 606 | 611 | 616 | 621 | 626 | 631 | 636 | 641 | 646 | 8 4.8 |
| 864 | 651 | 656 | 661 | 666 | 671 | 676 | 682 | 687 | 692 | 697 | 9 5.4 |
| 865 | 702 | 707 | 712 | 717 | 722 | 727 | 732 | 737 | 742 | 747 | |
| 866 | 752 | 757 | 762 | 767 | 772 | 777 | 782 | 787 | 792 | 797 | |
| 867 | 802 | 807 | 812 | 817 | 822 | 827 | 832 | 837 | 842 | 847 | |
| 868 | 852 | 857 | 862 | 867 | 872 | 877 | 882 | 887 | 892 | 897 | |
| 869 | 902 | 907 | 912 | 917 | 922 | 927 | 932 | 937 | 942 | 947 | |
| **870** | 952 | 957 | 962 | 967 | 972 | 977 | 982 | 987 | 992 | 997 | |
| 871 | 94 002 | 007 | 012 | 017 | 022 | 027 | 032 | 037 | 042 | 047 | **5** |
| 872 | 052 | 057 | 062 | 067 | 072 | 077 | 082 | 086 | 091 | 096 | 1 0.5 |
| 873 | 101 | 106 | 111 | 116 | 121 | 126 | 131 | 136 | 141 | 146 | 2 1.0 |
| 874 | 151 | 156 | 161 | 166 | 171 | 176 | 181 | 186 | 191 | 196 | 3 1.5 |
| 875 | 201 | 206 | 211 | 216 | 221 | 226 | 231 | 236 | 240 | 245 | 4 2.0 |
| 876 | 250 | 255 | 260 | 265 | 270 | 275 | 280 | 285 | 290 | 295 | 5 2.5 |
| 877 | 300 | 305 | 310 | 315 | 320 | 325 | 330 | 335 | 340 | 345 | 6 3.0 |
| 878 | 349 | 354 | 359 | 364 | 369 | 374 | 379 | 384 | 389 | 394 | 7 3.5 |
| 879 | 399 | 404 | 409 | 414 | 419 | 424 | 429 | 433 | 438 | 443 | 8 4.0 |
| | | | | | | | | | | | 9 4.5 |
| **880** | 448 | 453 | 458 | 463 | 468 | 473 | 478 | 483 | 488 | 493 | |
| 881 | 498 | 503 | 507 | 512 | 517 | 522 | 527 | 532 | 537 | 542 | |
| 882 | 547 | 552 | 557 | 562 | 567 | 571 | 576 | 581 | 586 | 591 | |
| 883 | 596 | 601 | 606 | 611 | 616 | 621 | 626 | 630 | 635 | 640 | |
| 884 | 645 | 650 | 655 | 660 | 665 | 670 | 675 | 680 | 685 | 689 | **4** |
| 885 | 694 | 699 | 704 | 709 | 714 | 719 | 724 | 729 | 734 | 738 | 1 0.4 |
| 886 | 743 | 748 | 753 | 758 | 763 | 768 | 773 | 778 | 783 | 787 | 2 0.8 |
| 887 | 792 | 797 | 802 | 807 | 812 | 817 | 822 | 827 | 832 | 836 | 3 1.2 |
| 888 | 841 | 846 | 851 | 856 | 861 | 866 | 871 | 876 | 880 | 885 | 4 1.6 |
| 889 | 890 | 895 | 900 | 905 | 910 | 915 | 919 | 924 | 929 | 934 | 5 2.0 |
| | | | | | | | | | | | 6 2.4 |
| **890** | 939 | 944 | 949 | 954 | 959 | 963 | 968 | 973 | 978 | 983 | 7 2.8 |
| 891 | 988 | 993 | 998 | *002 | *007 | *012 | *017 | *022 | *027 | *032 | 8 3.2 |
| 892 | 95 036 | 041 | 046 | 051 | 056 | 061 | 066 | 071 | 075 | 080 | 9 3.6 |
| 893 | 085 | 090 | 095 | 100 | 105 | 109 | 114 | 119 | 124 | 129 | |
| 894 | 134 | 139 | 143 | 148 | 153 | 158 | 163 | 168 | 173 | 177 | |
| 895 | 182 | 187 | 192 | 197 | 202 | 207 | 211 | 216 | 221 | 226 | |
| 896 | 231 | 236 | 240 | 245 | 250 | 255 | 260 | 265 | 270 | 274 | |
| 897 | 279 | 284 | 289 | 294 | 299 | 303 | 308 | 313 | 318 | 323 | |
| 898 | 328 | 332 | 337 | 342 | 347 | 352 | 357 | 361 | 366 | 371 | |
| 899 | 376 | 381 | 386 | 390 | 395 | 400 | 405 | 410 | 415 | 419 | |
| **900** | 424 | 429 | 434 | 439 | 444 | 448 | 453 | 458 | 463 | 468 | |
| N. | 0 | 1 | 2 | 3 | 4 | 5 | 6 | 7 | 8 | 9 | Proportional parts |

| N. | 0 | 1 | 2 | 3 | 4 | 5 | 6 | 7 | 8 | 9 |
|---|---|---|---|---|---|---|---|---|---|---|
| **900** | 95 424 | 429 | 434 | 439 | 444 | 448 | 453 | 458 | 463 | 468 |
| 901 | 472 | 477 | 482 | 487 | 492 | 497 | 501 | 506 | 511 | 516 |
| 902 | 521 | 525 | 530 | 535 | 540 | 545 | 550 | 554 | 559 | 564 |
| 903 | 569 | 574 | 578 | 583 | 588 | 593 | 598 | 602 | 607 | 612 |
| 904 | 617 | 622 | 626 | 631 | 636 | 641 | 646 | 650 | 655 | 660 |
| 905 | 665 | 670 | 674 | 679 | 684 | 689 | 694 | 698 | 703 | 708 |
| 906 | 713 | 718 | 722 | 727 | 732 | 737 | 742 | 746 | 751 | 756 |
| 907 | 761 | 766 | 770 | 775 | 780 | 785 | 789 | 794 | 799 | 804 |
| 908 | 809 | 813 | 818 | 823 | 828 | 832 | 837 | 842 | 847 | 852 |
| 909 | 856 | 861 | 866 | 871 | 875 | 880 | 885 | 890 | 895 | 899 |
| **910** | 904 | 909 | 914 | 918 | 923 | 928 | 933 | 938 | 942 | 947 |
| 911 | 952 | 957 | 961 | 966 | 971 | 976 | 980 | 985 | 990 | 995 |
| 912 | 999 | *004 | *009 | *014 | *019 | *023 | *028 | *033 | *038 | *042 |
| 913 | 96 047 | 052 | 057 | 061 | 066 | 071 | 076 | 080 | 085 | 090 |
| 914 | 095 | 099 | 104 | 109 | 114 | 118 | 123 | 128 | 133 | 137 |
| 915 | 142 | 147 | 152 | 156 | 161 | 166 | 171 | 175 | 180 | 185 |
| 916 | 190 | 194 | 199 | 204 | 209 | 213 | 218 | 223 | 227 | 232 |
| 917 | 237 | 242 | 246 | 251 | 256 | 261 | 265 | 270 | 275 | 280 |
| 918 | 284 | 289 | 294 | 298 | 303 | 308 | 313 | 317 | 322 | 327 |
| 919 | 332 | 336 | 341 | 346 | 350 | 355 | 360 | 365 | 369 | 374 |
| **920** | 379 | 384 | 388 | 393 | 398 | 402 | 407 | 412 | 417 | 421 |
| 921 | 426 | 431 | 435 | 440 | 445 | 450 | 454 | 459 | 464 | 468 |
| 922 | 473 | 478 | 483 | 487 | 492 | 497 | 501 | 506 | 511 | 515 |
| 923 | 520 | 525 | 530 | 534 | 539 | 544 | 548 | 553 | 558 | 562 |
| 924 | 567 | 572 | 577 | 581 | 586 | 591 | 595 | 600 | 605 | 609 |
| 925 | 614 | 619 | 624 | 628 | 633 | 638 | 642 | 647 | 652 | 656 |
| 926 | 661 | 666 | 670 | 675 | 680 | 685 | 689 | 694 | 699 | 703 |
| 927 | 708 | 713 | 717 | 722 | 727 | 731 | 736 | 741 | 745 | 750 |
| 928 | 755 | 759 | 764 | 769 | 774 | 778 | 783 | 788 | 792 | 797 |
| 929 | 802 | 806 | 811 | 816 | 820 | 825 | 830 | 834 | 839 | 844 |
| **930** | 848 | 853 | 858 | 862 | 867 | 872 | 876 | 881 | 886 | 890 |
| 931 | 895 | 900 | 904 | 909 | 914 | 918 | 923 | 928 | 932 | 937 |
| 932 | 942 | 946 | 951 | 956 | 960 | 965 | 970 | 974 | 979 | 984 |
| 933 | 988 | 993 | 997 | *002 | *007 | *011 | *016 | *021 | *025 | *030 |
| 934 | 97 035 | 039 | 044 | 049 | 053 | 058 | 063 | 067 | 072 | 077 |
| 935 | 081 | 086 | 090 | 095 | 100 | 104 | 109 | 114 | 118 | 123 |
| 936 | 128 | 132 | 137 | 142 | 146 | 151 | 155 | 160 | 165 | 169 |
| 937 | 174 | 179 | 183 | 188 | 192 | 197 | 202 | 206 | 211 | 216 |
| 938 | 220 | 225 | 230 | 234 | 239 | 243 | 248 | 253 | 257 | 262 |
| 939 | 267 | 271 | 276 | 280 | 285 | 290 | 294 | 299 | 304 | 308 |
| **940** | 313 | 317 | 322 | 327 | 331 | 336 | 340 | 345 | 350 | 354 |
| 941 | 359 | 364 | 368 | 373 | 377 | 382 | 387 | 391 | 396 | 400 |
| 942 | 405 | 410 | 414 | 419 | 424 | 428 | 433 | 437 | 442 | 447 |
| 943 | 451 | 456 | 460 | 465 | 470 | 474 | 479 | 483 | 488 | 493 |
| 944 | 497 | 502 | 506 | 511 | 516 | 520 | 525 | 529 | 534 | 539 |
| 945 | 543 | 548 | 552 | 557 | 562 | 566 | 571 | 575 | 580 | 585 |
| 946 | 589 | 594 | 598 | 603 | 607 | 612 | 617 | 621 | 626 | 630 |
| 947 | 635 | 640 | 644 | 649 | 653 | 658 | 663 | 667 | 672 | 676 |
| 948 | 681 | 685 | 690 | 695 | 699 | 704 | 708 | 713 | 717 | 722 |
| 949 | 727 | 731 | 736 | 740 | 745 | 749 | 754 | 759 | 763 | 768 |
| **950** | 772 | 777 | 782 | 786 | 791 | 795 | 800 | 804 | 809 | 813 |

Proportional parts

**5**

| 1 | 0.5 |
|---|---|
| 2 | 1.0 |
| 3 | 1.5 |
| 4 | 2.0 |
| 5 | 2.5 |
| 6 | 3.0 |
| 7 | 3.5 |
| 8 | 4.0 |
| 9 | 4.5 |

**4**

| 1 | 0.4 |
|---|---|
| 2 | 0.8 |
| 3 | 1.2 |
| 4 | 1.6 |
| 5 | 2.0 |
| 6 | 2.4 |
| 7 | 2.8 |
| 8 | 3.2 |
| 9 | 3.6 |

| N. | 0 | 1 | 2 | 3 | 4 | 5 | 6 | 7 | 8 | 9 | Proportional parts |
|---|---|---|---|---|---|---|---|---|---|---|---|
| **950** | 97 772 | 777 | 782 | 786 | 791 | 795 | 800 | 804 | 809 | 813 | |
| 951 | 818 | 823 | 827 | 832 | 836 | 841 | 845 | 850 | 855 | 859 | |
| 952 | 864 | 868 | 873 | 877 | 882 | 886 | 891 | 896 | 900 | 905 | |
| 953 | 909 | 914 | 918 | 923 | 928 | 932 | 937 | 941 | 946 | 950 | |
| 954 | 955 | 959 | 964 | 968 | 973 | 978 | 982 | 987 | 991 | 996 | |
| 955 | 98 000 | 005 | 009 | 014 | 019 | 023 | 028 | 032 | 037 | 041 | |
| 956 | 046 | 050 | 055 | 059 | 064 | 068 | 073 | 078 | 082 | 087 | |
| 957 | 091 | 096 | 100 | 105 | 109 | 114 | 118 | 123 | 127 | 132 | |
| 958 | 137 | 141 | 146 | 150 | 155 | 159 | 164 | 168 | 173 | 177 | |
| 959 | 182 | 186 | 191 | 195 | 200 | 204 | 209 | 214 | 218 | 223 | |
| **960** | 227 | 232 | 236 | 241 | 245 | 250 | 254 | 259 | 263 | 268 | **5** |
| 961 | 272 | 277 | 281 | 286 | 290 | 295 | 299 | 304 | 308 | 313 | 1 \| 0.5 |
| 962 | 318 | 322 | 327 | 331 | 336 | 340 | 345 | 349 | 354 | 358 | 2 \| 1.0 |
| 963 | 363 | 367 | 372 | 376 | 381 | 385 | 390 | 394 | 399 | 403 | 3 \| 1.5 |
| 964 | 408 | 412 | 417 | 421 | 426 | 430 | 435 | 439 | 444 | 448 | 4 \| 2.0 |
| 965 | 453 | 457 | 462 | 466 | 471 | 475 | 480 | 484 | 489 | 493 | 5 \| 2.5 |
| 966 | 498 | 502 | 507 | 511 | 516 | 520 | 525 | 529 | 534 | 538 | 6 \| 3.0 |
| 967 | 543 | 547 | 552 | 556 | 561 | 565 | 570 | 574 | 579 | 583 | 7 \| 3.5 |
| 968 | 588 | 592 | 597 | 601 | 605 | 610 | 614 | 619 | 623 | 628 | 8 \| 4.0 |
| 969 | 632 | 637 | 641 | 646 | 650 | 655 | 659 | 664 | 668 | 673 | 9 \| 4.5 |
| **970** | 677 | 682 | 686 | 691 | 695 | 700 | 704 | 709 | 713 | 717 | |
| 971 | 722 | 726 | 731 | 735 | 740 | 744 | 749 | 753 | 758 | 762 | |
| 972 | 767 | 771 | 776 | 780 | 784 | 789 | 793 | 798 | 802 | 807 | |
| 973 | 811 | 816 | 820 | 825 | 829 | 834 | 838 | 843 | 847 | 851 | |
| 974 | 856 | 860 | 865 | 869 | 874 | 878 | 883 | 887 | 892 | 896 | |
| 975 | 900 | 905 | 909 | 914 | 918 | 923 | 927 | 932 | 936 | 941 | |
| 976 | 945 | 949 | 954 | 958 | 963 | 967 | 972 | 976 | 981 | 985 | |
| 977 | 989 | 994 | 998 | *003 | *007 | *012 | *016 | *021 | *025 | *029 | |
| 978 | 99 034 | 038 | 043 | 047 | 052 | 056 | 061 | 065 | 069 | 074 | |
| 979 | 078 | 083 | 087 | 092 | 096 | 100 | 105 | 109 | 114 | 118 | |
| **980** | 123 | 127 | 131 | 136 | 140 | 145 | 149 | 154 | 158 | 162 | **4** |
| 981 | 167 | 171 | 176 | 180 | 185 | 189 | 193 | 198 | 202 | 207 | 1 \| 0.4 |
| 982 | 211 | 216 | 220 | 224 | 229 | 233 | 238 | 242 | 247 | 251 | 2 \| 0.8 |
| 983 | 255 | 260 | 264 | 269 | 273 | 277 | 282 | 286 | 291 | 295 | 3 \| 1.2 |
| 984 | 300 | 304 | 308 | 313 | 317 | 322 | 326 | 330 | 335 | 339 | 4 \| 1.6 |
| 985 | 344 | 348 | 352 | 357 | 361 | 366 | 370 | 374 | 379 | 383 | 5 \| 2.0 |
| 986 | 388 | 392 | 396 | 401 | 405 | 410 | 414 | 419 | 423 | 427 | 6 \| 2.4 |
| 987 | 432 | 436 | 441 | 445 | 449 | 454 | 458 | 463 | 467 | 471 | 7 \| 2.8 |
| 988 | 476 | 480 | 484 | 489 | 493 | 498 | 502 | 506 | 511 | 515 | 8 \| 3.2 |
| 989 | 520 | 524 | 528 | 533 | 537 | 542 | 546 | 550 | 555 | 559 | 9 \| 3.6 |
| **990** | 564 | 568 | 572 | 577 | 581 | 585 | 590 | 594 | 599 | 603 | |
| 991 | 607 | 612 | 616 | 621 | 625 | 629 | 634 | 638 | 642 | 647 | |
| 992 | 651 | 656 | 660 | 664 | 669 | 673 | 677 | 682 | 686 | 691 | |
| 993 | 695 | 699 | 704 | 708 | 712 | 717 | 721 | 726 | 730 | 734 | |
| 994 | 739 | 743 | 747 | 752 | 756 | 760 | 765 | 769 | 774 | 778 | |
| 995 | 782 | 787 | 791 | 795 | 800 | 804 | 808 | 813 | 817 | 822 | |
| 996 | 826 | 830 | 835 | 839 | 843 | 848 | 852 | 856 | 861 | 865 | |
| 997 | 870 | 874 | 878 | 883 | 887 | 891 | 896 | 900 | 904 | 909 | |
| 998 | 913 | 917 | 922 | 926 | 930 | 935 | 939 | 944 | 948 | 952 | |
| 999 | 957 | 961 | 965 | 970 | 974 | 978 | 983 | 987 | 991 | 996 | |
| **1000** | 00 000 | 004 | 009 | 013 | 017 | 022 | 026 | 030 | 035 | 039 | |
| N. | 0 | 1 | 2 | 3 | 4 | 5 | 6 | 7 | 8 | 9 | Proportional parts |

| N. | 0 | 1 | 2 | 3 | 4 | 5 | 6 | 7 | 8 | 9 | d. |
|---|---|---|---|---|---|---|---|---|---|---|---|
| 1000 | 000 0000 | 0434 | 0869 | 1303 | 1737 | 2171 | 2605 | 3039 | 3473 | 3907 | 434 |
| 1001 | 4341 | 4775 | 5208 | 5642 | 6076 | 6510 | 6943 | 7377 | 7810 | 8244 | 434 |
| 1002 | 8677 | 9111 | 9544 | 9977 | *0411 | *0844 | *1277 | *1710 | *2143 | *2576 | 433 |
| 1003 | 001 3009 | 3442 | 3875 | 4308 | 4741 | 5174 | 5607 | 6039 | 6472 | 6905 | 433 |
| 1004 | 7337 | 7770 | 8202 | 8635 | 9067 | 9499 | 9932 | *0366 | *0796 | *1228 | 433 |
| 1005 | 002 1661 | 2093 | 2525 | 2957 | 3389 | 3821 | 4253 | 4685 | 5116 | 5548 | 432 |
| 1006 | 5980 | 6411 | 6843 | 7275 | 7706 | 8138 | 8569 | 9001 | 9432 | 9863 | 431 |
| 1007 | 003 0295 | 0726 | 1157 | 1588 | 2019 | 2451 | 2882 | 3313 | 3744 | 4174 | 431 |
| 1008 | 4605 | 5036 | 5467 | 5898 | 6328 | 6759 | 7190 | 7620 | 8051 | 8481 | 431 |
| 1009 | 8912 | 9342 | 9772 | *0203 | *0633 | *1063 | *1493 | *1924 | *2354 | *2784 | 430 |
| 1010 | 004 3214 | 3644 | 4074 | 4504 | 4933 | 5363 | 5793 | 6223 | 6652 | 7082 | 430 |
| 1011 | 7512 | 7941 | 8371 | 8800 | 9229 | 9659 | *0088 | *0517 | *0947 | *1376 | 429 |
| 1012 | 005 1805 | 2234 | 2663 | 3092 | 3521 | 3950 | 4379 | 4808 | 5237 | 5666 | 429 |
| 1013 | 6094 | 6523 | 6952 | 7380 | 7809 | 8238 | 8666 | 9094 | 9523 | 9951 | 429 |
| 1014 | 006 0380 | 0808 | 1236 | 1664 | 2092 | 2521 | 2949 | 3377 | 3805 | 4233 | 428 |
| 1015 | 4660 | 5088 | 5516 | 5944 | 6372 | 6799 | 7227 | 7655 | 8082 | 8510 | 428 |
| 1016 | 8937 | 9365 | 9792 | *0219 | *0647 | *1074 | *1501 | *1928 | *2355 | *2782 | 427 |
| 1017 | 007 3210 | 3637 | 4064 | 4490 | 4917 | 5344 | 5771 | 6198 | 6624 | 7051 | 427 |
| 1018 | 7478 | 7904 | 8331 | 8757 | 9184 | 9610 | *0037 | *0463 | *0889 | *1316 | 426 |
| 1019 | 008 1742 | 2168 | 2594 | 3020 | 3446 | 3872 | 4298 | 4724 | 5150 | 5576 | 426 |
| 1020 | 6002 | 6427 | 6853 | 7279 | 7704 | 8130 | 8556 | 8981 | 9407 | 9832 | 426 |
| 1021 | 009 0257 | 0683 | 1108 | 1533 | 1959 | 2384 | 2809 | 3234 | 3659 | 4084 | 425 |
| 1022 | 4509 | 4934 | 5359 | 5784 | 6208 | 6633 | 7058 | 7483 | 7907 | 8332 | 425 |
| 1023 | 8756 | 9181 | 9605 | *0030 | *0454 | *0878 | *1303 | *1727 | *2151 | *2575 | 424 |
| 1024 | 010 3000 | 3424 | 3848 | 4272 | 4696 | 5120 | 5544 | 5967 | 6391 | 6815 | 424 |
| 1025 | 7239 | 7662 | 8086 | 8510 | 8933 | 9357 | 9780 | *0204 | *0627 | *1050 | 424 |
| 1026 | 011 1474 | 1897 | 2320 | 2743 | 3166 | 3590 | 4013 | 4436 | 4859 | 5282 | 423 |
| 1027 | 5704 | 6127 | 6550 | 6973 | 7396 | 7818 | 8241 | 8664 | 9086 | 9509 | 423 |
| 1028 | 9931 | *0354 | *0776 | *1198 | *1621 | *2043 | *2465 | *2887 | *3310 | *3732 | 422 |
| 1029 | 012 4154 | 4576 | 4998 | 5420 | 5842 | 6264 | 6685 | 7107 | 7529 | 7951 | 422 |
| 1030 | 8372 | 8794 | 9215 | 9637 | *0059 | *0480 | *0901 | *1323 | *1744 | *2165 | 422 |
| 1031 | 013 2587 | 3008 | 3429 | 3850 | 4271 | 4692 | 5113 | 5534 | 5955 | 6376 | 421 |
| 1032 | 6797 | 7218 | 7639 | 8059 | 8480 | 8901 | 9321 | 9742 | *0162 | *0583 | 421 |
| 1033 | 014 1003 | 1424 | 1844 | 2264 | 2685 | 3105 | 3525 | 3945 | 4365 | 4785 | 420 |
| 1034 | 5205 | 5625 | 6045 | 6465 | 6885 | 7305 | 7725 | 8144 | 8564 | 8984 | 420 |
| 1035 | 9403 | 9823 | *0243 | *0662 | *1082 | *1501 | *1920 | *2340 | *2759 | *3178 | 420 |
| 1036 | 015 3598 | 4017 | 4436 | 4855 | 5274 | 5693 | 6112 | 6531 | 6950 | 7369 | 419 |
| 1037 | 7788 | 8206 | 8625 | 9044 | 9462 | 9881 | *0300 | *0718 | *1137 | *1555 | 419 |
| 1038 | 016 1974 | 2392 | 2810 | 3229 | 3647 | 4065 | 4483 | 4901 | 5319 | 5737 | 418 |
| 1039 | 6155 | 6573 | 6991 | 7409 | 7827 | 8245 | 8663 | 9080 | 9498 | 9916 | 418 |
| 1040 | 017 0333 | 0751 | 1168 | 1586 | 2003 | 2421 | 2838 | 3256 | 3673 | 4090 | 417 |
| 1041 | 4507 | 4924 | 5342 | 5759 | 6176 | 6593 | 7010 | 7427 | 7844 | 8260 | 417 |
| 1042 | 8677 | 9094 | 9511 | 9927 | *0344 | *0761 | *1177 | *1594 | *2010 | *2427 | 417 |
| 1043 | 018 2843 | 3259 | 3676 | 4092 | 4508 | 4925 | 5341 | 5757 | 6173 | 6589 | 416 |
| 1044 | 7005 | 7421 | 7837 | 8253 | 8669 | 9084 | 9500 | 9916 | *0332 | *0747 | 416 |
| 1045 | 019 1163 | 1578 | 1994 | 2410 | 2825 | 3240 | 3656 | 4071 | 4486 | 4902 | 415 |
| 1046 | 5317 | 5732 | 6147 | 6562 | 6977 | 7392 | 7807 | 8222 | 8637 | 9052 | 415 |
| 1047 | 9467 | 9882 | *0296 | *0711 | *1126 | *1540 | *1955 | *2369 | *2784 | *3198 | 415 |
| 1048 | 020 3613 | 4027 | 4442 | 4856 | 5270 | 5684 | 6099 | 6513 | 6927 | 7341 | 414 |
| 1049 | 7755 | 8169 | 8583 | 8997 | 9411 | 9824 | *0238 | *0652 | *1066 | *1479 | 414 |
| 1050 | 021 1893 | 2307 | 2720 | 3134 | 3547 | 3961 | 4374 | 4787 | 5201 | 5614 | 413 |
| N. | 0 | 1 | 2 | 3 | 4 | 5 | 6 | 7 | 8 | 9 | d. |

| N. | 0 | 1 | 2 | 3 | 4 | 5 | 6 | 7 | 8 | 9 | d. |
|---|---|---|---|---|---|---|---|---|---|---|---|
| **1050** | 021 1893 | 2307 | 2720 | 3134 | 3547 | 3961 | 4374 | 4787 | 5201 | 5614 | 413 |
| 1051 | 6027 | 6440 | 6854 | 7267 | 7680 | 8093 | 8506 | 8919 | 9332 | 9745 | 413 |
| 1052 | 022 0157 | 0570 | 0983 | 1396 | 1808 | 2221 | 2634 | 3046 | 3459 | 3871 | 413 |
| 1053 | 4284 | 4696 | 5109 | 5521 | 5933 | 6345 | 6758 | 7170 | 7582 | 7994 | 412 |
| 1054 | 8406 | 8818 | 9230 | 9642 | *0054 | *0466 | *0878 | *1289 | *1701 | *2113 | 412 |
| 1055 | 023 2525 | 2936 | 3348 | 3759 | 4171 | 4582 | 4994 | 5405 | 5817 | 6228 | 411 |
| 1056 | 6639 | 7050 | 7462 | 7873 | 8284 | 8695 | 9106 | 9517 | 9928 | *0339 | 411 |
| 1057 | 024 0750 | 1161 | 1572 | 1982 | 2393 | 2804 | 3214 | 3625 | 4036 | 4446 | 411 |
| 1058 | 4857 | 5267 | 5678 | 6088 | 6498 | 6909 | 7319 | 7729 | 8139 | 8549 | 410 |
| 1059 | 8960 | 9370 | 9780 | *0190 | *0600 | *1010 | *1419 | *1829 | *2239 | *2649 | 410 |
| **1060** | 025 3059 | 3468 | 3878 | 4288 | 4697 | 5107 | 5516 | 5926 | 6335 | 6744 | 410 |
| 1061 | 7154 | 7563 | 7972 | 8382 | 8791 | 9200 | 9609 | *0018 | *0427 | *0836 | 409 |
| 1062 | 026 1245 | 1654 | 2063 | 2472 | 2881 | 3289 | 3698 | 4107 | 4515 | 4924 | 409 |
| 1063 | 5333 | 5741 | 6150 | 6558 | 6967 | 7375 | 7783 | 8192 | 8600 | 9008 | 408 |
| 1064 | 9416 | 9824 | *0233 | *0641 | *1049 | *1457 | *1865 | *2273 | *2680 | *3088 | 408 |
| 1065 | 027 3496 | 3904 | 4312 | 4719 | 5127 | 5535 | 5942 | 6350 | 6757 | 7165 | 408 |
| 1066 | 7572 | 7979 | 8387 | 8794 | 9201 | 9609 | *0016 | *0423 | *0830 | *1237 | 407 |
| 1067 | 028 1644 | 2051 | 2458 | 2865 | 3272 | 3679 | 4086 | 4492 | 4899 | 5306 | 407 |
| 1068 | 5713 | 6119 | 6526 | 6932 | 7339 | 7745 | 8152 | 8558 | 8964 | 9371 | 406 |
| 1069 | 9777 | *0183 | *0590 | *0996 | *1402 | *1808 | *2214 | *2620 | *3026 | *3432 | 406 |
| **1070** | 029 3838 | 4244 | 4649 | 5055 | 5461 | 5867 | 6272 | 6678 | 7084 | 7489 | 406 |
| 1071 | 7895 | 8300 | 8706 | 9111 | 9516 | 9922 | *0327 | *0732 | *1138 | *1543 | 405 |
| 1072 | 030 1948 | 2353 | 2758 | 3163 | 3568 | 3973 | 4378 | 4783 | 5188 | 5592 | 405 |
| 1073 | 5997 | 6402 | 6807 | 7211 | 7616 | 8020 | 8425 | 8830 | 9234 | 9638 | 405 |
| 1074 | 031 0043 | 0447 | 0851 | 1256 | 1660 | 2064 | 2468 | 2872 | 3277 | 3681 | 404 |
| 1075 | 4085 | 4489 | 4893 | 5296 | 5700 | 6104 | 6508 | 6912 | 7315 | 7719 | 404 |
| 1076 | 8123 | 8526 | 8930 | 9333 | 9737 | *0140 | *0544 | *0947 | *1350 | *1754 | 403 |
| 1077 | 032 2157 | 2560 | 2963 | 3367 | 3770 | 4173 | 4576 | 4979 | 5382 | 5785 | 403 |
| 1078 | 6188 | 6590 | 6993 | 7396 | 7799 | 8201 | 8604 | 9007 | 9409 | 9812 | 403 |
| 1079 | 033 0214 | 0617 | 1019 | 1422 | 1824 | 2226 | 2629 | 3031 | 3433 | 3835 | 402 |
| **1080** | 4238 | 4640 | 5042 | 5444 | 5846 | 6248 | 6650 | 7052 | 7453 | 7855 | 402 |
| 1081 | 8257 | 8659 | 9060 | 9462 | 9864 | *0265 | *0667 | *1068 | *1470 | *1871 | 402 |
| 1082 | 034 2273 | 2674 | 3075 | 3477 | 3878 | 4279 | 4680 | 5081 | 5482 | 5884 | 401 |
| 1083 | 6285 | 6686 | 7087 | 7487 | 7888 | 8289 | 8690 | 9091 | 9491 | 9892 | 401 |
| 1084 | 035 0293 | 0693 | 1094 | 1495 | 1895 | 2296 | 2696 | 3096 | 3497 | 3897 | 400 |
| 1085 | 4297 | 4698 | 5098 | 5498 | 5898 | 6298 | 6698 | 7098 | 7498 | 7898 | 400 |
| 1086 | 8298 | 8698 | 9098 | 9498 | 9898 | *0297 | *0697 | *1097 | *1496 | *1896 | 400 |
| 1087 | 036 2295 | 2695 | 3094 | 3494 | 3893 | 4293 | 4692 | 5091 | 5491 | 5890 | 399 |
| 1088 | 6289 | 6688 | 7087 | 7486 | 7885 | 8284 | 8683 | 9082 | 9481 | 9880 | 399 |
| 1089 | 037 0279 | 0678 | 1076 | 1475 | 1874 | 2272 | 2671 | 3070 | 3468 | 3867 | 399 |
| **1090** | 4265 | 4663 | 5062 | 5460 | 5858 | 6257 | 6655 | 7053 | 7451 | 7849 | 398 |
| 1091 | 8248 | 8646 | 9044 | 9442 | 9839 | *0237 | *0635 | *1033 | *1431 | *1829 | 398 |
| 1092 | 038 2226 | 2624 | 3022 | 3419 | 3817 | 4214 | 4612 | 5009 | 5407 | 5804 | 398 |
| 1093 | 6202 | 6599 | 6996 | 7393 | 7791 | 8188 | 8585 | 8982 | 9379 | 9776 | 397 |
| 1094 | 039 0173 | 0570 | 0967 | 1364 | 1761 | 2158 | 2554 | 2951 | 3348 | 3745 | 397 |
| 1095 | 4141 | 4538 | 4934 | 5331 | 5727 | 6124 | 6520 | 6917 | 7313 | 7709 | 397 |
| 1096 | 8106 | 8502 | 8898 | 9294 | 9690 | *0086 | *0482 | *0878 | *1274 | *1670 | 396 |
| 1097 | 040 2066 | 2462 | 2858 | 3254 | 3650 | 4045 | 4441 | 4837 | 5232 | 5628 | 396 |
| 1098 | 6023 | 6419 | 6814 | 7210 | 7605 | 8001 | 8396 | 8791 | 9187 | 9582 | 395 |
| 1099 | 9977 | *0372 | *0767 | *1162 | *1557 | *1952 | *2347 | *2742 | *3137 | *3532 | 395 |
| **1100** | 041 3927 | 4322 | 4716 | 5111 | 5506 | 5900 | 6295 | 6690 | 7084 | 7479 | 395 |
| N. | 0 | 1 | 2 | 3 | 4 | 5 | 6 | 7 | 8 | 9 | d. |

# LOGARITHMS—(Continued)

| N | 0 | 1 | 2 | 3 | 4 | 5 | 6 | 7 | 8 | 9 | d. |
|---|---|---|---|---|---|---|---|---|---|---|---|
| **1100** | 041 3927 | 4322 | 4716 | 5111 | 5506 | 5900 | 6295 | 6690 | 7084 | 7479 | 395 |
| 1101 | 7873 | 8268 | 8662 | 9056 | 9451 | 9845 | *0239 | *0633 | *1028 | *1422 | 394 |
| 1102 | 042 1816 | 2210 | 2604 | 2998 | 3392 | 3786 | 4180 | 4574 | 4968 | 5361 | 394 |
| 1103 | 5755 | 6149 | 6543 | 6936 | 7330 | 7723 | 8117 | 8510 | 8904 | 9297 | 394 |
| 1104 | 9691 | '0084 | *0477 | *0871 | *1264 | *1657 | *2050 | *2444 | *2837 | *3230 | 393 |
| 1105 | 043 3623 | 4016 | 4409 | 4802 | 5195 | 5587 | 5980 | 6373 | 6766 | 7159 | 393 |
| 1106 | 7551 | 7944 | 8337 | 8729 | 9122 | 9514 | 9907 | *0299 | *0692 | *1084 | 393 |
| 1107 | 044 1476 | 1869 | 2261 | 2653 | 3045 | 3437 | 3829 | 4222 | 4614 | 5006 | 392 |
| 1108 | 5398 | 5790 | 6181 | 6573 | 6965 | 7357 | 7749 | 8140 | 8532 | 8924 | 392 |
| 1109 | 9315 | 9707 | *0099 | *0490 | *0882 | *1273 | *1664 | *2056 | *2447 | *2839 | 392 |
| **1110** | 045 3230 | 3621 | 4012 | 4403 | 4795 | 5186 | 5577 | 5968 | 6359 | 6750 | 391 |
| 1111 | 7141 | 7531 | 7922 | 8313 | 8704 | 9095 | 9485 | 9876 | *0267 | *0657 | 391 |
| 1112 | 046 1048 | 1438 | 1829 | 2219 | 2610 | 3000 | 3391 | 3781 | 4171 | 4561 | 390 |
| 1113 | 4952 | 5342 | 5732 | 6122 | 6512 | 6902 | 7292 | 7682 | 8072 | 8462 | 390 |
| 1114 | 8852 | 9242 | 9632 | *0021 | *0411 | *0801 | *1190 | *1580 | *1970 | *2359 | 390 |
| 1115 | 047 2749 | 3138 | 3528 | 3917 | 4306 | 4696 | 5085 | 5474 | 5864 | 6253 | 389 |
| 1116 | 6642 | 7031 | 7420 | 7809 | 8198 | 8587 | 8976 | 9365 | 9754 | *0143 | 389 |
| 1117 | 048 0532 | 0921 | 1309 | 1698 | 2087 | 2475 | 2864 | 3253 | 3641 | 4030 | 389 |
| 1118 | 4418 | 4806 | 5195 | 5583 | 5972 | 6360 | 6748 | 7136 | 7525 | 7913 | 388 |
| 1119 | 8301 | 8689 | 9077 | 9465 | 9853 | *0241 | *0629 | *1017 | *1405 | *1792 | 388 |
| **1120** | 049 2180 | 2568 | 2956 | 3343 | 3731 | 4119 | 4506 | 4894 | 5281 | 5669 | 388 |
| 1121 | 6056 | 6444 | 6831 | 7218 | 7606 | 7993 | 8380 | 8767 | 9154 | 9541 | 387 |
| 1122 | 9929 | *0316 | *0703 | *1090 | *1477 | *1863 | *2250 | *2637 | *3024 | *3411 | 387 |
| 1123 | 050 3798 | 4184 | 4571 | 4958 | 5344 | 5731 | 6117 | 6504 | 6890 | 7277 | 387 |
| 1124 | 7663 | 8049 | 8436 | 8822 | 9208 | 9595 | 9981 | *0367 | *0753 | *1139 | 386 |
| 1125 | 051 1525 | 1911 | 2297 | 2683 | 3069 | 3455 | 3841 | 4227 | 4612 | 4998 | 386 |
| 1126 | 5384 | 5770 | 6155 | 6541 | 6926 | 7312 | 7697 | 8083 | 8468 | 8854 | 386 |
| 1127 | 9239 | 9624 | *0010 | *0395 | *0780 | *1166 | *1551 | *1936 | *2321 | *2706 | 385 |
| 1128 | 052 3091 | 3476 | 3861 | 4246 | 4631 | 5016 | 5400 | 5785 | 6170 | 6555 | 385 |
| 1129 | 6939 | 7324 | 7709 | 8093 | 8478 | 8862 | 9247 | 9631 | *0016 | *0400 | 385 |
| **1130** | 053 0784 | 1169 | 1553 | 1937 | 2321 | 2706 | 3090 | 3474 | 3858 | 4242 | 384 |
| 1131 | 4626 | 5010 | 5394 | 5778 | 6162 | 6546 | 6929 | 7313 | 7697 | 8081 | 384 |
| 1132 | 8464 | 8848 | 9232 | 9615 | 9999 | *0382 | *0766 | *1149 | *1532 | *1916 | 384 |
| 1133 | 054 2299 | 2682 | 3066 | 3449 | 3832 | 4215 | 4598 | 4981 | 5365 | 5748 | 383 |
| 1134 | 6131 | 6514 | 6896 | 7279 | 7662 | 8045 | 8428 | 8811 | 9193 | 9576 | 383 |
| 1135 | 9959 | *0341 | *0724 | *1106 | *1489 | *1871 | *2254 | *2636 | *3019 | *3401 | 382 |
| 1136 | 055 3783 | 4166 | 4548 | 4930 | 5312 | 5694 | 6077 | 6459 | 6841 | 7223 | 382 |
| 1137 | 7605 | 7987 | 8369 | 8750 | 9132 | 9514 | 9896 | *0278 | *0659 | *1041 | 382 |
| 1138 | 056 1423 | 1804 | 2186 | 2567 | 2949 | 3330 | 3712 | 4093 | 4475 | 4856 | 381 |
| 1139 | 5237 | 5619 | 6000 | 6381 | 6762 | 7143 | 7524 | 7905 | 8287 | 8668 | 381 |
| **1140** | 9049 | 9429 | 9810 | *0191 | *0572 | *0953 | *1334 | *1714 | *2095 | *2476 | 381 |
| 1141 | 057 2856 | 3237 | 3618 | 3998 | 4379 | 4759 | 5140 | 5520 | 5900 | 6281 | 381 |
| 1142 | 6661 | 7041 | 7422 | 7802 | 8182 | 8562 | 8942 | 9322 | 9702 | *0082 | 380 |
| 1143 | 058 0462 | 0842 | 1222 | 1602 | 1982 | 2362 | 2741 | 3121 | 3501 | 3881 | 380 |
| 1144 | 4260 | 4640 | 5019 | 5399 | 5778 | 6158 | 6537 | 6917 | 7296 | 7676 | 380 |
| 1145 | 8055 | 8434 | 8813 | 9193 | 9572 | 9951 | *0330 | *0709 | *1088 | *1467 | 379 |
| 1146 | 059 1846 | 2225 | 2604 | 2983 | 3362 | 3741 | 4119 | 4498 | 4877 | 5256 | 379 |
| 1147 | 5634 | 6013 | 6391 | 6770 | 7148 | 7527 | 7905 | 8284 | 8662 | 9041 | 379 |
| 1148 | 9419 | 9797 | *0175 | *0554 | *0932 | *1310 | *1688 | *2066 | *2444 | *2822 | 378 |
| 1149 | 060 3200 | 3578 | 3956 | 4334 | 4712 | 5090 | 5468 | 5845 | 6223 | 6601 | 378 |
| **1150** | 6978 | 7356 | 7734 | 8111 | 8489 | 8866 | 9244 | 9621 | 9999 | *0376 | 378 |
| N | 0 | 1 | 2 | 3 | 4 | 5 | 6 | 7 | 8 | 9 | d. |

| N | 0 | 1 | 2 | 3 | 4 | 5 | 6 | 7 | 8 | 9 | d. |
|---|---|---|---|---|---|---|---|---|---|---|---|
| 1150 | 060 6978 | 7356 | 7734 | 8111 | 8489 | 8866 | 9244 | 9621 | 9999 | *0376 | 378 |
| 1151 | 061 0753 | 1131 | 1508 | 1885 | 2262 | 2639 | 3017 | 3394 | 3771 | 4148 | 377 |
| 1152 | 4525 | 4902 | 5279 | 5656 | 6032 | 6409 | 6786 | 7163 | 7540 | 7916 | 377 |
| 1153 | 8293 | 8670 | 9046 | 9423 | 9799 | *0176 | *0552 | *0929 | *1305 | *1682 | 377 |
| 1154 | 062 2058 | 2434 | 2811 | 3187 | 3563 | 3939 | 4316 | 4692 | 5068 | 5444 | 376 |
| 1155 | 5820 | 6196 | 6572 | 6948 | 7324 | 7699 | 8075 | 8451 | 8827 | 9203 | 376 |
| 1156 | 9578 | 9954 | *0330 | *0705 | *1081 | *1456 | *1832 | *2207 | *2583 | *2958 | 376 |
| 1157 | 063 3334 | 3709 | 4084 | 4460 | 4835 | 5210 | 5585 | 5960 | 6335 | 6711 | 375 |
| 1158 | 7086 | 7461 | 7836 | 8211 | 8585 | 8960 | 9335 | 9710 | *0085 | *0460 | 375 |
| 1159 | 064 0834 | 1209 | 1584 | 1958 | 2333 | 2708 | 3082 | 3457 | 3831 | 4205 | 375 |
| 1160 | 4580 | 4954 | 5329 | 5703 | 6077 | 6451 | 6826 | 7200 | 7574 | 7948 | 374 |
| 1161 | 8322 | 8696 | 9070 | 9444 | 9818 | *0192 | *0566 | *0940 | *1314 | *1688 | 374 |
| 1162 | 065 2061 | 2435 | 2809 | 3182 | 3556 | 3930 | 4303 | 4677 | 5050 | 5424 | 374 |
| 1163 | 5797 | 6171 | 6544 | 6917 | 7291 | 7664 | 8037 | 8410 | 8784 | 9157 | 373 |
| 1164 | 9530 | 9903 | *0276 | *0649 | *1022 | *1395 | *1768 | *2141 | *2514 | *2886 | 373 |
| 1165 | 066 3259 | 3632 | 4005 | 4377 | 4750 | 5123 | 5495 | 5868 | 6241 | 6613 | 373 |
| 1166 | 6986 | 7358 | 7730 | 8103 | 8475 | 8847 | 9220 | 9592 | 9964 | *0336 | 372 |
| 1167 | 067 0709 | 1081 | 1453 | 1825 | 2197 | 2569 | 2941 | 3313 | 3685 | 4057 | 372 |
| 1168 | 4428 | 4800 | 5172 | 5544 | 5915 | 6287 | 6659 | 7030 | 7402 | 7774 | 372 |
| 1169 | 8145 | 8517 | 8888 | 9259 | 9631 | *0002 | *0374 | *0745 | *1116 | *1487 | 371 |
| 1170 | 068 1859 | 2230 | 2601 | 2972 | 3343 | 3714 | 4085 | 4456 | 4827 | 5198 | 371 |
| 1171 | 5569 | 5940 | 6311 | 6681 | 7052 | 7423 | 7794 | 8164 | 8535 | 8906 | 371 |
| 1172 | 9276 | 9647 | *0017 | *0388 | *0758 | *1129 | *1499 | *1869 | *2240 | *2610 | 370 |
| 1173 | 069 2980 | 3350 | 3721 | 4091 | 4461 | 4831 | 5201 | 5571 | 5941 | 6311 | 370 |
| 1174 | 6681 | 7051 | 7421 | 7791 | 8160 | 8530 | 8900 | 9270 | 9639 | *0009 | 370 |
| 1175 | 070 0379 | 0748 | 1118 | 1487 | 1857 | 2226 | 2596 | 2965 | 3335 | 3704 | 369 |
| 1176 | 4073 | 4442 | 4812 | 5181 | 5550 | 5919 | 6288 | 6658 | 7027 | 7396 | 369 |
| 1177 | 7765 | 8134 | 8503 | 8871 | 9240 | 9609 | 9978 | *0347 | *0715 | *1084 | 369 |
| 1178 | 071 1453 | 1822 | 2190 | 2559 | 2927 | 3296 | 3664 | 4033 | 4401 | 4770 | 369 |
| 1179 | 5138 | 5506 | 5875 | 6243 | 6611 | 6979 | 7348 | 7716 | 8084 | 8452 | 368 |
| 1180 | 8820 | 9188 | 9556 | 9924 | *0292 | *0660 | *1028 | *1396 | *1763 | *2131 | 368 |
| 1181 | 072 2499 | 2867 | 3234 | 3602 | 3970 | 4337 | 4705 | 5072 | 5440 | 5807 | 368 |
| 1182 | 6175 | 6542 | 6910 | 7277 | 7644 | 8011 | 8379 | 8746 | 9113 | 9480 | 367 |
| 1183 | 9847 | *0215 | *0582 | *0949 | *1316 | *1683 | *2050 | *2416 | *2783 | *3150 | 367 |
| 1184 | 073 3517 | 3884 | 4251 | 4617 | 4984 | 5351 | 5717 | 6084 | 6450 | 6817 | 367 |
| 1185 | 7184 | 7550 | 7916 | 8283 | 8649 | 9016 | 9382 | 9748 | *0114 | *0481 | 366 |
| 1186 | 074 0847 | 1213 | 1579 | 1945 | 2311 | 2677 | 3043 | 3409 | 3775 | 4141 | 366 |
| 1187 | 4507 | 4873 | 5239 | 5605 | 5970 | 6336 | 6702 | 7068 | 7433 | 7799 | 366 |
| 1188 | 8164 | 8530 | 8895 | 9261 | 9626 | 9992 | *0357 | *0723 | *1088 | *1453 | 365 |
| 1189 | 075 1819 | 2184 | 2549 | 2914 | 3279 | 3644 | 4010 | 4375 | 4740 | 5105 | 365 |
| 1190 | 5470 | 5835 | 6199 | 6564 | 6929 | 7294 | 7659 | 8024 | 8388 | 8753 | 365 |
| 1191 | 9118 | 9482 | 9847 | *0211 | *0576 | *0940 | *1305 | *1669 | *2034 | *2398 | 364 |
| 1192 | 076 2763 | 3127 | 3491 | 3855 | 4220 | 4584 | 4948 | 5312 | 5676 | 6040 | 364 |
| 1193 | 6404 | 6768 | 7132 | 7496 | 7860 | 8224 | 8588 | 8952 | 9316 | 9680 | 364 |
| 1194 | 077 0043 | 0407 | 0771 | 1134 | 1498 | 1862 | 2225 | 2589 | 2952 | 3316 | 364 |
| 1195 | 3679 | 4042 | 4406 | 4769 | 5133 | 5496 | 5859 | 6222 | 6585 | 6949 | 363 |
| 1196 | 7312 | 7675 | 8038 | 8401 | 8764 | 9127 | 9490 | 9853 | *0216 | *0579 | 363 |
| 1197 | 078 0942 | 1304 | 1667 | 2030 | 2393 | 2755 | 3118 | 3480 | 3843 | 4206 | 363 |
| 1198 | 4568 | 4931 | 5293 | 5656 | 6018 | 6380 | 6743 | 7105 | 7467 | 7830 | 362 |
| 1199 | 8192 | 8554 | 8916 | 9278 | 9640 | *0003 | *0365 | *0727 | *1089 | *1451 | 362 |
| 1200 | 079 1812 | 2174 | 2536 | 2898 | 3260 | 3622 | 3983 | 4345 | 4707 | 5068 | 362 |
| N | 0 | 1 | 2 | 3 | 4 | 5 | 6 | 7 | 8 | 9 | d. |

# LOGARITHMS OF THE TRIGONOMETRIC FUNCTIONS

Logarithms of the functions are given for each minute from 0-360°.

The quantity −10 is to be appended to all logarithms of the sine and cosine, to logarithms of the tangent from 0-45° and of the cotangent from 45-90°.

With degrees indicated at either side of the top of the page use the column headings at the top. With degrees stated at the bottom of the page use the column designations at the bottom.

With degrees at the left (top or bottom) use the minute column at the left, and with degrees on the right side of the page use the minute column at the right.

The method of determining the functions of small angles by the auxiliary quantities S and T is given in the section explaining the use of the mathematical tables at the front of the volume.

# LOGARITHMS OF TRIGONOMETRIC FUNCTIONS

| Min. | Values of S, −10 to be appended | | | | | Values of T, −10 to be appended | | | | | Sec. |
|---|---|---|---|---|---|---|---|---|---|---|---|
| | 0° | 1° | 2° | 3° | 4° | 0° | 1° | 2° | 3° | 4° | |
| 0′ | 4.68 557 | 555 | 549 | 538 | 522 | 4.68 557 | 562 | 575 | 597 | 628 | 0′ |
| 1 | 557 | 555 | 549 | 537 | 522 | 557 | 562 | 575 | 598 | 629 | 60 |
| 2 | 557 | 555 | 548 | 537 | 522 | 557 | 562 | 576 | 598 | 629 | 120 |
| 3 | 557 | 555 | 548 | 537 | 521 | 557 | 562 | 576 | 599 | 630 | 180 |
| 4 | 557 | 555 | 548 | 537 | 521 | 558 | 563 | 576 | 599 | 631 | 240 |
| 5 | 557 | 555 | 548 | 537 | 521 | 558 | 563 | 577 | 599 | 631 | 300 |
| 6 | 557 | 555 | 548 | 536 | 520 | 558 | 563 | 577 | 600 | 632 | 360 |
| 7 | 557 | 555 | 548 | 536 | 520 | 558 | 563 | 577 | 600 | 632 | 420 |
| 8 | 557 | 555 | 548 | 536 | 520 | 558 | 563 | 578 | 601 | 633 | 480 |
| 9 | 557 | 555 | 547 | 536 | 520 | 558 | 563 | 578 | 601 | 634 | 540 |
| 10 | 4.68 557 | 555 | 547 | 535 | 519 | 4.68 558 | 564 | 578 | 602 | 634 | 600 |
| 11 | 557 | 554 | 547 | 535 | 519 | 558 | 564 | 579 | 602 | 635 | 660 |
| 12 | 557 | 554 | 547 | 535 | 519 | 558 | 564 | 579 | 603 | 635 | 720 |
| 13 | 557 | 554 | 547 | 535 | 518 | 558 | 564 | 579 | 603 | 636 | 780 |
| 14 | 557 | 554 | 547 | 534 | 518 | 558 | 564 | 580 | 604 | 637 | 840 |
| 15 | 557 | 554 | 546 | 534 | 518 | 558 | 564 | 580 | 604 | 637 | 900 |
| 16 | 557 | 554 | 546 | 534 | 517 | 558 | 565 | 580 | 605 | 638 | 960 |
| 17 | 557 | 554 | 546 | 534 | 517 | 558 | 565 | 581 | 605 | 639 | 1020 |
| 18 | 557 | 554 | 546 | 534 | 517 | 558 | 565 | 581 | 606 | 639 | 1080 |
| 19 | 557 | 554 | 546 | 533 | 516 | 558 | 565 | 581 | 606 | 640 | 1140 |
| 20 | 4.68 557 | 554 | 546 | 533 | 516 | 4.68 558 | 565 | 582 | 607 | 640 | 1200 |
| 21 | 557 | 554 | 545 | 533 | 516 | 558 | 566 | 582 | 607 | 641 | 1260 |
| 22 | 557 | 553 | 545 | 533 | 515 | 558 | 566 | 582 | 608 | 642 | 1320 |
| 23 | 557 | 553 | 545 | 532 | 515 | 558 | 566 | 583 | 608 | 642 | 1380 |
| 24 | 557 | 553 | 545 | 532 | 515 | 558 | 566 | 583 | 609 | 643 | 1440 |
| 25 | 557 | 553 | 545 | 532 | 515 | 558 | 566 | 583 | 609 | 644 | 1500 |
| 26 | 557 | 553 | 544 | 532 | 514 | 558 | 567 | 584 | 610 | 644 | 1560 |
| 27 | 557 | 553 | 544 | 531 | 514 | 558 | 567 | 584 | 610 | 645 | 1620 |
| 28 | 557 | 553 | 544 | 531 | 514 | 558 | 567 | 584 | 611 | 646 | 1680 |
| 29 | 557 | 553 | 544 | 531 | 513 | 559 | 567 | 585 | 611 | 646 | 1740 |
| 30 | 4.68 557 | 553 | 544 | 531 | 513 | 4.68 559 | 567 | 585 | 612 | 647 | 1800 |
| 31 | 557 | 552 | 544 | 530 | 513 | 559 | 568 | 585 | 612 | 648 | 1860 |
| 32 | 557 | 552 | 543 | 530 | 512 | 559 | 568 | 586 | 613 | 648 | 1920 |
| 33 | 557 | 552 | 543 | 530 | 512 | 559 | 568 | 586 | 613 | 649 | 1980 |
| 34 | 557 | 552 | 543 | 529 | 512 | 559 | 568 | 587 | 614 | 650 | 2040 |
| 35 | 557 | 552 | 543 | 529 | 511 | 559 | 569 | 587 | 614 | 650 | 2100 |
| 36 | 557 | 552 | 543 | 529 | 511 | 559 | 569 | 587 | 615 | 651 | 2160 |
| 37 | 557 | 552 | 542 | 529 | 511 | 559 | 569 | 588 | 615 | 652 | 2220 |
| 38 | 557 | 552 | 542 | 528 | 510 | 559 | 569 | 588 | 616 | 652 | 2280 |
| 39 | 557 | 552 | 542 | 528 | 510 | 559 | 570 | 589 | 616 | 653 | 2340 |
| 40 | 4.68 557 | 551 | 542 | 528 | 510 | 4.68 559 | 570 | 589 | 617 | 654 | 2400 |
| 41 | 556 | 551 | 542 | 528 | 509 | 560 | 570 | 589 | 617 | 654 | 2460 |
| 42 | 556 | 551 | 541 | 527 | 509 | 560 | 570 | 590 | 618 | 655 | 2520 |
| 43 | 556 | 551 | 541 | 527 | 508 | 560 | 571 | 590 | 619 | 656 | 2580 |
| 44 | 556 | 551 | 541 | 527 | 508 | 560 | 571 | 591 | 619 | 656 | 2640 |
| 45 | 556 | 551 | 541 | 527 | 508 | 560 | 571 | 591 | 620 | 657 | 2700 |
| 46 | 556 | 551 | 541 | 526 | 507 | 560 | 571 | 591 | 620 | 658 | 2760 |
| 47 | 556 | 551 | 540 | 526 | 507 | 560 | 572 | 592 | 621 | 659 | 2820 |
| 48 | 556 | 550 | 540 | 526 | 507 | 560 | 572 | 592 | 621 | 659 | 2880 |
| 49 | 556 | 550 | 540 | 525 | 506 | 560 | 572 | 593 | 622 | 660 | 2940 |
| 50 | 4.68 556 | 550 | 540 | 525 | 506 | 4.68 561 | 572 | 593 | 622 | 661 | 3000 |
| 51 | 556 | 550 | 540 | 525 | 506 | 561 | 573 | 593 | 623 | 661 | 3060 |
| 52 | 556 | 550 | 539 | 525 | 505 | 561 | 573 | 594 | 624 | 662 | 3120 |
| 53 | 556 | 550 | 539 | 524 | 505 | 561 | 573 | 594 | 624 | 663 | 3180 |
| 54 | 556 | 550 | 539 | 524 | 505 | 561 | 573 | 595 | 625 | 664 | 3240 |
| 55 | 556 | 549 | 539 | 524 | 504 | 561 | 574 | 595 | 625 | 664 | 3300 |
| 56 | 556 | 549 | 539 | 523 | 504 | 561 | 574 | 596 | 626 | 665 | 3360 |
| 57 | 556 | 549 | 538 | 523 | 503 | 562 | 574 | 596 | 626 | 666 | 3420 |
| 58 | 555 | 549 | 538 | 523 | 503 | 562 | 575 | 596 | 627 | 667 | 3480 |
| 59 | 555 | 549 | 538 | 523 | 503 | 562 | 575 | 597 | 628 | 667 | 3540 |
| 60 | 4.68 555 | 549 | 538 | 522 | 502 | 4.68 562 | 575 | 597 | 628 | 668 | 3600 |

| ″ | ′ | L. Sin. | *d. | C. S. | C. T. | L. Tan. | c.d. | L. Cot. | L. Cos. | ′ |
|---|---|---------|-----|-------|-------|---------|------|---------|---------|---|
| 0 | 0 | — | | — | — | — | | — | 0.00 000 | 60 |
| 60 | 1 | 6.46 373 | 30103 | 5.31 443 | 5.31 443 | 6.46 373 | 30103 | 3.53 627 | 0.00 000 | 59 |
| 120 | 2 | 6.76 476 | 17609 | 5.31 443 | 5.31 443 | 6.76 476 | 17609 | 3.23 524 | 0.00 000 | 58 |
| 180 | 3 | 6.94 085 | 12494 | 5.31 443 | 5.31 443 | 6.94 085 | 12494 | 3.05 915 | 0.00 000 | 57 |
| 240 | 4 | 7.06 579 | 9691 | 5.31 443 | 5.31 442 | 7.06 579 | 9691 | 2.93 421 | 0.00 000 | 56 |
| 300 | 5 | 7.16 270 | 7918 | 5.31 443 | 5.31 442 | 7.16 270 | 7918 | 2.83 730 | 0.00 000 | 55 |
| 660 | 6 | 7.24 188 | 6694 | 5.31 443 | 5.31 442 | 7.24 188 | 6694 | 2.75 812 | 0.00 000 | 54 |
| 420 | 7 | 7.30 882 | 5800 | 5.31 443 | 5.31 442 | 7.30 882 | 5800 | 2.69 118 | 0.00 000 | 53 |
| 480 | 8 | 7.36 682 | 5115 | 5.31 443 | 5.31 442 | 7.36 682 | 5115 | 2.63 318 | 0.00 000 | 52 |
| 540 | 9 | 7.41 797 | 4576 | 5.31 443 | 5.31 442 | 7.41 797 | 4576 | 2.58 203 | 0.00 000 | 51 |
| 600 | 10 | 7.46 373 | 4139 | 5.31 443 | 5.31 442 | 7.46 373 | 4139 | 2.53 627 | 0.00 000 | 50 |
| 660 | 11 | 7.50 512 | 3779 | 5.31 443 | 5.31 442 | 7.50 512 | 3779 | 2.49 488 | 0.00 000 | 49 |
| 720 | 12 | 7.54 291 | 3476 | 5.31 443 | 5.31 442 | 7.54 291 | 3476 | 2.45 709 | 0.00 000 | 48 |
| 780 | 13 | 7.57 767 | 3218 | 5.31 443 | 5.31 442 | 7.57 767 | 3219 | 2.42 233 | 0.00 000 | 47 |
| 840 | 14 | 7.60 985 | 2997 | 5.31 443 | 5.31 442 | 7.60 986 | 2996 | 2.39 014 | 0.00 000 | 46 |
| 900 | 15 | 7.63 982 | 2802 | 5.31 443 | 5.31 442 | 7.63 982 | 2803 | 2.36 018 | 0.00 000 | 45 |
| 960 | 16 | 7.66 784 | 2633 | 5.31 443 | 5.31 442 | 7.66 785 | 2633 | 2.33 215 | 0.00 000 | 44 |
| 1020 | 17 | 7.69 417 | 2483 | 5.31 443 | 5.31 442 | 7.69 418 | 2482 | 2.30 582 | 9.99 999 | 43 |
| 1080 | 18 | 7.71 900 | 2348 | 5.31 443 | 5.31 442 | 7.71 900 | 2348 | 2.28 100 | 9.99 999 | 42 |
| 1140 | 19 | 7.74 248 | 2227 | 5.31 443 | 5.31 442 | 7.74 248 | 2228 | 2.25 752 | 9.99 999 | 41 |
| 1200 | 20 | 7.76 475 | 2119 | 5.31 443 | 5.31 442 | 7.76 476 | 2119 | 2.23 524 | 9.99 999 | 40 |
| 1260 | 21 | 7.78 594 | 2021 | 5.31 443 | 5.31 442 | 7.78 595 | 2020 | 2.21 405 | 9.99 999 | 39 |
| 1320 | 22 | 7.80 615 | 1930 | 5.31 443 | 5.31 442 | 7.80 615 | 1931 | 2.19 385 | 9.99 999 | 38 |
| 1380 | 23 | 7.82 545 | 1848 | 5.31 443 | 5.31 442 | 7.82 546 | 1848 | 2.17 454 | 9.99 999 | 37 |
| 1440 | 24 | 7.84 393 | 1773 | 5.31 443 | 5.31 442 | 7.84 394 | 1773 | 2.15 606 | 9.99 999 | 36 |
| 1500 | 25 | 7.86 166 | 1704 | 5.31 443 | 5.31 442 | 7.86 166 | 1704 | 2.13 833 | 9.99 999 | 35 |
| 1560 | 26 | 7.87 870 | 1639 | 5.31 443 | 5.31 442 | 7.87 871 | 1639 | 2.12 129 | 9.99 999 | 34 |
| 1620 | 27 | 7.89 509 | 1579 | 5.31 443 | 5.31 442 | 7.89 510 | 1579 | 2.10 490 | 9.99 999 | 33 |
| 1680 | 28 | 7.91 088 | 1524 | 5.31 443 | 5.31 442 | 7.91 089 | 1524 | 2.08 911 | 9.99 999 | 32 |
| 1740 | 29 | 7.92 612 | 1472 | 5.31 443 | 5.31 441 | 7.92 613 | 1473 | 2.07 387 | 9.99 998 | 31 |
| 1800 | 30 | 7.94 084 | 1424 | 5.31 443 | 5.31 441 | 7.94 086 | 1424 | 2.05 914 | 9.99 998 | 30 |
| 1860 | 31 | 7.95 508 | 1379 | 5.31 443 | 5.31 441 | 7.95 510 | 1379 | 2.04 490 | 9.99 998 | 29 |
| 1920 | 32 | 7.96 887 | 1336 | 5.31 443 | 5.31 441 | 7.96 889 | 1336 | 2.03 111 | 9.99 998 | 28 |
| 1980 | 33 | 7.98 223 | 1297 | 5.31 443 | 5.31 441 | 7.98 225 | 1297 | 2.01 775 | 9.99 998 | 27 |
| 2040 | 34 | 7.99 520 | 1259 | 5.31 443 | 5.31 441 | 7.99 522 | 1259 | 2.00 478 | 9.99 998 | 26 |
| 2100 | 35 | 8.00 779 | 1223 | 5.31 443 | 5.31 441 | 8.00 781 | 1223 | 1.99 219 | 9.99 998 | 25 |
| 2160 | 36 | 8.02 002 | 1190 | 5.31 443 | 5.31 441 | 8.02 004 | 1190 | 1.97 996 | 9.99 998 | 24 |
| 2220 | 37 | 8.03 192 | 1158 | 5.31 443 | 5.31 441 | 8.03 194 | 1159 | 1.96 806 | 9.99 997 | 23 |
| 2280 | 38 | 8.04 350 | 1128 | 5.31 443 | 5.31 441 | 8.04 353 | 1128 | 1.95 647 | 9.99 997 | 22 |
| 2340 | 39 | 8.05 478 | 1100 | 5.31 443 | 5.31 441 | 8.05 481 | 1100 | 1.94 519 | 9.99 997 | 21 |
| 2400 | 40 | 8.06 578 | 1072 | 5.31 443 | 5.31 441 | 8.06 581 | 1072 | 1.93 419 | 9.99 997 | 20 |
| 2460 | 41 | 8.07 650 | 1046 | 5.31 443 | 5.31 440 | 8.07 653 | 1047 | 1.92 347 | 9.99 997 | 19 |
| 2520 | 42 | 8.08 696 | 1022 | 5.31 444 | 5.31 440 | 8.08 700 | 1022 | 1.91 300 | 9.99 997 | 18 |
| 2580 | 43 | 8.09 718 | 999 | 5.31 444 | 5.31 440 | 8.09 722 | 998 | 1.90 278 | 9.99 997 | 17 |
| 2640 | 44 | 8.10 717 | 976 | 5.31 444 | 5.31 440 | 8.10 720 | 976 | 1.89 280 | 9.99 996 | 16 |
| 2700 | 45 | 8.11 693 | 954 | 5.31 444 | 5.31 440 | 8.11 696 | 955 | 1.88 304 | 9.99 996 | 15 |
| 2760 | 46 | 8.12 647 | 934 | 5.31 444 | 5.31 440 | 8.12 651 | 934 | 1.87 349 | 9.99 996 | 14 |
| 2820 | 47 | 8.13 581 | 914 | 5.31 444 | 5.31 440 | 8.13 585 | 915 | 1.86 415 | 9.99 996 | 13 |
| 2880 | 48 | 8.14 495 | 896 | 5.31 444 | 5.31 440 | 8.14 500 | 895 | 1.85 500 | 9.99 996 | 12 |
| 2940 | 49 | 8.15 391 | 877 | 5.31 444 | 5.31 440 | 8.15 395 | 878 | 1.84 605 | 9.99 996 | 11 |
| 3000 | 50 | 8.16 268 | 860 | 5.31 444 | 5.31 439 | 8.16 273 | 860 | 1.83 727 | 9.99 995 | 10 |
| 3060 | 51 | 8.17 128 | 843 | 5.31 444 | 5.31 439 | 8.17 133 | 843 | 1.82 867 | 9.99 995 | 9 |
| 8120 | 52 | 8.17 971 | 827 | 5.31 444 | 5.31 439 | 8.17 976 | 828 | 1.82 024 | 9.99 995 | 8 |
| 8180 | 53 | 8.18 798 | 812 | 5.31 444 | 5.31 439 | 8.18 804 | 812 | 1.81 196 | 9.99 995 | 7 |
| 8240 | 54 | 8.19 610 | 797 | 5.31 444 | 5.31 439 | 8.19 616 | 797 | 1.80 384 | 9.99 995 | 6 |
| 3300 | 55 | 8.20 407 | 782 | 5.31 444 | 5.31 439 | 8.20 413 | 782 | 1.79 587 | 9.99 994 | 5 |
| 3360 | 56 | 8.21 189 | 769 | 5.31 444 | 5.31 439 | 8.21 195 | 769 | 1.78 805 | 9.99 994 | 4 |
| 3420 | 57 | 8.21 958 | 755 | 5.31 445 | 5.31 439 | 8.21 964 | 756 | 1.78 036 | 9.99 994 | 3 |
| 3480 | 58 | 8.22 713 | 743 | 5.31 445 | 5.31 438 | 8.22 720 | 742 | 1.77 280 | 9.99 994 | 2 |
| 3540 | 59 | 8.23 456 | 730 | 5.31 445 | 5.31 438 | 8.23 462 | 730 | 1.76 538 | 9.99 994 | 1 |
| 3000 | 60 | 8.24 186 | | 5.31 445 | 5.31 438 | 8.24 192 | | 1.75 808 | 9.99 993 | 0 |
| ′ | | L. Cos. | d. | | | L. Cot. | c.d. | L. Tan. | L. Sin. | ′ |

* Interpolation in this section of the table is not accurate.

| '' | ' | L. Sin. | *d. | C. S. | C. T. | L. Tan. | *c.d. | L. Cot. | L. Cos. | ' |
|---|---|---|---|---|---|---|---|---|---|---|
| 8600 | 0 | 8.24 186 | 717 | 5.31 445 | 5.31 438 | 8.24 192 | 718 | 1.75 808 | 9.99 993 | 60 |
| 8660 | 1 | 8.24 903 | 706 | 5.31 445 | 5.31 438 | 8.24 910 | 706 | 1.75 090 | 9.99 993 | 59 |
| 8720 | 2 | 8.25 609 | 695 | 5.31 445 | 5.31 438 | 8.25 616 | 696 | 1.74 384 | 9.99 993 | 58 |
| 3780 | 3 | 8.26 304 | 684 | 5.31 445 | 5.31 438 | 8.26 312 | 684 | 1.73 688 | 9.99 993 | 57 |
| 3840 | 4 | 8.26 988 | 673 | 5.31 445 | 5.31 437 | 8.26 996 | 673 | 1.73 004 | 9.99 992 | 56 |
| 3900 | 5 | 8.27 661 | 663 | 5.31 445 | 5.31 437 | 8.27 669 | 663 | 1.72 331 | 9.99 992 | 55 |
| 3960 | 6 | 8.28 324 | 653 | 5.31 445 | 5.31 437 | 8.28 332 | 654 | 1.71 668 | 9.99 992 | 54 |
| 4020 | 7 | 8.28 977 | 644 | 5.31 445 | 5.31 437 | 8.28 986 | 643 | 1.71 014 | 9.99 992 | 53 |
| 4080 | 8 | 8.29 621 | 634 | 5.31 445 | 5.31 437 | 8.29 629 | 634 | 1.70 371 | 9.99 992 | 52 |
| 4140 | 9 | 8.30 255 | 624 | 5.31 445 | 5.31 437 | 8.30 263 | 625 | 1.69 737 | 9.99 991 | 51 |
| 4200 | 10 | 8.30 879 | 616 | 5.31 446 | 5.31 437 | 8.30 888 | 617 | 1.69 112 | 9.99 991 | 50 |
| 4260 | 11 | 8.31 495 | 608 | 5.31 446 | 5.31 436 | 8.31 505 | 607 | 1.68 495 | 9.99 991 | 49 |
| 4320 | 12 | 8.32 103 | 599 | 5.31 446 | 5.31 436 | 8.32 112 | 599 | 1.67 888 | 9.99 990 | 48 |
| 4380 | 13 | 8.32 702 | 590 | 5.31 446 | 5.31 436 | 8.32 711 | 591 | 1.67 289 | 9.99 990 | 47 |
| 4440 | 14 | 8.33 292 | 583 | 5.31 446 | 5.31 436 | 8.33 302 | 584 | 1.66 698 | 9.99 990 | 46 |
| 4500 | 15 | 8.33 875 | 575 | 5.31 446 | 5.31 436 | 8.33 886 | 575 | 1.66 114 | 9.99 990 | 45 |
| 4560 | 16 | 8.34 450 | 568 | 5.31 446 | 5.31 435 | 8.34 461 | 568 | 1.65 539 | 9.99 989 | 44 |
| 4620 | 17 | 8.35 018 | 560 | 5.31 446 | 5.31 435 | 8.35 029 | 561 | 1.64 971 | 9.99 989 | 43 |
| 4680 | 18 | 8.35 578 | 553 | 5.31 446 | 5.31 435 | 8.35 590 | 553 | 1.64 410 | 9.99 989 | 42 |
| 4740 | 19 | 8.36 131 | 547 | 5.31 446 | 5.31 435 | 8.36 143 | 546 | 1.63 857 | 9.99 989 | 41 |
| 4800 | 20 | 8.36 678 | 539 | 5.31 446 | 5.31 435 | 8.36 689 | 540 | 1.63 311 | 9.99 988 | 40 |
| 4860 | 21 | 8.37 217 | 533 | 5.31 447 | 5.31 434 | 8.37 229 | 533 | 1.62 771 | 9.99 988 | 39 |
| 4920 | 22 | 8.37 750 | 526 | 5.31 447 | 5.31 434 | 8.37 762 | 527 | 1.62 238 | 9.99 988 | 38 |
| 4980 | 23 | 8.38 276 | 520 | 5.31 447 | 5.31 434 | 8.38 289 | 520 | 1.61 711 | 9.99 987 | 37 |
| 5040 | 24 | 8.38 796 | 514 | 5.31 447 | 5.31 434 | 8.38 809 | 514 | 1.61 191 | 9.99 987 | 36 |
| 5100 | 25 | 8.39 310 | 508 | 5.31 447 | 5.31 434 | 8.39 323 | 509 | 1.60 677 | 9.99 987 | 35 |
| 5160 | 26 | 8.39 818 | 502 | 5.31 447 | 5.31 433 | 8.39 832 | 502 | 1.60 168 | 9.99 986 | 34 |
| 5220 | 27 | 8.40 320 | 496 | 5.31 447 | 5.31 433 | 8.40 334 | 496 | 1.59 666 | 9.99 986 | 33 |
| 5280 | 28 | 8.40 816 | 491 | 5.31 447 | 5.31 433 | 8.40 830 | 491 | 1.59 170 | 9.99 986 | 32 |
| 5340 | 29 | 8.41 307 | 485 | 5.31 447 | 5.31 433 | 8.41 321 | 486 | 1.58 679 | 9.99 985 | 31 |
| 5400 | 30 | 8.41 792 | 480 | 5.31 447 | 5.31 433 | 8.41 807 | 480 | 1.58 193 | 9.99 985 | 30 |
| 5460 | 31 | 8.42 272 | 474 | 5.31 448 | 5.31 432 | 8.42 287 | 475 | 1.57 713 | 9.99 985 | 29 |
| 5520 | 32 | 8.42 746 | 470 | 5.31 448 | 5.31 432 | 8.42 762 | 470 | 1.57 238 | 9.99 984 | 28 |
| 5580 | 33 | 8.43 216 | 464 | 5.31 448 | 5.31 432 | 8.43 232 | 464 | 1.56 768 | 9.99 984 | 27 |
| 5640 | 34 | 8.43 680 | 459 | 5.31 448 | 5.31 432 | 8.43 696 | 460 | 1.56 304 | 9.99 984 | 26 |
| 5700 | 35 | 8.44 139 | 455 | 5.31 448 | 5.31 431 | 8.44 156 | 455 | 1.55 844 | 9.99 983 | 25 |
| 5760 | 36 | 8.44 594 | 450 | 5.31 448 | 5.31 431 | 8.44 611 | 450 | 1.55 389 | 9.99 983 | 24 |
| 5820 | 37 | 8.45 044 | 445 | 5.31 448 | 5.31 431 | 8.45 061 | 446 | 1.54 939 | 9.99 983 | 23 |
| 5880 | 38 | 8.45 489 | 441 | 5.31 448 | 5.31 431 | 8.45 507 | 441 | 1.54 493 | 9.99 982 | 22 |
| 5940 | 39 | 8.45 930 | 436 | 5.31 449 | 5.31 431 | 8.45 948 | 437 | 1.54 052 | 9.99 982 | 21 |
| 6000 | 40 | 8.46 366 | 433 | 5.31 449 | 5.31 430 | 8.46 386 | 432 | 1.53 615 | 9.99 982 | 20 |
| 6060 | 41 | 8.46 799 | 427 | 5.31 449 | 5.31 430 | 8.46 817 | 428 | 1.53 183 | 9.99 981 | 19 |
| 6120 | 42 | 8.47 226 | 424 | 5.31 449 | 5.31 430 | 8.47 245 | 424 | 1.52 755 | 9.99 981 | 18 |
| 6180 | 43 | 8.47 650 | 419 | 5.31 449 | 5.31 430 | 8.47 669 | 420 | 1.52 331 | 9.99 981 | 17 |
| 6240 | 44 | 8.48 069 | 416 | 5.31 449 | 5.31 429 | 8.48 089 | 416 | 1.51 911 | 9.99 980 | 16 |
| 6300 | 45 | 8.48 485 | 411 | 5.31 449 | 5.31 429 | 8.48 505 | 412 | 1.51 495 | 9.99 980 | 15 |
| 6360 | 46 | 8.48 896 | 408 | 5.31 449 | 5.31 429 | 8.48 917 | 408 | 1.51 083 | 9.99 979 | 14 |
| 6420 | 47 | 8.49 304 | 404 | 5.31 450 | 5.31 428 | 8.49 325 | 404 | 1.50 675 | 9.99 979 | 13 |
| 6480 | 48 | 8.49 708 | 400 | 5.31 450 | 5.31 428 | 8.49 729 | 401 | 1.50 271 | 9.99 979 | 12 |
| 6540 | 49 | 8.50 108 | 396 | 5.31 450 | 5.31 428 | 8.50 130 | 397 | 1.49 870 | 9.99 978 | 11 |
| 6600 | 50 | 8.50 504 | 393 | 5.31 450 | 5.31 428 | 8.50 527 | 393 | 1.49 473 | 9.99 978 | 10 |
| 6660 | 51 | 8.50 897 | 390 | 5.31 450 | 5.31 427 | 8.50 920 | 390 | 1.49 080 | 9.99 977 | 9 |
| 6720 | 52 | 8.51 287 | 386 | 5.31 450 | 5.31 427 | 8.51 310 | 386 | 1.48 690 | 9.99 977 | 8 |
| 6780 | 53 | 8.51 673 | 382 | 5.31 450 | 5.31 427 | 8.51 696 | 383 | 1.48 304 | 9.99 977 | 7 |
| 6840 | 54 | 8.52 055 | 379 | 5.31 450 | 5.31 427 | 8.52 079 | 380 | 1.47 921 | 9.99 976 | 6 |
| 6900 | 55 | 8.52 434 | 376 | 5.31 451 | 5.31 426 | 8.52 459 | 376 | 1.47 541 | 9.99 976 | 5 |
| 6960 | 56 | 8.52 810 | 373 | 5.31 451 | 5.31 426 | 8.52 835 | 373 | 1.47 165 | 9.99 975 | 4 |
| 7020 | 57 | 8.53 183 | 369 | 5.31 451 | 5.31 426 | 8.53 208 | 370 | 1.46 792 | 9.99 975 | 3 |
| 7080 | 58 | 8.53 552 | 367 | 5.31 451 | 5.31 425 | 8.53 578 | 367 | 1.46 422 | 9.99 974 | 2 |
| 7140 | 59 | 8.53 919 | 363 | 5.31 451 | 5.31 425 | 8.53 945 | 363 | 1.46 055 | 9.99 974 | 1 |
| 7200 | 60 | 8.54 282 | | 5.31 451 | 5.31 425 | 8.54 308 | | 1.45 692 | 9.99 974 | 0 |
| | ' | L. Cos. | d. | | | L. Cot. | c.d. | L. Tan. | L. Sin. | ' |

* Interpolation in this section of the table is not accurate.

| | ′ | L. Sin. | *d. | C. S. | C. T. | L. Tan. | *c.d | L. Cot. | L. Cos. | ′ |
|---|---|---|---|---|---|---|---|---|---|---|
| 7200 | 0 | 8.54 282 | 360 | 5.31 451 | 5.31 425 | 8.54 308 | 361 | 1.45 692 | 9.99 974 | 60 |
| 7260 | 1 | 8.54 642 | 357 | 5.31 451 | 5.31 425 | 8.54 669 | 358 | 1.45 331 | 9.99 973 | 59 |
| 7320 | 2 | 8.54 999 | 355 | 5.31 452 | 5.31 424 | 8.55 027 | 355 | 1.44 973 | 9.99 973 | 58 |
| 7380 | 3 | 8.55 354 | 351 | 5.31 452 | 5.31 424 | 8.55 382 | 352 | 1.44 618 | 9.99 972 | 57 |
| 7440 | 4 | 8.55 705 | 349 | 5.31 452 | 5.31 424 | 8.55 734 | 349 | 1.44 266 | 9.99 972 | 56 |
| 7500 | 5 | 8.56 054 | 346 | 5.31 452 | 5.31 423 | 8.56 083 | 346 | 1.43 917 | 9.99 971 | 55 |
| 7560 | 6 | 8.56 400 | 343 | 5.31 452 | 5.31 423 | 8.56 429 | 344 | 1.43 571 | 9.99 971 | 54 |
| 7620 | 7 | 8.56 743 | 341 | 5.31 452 | 5.31 423 | 8.56 773 | 341 | 1.43 227 | 9.99 970 | 53 |
| 7680 | 8 | 8.57 084 | 337 | 5.31 453 | 5.31 422 | 8.57 114 | 338 | 1.42 886 | 9.99 970 | 52 |
| 7740 | 9 | 8.57 421 | 336 | 5.31 453 | 5.31 422 | 8.57 452 | 336 | 1.42 548 | 9.99 969 | 51 |
| 7800 | 10 | 8.57 757 | 332 | 5.31 453 | 5.31 422 | 8.57 788 | 333 | 1.42 212 | 9.99 969 | 50 |
| 7860 | 11 | 8.58 089 | 330 | 5.31 453 | 5.31 421 | 8.58 121 | 331 | 1.41 879 | 9.99 968 | 49 |
| 7920 | 12 | 8.58 419 | 328 | 5.31 453 | 5.31 421 | 8.58 453 | 328 | 1.41 549 | 9.99 968 | 48 |
| 7980 | 13 | 8.58 747 | 325 | 5.31 453 | 5.31 421 | 8.58 779 | 326 | 1.41 221 | 9.99 967 | 47 |
| 8040 | 14 | 8.59 072 | 323 | 5.31 454 | 5.31 421 | 8.59 105 | 323 | 1.40 895 | 9.99 967 | 46 |
| 8100 | 15 | 8.59 395 | 320 | 5.31 454 | 5.31 420 | 8.59 428 | 321 | 1.40 572 | 9.99 967 | 45 |
| 8160 | 16 | 8.59 715 | 318 | 5.31 454 | 5.31 420 | 8.59 749 | 319 | 1.40 251 | 9.99 966 | 44 |
| 8220 | 17 | 8.60 033 | 316 | 5.31 454 | 5.31 420 | 8.60 068 | 316 | 1.39 932 | 9.99 966 | 43 |
| 8280 | 18 | 8.60 349 | 313 | 5.31 454 | 5.31 419 | 8.60 384 | 314 | 1.39 616 | 9.99 965 | 42 |
| 8340 | 19 | 8.60 662 | 311 | 5.31 454 | 5.31 419 | 8.60 698 | 311 | 1.39 302 | 9.99 964 | 41 |
| 8400 | 20 | 8.60 973 | 309 | 5.31 455 | 5.31 418 | 8.61 009 | 310 | 1.38 991 | 9.99 964 | 40 |
| 8460 | 21 | 8.61 282 | 307 | 5.31 455 | 5.31 418 | 8.61 319 | 307 | 1.38 681 | 9.99 963 | 39 |
| 8520 | 22 | 8.61 589 | 305 | 5.31 455 | 5.31 418 | 8.61 626 | 305 | 1.38 374 | 9.99 963 | 38 |
| 8580 | 23 | 8.61 894 | 302 | 5.31 455 | 5.31 417 | 8.61 931 | 303 | 1.38 069 | 9.99 962 | 37 |
| 8640 | 24 | 8.62 196 | 301 | 5.31 455 | 5.31 417 | 8.62 234 | 301 | 1.37 766 | 9.99 962 | 36 |
| 8700 | 25 | 8.62 497 | 298 | 5.31 455 | 5.31 417 | 8.62 535 | 299 | 1.37 465 | 9.99 961 | 35 |
| 8760 | 26 | 8.62 795 | 296 | 5.31 456 | 5.31 416 | 8.62 834 | 297 | 1.37 166 | 9.99 961 | 34 |
| 8820 | 27 | 8.63 091 | 294 | 5.31 456 | 5.31 416 | 8.63 131 | 295 | 1.36 869 | 9.99 960 | 33 |
| 8880 | 28 | 8.63 385 | 293 | 5.31 456 | 5.31 416 | 8.63 426 | 292 | 1.36 574 | 9.99 960 | 32 |
| 8940 | 29 | 8.63 678 | 290 | 5.31 456 | 5.31 415 | 8.63 718 | 291 | 1.36 282 | 9.99 959 | 31 |
| 9000 | 30 | 8.63 968 | 288 | 5.31 456 | 5.31 415 | 8.64 009 | 289 | 1.35 991 | 9.99 959 | 30 |
| 9060 | 31 | 8.64 256 | 287 | 5.31 456 | 5.31 415 | 8.64 298 | 287 | 1.35 702 | 9.99 958 | 29 |
| 9120 | 32 | 8.64 543 | 284 | 5.31 457 | 5.31 414 | 8.64 585 | 285 | 1.35 415 | 9.99 958 | 28 |
| 9180 | 33 | 8.64 827 | 283 | 5.31 457 | 5.31 414 | 8.64 870 | 284 | 1.35 130 | 9.99 957 | 27 |
| 9240 | 34 | 8.65 110 | 281 | 5.31 457 | 5.31 413 | 8.65 154 | 281 | 1.34 846 | 9.99 957 | 26 |
| 9300 | 35 | 8.65 391 | 279 | 5.31 457 | 5.31 413 | 8.65 435 | 280 | 1.34 565 | 9.99 956 | 25 |
| 9360 | 36 | 8.65 670 | 277 | 5.31 457 | 5.31 413 | 8.65 715 | 278 | 1.34 285 | 9.99 955 | 24 |
| 9420 | 37 | 8.65 947 | 276 | 5.31 458 | 5.31 412 | 8.65 993 | 276 | 1.34 007 | 9.99 955 | 23 |
| 9480 | 38 | 8.66 223 | 274 | 5.31 458 | 5.31 412 | 8.66 269 | 274 | 1.33 731 | 9.99 954 | 22 |
| 9540 | 39 | 8.66 497 | 272 | 5.31 458 | 5.31 412 | 8.66 543 | 273 | 1.33 457 | 9.99 954 | 21 |
| 9600 | 40 | 8.66 769 | 270 | 5.31 458 | 5.31 411 | 8.66 816 | 271 | 1.33 184 | 9.99 953 | 20 |
| 9660 | 41 | 8.67 039 | 269 | 5.31 458 | 5.31 411 | 8.67 087 | 269 | 1.32 913 | 9.99 952 | 19 |
| 9720 | 42 | 8.67 308 | 267 | 5.31 459 | 5.31 410 | 8.67 356 | 268 | 1.32 644 | 9.99 952 | 18 |
| 9780 | 43 | 8.67 575 | 266 | 5.31 459 | 5.31 410 | 8.67 624 | 266 | 1.32 376 | 9.99 951 | 17 |
| 9840 | 44 | 8.67 841 | 263 | 5.31 459 | 5.31 410 | 8.67 890 | 264 | 1.32 110 | 9.99 951 | 16 |
| 9900 | 45 | 8.68 104 | 263 | 5.31 459 | 5.31 409 | 8.68 154 | 263 | 1.31 846 | 9.99 950 | 15 |
| 9960 | 46 | 8.68 367 | 260 | 5.31 459 | 5.31 409 | 8.68 417 | 261 | 1.31 583 | 9.99 949 | 14 |
| 10020 | 47 | 8.68 627 | 259 | 5.31 460 | 5.31 408 | 8.68 678 | 260 | 1.31 322 | 9.99 949 | 13 |
| 10080 | 48 | 8.68 886 | 258 | 5.31 460 | 5.31 408 | 8.68 938 | 258 | 1.31 062 | 9.99 948 | 12 |
| 10140 | 49 | 8.69 144 | 256 | 5.31 460 | 5.31 408 | 8.69 196 | 257 | 1.30 804 | 9.99 948 | 11 |
| 10200 | 50 | 8.69 400 | 254 | 5.31 460 | 5.31 407 | 8.69 453 | 255 | 1.30 547 | 9.99 947 | 10 |
| 10260 | 51 | 8.69 654 | 253 | 5.31 460 | 5.31 407 | 8.69 708 | 254 | 1.30 292 | 9.99 946 | 9 |
| 10320 | 52 | 8.69 907 | 252 | 5.31 461 | 5.31 406 | 8.69 962 | 252 | 1.30 038 | 9.99 946 | 8 |
| 10380 | 53 | 8.70 159 | 250 | 5.31 461 | 5.31 406 | 8.70 214 | 251 | 1.29 786 | 9.99 945 | 7 |
| 10440 | 54 | 8.70 409 | 249 | 5.31 461 | 5.31 405 | 8.70 465 | 249 | 1.29 535 | 9.99 944 | 6 |
| 10500 | 55 | 8.70 658 | 247 | 5.31 461 | 5.31 405 | 8.70 714 | 248 | 1.29 286 | 9.99 944 | 5 |
| 10560 | 56 | 8.70 905 | 246 | 5.31 461 | 5.31 405 | 8.70 962 | 246 | 1.29 038 | 9.99 943 | 4 |
| 10620 | 57 | 8.71 151 | 244 | 5.31 462 | 5.31 404 | 8.71 208 | 245 | 1.28 792 | 9.99 942 | 3 |
| 10680 | 58 | 8.71 395 | 243 | 5.31 462 | 5.31 404 | 8.71 453 | 244 | 1.28 547 | 9.99 942 | 2 |
| 10740 | 59 | 8.71 638 | 242 | 5.31 462 | 5.31 403 | 8.71 697 | 243 | 1.28 303 | 9.99 941 | 1 |
| 10800 | 60 | 8.71 880 | | 5.31 462 | 5.31 403 | 8.71 940 | | 1.28 060 | 9.99 940 | 0 |
| | ′ | L. Cos. | d. | | | L. Cot. | c.d. | L. Tan. | L. Sin. | ′ |

* Interpolation in this section of the table is not accurate.

(183°)     (356°) 176°

| ' | L. Sin. | *d. | L. Tan. | *c.d. | L. Cot. | L. Cos. | ' |
|---|---------|-----|---------|-------|---------|---------|---|
| 0 | 8.71 880 | 240 | 8.71 940 | 241 | 1.28 060 | 9.99 940 | 60 |
| 1 | 8.72 120 | 239 | 8.72 181 | 241 | 1.27 819 | 9.99 940 | 59 |
| 2 | 8.72 359 | 238 | 8.72 420 | 239 | 1.27 580 | 9.99 939 | 58 |
| 3 | 8.72 597 | 237 | 8.72 659 | 237 | 1.27 341 | 9.99 938 | 57 |
| 4 | 8.72 834 | 235 | 8.72 896 | 236 | 1.27 104 | 9.99 938 | 56 |
| 5 | 8.73 069 | 234 | 8.73 132 | 234 | 1.26 868 | 9.99 937 | 55 |
| 6 | 8.73 303 | 232 | 8.73 366 | 234 | 1.26 634 | 9.99 936 | 54 |
| 7 | 8.73 535 | 232 | 8.73 600 | 232 | 1.26 400 | 9.99 936 | 53 |
| 8 | 8.73 767 | 230 | 8.73 832 | 231 | 1.26 168 | 9.99 935 | 52 |
| 9 | 8.73 997 | 229 | 8.74 063 | 229 | 1.25 937 | 9.99 934 | 51 |
| 10 | 8.74 226 | 228 | 8.74 292 | 229 | 1.25 708 | 9.99 934 | 50 |
| 11 | 8.74 454 | 226 | 8.74 521 | 227 | 1.25 479 | 9.99 933 | 49 |
| 12 | 8.74 680 | 226 | 8.74 748 | 226 | 1.25 252 | 9.99 932 | 48 |
| 13 | 8.74 906 | 224 | 8.74 974 | 225 | 1.25 026 | 9.99 932 | 47 |
| 14 | 8.75 130 | 223 | 8.75 199 | 224 | 1.24 801 | 9.99 931 | 46 |
| 15 | 8.75 353 | 222 | 8.75 423 | 222 | 1.24 577 | 9.99 931 | 45 |
| 16 | 8.75 575 | 220 | 8.75 645 | 222 | 1.24 355 | 9.99 929 | 44 |
| 17 | 8.75 795 | 220 | 8.75 867 | 220 | 1.24 133 | 9.99 929 | 43 |
| 18 | 8.76 015 | 219 | 8.76 087 | 219 | 1.23 913 | 9.99 928 | 42 |
| 19 | 8.76 234 | 217 | 8.76 306 | 219 | 1.23 694 | 9.99 927 | 41 |
| 20 | 8.76 451 | 216 | 8.76 525 | 217 | 1.23 475 | 9.99 926 | 40 |
| 21 | 8.76 667 | 216 | 8.76 742 | 216 | 1.23 258 | 9.99 926 | 39 |
| 22 | 8.76 883 | 214 | 8.76 958 | 215 | 1.23 042 | 9.99 925 | 38 |
| 23 | 8.77 097 | 213 | 8.77 173 | 214 | 1.22 827 | 9.99 924 | 37 |
| 24 | 8.77 310 | 212 | 8.77 387 | 213 | 1.22 613 | 9.99 923 | 36 |
| 25 | 8.77 522 | 211 | 8.77 600 | 211 | 1.22 400 | 9.99 923 | 35 |
| 26 | 8.77 733 | 210 | 8.77 811 | 211 | 1.22 189 | 9.99 922 | 34 |
| 27 | 8.77 943 | 209 | 8.78 022 | 210 | 1.21 978 | 9.99 921 | 33 |
| 28 | 8.78 152 | 208 | 8.78 232 | 209 | 1.21 768 | 9.99 920 | 32 |
| 29 | 8.78 360 | 208 | 8.78 441 | 208 | 1.21 559 | 9.99 920 | 31 |
| 30 | 8.78 568 | 206 | 8.78 649 | 206 | 1.21 351 | 9.99 919 | 30 |
| 31 | 8.78 774 | 205 | 8.78 855 | 206 | 1.21 145 | 9.99 918 | 29 |
| 32 | 8.78 979 | 204 | 8.79 061 | 205 | 1.20 939 | 9.99 917 | 28 |
| 33 | 8.79 183 | 203 | 8.79 266 | 204 | 1.20 734 | 9.99 917 | 27 |
| 34 | 8.79 386 | 202 | 8.79 470 | 203 | 1.20 530 | 9.99 916 | 26 |
| 35 | 8.79 588 | 201 | 8.79 673 | 202 | 1.20 327 | 9.99 915 | 25 |
| 36 | 8.79 789 | 201 | 8.79 875 | 201 | 1.20 125 | 9.99 914 | 24 |
| 37 | 8.79 990 | 199 | 8.80 076 | 201 | 1.19 924 | 9.99 913 | 23 |
| 38 | 8.80 189 | 199 | 8.80 277 | 199 | 1.19 723 | 9.99 913 | 22 |
| 39 | 8.80 388 | 197 | 8.80 476 | 198 | 1.19 524 | 9.99 912 | 21 |
| 40 | 8.80 585 | 197 | 8.80 674 | 198 | 1.19 326 | 9.99 911 | 20 |
| 41 | 8.80 782 | 196 | 8.80 872 | 196 | 1.19 128 | 9.99 910 | 19 |
| 42 | 8.80 978 | 195 | 8.81 068 | 196 | 1.18 932 | 9.99 909 | 18 |
| 43 | 8.81 173 | 194 | 8.81 264 | 195 | 1.18 736 | 9.99 909 | 17 |
| 44 | 8.81 367 | 193 | 8.81 459 | 194 | 1.18 541 | 9.99 908 | 16 |
| 45 | 8.81 560 | 192 | 8.81 653 | 193 | 1.18 347 | 9.99 907 | 15 |
| 46 | 8.81 752 | 192 | 8.81 846 | 192 | 1.18 154 | 9.99 906 | 14 |
| 47 | 8.81 944 | 190 | 8.82 038 | 192 | 1.17 962 | 9.99 905 | 13 |
| 48 | 8.82 134 | 190 | 8.82 230 | 190 | 1.17 770 | 9.99 904 | 12 |
| 49 | 8.82 324 | 189 | 8.82 420 | 190 | 1.17 580 | 9.99 904 | 11 |
| 50 | 8.82 513 | 188 | 8.82 610 | 189 | 1.17 390 | 9.99 903 | 10 |
| 51 | 8.82 701 | 187 | 8.82 799 | 188 | 1.17 201 | 9.99 902 | 9 |
| 52 | 8.82 888 | 187 | 8.82 987 | 188 | 1.17 013 | 9.99 901 | 8 |
| 53 | 8.83 075 | 186 | 8.83 175 | 186 | 1.16 825 | 9.99 900 | 7 |
| 54 | 8.83 261 | 185 | 8.83 361 | 186 | 1.16 639 | 9.99 899 | 6 |
| 55 | 8.83 446 | 184 | 8.83 547 | 185 | 1.16 453 | 9.99 898 | 5 |
| 56 | 8.83 630 | 183 | 8.83 732 | 184 | 1.16 268 | 9.99 898 | 4 |
| 57 | 8.83 813 | 183 | 8.83 916 | 184 | 1.16 084 | 9.99 897 | 3 |
| 58 | 8.83 996 | 181 | 8.84 100 | 182 | 1.15 900 | 9.99 896 | 2 |
| 59 | 8.84 177 | 181 | 8.84 282 | 182 | 1.15 718 | 9.99 896 | 1 |
| 60 | 8.84 358 | | 8.84 464 | | 1.15 536 | 9.99 894 | 0 |

| ' | L. Cos. | d. | L. Cot. | c.d. | L. Tan. | L. Sin. | ' |
|---|---------|----|---------|------|---------|---------|---|

P. P.

| '' | 241 | 239 | 237 | 235 | 234 |
|----|-----|-----|-----|-----|-----|
| 1 | 4.0 | 4.0 | 4.0 | 3.9 | 3.9 |
| 2 | 8.0 | 8.0 | 7.9 | 7.8 | 7.8 |
| 3 | 12.0 | 12.0 | 11.8 | 11.8 | 11.7 |
| 4 | 16.1 | 15.9 | 15.8 | 15.7 | 15.6 |
| 5 | 20.1 | 19.9 | 19.8 | 19.6 | 19.5 |
| 6 | 24.1 | 23.9 | 23.7 | 23.5 | 23.4 |
| 7 | 28.1 | 27.9 | 27.6 | 27.4 | 27.3 |
| 8 | 32.1 | 31.9 | 31.6 | 31.3 | 31.2 |
| 9 | 36.2 | 35.8 | 35.6 | 35.2 | 35.1 |

| '' | 232 | 229 | 227 | 225 | 223 |
|----|-----|-----|-----|-----|-----|
| 1 | 3.9 | 3.8 | 3.8 | 3.8 | 3.7 |
| 2 | 7.7 | 7.6 | 7.6 | 7.5 | 7.4 |
| 3 | 11.6 | 11.4 | 11.4 | 11.2 | 11.2 |
| 4 | 15.5 | 15.3 | 15.1 | 15.0 | 14.9 |
| 5 | 19 3 | 19.1 | 18.9 | 18.8 | 18.6 |
| 6 | 23.2 | 22.9 | 22.7 | 22.5 | 22.3 |
| 7 | 27.1 | 26.7 | 26.5 | 26.2 | 26.0 |
| 8 | 30.9 | 30.5 | 30.3 | 30.0 | 29.7 |
| 9 | 34.8 | 34.4 | 34.0 | 33.8 | 33.4 |

| '' | 222 | 220 | 217 | 215 | 213 |
|----|-----|-----|-----|-----|-----|
| 1 | 3.7 | 3.7 | 3.6 | 3.6 | 3.6 |
| 2 | 7.4 | 7.3 | 7.2 | 7.2 | 7.1 |
| 3 | 11.1 | 11.0 | 10.8 | 10.8 | 10.6 |
| 4 | 14.8 | 14.7 | 14.5 | 14.3 | 14.2 |
| 5 | 18.5 | 18.3 | 18.1 | 17.9 | 17.8 |
| 6 | 22.2 | 22.0 | 21.7 | 21.5 | 21.3 |
| 7 | 25.9 | 25.7 | 25.3 | 25.1 | 24.8 |
| 8 | 29.6 | 29.3 | 28.9 | 28.7 | 28.4 |
| 9 | 33.3 | 33.0 | 32.6 | 32.2 | 32.0 |

| '' | 211 | 208 | 206 | 203 | 201 |
|----|-----|-----|-----|-----|-----|
| 1 | 3.5 | 3.5 | 3.4 | 3.4 | 3.4 |
| 2 | 7.0 | 6.9 | 6.9 | 6.8 | 6.7 |
| 3 | 10.6 | 10.4 | 10.3 | 10.2 | 10.0 |
| 4 | 14.1 | 13.9 | 13.7 | 13.5 | 13.4 |
| 5 | 17.6 | 17.3 | 17.2 | 16.9 | 16.8 |
| 6 | 21.1 | 20.8 | 20.6 | 20.3 | 20.1 |
| 7 | 24.6 | 24.3 | 24.0 | 23.7 | 23.4 |
| 8 | 28.1 | 27.7 | 27.5 | 27.1 | 26.8 |
| 9 | 31.6 | 31.2 | 30.9 | 30.4 | 30.2 |

| '' | 199 | 197 | 195 | 193 | 192 |
|----|-----|-----|-----|-----|-----|
| 1 | 3.3 | 3.3 | 3.2 | 3.2 | 3.2 |
| 2 | 6.6 | 6.6 | 6.5 | 6.4 | 6.4 |
| 3 | 10.0 | 9.8 | 9.8 | 9.6 | 9.6 |
| 4 | 13.3 | 13.1 | 13.0 | 12.9 | 12.8 |
| 5 | 16.6 | 16.4 | 16.2 | 16.1 | 16.0 |
| 6 | 19.9 | 19.7 | 19.5 | 19.3 | 19.2 |
| 7 | 23.2 | 23.0 | 22.8 | 22.5 | 22.4 |
| 8 | 26.5 | 26.3 | 26.0 | 25.7 | 25.6 |
| 9 | 29.8 | 29.6 | 29.2 | 29.0 | 28.8 |

| '' | 189 | 187 | 185 | 183 | 181 |
|----|-----|-----|-----|-----|-----|
| 1 | 3.2 | 3.1 | 3.1 | 3.0 | 3.0 |
| 2 | 6.3 | 6.2 | 6.2 | 6.1 | 6.0 |
| 3 | 9.4 | 9.4 | 9.2 | 9.2 | 9.0 |
| 4 | 12.6 | 12.5 | 12.3 | 12.2 | 12.1 |
| 5 | 15.8 | 15.6 | 15.4 | 15.2 | 15.1 |
| 6 | 18.9 | 18.7 | 18.5 | 18.3 | 18.1 |
| 7 | 22.0 | 21.8 | 21.6 | 21.4 | 21.1 |
| 8 | 25.2 | 24.9 | 24.7 | 24.4 | 24.1 |
| 9 | 28.4 | 28.0 | 27.8 | 27.4 | 27.2 |
| 10 | 31.5 | 31.2 | 30.8 | 30.5 | 30.2 |

93° (273°)     (266°) 86°

* Interpolation in this section of the table is not accurate.

4° (184°)          (355°) 175°

| ' | L. Sin. | d | L. Tan. | c.d | L. Cot. | L. Cos. | ' |
|---|---------|---|---------|-----|---------|---------|---|
| 0 | 8.84 358 | 181 | 8.84 464 | 182 | 1.15 536 | 9.99 894 | 60 |
| 1 | 8.84 539 | 179 | 8.84 646 | 180 | 1.15 354 | 9.99 893 | 59 |
| 2 | 8.84 718 | 179 | 8.84 826 | 180 | 1.15 174 | 9.99 892 | 58 |
| 3 | 8.84 897 | 178 | 8.85 006 | 179 | 1.14 994 | 9.99 891 | 57 |
| 4 | 8.85 075 | 177 | 8.85 185 | 178 | 1.14 815 | 9.99 891 | 56 |
| 5 | 8.85 252 | 177 | 8.85 363 | 177 | 1.14 637 | 9.99 890 | 55 |
| 6 | 8.85 429 | 176 | 8.85 540 | 177 | 1.14 460 | 9.99 889 | 54 |
| 7 | 8.85 605 | 175 | 8.85 717 | 177 | 1.14 283 | 9.99 888 | 53 |
| 8 | 8.85 780 | 175 | 8.85 893 | 176 | 1.14 107 | 9.99 887 | 52 |
| 9 | 8.85 955 | 173 | 8.86 069 | 174 | 1.13 931 | 9.99 886 | 51 |
| 10 | 8.86 128 | 173 | 8.86 243 | 174 | 1.13 757 | 9.99 885 | 50 |
| 11 | 8.86 301 | 173 | 8.86 417 | 174 | 1.13 583 | 9.99 884 | 49 |
| 12 | 8.86 474 | 171 | 8.86 591 | 172 | 1.13 409 | 9.99 883 | 48 |
| 13 | 8.86 645 | 171 | 8.86 763 | 172 | 1.13 237 | 9.99 882 | 47 |
| 14 | 8.86 816 | 171 | 8.86 935 | 171 | 1.13 065 | 9.99 881 | 46 |
| 15 | 8.86 987 | 169 | 8.87 106 | 171 | 1.12 894 | 9.99 880 | 45 |
| 16 | 8.87 156 | 169 | 8.87 277 | 170 | 1.12 723 | 9.99 879 | 44 |
| 17 | 8.87 325 | 169 | 8.87 447 | 169 | 1.12 553 | 9.99 879 | 43 |
| 18 | 8.87 494 | 167 | 8.87 616 | 169 | 1.12 384 | 9.99 878 | 42 |
| 19 | 8.87 661 | 168 | 8.87 785 | 168 | 1.12 215 | 9.99 877 | 41 |
| 20 | 8.87 829 | 166 | 8.87 953 | 167 | 1.12 047 | 9.99 876 | 40 |
| 21 | 8.87 995 | 166 | 8.88 120 | 167 | 1.11 880 | 9.99 875 | 39 |
| 22 | 8.88 161 | 165 | 8.88 287 | 166 | 1.11 713 | 9.99 874 | 38 |
| 23 | 8.88 326 | 164 | 8.88 453 | 165 | 1.11 547 | 9.99 873 | 37 |
| 24 | 8.88 490 | 164 | 8.88 618 | 165 | 1.11 382 | 9.99 872 | 36 |
| 25 | 8.88 654 | 163 | 8.88 783 | 165 | 1.11 217 | 9.99 871 | 35 |
| 26 | 8.88 817 | 163 | 8.88 948 | 163 | 1.11 052 | 9.99 870 | 34 |
| 27 | 8.88 980 | 162 | 8.89 111 | 163 | 1.10 889 | 9.99 869 | 33 |
| 28 | 8.89 142 | 162 | 8.89 274 | 163 | 1.10 726 | 9.99 868 | 32 |
| 29 | 8.89 304 | 160 | 8.89 437 | 161 | 1.10 563 | 9.99 867 | 31 |
| 30 | 8.89 464 | 161 | 8.89 598 | 162 | 1.10 402 | 9.99 866 | 30 |
| 31 | 8.89 625 | 159 | 8.89 760 | 160 | 1.10 240 | 9.99 865 | 29 |
| 32 | 8.89 784 | 159 | 8.89 920 | 160 | 1.10 080 | 9.99 864 | 28 |
| 33 | 8.89 943 | 159 | 8.90 080 | 160 | 1.09 920 | 9.99 863 | 27 |
| 34 | 8.90 102 | 158 | 8.90 240 | 159 | 1.09 760 | 9.99 862 | 26 |
| 35 | 8.90 260 | 157 | 8.90 399 | 158 | 1.09 601 | 9.99 861 | 25 |
| 36 | 8.90 417 | 157 | 8.90 557 | 158 | 1.09 443 | 9.99 860 | 24 |
| 37 | 8.90 574 | 156 | 8.90 715 | 157 | 1.09 285 | 9.99 859 | 23 |
| 38 | 8.90 730 | 155 | 8.90 872 | 157 | 1.09 128 | 9.99 858 | 22 |
| 39 | 8.90 885 | 155 | 8.91 029 | 156 | 1.08 971 | 9.99 857 | 21 |
| 40 | 8.91 040 | 155 | 8.91 185 | 155 | 1.08 815 | 9.99 856 | 20 |
| 41 | 8.91 195 | 154 | 8.91 340 | 155 | 1.08 660 | 9.99 855 | 19 |
| 42 | 8.91 349 | 153 | 8.91 495 | 155 | 1.08 505 | 9.99 854 | 18 |
| 43 | 8.91 502 | 153 | 8.91 650 | 153 | 1.08 350 | 9.99 853 | 17 |
| 44 | 8.91 655 | 152 | 8.91 803 | 154 | 1.08 197 | 9.99 852 | 16 |
| 45 | 8.91 807 | 152 | 8.91 957 | 153 | 1.08 043 | 9.99 851 | 15 |
| 46 | 8.91 959 | 151 | 8.92 110 | 152 | 1.07 890 | 9.99 850 | 14 |
| 47 | 8.92 110 | 151 | 8.92 262 | 152 | 1.07 738 | 9.99 848 | 13 |
| 48 | 8.92 261 | 150 | 8.92 414 | 151 | 1.07 586 | 9.99 847 | 12 |
| 49 | 8.92 411 | 150 | 8.92 565 | 151 | 1.07 435 | 9.99 846 | 11 |
| 50 | 8.92 561 | 149 | 8.92 716 | 150 | 1.07 284 | 9.99 845 | 10 |
| 51 | 8.92 710 | 149 | 8.92 866 | 150 | 1.07 134 | 9.99 844 | 9 |
| 52 | 8.92 859 | 148 | 8.93 016 | 149 | 1.06 984 | 9.99 843 | 8 |
| 53 | 8.93 007 | 147 | 8.93 165 | 148 | 1.06 835 | 9.99 842 | 7 |
| 54 | 8.93 154 | 147 | 8.93 313 | 149 | 1.06 687 | 9.99 841 | 6 |
| 55 | 8.93 301 | 147 | 8.93 462 | 147 | 1.06 538 | 9.99 840 | 5 |
| 56 | 8.93 448 | 146 | 8.93 609 | 147 | 1.06 391 | 9.99 839 | 4 |
| 57 | 8.93 594 | 146 | 8.93 756 | 147 | 1.06 244 | 9.99 838 | 3 |
| 58 | 8.93 740 | 145 | 8.93 903 | 146 | 1.06 097 | 9.99 837 | 2 |
| 59 | 8.93 885 | 145 | 8.94 049 | 146 | 1.05 951 | 9.99 836 | 1 |
| 60 | 8.94 030 |  | 8.94 195 |  | 1.05 805 | 9.99 834 | 0 |

**P.P.**

| " | 182 | 181 | 179 | 178 | 177 |
|---|-----|-----|-----|-----|-----|
| 1 | 3.0 | 3.0 | 3.0 | 3.0 | 3.0 |
| 2 | 6.1 | 6.0 | 6.0 | 5.9 | 5.9 |
| 3 | 9.1 | 9.0 | 9.0 | 8.9 | 8.8 |
| 4 | 12.1 | 12.1 | 11.9 | 11.9 | 11.8 |
| 5 | 15.2 | 15.1 | 14.9 | 14.8 | 14.8 |
| 6 | 18.2 | 18.1 | 17.9 | 17.8 | 17.7 |
| 7 | 21.2 | 21.1 | 20.9 | 20.8 | 20.6 |
| 8 | 24.3 | 24.1 | 23.9 | 23.7 | 23.6 |
| 9 | 27.3 | 27.2 | 26.8 | 26.7 | 26.6 |

| " | 176 | 175 | 174 | 173 | 172 |
|---|-----|-----|-----|-----|-----|
| 1 | 2.9 | 2.9 | 2.9 | 2.9 | 2.9 |
| 2 | 5.9 | 5.8 | 5.8 | 5.8 | 5.7 |
| 3 | 8.8 | 8.8 | 8.7 | 8.6 | 8.6 |
| 4 | 11.7 | 11.7 | 11.6 | 11.5 | 11.5 |
| 5 | 14.7 | 14.6 | 14.5 | 14.4 | 14.3 |
| 6 | 17.6 | 17.5 | 17.4 | 17.3 | 17.2 |
| 7 | 20.5 | 20.4 | 20.3 | 20.2 | 20.1 |
| 8 | 23.5 | 23.3 | 23.2 | 23.1 | 22.9 |
| 9 | 26.4 | 26.2 | 26.1 | 26.0 | 25.8 |

| " | 171 | 170 | 169 | 168 | 167 |
|---|-----|-----|-----|-----|-----|
| 1 | 2.8 | 2.8 | 2.8 | 2.8 | 2.8 |
| 2 | 5.7 | 5.7 | 5.6 | 5.6 | 5.6 |
| 3 | 8.6 | 8.5 | 8.4 | 8.4 | 8.4 |
| 4 | 11.4 | 11.3 | 11.3 | 11.2 | 11.1 |
| 5 | 14.2 | 14.2 | 14.1 | 14.0 | 13.9 |
| 6 | 17.1 | 17.0 | 16.9 | 16.8 | 16.7 |
| 7 | 20.0 | 19.8 | 19.7 | 19.6 | 19.5 |
| 8 | 22.8 | 22.7 | 22.5 | 22.4 | 22.3 |
| 9 | 25.6 | 25.5 | 25.4 | 25.2 | 25.0 |

| " | 166 | 165 | 164 | 163 | 162 |
|---|-----|-----|-----|-----|-----|
| 1 | 2.8 | 2.8 | 2.7 | 2.7 | 2.7 |
| 2 | 5.5 | 5.5 | 5.5 | 5.4 | 5.4 |
| 3 | 8.3 | 8.2 | 8.2 | 8.2 | 8.1 |
| 4 | 11.1 | 11.0 | 10.9 | 10.9 | 10.8 |
| 5 | 13.8 | 13.8 | 13.7 | 13.6 | 13.5 |
| 6 | 16.6 | 16.5 | 16.4 | 16.3 | 16.2 |
| 7 | 19.4 | 19.2 | 19.1 | 19.0 | 18.9 |
| 8 | 22.1 | 22.0 | 21.9 | 21.7 | 21.6 |
| 9 | 24.9 | 24.8 | 24.6 | 24.4 | 24.3 |

| " | 161 | 160 | 159 | 158 | 157 |
|---|-----|-----|-----|-----|-----|
| 1 | 2.7 | 2.7 | 2.6 | 2.6 | 2.6 |
| 2 | 5.4 | 5.3 | 5.3 | 5.3 | 5.2 |
| 3 | 8.0 | 8.0 | 8.0 | 7.9 | 7.8 |
| 4 | 10.7 | 10.7 | 10.6 | 10.5 | 10.5 |
| 5 | 13.4 | 13.3 | 13.2 | 13.1 | 13.1 |
| 6 | 16.1 | 16.0 | 15.9 | 15.8 | 15.7 |
| 7 | 18.8 | 18.7 | 18.6 | 18.4 | 18.3 |
| 8 | 21.5 | 21.3 | 21.2 | 21.1 | 20.9 |
| 9 | 24.2 | 24.0 | 23.8 | 23.7 | 23.6 |

| " | 156 | 155 | 154 | 153 | 152 |
|---|-----|-----|-----|-----|-----|
| 1 | 2.6 | 2.6 | 2.6 | 2.6 | 2.5 |
| 2 | 5.2 | 5.2 | 5.1 | 5.1 | 5.1 |
| 3 | 7.8 | 7.8 | 7.7 | 7.6 | 7.6 |
| 4 | 10.4 | 10.3 | 10.3 | 10.2 | 10.1 |
| 5 | 13.0 | 12.9 | 12.8 | 12.8 | 12.7 |
| 6 | 15.6 | 15.5 | 15.4 | 15.3 | 15.2 |
| 7 | 18.2 | 18.1 | 18.0 | 17.8 | 17.7 |
| 8 | 20.8 | 20.7 | 20.5 | 20.4 | 20.3 |
| 9 | 23.4 | 23.2 | 23.1 | 23.0 | 22.8 |
| 10 | 26.0 | 25.8 | 25.7 | 25.5 | 25.3 |

| ' | L. Cos. | d. | L. Cot. | c.d. | L. Tan. | L. Sin. | ' | P. P. |
|---|---------|----|---------|------|---------|---------|---|-------|

94° (274°)          (265°) 85°

* Interpolation in this section of the table is not accurate.

| ' | L. Sin. | d. | L. Tan. | c.d. | L. Cot. | L. Cos. | ' |
|---|---------|-----|---------|------|---------|---------|---|
| 0 | 8.94 030 | 144 | 8.94 195 | 145 | 1.05 805 | 9.99 834 | 60 |
| 1 | 8.94 174 | 144 | 8.94 340 | 145 | 1.05 660 | 9.99 833 | 59 |
| 2 | 8.94 317 | 143 | 8.94 485 | 145 | 1.05 515 | 9.99 832 | 58 |
| 3 | 8.94 461 | 144 | 8.94 630 | 145 | 1.05 370 | 9.99 831 | 57 |
| 4 | 8.94 603 | 142 | 8.94 773 | 143 | 1.05 227 | 9.99 830 | 56 |
| 5 | 8.94 746 | 143 / 141 | 8.94 917 | 144 | 1.05 083 | 9.99 829 | 55 |
| 6 | 8.94 887 | 141 | 8.95 060 | 143 | 1.04 940 | 9.99 828 | 54 |
| 7 | 8.95 029 | 142 | 8.95 202 | 142 | 1.04 798 | 9.99 827 | 53 |
| 8 | 8.95 170 | 141 | 8.95 344 | 142 | 1.04 656 | 9.99 825 | 52 |
| 9 | 8.95 310 | 140 | 8.95 486 | 142 | 1.04 514 | 9.99 824 | 51 |
| 10 | 8.95 450 | 140 / 139 | 8.95 627 | 141 | 1.04 373 | 9.99 823 | 50 |
| 11 | 8.95 589 | 139 | 8.95 767 | 140 | 1.04 233 | 9.99 822 | 49 |
| 12 | 8.95 728 | 139 | 8.95 908 | 141 | 1.04 092 | 9.99 821 | 48 |
| 13 | 8.95 867 | 139 | 8.96 047 | 140 | 1.03 953 | 9.99 820 | 47 |
| 14 | 8.96 005 | 138 | 8.96 187 | 139 | 1.03 813 | 9.99 819 | 46 |
| 15 | 8.96 143 | 138 / 137 | 8.96 325 | 138 | 1.03 675 | 9.99 817 | 45 |
| 16 | 8.96 280 | 137 | 8.96 464 | 139 | 1.03 536 | 9.99 816 | 44 |
| 17 | 8.96 417 | 137 | 8.96 602 | 138 | 1.03 398 | 9.99 815 | 43 |
| 18 | 8.96 553 | 136 | 8.96 739 | 137 | 1.03 261 | 9.99 814 | 42 |
| 19 | 8.96 689 | 136 | 8.96 877 | 138 | 1.03 123 | 9.99 813 | 41 |
| 20 | 8.96 825 | 136 / 135 | 8.97 013 | 136 | 1.02 987 | 9.99 812 | 40 |
| 21 | 8.96 960 | 135 | 8.97 150 | 137 | 1.02 850 | 9.99 810 | 39 |
| 22 | 8.97 095 | 135 | 8.97 285 | 135 | 1.02 715 | 9.99 809 | 38 |
| 23 | 8.97 229 | 134 | 8.97 421 | 136 | 1.02 579 | 9.99 808 | 37 |
| 24 | 8.97 363 | 134 | 8.97 556 | 135 | 1.02 444 | 9.99 807 | 36 |
| 25 | 8.97 496 | 133 | 8.97 691 | 135 | 1.02 309 | 9.99 806 | 35 |
| 26 | 8.97 629 | 133 | 8.97 825 | 134 | 1.02 175 | 9.99 804 | 34 |
| 27 | 8.97 762 | 133 | 8.97 959 | 134 | 1.02 041 | 9.99 803 | 33 |
| 28 | 8.97 894 | 132 | 8.98 092 | 133 | 1.01 908 | 9.99 802 | 32 |
| 29 | 8.98 026 | 132 | 8.98 225 | 133 | 1.01 775 | 9.99 801 | 31 |
| 30 | 8.98 157 | 131 | 8.98 358 | 133 | 1.01 642 | 9.99 800 | 30 |
| 31 | 8.98 288 | 131 | 8.98 490 | 132 | 1.01 510 | 9.99 798 | 29 |
| 32 | 8.98 419 | 131 | 8.98 622 | 132 | 1.01 378 | 9.99 797 | 28 |
| 33 | 8.98 549 | 130 | 8.98 753 | 131 | 1.01 247 | 9.99 796 | 27 |
| 34 | 8.98 679 | 130 | 8.98 884 | 131 | 1.01 116 | 9.99 795 | 26 |
| 35 | 8.98 808 | 129 | 8.99 015 | 131 | 1.00 985 | 9.99 793 | 25 |
| 36 | 8.98 937 | 129 | 8.99 145 | 130 | 1.00 855 | 9.99 792 | 24 |
| 37 | 8.99 066 | 129 | 8.99 275 | 130 | 1.00 725 | 9.99 791 | 23 |
| 38 | 8.99 194 | 128 | 8.99 405 | 130 | 1.00 595 | 9.99 790 | 22 |
| 39 | 8.99 322 | 128 | 8.99 534 | 129 | 1.00 466 | 9.99 788 | 21 |
| 40 | 8.99 450 | 128 / 127 | 8.99 662 | 128 | 1.00 338 | 9.99 787 | 20 |
| 41 | 8.99 577 | 127 | 8.99 791 | 129 | 1.00 209 | 9.99 786 | 19 |
| 42 | 8.99 704 | 127 | 8.99 919 | 128 | 1.00 081 | 9.99 785 | 18 |
| 43 | 8.99 830 | 126 | 9.00 046 | 127 | 0.99 954 | 9.99 783 | 17 |
| 44 | 8.99 956 | 126 | 9.00 174 | 128 | 0.99 826 | 9.99 782 | 16 |
| 45 | 9.00 082 | 126 / 125 | 9.00 301 | 127 | 0.99 699 | 9.99 781 | 15 |
| 46 | 9.00 207 | 125 | 9.00 427 | 126 | 0.99 573 | 9.99 780 | 14 |
| 47 | 9.00 332 | 125 | 9.00 553 | 126 | 0.99 447 | 9.99 778 | 13 |
| 48 | 9.00 456 | 124 | 9.00 679 | 126 | 0.99 321 | 9.99 777 | 12 |
| 49 | 9.00 581 | 125 | 9.00 805 | 126 | 0.99 195 | 9.99 776 | 11 |
| 50 | 9.00 704 | 123 | 9.00 930 | 125 | 0.99 070 | 9.99 775 | 10 |
| 51 | 9.00 828 | 124 | 9.01 055 | 125 | 0.98 945 | 9.99 773 | 9 |
| 52 | 9.00 951 | 123 | 9.01 179 | 124 | 0.98 821 | 9.99 772 | 8 |
| 53 | 9.01 074 | 123 | 9.01 303 | 124 | 0.98 697 | 9.99 771 | 7 |
| 54 | 9.01 196 | 122 | 9.01 427 | 124 | 0.98 573 | 9.99 769 | 6 |
| 55 | 9.01 318 | 122 | 9.01 550 | 123 | 0.98 450 | 9.99 768 | 5 |
| 56 | 9.01 440 | 122 / 121 | 9.01 673 | 123 | 0.98 327 | 9.99 767 | 4 |
| 57 | 9.01 561 | 121 | 9.01 796 | 123 | 0.98 204 | 9.99 765 | 3 |
| 58 | 9.01 682 | 121 | 9.01 918 | 122 | 0.98 082 | 9.99 764 | 2 |
| 59 | 9.01 803 | 121 / 120 | 9.02 040 | 122 | 0.97 960 | 9.99 762 | 1 |
| 60 | 9.01 923 | | 9.02 162 | | 0.97 838 | 9.99 761 | 0 |

P.P.

| " | 151 | 149 | 148 | 147 | 146 |
|---|-----|-----|-----|-----|-----|
| 1 | 2.5 | 2.5 | 2.5 | 2.4 | 2.4 |
| 2 | 5.0 | 5.0 | 4.9 | 4.9 | 4.9 |
| 3 | 7.6 | 7.4 | 7.4 | 7.4 | 7.3 |
| 4 | 10.1 | 9.9 | 9.9 | 9.8 | 9.7 |
| 5 | 12.6 | 12.4 | 12.3 | 12.2 | 12.2 |
| 6 | 15.1 | 14.9 | 14.8 | 14.7 | 14.6 |
| 7 | 17.6 | 17.4 | 17.3 | 17.2 | 17.0 |
| 8 | 20.1 | 19.9 | 19.7 | 19.6 | 19.5 |
| 9 | 22.6 | 22.4 | 22.2 | 22.0 | 21.9 |

| " | 145 | 144 | 143 | 142 | 141 |
|---|-----|-----|-----|-----|-----|
| 1 | 2.4 | 2.4 | 2.4 | 2.4 | 2.4 |
| 2 | 4.8 | 4.8 | 4.8 | 4.7 | 4.7 |
| 3 | 7.2 | 7.2 | 7.2 | 7.1 | 7.0 |
| 4 | 9.7 | 9.6 | 9.5 | 9.5 | 9.4 |
| 5 | 12.1 | 12.0 | 11.9 | 11.8 | 11.8 |
| 6 | 14.5 | 14.4 | 14.3 | 14.2 | 14.1 |
| 7 | 16.9 | 16.8 | 16.7 | 16.6 | 16.4 |
| 8 | 19.3 | 19.2 | 19.1 | 18.9 | 18.8 |
| 9 | 21.8 | 21.6 | 21.4 | 21.3 | 21.2 |

| " | 140 | 139 | 138 | 137 | 136 |
|---|-----|-----|-----|-----|-----|
| 1 | 2.3 | 2.3 | 2.3 | 2.3 | 2.3 |
| 2 | 4.7 | 4.6 | 4.6 | 4.6 | 4.5 |
| 3 | 7.0 | 7.0 | 6.9 | 6.8 | 6.8 |
| 4 | 9.3 | 9.3 | 9.2 | 9.1 | 9.1 |
| 5 | 11.7 | 11.6 | 11.5 | 11.4 | 11.3 |
| 6 | 14.0 | 13.9 | 13.8 | 13.7 | 13.6 |
| 7 | 16.3 | 16.2 | 16.1 | 16.0 | 15.9 |
| 8 | 18.7 | 18.5 | 18.4 | 18.3 | 18.1 |
| 9 | 21.0 | 20.8 | 20.7 | 20.6 | 20.4 |

| " | 135 | 134 | 133 | 132 | 131 |
|---|-----|-----|-----|-----|-----|
| 1 | 2.2 | 2.2 | 2.2 | 2.2 | 2.2 |
| 2 | 4.5 | 4.5 | 4.4 | 4.4 | 4.4 |
| 3 | 6.8 | 6.7 | 6.6 | 6.6 | 6.6 |
| 4 | 9.0 | 8.9 | 8.9 | 8.8 | 8.7 |
| 5 | 11.2 | 11.2 | 11.1 | 11.0 | 10.9 |
| 6 | 13.5 | 13.4 | 13.3 | 13.2 | 13.1 |
| 7 | 15.8 | 15.6 | 15.5 | 15.4 | 15.3 |
| 8 | 18.0 | 17.9 | 17.7 | 17.6 | 17.5 |
| 9 | 20.2 | 20.1 | 20.0 | 19.8 | 19.6 |

| " | 130 | 129 | 128 | 127 | 126 |
|---|-----|-----|-----|-----|-----|
| 1 | 2.2 | 2.2 | 2.1 | 2.1 | 2.1 |
| 2 | 4.3 | 4.3 | 4.3 | 4.2 | 4.2 |
| 3 | 6.5 | 6.4 | 6.4 | 6.4 | 6.3 |
| 4 | 8.7 | 8.6 | 8.5 | 8.5 | 8.4 |
| 5 | 10.8 | 10.8 | 10.7 | 10.6 | 10.5 |
| 6 | 13.0 | 12.9 | 12.8 | 12.7 | 12.6 |
| 7 | 15.2 | 15.0 | 14.9 | 14.8 | 14.7 |
| 8 | 17.3 | 17.2 | 17.1 | 16.9 | 16.8 |
| 9 | 19.5 | 19.4 | 19.2 | 19.0 | 18.9 |

| " | 125 | 124 | 123 | 122 | 121 |
|----|-----|-----|-----|-----|-----|
| 1 | 2.1 | 2.1 | 2.0 | 2.0 | 2.0 |
| 2 | 4.2 | 4.1 | 4.1 | 4.1 | 4.0 |
| 3 | 6.2 | 6.2 | 6.2 | 6.1 | 6.0 |
| 4 | 8.3 | 8.3 | 8.2 | 8.1 | 8.1 |
| 5 | 10.4 | 10.3 | 10.2 | 10.2 | 10.1 |
| 6 | 12.5 | 12.4 | 12.3 | 12.2 | 12.1 |
| 7 | 14.6 | 14.5 | 14.4 | 14.2 | 14.1 |
| 8 | 16.7 | 16.5 | 16.4 | 16.3 | 16.1 |
| 9 | 18.8 | 18.6 | 18.4 | 18.3 | 18.2 |
| 10 | 20.8 | 20.7 | 20.5 | 20.3 | 20.2 |

| ' | L. Cos. | d. | L. Cot. | c.d. | L. Tan. | L. Sin. | ' | P.P. |
|---|---------|-----|---------|------|---------|---------|---|------|

| ' | L. Sin. | d. | L. Tan. | c.d. | L. Cot. | L. Cos. | ' | P. P. | | | |
|---|---------|-----|---------|------|---------|---------|---|---|---|---|---|
| **0** | 9.01 923 | | 9.02 162 | | 0.97 838 | 9.99 761 | **60** | **"** | **121** | **120** | **119** | **118** |
| 1 | 9.02 043 | 120 | 9.02 283 | 121 | 0.97 717 | 9.99 760 | 59 | 1 | 2.0 | 2.0 | 2.0 | 2.0 |
| 2 | 9.02 163 | 120 | 9.02 404 | 121 | 0.97 596 | 9.99 759 | 58 | 2 | 4.0 | 4.0 | 4.0 | 3.9 |
| 3 | 9.02 283 | 120 | 9.02 525 | 121 | 0.97 475 | 9.99 757 | 57 | 3 | 6.0 | 6.0 | 6.0 | 5.9 |
| 4 | 9.02 402 | 119 | 9.02 645 | 120 | 0.97 355 | 9.99 756 | 56 | 4 | 8.1 | 8.0 | 7.9 | 7.9 |
| | | 118 | | 121 | | | | | | | | |
| **5** | 9.02 520 | | 9.02 766 | | 0.97 234 | 9.99 755 | **55** | 5 | 10.1 | 10.0 | 9.9 | 9.8 |
| 6 | 9.02 639 | 119 | 9.02 885 | 119 | 0.97 115 | 9.99 753 | 54 | 6 | 12.1 | 12.0 | 11.9 | 11.8 |
| 7 | 9.02 757 | 118 | 9.03 005 | 120 | 0.96 995 | 9.99 752 | 53 | 7 | 14.1 | 14.0 | 13.9 | 13.8 |
| 8 | 9.02 874 | 117 | 9.03 124 | 119 | 0.96 876 | 9.99 751 | 52 | 8 | 16.1 | 16.0 | 15.9 | 15.7 |
| 9 | 9.02 992 | 118 | 9.03 242 | 119 | 0.96 758 | 9.99 749 | 51 | 9 | 18.2 | 18.0 | 17.8 | 17.7 |
| | | 117 | | 119 | | | | | | | | |
| **10** | 9.03 109 | | 9.03 361 | | 0.96 639 | 9.99 748 | **50** | 10 | 20.2 | 20.0 | 19.8 | 19.7 |
| 11 | 9.03 226 | 117 | 9.03 479 | 118 | 0.96 521 | 9.99 747 | 49 | 20 | 40.3 | 40.0 | 39.7 | 39.3 |
| 12 | 9.03 342 | 116 | 9.03 597 | 118 | 0.96 403 | 9.99 745 | 48 | 30 | 60.5 | 60.0 | 59.5 | 59.0 |
| 13 | 9.03 458 | 116 | 9.03 714 | 117 | 0.96 286 | 9.99 744 | 47 | 40 | 80.7 | 80.0 | 79.3 | 78.7 |
| 14 | 9.03 574 | 116 | 9.03 832 | 118 | 0.96 168 | 9.99 742 | 46 | 50 | 100.8 | 100.0 | 99.2 | 98.3 |
| | | 116 | | 116 | | | | | | | | |
| **15** | 9.03 690 | | 9.03 948 | | 0.96 052 | 9.99 741 | **45** | **"** | **117** | **116** | **115** | **114** |
| 16 | 9.03 805 | 115 | 9.04 065 | 117 | 0.95 935 | 9.99 740 | 44 | 1 | 2.0 | 1.9 | 1.9 | 1.9 |
| 17 | 9.03 920 | 115 | 9.04 181 | 116 | 0.95 819 | 9.99 738 | 43 | 2 | 3.9 | 3.9 | 3.8 | 3.8 |
| 18 | 9.04 034 | 114 | 9.04 297 | 116 | 0.95 703 | 9.99 737 | 42 | 3 | 5.8 | 5.8 | 5.8 | 5.7 |
| 19 | 9.04 149 | 115 | 9.04 413 | 116 | 0.95 587 | 9.99 736 | 41 | 4 | 7.8 | 7.7 | 7.7 | 7.6 |
| | | 113 | | 115 | | | | | | | | |
| **20** | 9.04 262 | | 9.04 528 | | 0.95 472 | 9.99 734 | **40** | 5 | 9.8 | 9.7 | 9.6 | 9.5 |
| 21 | 9.04 376 | 114 | 9.04 643 | 115 | 0.95 357 | 9.99 733 | 39 | 6 | 11.7 | 11.6 | 11.5 | 11.4 |
| 22 | 9.04 490 | 114 | 9.04 758 | 115 | 0.95 242 | 9.99 731 | 38 | 7 | 13.6 | 13.5 | 13.4 | 13.3 |
| 23 | 9.04 603 | 113 | 9.04 873 | 115 | 0.95 127 | 9.99 730 | 37 | 8 | 15.6 | 15.5 | 15.3 | 15.2 |
| 24 | 9.04 715 | 112 | 9.04 987 | 114 | 0.95 013 | 9.99 728 | 36 | 9 | 17.6 | 17.4 | 17.2 | 17.1 |
| | | 113 | | 114 | | | | | | | | |
| **25** | 9.04 828 | | 9.05 101 | | 0.94 899 | 9.99 727 | **35** | 10 | 19.5 | 19.3 | 19.2 | 19.0 |
| 26 | 9.04 940 | 112 | 9.05 214 | 113 | 0.94 786 | 9.99 726 | 34 | 20 | 39.0 | 38.7 | 38.3 | 38.0 |
| 27 | 9.05 052 | 112 | 9.05 328 | 114 | 0.94 672 | 9.99 724 | 33 | 30 | 58.5 | 58.0 | 57.5 | 57.0 |
| 28 | 9.05 164 | 112 | 9.05 441 | 113 | 0.94 559 | 9.99 723 | 32 | 40 | 78.0 | 77.3 | 76.7 | 76.0 |
| 29 | 9.05 275 | 111 | 9.05 553 | 112 | 0.94 447 | 9.99 721 | 31 | 50 | 97.5 | 96.7 | 95.8 | 95.0 |
| | | 111 | | 113 | | | | | | | | |
| **30** | 9.05 386 | | 9.05 666 | | 0.94 334 | 9.99 720 | **30** | **"** | **113** | **112** | **111** | **110** |
| 31 | 9.05 497 | 111 | 9.05 778 | 112 | 0.94 222 | 9.99 718 | 29 | 1 | 1.9 | 1.9 | 1.8 | 1.8 |
| 32 | 9.05 607 | 110 | 9.05 890 | 112 | 0.94 110 | 9.99 717 | 28 | 2 | 3.8 | 3.7 | 3.7 | 3.7 |
| 33 | 9.05 717 | 110 | 9.06 002 | 112 | 0.93 998 | 9.99 716 | 27 | 3 | 5.6 | 5.6 | 5.6 | 5.5 |
| 34 | 9.05 827 | 110 | 9.06 113 | 111 | 0.93 887 | 9.99 714 | 26 | 4 | 7.5 | 7.5 | 7.4 | 7.3 |
| | | 110 | | 111 | | | | | | | | |
| **35** | 9.05 937 | | 9.06 224 | | 0.93 776 | 9.99 713 | **25** | 5 | 9.4 | 9.3 | 9.2 | 9.2 |
| 36 | 9.06 046 | 109 | 9.06 335 | 111 | 0.93 665 | 9.99 711 | 24 | 6 | 11.3 | 11.2 | 11.1 | 11.0 |
| 37 | 9.06 155 | 109 | 9.06 445 | 110 | 0.93 555 | 9.99 710 | 23 | 7 | 13.2 | 13.1 | 13.0 | 12.8 |
| 38 | 9.06 264 | 109 | 9.06 556 | 111 | 0.93 444 | 9.99 708 | 22 | 8 | 15.1 | 14.9 | 14.8 | 14.7 |
| 39 | 9.06 372 | 108 | 9.06 666 | 110 | 0.93 334 | 9.99 707 | 21 | 9 | 17.0 | 16.8 | 16.6 | 16.5 |
| | | 109 | | 109 | | | | | | | | |
| **40** | 9.06 481 | | 9.06 775 | | 0.93 225 | 9.99 705 | **20** | 10 | 18.8 | 18.7 | 18.5 | 18.3 |
| 41 | 9.06 589 | 108 | 9.06 885 | 110 | 0.93 115 | 9.99 704 | 19 | 20 | 37.7 | 37.3 | 37.0 | 36.7 |
| 42 | 9.06 696 | 107 | 9.06 994 | 109 | 0.93 006 | 9.99 702 | 18 | 30 | 56.5 | 56.0 | 55.5 | 55.0 |
| 43 | 9.06 804 | 108 | 9.07 103 | 109 | 0.92 897 | 9.99 701 | 17 | 40 | 75.3 | 74.7 | 74.0 | 73.3 |
| 44 | 9.06 911 | 107 | 9.07 211 | 108 | 0.92 789 | 9.99 699 | 16 | 50 | 94.2 | 93.3 | 92.5 | 91.7 |
| | | 107 | | 109 | | | | | | | | |
| **45** | 9.07 018 | | 9.07 320 | | 0.92 680 | 9.99 698 | **15** | **"** | **109** | **108** | **107** | **106** |
| 46 | 9.07 124 | 106 | 9.07 428 | 108 | 0.92 572 | 9.99 696 | 14 | 1 | 1.8 | 1.8 | 1.8 | 1.8 |
| 47 | 9.07 231 | 107 | 9.07 536 | 108 | 0.92 464 | 9.99 695 | 13 | 2 | 3.6 | 3.6 | 3.6 | 3.5 |
| 48 | 9.07 337 | 106 | 9.07 643 | 107 | 0.92 357 | 9.99 693 | 12 | 3 | 5.4 | 5.4 | 5.4 | 5.3 |
| 49 | 9.07 442 | 105 | 9.07 751 | 108 | 0.92 249 | 9.99 692 | 11 | 4 | 7.3 | 7.2 | 7.1 | 7.1 |
| | | 106 | | 107 | | | | | | | | |
| **50** | 9.07 548 | | 9.07 858 | | 0.92 142 | 9.99 690 | **10** | 5 | 9.1 | 9.0 | 8.9 | 8.8 |
| 51 | 9.07 653 | 105 | 9.07 964 | 106 | 0.92 036 | 9.99 689 | 9 | 6 | 10.9 | 10.8 | 10.7 | 10.6 |
| 52 | 9.07 758 | 105 | 9.08 071 | 107 | 0.91 929 | 9.99 687 | 8 | 7 | 12.7 | 12.6 | 12.5 | 12.4 |
| 53 | 9.07 863 | 105 | 9.08 177 | 106 | 0.91 823 | 9.99 686 | 7 | 8 | 14.5 | 14.4 | 14.3 | 14.1 |
| 54 | 9.07 968 | 105 | 9.08 283 | 106 | 0.91 717 | 9.99 684 | 6 | 9 | 16.4 | 16.2 | 16.0 | 15.9 |
| | | 104 | | 106 | | | | | | | | |
| **55** | 9.08 072 | | 9.08 389 | | 0.91 611 | 9.99 683 | **5** | 10 | 18.2 | 18.0 | 17.8 | 17.7 |
| 56 | 9.08 176 | 104 | 9.08 495 | 106 | 0.91 505 | 9.99 681 | 4 | 20 | 36.3 | 36.0 | 35.7 | 35.3 |
| 57 | 9.08 280 | 104 | 9.08 600 | 105 | 0.91 400 | 9.99 680 | 3 | 30 | 54.5 | 54.0 | 53.5 | 53.0 |
| 58 | 9.08 383 | 103 | 9.08 705 | 105 | 0.91 295 | 9.99 678 | 2 | 40 | 72.7 | 72.0 | 71.3 | 70.7 |
| 59 | 9.08 486 | 103 | 9.08 810 | 105 | 0.91 190 | 9.99 677 | 1 | 50 | 90.8 | 90.0 | 89.2 | 88.8 |
| | | 103 | | 104 | | | | | | | | |
| **60** | 9.08 589 | | 9.08 914 | | 0.91 086 | 9.99 675 | **0** | | | | | |
| ' | L. Cos. | d. | L. Cot. | c.d. | L. Tan. | L. Sin. | ' | | P. P. | | |

| ′ | L. Sin. | d. | L. Tan. | c.d. | L. Cot. | L. Cos. | ′ | P. P. | | | |
|---|---------|----|---------|------|---------|---------|---|----|----|----|----|
| **0** | 9.08 589 | 103 | 9.08 914 | 105 | 0.91 086 | 9.99 675 | **60** | ″ | 105 | 104 | 103 | 102 |
| 1 | 9.08 692 | 103 | 9.09 019 | 104 | 0.90 981 | 9.99 674 | 59 | 1 | 1.8 | 1.7 | 1.7 | 1.7 |
| 2 | 9.08 795 | 102 | 9.09 123 | 104 | 0.90 877 | 9.99 672 | 58 | 2 | 3.5 | 3.5 | 3.4 | 3.4 |
| 3 | 9.08 897 | 102 | 9.09 227 | 103 | 0.90 773 | 9.99 670 | 57 | 3 | 5.2 | 5.2 | 5.2 | 5.1 |
| 4 | 9.08 999 | 102 | 9.09 330 | 104 | 0.90 670 | 9.99 669 | 56 | 4 | 7.0 | 6.9 | 6.9 | 6.8 |
| **5** | 9.09 101 | 101 | 9.09 434 | 103 | 0.90 566 | 9.99 667 | 55 | 5 | 8.8 | 8.7 | 8.6 | 8.5 |
| 6 | 9.09 202 | 102 | 9.09 537 | 103 | 0.90 463 | 9.99 666 | 54 | 6 | 10.5 | 10.4 | 10.3 | 10.2 |
| 7 | 9.09 304 | 101 | 9.09 640 | 102 | 0.90 360 | 9.99 664 | 53 | 7 | 12.2 | 12.1 | 12.0 | 11.9 |
| 8 | 9.09 405 | 101 | 9.09 742 | 103 | 0.90 258 | 9.99 663 | 52 | 8 | 14.0 | 13.9 | 13.7 | 13.6 |
| 9 | 9.09 506 | 100 | 9.09 845 | 102 | 0.90 155 | 9.99 661 | 51 | 9 | 15.8 | 15.6 | 15.4 | 15.3 |
| **10** | 9.09 606 | 101 | 9.09 947 | 102 | 0.90 053 | 9.99 659 | **50** | 10 | 17.5 | 17.3 | 17.2 | 17.0 |
| 11 | 9.09 707 | 100 | 9.10 049 | 101 | 0.89 951 | 9.99 658 | 49 | 20 | 35.0 | 34.7 | 34.3 | 34.0 |
| 12 | 9.09 807 | 100 | 9.10 150 | 102 | 0.89 850 | 9.99 656 | 48 | 30 | 52.5 | 52.0 | 51.5 | 51.0 |
| 13 | 9.09 907 | 99 | 9.10 252 | 101 | 0.89 748 | 9.99 655 | 47 | 40 | 70.0 | 69.3 | 68.7 | 68.0 |
| 14 | 9.10 006 | 100 | 9.10 353 | 101 | 0.89 647 | 9.99 653 | 46 | 50 | 87.5 | 86.7 | 85.8 | 85.0 |
| **15** | 9.10 106 | 99 | 9.10 454 | 101 | 0.89 546 | 9.99 651 | 45 | ″ | 101 | 100 | 99 | 98 |
| 16 | 9.10 205 | 99 | 9.10 555 | 101 | 0.89 445 | 9.99 650 | 44 | 1 | 1.7 | 1.7 | 1.6 | 1.6 |
| 17 | 9.10 304 | 98 | 9.10 656 | 100 | 0.89 344 | 9.99 648 | 43 | 2 | 3.4 | 3.3 | 3.3 | 3.3 |
| 18 | 9.10 402 | 99 | 9.10 756 | 100 | 0.89 244 | 9.99 647 | 42 | 3 | 5.0 | 5.0 | 4.9 | 4.9 |
| 19 | 9.10 501 | 98 | 9.10 856 | 100 | 0.89 144 | 9.99 645 | 41 | 4 | 6.7 | 6.7 | 6.6 | 6.5 |
| **20** | 9.10 599 | 98 | 9.10 956 | 100 | 0.89 044 | 9.99 643 | **40** | 5 | 8.4 | 8.3 | 8.2 | 8.2 |
| 21 | 9.10 697 | 98 | 9.11 056 | 99 | 0.88 944 | 9.99 642 | 39 | 6 | 10.1 | 10.0 | 9.9 | 9.8 |
| 22 | 9.10 795 | 98 | 9.11 155 | 99 | 0.88 845 | 9.99 640 | 38 | 7 | 11.8 | 11.7 | 11.6 | 11.4 |
| 23 | 9.10 893 | 97 | 9.11 254 | 99 | 0.88 746 | 9.99 638 | 37 | 8 | 13.5 | 13.3 | 13.2 | 13.1 |
| 24 | 9.10 990 | 97 | 9.11 353 | 99 | 0.88 647 | 9.99 637 | 36 | 9 | 15.2 | 15.0 | 14.8 | 14.7 |
| **25** | 9.11 087 | 97 | 9.11 452 | 99 | 0.88 548 | 9.99 635 | 35 | 10 | 16.8 | 16.7 | 16.5 | 16.3 |
| 26 | 9.11 184 | 97 | 9.11 551 | 98 | 0.88 449 | 9.99 633 | 34 | 20 | 33.7 | 33.3 | 33.0 | 32.7 |
| 27 | 9.11 281 | 96 | 9.11 649 | 98 | 0.88 351 | 9.99 632 | 33 | 30 | 50.5 | 50.0 | 49.5 | 49.0 |
| 28 | 9.11 377 | 97 | 9.11 747 | 98 | 0.88 253 | 9.99 630 | 32 | 40 | 67.3 | 66.7 | 66.0 | 65.3 |
| 29 | 9.11 474 | 96 | 9.11 845 | 98 | 0.88 155 | 9.99 629 | 31 | 50 | 84.2 | 83.3 | 82.5 | 81.7 |
| **30** | 9.11 570 | 96 | 9.11 943 | 97 | 0.88 057 | 9.99 627 | **30** | ″ | 97 | 96 | 95 | 94 |
| 31 | 9.11 666 | 95 | 9.12 040 | 98 | 0.87 960 | 9.99 625 | 29 | 1 | 1.6 | 1.6 | 1.6 | 1.6 |
| 32 | 9.11 761 | 96 | 9.12 138 | 97 | 0.87 862 | 9.99 624 | 28 | 2 | 3.2 | 3.2 | 3.2 | 3.1 |
| 33 | 9.11 857 | 95 | 9.12 235 | 97 | 0.87 765 | 9.99 622 | 27 | 3 | 4.8 | 4.8 | 4.8 | 4.7 |
| 34 | 9.11 952 | 95 | 9.12 332 | 96 | 0.87 668 | 9.99 620 | 26 | 4 | 6.5 | 6.4 | 6.3 | 6.3 |
| **35** | 9.12 047 | 95 | 9.12 428 | 97 | 0.87 572 | 9.99 618 | 25 | 5 | 8.1 | 8.0 | 7.9 | 7.8 |
| 36 | 9.12 142 | 94 | 9.12 525 | 96 | 0.87 475 | 9.99 617 | 24 | 6 | 9.7 | 9.6 | 9.5 | 9.4 |
| 37 | 9.12 236 | 95 | 9.12 621 | 96 | 0.87 379 | 9.99 615 | 23 | 7 | 11.3 | 11.2 | 11.1 | 11.0 |
| 38 | 9.12 331 | 94 | 9.12 717 | 96 | 0.87 283 | 9.99 613 | 22 | 8 | 12.9 | 12.8 | 12.7 | 12.5 |
| 39 | 9.12 425 | 94 | 9.12 813 | 96 | 0.87 187 | 9.99 612 | 21 | 9 | 14.6 | 14.4 | 14.2 | 14.1 |
| **40** | 9.12 519 | 93 | 9.12 909 | 95 | 0.87 091 | 9.99 610 | **20** | 10 | 16.2 | 16.0 | 15.8 | 15.7 |
| 41 | 9.12 612 | 94 | 9.13 004 | 95 | 0.86 996 | 9.99 608 | 19 | 20 | 32.3 | 32.0 | 31.7 | 31.3 |
| 42 | 9.12 706 | 93 | 9.13 099 | 95 | 0.86 901 | 9.99 607 | 18 | 30 | 48.5 | 48.0 | 47.5 | 47.0 |
| 43 | 9.12 799 | 93 | 9.13 194 | 95 | 0.86 806 | 9.99 605 | 17 | 40 | 64.7 | 64.0 | 63.3 | 62.7 |
| 44 | 9.12 892 | 93 | 9.13 289 | 95 | 0.86 711 | 9.99 603 | 16 | 50 | 80.8 | 80.0 | 79.2 | 78.3 |
| **45** | 9.12 985 | 93 | 9.13 384 | 94 | 0.86 616 | 9.99 601 | 15 | ″ | 93 | 92 | 91 | 90 |
| 46 | 9.13 078 | 93 | 9.13 478 | 95 | 0.86 522 | 9.99 600 | 14 | 1 | 1.6 | 1.5 | 1.5 | 1.5 |
| 47 | 9.13 171 | 92 | 9.13 573 | 94 | 0.86 427 | 9.99 598 | 13 | 2 | 3.1 | 3.1 | 3.9 | 3.0 |
| 48 | 9.13 263 | 92 | 9.13 667 | 94 | 0.86 333 | 9.99 596 | 12 | 3 | 4.6 | 4 6 | 4.6 | 4.5 |
| 49 | 9.13 355 | 92 | 9.13 761 | 93 | 0.86 239 | 9.99 595 | 11 | 4 | 6.2 | 6 1 | 6.1 | 6.0 |
| **50** | 9.13 447 | 92 | 9.13 854 | 94 | 0.86 146 | 9.99 593 | **10** | 5 | 7.8 | 7.7 | 7.6 | 7.5 |
| 51 | 9.13 539 | 91 | 9.13 948 | 93 | 0.86 052 | 9.99 591 | 9 | 6 | 9.3 | 9.2 | 9.1 | 9.0 |
| 52 | 9.13 630 | 92 | 9.14 041 | 93 | 0.85 959 | 9.99 589 | 8 | 7 | 10.8 | 10.7 | 10.6 | 10.5 |
| 53 | 9.13 722 | 91 | 9.14 134 | 93 | 0.85 866 | 9.99 588 | 7 | 8 | 12.4 | 12.3 | 12.1 | 12.0 |
| 54 | 9.13 813 | 91 | 9.14 227 | 93 | 0.85 773 | 9.99 586 | 6 | 9 | 14.0 | 13.8 | 13.6 | 13.5 |
| **55** | 9.13 904 | 90 | 9.14 320 | 92 | 0.85 680 | 9.99 584 | 5 | 10 | 15.5 | 15.3 | 15.2 | 15.0 |
| 56 | 9.13 994 | 91 | 9.14 412 | 92 | 0.85 588 | 9.99 582 | 4 | 20 | 31.0 | 30.7 | 30.3 | 30.0 |
| 57 | 9.14 085 | 90 | 9.14 504 | 93 | 0.85 496 | 9.99 581 | 3 | 30 | 46.5 | 46.0 | 45.5 | 45.0 |
| 58 | 9.14 175 | 91 | 9.14 597 | 91 | 0.85 403 | 9.99 579 | 2 | 40 | 62.0 | 61.3 | 60.7 | 60.0 |
| 59 | 9.14 266 | 90 | 9.14 688 | 92 | 0.85 312 | 9.99 577 | 1 | 50 | 77.5 | 76.7 | 75.8 | 75.0 |
| **60** | 9.14 356 | | 9.14 780 | | 0.85 220 | 9.99 575 | **0** | | | | | |
| ′ | L. Cos. | d. | L. Cot. | c.d. | L. Tan. | L. Sin. | ′ | | | P. P. | | |

| ' | L. Sin | d. | L. Tan. | c. d. | L. Cot. | L. Cos. | ' |
|---|---|---|---|---|---|---|---|
| 0 | 9.14 356 | 89 | 9.14 780 | 92 | 0.85 220 | 9.99 575 | 60 |
| 1 | 9.14 445 | 90 | 9.14 872 | 91 | 0.85 128 | 9.99 574 | 59 |
| 2 | 9.14 535 | 89 | 9.14 963 | 91 | 0.85 037 | 9.99 572 | 58 |
| 3 | 9.14 624 | 90 | 9.15 054 | 91 | 0.84 946 | 9.99 570 | 57 |
| 4 | 9.14 714 | 89 | 9.15 145 | 91 | 0.84 855 | 9.99 568 | 56 |
| 5 | 9.14 803 | 88 | 9.15 236 | 91 | 0.84 764 | 9.99 566 | 55 |
| 6 | 9.14 891 | 89 | 9.15 327 | 90 | 0.84 673 | 9.99 565 | 54 |
| 7 | 9.14 980 | 89 | 9.15 417 | 91 | 0.84 583 | 9.99 563 | 53 |
| 8 | 9.15 069 | 88 | 9.15 508 | 90 | 0.84 492 | 9.99 561 | 52 |
| 9 | 9.15 157 | 88 | 9.15 598 | 90 | 0.84 402 | 9.99 559 | 51 |
| 10 | 9.15 245 | 88 | 9.15 688 | 89 | 0.84 312 | 9.99 557 | 50 |
| 11 | 9.15 333 | 88 | 9.15 777 | 90 | 0.84 223 | 9.99 556 | 49 |
| 12 | 9.15 421 | 87 | 9.15 867 | 89 | 0.84 133 | 9.99 554 | 48 |
| 13 | 9.15 508 | 88 | 9.15 956 | 90 | 0.84 044 | 9.99 552 | 47 |
| 14 | 9.15 596 | 87 | 9.16 046 | 89 | 0.83 954 | 9.99 550 | 46 |
| 15 | 9.15 683 | 87 | 9.16 135 | 89 | 0.83 865 | 9.99 548 | 45 |
| 16 | 9.15 770 | 87 | 9.16 224 | 88 | 0.83 776 | 9.99 546 | 44 |
| 17 | 9.15 857 | 87 | 9.16 312 | 89 | 0.83 688 | 9.99 545 | 43 |
| 18 | 9.15 944 | 86 | 9.16 401 | 88 | 0.83 599 | 9.99 543 | 42 |
| 19 | 9.16 030 | 86 | 9.16 489 | 88 | 0.83 511 | 9.99 541 | 41 |
| 20 | 9.16 116 | 87 | 9.16 577 | 88 | 0.83 423 | 9.99 539 | 40 |
| 21 | 9.16 203 | 86 | 9.16 665 | 88 | 0.83 335 | 9.99 537 | 39 |
| 22 | 9.16 289 | 85 | 9.16 753 | 88 | 0.83 247 | 9.99 535 | 38 |
| 23 | 9.16 374 | 86 | 9.16 841 | 87 | 0.83 159 | 9.99 533 | 37 |
| 24 | 9.16 460 | 85 | 9.16 928 | 88 | 0.83 072 | 9.99 532 | 36 |
| 25 | 9.16 545 | 86 | 9.17 016 | 87 | 0.82 984 | 9.99 530 | 35 |
| 26 | 9.16 631 | 85 | 9.17 103 | 87 | 0.82 897 | 9.99 528 | 34 |
| 27 | 9.16 716 | 85 | 9.17 190 | 87 | 0.82 810 | 9.99 526 | 33 |
| 28 | 9.16 801 | 85 | 9.17 277 | 86 | 0.82 723 | 9.99 524 | 32 |
| 29 | 9.16 886 | 84 | 9.17 363 | 87 | 0.82 637 | 9.99 522 | 31 |
| 30 | 9.16 970 | 85 | 9.17 450 | 86 | 0.82 550 | 9.99 520 | 30 |
| 31 | 9.17 055 | 84 | 9.17 536 | 86 | 0.82 464 | 9.99 518 | 29 |
| 32 | 9.17 139 | 84 | 9.17 622 | 86 | 0.82 378 | 9.99 517 | 28 |
| 33 | 9.17 223 | 84 | 9.17 708 | 86 | 0.82 292 | 9.99 515 | 27 |
| 34 | 9.17 307 | 84 | 9.17 794 | 86 | 0.82 206 | 9.99 513 | 26 |
| 35 | 9.17 391 | 83 | 9.17 880 | 85 | 0.82 120 | 9.99 511 | 25 |
| 36 | 9.17 474 | 84 | 9.17 965 | 86 | 0.82 035 | 9.99 509 | 24 |
| 37 | 9.17 558 | 83 | 9.18 051 | 85 | 0.81 949 | 9.99 507 | 23 |
| 38 | 9.17 641 | 83 | 9.18 136 | 85 | 0.81 864 | 9.99 505 | 22 |
| 39 | 9.17 724 | 83 | 9.18 221 | 85 | 0.81 779 | 9.99 503 | 21 |
| 40 | 9.17 807 | 83 | 9.18 306 | 85 | 0.81 694 | 9.99 501 | 20 |
| 41 | 9.17 890 | 83 | 9.18 391 | 84 | 0.81 609 | 9.99 499 | 19 |
| 42 | 9.17 973 | 82 | 9.18 475 | 85 | 0.81 525 | 9.99 497 | 18 |
| 43 | 9.18 055 | 82 | 9.18 560 | 84 | 0.81 440 | 9.99 495 | 17 |
| 44 | 9.18 137 | 83 | 9.18 644 | 84 | 0.81 356 | 9.99 494 | 16 |
| 45 | 9.18 220 | 82 | 9.18 728 | 84 | 0.81 272 | 9.99 492 | 15 |
| 46 | 9.18 302 | 81 | 9.18 812 | 84 | 0.81 188 | 9.99 490 | 14 |
| 47 | 9.18 383 | 82 | 9.18 896 | 83 | 0.81 104 | 9.99 488 | 13 |
| 48 | 9.18 465 | 82 | 9.18 979 | 84 | 0.81 021 | 9.99 486 | 12 |
| 49 | 9.18 547 | 81 | 9.19 063 | 83 | 0.80 937 | 9.99 484 | 11 |
| 50 | 9.18 628 | 81 | 9.19 146 | 83 | 0.80 854 | 9.99 482 | 10 |
| 51 | 9.18 709 | 81 | 9.19 229 | 83 | 0.80 771 | 9.99 480 | 9 |
| 52 | 9.18 790 | 81 | 9.19 312 | 83 | 0.80 688 | 9.99 478 | 8 |
| 53 | 9.18 871 | 81 | 9.19 395 | 83 | 0.80 605 | 9.99 476 | 7 |
| 54 | 9.18 952 | 81 | 9.19 478 | 83 | 0.80 522 | 9.99 474 | 6 |
| 55 | 9.19 033 | 80 | 9.19 561 | 82 | 0.80 439 | 9.99 472 | 5 |
| 56 | 9.19 113 | 80 | 9.19 643 | 82 | 0.80 357 | 9.99 470 | 4 |
| 57 | 9.19 193 | 80 | 9.19 725 | 82 | 0.80 275 | 9.99 468 | 3 |
| 58 | 9.19 273 | 80 | 9.19 807 | 82 | 0.80 193 | 9.99 466 | 2 |
| 59 | 9.19 353 | 80 | 9.19 889 | 82 | 0.80 111 | 9.99 464 | 1 |
| 60 | 9.19 433 | | 9.19 971 | | 0.80 029 | 9.99 462 | 0 |
| ' | L. Cos. | d. | L. Cot. | c. d. | L. Tan. | L. Sin. | ' |

**P. P.**

| " | 92 | 91 | 90 |
|---|---|---|---|
| 1 | 1.5 | 1.5 | 1.5 |
| 2 | 3.1 | 3.0 | 3.0 |
| 3 | 4.6 | 4.6 | 4.5 |
| 4 | 6.1 | 6.1 | 6.0 |
| 5 | 7.7 | 7.6 | 7.5 |
| 6 | 9.2 | 9.1 | 9.0 |
| 7 | 10.7 | 10.6 | 10.5 |
| 8 | 12.3 | 12.1 | 12.0 |
| 9 | 13.8 | 13.6 | 13.5 |
| 10 | 15.3 | 15.2 | 15.0 |
| 20 | 30.7 | 30.3 | 30.0 |
| 30 | 46.0 | 45.5 | 45.0 |
| 40 | 61.3 | 60.7 | 60.0 |
| 50 | 76.7 | 75.8 | 75.0 |

| " | 89 | 88 | 87 |
|---|---|---|---|
| 1 | 1.5 | 1.5 | 1.4 |
| 2 | 3.0 | 2.9 | 2.9 |
| 3 | 4.4 | 4.4 | 4.4 |
| 4 | 5.9 | 5.9 | 5.8 |
| 5 | 7.4 | 7.3 | 7.2 |
| 6 | 8.9 | 8.8 | 8.7 |
| 7 | 10.4 | 10.3 | 10.2 |
| 8 | 11.9 | 11.7 | 11.6 |
| 9 | 13.4 | 13.2 | 13.0 |
| 10 | 14.8 | 14.7 | 14.5 |
| 20 | 29.7 | 29.3 | 29.0 |
| 30 | 44.5 | 44.0 | 43.5 |
| 40 | 59.3 | 58.7 | 58.0 |
| 50 | 74.2 | 73.3 | 72.5 |

| " | 86 | 85 | 84 |
|---|---|---|---|
| 1 | 1.4 | 1.4 | 1.4 |
| 2 | 2.9 | 2.8 | 2.8 |
| 3 | 4.3 | 4.2 | 4.2 |
| 4 | 5.7 | 5.7 | 5.6 |
| 5 | 7.2 | 7.1 | 7.0 |
| 6 | 8.6 | 8.5 | 8.4 |
| 7 | 10.0 | 9.9 | 9.8 |
| 8 | 11.5 | 11.3 | 11.2 |
| 9 | 12.9 | 12.8 | 12.6 |
| 10 | 14.3 | 14.2 | 14.0 |
| 20 | 28.7 | 28.3 | 28.0 |
| 30 | 43.0 | 42.5 | 42.0 |
| 40 | 57.3 | 56.7 | 56.0 |
| 50 | 71.7 | 70.8 | 70.0 |

| " | 83 | 82 | 81 |
|---|---|---|---|
| 1 | 1.4 | 1.4 | 1.4 |
| 2 | 2.8 | 2.7 | 2.7 |
| 3 | 4.2 | 4.1 | 4.0 |
| 4 | 5.5 | 5.5 | 5.4 |
| 5 | 6.9 | 6.8 | 6.8 |
| 6 | 8.3 | 8.2 | 8.1 |
| 7 | 9.7 | 9.6 | 9.4 |
| 8 | 11.1 | 10.9 | 10.8 |
| 9 | 12.4 | 12.3 | 12.2 |
| 10 | 13.8 | 13.7 | 13.5 |
| 20 | 27.7 | 27.3 | 27.0 |
| 30 | 41.5 | 41.0 | 40.5 |
| 40 | 55.3 | 54.7 | 54.0 |
| 50 | 69.2 | 68.3 | 67.5 |

# LOGARITHMS OF THE FUNCTIONS (Continued)

| ′ | L. Sin. | d. | L. Tan. | c.d. | L. Cot. | L. Cos. | ′ |
|---|---|---|---|---|---|---|---|
| 0 | 9.19433 | 80 | 9.19971 | 82 | 0.80029 | 9.99462 | 60 |
| 1 | 9.19513 | 79 | 9.20053 | 81 | 0.79947 | 9.99460 | 59 |
| 2 | 9.19592 | 80 | 9.20134 | 82 | 0.79866 | 9.99458 | 58 |
| 3 | 9.19672 | 79 | 9.20216 | 81 | 0.79784 | 9.99456 | 57 |
| 4 | 9.19751 | 79 | 9.20297 | 81 | 0.79703 | 9.99454 | 56 |
| 5 | 9.19830 | 79 | 9.20378 | 81 | 0.79622 | 9.99452 | 55 |
| 6 | 9.19909 | 79 | 9.20459 | 81 | 0.79541 | 9.99450 | 54 |
| 7 | 9.19988 | 79 | 9.20540 | 81 | 0.79460 | 9.99448 | 53 |
| 8 | 9.20067 | 78 | 9.20621 | 80 | 0.79379 | 9.99446 | 52 |
| 9 | 9.20145 | 78 | 9.20701 | 81 | 0.79299 | 9.99444 | 51 |
| 10 | 9.20223 | 79 | 9.20782 | 80 | 0.79218 | 9.99442 | 50 |
| 11 | 9.20302 | 78 | 9.20862 | 80 | 0.79138 | 9.99440 | 49 |
| 12 | 9.20380 | 78 | 9.20942 | 80 | 0.79058 | 9.99438 | 48 |
| 13 | 9.20458 | 77 | 9.21022 | 80 | 0.78978 | 9.99436 | 47 |
| 14 | 9.20535 | 78 | 9.21102 | 80 | 0.78898 | 9.99434 | 46 |
| 15 | 9.20613 | 78 | 9.21182 | 79 | 0.78818 | 9.99432 | 45 |
| 16 | 9.20691 | 77 | 9.21261 | 80 | 0.78739 | 9.99429 | 44 |
| 17 | 9.20768 | 77 | 9.21341 | 79 | 0.78659 | 9.99427 | 43 |
| 18 | 9.20845 | 77 | 9.21420 | 79 | 0.78580 | 9.99425 | 42 |
| 19 | 9.20922 | 77 | 9.21499 | 79 | 0.78501 | 9.99423 | 41 |
| 20 | 9.20999 | 77 | 9.21578 | 79 | 0.78422 | 9.99421 | 40 |
| 21 | 9.21076 | 77 | 9.21657 | 79 | 0.78343 | 9.99419 | 39 |
| 22 | 9.21153 | 76 | 9.21736 | 78 | 0.78264 | 9.99417 | 38 |
| 23 | 9.21229 | 77 | 9.21814 | 79 | 0.78186 | 9.99415 | 37 |
| 24 | 9.21306 | 76 | 9.21893 | 78 | 0.78107 | 9.99413 | 36 |
| 25 | 9.21382 | 76 | 9.21971 | 78 | 0.78029 | 9.99411 | 35 |
| 26 | 9.21458 | 76 | 9.22049 | 78 | 0.77951 | 9.99409 | 34 |
| 27 | 9.21534 | 76 | 9.22127 | 78 | 0.77873 | 9.99407 | 33 |
| 28 | 9.21610 | 75 | 9.22205 | 78 | 0.77795 | 9.99404 | 32 |
| 29 | 9.21685 | 76 | 9.22283 | 78 | 0.77717 | 9.99402 | 31 |
| 30 | 9.21761 | 75 | 9.22361 | 77 | 0.77639 | 9.99400 | 30 |
| 31 | 9.21836 | 76 | 9.22438 | 78 | 0.77562 | 9.99398 | 29 |
| 32 | 9.21912 | 75 | 9.22516 | 77 | 0.77484 | 9.99396 | 28 |
| 33 | 9.21987 | 75 | 9.22593 | 77 | 0.77407 | 9.99394 | 27 |
| 34 | 9.22062 | 75 | 9.22670 | 77 | 0.77330 | 9.99392 | 26 |
| 35 | 9.22137 | 74 | 9.22747 | 77 | 0.77253 | 9.99390 | 25 |
| 36 | 9.22211 | 75 | 9.22824 | 77 | 0.77176 | 9.99388 | 24 |
| 37 | 9.22286 | 75 | 9.22901 | 76 | 0.77099 | 9.99385 | 23 |
| 38 | 9.22361 | 74 | 9.22977 | 77 | 0.77023 | 9.99383 | 22 |
| 39 | 9.22435 | 74 | 9.23054 | 76 | 0.76946 | 9.99381 | 21 |
| 40 | 9.22509 | 74 | 9.23130 | 76 | 0.76870 | 9.99379 | 20 |
| 41 | 9.22583 | 74 | 9.23206 | 77 | 0.76794 | 9.99377 | 19 |
| 42 | 9.22657 | 74 | 9.23283 | 76 | 0.76717 | 9.99375 | 18 |
| 43 | 9.22731 | 74 | 9.23359 | 76 | 0.76641 | 9.99372 | 17 |
| 44 | 9.22805 | 73 | 9.23435 | 75 | 0.76565 | 9.99370 | 16 |
| 45 | 9.22878 | 74 | 9.23510 | 76 | 0.76490 | 9.99368 | 15 |
| 46 | 9.22952 | 73 | 9.23586 | 75 | 0.76414 | 9.99366 | 14 |
| 47 | 9.23025 | 73 | 9.23661 | 76 | 0.76339 | 9.99364 | 13 |
| 48 | 9.23098 | 73 | 9.23737 | 75 | 0.76263 | 9.99362 | 12 |
| 49 | 9.23171 | 73 | 9.23812 | 75 | 0.76188 | 9.99359 | 11 |
| 50 | 9.23244 | 73 | 9.23887 | 75 | 0.76113 | 9.99357 | 10 |
| 51 | 9.23317 | 73 | 9.23962 | 75 | 0.76038 | 9.99355 | 9 |
| 52 | 9.23390 | 72 | 9.24037 | 75 | 0.75963 | 9.99353 | 8 |
| 53 | 9.23462 | 73 | 9.24112 | 74 | 0.75888 | 9.99351 | 7 |
| 54 | 9.23535 | 72 | 9.24186 | 75 | 0.75814 | 9.99348 | 6 |
| 55 | 9.23607 | 72 | 9.24261 | 74 | 0.75739 | 9.99346 | 5 |
| 56 | 9.23679 | 73 | 9.24335 | 75 | 0.75665 | 9.99344 | 4 |
| 57 | 9.23752 | 71 | 9.24410 | 74 | 0.75590 | 9.99342 | 3 |
| 58 | 9.23823 | 72 | 9.24484 | 74 | 0.75516 | 9.99340 | 2 |
| 59 | 9.23895 | 72 | 9.24558 | 74 | 0.75442 | 9.99337 | 1 |
| 60 | 9.23967 | | 9.24632 | | 0.75368 | 9.99335 | 0 |

| | L. Cos. | d. | L. Cot. | c.d. | L. Tan. | L. Sin. | ′ |
|---|---|---|---|---|---|---|---|

## P. P.

| ″ | 80 | 79 | 78 | 77 |
|---|---|---|---|---|
| 1 | 1.3 | 1.3 | 1.3 | 1.3 |
| 2 | 2.7 | 2.6 | 2.6 | 2.6 |
| 3 | 4.0 | 4.0 | 3.9 | 3.8 |
| 4 | 5.3 | 5.3 | 5.2 | 5.1 |
| 5 | 6.7 | 6.6 | 6.5 | 6.4 |
| 6 | 8.0 | 7.9 | 7.8 | 7.7 |
| 7 | 9.3 | 9.2 | 9.1 | 9.0 |
| 8 | 10.7 | 10.5 | 10.4 | 10.3 |
| 9 | 12.0 | 11.8 | 11.7 | 11.6 |
| 10 | 13.3 | 13.2 | 13.0 | 12.8 |
| 20 | 26.7 | 26.3 | 26.0 | 25.7 |
| 30 | 40.0 | 39.5 | 39.0 | 38.5 |
| 40 | 53.3 | 52.7 | 52.0 | 51.3 |
| 50 | 66.7 | 65.8 | 65.0 | 64.2 |

| ″ | 76 | 75 | 74 | 73 |
|---|---|---|---|---|
| 1 | 1.3 | 1.2 | 1.2 | 1.2 |
| 2 | 2.5 | 2.5 | 2.5 | 2.4 |
| 3 | 3.8 | 3.8 | 3.7 | 3.6 |
| 4 | 5.1 | 5.0 | 4.9 | 4.9 |
| 5 | 6.3 | 6.2 | 6.2 | 6.1 |
| 6 | 7.6 | 7.5 | 7.4 | 7.3 |
| 7 | 8.9 | 8.8 | 8.6 | 8.5 |
| 8 | 10.1 | 10.0 | 9.9 | 9.7 |
| 9 | 11.4 | 11.2 | 11.1 | 11.0 |
| 10 | 12.7 | 12.5 | 12.3 | 12.2 |
| 20 | 25.3 | 25.0 | 24.7 | 24.3 |
| 30 | 38.0 | 37.5 | 37.0 | 36.5 |
| 40 | 50.7 | 50.0 | 49.3 | 48.7 |
| 50 | 63.3 | 62.5 | 61.7 | 60.8 |

| ″ | 72 | 71 | 3 | 2 |
|---|---|---|---|---|
| 1 | 1.2 | 1.2 | 0.0 | 0.0 |
| 2 | 2.4 | 2.4 | 0.1 | 0.1 |
| 3 | 3.6 | 3.6 | 0.2 | 0.1 |
| 4 | 4.8 | 4.7 | 0.2 | 0.1 |
| 5 | 6.0 | 5.9 | 0.2 | 0.2 |
| 6 | 7.2 | 7.1 | 0.3 | 0.2 |
| 7 | 8.4 | 8.3 | 0.4 | 0.2 |
| 8 | 9.6 | 9.5 | 0.4 | 0.3 |
| 9 | 10.8 | 10.6 | 0.4 | 0.3 |
| 10 | 12.0 | 11.8 | 0.5 | 0.3 |
| 20 | 24.0 | 23.7 | 1.0 | 0.7 |
| 30 | 36.0 | 35.5 | 1.5 | 1.0 |
| 40 | 48.0 | 47.3 | 2.0 | 1.3 |
| 50 | 60.0 | 59.2 | 2.5 | 1.7 |

| | $\frac{3}{79}$ | $\frac{3}{78}$ | $\frac{3}{77}$ |
|---|---|---|---|
| 0 | 13.2 | 13.0 | 12.8 |
| 1 | 39.5 | 39.0 | 38.5 |
| 2 | 65.8 | 65.0 | 64.2 |
| 3 | | | |

| | $\frac{3}{76}$ | $\frac{3}{75}$ | $\frac{3}{74}$ |
|---|---|---|---|
| 0 | 12.7 | 12.5 | 12.3 |
| 1 | 38.0 | 37.5 | 37.0 |
| 2 | 63.3 | 62.5 | 61.7 |
| 3 | | | |

| ′ | L. Sin. | d. | L. Tan. | c.d. | L. Cot. | L. Cos. | d. | ′ |
|---|---------|----|---------|------|---------|---------|----|----|
| 0 | 9.23 967 | 72 | 9.24 632 | 74 | 0.75 368 | 9.99 335 | 2 | 60 |
| 1 | 9.24 039 | 71 | 9.24 706 | 73 | 0.75 294 | 9.99 333 | 2 | 59 |
| 2 | 9.24 110 | 71 | 9.24 779 | 74 | 0.75 221 | 9.99 331 | 3 | 58 |
| 3 | 9.24 181 | 72 | 9.24 853 | 73 | 0 75 147 | 9 99 328 | 2 | 57 |
| 4 | 9.24 253 | 71 | 9.24 926 | 74 | 0.75 074 | 9.99 326 | 2 | 56 |
| 5 | 9.24 324 | 71 | 9.25 000 | 73 | 0.75 000 | 9.99 324 | 2 | 55 |
| 6 | 9.24 395 | 71 | 9.25 073 | 73 | 0.74 927 | 9.99 322 | 3 | 54 |
| 7 | 9.24 466 | 70 | 9.25 146 | 73 | 0.74 854 | 9.99 319 | 2 | 53 |
| 8 | 9.24 536 | 71 | 9.25 219 | 73 | 0.74 781 | 9.99 317 | 2 | 52 |
| 9 | 9.24 607 | 70 | 9.25 292 | 73 | 0.74 708 | 9.99 315 | 2 | 51 |
| 10 | 9.24 677 | 71 | 9.25 365 | 72 | 0.74 635 | 9.99 313 | 3 | 50 |
| 11 | 9.24 748 | 70 | 9.25 437 | 73 | 0.74 563 | 9.99 310 | 2 | 49 |
| 12 | 9.24 818 | 70 | 9.25 510 | 72 | 0.74 490 | 9.99 308 | 2 | 48 |
| 13 | 9.24 888 | 70 | 9.25 582 | 73 | 0.74 418 | 9.99 306 | 2 | 47 |
| 14 | 9.24 958 | 70 | 9.25 655 | 72 | 0.74 345 | 9.99 304 | 3 | 46 |
| 15 | 9.25 028 | 70 | 9.25 727 | 72 | 0.74 273 | 9.99 301 | 2 | 45 |
| 16 | 9.25 098 | 70 | 9.25 799 | 72 | 0.74 201 | 9.99 299 | 2 | 44 |
| 17 | 9.25 168 | 69 | 9.25 871 | 72 | 0.74 129 | 9.99 297 | 3 | 43 |
| 18 | 9.25 237 | 70 | 9.25 943 | 72 | 0.74 057 | 9.99 294 | 2 | 42 |
| 19 | 9.25 307 | 69 | 9.26 015 | 71 | 0 73 985 | 9.99 292 | 2 | 41 |
| 20 | 9.25 376 | 69 | 9.26 086 | 72 | 0.73 914 | 9.99 290 | 2 | 40 |
| 21 | 9.25 445 | 69 | 9.26 158 | 71 | 0.73 842 | 9.99 288 | 3 | 39 |
| 22 | 9.25 514 | 69 | 9.26 229 | 72 | 0.73 771 | 9.99 285 | 2 | 38 |
| 23 | 9.25 583 | 69 | 9.26 301 | 71 | 0.73 699 | 9.99 283 | 2 | 37 |
| 24 | 9.25 652 | 69 | 9.26 372 | 71 | 0.73 628 | 9.99 281 | 3 | 36 |
| 25 | 9.25 721 | 69 | 9.26 443 | 71 | 0.73 557 | 9.99 278 | 2 | 35 |
| 26 | 9.25 790 | 68 | 9.26 514 | 71 | 0.73 486 | 9.99 276 | 2 | 34 |
| 27 | 9.25 858 | 69 | 9.26 585 | 70 | 0.73 415 | 9.99 274 | 3 | 33 |
| 28 | 9.25 927 | 68 | 9.26 655 | 71 | 0.73 345 | 9.99 271 | 2 | 32 |
| 29 | 9.25 995 | 68 | 9.26 726 | 71 | 0.73 274 | 9.99 269 | 2 | 31 |
| 30 | 9.26 063 | 68 | 9.26 797 | 70 | 0.73 203 | 9.99 267 | 3 | 30 |
| 31 | 9.26 131 | 68 | 9.26 867 | 70 | 0.73 133 | 9.99 264 | 2 | 29 |
| 32 | 9.26 199 | 68 | 9.26 937 | 71 | 0 73 063 | 9.99 262 | 2 | 28 |
| 33 | 9.26 267 | 68 | 9.27 008 | 70 | 0.72 992 | 9.99 260 | 3 | 27 |
| 34 | 9.26 335 | 68 | 9.27 078 | 70 | 0.72 922 | 9.99 257 | 2 | 26 |
| 35 | 9.26 403 | 67 | 9.27 148 | 70 | 0.72 852 | 9.99 255 | 2 | 25 |
| 36 | 9.26 470 | 68 | 9.27 218 | 70 | 0.72 782 | 9.99 252 | 3 | 24 |
| 37 | 9.26 538 | 67 | 9.27 288 | 69 | 0.72 712 | 9.99 250 | 2 | 23 |
| 38 | 9.26 605 | 67 | 9.27 357 | 70 | 0.72 643 | 9.99 248 | 2 | 22 |
| 39 | 9.26 672 | 67 | 9.27 427 | 69 | 0.72 573 | 9.99 245 | 3 | 21 |
| 40 | 9.26 739 | 67 | 9.27 496 | 70 | 0.72 504 | 9.99 243 | 2 | 20 |
| 41 | 9.26 806 | 67 | 9.27 566 | 69 | 0.72 434 | 9.99 241 | 2 | 19 |
| 42 | 9.26 873 | 67 | 9.27 635 | 69 | 0.72 365 | 9.99 238 | 3 | 18 |
| 43 | 9.26 940 | 67 | 9.27 704 | 69 | 0.72 296 | 9.99 236 | 2 | 17 |
| 44 | 9.27 007 | 66 | 9.27 773 | 69 | 0.72 227 | 9.99 233 | 2 | 16 |
| 45 | 9.27 073 | 67 | 9.27 842 | 69 | 0.72 158 | 9.99 231 | 2 | 15 |
| 46 | 9.27 140 | 66 | 9.27 911 | 69 | 0.72 089 | 9.99 229 | 3 | 14 |
| 47 | 9.27 206 | 67 | 9.27 980 | 69 | 0.72 020 | 9.99 226 | 3 | 13 |
| 48 | 9.27 273 | 66 | 9.28 049 | 68 | 0.71 951 | 9.99 224 | 3 | 12 |
| 49 | 9.27 339 | 66 | 9.28 117 | 69 | 0.71 883 | 9.99 221 | 2 | 11 |
| 50 | 9.27 405 | 66 | 9.28 186 | 68 | 0.71 814 | 9.99 219 | 2 | 10 |
| 51 | 9.27 471 | 66 | 9.28 254 | 69 | 0.71 746 | 9.99 217 | 3 | 9 |
| 52 | 9.27 537 | 65 | 9.28 323 | 68 | 0.71 677 | 9.99 214 | 2 | 8 |
| 53 | 9.27 602 | 66 | 9.28 391 | 68 | 0.71 609 | 9.99 212 | 3 | 7 |
| 54 | 9.27 668 | 66 | 9.28 459 | 68 | 0.71 541 | 9.99 209 | 2 | 6 |
| 55 | 9.27 734 | 65 | 9.28 527 | 68 | 0.71 473 | 9.99 207 | 3 | 5 |
| 56 | 9.27 799 | 65 | 9.28 595 | 67 | 0.71 405 | 9.99 204 | 2 | 4 |
| 57 | 9.27 864 | 66 | 9.28 662 | 68 | 0.71 338 | 9.99 202 | 2 | 3 |
| 58 | 9.27 930 | 65 | 9.28 730 | 68 | 0.71 270 | 9.99 200 | 3 | 2 |
| 59 | 9.27 995 | 65 | 9.28 798 | 67 | 0.71 202 | 9.99 197 | 2 | 1 |
| 60 | 9.28 060 | | 9.28 865 | | 0.71 135 | 9.99 195 | | 0 |

| ′ | L. Cos. | d. | L. Cot. | c.d. | L. Tan. | L. Sin. | d. | ′ |
|---|---------|----|---------|------|---------|---------|----|----|

**P. P.**

| ″ | 74 | 73 | 72 |
|---|----|----|----|
| 1 | 1.2 | 1.2 | 1.2 |
| 2 | 2 5 | 2 4 | 2.4 |
| 3 | 3 7 | 3 6 | 3.6 |
| 4 | 4.9 | 4.9 | 4.8 |
| 5 | 6.2 | 6 1 | 6.0 |
| 6 | 7 4 | 7 3 | 7.2 |
| 7 | 8.6 | 8 5 | 8.4 |
| 8 | 9.9 | 9.7 | 9.6 |
| 9 | 11.1 | 11.0 | 10.8 |
| 10 | 12.3 | 12.2 | 12.0 |
| 20 | 24 7 | 24.3 | 24.0 |
| 30 | 37 0 | 36.5 | 36.0 |
| 40 | 49.3 | 48.7 | 48.0 |
| 50 | 61.7 | 60.8 | 60.0 |

| ″ | 71 | 70 | 69 |
|---|----|----|----|
| 1 | 1.2 | 1.2 | 1.2 |
| 2 | 2 4 | 2.3 | 2.3 |
| 3 | 3 6 | 3.5 | 3.4 |
| 4 | 4.7 | 4.7 | 4.6 |
| 5 | 5.9 | 5.8 | 5.8 |
| 6 | 7.1 | 7.0 | 6.9 |
| 7 | 8.3 | 8.2 | 8.0 |
| 8 | 9.5 | 9.3 | 9.2 |
| 9 | 10.6 | 10.5 | 10.4 |
| 10 | 11.8 | 11.7 | 11.5 |
| 20 | 23.7 | 23.3 | 23.0 |
| 30 | 35.5 | 35.0 | 34.5 |
| 40 | 47.3 | 46.7 | 46.0 |
| 50 | 59.2 | 58.3 | 57.5 |

| ″ | 68 | 67 | 66 |
|---|----|----|----|
| 1 | 1.1 | 1.1 | 1.1 |
| 2 | 2.3 | 2.2 | 2.2 |
| 3 | 3.4 | 3.4 | 3.3 |
| 4 | 4.5 | 4.5 | 4.4 |
| 5 | 5.7 | 5.6 | 5.5 |
| 6 | 6.8 | 6.7 | 6.6 |
| 7 | 7.9 | 7.8 | 7.7 |
| 8 | 9.1 | 8.9 | 8.8 |
| 9 | 10.2 | 10.0 | 9.9 |
| 10 | 11.3 | 11.2 | 11 0 |
| 20 | 22.7 | 22.3 | 22 0 |
| 30 | 34.0 | 33.5 | 33.0 |
| 40 | 45.3 | 44.7 | 44.0 |
| 50 | 56.7 | 55.8 | 55.0 |

| | $\frac{3}{74}$ | $\frac{3}{73}$ | $\frac{3}{72}$ |
|---|----|----|----|
| 0 1 | 12.3 | 12.2 | 12.0 |
| 1 2/3 | 37.0 | 36.5 | 36 0 |
| | 61.7 | 60.8 | 60.0 |

| | $\frac{3}{71}$ | $\frac{3}{70}$ | $\frac{3}{69}$ | $\frac{3}{68}$ |
|---|----|----|----|----|
| 0 1 | 11.8 | 11.7 | 11.5 | 11.3 |
| 1/2 2/3 | 35.5 | 35.0 | 34.5 | 34.0 |
| | 59.2 | 58.3 | 57.5 | 56.7 |

**P. P.**

| ′ | L. Sin. | d. | L. Tan. | c.d. | L. Cot. | L. Cos. | d. | ′ |
|---|---------|----|---------|------|---------|---------|----|---|
| 0 | 9.28 060 | 65 | 9.28 865 | 68 | 0.71 135 | 9.99 195 | 3 | 60 |
| 1 | 9.28 125 | 65 | 9.28 933 | 68 | 0.71 067 | 9.99 192 | 3 | 59 |
| 2 | 9.28 190 | 64 | 9.29 000 | 67 | 0.71 000 | 9.99 190 | 3 | 58 |
| 3 | 9.28 254 | 65 | 9.29 067 | 67 | 0.70 933 | 9.99 187 | 2 | 57 |
| 4 | 9.28 319 | 65 | 9.29 134 | 67 | 0.70 866 | 9.99 185 | 3 | 56 |
| 5 | 9.28 384 | 64 | 9.29 201 | 67 | 0.70 799 | 9.99 182 | 2 | 55 |
| 6 | 9.28 448 | 64 | 9.29 268 | 67 | 0.70 732 | 9.99 180 | 3 | 54 |
| 7 | 9.28 512 | 65 | 9.29 335 | 67 | 0.70 665 | 9.99 177 | 2 | 53 |
| 8 | 9.28 577 | 64 | 9.29 402 | 66 | 0.70 598 | 9.99 175 | 3 | 52 |
| 9 | 9.28 641 | 64 | 9.29 468 | 67 | 0.70 532 | 9.99 172 | 2 | 51 |
| 10 | 9.28 705 | 64 | 9.29 535 | 66 | 0.70 465 | 9.99 170 | 3 | 50 |
| 11 | 9.28 769 | 64 | 9.29 601 | 67 | 0.70 399 | 9.99 167 | 2 | 49 |
| 12 | 9.28 833 | 63 | 9.29 668 | 66 | 0.70 332 | 9.99 165 | 3 | 48 |
| 13 | 9.28 896 | 64 | 9.29 734 | 66 | 0.70 266 | 9.99 162 | 2 | 47 |
| 14 | 9.28 960 | 64 | 9.29 800 | 66 | 0.70 200 | 9.99 160 | 3 | 46 |
| 15 | 9.29 024 | 63 | 9.29 866 | 66 | 0.70 134 | 9.99 157 | 2 | 45 |
| 16 | 9.29 087 | 63 | 9.29 932 | 66 | 0.70 068 | 9.99 155 | 3 | 44 |
| 17 | 9.29 150 | 64 | 9.29 998 | 66 | 0.70 002 | 9.99 152 | 3 | 43 |
| 18 | 9.29 214 | 63 | 9.30 064 | 66 | 0.69 936 | 9.99 150 | 2 | 42 |
| 19 | 9.29 277 | 63 | 9.30 130 | 66 | 0.69 870 | 9.99 147 | 2 | 41 |
| 20 | 9.29 340 | 63 | 9.30 195 | 66 | 0.69 805 | 9.99 145 | 3 | 40 |
| 21 | 9.29 403 | 63 | 9.30 261 | 65 | 0.69 739 | 9.99 142 | 2 | 39 |
| 22 | 9.29 466 | 63 | 9.30 326 | 65 | 0.69 674 | 9.99 140 | 3 | 38 |
| 23 | 9.29 529 | 62 | 9.30 391 | 66 | 0.69 609 | 9.99 137 | 2 | 37 |
| 24 | 9.29 591 | 63 | 9.30 457 | 65 | 0.69 543 | 9.99 135 | 3 | 36 |
| 25 | 9.29 654 | 62 | 9.30 522 | 65 | 0.69 478 | 9.99 132 | 2 | 35 |
| 26 | 9.29 716 | 63 | 9.30 587 | 65 | 0.69 413 | 9.99 130 | 3 | 34 |
| 27 | 9.29 779 | 62 | 9.30 652 | 65 | 0.69 348 | 9.99 127 | 2 | 33 |
| 28 | 9.29 841 | 62 | 9.30 717 | 65 | 0.69 283 | 9.99 124 | 2 | 32 |
| 29 | 9.29 903 | 63 | 9.30 782 | 64 | 0.69 218 | 9.99 122 | 3 | 31 |
| 30 | 9.29 966 | 62 | 9.30 846 | 65 | 0.69 154 | 9.99 119 | 2 | 30 |
| 31 | 9.30 028 | 62 | 9.30 911 | 64 | 0.69 089 | 9.99 117 | 3 | 29 |
| 32 | 9.30 090 | 61 | 9.30 975 | 65 | 0.69 025 | 9.99 114 | 2 | 28 |
| 33 | 9.30 151 | 62 | 9.31 040 | 64 | 0.68 960 | 9.99 112 | 3 | 27 |
| 34 | 9.30 213 | 62 | 9.31 104 | 64 | 0.68 896 | 9.99 109 | 3 | 26 |
| 35 | 9.30 275 | 61 | 9.31 168 | 65 | 0.68 832 | 9.99 106 | 2 | 25 |
| 36 | 9.30 336 | 62 | 9.31 233 | 64 | 0.68 767 | 9.99 104 | 3 | 24 |
| 37 | 9.30 398 | 61 | 9.31 297 | 64 | 0.68 703 | 9.99 101 | 2 | 23 |
| 38 | 9.30 459 | 62 | 9.31 361 | 64 | 0.68 639 | 9.99 099 | 3 | 22 |
| 39 | 9.30 521 | 61 | 9.31 425 | 64 | 0.68 575 | 9.99 096 | 3 | 21 |
| 40 | 9.30 582 | 61 | 9.31 489 | 63 | 0.68 511 | 9.99 093 | 2 | 20 |
| 41 | 9.30 643 | 61 | 9.31 552 | 64 | 0.68 448 | 9.99 091 | 3 | 19 |
| 42 | 9.30 704 | 61 | 9.31 616 | 63 | 0.68 384 | 9.99 088 | 3 | 18 |
| 43 | 9.30 765 | 61 | 9.31 679 | 64 | 0.68 321 | 9.99 086 | 3 | 17 |
| 44 | 9.30 826 | 61 | 9.31 743 | 63 | 0.68 257 | 9.99 083 | 3 | 16 |
| 45 | 9.30 887 | 60 | 9.31 806 | 64 | 0.68 194 | 9.99 080 | 2 | 15 |
| 46 | 9.30 947 | 61 | 9.31 870 | 63 | 0.68 130 | 9.99 078 | 3 | 14 |
| 47 | 9.31 008 | 60 | 9.31 933 | 63 | 0.68 067 | 9.99 075 | 3 | 13 |
| 48 | 9.31 068 | 61 | 9.31 996 | 63 | 0.68 004 | 9.99 072 | 2 | 12 |
| 49 | 9.31 129 | 60 | 9.32 059 | 63 | 0.67 941 | 9.99 070 | 3 | 11 |
| 50 | 9.31 189 | 60 | 9.32 122 | 63 | 0.67 878 | 9.99 067 | 3 | 10 |
| 51 | 9.31 249 | 61 | 9.32 185 | 63 | 0.67 815 | 9.99 064 | 2 | 9 |
| 52 | 9.31 310 | 60 | 9.32 248 | 63 | 0.67 752 | 9.99 062 | 3 | 8 |
| 53 | 9.31 370 | 60 | 9.32 311 | 62 | 0.67 689 | 9.99 059 | 3 | 7 |
| 54 | 9.31 430 | 60 | 9.32 373 | 63 | 0.67 627 | 9.99 056 | 2 | 6 |
| 55 | 9.31 490 | 59 | 9.32 436 | 62 | 0.67 564 | 9.99 054 | 3 | 5 |
| 56 | 9.31 549 | 60 | 9.32 498 | 63 | 0.67 502 | 9.99 051 | 3 | 4 |
| 57 | 9.31 609 | 60 | 9.32 561 | 62 | 0.67 439 | 9.99 048 | 3 | 3 |
| 58 | 9.31 669 | 59 | 9.32 623 | 62 | 0.67 377 | 9.99 046 | 3 | 2 |
| 59 | 9.31 728 | 60 | 9.32 685 | 62 | 0.67 315 | 9.99 043 | 3 | 1 |
| 60 | 9.31 788 |  | 9.32 747 |  | 0.67 253 | 9.99 040 |  | 0 |
| ′ | L. Cos. | d. | L. Cot. | c.d. | L. Tan. | L. Sin. | d. | ′ |

**P. P.**

|  | 65 | 64 | 63 |
|---|----|----|----|
| 1 | 1.1 | 1.1 | 1.0 |
| 2 | 2.2 | 2.1 | 2.1 |
| 3 | 3.2 | 3.2 | 3.2 |
| 4 | 4.3 | 4.3 | 4.2 |
| 5 | 5.4 | 5.3 | 5.2 |
| 6 | 6.5 | 6.4 | 6.3 |
| 7 | 7.6 | 7.5 | 7.4 |
| 8 | 8.7 | 8.5 | 8.4 |
| 9 | 9.8 | 9.6 | 9.4 |
| 10 | 10.8 | 10.7 | 10.5 |
| 20 | 21.7 | 21.3 | 21.0 |
| 30 | 32.5 | 32.0 | 31.5 |
| 40 | 43.3 | 42.7 | 42.0 |
| 50 | 54.2 | 53.3 | 52.5 |

|  | 62 | 61 | 60 |
|---|----|----|----|
| 1 | 1.0 | 1.0 | 1.0 |
| 2 | 2.1 | 2.0 | 2.0 |
| 3 | 3.1 | 3.0 | 3.0 |
| 4 | 4.1 | 4.1 | 4.0 |
| 5 | 5.2 | 5.1 | 5.0 |
| 6 | 6.2 | 6.1 | 6.0 |
| 7 | 7.2 | 7.1 | 7.0 |
| 8 | 8.3 | 8.1 | 8.0 |
| 9 | 9.3 | 9.2 | 9.0 |
| 10 | 10.3 | 10.2 | 10.0 |
| 20 | 20.7 | 20.3 | 20.0 |
| 30 | 31.0 | 30.5 | 30.0 |
| 40 | 41.3 | 40.7 | 40.0 |
| 50 | 51.7 | 50.8 | 50.0 |

|  | 59 | 3 | 2 |
|---|----|----|----|
| 1 | 1.0 | 0.0 | 0.0 |
| 2 | 2.0 | 0.1 | 0.1 |
| 3 | 3.0 | 0.2 | 0.1 |
| 4 | 3.9 | 0.2 | 0.1 |
| 5 | 4.9 | 0.2 | 0.2 |
| 6 | 5.9 | 0.3 | 0.2 |
| 7 | 6.9 | 0.4 | 0.2 |
| 8 | 7.9 | 0.4 | 0.3 |
| 9 | 8.8 | 0.4 | 0.3 |
| 10 | 9.8 | 0.5 | 0.3 |
| 20 | 19.7 | 1.0 | 0.7 |
| 30 | 29.5 | 1.5 | 1.0 |
| 40 | 39.3 | 2.0 | 1.3 |
| 50 | 49.2 | 2.5 | 1.7 |

|  | $\frac{3}{67}$ | $\frac{3}{66}$ | $\frac{3}{65}$ |
|---|----|----|----|
| 1 | 11.2 | 11.0 | 10.8 |
| 2 | 33.5 | 33.0 | 32.5 |
| 3 | 55.8 | 55.0 | 54.2 |

|  | $\frac{3}{64}$ | $\frac{3}{63}$ | $\frac{3}{62}$ |
|---|----|----|----|
| 1 | 10.7 | 10.5 | 10.3 |
| 2 | 32.0 | 31.5 | 31.0 |
| 3 | 53.3 | 52.5 | 51.7 |

## LOGARITHMS OF THE FUNCTIONS (Continued)

| ' | L. Sin. | d. | L. Tan. | c.d. | L. Cot. | L. Cos. | d. | ' |
|---|---|---|---|---|---|---|---|---|
| 0 | 9.31 788 | 59 | 9.32 747 | 63 | 0.67 253 | 9.99 040 | 2 | 60 |
| 1 | 9.31 847 | 60 | 9.32 810 | 62 | 0.67 190 | 9.99 038 | 2 | 59 |
| 2 | 9.31 907 | 59 | 9.32 872 | 61 | 0.67 128 | 9.99 035 | 3 | 58 |
| 3 | 9.31 966 | 59 | 9.32 933 | 62 | 0.67 067 | 9.99 032 | 3 | 57 |
| 4 | 9.32 025 | 59 | 9.32 995 | 62 | 0.67 005 | 9.99 030 | 2 | 56 |
| 5 | 9.32 084 | 59 | 9.33 057 | 62 | 0.66 943 | 9.99 027 | 3 | 55 |
| 6 | 9.32 143 | 59 | 9.33 119 | 61 | 0.66 881 | 9.99 024 | 3 | 54 |
| 7 | 9.32 202 | 59 | 9.33 180 | 62 | 0.66 820 | 9.99 022 | 2 | 53 |
| 8 | 9.32 261 | 58 | 9.33 242 | 61 | 0.66 758 | 9.99 019 | 3 | 52 |
| 9 | 9.32 319 | 59 | 9.33 303 | 62 | 0.66 697 | 9.99 016 | 3 | 51 |
| 10 | 9.32 378 | 59 | 9.33 365 | 61 | 0.66 635 | 9.99 013 | 2 | 50 |
| 11 | 9.32 437 | 58 | 9.33 426 | 61 | 0.66 574 | 9.99 011 | 2 | 49 |
| 12 | 9.32 495 | 58 | 9.33 487 | 61 | 0.66 513 | 9.99 008 | 3 | 48 |
| 13 | 9.32 553 | 59 | 9.33 548 | 61 | 0.66 452 | 9.99 005 | 3 | 47 |
| 14 | 9.32 612 | 58 | 9.33 609 | 61 | 0.66 391 | 9.99 002 | 2 | 46 |
| 15 | 9.32 670 | 58 | 9.33 670 | 61 | 0.66 330 | 9.99 000 | 3 | 45 |
| 16 | 9.32 728 | 58 | 9.33 731 | 61 | 0.66 269 | 9.98 997 | 3 | 44 |
| 17 | 9.32 786 | 58 | 9.33 792 | 61 | 0.66 208 | 9.98 994 | 3 | 43 |
| 18 | 9.32 844 | 58 | 9.33 853 | 60 | 0.66 147 | 9.98 991 | 2 | 42 |
| 19 | 9.32 902 | 58 | 9.33 913 | 61 | 0.66 087 | 9.98 989 | 3 | 41 |
| 20 | 9.32 960 | 58 | 9.33 974 | 60 | 0.66 026 | 9.98 986 | 3 | 40 |
| 21 | 9.33 018 | 57 | 9.34 034 | 61 | 0.65 966 | 9.98 983 | 3 | 39 |
| 22 | 9.33 075 | 58 | 9.34 095 | 60 | 0.65 905 | 9.98 980 | 2 | 38 |
| 23 | 9.33 133 | 57 | 9.34 155 | 60 | 0.65 845 | 9.98 978 | 3 | 37 |
| 24 | 9.33 190 | 58 | 9.34 215 | 61 | 0.65 785 | 9.98 975 | 3 | 36 |
| 25 | 9.33 248 | 57 | 9.34 276 | 60 | 0.65 724 | 9.98 972 | 3 | 35 |
| 26 | 9.33 305 | 57 | 9.34 336 | 60 | 0.65 664 | 9.98 969 | 2 | 34 |
| 27 | 9.33 362 | 58 | 9.34 396 | 60 | 0.65 604 | 9.98 967 | 3 | 33 |
| 28 | 9.33 420 | 57 | 9.34 456 | 60 | 0.65 544 | 9.98 964 | 3 | 32 |
| 29 | 9.33 477 | 57 | 9.34 516 | 60 | 0.65 484 | 9.98 961 | 3 | 31 |
| 30 | 9.33 534 | 57 | 9.34 576 | 59 | 0.65 424 | 9.98 958 | 3 | 30 |
| 31 | 9.33 591 | 56 | 9.34 635 | 60 | 0.65 365 | 9.98 955 | 2 | 29 |
| 32 | 9.33 647 | 57 | 9.34 695 | 60 | 0.65 305 | 9.98 953 | 2 | 28 |
| 33 | 9.33 704 | 57 | 9.34 755 | 59 | 0.65 245 | 9.98 950 | 3 | 27 |
| 34 | 9.33 761 | 57 | 9.34 814 | 60 | 0.65 186 | 9.98 947 | 3 | 26 |
| 35 | 9.33 818 | 56 | 9.34 874 | 59 | 0.65 126 | 9.98 944 | 3 | 25 |
| 36 | 9.33 874 | 57 | 9.34 933 | 59 | 0.65 067 | 9.98 941 | 3 | 24 |
| 37 | 9.33 931 | 56 | 9.34 992 | 59 | 0.65 008 | 9.98 938 | 2 | 23 |
| 38 | 9.33 987 | 56 | 9.35 051 | 60 | 0.64 949 | 9.98 936 | 3 | 22 |
| 39 | 9.34 043 | 57 | 9.35 111 | 59 | 0.64 889 | 9.98 933 | 3 | 21 |
| 40 | 9.34 100 | 56 | 9.35 170 | 59 | 0.64 830 | 9.98 930 | 3 | 20 |
| 41 | 9.34 156 | 56 | 9.35 229 | 59 | 0.64 771 | 9.98 927 | 3 | 19 |
| 42 | 9.34 212 | 56 | 9.35 288 | 59 | 0.64 712 | 9.98 924 | 3 | 18 |
| 43 | 9.34 268 | 56 | 9.35 347 | 58 | 0.64 653 | 9.98 921 | 2 | 17 |
| 44 | 9.34 324 | 56 | 9.35 405 | 59 | 0.64 595 | 9.98 919 | 3 | 16 |
| 45 | 9.34 380 | 56 | 9.35 464 | 59 | 0.64 536 | 9.98 916 | 3 | 15 |
| 46 | 9.34 436 | 55 | 9.35 523 | 58 | 0.64 477 | 9.98 913 | 3 | 14 |
| 47 | 9.34 491 | 56 | 9.35 581 | 59 | 0.64 419 | 9.98 910 | 3 | 13 |
| 48 | 9.34 547 | 55 | 9.35 640 | 58 | 0.64 360 | 9.98 907 | 3 | 12 |
| 49 | 9.34 602 | 56 | 9.35 698 | 59 | 0.64 302 | 9.98 904 | 3 | 11 |
| 50 | 9.34 658 | 55 | 9.35 757 | 58 | 0.64 243 | 9.98 901 | 3 | 10 |
| 51 | 9.34 713 | 56 | 9.35 815 | 58 | 0.64 185 | 9.98 898 | 2 | 9 |
| 52 | 9.34 769 | 55 | 9.35 873 | 58 | 0.64 127 | 9.98 896 | 3 | 8 |
| 53 | 9.34 824 | 55 | 9.35 931 | 58 | 0.64 069 | 9.98 893 | 3 | 7 |
| 54 | 9.34 879 | 55 | 9.35 989 | 58 | 0.64 011 | 9.98 890 | 3 | 6 |
| 55 | 9.34 934 | 55 | 9.36 047 | 58 | 0.63 953 | 9.98 887 | 3 | 5 |
| 56 | 9.34 989 | 55 | 9.36 105 | 58 | 0.63 895 | 9.98 884 | 3 | 4 |
| 57 | 9.35 044 | 55 | 9.36 163 | 58 | 0.63 837 | 9.98 881 | 3 | 3 |
| 58 | 9.35 099 | 55 | 9.36 221 | 58 | 0.63 779 | 9.98 878 | 3 | 2 |
| 59 | 9.35 154 | 55 | 9.36 279 | 57 | 0.63 721 | 9.98 875 | 3 | 1 |
| 60 | 9.35 209 | | 9.36 336 | | 0.63 664 | 9.98 872 | | 0 |

| L. Cos. | d. | L. Cot. | c.d. | L. Tan. | L. Sin. | d. | ' | P. P. |
|---|---|---|---|---|---|---|---|---|

### P. P.

| | 63 | 62 | 61 |
|---|---|---|---|
| " | | | |
| 1 | 1.0 | 1.0 | 1.0 |
| 2 | 2.1 | 2.1 | 2.0 |
| 3 | 3.2 | 3.1 | 3.0 |
| 4 | 4.2 | 4.1 | 4.1 |
| 5 | 5.2 | 5.2 | 5.1 |
| 6 | 6.3 | 6.2 | 6.1 |
| 7 | 7.4 | 7.2 | 7.1 |
| 8 | 8.4 | 8.3 | 8.1 |
| 9 | 9.4 | 9.3 | 9.2 |
| 10 | 10.5 | 10.3 | 10.2 |
| 20 | 21.0 | 20.7 | 20.3 |
| 30 | 31.5 | 31.0 | 30.5 |
| 40 | 42.0 | 41.3 | 40.7 |
| 50 | 52.5 | 51.7 | 50.8 |

| | 60 | 59 | 58 |
|---|---|---|---|
| " | | | |
| 1 | 1.0 | 1.0 | 1.0 |
| 2 | 2.0 | 2.0 | 1.9 |
| 3 | 3.0 | 3.0 | 2.9 |
| 4 | 4.0 | 3.9 | 3.9 |
| 5 | 5.0 | 4.9 | 4.8 |
| 6 | 6.0 | 5.9 | 5.8 |
| 7 | 7.0 | 6.9 | 6.8 |
| 8 | 8.0 | 7.9 | 7.7 |
| 9 | 9.0 | 8.8 | 8.7 |
| 10 | 10.0 | 9.8 | 9.7 |
| 20 | 20.0 | 19.7 | 19.3 |
| 30 | 30.0 | 29.5 | 29.0 |
| 40 | 40.0 | 39.3 | 38.7 |
| 50 | 50.0 | 49.2 | 48.3 |

| | 57 | 56 | 55 |
|---|---|---|---|
| " | | | |
| 1 | 1.0 | 0.9 | 0.9 |
| 2 | 1.9 | 1.9 | 1.8 |
| 3 | 2.8 | 2.8 | 2.8 |
| 4 | 3.8 | 3.7 | 3.7 |
| 5 | 4.8 | 4.7 | 4.6 |
| 6 | 5.7 | 5.6 | 5.5 |
| 7 | 6.6 | 6.5 | 6.4 |
| 8 | 7.6 | 7.5 | 7.3 |
| 9 | 8.6 | 8.4 | 8.2 |
| 10 | 9.5 | 9.3 | 9.2 |
| 20 | 19.0 | 18.7 | 18.3 |
| 30 | 28.5 | 28.0 | 27.5 |
| 40 | 38.0 | 37.3 | 36.7 |
| 50 | 47.5 | 46.7 | 45.8 |

| | 3/62 | 3/61 | 3/60 |
|---|---|---|---|
| 0 | | | |
| 1 | 10.3 | 10.2 | 10.0 |
| 2 | 31.0 | 30.5 | 30.0 |
| 3 | 51.7 | 50.8 | 50.0 |

| | 3/59 | 3/58 | 3/57 |
|---|---|---|---|
| 0 | | | |
| 1 | 9.8 | 9.7 | 9.5 |
| 2 | 29.5 | 29.0 | 28.5 |
| 3 | 49.2 | 48.3 | 47.5 |

| ' | L. Sin. | d. | L. Tan. | c.d. | L. Cot. | L. Cos. | d. | ' |
|---|---|---|---|---|---|---|---|---|
| 0 | 9.35 209 | 54 | 9.36 336 | 58 | 0.63 664 | 9.98 872 | 3 | 60 |
| 1 | 9.35 263 | 55 | 9.36 394 | 58 | 0.63 606 | 9.98 869 | 2 3 | 59 |
| 2 | 9.35 318 | 55 | 9.36 452 | 58 | 0.63 548 | 9.98 867 | 3 | 58 |
| 3 | 9.35 373 | 55 | 9.36 509 | 57 | 0.63 491 | 9.98 864 | 3 | 57 |
| 4 | 9.35 427 | 54 | 9.36 566 | 58 | 0.63 434 | 9.98 861 | 3 | 56 |
| 5 | 9.35 481 | 54 | 9.36 624 | | 0.63 376 | 9.98 858 | 3 | 55 |
| 6 | 9.35 536 | 55 | 9.36 681 | 57 | 0.63 319 | 9.98 855 | 3 | 54 |
| 7 | 9.35 590 | 54 | 9.36 738 | 57 | 0.63 262 | 9.98 852 | 3 | 53 |
| 8 | 9.35 644 | 54 | 9.36 795 | 57 | 0.63 205 | 9.98 849 | 3 | 52 |
| 9 | 9.35 698 | 54 | 9.36 852 | 57 | 0.63 148 | 9.98 846 | 3 | 51 |
| 10 | 9.35 752 | 54 | 9.36 909 | 57 | 0.63 091 | 9.98 843 | 3 | 50 |
| 11 | 9.35 806 | 54 | 9.36 966 | 57 | 0.63 034 | 9.98 840 | 3 | 49 |
| 12 | 9.35 860 | 54 | 9.37 023 | 57 | 0.62 977 | 9.98 837 | 3 | 48 |
| 13 | 9.35 914 | 54 | 9.37 080 | 57 | 0.62 920 | 9.98 834 | 3 | 47 |
| 14 | 9.35 968 | 54 | 9.37 137 | 56 | 0.62 863 | 9.98 831 | 3 | 46 |
| 15 | 9.36 022 | 53 | 9.37 193 | 57 | 0.62 807 | 9.98 828 | 3 | 45 |
| 16 | 9.36 075 | 54 | 9.37 250 | 56 | 0.62 750 | 9.98 825 | 3 | 44 |
| 17 | 9.36 129 | 53 | 9.37 306 | 57 | 0.62 694 | 9.98 822 | 3 | 43 |
| 18 | 9.36 182 | 54 | 9.37 363 | 56 | 0.62 637 | 9.98 819 | 3 | 42 |
| 19 | 9.36 236 | 53 | 9.37 419 | 57 | 0.62 581 | 9.98 816 | 3 | 41 |
| 20 | 9.36 289 | 53 | 9.37 476 | 56 | 0.62 524 | 9.98 813 | 3 | 40 |
| 21 | 9.36 342 | 53 | 9.37 532 | 56 | 0.62 468 | 9.98 810 | 3 | 39 |
| 22 | 9.36 395 | 54 | 9.37 588 | 56 | 0.62 412 | 9.98 807 | 3 | 38 |
| 23 | 9.36 449 | 53 | 9.37 644 | 56 | 0.62 356 | 9.98 804 | 3 | 37 |
| 24 | 9.36 502 | 53 | 9.37 700 | 56 | 0.62 300 | 9.98 801 | 3 | 36 |
| 25 | 9.36 555 | 53 | 9.37 756 | 56 | 0.62 244 | 9.98 798 | 3 | 35 |
| 26 | 9.36 608 | 52 | 9.37 812 | 56 | 0.62 188 | 9.98 795 | 3 | 34 |
| 27 | 9.36 660 | 53 | 9.37 868 | 56 | 0.62 132 | 9.98 792 | 3 | 33 |
| 28 | 9.36 713 | 53 | 9.37 924 | 56 | 0.62 076 | 9.98 789 | 3 | 32 |
| 29 | 9.36 766 | 53 | 9.37 980 | 55 | 0.62 020 | 9.98 786 | 3 | 31 |
| 30 | 9.36 819 | 52 | 9.38 035 | 56 | 0.61 965 | 9.98 783 | 3 | 30 |
| 31 | 9.36 871 | 53 | 9.38 091 | 56 | 0.61 909 | 9.98 780 | 3 | 29 |
| 32 | 9.36 924 | 52 | 9.38 147 | 55 | 0.61 853 | 9.98 777 | 3 | 28 |
| 33 | 9.36 976 | 52 | 9.38 202 | 55 | 0.61 798 | 9.98 774 | 3 | 27 |
| 34 | 9.37 028 | 53 | 9.38 257 | 56 | 0.61 743 | 9.98 771 | 3 | 26 |
| 35 | 9.37 081 | 52 | 9.38 313 | 55 | 0.61 687 | 9.98 768 | 3 | 25 |
| 36 | 9.37 133 | 52 | 9.38 368 | 55 | 0.61 632 | 9.98 765 | 3 | 24 |
| 37 | 9.37 185 | 52 | 9.38 423 | 55 | 0.61 577 | 9.98 762 | 3 | 23 |
| 38 | 9.37 237 | 52 | 9.38 479 | 56 | 0.61 521 | 9.98 759 | 3 | 22 |
| 39 | 9.37 289 | 52 | 9.38 534 | 55 | 0.61 466 | 9.98 756 | 3 | 21 |
| 40 | 9.37 341 | 52 | 9.38 589 | 55 | 0.61 411 | 9.98 753 | 3 | 20 |
| 41 | 9.37 393 | 52 | 9.38 644 | 55 | 0.61 356 | 9.98 750 | 3 | 19 |
| 42 | 9.37 445 | 52 | 9.38 699 | 55 | 0.61 301 | 9.98 746 | 4 | 18 |
| 43 | 9.37 497 | 52 | 9.38 754 | 55 | 0.61 246 | 9.98 743 | 3 | 17 |
| 44 | 9.37 549 | 51 | 9.38 808 | 54 | 0.61 192 | 9.98 740 | 3 | 16 |
| 45 | 9.37 600 | 52 | 9.38 863 | 55 | 0.61 137 | 9.98 737 | 3 | 15 |
| 46 | 9.37 652 | 51 | 9.38 918 | 55 | 0.61 082 | 9.98 734 | 3 | 14 |
| 47 | 9.37 703 | 52 | 9.38 972 | 54 | 0.61 028 | 9.98 731 | 3 | 13 |
| 48 | 9.37 755 | 51 | 9.39 027 | 55 | 0.60 973 | 9.98 728 | 3 | 12 |
| 49 | 9.37 806 | 52 | 9.39 082 | 55 | 0.60 918 | 9.98 725 | 3 | 11 |
| 50 | 9.37 858 | 51 | 9.39 136 | 54 | 0.60 864 | 9.98 722 | 3 | 10 |
| 51 | 9.37 909 | 51 | 9.39 190 | 54 | 0.60 810 | 9.98 719 | 3 | 9 |
| 52 | 9.37 960 | 51 | 9.39 245 | 55 | 0.60 755 | 9.98 715 | 4 | 8 |
| 53 | 9.38 011 | 51 | 9.39 299 | 54 | 0.60 701 | 9.98 712 | 3 | 7 |
| 54 | 9.38 062 | 51 | 9.39 353 | 54 | 0.60 647 | 9.98 709 | 3 | 6 |
| 55 | 9.38 113 | 51 | 9.39 407 | 54 | 0.60 593 | 9.98 706 | 3 | 5 |
| 56 | 9.38 164 | 51 | 9.39 461 | 54 | 0.60 539 | 9.98 703 | 3 | 4 |
| 57 | 9.38 215 | 51 | 9.39 515 | 54 | 0.60 485 | 9.98 700 | 3 | 3 |
| 58 | 9.38 266 | 51 | 9.39 569 | 54 | 0.60 431 | 9.98 697 | 3 | 2 |
| 59 | 9.38 317 | 51 | 9.39 623 | 54 | 0.60 377 | 9.98 694 | 3 | 1 |
| 60 | 9.38 368 | | 9.39 677 | | 0.60 323 | 9.98 690 | | 0 |

| | L. Cos. | d. | L. Cot. | c.d. | L. Tan. | | L. Sin. | d. | ' |

**P. P.**

| | 57 | 56 | 55 |
|---|---|---|---|
| 1 | 1.0 | 0.9 | 0.9 |
| 2 | 1.9 | 1.9 | 1.8 |
| 3 | 2.8 | 2.8 | 2.8 |
| 4 | 3.8 | 3.7 | 3.7 |
| 5 | 4.8 | 4.7 | 4.6 |
| 6 | 5.7 | 5.6 | 5.5 |
| 7 | 6.6 | 6.5 | 6.4 |
| 8 | 7.6 | 7.5 | 7.3 |
| 9 | 8.6 | 8.4 | 8.2 |
| 10 | 9.5 | 9.3 | 9.2 |
| 20 | 19.0 | 18.7 | 18.3 |
| 30 | 28.5 | 28.0 | 27.5 |
| 40 | 38.0 | 37.3 | 36.7 |
| 50 | 47.5 | 46.7 | 45.8 |

| | 54 | 53 | 52 |
|---|---|---|---|
| 1 | 0.9 | 0.9 | 0.9 |
| 2 | 1.8 | 1.8 | 1.7 |
| 3 | 2.7 | 2.6 | 2.6 |
| 4 | 3.6 | 3.5 | 3.5 |
| 5 | 4.5 | 4.4 | 4.3 |
| 6 | 5.4 | 5.3 | 5.2 |
| 7 | 6.3 | 6.2 | 6.1 |
| 8 | 7.2 | 7.1 | 6.9 |
| 9 | 8.1 | 8.0 | 7.8 |
| 10 | 9.0 | 8.8 | 8.7 |
| 20 | 18.0 | 17.7 | 17.3 |
| 30 | 27.0 | 26.5 | 26.0 |
| 40 | 36.0 | 35.3 | 34.7 |
| 50 | 45.0 | 44.2 | 43.3 |

| | 51 | 4 | 3 | 2 |
|---|---|---|---|---|
| 1 | 0.8 | 0.1 | 0.0 | 0.0 |
| 2 | 1.7 | 0.1 | 0.1 | 0.1 |
| 3 | 2.6 | 0.2 | 0.2 | 0.1 |
| 4 | 3.4 | 0.3 | 0.2 | 0.1 |
| 5 | 4.2 | 0.3 | 0.2 | 0.2 |
| 6 | 5.1 | 0.4 | 0.3 | 0.2 |
| 7 | 6.0 | 0.5 | 0.4 | 0.2 |
| 8 | 6.8 | 0.5 | 0.4 | 0.3 |
| 9 | 7.6 | 0.6 | 0.4 | 0.3 |
| 10 | 8.5 | 0.7 | 0.5 | 0.3 |
| 20 | 17.0 | 1.3 | 1.0 | 0.7 |
| 30 | 25.5 | 2.0 | 1.5 | 1.0 |
| 40 | 34.0 | 2.7 | 2.0 | 1.3 |
| 50 | 42.5 | 3.3 | 2.5 | 1.7 |

| | 4 | 4 | 3 | 3 |
|---|---|---|---|---|
| | 55 | 54 | 58 | 57 |
| 0 | 6.9 | 6.8 | 9.7 | 9.5 |
| 1 | 20.6 | 20.2 | 29.0 | 28.5 |
| 2 | 34.4 | 33.8 | 48.3 | 47.5 |
| 4 | 48.1 | 47.2 | — | — |

| | 3 | 3 | 3 |
|---|---|---|---|
| | 56 | 55 | 54 |
| 1 | 9.3 | 9.2 | 9.0 |
| 2 | 28.0 | 27.5 | 27.0 |
| 3 | 46.7 | 45.8 | 45.0 |

| ′ | L. Sin. | d. | L. Tan. | c.d. | L. Cot. | L. Cos. | d. | ′ |
|---|---------|----|---------|------|---------|---------|----|----|
| 0 | 9.38 368 | 50 | 9.39 677 | 54 | 0.60 323 | 9.98 690 | 3 | 60 |
| 1 | 9.38 418 | 51 | 9.39 731 | 54 | 0.60 269 | 9.98 687 | 3 | 59 |
| 2 | 9.38 469 | 50 | 9.39 785 | 53 | 0.60 215 | 9.98 684 | 3 | 58 |
| 3 | 9.38 519 | 51 | 9.39 838 | 54 | 0.60 162 | 9.98 681 | 3 | 57 |
| 4 | 9.38 570 | 50 | 9.39 892 | 53 | 0.60 108 | 9.98 678 | 3 | 56 |
| 5 | 9.38 620 | 50 | 9.39 945 | 54 | 0.60 055 | 9.98 675 | 4 | 55 |
| 6 | 9.38 670 | 50 | 9.39 999 | 53 | 0.60 001 | 9.98 671 | 3 | 54 |
| 7 | 9.38 721 | 51 | 9.40 052 | 54 | 0.59 948 | 9.98 668 | 3 | 53 |
| 8 | 9.38 771 | 50 | 9.40 106 | 53 | 0.59 894 | 9.98 665 | 3 | 52 |
| 9 | 9.38 821 | 50 | 9.40 159 | 53 | 0.59 841 | 9.98 662 | 3 | 51 |
| 10 | 9.38 871 | 50 | 9.40 212 | 54 | 0.59 788 | 9.98 659 | 3 | 50 |
| 11 | 9.38 921 | 50 | 9.40 266 | 53 | 0.59 734 | 9.98 656 | 4 | 49 |
| 12 | 9.38 971 | 50 | 9.40 319 | 53 | 0.59 681 | 9.98 652 | 3 | 48 |
| 13 | 9.39 021 | 50 | 9.40 372 | 53 | 0.59 628 | 9.98 649 | 3 | 47 |
| 14 | 9.39 071 | 50 | 9.40 425 | 53 | 0.59 575 | 9.98 646 | 3 | 46 |
| 15 | 9.39 121 | 49 | 9.40 478 | 53 | 0.59 522 | 9.98 643 | 3 | 45 |
| 16 | 9.39 170 | 50 | 9.40 531 | 53 | 0.59 469 | 9.98 640 | 4 | 44 |
| 17 | 9.39 220 | 50 | 9.40 584 | 53 | 0.59 416 | 9.98 636 | 3 | 43 |
| 18 | 9.39 270 | 49 | 9.40 636 | 53 | 0.59 364 | 9.98 633 | 3 | 42 |
| 19 | 9.39 319 | 50 | 9.40 689 | 53 | 0.59 311 | 9.98 630 | 3 | 41 |
| 20 | 9.39 369 | 49 | 9.40 742 | 53 | 0.59 258 | 9.98 627 | 4 | 40 |
| 21 | 9.39 418 | 49 | 9.40 795 | 52 | 0.59 205 | 9.98 623 | 3 | 39 |
| 22 | 9.39 467 | 50 | 9.40 847 | 53 | 0.59 153 | 9.98 620 | 3 | 38 |
| 23 | 9.39 517 | 49 | 9.40 900 | 52 | 0.59 100 | 9.98 617 | 3 | 37 |
| 24 | 9.39 566 | 49 | 9.40 952 | 53 | 0.59 048 | 9.98 614 | 4 | 36 |
| 25 | 9.39 615 | 49 | 9.41 005 | 52 | 0.58 995 | 9.98 610 | 3 | 35 |
| 26 | 9.39 664 | 49 | 9.41 057 | 52 | 0.58 943 | 9.98 607 | 3 | 34 |
| 27 | 9.39 713 | 49 | 9.41 109 | 52 | 0.58 891 | 9.98 604 | 3 | 33 |
| 28 | 9.39 762 | 49 | 9.41 161 | 53 | 0.58 839 | 9.98 601 | 4 | 32 |
| 29 | 9.39 811 | 49 | 9.41 214 | 52 | 0.58 786 | 9.98 597 | 3 | 31 |
| 30 | 9.39 860 | 49 | 9.41 266 | 52 | 0.58 734 | 9.98 594 | 3 | 30 |
| 31 | 9.39 909 | 49 | 9.41 318 | 52 | 0.58 682 | 9.98 591 | 3 | 29 |
| 32 | 9.39 958 | 48 | 9.41 370 | 52 | 0.58 630 | 9.98 588 | 4 | 28 |
| 33 | 9.40 006 | 49 | 9.41 422 | 52 | 0.58 578 | 9.98 584 | 3 | 27 |
| 34 | 9.40 055 | 48 | 9.41 474 | 52 | 0.58 526 | 9.98 581 | 3 | 26 |
| 35 | 9.40 103 | 49 | 9.41 526 | 52 | 0.58 474 | 9.98 578 | 4 | 25 |
| 36 | 9.40 152 | 48 | 9.41 578 | 51 | 0.58 422 | 9.98 574 | 3 | 24 |
| 37 | 9.40 200 | 49 | 9.41 629 | 52 | 0.58 371 | 9.98 571 | 3 | 23 |
| 38 | 9.40 249 | 48 | 9.41 681 | 52 | 0.58 319 | 9.98 568 | 3 | 22 |
| 39 | 9.40 297 | 49 | 9.41 733 | 51 | 0.58 267 | 9.98 565 | 4 | 21 |
| 40 | 9.40 346 | 48 | 9.41 784 | 52 | 0.58 216 | 9.98 561 | 3 | 20 |
| 41 | 9.40 394 | 48 | 9.41 836 | 51 | 0.58 164 | 9.98 558 | 3 | 19 |
| 42 | 9.40 442 | 48 | 9.41 887 | 52 | 0.58 113 | 9.98 555 | 4 | 18 |
| 43 | 9.40 490 | 48 | 9.41 939 | 51 | 0.58 061 | 9.98 551 | 3 | 17 |
| 44 | 9.40 538 | 48 | 9.41 990 | 51 | 0.58 010 | 9.98 548 | 3 | 16 |
| 45 | 9.40 586 | 48 | 9.42 041 | 52 | 0.57 959 | 9.98 545 | 4 | 15 |
| 46 | 9.40 634 | 48 | 9.42 093 | 51 | 0.57 907 | 9.98 541 | 3 | 14 |
| 47 | 9.40 682 | 48 | 9.42 144 | 51 | 0.57 856 | 9.98 538 | 3 | 13 |
| 48 | 9.40 730 | 48 | 9.42 195 | 51 | 0.57 805 | 9.98 535 | 4 | 12 |
| 49 | 9.40 778 | 47 | 9.42 246 | 51 | 0.57 754 | 9.98 531 | 3 | 11 |
| 50 | 9.40 825 | 48 | 9.42 297 | 51 | 0.57 703 | 9.98 528 | 3 | 10 |
| 51 | 9.40 873 | 48 | 9.42 348 | 51 | 0.57 652 | 9.98 525 | 3 | 9 |
| 52 | 9.40 921 | 47 | 9.42 399 | 51 | 0.57 601 | 9.98 521 | 3 | 8 |
| 53 | 9.40 968 | 48 | 9.42 450 | 51 | 0.57 550 | 9.98 518 | 3 | 7 |
| 54 | 9.41 016 | 47 | 9.42 501 | 51 | 0.57 499 | 9.98 515 | 4 | 6 |
| 55 | 9.41 063 | 48 | 9.42 552 | 51 | 0.57 448 | 9.98 511 | 3 | 5 |
| 56 | 9.41 111 | 47 | 9.42 603 | 50 | 0.57 397 | 9.98 508 | 3 | 4 |
| 57 | 9.41 158 | 47 | 9.42 653 | 51 | 0.57 347 | 9.98 505 | 4 | 3 |
| 58 | 9.41 205 | 47 | 9.42 704 | 51 | 0.57 296 | 9.98 501 | 3 | 2 |
| 59 | 9.41 252 | 48 | 9.42 755 | 50 | 0.57 245 | 9.98 498 | 4 | 1 |
| 60 | 9.41 300 |  | 9.42 805 |  | 0.57 195 | 9.98 494 |  | 0 |

**P. P.**

| ′ | 54 | 53 | 52 |
|---|----|----|----|
| 1 | 0.9 | 0.9 | 0.9 |
| 2 | 1.8 | 1.8 | 1.7 |
| 3 | 2.7 | 2.6 | 2.6 |
| 4 | 3.6 | 3.5 | 3.5 |
| 5 | 4.5 | 4.4 | 4.3 |
| 6 | 5.4 | 5.3 | 5.2 |
| 7 | 6.3 | 6.2 | 6 1 |
| 8 | 7.2 | 7.1 | 6 9 |
| 9 | 8.1 | 8.0 | 7 8 |
| 10 | 9.0 | 8.8 | 8 7 |
| 20 | 18.0 | 17.7 | 17 3 |
| 30 | 27.0 | 26.5 | 26 0 |
| 40 | 36.0 | 35.3 | 34 7 |
| 50 | 45.0 | 44.2 | 43.3 |

| ′ | 51 | 50 | 49 |
|---|----|----|----|
| 1 | 0.8 | 0.8 | 0.8 |
| 2 | 1.7 | 1.7 | 1.6 |
| 3 | 2.6 | 2.5 | 2.4 |
| 4 | 3.4 | 3.3 | 3.3 |
| 5 | 4.2 | 4.2 | 4.1 |
| 6 | 5.1 | 5.0 | 4.9 |
| 7 | 6.0 | 5.8 | 5.7 |
| 8 | 6.8 | 6.7 | 6.6 |
| 9 | 7.6 | 7.5 | 7.4 |
| 10 | 8.5 | 8.3 | 8.2 |
| 20 | 17.0 | 16.7 | 16.3 |
| 30 | 25.5 | 25.0 | 24.5 |
| 40 | 34.0 | 33.3 | 32.7 |
| 50 | 42.5 | 41.7 | 40.8 |

| ′ | 48 | 47 | 4 | 3 |
|---|----|----|----|----|
| 1 | 0.8 | 0.8 | 0.1 | 0.0 |
| 2 | 1.6 | 1.6 | 0.1 | 0.1 |
| 3 | 2.4 | 2.4 | 0.2 | 0.2 |
| 4 | 3.2 | 3.1 | 0.3 | 0.2 |
| 5 | 4.0 | 3.9 | 0.3 | 0.2 |
| 6 | 4.8 | 4.7 | 0.4 | 0.3 |
| 7 | 5.6 | 5.5 | 0.5 | 0.4 |
| 8 | 6.4 | 6.3 | 0.5 | 0.4 |
| 9 | 7.2 | 7.0 | 0.6 | 0.4 |
| 10 | 8.0 | 7.8 | 0.7 | 0.5 |
| 20 | 16.0 | 15.7 | 1.3 | 1.0 |
| 30 | 24.0 | 23.5 | 2.0 | 1.5 |
| 40 | 32.0 | 31.3 | 2.7 | 2.0 |
| 50 | 40.0 | 39.2 | 3.3 | 2.5 |

| | $\frac{4}{54}$ | $\frac{4}{53}$ | $\frac{4}{52}$ | $\frac{4}{51}$ |
|---|----|----|----|----|
| 0 | 6.8 | 6.6 | 6.5 | 6.4 |
| 1 | 20.2 | 19.9 | 19.5 | 19.1 |
| 2 | 33.8 | 33.1 | 32.5 | 31.9 |
| 3 | 47.2 | 46.4 | 45.5 | 44.6 |

| | $\frac{3}{54}$ | $\frac{3}{53}$ | $\frac{3}{52}$ | $\frac{3}{51}$ |
|---|----|----|----|----|
| 0 | 9.0 | 8.8 | 8.7 | 8.5 |
| 1 | 27.0 | 26.5 | 26.0 | 25.5 |
| 2 | 45.0 | 44.2 | 43.3 | 42.5 |

| ′ | L. Cos. | d. | L. Cot. | c.d. | L. Tan. | L. Sin. | d. | ′ | P. P. |
|---|---------|----|---------|------|---------|---------|----|----|-------|

**15° (195°)**  (344°) **164°**

| ' | L. Sin. | d. | L. Tan. | c.d. | L. Cot. | L. Cos. | d. | ' |
|---|---------|----|---------|------|---------|---------|----|----|
| 0 | 9.41 300 |    | 9.42 805 |    | 0.57 195 | 9.98 494 |   | 60 |
| 1 | 9.41 347 | 47 | 9.42 856 | 51 | 0.57 144 | 9.98 491 | 3 | 59 |
| 2 | 9.41 394 | 47 | 9.42 906 | 50 | 0.57 094 | 9.98 488 | 3 | 58 |
| 3 | 9.41 441 | 47 | 9.42 957 | 51 | 0.57 043 | 9.98 484 | 4 | 57 |
| 4 | 9.41 488 | 47 | 9.43 007 | 50 | 0.56 993 | 9.98 481 | 3 | 56 |
| 5 | 9.41 535 | 47 | 9.43 057 | 50 | 0.56 943 | 9.98 477 | 4 | 55 |
| 6 | 9.41 582 | 47 | 9.43 108 | 51 | 0.56 892 | 9.98 474 | 3 | 54 |
| 7 | 9.41 628 | 46 | 9.43 158 | 50 | 0.56 842 | 9.98 471 | 3 | 53 |
| 8 | 9.41 675 | 47 | 9.43 208 | 50 | 0.56 792 | 9.98 467 | 4 | 52 |
| 9 | 9.41 722 | 47 | 9.43 258 | 50 | 0.56 742 | 9.98 464 | 3 | 51 |
| 10 | 9.41 768 | 46 | 9.43 308 | 50 | 0.56 692 | 9.98 460 | 4 | 50 |
| 11 | 9.41 815 | 47 | 9.43 358 | 50 | 0.56 642 | 9.98 457 | 3 | 49 |
| 12 | 9.41 861 | 46 | 9.43 408 | 50 | 0.56 592 | 9.98 453 | 4 | 48 |
| 13 | 9.41 908 | 47 | 9.43 458 | 50 | 0.56 542 | 9.98 450 | 3 | 47 |
| 14 | 9.41 954 | 46 | 9.43 508 | 50 | 0.56 492 | 9.98 446 | 4 | 46 |
| 15 | 9.42 001 | 47 | 9.43 558 | 49 | 0.56 442 | 9.98 443 | 3 | 45 |
| 16 | 9.42 047 | 46 | 9.43 607 | 50 | 0.56 393 | 9.98 440 | 3 | 44 |
| 17 | 9.42 093 | 46 | 9.43 657 | 50 | 0.56 343 | 9.98 436 | 4 | 43 |
| 18 | 9.42 140 | 47 | 9.43 707 | 49 | 0.56 293 | 9.98 433 | 3 | 42 |
| 19 | 9.42 186 | 46 | 9.43 756 | 50 | 0.56 244 | 9.98 429 | 4 | 41 |
| 20 | 9.42 232 | 46 | 9.43 806 | 49 | 0.56 194 | 9.98 426 | 3 | 40 |
| 21 | 9.42 278 | 46 | 9.43 855 | 50 | 0.56 145 | 9.98 422 | 4 | 39 |
| 22 | 9.42 324 | 46 | 9.43 905 | 49 | 0.56 095 | 9.98 419 | 3 | 38 |
| 23 | 9.42 370 | 46 | 9.43 954 | 50 | 0.56 046 | 9.98 415 | 4 | 37 |
| 24 | 9.42 416 | 45 | 9.44 004 | 49 | 0.55 996 | 9.98 412 | 3 | 36 |
| 25 | 9.42 461 | 46 | 9.44 053 | 49 | 0.55 947 | 9.98 409 | 4 | 35 |
| 26 | 9.42 507 | 46 | 9.44 102 | 49 | 0.55 898 | 9.98 405 | 3 | 34 |
| 27 | 9.42 553 | 46 | 9.44 151 | 50 | 0.55 849 | 9.98 402 | 4 | 33 |
| 28 | 9.42 599 | 45 | 9.44 201 | 49 | 0.55 799 | 9.98 398 | 3 | 32 |
| 29 | 9.42 644 | 46 | 9.44 250 | 49 | 0.55 750 | 9.98 395 | 4 | 31 |
| 30 | 9.42 690 | 45 | 9.44 299 | 49 | 0.55 701 | 9.98 391 | 3 | 30 |
| 31 | 9.42 735 | 46 | 9.44 348 | 49 | 0.55 652 | 9.98 388 | 4 | 29 |
| 32 | 9.42 781 | 45 | 9.44 397 | 49 | 0.55 603 | 9.98 384 | 3 | 28 |
| 33 | 9.42 826 | 46 | 9.44 446 | 49 | 0.55 554 | 9.98 381 | 4 | 27 |
| 34 | 9.42 872 | 45 | 9.44 495 | 49 | 0.55 505 | 9.98 377 | 4 | 26 |
| 35 | 9.42 917 | 45 | 9.44 544 | 48 | 0.55 456 | 9.98 373 | 3 | 25 |
| 36 | 9.42 962 | 46 | 9.44 592 | 49 | 0.55 408 | 9.98 370 | 4 | 24 |
| 37 | 9.43 008 | 45 | 9.44 641 | 49 | 0.55 359 | 9.98 366 | 3 | 23 |
| 38 | 9.43 053 | 45 | 9.44 690 | 48 | 0.55 310 | 9.98 363 | 4 | 22 |
| 39 | 9.43 098 | 45 | 9.44 738 | 49 | 0.55 262 | 9.98 359 | 3 | 21 |
| 40 | 9.43 143 | 45 | 9.44 787 | 49 | 0.55 213 | 9.98 356 | 4 | 20 |
| 41 | 9.43 188 | 45 | 9.44 836 | 48 | 0.55 164 | 9.98 352 | 3 | 19 |
| 42 | 9.43 233 | 45 | 9.44 884 | 49 | 0.55 116 | 9.98 349 | 4 | 18 |
| 43 | 9.43 278 | 45 | 9.44 933 | 48 | 0.55 067 | 9.98 345 | 3 | 17 |
| 44 | 9.43 323 | 44 | 9.44 981 | 48 | 0.55 019 | 9.98 342 | 4 | 16 |
| 45 | 9.43 367 | 45 | 9.45 029 | 49 | 0.54 971 | 9.98 338 | 4 | 15 |
| 46 | 9.43 412 | 45 | 9.45 078 | 48 | 0.54 922 | 9.98 334 | 3 | 14 |
| 47 | 9.43 457 | 45 | 9.45 126 | 48 | 0.54 874 | 9.98 331 | 4 | 13 |
| 48 | 9.43 502 | 44 | 9.45 174 | 48 | 0.54 826 | 9.98 327 | 3 | 12 |
| 49 | 9.43 546 | 45 | 9.45 222 | 49 | 0.54 778 | 9.98 324 | 4 | 11 |
| 50 | 9.43 591 | 44 | 9.45 271 | 48 | 0.54 729 | 9.98 320 | 3 | 10 |
| 51 | 9.43 635 | 45 | 9.45 319 | 48 | 0.54 681 | 9.98 317 | 4 | 9 |
| 52 | 9.43 680 | 44 | 9.45 367 | 48 | 0.54 633 | 9.98 313 | 4 | 8 |
| 53 | 9.43 724 | 45 | 9.45 415 | 48 | 0.54 585 | 9.98 309 | 3 | 7 |
| 54 | 9.43 769 | 44 | 9.45 463 | 48 | 0.54 537 | 9.98 306 | 4 | 6 |
| 55 | 9.43 813 | 44 | 9.45 511 | 48 | 0.54 489 | 9.98 302 | 3 | 5 |
| 56 | 9.43 857 | 44 | 9.45 559 | 47 | 0.54 441 | 9.98 299 | 4 | 4 |
| 57 | 9.43 901 | 45 | 9.45 606 | 48 | 0.54 394 | 9.98 295 | 4 | 3 |
| 58 | 9.43 946 | 44 | 9.45 654 | 48 | 0.54 346 | 9.98 291 | 3 | 2 |
| 59 | 9.43 990 | 44 | 9.45 702 | 48 | 0.54 298 | 9.98 288 | 4 | 1 |
| 60 | 9.44 034 |    | 9.45 750 |    | 0.54 250 | 9.98 284 |   | 0 |

**P. P.**

| '' | 51 | 50 | 49 |
|----|----|----|----|
| 1 | 0.8 | 0.8 | 0.8 |
| 2 | 1.7 | 1.7 | 1.6 |
| 3 | 2.6 | 2.5 | 2.4 |
| 4 | 3.4 | 3.3 | 3.3 |
| 5 | 4.2 | 4.2 | 4.1 |
| 6 | 5.1 | 5.0 | 4.9 |
| 7 | 6.0 | 5.8 | 5.7 |
| 8 | 6.8 | 6.7 | 6.5 |
| 9 | 7.6 | 7.5 | 7.4 |
| 10 | 8.5 | 8.3 | 8.2 |
| 20 | 17.0 | 16.7 | 16.3 |
| 30 | 25.5 | 25.0 | 24.5 |
| 40 | 34.0 | 33.3 | 32.7 |
| 50 | 42.5 | 41.7 | 40.8 |

| '' | 48 | 47 | 46 |
|----|----|----|----|
| 1 | 0.8 | 0.8 | 0.8 |
| 2 | 1.6 | 1.6 | 1.5 |
| 3 | 2.4 | 2.4 | 2.3 |
| 4 | 3.2 | 3.1 | 3.1 |
| 5 | 4.0 | 3.9 | 3.8 |
| 6 | 4.8 | 4.7 | 4.6 |
| 7 | 5.6 | 5.5 | 5.4 |
| 8 | 6.4 | 6.3 | 6.1 |
| 9 | 7.2 | 7.0 | 6.9 |
| 10 | 8.0 | 7.8 | 7.7 |
| 20 | 16.0 | 15.7 | 15.3 |
| 30 | 24.0 | 23.5 | 23.0 |
| 40 | 32.0 | 31.3 | 30.7 |
| 50 | 40.0 | 39.2 | 38.3 |

| '' | 45 | 44 | 4 | 3 |
|----|----|----|---|---|
| 1 | 0.8 | 0.7 | 0.1 | 0.0 |
| 2 | 1.5 | 1.5 | 0.1 | 0.1 |
| 3 | 2.2 | 2.2 | 0.2 | 0.2 |
| 4 | 3.0 | 2.9 | 0.3 | 0.2 |
| 5 | 3.8 | 3.7 | 0.3 | 0.2 |
| 6 | 4.5 | 4.4 | 0.4 | 0.3 |
| 7 | 5.2 | 5.1 | 0.5 | 0.4 |
| 8 | 6.0 | 5.9 | 0.5 | 0.4 |
| 9 | 6.8 | 6.6 | 0.6 | 0.4 |
| 10 | 7.5 | 7.3 | 0.7 | 0.5 |
| 20 | 15.0 | 14.7 | 1.3 | 1.0 |
| 30 | 22.5 | 22.0 | 2.0 | 1.5 |
| 40 | 30.0 | 29.3 | 2.7 | 2.0 |
| 50 | 37.5 | 36.7 | 3.3 | 2.5 |

| | $\frac{4}{50}$ | $\frac{4}{49}$ | $\frac{4}{48}$ | $\frac{4}{47}$ |
|---|---|---|---|---|
| 0 | 6.2 | 6.1 | 6.0 | 5.9 |
| 1 | 18.8 | 18.4 | 18.0 | 17.6 |
| 2 | 31.2 | 30.6 | 30.0 | 29.4 |
| 3 | 43.8 | 42.9 | 42.0 | 41.1 |

| | $\frac{3}{51}$ | $\frac{3}{50}$ | $\frac{3}{49}$ | $\frac{3}{48}$ |
|---|---|---|---|---|
| 0 | 8.5 | 8.3 | 8.2 | 8.0 |
| 1 | 25.5 | 25.0 | 24.5 | 24.0 |
| 2 | 42.5 | 41.7 | 40.8 | 40.0 |

| ' | L. Cos. | d. | L. Cot. | c.d. | L. Tan. | L. Sin. | d. | ' | P. P. |
|---|---------|----|---------|------|---------|---------|----|----|-------|

# LOGARITHMS OF THE FUNCTIONS

| ′ | L. Sin. | d. | L. Tan. | c.d. | L. Cot. | L. Cos. | d. | ′ |
|---|---------|----|---------|------|---------|---------|----|---|
| 0 | 9.44 034 | 44 | 9.45 750 | 47 | 0.54 250 | 9.98 284 | 3 | 60 |
| 1 | 9.44 078 | 44 | 9.45 797 | 47 | 0.54 203 | 9.98 281 | 3 | 59 |
| 2 | 9.44 122 | 44 | 9.45 845 | 48 | 0.54 155 | 9.98 277 | 4 | 58 |
| 3 | 9.44 166 | 44 | 9.45 892 | 47 | 0.54 108 | 9.98 273 | 3 | 57 |
| 4 | 9.44 210 | 44 | 9.45 940 | 48 | 0.54 060 | 9.98 270 | 4 | 56 |
| 5 | 9.44 253 | 43 | 9.45 987 | 47 | 0.54 013 | 9.98 266 | 4 | 55 |
| 6 | 9.44 297 | 44 | 9.46 035 | 48 | 0.53 965 | 9.98 262 | 3 | 54 |
| 7 | 9.44 341 | 44 | 9.46 082 | 47 | 0.53 918 | 9.98 259 | 4 | 53 |
| 8 | 9.44 385 | 44 | 9.46 130 | 48 | 0.53 870 | 9.98 255 | 4 | 52 |
| 9 | 9.44 428 | 43 | 9.46 177 | 47 | 0.53 823 | 9.98 251 | 3 | 51 |
| 10 | 9.44 472 | 44 | 9.46 224 | 47 | 0.53 776 | 9.98 248 | | 50 |
| 11 | 9.44 516 | 43 | 9.46 271 | 48 | 0.53 729 | 9.98 244 | 4 | 49 |
| 12 | 9.44 559 | 43 | 9.46 319 | 47 | 0.53 681 | 9.98 240 | 4 | 48 |
| 13 | 9.44 602 | 44 | 9.46 366 | 47 | 0.53 634 | 9.98 237 | 3 | 47 |
| 14 | 9.44 646 | 43 | 9.46 413 | 47 | 0.53 587 | 9.98 233 | 4 | 46 |
| 15 | 9.44 689 | 44 | 9.46 460 | 47 | 0.53 540 | 9.98 229 | 4 | 45 |
| 16 | 9.44 733 | 43 | 9.46 507 | 47 | 0.53 493 | 9.98 226 | 3 | 44 |
| 17 | 9.44 776 | 43 | 9.46 554 | 47 | 0.53 446 | 9.98 222 | 4 | 43 |
| 18 | 9.44 819 | 43 | 9.46 601 | 47 | 0.53 399 | 9.98 218 | 4 | 42 |
| 19 | 9.44 862 | 43 | 9.46 648 | 46 | 0.53 352 | 9.98 215 | 4 | 41 |
| 20 | 9.44 905 | 43 | 9.46 694 | 47 | 0.53 306 | 9.98 211 | | 40 |
| 21 | 9.44 948 | 44 | 9.46 741 | 47 | 0.53 259 | 9.98 207 | 4 | 39 |
| 22 | 9.44 992 | 43 | 9.46 788 | 47 | 0.53 212 | 9.98 204 | 3 | 38 |
| 23 | 9.45 035 | 42 | 9.46 835 | 46 | 0.53 165 | 9.98 200 | 4 | 37 |
| 24 | 9.45 077 | 43 | 9.46 881 | 47 | 0.53 119 | 9.98 196 | 4 | 36 |
| 25 | 9.45 120 | 43 | 9.46 928 | 47 | 0.53 072 | 9.98 192 | | 35 |
| 26 | 9.45 163 | 43 | 9.46 975 | 46 | 0.53 025 | 9.98 189 | 3 | 34 |
| 27 | 9.45 206 | 43 | 9.47 021 | 47 | 0.52 979 | 9.98 185 | 4 | 33 |
| 28 | 9.45 249 | 43 | 9.47 068 | 46 | 0.52 932 | 9.98 181 | 4 | 32 |
| 29 | 9.45 292 | 42 | 9.47 114 | 46 | 0.52 886 | 9.98 177 | 4 | 31 |
| 30 | 9.45 334 | 43 | 9.47 160 | 47 | 0.52 840 | 9.98 174 | | 30 |
| 31 | 9.45 377 | 42 | 9.47 207 | 46 | 0.52 793 | 9.98 170 | 4 | 29 |
| 32 | 9.45 419 | 43 | 9.47 253 | 46 | 0.52 747 | 9.98 166 | 4 | 28 |
| 33 | 9.45 462 | 42 | 9.47 299 | 47 | 0.52 701 | 9.98 162 | 3 | 27 |
| 34 | 9.45 504 | 43 | 9.47 346 | 46 | 0.52 654 | 9.98 159 | 4 | 26 |
| 35 | 9.45 547 | 42 | 9.47 392 | 46 | 0.52 608 | 9.98 155 | | 25 |
| 36 | 9.45 589 | 43 | 9.47 438 | 46 | 0.52 562 | 9.98 151 | 4 | 24 |
| 37 | 9.45 632 | 42 | 9.47 484 | 46 | 0.52 516 | 9.98 147 | 3 | 23 |
| 38 | 9.45 674 | 42 | 9.47 530 | 46 | 0.52 470 | 9.98 144 | 4 | 22 |
| 39 | 9.45 716 | 42 | 9.47 576 | 46 | 0.52 424 | 9.98 140 | 4 | 21 |
| 40 | 9.45 758 | 43 | 9.47 622 | 46 | 0.52 378 | 9.98 136 | | 20 |
| 41 | 9.45 801 | 42 | 9.47 668 | 46 | 0.52 332 | 9.98 132 | 4 | 19 |
| 42 | 9.45 843 | 42 | 9.47 714 | 46 | 0.52 286 | 9.98 129 | 3 | 18 |
| 43 | 9.45 885 | 42 | 9.47 760 | 46 | 0.52 240 | 9.98 125 | 4 | 17 |
| 44 | 9.45 927 | 42 | 9.47 806 | 46 | 0.52 194 | 9.98 121 | 4 | 16 |
| 45 | 9.45 969 | 42 | 9.47 852 | 45 | 0.52 148 | 9.98 117 | | 15 |
| 46 | 9.46 011 | 42 | 9.47 897 | 46 | 0.52 103 | 9.98 113 | 4 | 14 |
| 47 | 9.46 053 | 42 | 9.47 943 | 46 | 0.52 057 | 9.98 110 | 3 | 13 |
| 48 | 9.46 095 | 41 | 9.47 989 | 46 | 0.52 011 | 9.98 106 | 4 | 12 |
| 49 | 9.46 136 | 42 | 9.48 035 | 45 | 0.51 965 | 9.98 102 | 4 | 11 |
| 50 | 9.46 178 | 42 | 9.48 080 | 46 | 0.51 920 | 9.98 098 | 4 | 10 |
| 51 | 9.46 220 | 42 | 9.48 126 | 45 | 0.51 874 | 9.98 094 | 4 | 9 |
| 52 | 9.46 262 | 41 | 9.48 171 | 46 | 0.51 829 | 9.98 090 | 3 | 8 |
| 53 | 9.46 303 | 42 | 9.48 217 | 45 | 0.51 783 | 9.98 087 | 4 | 7 |
| 54 | 9.46 345 | 41 | 9.48 262 | 45 | 0.51 738 | 9.98 083 | 4 | 6 |
| 55 | 9.46 386 | 42 | 9.48 307 | 46 | 0.51 693 | 9.98 079 | 4 | 5 |
| 56 | 9.46 428 | 41 | 9.48 353 | 45 | 0.51 647 | 9.98 075 | 4 | 4 |
| 57 | 9.46 469 | 41 | 9.48 398 | 45 | 0.51 602 | 9.98 071 | 4 | 3 |
| 58 | 9.46 511 | 41 | 9.48 443 | 45 | 0.51 557 | 9.98 067 | 4 | 2 |
| 59 | 9.46 552 | 42 | 9.48 489 | 45 | 0.51 511 | 9.98 063 | 3 | 1 |
| 60 | 9.46 594 | | 9.48 534 | | 0.51 466 | 9.98 060 | | 0 |

| | L. Cos. | d. | L. Cot. | c.d. | L. Tan. | L. Sin. | d. | ′ |

### P.P.

| ″ | 48 | 47 | 46 |
|---|----|----|----|
| 1 | 0.8 | 0.8 | 0.8 |
| 2 | 1.6 | 1.6 | 1.8 |
| 3 | 2.4 | 2.4 | 2.3 |
| 4 | 3.2 | 3.1 | 3.1 |
| 5 | 4.0 | 3.9 | 3.8 |
| 6 | 4.8 | 4.7 | 4.6 |
| 7 | 5.6 | 5.5 | 5.4 |
| 8 | 6.4 | 6.3 | 6.1 |
| 9 | 7.2 | 7.0 | 6.9 |
| 10 | 8.0 | 7.8 | 7.7 |
| 20 | 16.0 | 15.7 | 15.3 |
| 30 | 24.0 | 23.5 | 23.0 |
| 40 | 32.0 | 31.3 | 30.7 |
| 50 | 40.0 | 39.2 | 38.3 |

| ″ | 45 | 44 | 43 |
|---|----|----|----|
| 1 | 0.8 | 0.7 | 0.7 |
| 2 | 1.5 | 1.5 | 1.4 |
| 3 | 2.2 | 2.2 | 2.2 |
| 4 | 3.0 | 2.9 | 2.9 |
| 5 | 3.8 | 3.7 | 3.6 |
| 6 | 4.5 | 4.4 | 4.3 |
| 7 | 5.2 | 5.1 | 5.0 |
| 8 | 6.0 | 5.9 | 5.7 |
| 9 | 6.8 | 6.6 | 6.4 |
| 10 | 7.5 | 7.3 | 7.2 |
| 20 | 15.0 | 14.7 | 14.3 |
| 30 | 22.5 | 22.0 | 21.5 |
| 40 | 30.0 | 29.3 | 28.7 |
| 50 | 37.5 | 36.7 | 35.8 |

| ″ | 42 | 41 | 4 | 3 |
|---|----|----|---|---|
| 1 | 0.7 | 0.7 | 0.1 | 0.0 |
| 2 | 1.4 | 1.4 | 0.1 | 0.1 |
| 3 | 2.1 | 2.0 | 0.2 | 0.2 |
| 4 | 2.8 | 2.7 | 0.3 | 0.2 |
| 5 | 3.5 | 3.4 | 0.3 | 0.2 |
| 6 | 4.2 | 4.1 | 0.4 | 0.3 |
| 7 | 4.9 | 4.8 | 0.5 | 0.4 |
| 8 | 5.6 | 5.5 | 0.5 | 0.4 |
| 9 | 6.3 | 6.2 | 0.6 | 0.4 |
| 10 | 7.0 | 6.8 | 0.7 | 0.5 |
| 20 | 14.0 | 13.7 | 1.3 | 1.0 |
| 30 | 21.0 | 20.5 | 2.0 | 1.5 |
| 40 | 28.0 | 27.3 | 2.7 | 2.0 |
| 50 | 35.0 | 34.2 | 3.3 | 2.5 |

| | 4 | 4 | 4 | 4 |
|---|----|----|----|----|
| | 48 | 47 | 46 | 45 |
| 1 | 6.0 | 5.9 | 5.8 | 5.6 |
| 2 | 18.0 | 17.6 | 17.2 | 16.9 |
| 3 | 30.0 | 29.4 | 28.8 | 28.1 |
| 4 | 42.0 | 41.1 | 40.2 | 39.4 |

| | 3 | 3 | 3 | 3 |
|---|----|----|----|----|
| | 48 | 47 | 46 | 45 |
| 1 | 8.0 | 7.8 | 7.7 | 7.5 |
| 2 | 24.0 | 23.5 | 23.0 | 22.5 |
| 3 | 40.0 | 39.2 | 38.3 | 37.5 |

| | P.P. |

# LOGARITHMS OF THE FUNCTIONS (Continued)

| ' | L. Sin. | d. | L. Tan. | c.d. | L. Cot. | L. Cos. | d. | ' |
|---|---|---|---|---|---|---|---|---|
| 0 | 9.46 594 | 41 | 9.48 534 | 45 | 0.51 466 | 9.98 060 | 4 | 60 |
| 1 | 9.46 635 | 41 | 9.48 579 | 45 | 0.51 421 | 9.98 056 | 4 | 59 |
| 2 | 9.46 676 | 41 | 9.48 624 | 45 | 0.51 376 | 9.98 052 | 4 | 58 |
| 3 | 9.46 717 | 41 | 9.48 669 | 45 | 0.51 331 | 9.98 048 | 4 | 57 |
| 4 | 9.46 758 | 42 | 9.48 714 | 45 | 0.51 286 | 9.98 044 | 4 | 56 |
| 5 | 9.46 800 | 41 | 9.48 759 | 45 | 0.51 241 | 9.98 040 | 4 | 55 |
| 6 | 9.46 841 | 41 | 9.48 804 | 45 | 0.51 196 | 9.98 036 | 4 | 54 |
| 7 | 9.46 882 | 41 | 9.48 849 | 45 | 0.51 151 | 9.98 032 | 4 | 53 |
| 8 | 9.46 923 | 41 | 9.48 894 | 45 | 0.51 106 | 9.98 029 | 3 | 52 |
| 9 | 9.46 964 | 41 | 9.48 939 | 45 | 0.51 061 | 9.98 025 | 4 | 51 |
| 10 | 9.47 005 | 40 | 9.48 984 | 45 | 0.51 016 | 9.98 021 | 4 | 50 |
| 11 | 9.47 045 | 41 | 9.49 029 | 44 | 0.50 971 | 9.98 017 | 4 | 49 |
| 12 | 9.47 086 | 41 | 9.49 073 | 45 | 0.50 927 | 9.98 013 | 4 | 48 |
| 13 | 9.47 127 | 41 | 9.49 118 | 45 | 0.50 882 | 9.98 009 | 4 | 47 |
| 14 | 9.47 168 | 41 | 9.49 163 | 44 | 0.50 837 | 9.98 005 | 4 | 46 |
| 15 | 9.47 209 | 40 | 9.49 207 | 45 | 0.50 793 | 9.98 001 | 4 | 45 |
| 16 | 9.47 249 | 41 | 9.49 252 | 44 | 0.50 748 | 9.97 997 | 4 | 44 |
| 17 | 9.47 290 | 40 | 9.49 296 | 45 | 0.50 704 | 9.97 993 | 4 | 43 |
| 18 | 9.47 330 | 41 | 9.49 341 | 44 | 0.50 659 | 9.97 989 | 4 | 42 |
| 19 | 9.47 371 | 40 | 9.49 385 | 45 | 0.50 615 | 9.97 986 | 3 | 41 |
| 20 | 9.47 411 | 41 | 9.49 430 | 44 | 0.50 570 | 9.97 982 | 4 | 40 |
| 21 | 9.47 452 | 40 | 9.49 474 | 45 | 0.50 526 | 9.97 978 | 4 | 39 |
| 22 | 9.47 492 | 41 | 9.49 519 | 44 | 0.50 481 | 9.97 974 | 4 | 38 |
| 23 | 9.47 533 | 40 | 9.49 563 | 44 | 0.50 437 | 9.97 970 | 4 | 37 |
| 24 | 9.47 573 | 40 | 9.49 607 | 45 | 0.50 393 | 9.97 966 | 4 | 36 |
| 25 | 9.47 613 | 41 | 9.49 652 | 44 | 0.50 348 | 9.97 962 | 4 | 35 |
| 26 | 9.47 654 | 40 | 9.49 696 | 44 | 0.50 304 | 9.97 958 | 4 | 34 |
| 27 | 9.47 694 | 40 | 9.49 740 | 44 | 0.50 260 | 9.97 954 | 4 | 33 |
| 28 | 9.47 734 | 40 | 9.49 784 | 44 | 0.50 216 | 9.97 950 | 4 | 32 |
| 29 | 9.47 774 | 40 | 9.49 828 | 44 | 0.50 172 | 9.97 946 | 4 | 31 |
| 30 | 9.47 814 | 40 | 9.49 872 | 44 | 0.50 128 | 9.97 942 | 4 | 30 |
| 31 | 9.47 854 | 40 | 9.49 916 | 44 | 0.50 084 | 9.97 938 | 4 | 29 |
| 32 | 9.47 894 | 40 | 9.49 960 | 44 | 0.50 040 | 9.97 934 | 4 | 28 |
| 33 | 9.47 934 | 40 | 9.50 004 | 44 | 0.49 996 | 9.97 930 | 4 | 27 |
| 34 | 9.47 974 | 40 | 9.50 048 | 44 | 0.49 952 | 9.97 926 | 4 | 26 |
| 35 | 9.48 014 | 40 | 9.50 092 | 44 | 0.49 908 | 9.97 922 | 4 | 25 |
| 36 | 9.48 054 | 40 | 9.50 136 | 44 | 0.49 864 | 9.97 918 | 4 | 24 |
| 37 | 9.48 094 | 40 | 9.50 180 | 44 | 0.49 820 | 9.97 914 | 4 | 23 |
| 38 | 9.48 133 | 40 | 9.50 223 | 43 | 0.49 777 | 9.97 910 | 4 | 22 |
| 39 | 9.48 173 | 40 | 9.50 267 | 44 | 0.49 733 | 9.97 906 | 4 | 21 |
| 40 | 9.48 213 | 40 | 9.50 311 | 44 | 0.49 689 | 9.97 902 | 4 | 20 |
| 41 | 9.48 252 | 40 | 9.50 355 | 43 | 0.49 645 | 9.97 898 | 4 | 19 |
| 42 | 9.48 292 | 40 | 9.50 398 | 44 | 0.49 602 | 9.97 894 | 4 | 18 |
| 43 | 9.48 332 | 40 | 9.50 442 | 43 | 0.49 558 | 9.97 890 | 4 | 17 |
| 44 | 9.48 371 | 40 | 9.50 485 | 44 | 0.49 515 | 9.97 886 | 4 | 16 |
| 45 | 9.48 411 | 39 | 9.50 529 | 43 | 0.49 471 | 9.97 882 | 4 | 15 |
| 46 | 9.48 450 | 40 | 9.50 572 | 44 | 0.49 428 | 9.97 878 | 4 | 14 |
| 47 | 9.48 490 | 39 | 9.50 616 | 43 | 0.49 384 | 9.97 874 | 4 | 13 |
| 48 | 9.48 529 | 39 | 9.50 659 | 44 | 0.49 341 | 9.97 870 | 4 | 12 |
| 49 | 9.48 568 | 39 | 9.50 703 | 43 | 0.49 297 | 9.97 866 | 5 | 11 |
| 50 | 9.48 607 | 40 | 9.50 746 | 43 | 0.49 254 | 9.97 861 | 4 | 10 |
| 51 | 9.48 647 | 39 | 9.50 789 | 44 | 0.49 211 | 9.97 857 | 4 | 9 |
| 52 | 9.48 686 | 39 | 9.50 833 | 43 | 0.49 167 | 9.97 853 | 4 | 8 |
| 53 | 9.48 725 | 39 | 9.50 876 | 43 | 0.49 124 | 9.97 849 | 4 | 7 |
| 54 | 9.48 764 | 39 | 9.50 919 | 43 | 0.49 081 | 9.97 845 | 4 | 6 |
| 55 | 9.48 803 | 39 | 9.50 962 | 43 | 0.49 038 | 9.97 841 | 4 | 5 |
| 56 | 9.48 842 | 39 | 9.51 005 | 43 | 0.48 995 | 9.97 837 | 4 | 4 |
| 57 | 9.48 881 | 39 | 9.51 048 | 43 | 0.48 952 | 9.97 833 | 4 | 3 |
| 58 | 9.48 920 | 39 | 9.51 092 | 44 | 0.48 908 | 9.97 829 | 4 | 2 |
| 59 | 9.48 959 | 39 | 9.51 135 | 43 | 0.48 865 | 9.97 825 | 4 | 1 |
| 60 | 9.48 998 |  | 9.51 178 |  | 0.48 822 | 9.97 821 |  | 0 |

**P.P.**

| " | 45 | 44 | 43 |
|---|---|---|---|
| 1 | 0.8 | 0.7 | 0.7 |
| 2 | 1.5 | 1.5 | 1.4 |
| 3 | 2.2 | 2.2 | 2.2 |
| 4 | 3.0 | 2.9 | 2.9 |
| 5 | 3.8 | 3.7 | 3.6 |
| 6 | 4.5 | 4.4 | 4.3 |
| 7 | 5.2 | 5.1 | 5.0 |
| 8 | 6.0 | 5.9 | 5.7 |
| 9 | 6.8 | 6.6 | 6.4 |
| 10 | 7.5 | 7.3 | 7.2 |
| 20 | 15.0 | 14.7 | 14.3 |
| 30 | 22.5 | 22.0 | 21.5 |
| 40 | 30.0 | 29.3 | 28.7 |
| 50 | 37.5 | 36.7 | 35.8 |

| " | 42 | 41 | 40 |
|---|---|---|---|
| 1 | 0.7 | 0.7 | 0.7 |
| 2 | 1.4 | 1.4 | 1.3 |
| 3 | 2.1 | 2.0 | 2.0 |
| 4 | 2.8 | 2.7 | 2.7 |
| 5 | 3.5 | 3.4 | 3.3 |
| 6 | 4.2 | 4.1 | 4.0 |
| 7 | 4.9 | 4.8 | 4.7 |
| 8 | 5.6 | 5.5 | 5.3 |
| 9 | 6.3 | 6.2 | 6.0 |
| 10 | 7.0 | 6.8 | 6.7 |
| 20 | 14.0 | 13.7 | 13.3 |
| 30 | 21.0 | 20.5 | 20.0 |
| 40 | 28.0 | 27.3 | 26.7 |
| 50 | 35.0 | 34.2 | 33.3 |

| " | 39 | 5 | 4 | 3 |
|---|---|---|---|---|
| 1 | 0.6 | 0.1 | 0.1 | 0.0 |
| 2 | 1.3 | 0.2 | 0.1 | 0.1 |
| 3 | 2.0 | 0.2 | 0.2 | 0.2 |
| 4 | 2.6 | 0.3 | 0.3 | 0.2 |
| 5 | 3.2 | 0.4 | 0.3 | 0.2 |
| 6 | 3.9 | 0.5 | 0.4 | 0.3 |
| 7 | 4.6 | 0.6 | 0.5 | 0.4 |
| 8 | 5.2 | 0.7 | 0.5 | 0.4 |
| 9 | 5.8 | 0.8 | 0.6 | 0.4 |
| 10 | 6.5 | 0.8 | 0.7 | 0.5 |
| 20 | 13.0 | 1.7 | 1.3 | 1.0 |
| 30 | 19.5 | 2.5 | 2.0 | 1.5 |
| 40 | 26.0 | 3.3 | 2.7 | 2.0 |
| 50 | 32.5 | 4.2 | 3.3 | 2.5 |

| | 5 | 4 | 4 |
|---|---|---|---|
| | 43 | 45 | 44 |
| 0 | 4.3 | 5.6 | 5.5 |
| 1 | 12.9 | 16.9 | 16.5 |
| 2 | 21.5 | 28.1 | 27.5 |
| 3 | 30.1 | 39.4 | 38.5 |
| 4 | 38.7 | — | — |
| 5 |  |  |  |

| | 4 | 3 | 3 |
|---|---|---|---|
| | 43 | 45 | 44 |
| 0 | 5.4 | 7.5 | 7.3 |
| 1 | 16.1 | 22.5 | 22.0 |
| 2 | 26.9 | 37.5 | 36.7 |
| 3 | 37.6 |  |  |
| 4 |  |  |  |

| ' | L. Cos. | d. | L. Cot. | c.d. | L. Tan. | L. Sin. | d. | ' | P.P. |
|---|---|---|---|---|---|---|---|---|---|

| ′ | L. Sin. | d. | L. Tan. | c.d. | L. Cot. | L. Cos. | d | ′ |
|---|---------|----|---------|------|---------|---------|---|---|
| 0 | 9.48 998 | 39 | 9.51 178 | 43 | 0.48 822 | 9.97 821 | 4 | 60 |
| 1 | 9.49 037 | 39 | 9.51 221 | 43 | 0.48 779 | 9.97 817 | 5 | 59 |
| 2 | 9.49 076 | 39 | 9.51 264 | 42 | 0.48 736 | 9.97 812 | 4 | 58 |
| 3 | 9.49 115 | 38 | 9.51 306 | 43 | 0.48 694 | 9.97 808 | 4 | 57 |
| 4 | 9.49 153 | 39 | 9.51 349 | 43 | 0.48 651 | 9.97 804 | 4 | 56 |
| 5 | 9.49 192 | 39 | 9.51 392 | 43 | 0.48 608 | 9.97 800 | 4 | 55 |
| 6 | 9.49 231 | 38 | 9.51 435 | 43 | 0.48 565 | 9.97 796 | 4 | 54 |
| 7 | 9.49 269 | 39 | 9.51 478 | 42 | 0.48 522 | 9.97 792 | 4 | 53 |
| 8 | 9.49 308 | 39 | 9.51 520 | 43 | 0.48 480 | 9.97 788 | 4 | 52 |
| 9 | 9.49 347 | 38 | 9.51 563 | 43 | 0.48 437 | 9.97 784 | 5 | 51 |
| 10 | 9.49 385 | 39 | 9.51 606 | 42 | 0.48 394 | 9.97 779 | 4 | 50 |
| 11 | 9.49 424 | 38 | 9.51 648 | 43 | 0.48 352 | 9.97 775 | 4 | 49 |
| 12 | 9.49 462 | 38 | 9.51 691 | 43 | 0.48 309 | 9.97 771 | 4 | 48 |
| 13 | 9.49 500 | 39 | 9.51 734 | 42 | 0.48 266 | 9.97 767 | 4 | 47 |
| 14 | 9.49 539 | 38 | 9.51 776 | 43 | 0.48 224 | 9.97 763 | 4 | 46 |
| 15 | 9.49 577 | 38 | 9.51 819 | 42 | 0.48 181 | 9.97 759 | 5 | 45 |
| 16 | 9.49 615 | 39 | 9.51 861 | 42 | 0.48 139 | 9.97 754 | 4 | 44 |
| 17 | 9.49 654 | 38 | 9.51 903 | 43 | 0.48 097 | 9.97 750 | 4 | 43 |
| 18 | 9.49 692 | 38 | 9.51 946 | 42 | 0.48 054 | 9.97 746 | 4 | 42 |
| 19 | 9.49 730 | 38 | 9.51 988 | 43 | 0.48 012 | 9.97 742 | 4 | 41 |
| 20 | 9.49 768 | 38 | 9.52 031 | 42 | 0.47 969 | 9.97 738 | 4 | 40 |
| 21 | 9.49 806 | 38 | 9.52 073 | 42 | 0.47 927 | 9.97 734 | 5 | 39 |
| 22 | 9.49 844 | 38 | 9.52 115 | 42 | 0.47 885 | 9.97 729 | 4 | 38 |
| 23 | 9.49 882 | 38 | 9.52 157 | 43 | 0.47 843 | 9.97 725 | 4 | 37 |
| 24 | 9.49 920 | 38 | 9.52 200 | 42 | 0.47 800 | 9.97 721 | 4 | 36 |
| 25 | 9.49 958 | 38 | 9.52 242 | 42 | 0.47 758 | 9.97 717 | 4 | 35 |
| 26 | 9.49 996 | 38 | 9.52 284 | 42 | 0.47 716 | 9.97 713 | 5 | 34 |
| 27 | 9.50 034 | 38 | 9.52 326 | 42 | 0.47 674 | 9.97 708 | 4 | 33 |
| 28 | 9.50 072 | 38 | 9.52 368 | 42 | 0.47 632 | 9.97 704 | 4 | 32 |
| 29 | 9.50 110 | 38 | 9.52 410 | 42 | 0.47 590 | 9.97 700 | 4 | 31 |
| 30 | 9.50 148 | 37 | 9.52 452 | 42 | 0.47 548 | 9.97 696 | 5 | 30 |
| 31 | 9.50 185 | 38 | 9.52 494 | 42 | 0.47 506 | 9.97 691 | 4 | 29 |
| 32 | 9.50 223 | 38 | 9.52 536 | 42 | 0.47 464 | 9.97 687 | 4 | 28 |
| 33 | 9.50 261 | 37 | 9.52 578 | 42 | 0.47 422 | 9.97 683 | 4 | 27 |
| 34 | 9.50 298 | 38 | 9.52 620 | 41 | 0.47 380 | 9.97 679 | 5 | 26 |
| 35 | 9.50 336 | 38 | 9.52 661 | 42 | 0.47 339 | 9.97 674 | 4 | 25 |
| 36 | 9.50 374 | 37 | 9.52 703 | 42 | 0.47 297 | 9.97 670 | 4 | 24 |
| 37 | 9.50 411 | 38 | 9.52 745 | 42 | 0.47 255 | 9.97 666 | 4 | 23 |
| 38 | 9.50 449 | 37 | 9.52 787 | 42 | 0.47 213 | 9.97 662 | 5 | 22 |
| 39 | 9.50 486 | 37 | 9.52 829 | 41 | 0.47 171 | 9.97 657 | 4 | 21 |
| 40 | 9.50 523 | 38 | 9.52 870 | 42 | 0.47 130 | 9.97 653 | 4 | 20 |
| 41 | 9.50 561 | 37 | 9.52 912 | 41 | 0.47 088 | 9.97 649 | 4 | 19 |
| 42 | 9.50 598 | 37 | 9.52 953 | 42 | 0.47 047 | 9.97 645 | 5 | 18 |
| 43 | 9.50 635 | 38 | 9.52 995 | 42 | 0.47 005 | 9.97 640 | 4 | 17 |
| 44 | 9.50 673 | 37 | 9.53 037 | 41 | 0.46 963 | 9.97 636 | 4 | 16 |
| 45 | 9.50 710 | 37 | 9.53 078 | 42 | 0.46 922 | 9.97 632 | 4 | 15 |
| 46 | 9.50 747 | 37 | 9.53 120 | 41 | 0.46 880 | 9.97 628 | 5 | 14 |
| 47 | 9.50 784 | 37 | 9.53 161 | 41 | 0.46 839 | 9.97 623 | 4 | 13 |
| 48 | 9.50 821 | 37 | 9.53 202 | 42 | 0.46 798 | 9.97 619 | 4 | 12 |
| 49 | 9.50 858 | 38 | 9.53 244 | 41 | 0.46 756 | 9.97 615 | 5 | 11 |
| 50 | 9.50 896 | 37 | 9.53 285 | 42 | 0.46 715 | 9.97 610 | 4 | 10 |
| 51 | 9.50 933 | 37 | 9.53 327 | 41 | 0.46 673 | 9.97 606 | 4 | 9 |
| 52 | 9.50 970 | 37 | 9.53 368 | 41 | 0.46 632 | 9.97 602 | 5 | 8 |
| 53 | 9.51 007 | 36 | 9.53 409 | 41 | 0.46 591 | 9.97 597 | 4 | 7 |
| 54 | 9.51 043 | 37 | 9.53 450 | 42 | 0.46 550 | 9.97 593 | 4 | 6 |
| 55 | 9.51 080 | 37 | 9.53 492 | 41 | 0.46 508 | 9.97 589 | 5 | 5 |
| 56 | 9.51 117 | 37 | 9.53 533 | 41 | 0.46 467 | 9.97 584 | 4 | 4 |
| 57 | 9.51 154 | 37 | 9.53 574 | 41 | 0.46 426 | 9.97 580 | 4 | 3 |
| 58 | 9.51 191 | 36 | 9.53 615 | 41 | 0.46 385 | 9.97 576 | 5 | 2 |
| 59 | 9.51 227 | 37 | 9.53 656 | 41 | 0.46 344 | 9.97 571 | 4 | 1 |
| 60 | 9.51 264 |  | 9.53 697 |  | 0.46 303 | 9.97 567 |  | 0 |

| ′ | L. Cos. | d. | L. Cot. | c.d. | L. Tan. | L. Sin. | d | ′ |

**P. P.**

| ″ | 43 | 42 | 41 |
|---|----|----|----|
| 1 | 0.7 | 0.7 | 0.7 |
| 2 | 1.4 | 1.4 | 1.4 |
| 3 | 2.2 | 2.1 | 2.0 |
| 4 | 2.9 | 2.8 | 2.7 |
| 5 | 3.6 | 3.5 | 3.4 |
| 6 | 4.3 | 4.2 | 4.1 |
| 7 | 5.0 | 4.9 | 4.8 |
| 8 | 5.7 | 5.6 | 5.5 |
| 9 | 6.4 | 6.3 | 6.2 |
| 10 | 7.2 | 7.0 | 6.8 |
| 20 | 14.3 | 14.0 | 13.7 |
| 30 | 21.5 | 21.0 | 20.5 |
| 40 | 28.7 | 28.0 | 27.3 |
| 50 | 35.8 | 35.0 | 34.2 |

| ″ | 39 | 38 | 37 |
|---|----|----|----|
| 1 | 0.6 | 0.6 | 0.6 |
| 2 | 1.3 | 1.3 | 1.2 |
| 3 | 2.0 | 1.9 | 1.8 |
| 4 | 2.6 | 2.5 | 2.5 |
| 5 | 3.2 | 3.2 | 3.1 |
| 6 | 3.9 | 3.8 | 3.7 |
| 7 | 4.6 | 4.4 | 4.3 |
| 8 | 5.2 | 5.1 | 4.9 |
| 9 | 5.8 | 5.7 | 5.6 |
| 10 | 6.5 | 6.3 | 6.2 |
| 20 | 13.0 | 12.7 | 12.3 |
| 30 | 19.5 | 19.0 | 18.5 |
| 40 | 26.0 | 25.3 | 24.7 |
| 50 | 32.5 | 31.7 | 30.8 |

| ″ | 36 | 5 | 4 |
|---|----|----|----|
| 1 | 0.6 | 0.1 | 0.1 |
| 2 | 1.2 | 0.2 | 0.1 |
| 3 | 1.8 | 0.2 | 0.2 |
| 4 | 2.4 | 0.3 | 0.3 |
| 5 | 3.0 | 0.4 | 0.3 |
| 6 | 3.6 | 0.5 | 0.4 |
| 7 | 4.2 | 0.6 | 0.5 |
| 8 | 4.8 | 0.7 | 0.5 |
| 9 | 5.4 | 0.8 | 0.6 |
| 10 | 6.0 | 0.8 | 0.7 |
| 20 | 12.0 | 1.7 | 1.3 |
| 30 | 18.0 | 2.5 | 2.0 |
| 40 | 24.0 | 3.3 | 2.7 |
| 50 | 30.0 | 4.2 | 3.3 |

| 5 | 5 | 5 |
|---|---|---|
| 43 | 42 | 41 |
| 4.3 | 4.2 | 4.1 |
| 12.9 | 12.6 | 12.3 |
| 21.5 | 21.0 | 20.5 |
| 30.1 | 29.4 | 28.7 |
| 38.7 | 37.8 | 36.9 |

| 4 | 4 | 4 |
|---|---|---|
| 43 | 42 | 41 |
| 5.4 | 5.2 | 5.1 |
| 16.1 | 15.8 | 15.4 |
| 26.9 | 26.2 | 25.6 |
| 37.6 | 36.8 | 35.9 |

# LOGARITHMS OF THE FUNCTIONS (Continued)

| ' | L. Sin. | d. | L. Tan. | c.d. | L. Cot. | L. Cos. | d. | ' |
|---|---------|----|---------|------|---------|---------|----|---|
| 0 | 9.51 264 | 37 | 9.53 697 | 41 | 0.46 303 | 9.97 567 | 4 | 60 |
| 1 | 9.51 301 | 37 | 9.53 738 | 41 | 0.46 262 | 9.97 563 | 5 | 59 |
| 2 | 9.51 338 | 36 | 9.53 779 | 41 | 0.46 221 | 9.97 558 | 4 | 58 |
| 3 | 9.51 374 | 37 | 9.53 820 | 41 | 0.46 180 | 9.97 554 | 4 | 57 |
| 4 | 9.51 411 | 36 | 9.53 861 | 41 | 0.46 139 | 9.97 550 | 5 | 56 |
| 5 | 9.51 447 | 37 | 9.53 902 | 41 | 0.46 098 | 9.97 545 | 4 | 55 |
| 6 | 9.51 484 | 36 | 9.53 943 | 41 | 0.46 057 | 9.97 541 | 5 | 54 |
| 7 | 9.51 520 | 37 | 9.53 984 | 41 | 0.46 016 | 9.97 536 | 4 | 53 |
| 8 | 9.51 557 | 36 | 9.54 025 | 40 | 0.45 975 | 9.97 532 | 4 | 52 |
| 9 | 9.51 593 | 36 | 9.54 065 | 41 | 0.45 935 | 9.97 528 | 5 | 51 |
| 10 | 9.51 629 | 37 | 9.54 106 | 41 | 0.45 894 | 9.97 523 | 4 | 50 |
| 11 | 9.51 666 | 36 | 9.54 147 | 40 | 0.45 853 | 9.97 519 | 4 | 49 |
| 12 | 9.51 702 | 36 | 9.54 187 | 41 | 0.45 813 | 9.97 515 | 5 | 48 |
| 13 | 9.51 738 | 36 | 9.54 228 | 41 | 0.45 772 | 9.97 510 | 4 | 47 |
| 14 | 9.51 774 | 37 | 9.54 269 | 40 | 0.45 731 | 9.97 506 | 5 | 46 |
| 15 | 9.51 811 | 36 | 9.54 309 | 41 | 0.45 691 | 9.97 501 | 4 | 45 |
| 16 | 9.51 847 | 36 | 9.54 350 | 40 | 0.45 650 | 9.97 497 | 5 | 44 |
| 17 | 9.51 883 | 36 | 9.54 390 | 41 | 0.45 610 | 9.97 492 | 4 | 43 |
| 18 | 9.51 919 | 36 | 9.54 431 | 40 | 0.45 569 | 9.97 488 | 4 | 42 |
| 19 | 9.51 955 | 36 | 9.54 471 | 41 | 0.45 529 | 9.97 484 | 5 | 41 |
| 20 | 9.51 991 | 36 | 9.54 512 | 40 | 0.45 488 | 9.97 479 | 4 | 40 |
| 21 | 9.52 027 | 36 | 9.54 552 | 41 | 0.45 448 | 9.97 475 | 5 | 39 |
| 22 | 9.52 063 | 36 | 9.54 593 | 40 | 0.45 407 | 9.97 470 | 4 | 38 |
| 23 | 9.52 099 | 36 | 9.54 633 | 40 | 0.45 367 | 9.97 466 | 5 | 37 |
| 24 | 9.52 135 | 36 | 9.54 673 | 41 | 0.45 327 | 9.97 461 | 4 | 36 |
| 25 | 9.52 171 | 36 | 9.54 714 | 40 | 0.45 286 | 9.97 457 | 4 | 35 |
| 26 | 9.52 207 | 36 | 9.54 754 | 40 | 0.45 246 | 9.97 453 | 5 | 34 |
| 27 | 9.52 242 | 36 | 9.54 794 | 41 | 0.45 206 | 9.97 448 | 4 | 33 |
| 28 | 9.52 278 | 36 | 9.54 835 | 40 | 0.45 165 | 9.97 444 | 5 | 32 |
| 29 | 9.52 314 | 36 | 9.54 875 | 40 | 0.45 125 | 9.97 439 | 4 | 31 |
| 30 | 9.52 350 | 35 | 9.54 915 | 40 | 0.45 085 | 9.97 435 | 5 | 30 |
| 31 | 9.52 385 | 36 | 9.54 955 | 40 | 0.45 045 | 9.97 430 | 4 | 29 |
| 32 | 9.52 421 | 35 | 9.54 995 | 40 | 0.45 005 | 9.97 426 | 5 | 28 |
| 33 | 9.52 456 | 36 | 9.55 035 | 40 | 0.44 965 | 9.97 421 | 4 | 27 |
| 34 | 9.52 492 | 35 | 9.55 075 | 40 | 0.44 925 | 9.97 417 | 5 | 26 |
| 35 | 9.52 527 | 36 | 9.55 115 | 40 | 0.44 885 | 9.97 412 | 4 | 25 |
| 36 | 9.52 563 | 35 | 9.55 155 | 40 | 0.44 845 | 9.97 408 | 5 | 24 |
| 37 | 9.52 598 | 36 | 9.55 195 | 40 | 0.44 805 | 9.97 403 | 4 | 23 |
| 38 | 9.52 634 | 35 | 9.55 235 | 40 | 0.44 765 | 9.97 399 | 5 | 22 |
| 39 | 9.52 669 | 36 | 9.55 275 | 40 | 0.44 725 | 9.97 394 | 4 | 21 |
| 40 | 9.52 705 | 35 | 9.55 315 | 40 | 0.44 685 | 9.97 390 | 5 | 20 |
| 41 | 9.52 740 | 35 | 9.55 355 | 40 | 0.44 645 | 9.97 385 | 4 | 19 |
| 42 | 9.52 775 | 36 | 9.55 395 | 39 | 0.44 605 | 9.97 381 | 5 | 18 |
| 43 | 9.52 811 | 35 | 9.55 434 | 40 | 0.44 566 | 9.97 376 | 4 | 17 |
| 44 | 9.52 846 | 35 | 9.55 474 | 40 | 0.44 526 | 9.97 372 | 5 | 16 |
| 45 | 9.52 881 | 35 | 9.55 514 | 40 | 0.44 486 | 9.97 367 | 4 | 15 |
| 46 | 9.52 916 | 35 | 9.55 554 | 39 | 0.44 446 | 9.97 363 | 4 | 14 |
| 47 | 9.52 951 | 35 | 9.55 593 | 40 | 0.44 407 | 9.97 358 | 5 | 13 |
| 48 | 9.52 986 | 35 | 9.55 633 | 40 | 0.44 367 | 9.97 353 | 4 | 12 |
| 49 | 9.53 021 | 35 | 9.55 673 | 39 | 0.44 327 | 9.97 349 | 5 | 11 |
| 50 | 9.53 056 | 36 | 9.55 712 | 40 | 0.44 288 | 9.97 344 | 4 | 10 |
| 51 | 9.53 092 | 34 | 9.55 752 | 39 | 0.44 248 | 9.97 340 | 5 | 9 |
| 52 | 9.53 126 | 35 | 9.55 791 | 40 | 0.44 209 | 9.97 335 | 4 | 8 |
| 53 | 9.53 161 | 35 | 9.55 831 | 39 | 0.44 169 | 9.97 331 | 5 | 7 |
| 54 | 9.53 196 | 35 | 9.55 870 | 40 | 0.44 130 | 9.97 326 | 4 | 6 |
| 55 | 9.53 231 | 35 | 9.55 910 | 39 | 0.44 090 | 9.97 322 | 5 | 5 |
| 56 | 9.53 266 | 35 | 9.55 949 | 40 | 0.44 051 | 9.97 317 | 5 | 4 |
| 57 | 9.53 301 | 35 | 9.55 989 | 39 | 0.44 011 | 9.97 312 | 4 | 3 |
| 58 | 9.53 336 | 34 | 9.56 028 | 39 | 0.43 972 | 9.97 308 | 5 | 2 |
| 59 | 9.53 370 | 35 | 9.56 067 | 39 | 0.43 933 | 9.97 303 | 4 | 1 |
| 60 | 9.53 405 |  | 9.56 107 |  | 0.43 893 | 9.97 299 |  | 0 |

| ' | L. Cos. | d. | L. Cot. | c.d. | L. Tan. | L. Sin. | d. | ' |
|---|---------|----|---------|------|---------|---------|----|---|

## P. P.

| | 41 | 40 | 39 |
|---|-----|-----|-----|
| 1 | 0.7 | 0.7 | 0.6 |
| 2 | 1.4 | 1.3 | 1.3 |
| 3 | 2.0 | 2.0 | 2.0 |
| 4 | 2.7 | 2.7 | 2.6 |
| 5 | 3.4 | 3.3 | 3.2 |
| 6 | 4.1 | 4.0 | 3.9 |
| 7 | 4.8 | 4.7 | 4.6 |
| 8 | 5.5 | 5.3 | 5.2 |
| 9 | 6.2 | 6.0 | 5.8 |
| 10 | 6.8 | 6.7 | 6.5 |
| 20 | 13.7 | 13.3 | 13.0 |
| 30 | 20.5 | 20.0 | 19.5 |
| 40 | 27.3 | 26.7 | 26.0 |
| 50 | 34.2 | 33.3 | 32.5 |

| | 37 | 36 | 35 |
|---|-----|-----|-----|
| 1 | 0.6 | 0.6 | 0.6 |
| 2 | 1.2 | 1.2 | 1.2 |
| 3 | 1.8 | 1.8 | 1.8 |
| 4 | 2.5 | 2.4 | 2.3 |
| 5 | 3.1 | 3.0 | 2.9 |
| 6 | 3.7 | 3.6 | 3.5 |
| 7 | 4.3 | 4.2 | 4.1 |
| 8 | 4.9 | 4.8 | 4.7 |
| 9 | 5.6 | 5.4 | 5.2 |
| 10 | 6.2 | 6.0 | 5.8 |
| 20 | 12.3 | 12.0 | 11.7 |
| 30 | 18.5 | 18.0 | 17.5 |
| 40 | 24.7 | 24.0 | 23.3 |
| 50 | 30.8 | 30.0 | 29.2 |

| | 34 | 5 | 4 |
|---|-----|-----|-----|
| 1 | 0.6 | 0.1 | 0.1 |
| 2 | 1.1 | 0.2 | 0.1 |
| 3 | 1.7 | 0.2 | 0.2 |
| 4 | 2.3 | 0.3 | 0.3 |
| 5 | 2.8 | 0.4 | 0.3 |
| 6 | 3.4 | 0.5 | 0.4 |
| 7 | 4.0 | 0.6 | 0.5 |
| 8 | 4.5 | 0.7 | 0.5 |
| 9 | 5.1 | 0.8 | 0.6 |
| 10 | 5.7 | 0.8 | 0.7 |
| 20 | 11.3 | 1.7 | 1.3 |
| 30 | 17.0 | 2.5 | 2.0 |
| 40 | 22.7 | 3.3 | 2.7 |
| 50 | 28.3 | 4.2 | 3.3 |

| | 5 | 5 | 5 |
|---|-----|-----|-----|
| | 41 | 40 | 39 |
| 1 | 4.1 | 4.0 | 3.9 |
| 2 | 12.3 | 12.0 | 11.7 |
| 3 | 20.5 | 20.0 | 19.5 |
| 4 | 28.7 | 28.0 | 27.3 |
| 5 | 36.9 | 36.0 | 35.1 |

| | 4 | 4 | 4 |
|---|-----|-----|-----|
| | 41 | 40 | 39 |
| 1 | 5.1 | 5.0 | 4.2 |
| 2 | 15.4 | 15.0 | 14.6 |
| 3 | 25.6 | 25.0 | 24.4 |
| 4 | 35.9 | 35.0 | 34.1 |

# LOGARITHMS OF THE FUNCTIONS (Continued)

| ' | L. Sin. | d. | L. Tan. | c.d. | L. Cot. | L. Cos. | d. | ' |
|---|---|---|---|---|---|---|---|---|
| 0 | 9.53 405 | 35 | 9.56 107 | 39 | 0.43 893 | 9.97 299 | 5 | 60 |
| 1 | 9.53 440 | 35 | 9.56 146 | 39 | 0.43 854 | 9.97 294 | 5 | 59 |
| 2 | 9.53 475 | 34 | 9.56 185 | 39 | 0.43 815 | 9.97 289 | 4 | 58 |
| 3 | 9.53 509 | 35 | 9.56 224 | 40 | 0.43 776 | 9.97 285 | 5 | 57 |
| 4 | 9.53 544 | 34 | 9.56 264 | 39 | 0.43 736 | 9.97 280 | 4 | 56 |
| 5 | 9.53 578 | 35 | 9.56 303 | 39 | 0.43 697 | 9.97 276 | 5 | 55 |
| 6 | 9.53 613 | 34 | 9.56 342 | 39 | 0.43 658 | 9.97 271 | 5 | 54 |
| 7 | 9.53 647 | 35 | 9.56 381 | 39 | 0.43 619 | 9.97 266 | 4 | 53 |
| 8 | 9.53 682 | 34 | 9.56 420 | 39 | 0.43 580 | 9.97 262 | 5 | 52 |
| 9 | 9.53 716 | 35 | 9.56 459 | 39 | 0.43 541 | 9.97 257 | 5 | 51 |
| 10 | 9.53 751 | 34 | 9.56 498 | 39 | 0.43 502 | 9.97 252 | 4 | 50 |
| 11 | 9.53 785 | 34 | 9.56 537 | 39 | 0.43 463 | 9.97 248 | 5 | 49 |
| 12 | 9.53 819 | 35 | 9.56 576 | 39 | 0.43 424 | 9.97 243 | 5 | 48 |
| 13 | 9.53 854 | 34 | 9.56 615 | 39 | 0.43 385 | 9.97 238 | 4 | 47 |
| 14 | 9.53 888 | 34 | 9.56 654 | 39 | 0.43 346 | 9.97 234 | 5 | 46 |
| 15 | 9.53 922 | 35 | 9.56 693 | 39 | 0.43 307 | 9.97 229 | 5 | 45 |
| 16 | 9.53 957 | 34 | 9.56 732 | 39 | 0.43 268 | 9.97 224 | 4 | 44 |
| 17 | 9.53 991 | 34 | 9.56 771 | 39 | 0.43 229 | 9.97 220 | 5 | 43 |
| 18 | 9.54 025 | 34 | 9.56 810 | 39 | 0.43 190 | 9.97 215 | 5 | 42 |
| 19 | 9.54 059 | 34 | 9.56 849 | 38 | 0.43 151 | 9.97 210 | 4 | 41 |
| 20 | 9.54 093 | 34 | 9.56 887 | 39 | 0.43 113 | 9.97 206 | 5 | 40 |
| 21 | 9.54 127 | 34 | 9.56 926 | 39 | 0.43 074 | 9.97 201 | 5 | 39 |
| 22 | 9.54 161 | 34 | 9.56 965 | 39 | 0.43 035 | 9.97 196 | 4 | 38 |
| 23 | 9.54 195 | 34 | 9.57 004 | 38 | 0.42 996 | 9.97 192 | 5 | 37 |
| 24 | 9.54 229 | 34 | 9.57 042 | 39 | 0.42 958 | 9.97 187 | 5 | 36 |
| 25 | 9.54 263 | 34 | 9.57 081 | 39 | 0.42 919 | 9.97 182 | 4 | 35 |
| 26 | 9.54 297 | 34 | 9.57 120 | 38 | 0.42 880 | 9.97 178 | 5 | 34 |
| 27 | 9.54 331 | 34 | 9.57 158 | 39 | 0.42 842 | 9.97 173 | 5 | 33 |
| 28 | 9.54 365 | 34 | 9.57 197 | 38 | 0.42 803 | 9.97 168 | 5 | 32 |
| 29 | 9.54 399 | 34 | 9.57 235 | 39 | 0.42 765 | 9.97 163 | 4 | 31 |
| 30 | 9.54 433 | 33 | 9.57 274 | 38 | 0.42 726 | 9.97 159 | 5 | 30 |
| 31 | 9.54 466 | 34 | 9.57 312 | 39 | 0.42 688 | 9.97 154 | 5 | 29 |
| 32 | 9.54 500 | 34 | 9.57 351 | 38 | 0.42 649 | 9.97 149 | 4 | 28 |
| 33 | 9.54 534 | 33 | 9.57 389 | 39 | 0.42 611 | 9.97 145 | 5 | 27 |
| 34 | 0.54 567 | 34 | 9.57 428 | 38 | 0.42 572 | 9.97 140 | 5 | 26 |
| 35 | 9.54 601 | 34 | 9.57 466 | 38 | 0.42 534 | 9.97 135 | 5 | 25 |
| 36 | 9.54 635 | 33 | 9.57 504 | 39 | 0.42 496 | 9.97 130 | 4 | 24 |
| 37 | 9.54 668 | 34 | 9.57 543 | 38 | 0.42 457 | 9.97 126 | 5 | 23 |
| 38 | 9.54 702 | 33 | 9.57 581 | 38 | 0.42 419 | 9.97 121 | 5 | 22 |
| 39 | 9.54 735 | 34 | 9.57 619 | 39 | 0.42 381 | 9.97 116 | 5 | 21 |
| 40 | 9.54 769 | 33 | 9.57 658 | 38 | 0.42 342 | 9.97 111 | 4 | 20 |
| 41 | 9.54 802 | 34 | 9.57 696 | 38 | 0.42 304 | 9.97 107 | 5 | 19 |
| 42 | 9.54 836 | 33 | 9.57 734 | 38 | 0.42 266 | 9.97 102 | 5 | 18 |
| 43 | 9.54 869 | 34 | 9.57 772 | 38 | 0.42 228 | 9.97 097 | 5 | 17 |
| 44 | 9.54 903 | 33 | 9.57 810 | 39 | 0.42 190 | 9.97 092 | 5 | 16 |
| 45 | 9.54 936 | 33 | 9.57 849 | 38 | 0.42 151 | 9.97 087 | 4 | 15 |
| 46 | 9.54 969 | 34 | 9.57 887 | 38 | 0.42 113 | 9.97 083 | 5 | 14 |
| 47 | 9.55 003 | 33 | 9.57 925 | 38 | 0.42 075 | 9.97 078 | 5 | 13 |
| 48 | 9.55 036 | 33 | 9.57 963 | 38 | 0.42 037 | 9.97 073 | 5 | 12 |
| 49 | 9.55 069 | 33 | 9.58 001 | 38 | 0.41 999 | 9.97 068 | 5 | 11 |
| 50 | 9.55 102 | 34 | 9.58 039 | 38 | 0.41 961 | 9.97 063 | 4 | 10 |
| 51 | 9.55 136 | 33 | 9.58 077 | 38 | 0.41 923 | 9.97 059 | 5 | 9 |
| 52 | 9.55 169 | 33 | 9.58 115 | 38 | 0.41 885 | 9.97 054 | 5 | 8 |
| 53 | 9.55 202 | 33 | 9.58 153 | 38 | 0.41 847 | 9.97 049 | 5 | 7 |
| 54 | 9.55 235 | 33 | 9.58 191 | 38 | 0.41 809 | 9.97 044 | 5 | 6 |
| 55 | 9.55 268 | 33 | 9.58 229 | 38 | 0.41 771 | 9.97 039 | 4 | 5 |
| 56 | 9.55 301 | 33 | 9.58 267 | 37 | 0.41 733 | 9.97 035 | 5 | 4 |
| 57 | 9.55 334 | 33 | 9.58 304 | 38 | 0.41 696 | 9.97 030 | 5 | 3 |
| 58 | 9.55 367 | 33 | 9.58 342 | 38 | 0.41 658 | 9.97 025 | 5 | 2 |
| 59 | 9.55 400 | 33 | 9.58 380 | 38 | 0.41 620 | 9.97 020 | 5 | 1 |
| 60 | 9.55 433 | | 9.58 418 | | 0.41 582 | 9.97 015 | | 0 |

| ' | L. Cos. | d. | L. Cot. | c.d. | L. Tan. | L. Sin. | d. | ' |
|---|---|---|---|---|---|---|---|---|

## P. P.

| | 40 | 39 | 38 |
|---|---|---|---|
| 1 | 0.7 | 0.6 | 0.6 |
| 2 | 1.3 | 1.3 | 1.3 |
| 3 | 2.0 | 2.0 | 1.9 |
| 4 | 2.7 | 2.6 | 2.5 |
| 5 | 3.3 | 3.2 | 3.2 |
| 6 | 4.0 | 3.9 | 3.8 |
| 7 | 4.7 | 4.6 | 4.4 |
| 8 | 5.3 | 5.2 | 5.1 |
| 9 | 6.0 | 5.8 | 5.7 |
| 10 | 6.7 | 6.5 | 6.3 |
| 20 | 13.3 | 13.0 | 12.7 |
| 30 | 20.0 | 19.5 | 19.0 |
| 40 | 26.7 | 26.0 | 25.3 |
| 50 | 33.3 | 32.5 | 31.7 |

| | 37 | 35 | 34 |
|---|---|---|---|
| 1 | 0.6 | 0.6 | 0.6 |
| 2 | 1.2 | 1.2 | 1.1 |
| 3 | 1.8 | 1.8 | 1.7 |
| 4 | 2.5 | 2.3 | 2.3 |
| 5 | 3.1 | 2.9 | 2.8 |
| 6 | 3.7 | 3.5 | 3.4 |
| 7 | 4.3 | 4.1 | 4.0 |
| 8 | 4.9 | 4.7 | 4.5 |
| 9 | 5.6 | 5.2 | 5.1 |
| 10 | 6.2 | 5.8 | 5.7 |
| 20 | 12.3 | 11.7 | 11.3 |
| 30 | 18.5 | 17.5 | 17.0 |
| 40 | 24.7 | 23.3 | 22.7 |
| 50 | 30.8 | 29.2 | 28.3 |

| | 33 | 5 | 4 |
|---|---|---|---|
| 1 | 0.6 | 0.1 | 0.1 |
| 2 | 1.1 | 0.2 | 0.1 |
| 4 | 1.6 | 0.2 | 0.2 |
| 4 | 2.2 | 0.3 | 0.3 |
| 5 | 2.8 | 0.4 | 0.3 |
| 6 | 3.3 | 0.5 | 0.4 |
| 7 | 3.8 | 0.6 | 0.5 |
| 8 | 4.4 | 0.7 | 0.5 |
| 9 | 5.0 | 0.8 | 0.6 |
| 10 | 5.5 | 0.8 | 0.7 |
| 20 | 11.0 | 1.7 | 1.3 |
| 30 | 16.5 | 2.5 | 2.0 |
| 40 | 22.0 | 3.3 | 2.7 |
| 50 | 27.5 | 4.2 | 3.3 |

| | 5 | 5 | 5 |
|---|---|---|---|

| | | 40 | 39 | 38 |
|---|---|---|---|---|
| 0 | 1 | 4.0 | 3.9 | 3.8 |
| | 2 | 12.0 | 11.7 | 11.4 |
| | | 20.0 | 19.5 | 19.0 |
| | 3 | 28.0 | 27.3 | 26.6 |
| | 4 | 36.0 | 35.1 | 34.2 |
| | 5 | | | |

| | 5 | 4 | 4 |
|---|---|---|---|
| | 37 | 39 | 38 |

| | | 37 | 39 | 38 |
|---|---|---|---|---|
| 0 | 1 | 3.7 | 4.9 | 4.8 |
| | 2 | 11.1 | 14.6 | 14.2 |
| | 3 | 18.5 | 24.4 | 23.8 |
| | 4 | 25.9 | 34.1 | 33.2 |
| | 5 | 33.3 | — | — |

| ′ | L. Sin. | d. | L. Tan. | c.d. | L. Cot. | L. Cos. | d. | ′ |
|---|---------|----|---------|------|---------|---------|----|---|
| 0 | 9.55 433 |    | 9.58 418 |    | 0.41 582 | 9.97 015 |   | 60 |
| 1 | 9.55 466 | 33 | 9.58 455 | 37 | 0.41 545 | 9.97 010 | 5 | 59 |
| 2 | 9.55 499 | 33 | 9.58 493 | 38 | 0.41 507 | 9.97 005 | 5 | 58 |
| 3 | 9.55 532 | 33 | 9.58 531 | 38 | 0.41 469 | 9.97 001 | 4 | 57 |
| 4 | 9.55 564 | 32 | 9.58 569 | 38 | 0.41 431 | 9.96 996 | 5 | 56 |
| 5 | 9.55 597 | 33 | 9.58 606 | 37 | 0.41 394 | 9.96 991 | 5 | 55 |
| 6 | 9.55 630 | 33 | 9.58 644 | 38 | 0.41 356 | 9.96 986 | 5 | 54 |
| 7 | 9.55 663 | 33 | 9.58 681 | 37 | 0.41 319 | 9.96 981 | 5 | 53 |
| 8 | 9.55 695 | 32 | 9.58 719 | 38 | 0.41 281 | 9.96 976 | 5 | 52 |
| 9 | 9.55 728 | 33 | 9.58 757 | 38 | 0.41 243 | 9.96 971 | 5 | 51 |
| 10 | 9.55 761 | 33 | 9.58 794 | 37 | 0.41 206 | 9.96 966 | 5 | 50 |
| 11 | 9.55 793 | 32 | 9.58 832 | 38 | 0.41 168 | 9.96 962 | 4 | 49 |
| 12 | 9.55 826 | 33 | 9.58 869 | 37 | 0.41 131 | 9.96 957 | 5 | 48 |
| 13 | 9.55 858 | 32 | 9.58 907 | 38 | 0.41 093 | 9.96 952 | 5 | 47 |
| 14 | 9.55 891 | 33 | 9.58 944 | 37 | 0.41 056 | 9.96 947 | 5 | 46 |
| 15 | 9.55 923 | 32 | 9.58 981 | 38 | 0.41 019 | 9.96 942 | 5 | 45 |
| 16 | 9.55 956 | 33 | 9.59 019 | 37 | 0.40 981 | 9.96 937 | 5 | 44 |
| 17 | 9.55 988 | 32 | 9.59 056 | 38 | 0.40 944 | 9.96 932 | 5 | 43 |
| 18 | 9.56 021 | 33 | 9.59 094 | 37 | 0.40 906 | 9.96 927 | 5 | 42 |
| 19 | 9.56 053 | 32 | 9.59 131 | 37 | 0.40 869 | 9.96 922 | 5 | 41 |
| 20 | 9.56 085 | 33 | 9.59 168 | 37 | 0.40 832 | 9.96 917 | 5 | 40 |
| 21 | 9.56 118 | 32 | 9.59 205 | 38 | 0.40 795 | 9.96 912 | 5 | 39 |
| 22 | 9.56 150 | 32 | 9.59 243 | 37 | 0.40 757 | 9.96 907 | 4 | 38 |
| 23 | 9.56 182 | 33 | 9.59 280 | 37 | 0.40 720 | 9.96 903 | 5 | 37 |
| 24 | 9.56 215 | 32 | 9.59 317 | 37 | 0.40 683 | 9.96 898 | 5 | 36 |
| 25 | 9.56 247 | 32 | 9.59 354 | 37 | 0.40 646 | 9.96 893 | 5 | 35 |
| 26 | 9.56 279 | 32 | 9.59 391 | 38 | 0.40 609 | 9.96 888 | 5 | 34 |
| 27 | 9.56 311 | 32 | 9.59 429 | 37 | 0.40 571 | 9.96 883 | 5 | 33 |
| 28 | 9.56 343 | 32 | 9.59 466 | 37 | 0.40 534 | 9.96 878 | 5 | 32 |
| 29 | 9.56 375 | 32 | 9.59 503 | 37 | 0.40 497 | 9 96 873 | 5 | 31 |
| 30 | 9.56 408 | 32 | 9.59 540 | 37 | 0.40 460 | 9.96 868 | 5 | 30 |
| 31 | 9.56 440 | 32 | 9.59 577 | 37 | 0.40 423 | 9.96 863 | 5 | 29 |
| 32 | 9.56 472 | 32 | 9.59 614 | 37 | 0.40 386 | 9.96 858 | 5 | 28 |
| 33 | 9.56 504 | 32 | 9.59 651 | 37 | 0.40 349 | 9.96 853 | 5 | 27 |
| 34 | 9.56 536 | 32 | 9.59 688 | 37 | 0.40 312 | 9.96 848 | 5 | 26 |
| 35 | 9.56 568 | 31 | 9.59 725 | 37 | 0.40 275 | 9.96 843 | 5 | 25 |
| 36 | 9.56 599 | 32 | 9.59 762 | 37 | 0.40 238 | 9.96 838 | 5 | 24 |
| 37 | 9 56 631 | 31 | 9.59 799 | 37 | 0.40 201 | 9.96 833 | 5 | 23 |
| 38 | 9.56 663 | 32 | 9.59 835 | 36 | 0.40 165 | 9.96 828 | 5 | 22 |
| 39 | 9.56 695 | 32 | 9.59 872 | 37 | 0.40 128 | 9.96 823 | 5 | 21 |
| 40 | 9.56 727 | 32 | 9.59 909 | 37 | 0.40 091 | 9.96 818 | 5 | 20 |
| 41 | 9.56 759 | 31 | 9.59 946 | 37 | 0.40 054 | 9.96 813 | 5 | 19 |
| 42 | 9.56 790 | 32 | 9.59 983 | 37 | 0.40 017 | 9.96 808 | 5 | 18 |
| 43 | 9.56 822 | 32 | 9.60 019 | 36 | 0.39 981 | 9.96 803 | 5 | 17 |
| 44 | 9.56 854 | 32 | 9.60 056 | 37 | 0.39 944 | 9.96 798 | 5 | 16 |
| 45 | 9.56 886 | 31 | 9.60 093 | 37 | 0.39 907 | 9.96 793 | 5 | 15 |
| 46 | 9.56 917 | 32 | 9.60 130 | 37 | 0.39 870 | 9.96 788 | 5 | 14 |
| 47 | 9.56 949 | 31 | 9.60 166 | 36 | 0.39 834 | 9.96 783 | 5 | 13 |
| 48 | 9.56 980 | 32 | 9.60 203 | 37 | 0.39 797 | 9.96 778 | 6 | 12 |
| 49 | 9.57 012 | 32 | 9.60 240 | 37 | 0.39 760 | 9.96 772 | 5 | 11 |
| 50 | 9.57 044 | 31 | 9.60 276 | 36 | 0.39 724 | 9.96 767 | 5 | 10 |
| 51 | 9.57 075 | 32 | 9.60 313 | 37 | 0.39 687 | 9.96 762 | 5 | 9 |
| 52 | 9.57 107 | 31 | 9.60 349 | 36 | 0.39 651 | 9.96 757 | 5 | 8 |
| 53 | 9.57 138 | 31 | 9.60 386 | 37 | 0.39 614 | 9.96 752 | 5 | 7 |
| 54 | 9.57 169 | 32 | 9.60 422 | 36 | 0.39 578 | 9.96 747 | 5 | 6 |
| 55 | 9.57 201 | 31 | 9.60 459 | 37 | 0.39 541 | 9.96 742 | 5 | 5 |
| 56 | 9.57 232 | 32 | 9.60 495 | 36 | 0.39 505 | 9.96 737 | 5 | 4 |
| 57 | 9.57 264 | 31 | 9.60 532 | 37 | 0.39 468 | 9.96 732 | 5 | 3 |
| 58 | 9.57 295 | 31 | 9.60 568 | 36 | 0.39 432 | 9.96 727 | 5 | 2 |
| 59 | 9.57 326 | 32 | 9.60 605 | 37 | 0.39 395 | 9.96 722 | 5 | 1 |
| 60 | 9.57 358 |    | 9.60 641 | 36 | 0.39 359 | 9.96 717 | 5 | 0 |

**P. P.**

|    | 38 | 37 | 36 |
|----|----|----|----|
| 1  | 0.6 | 0.6 | 0.6 |
| 2  | 1.3 | 1.2 | 1.2 |
| 3  | 1.9 | 1.8 | 1.8 |
| 4  | 2.5 | 2.5 | 2.4 |
| 5  | 3.2 | 3.1 | 3.0 |
| 6  | 3.8 | 3.7 | 3.6 |
| 7  | 4.4 | 4.3 | 4.2 |
| 8  | 5.1 | 4.9 | 4.8 |
| 9  | 5.7 | 5.6 | 5.4 |
| 10 | 6.3 | 6.2 | 6.0 |
| 20 | 12.7 | 12.3 | 12.0 |
| 30 | 19.0 | 18.5 | 18.0 |
| 40 | 25.3 | 24.7 | 24.0 |
| 50 | 31.7 | 30.8 | 30.0 |

|    | 33 | 32 | 31 |
|----|----|----|----|
| 1  | 0.6 | 0.5 | 0.5 |
| 2  | 1.1 | 1.1 | 1.0 |
| 3  | 1.6 | 1.6 | 1.6 |
| 4  | 2.2 | 2.1 | 2.1 |
| 5  | 2.8 | 2.7 | 2.6 |
| 6  | 3.3 | 3.2 | 3.1 |
| 7  | 3.8 | 3.7 | 3.6 |
| 8  | 4.4 | 4.3 | 4.1 |
| 9  | 5.0 | 4.8 | 4.6 |
| 10 | 5.5 | 5.3 | 5.2 |
| 20 | 11.0 | 10.7 | 10.3 |
| 30 | 16.5 | 16.0 | 15.5 |
| 40 | 22.0 | 21.3 | 20.7 |
| 50 | 27.5 | 26.7 | 25.8 |

|    | 6 | 5 | 4 |
|----|---|---|---|
| 1  | 0.1 | 0.1 | 0.1 |
| 2  | 0.2 | 0.2 | 0.1 |
| 3  | 0.3 | 0.2 | 0.2 |
| 4  | 0.4 | 0.3 | 0.3 |
| 5  | 0.5 | 0.4 | 0.3 |
| 6  | 0.6 | 0.5 | 0.4 |
| 7  | 0.7 | 0.6 | 0.5 |
| 8  | 0.8 | 0.7 | 0.5 |
| 9  | 0.9 | 0.8 | 0.6 |
| 10 | 1.0 | 0.8 | 0.7 |
| 20 | 2.0 | 1.7 | 1.3 |
| 30 | 3.0 | 2.5 | 2.0 |
| 40 | 4.0 | 3.3 | 2.7 |
| 50 | 5.0 | 4.2 | 3.3 |

|   | 6 | 5 | 5 |
|---|----|----|----|
|   | 37 | 38 | 37 |
| 0 | 3.1 | 3.8 | 3.7 |
| 1 | 9.2 | 11.4 | 11.1 |
| 2 | 15.4 | 19.0 | 18.5 |
| 3 | 21.6 | 26.6 | 25.9 |
| 4 | 27.8 | 34.2 | 33.3 |
| 6 | 33.9 | — | — |

|   | 5 | 4 | 4 |
|---|----|----|----|
|   | 36 | 38 | 37 |
| 0 | 3.6 | 4.8 | 4.6 |
| 1 | 10.8 | 14.2 | 13.9 |
| 2 | 18.0 | 23.8 | 23.1 |
| 3 | 25.2 | 33.2 | 32.4 |
| 4 | 32.4 | — | — |

| ′ | L. Cos. | d. | L. Cot. | c d. | L. Tan. | L. Sin. | d. | ′ |
|---|---------|----|---------|------|---------|---------|----|---|

**22° (202)°**     **(337°) 157°**

| ' | L. Sin. | d. | L. Tan. | c.d. | L. Cot. | L. Cos. | d. | ' |
|---|---------|----|---------|------|---------|---------|----|---|
| 0 | 9.57 358 |   | 9.60 641 |   | 0.39 359 | 9.96 717 |   | 60 |
| 1 | 9.57 389 | 31 | 9.60 677 | 36 | 0.39 323 | 9.96 711 | 6 | 59 |
| 2 | 9.57 420 | 31 | 9.60 714 | 37 | 0.39 286 | 9.96 706 | 5 | 58 |
| 3 | 9.57 451 | 31 | 9.60 750 | 36 | 0.39 250 | 9.96 701 | 5 | 57 |
| 4 | 9.57 482 | 31 | 9.60 786 | 36 | 0.39 214 | 9.96 696 | 5 | 56 |
| 5 | 9.57 514 | 32 | 9.60 823 | 37 | 0.39 177 | 9.96 691 | 5 | 55 |
| 6 | 9.57 545 | 31 | 9.60 859 | 36 | 0.39 141 | 9.96 686 | 5 | 54 |
| 7 | 9.57 576 | 31 | 9.60 895 | 36 | 0.39 105 | 9.96 681 | 5 | 53 |
| 8 | 9.57 607 | 31 | 9.60 931 | 36 | 0.39 069 | 9.96 676 | 5 | 52 |
| 9 | 9.57 638 | 31 | 9.60 967 | 36 | 0.39 033 | 9.96 670 | 6 | 51 |
| 10 | 9.57 669 | 31 | 9.61 004 | 37 | 0.38 996 | 9.96 665 | 5 | 50 |
| 11 | 9.57 700 | 31 | 9.61 040 | 36 | 0.38 960 | 9.96 660 | 5 | 49 |
| 12 | 9.57 731 | 31 | 9.61 076 | 36 | 0.38 924 | 9.96 655 | 5 | 48 |
| 13 | 9.57 762 | 31 | 9.61 112 | 36 | 0.38 888 | 9.96 650 | 5 | 47 |
| 14 | 9.57 793 | 31 | 9.61 148 | 36 | 0.38 852 | 9.96 645 | 5 | 46 |
| 15 | 9.57 824 | 31 | 9.61 184 | 36 | 0.38 816 | 9.96 640 | 5 | 45 |
| 16 | 9.57 855 | 31 | 9.61 220 | 36 | 0.38 780 | 9.96 634 | 6 | 44 |
| 17 | 9.57 885 | 30 | 9.61 256 | 36 | 0.38 744 | 9.96 629 | 5 | 43 |
| 18 | 9.57 916 | 31 | 9.61 292 | 36 | 0.38 708 | 9.96 624 | 5 | 42 |
| 19 | 9.57 947 | 31 | 9.61 328 | 36 | 0.38 672 | 9.96 619 | 5 | 41 |
| 20 | 9.57 978 | 31 | 9.61 364 | 36 | 0.38 636 | 9.96 614 | 5 | 40 |
| 21 | 9.58 008 | 30 | 9.61 400 | 36 | 0.38 600 | 9.96 608 | 6 | 39 |
| 22 | 9.58 039 | 31 | 9.61 436 | 36 | 0.38 564 | 9.96 603 | 5 | 38 |
| 23 | 9.58 070 | 31 | 9.61 472 | 36 | 0.38 528 | 9.96 598 | 5 | 37 |
| 24 | 9.58 101 | 31 | 9.61 508 | 36 | 0.38 492 | 9.96 593 | 5 | 36 |
| 25 | 9.58 131 | 30 | 9.61 544 | 36 | 0.38 456 | 9.96 588 | 5 | 35 |
| 26 | 9.58 162 | 31 | 9.61 579 | 35 | 0.38 421 | 9.96 582 | 6 | 34 |
| 27 | 9.58 192 | 30 | 9.61 615 | 36 | 0.38 385 | 9.96 577 | 5 | 33 |
| 28 | 9.58 223 | 31 | 9.61 651 | 36 | 0.38 349 | 9.96 572 | 5 | 32 |
| 29 | 9.58 253 | 30 | 9.61 687 | 36 | 0.38 313 | 9.96 567 | 5 | 31 |
| 30 | 9.58 284 | 31 | 9.61 722 | 35 | 0.38 278 | 9.96 562 | 6 | 30 |
| 31 | 9.58 314 | 30 | 9.61 758 | 36 | 0.38 242 | 9.96 556 | 5 | 29 |
| 32 | 9.58 345 | 31 | 9.61 794 | 36 | 0.38 206 | 9.96 551 | 5 | 28 |
| 33 | 9.58 375 | 30 | 9.61 830 | 36 | 0.38 170 | 9.96 546 | 5 | 27 |
| 34 | 9.58 406 | 31 | 9.61 865 | 35 | 0.38 135 | 9.96 541 | 6 | 26 |
| 35 | 9.58 436 | 30 | 9.61 901 | 36 | 0.38 099 | 9.96 535 | 5 | 25 |
| 36 | 9.58 467 | 31 | 9.61 936 | 35 | 0.38 064 | 9.96 530 | 5 | 24 |
| 37 | 9.58 497 | 30 | 9.61 972 | 36 | 0.38 028 | 9.96 525 | 5 | 23 |
| 38 | 9.58 527 | 30 | 9.62 008 | 36 | 0.37 992 | 9.96 520 | 6 | 22 |
| 39 | 9.58 557 | 30 | 9.62 043 | 35 | 0.37 957 | 9.96 514 | 5 | 21 |
| 40 | 9.58 588 | 31 | 9.62 079 | 36 | 0.37 921 | 9.96 509 | 5 | 20 |
| 41 | 9.58 618 | 30 | 9.62 114 | 35 | 0.37 886 | 9.96 504 | 6 | 19 |
| 42 | 9.58 648 | 30 | 9.62 150 | 36 | 0.37 850 | 9.96 498 | 5 | 18 |
| 43 | 9.58 678 | 30 | 9.62 185 | 35 | 0.37 815 | 9.96 493 | 5 | 17 |
| 44 | 9.58 709 | 31 | 9.62 221 | 36 | 0.37 779 | 9.96 488 | 6 | 16 |
| 45 | 9.58 739 | 30 | 9.62 256 | 35 | 0.37 744 | 9.96 483 | 6 | 15 |
| 46 | 9.58 769 | 30 | 9.62 292 | 36 | 0.37 708 | 9.96 477 | 5 | 14 |
| 47 | 9.58 799 | 30 | 9.62 327 | 35 | 0.37 673 | 9.96 472 | 5 | 13 |
| 48 | 9.58 829 | 30 | 9.62 362 | 35 | 0.37 638 | 9.96 467 | 6 | 12 |
| 49 | 9.58 859 | 30 | 9.62 398 | 36 | 0.37 602 | 9.96 461 | 5 | 11 |
| 50 | 9.58 889 | 30 | 9.62 433 | 35 | 0.37 567 | 9.96 456 | 5 | 10 |
| 51 | 9.58 919 | 30 | 9.62 468 | 36 | 0.37 532 | 9.96 451 | 6 | 9 |
| 52 | 9.58 949 | 30 | 9.62 504 | 35 | 0.37 496 | 9.96 445 | 5 | 8 |
| 53 | 9.58 979 | 30 | 9.62 539 | 35 | 0.37 461 | 9.96 440 | 5 | 7 |
| 54 | 9.59 009 | 30 | 9.62 574 | 35 | 0.37 426 | 9.96 435 | 6 | 6 |
| 55 | 9.59 039 | 30 | 9.62 609 | 36 | 0.37 391 | 9.96 429 | 5 | 5 |
| 56 | 9.59 069 | 30 | 9.62 645 | 35 | 0.37 355 | 9.96 424 | 5 | 4 |
| 57 | 9.59 098 | 29 | 9.62 680 | 35 | 0.37 320 | 9.96 419 | 6 | 3 |
| 58 | 9.59 128 | 30 | 9.62 715 | 35 | 0.37 285 | 9.96 413 | 5 | 2 |
| 59 | 9.59 158 | 30 | 9.62 750 | 35 | 0.37 250 | 9.96 408 | 5 | 1 |
| 60 | 9.59 188 | 30 | 9.62 785 | 35 | 0.37 215 | 9.96 403 | 5 | 0 |
| ' | L. Cos. | d. | L. Cot. | c.d. | L. Tan. | L. Sin. | d. | ' |

**P. P.**

| " | 37 | 36 | 35 |
|---|----|----|----|
| 1 | 0.6 | 0.6 | 0.6 |
| 2 | 1.2 | 1.2 | 1.2 |
| 3 | 1.8 | 1.8 | 1.8 |
| 4 | 2.5 | 2.4 | 2.3 |
| 5 | 3.1 | 3.0 | 2.9 |
| 6 | 3.7 | 3.6 | 3.5 |
| 7 | 4.3 | 4.2 | 4.1 |
| 8 | 4.9 | 4.8 | 4.7 |
| 9 | 5.6 | 5.4 | 5.2 |
| 10 | 6.2 | 6.0 | 5.8 |
| 20 | 12.3 | 12.0 | 11.7 |
| 30 | 18.5 | 18.0 | 17.5 |
| 40 | 24.7 | 24.0 | 23.3 |
| 50 | 30.8 | 30.0 | 29.2 |

| " | 32 | 31 | 30 |
|---|----|----|----|
| 1 | 0.5 | 0.5 | 0.5 |
| 2 | 1.1 | 1.0 | 1.0 |
| 3 | 1.6 | 1.6 | 1.5 |
| 4 | 2.1 | 2.1 | 2.0 |
| 5 | 2.7 | 2.6 | 2.5 |
| 6 | 3.2 | 3.1 | 3.0 |
| 7 | 3.7 | 3.6 | 3.5 |
| 8 | 4.3 | 4.1 | 4.0 |
| 9 | 4.8 | 4.6 | 4.5 |
| 10 | 5.3 | 5.2 | 5.0 |
| 20 | 10.7 | 10.3 | 10.0 |
| 30 | 16.0 | 15.5 | 15.0 |
| 40 | 21.3 | 20.7 | 20.0 |
| 50 | 26.7 | 25.8 | 25.0 |

| " | 29 | 6 | 5 |
|---|----|---|---|
| 1 | 0.5 | 0.1 | 0.1 |
| 2 | 1.0 | 0.2 | 0.2 |
| 3 | 1.4 | 0.3 | 0.2 |
| 4 | 1.9 | 0.4 | 0.3 |
| 5 | 2.4 | 0.5 | 0.4 |
| 6 | 2.9 | 0.6 | 0.5 |
| 7 | 3.4 | 0.7 | 0.6 |
| 8 | 3.9 | 0.8 | 0.7 |
| 9 | 4.4 | 0.9 | 0.8 |
| 10 | 4.8 | 1.0 | 0.8 |
| 20 | 9.7 | 2.0 | 1.7 |
| 30 | 14.5 | 3.0 | 2.5 |
| 40 | 19.3 | 4.0 | 3.3 |
| 50 | 24.2 | 5.0 | 4.2 |

| | 6 / 36 | 6 / 35 |
|---|----|----|
| 0 | | |
| 1 | 3.0 | 2.9 |
| 2 | 9.0 | 8.8 |
| 3 | 15.0 | 14.6 |
| 4 | 21.0 | 20.4 |
| 5 | 27.0 | 26.2 |
| 6 | 33.0 | 32.1 |

| | 5 / 37 | 5 / 36 | 5 / 35 |
|---|----|----|----|
| 0 | | | |
| 1 | 3.7 | 3.6 | 3.5 |
| 2 | 11.1 | 10.8 | 10.5 |
| 3 | 18.5 | 18.0 | 17.5 |
| 4 | 25.9 | 25.2 | 24.5 |
| 5 | 33.3 | 32.4 | 31.5 |

**112° (292°)**     **(247°) 67°**

# LOGARITHMS OF THE FUNCTIONS (Continued)

**23° (203°)**          (336°) **156°**

| ′ | L. Sin. | d. | L. Tan. | c.d. | L. Cot. | L. Cos. | d. | ′ | P. P. | | |
|---|---------|----|---------|------|---------|---------|----|----|-------|---|---|
| 0 | 9.59 188 | 30 | 9.62 78̄5 | 35 | 0.37 21̄5 | 9.96 403 | 6 | 60 | ″ | 36 | 35 | 34 |
| 1 | 9.59 218 | 30 | 9.62 820 | 35 | 0.37 180 | 9.96 397 | 5 | 59 | 1 | 0.6 | 0.6 | 0.6 |
| 2 | 9.59 247 | 30 | 9.62 85̄5 | 35 | 0.37 14̄5 | 9.96 392 | 5 | 58 | 2 | 1.2 | 1.2 | 1.1 |
| 3 | 9.59 277 | 30 | 9.62 890 | 36 | 0.37 110 | 9.96 387 | 6 | 57 | 3 | 1.8 | 1.8 | 1.7 |
| 4 | 9.59 307 | 29 | 9.62 926 | 35 | 0.37 074 | 9.96 381 | 5 | 56 | 4 | 2.4 | 2.3 | 2.3 |
| 5 | 9.59 336 | 30 | 9.62 961 | 35 | 0.37 039 | 9.96 376 | 6 | 55 | 5 | 3.0 | 2.9 | 2.8 |
| 6 | 9.59 366 | 30 | 9.62 996 | 35 | 0.37 004 | 9.96 370 | 5 | 54 | 6 | 3.6 | 3.5 | 3.4 |
| 7 | 9.59 396 | 29 | 9.63 031 | 35 | 0.36 969 | 9.96 36̄5 | 5 | 53 | 7 | 4.2 | 4.1 | 4.0 |
| 8 | 9.59 42̄5 | 30 | 9.63 066 | 35 | 0.36 934 | 9.96 360 | 5 | 52 | 8 | 4.8 | 4.7 | 4.̄5 |
| 9 | 9.59 45̄5 | 29 | 9.63 101 | 34 | 0.36 899 | 9.96 354 | 5 | 51 | 9 | 5.4 | 5.2 | 5.1 |
| 10 | 9.59 484 | 30 | 9.63 13̄5 | 35 | 0.36 86̄5 | 9.96 349 | 6 | 50 | 10 | 6.0 | 5.8 | 5.7 |
| 11 | 9.59 514 | 29 | 9.63 170 | 35 | 0.36 830 | 9.96 343 | 5 | 49 | 20 | 12.0 | 11.7 | 11.3 |
| 12 | 9.59 543 | 30 | 9.63 20̄5 | 35 | 0.36 79̄5 | 9.96 338 | 5 | 48 | 30 | 18.0 | 17.5 | 17.0 |
| 13 | 9.59 573 | 29 | 9.63 240 | 35 | 0.36 760 | 9.96 333 | 6 | 47 | 40 | 24.0 | 23.3 | 22.7 |
| 14 | 9.59 602 | 30 | 9.63 27̄5 | 35 | 0.36 72̄5 | 9.96 327 | 5 | 46 | 50 | 30.0 | 29.2 | 28.3 |
| 15 | 9.59 632 | 29 | 9.63 310 | 35 | 0.36 690 | 9.96 322 | 6 | 45 | ″ | 30 | 29 | 28 |
| 16 | 9.59 661 | 29 | 9.63 34̄5 | 34 | 0.36 65̄5 | 9.96 316 | 5 | 44 | 1 | 0.5 | 0.̄5 | 0.̄5 |
| 17 | 9.59 690 | 30 | 9.63 379 | 35 | 0.36 621 | 9.96 311 | 6 | 43 | 2 | 1.0 | 1.0 | 0.9 |
| 18 | 9.59 720 | 29 | 9.63 414 | 35 | 0.36 586 | 9.96 30̄5 | 5 | 42 | 3 | 1.5 | 1.4 | 1.4 |
| 19 | 9.59 749 | 29 | 9.63 449 | 35 | 0.36 551 | 9.96 300 | 6 | 41 | 4 | 2.0 | 1.9 | 1.9 |
| 20 | 9.59 778 | 30 | 9.63 484 | 35 | 0.36 516 | 9.96 294 | 5 | 40 | 5 | 2.5 | 2.4 | 2.3 |
| 21 | 9.59 808 | 29 | 9.63 519 | 34 | 0.36 481 | 9.96 289 | 5 | 39 | 6 | 3.0 | 2.9 | 2.8 |
| 22 | 9.59 837 | 29 | 9.63 55̄3 | 35 | 0.36 447 | 9.96 284 | 6 | 38 | 7 | 3.5 | 3.4 | 3.3 |
| 23 | 9.59 866 | 29 | 9.63 588 | 35 | 0.36 412 | 9.96 278 | 5 | 37 | 8 | 4.0 | 3.9 | 3.7 |
| 24 | 9.59 89̄5 | 29 | 9.63 623 | 34 | 0.36 377 | 9.96 273 | 6 | 36 | 9 | 4.5 | 4.4 | 4.2 |
| 25 | 9.59 924 | 30 | 9.63 657 | 35 | 0.36 343 | 9.96 267 | 5 | 35 | 10 | 5.0 | 4.8 | 4.7 |
| 26 | 9.59 954 | 29 | 9.63 692 | 34 | 0.36 308 | 9.96 262 | 6 | 34 | 20 | 10.0 | 9.7 | 9.3 |
| 27 | 9.59 983 | 29 | 9.63 726 | 35 | 0.36 274 | 9.96 256 | 5 | 33 | 30 | 15.0 | 14.5 | 14.0 |
| 28 | 9.60 012 | 29 | 9.63 761 | 35 | 0.36 239 | 9.96 251 | 6 | 32 | 40 | 20.0 | 19.3 | 18.7 |
| 29 | 9.60 041 | 29 | 9.63 796 | 34 | 0.36 204 | 9.96 24̄5 | 5 | 31 | 50 | 25.0 | 24.2 | 23.3 |
| 30 | 9.60 070 | 29 | 9.63 830 | 35 | 0.36 170 | 9.96 240 | 6 | 30 | ″ | 6 | 5 | |
| 31 | 9.60 099 | 29 | 9.63 86̄5 | 34 | 0.36 13̄5 | 9.96 234 | 5 | 29 | 1 | 0.1 | 0.1 | |
| 32 | 9.60 128 | 29 | 9.63 899 | 35 | 0.36 101 | 9.96 229 | 6 | 28 | 2 | 0.2 | 0.2 | |
| 33 | 9.60 157 | 29 | 9.63 934 | 34 | 0.36 066 | 9.96 223 | 5 | 27 | 3 | 0.3 | 0.2 | |
| 34 | 9.60 186 | 29 | 9.63 968 | 35 | 0.36 032 | 9.96 218 | 6 | 26 | 4 | 0.4 | 0.3 | |
| 35 | 9.60 21̄5 | 29 | 9.64 003 | 34 | 0.35 997 | 9.96 212 | 5 | 25 | 5 | 0.5 | 0.4 | |
| 36 | 9.60 244 | 29 | 9.64 037 | 35 | 0.35 963 | 9.96 207 | 6 | 24 | 6 | 0.6 | 0.5 | |
| 37 | 9.60 273 | 29 | 9.64 072 | 34 | 0.35 928 | 9.96 201 | 5 | 23 | 7 | 0.7 | 0.6 | |
| 38 | 9.60 302 | 29 | 9.64 106 | 34 | 0.35 894 | 9.96 196 | 6 | 22 | 8 | 0.8 | 0.7 | |
| 39 | 9.60 331 | 28 | 9.64 140 | 35 | 0.35 860 | 9.96 190 | 5 | 21 | 9 | 0.9 | 0.8 | |
| 40 | 9.60 359 | 29 | 9.64 17̄5 | 34 | 0.35 82̄5 | 9.96 185 | 6 | 20 | 10 | 1.0 | 0.8 | |
| 41 | 9.60 388 | 29 | 9.64 209 | 34 | 0.35 791 | 9.96 179 | 5 | 19 | 20 | 2.0 | 1.7 | |
| 42 | 9.60 417 | 29 | 9.64 243 | 35 | 0.35 757 | 9.96 174 | 6 | 18 | 30 | 3.0 | 2.5 | |
| 43 | 9.60 446 | 28 | 9.64 278 | 34 | 0.35 722 | 9.96 168 | 6 | 17 | 40 | 4.0 | 3.3 | |
| 44 | 9.60 474 | 29 | 9.64 312 | 34 | 0.35 688 | 9.96 162 | 5 | 16 | 50 | 5.0 | 4.2 | |
| 45 | 9.60 503 | 29 | 9.64 346 | 35 | 0.35 654 | 9.96 157 | 6 | 15 | ″ | 6 | 6 | 6 |
| 46 | 9.60 532 | 29 | 9.64 381 | 34 | 0.35 619 | 9.96 151 | 5 | 14 | | 36 | 35 | 34 |
| 47 | 9.60 561 | 28 | 9.64 41̄5 | 34 | 0.35 58̄5 | 9.96 146 | 6 | 13 | 1 | 3.0 | 2.9 | 2.8 |
| 48 | 9.60 589 | 29 | 9.64 449 | 34 | 0.35 551 | 9.96 140 | 5 | 12 | 2 | 9.0 | 8.8 | 8.5 |
| 49 | 9.60 618 | 28 | 9.64 483 | 34 | 0.35 517 | 9.96 13̄5 | 6 | 11 | 3 | 15.0 | 14.6 | 14.2 |
| 50 | 9.60 646 | 29 | 9.64 517 | 35 | 0.35 483 | 9.96 129 | 6 | 10 | 4 | 21.0 | 20.4 | 19.8 |
| 51 | 9.60 67̄5 | 29 | 9.64 552 | 34 | 0.35 448 | 9.96 123 | 5 | 9 | 5 | 27.0 | 26.2 | 25.5 |
| 52 | 9.60 704 | 28 | 9.64 586 | 34 | 0.35 414 | 9.96 118 | 6 | 8 | 6 | 33.0 | 32.1 | 31.2 |
| 53 | 9.60 732 | 29 | 9.64 620 | 34 | 0.35 380 | 9.96 112 | 5 | 7 | | | | |
| 54 | 9.60 761 | 28 | 9.64 654 | 34 | 0.35 346 | 9.96 107 | 6 | 6 | ″ | 5 | 5 | |
| 55 | 9.60 789 | 29 | 9.64 688 | 34 | 0.35 312 | 9.96 101 | 5 | 5 | | 35 | 34 | |
| 56 | 9.60 818 | 28 | 9.64 722 | 34 | 0.35 278 | 9.96 09̄5 | 5 | 4 | 1 | 3.5 | 3.4 | |
| 57 | 9.60 846 | 29 | 9.64 756 | 34 | 0.35 244 | 9.96 090 | 6 | 3 | 2 | 10.5 | 10.2 | |
| 58 | 9.60 87̄5 | 28 | 9.64 790 | 34 | 0.35 210 | 9.96 084 | 5 | 2 | 3 | 17.5 | 17.0 | |
| 59 | 9.60 903 | 28 | 9.64 824 | 34 | 0.35 176 | 9.96 079 | 6 | 1 | 4 | 24.5 | 23.8 | |
| 60 | 9.60 931 | | 9.64 858 | | 0.35 142 | 9.96 073 | | 0 | 5 | 31.5 | 30.6 | |
| ′ | L. Cos. | d. | L. Cot. | c.d. | L. Tan. | L. Sin. | d. | ′ | P. P. | | |

**113° (293°)**          (246°) **66°**

69

**24° (204°)**  (335°) **155°**

| ' | L. Sin. | d. | L. Tan. | c.d. | L. Cot. | L. Cos. | d. | ' |
|---|---|---|---|---|---|---|---|---|
| 0 | 9.60 931 | 29 | 9.64 858 | 34 | 0.35 142 | 9.96 073 | 6 | 60 |
| 1 | 9.60 960 | 29 | 9.64 892 | 34 | 0.35 108 | 9.96 067 | 6 | 59 |
| 2 | 9.60 988 | 28 | 9.64 926 | 34 | 0.35 074 | 9.96 062 | 5 | 58 |
| 3 | 9.61 016 | 28 | 9.64 960 | 34 | 0.35 040 | 9.96 056 | 6 | 57 |
| 4 | 9.61 045̄ | 29 28 | 9.64 994 | 34 | 0.35 006 | 9.96 050̄ | 6 5 | 56 |
| 5 | 9.61 073 | | 9.65 028 | 34 | 0.34 972 | 9.96 045̄ | | 55 |
| 6 | 9.61 101 | 28 | 9.65 062 | 34 | 0.34 938 | 9.96 039 | 6 | 54 |
| 7 | 9.61 129 | 28 | 9.65 096 | 34 | 0.34 904 | 9.96 034 | 5 | 53 |
| 8 | 9.61 158 | 29 | 9.65 130 | 34 | 0.34 870 | 9.96 028 | 6 | 52 |
| 9 | 9.61 186 | 28 | 9.65 164 | 33 | 0.34 836 | 9.96 022 | 6 5 | 51 |
| 10 | 9.61 214 | 28 | 9.65 197 | 34 | 0.34 803 | 9.96 017 | 5 | 50 |
| 11 | 9.61 242 | 28 | 9.65 231 | 34 | 0.34 769 | 9.96 011 | 6 | 49 |
| 12 | 9.61 270 | 28 | 9.65 265̄ | 34 | 0.34 735̄ | 9.96 006 | 6 | 48 |
| 13 | 9.61 298 | 28 | 9.65 299 | 34 | 0.34 701 | 9.96 000 | 5 | 47 |
| 14 | 9.61 326 | 28 | 9.65 333 | 33 | 0.34 667 | 9.95 994 | 6 | 46 |
| 15 | 9.61 354 | 28 | 9.65 366 | 34 | 0.34 634 | 9.95 988 | 6 | 45 |
| 16 | 9.61 382 | 29 | 9.65 400 | 34 | 0.34 600 | 9.95 982 | 6 | 44 |
| 17 | 9.61 411 | 27 | 9.65 434 | 33 | 0.34 566 | 9.95 977 | 6 | 43 |
| 18 | 9.61 438 | 28 | 9.65 467 | 34 | 0.34 533 | 9.95 971 | 6 | 42 |
| 19 | 9.61 466 | 28 | 9.65 501 | 34 | 0.34 499 | 9.95 965̄ | 5 | 41 |
| 20 | 9.61 494 | 28 | 9.65 535̄ | 33 | 0.34 465̄ | 9.95 960 | 6 | 40 |
| 21 | 9.61 522 | 28 | 9.65 568 | 34 | 0.34 432 | 9.95 954 | 6 | 39 |
| 22 | 9.61 550̄ | 28 | 9.65 602 | 34 | 0.34 398 | 9.95 948 | 6 | 38 |
| 23 | 9.61 578 | 28 | 9.65 636 | 33 | 0.34 364 | 9.95 942 | 5 | 37 |
| 24 | 9.61 606 | 28 | 9.65 669 | 34 | 0.34 331 | 9.95 937 | 6 | 36 |
| 25 | 9.61 634 | | 9.65 703 | 33 | 0.34 297 | 9.95 931 | 6 | 35 |
| 26 | 9.61 662 | 28 | 9.65 736 | 34 | 0.34 264 | 9.95 925̄ | 5 | 34 |
| 27 | 9.61 689 | 27 | 9.65 770 | 33 | 0.34 230 | 9.95 920 | 6 | 33 |
| 28 | 9.61 717 | 28 | 9.65 803 | 34 | 0.34 197 | 9.95 914 | 5 | 32 |
| 29 | 9.61 745̄ | 28 | 9.65 837 | 33 | 0.34 163 | 9.95 908 | 6 | 31 |
| 30 | 9.61 773 | 28 | 9.65 870 | 34 | 0.34 130 | 9.95 902 | 6 | 30 |
| 31 | 9.61 800 | 27 | 9.65 904 | 34 | 0.34 096 | 9.95 897 | 5 | 29 |
| 32 | 9.61 828 | 28 | 9.65 937 | 34 | 0.34 063 | 9.95 891 | 6 | 28 |
| 33 | 9.61 856 | 28 | 9.65 971 | 34 | 0.34 029 | 9.95 885̄ | 6 | 27 |
| 34 | 9.61 883 | 27 28 | 9.66 004 | 33 | 0.33 996 | 9.95 879 | 6 | 26 |
| 35 | 9.61 911 | | 9.66 038 | 33 | 0.33 962 | 9.95 873 | 6 | 25 |
| 36 | 9.61 939 | 28 | 9.66 071 | 33 | 0.33 929 | 9.95 868 | 5 | 24 |
| 37 | 9.61 966 | 27 | 9.66 104 | 34 | 0.33 896 | 9.95 862 | 6 | 23 |
| 38 | 9.61 994 | 28 | 9.66 138 | 33 | 0.33 862 | 9.95 856 | 6 | 22 |
| 39 | 9.62 021 | 27 28 | 9.66 171 | 33 | 0.33 829 | 9.95 850̄ | 6 | 21 |
| 40 | 9.62 049 | | 9.66 204 | 34 | 0.33 796 | 9.95 844 | 6 | 20 |
| 41 | 9.62 076 | 27 | 9.66 238 | 33 | 0.33 762 | 9.95 839 | 5 | 19 |
| 42 | 9.62 104 | 28 | 9.66 271 | 33 | 0.33 729 | 9.95 833 | 6 | 18 |
| 43 | 9.62 131 | 27 | 9.66 304 | 33 | 0.33 696 | 9.95 827 | 6 | 17 |
| 44 | 9.62 159 | 28 27 | 9.66 337 | 34 | 0.33 663 | 9.95 821 | 6 | 16 |
| 45 | 9.62 186 | | 9.66 371 | 33 | 0.33 629 | 9.95 815̄ | 6 | 15 |
| 46 | 9.62 214 | 28 | 9.66 404 | 33 | 0.33 596 | 9.95 810̄ | 5 | 14 |
| 47 | 9.62 241 | 27 | 9.66 437 | 33 | 0.33 563 | 9.95 804 | 6 | 13 |
| 48 | 9.62 268 | 27 | 9.66 470 | 33 | 0.33 530 | 9.95 798 | 6 | 12 |
| 49 | 9.62 296 | 28 27 | 9.66 503 | 34 | 0.33 497 | 9.95 792 | 6 | 11 |
| 50 | 9.62 323 | | 9.66 537 | 33 | 0.33 463 | 9.95 786 | 6 | 10 |
| 51 | 9.62 350̄ | 27 | 9.66 570 | 33 | 0.33 430 | 9.95 780̄ | 6 | 9 |
| 52 | 9.62 377 | 28 | 9.66 603 | 33 | 0.33 397 | 9.95 775̄ | 5 | 8 |
| 53 | 9.62 405̄ | 27 | 9.66 636 | 33 | 0.33 364 | 9.95 769 | 6 | 7 |
| 54 | 9.62 432 | 27 | 9.66 669 | 33 | 0.33 331 | 9.95 763 | 6 | 6 |
| 55 | 9.62 459 | | 9.66 702 | 33 | 0.33 298 | 9.95 757 | 6 | 5 |
| 56 | 9.62 486 | 27 | 9.66 735̄ | 33 | 0.33 265̄ | 9.95 751 | 6 | 4 |
| 57 | 9.62 513 | 27 | 9.66 768 | 33 | 0.33 232 | 9.95 745̄ | 6 | 3 |
| 58 | 9.62 541 | 28 | 9.66 801 | 33 | 0.33 199 | 9.95 739 | 6 | 2 |
| 59 | 9.62 568 | 27 27 | 9.66 834 | 33 | 0.33 166 | 9.95 733 | 6 5 | 1 |
| 60 | 9.62 595̄ | | 9.66 867 | | 0.33 133 | 9.95 728 | | 0 |
| ' | L. Cos. | d. | L. Cot. | c.d. | L. Tan. | L. Sin. | d. | ' |

### P. P.

| '' | 34 | 33 |
|---|---|---|
| 1 | 0.6 | 0.6 |
| 2 | 1.1 | 1.1 |
| 3 | 1.7 | 1.6 |
| 4 | 2.3 | 2.2 |
| 5 | 2.8 | 2.8 |
| 6 | 3.4 | 3.3 |
| 7 | 4.0 | 3.8 |
| 8 | 4.5 | 4.4 |
| 9 | 5.1 | 5.0 |
| 10 | 5.7 | 5.5 |
| 20 | 11.3 | 11.0 |
| 30 | 17.0 | 16.5 |
| 40 | 22.7 | 22.0 |
| 50 | 28.3 | 27.5 |

| '' | 29 | 28 | 27 |
|---|---|---|---|
| 1 | 0.5̄ | 0.5̄ | 0.4 |
| 2 | 1.0 | 0.9 | 0.9 |
| 3 | 1.4 | 1.4 | 1.4 |
| 4 | 1.9 | 1.9 | 1.8 |
| 5 | 2.4 | 2.3 | 2.2 |
| 6 | 2.9 | 2.8 | 2.7 |
| 7 | 3.4 | 3.3 | 3.2 |
| 8 | 3.9 | 3.7 | 3.6 |
| 9 | 4.4 | 4.2 | 4.0 |
| 10 | 4.8 | 4.7 | 4.5 |
| 20 | 9.7 | 9.3 | 9.0 |
| 30 | 14.5 | 14.0 | 13.5 |
| 40 | 19.3 | 18.7 | 18.0 |
| 50 | 24.2 | 23.3 | 22.5 |

| '' | 6 | 5 |
|---|---|---|
| 1 | 0.1 | 0.1 |
| 2 | 0.2 | 0.2 |
| 3 | 0.3 | 0.2 |
| 4 | 0.4 | 0.3 |
| 5 | 0.5 | 0.4 |
| 6 | 0.6 | 0.5 |
| 7 | 0.7 | 0.6 |
| 8 | 0.8 | 0.7 |
| 9 | 0.9 | 0.8 |
| 10 | 1.0 | 0.8 |
| 20 | 2.0 | 1.7 |
| 30 | 3.0 | 2.5 |
| 40 | 4.0 | 3.3 |
| 50 | 5.0 | 4.2 |

| | $\frac{6}{34}$ | $\frac{6}{33}$ | $\frac{5}{34}$ |
|---|---|---|---|
| 0 1 | 2.8 | 2.8 | 3.4 |
| 2 | 8.5 | 8.2 | 10.2 |
| 3 | 14.2 | 13.8 | 17.0 |
| 4 | 19.8 | 19.2 | 23.8 |
| 5 | 25.5 | 24.8 | 30.6 |
| 6 | 31.2 | 30.2 | — |

| ′ | L. Sin. | d. | L. Tan. | c.d. | L. Cot. | L. Cos. | d. | ′ | P.P. |
|---|---|---|---|---|---|---|---|---|---|
| 0 | 9.62 595 | 27 | 9.66 867 | 33 | 0.33 133 | 9.95 728 | 6 | 60 | |
| 1 | 9.62 622 | 27 | 9.66 900 | 33 | 0.33 100 | 9.95 722 | 6 | 59 | |
| 2 | 9.62 649 | 27 | 9.66 933 | 33 | 0.33 067 | 9.95 716 | 6 | 58 | 33  32 |
| 3 | 9.62 676 | 27 | 9.66 966 | 33 | 0.33 034 | 9.95 710 | 6 | 57 | 1  0.6  0.5 |
| 4 | 9.62 703 | 27 | 9.66 999 | 33 | 0.33 001 | 9.95 704 | 6 | 56 | 2  1.1  1.1 |
| 5 | 9.62 730 | 27 | 9.67 032 | 33 | 0.32 968 | 9.95 698 | 6 | 55 | 3  1.6  1.6 |
| 6 | 9.62 757 | 27 | 9.67 065 | 33 | 0.32 935 | 9.95 692 | 6 | 54 | 4  2.2  2.1 |
| 7 | 9.62 784 | 27 | 9.67 098 | 33 | 0.32 902 | 9.95 686 | 6 | 53 | 5  2.8  2.7 |
| 8 | 9.62 811 | 27 | 9.67 131 | 33 | 0.32 869 | 9.95 680 | 6 | 52 | 6  3.3  3.2 |
| 9 | 9.62 838 | 27 | 9.67 163 | 32 | 0.32 837 | 9.95 674 | 6 | 51 | 7  3.8  3.7 |
| 10 | 9.62 865 | 27 | 9.67 196 | 33 | 0.32 804 | 9.95 668 | 5 | 50 | 8  4.4  4.3 |
| 11 | 9.62 892 | 27 | 9.67 229 | 33 | 0.32 771 | 9.95 663 | 6 | 49 | 9  5.0  4.8 |
| 12 | 9.62 918 | 26 | 9.67 262 | 33 | 0.32 738 | 9.95 657 | 6 | 48 | 10  5.5  5.3 |
| 13 | 9.62 945 | 27 | 9.67 295 | 33 | 0.32 705 | 9.95 651 | 6 | 47 | 20  11.0  10.7 |
| 14 | 9.62 972 | 27 | 9.67 327 | 32 | 0.32 673 | 9.95 645 | 6 | 46 | 30  16.5  16.0 |
| 15 | 9.62 999 | 27 | 9.67 360 | 33 | 0.32 640 | 9.95 639 | 6 | 45 | 40  22.0  21.3 |
| 16 | 9.63 026 | 26 | 9.67 393 | 33 | 0.32 607 | 9.95 633 | 6 | 44 | 50  27.5  26.7 |
| 17 | 9.63 052 | 27 | 9.67 426 | 32 | 0.32 574 | 9.95 627 | 6 | 43 | 27  26 |
| 18 | 9.63 079 | 27 | 9.67 458 | 33 | 0.32 542 | 9.95 621 | 6 | 42 | 1  0.4  0.4 |
| 19 | 9.63 106 | 27 | 9.67 491 | 33 | 0.32 509 | 9.95 615 | 6 | 41 | 2  0.9  0.9 |
| 20 | 9.63 133 | 26 | 9.67 524 | 32 | 0.32 476 | 9.95 609 | 6 | 40 | 3  1.4  1.3 |
| 21 | 9.63 159 | 27 | 9.67 556 | 33 | 0.32 444 | 9.95 603 | 6 | 39 | 4  1.8  1.7 |
| 22 | 9.63 186 | 27 | 9.67 589 | 33 | 0.32 411 | 9.95 597 | 6 | 38 | 5  2.2  2.2 |
| 23 | 9.63 213 | 26 | 9.67 622 | 32 | 0.32 378 | 9.95 591 | 6 | 37 | 6  2.7  2.6 |
| 24 | 9.63 239 | 27 | 9.67 654 | 33 | 0.32 346 | 9.95 585 | 6 | 36 | 7  3.2  3.0 |
| 25 | 9.63 266 | 26 | 9.67 687 | 32 | 0.32 313 | 9.95 579 | 6 | 35 | 8  3.6  3.5 |
| 26 | 9.63 292 | 27 | 9.67 719 | 33 | 0.32 281 | 9.95 573 | 6 | 34 | 9  4.0  3.9 |
| 27 | 9.63 319 | 26 | 9.67 752 | 33 | 0.32 248 | 9.95 567 | 6 | 33 | 10  4.5  4.3 |
| 28 | 9.63 345 | 27 | 9.67 785 | 32 | 0.32 215 | 9.95 561 | 6 | 32 | 20  9.0  8.7 |
| 29 | 9.63 372 | 26 | 9.67 817 | 33 | 0.32 183 | 9.95 555 | 6 | 31 | 30  13.5  13.0 |
| 30 | 9.63 398 | 27 | 9.67 850 | 32 | 0.32 150 | 9.95 549 | 6 | 30 | 40  18.0  17.3 |
| 31 | 9.63 425 | 26 | 9.67 882 | 33 | 0.32 118 | 9.95 543 | 6 | 29 | 50  22.5  21.7 |
| 32 | 9.63 451 | 27 | 9.67 915 | 32 | 0.32 085 | 9.95 537 | 6 | 28 | 7  6  6 |
| 33 | 9.63 478 | 26 | 9.67 947 | 33 | 0.32 053 | 9.95 531 | 6 | 27 | 1  0.1  0.1  0.1 |
| 34 | 9.63 504 | 27 | 9.67 980 | 32 | 0.32 020 | 9.95 525 | 6 | 26 | 2  0.2  0.2  0.2 |
| 35 | 9.63 531 | 26 | 9.68 012 | 32 | 0.31 988 | 9.95 519 | 6 | 25 | 3  0.4  0.3  0.3 |
| 36 | 9.63 557 | 26 | 9.68 044 | 33 | 0.31 956 | 9.95 513 | 6 | 24 | 4  0.5  0.4  0.3 |
| 37 | 9.63 583 | 27 | 9.68 077 | 32 | 0.31 923 | 9.95 507 | 6 | 23 | 5  0.6  0.5  0.4 |
| 38 | 9.63 610 | 26 | 9.68 109 | 33 | 0.31 891 | 9.95 500 | 7 | 22 | 6  0.7  0.6  0.5 |
| 39 | 9.63 636 | 26 | 9.68 142 | 32 | 0.31 858 | 9.95 494 | 6 | 21 | 7  0.8  0.7  0.6 |
| 40 | 9.63 662 | 27 | 9.68 174 | 32 | 0.31 826 | 9.95 488 | 6 | 20 | 8  0.9  0.8  0.7 |
| 41 | 9.63 689 | 26 | 9.68 206 | 33 | 0.31 794 | 9.95 482 | 6 | 19 | 9  1.0  0.9  0.8 |
| 42 | 9.63 715 | 26 | 9.68 239 | 32 | 0.31 761 | 9.95 476 | 6 | 18 | 10  1.2  1.0  0.8 |
| 43 | 9.63 741 | 26 | 9.68 271 | 32 | 0.31 729 | 9.95 470 | 6 | 17 | 20  2.3  2.0  1.7 |
| 44 | 9.63 767 | 27 | 9.68 303 | 33 | 0.31 697 | 9.95 464 | 6 | 16 | 30  3.5  3.0  2.5 |
| 45 | 9.63 794 | 26 | 9.68 336 | 32 | 0.31 664 | 9.95 458 | 6 | 15 | 40  4.7  4.0  3.3 |
| 46 | 9.63 820 | 26 | 9.68 368 | 32 | 0.31 632 | 9.95 452 | 6 | 14 | 50  5.8  5.0  4.2 |
| 47 | 9.63 846 | 26 | 9.68 400 | 32 | 0.31 600 | 9.95 446 | 6 | 13 | |
| 48 | 9.63 872 | 26 | 9.68 432 | 33 | 0.31 568 | 9.95 440 | 6 | 12 | |
| 49 | 9.63 898 | 26 | 9.68 465 | 32 | 0.31 535 | 9.95 434 | 7 | 11 | 7  6  5 |
| 50 | 9.63 924 | 26 | 9.68 497 | 32 | 0.31 503 | 9.95 427 | 6 | 10 | 32  32  33 |
| 51 | 9.63 950 | 26 | 9.68 529 | 32 | 0.31 471 | 9.95 421 | 6 | 9 | 0  2.3  2.7  3.8 |
| 52 | 9.63 976 | 26 | 9.68 561 | 32 | 0.31 439 | 9.95 415 | 6 | 8 | 1  6.9  8.0  9.9 |
| 53 | 9.64 002 | 26 | 9.68 593 | 33 | 0.31 407 | 9.95 409 | 6 | 7 | 2  11.4  13.3  16.5 |
| 54 | 9.64 028 | 26 | 9.68 626 | 32 | 0.31 374 | 9.95 403 | 6 | 6 | 3  16.0  18.7  23.1 |
| 55 | 9.64 054 | 26 | 9.68 658 | 32 | 0.31 342 | 9.95 397 | 6 | 5 | 4  20.6  24.0  29.7 |
| 56 | 9.64 080 | 26 | 9.68 690 | 32 | 0.31 310 | 9.95 391 | 7 | 4 | 5  25.1  29.3  — |
| 57 | 9.64 106 | 26 | 9.68 722 | 32 | 0.31 278 | 9.95 384 | 6 | 3 | 6  29.7  —  — |
| 58 | 9.64 132 | 26 | 9.68 754 | 32 | 0.31 246 | 9.95 378 | 6 | 2 | 7 |
| 59 | 9.64 158 | 26 | 9.68 786 | 32 | 0.31 214 | 9.95 372 | 6 | 1 | |
| 60 | 9.64 184 | | 9.68 818 | | 0.31 182 | 9.95 366 | | 0 | |
| ′ | L. Cos. | d. | L. Cot. | c.d. | L. Tan. | L. Sin. | d. | ′ | P.P. |

# LOGARITHMS OF THE FUNCTIONS (Continued)

**26° (206°)**  (333°) **153°**

| ' | L. Sin. | d. | L. Tan. | c.d. | L. Cot. | L. Cos. | d. | ' |
|---|---------|----|---------|------|---------|---------|----|----|
| 0 | 9.64 184 |    | 9.68 818 |    | 0.31 182 | 9.95 366 |   | 60 |
| 1 | 9.64 210 | 26 | 9.68 850 | 32 | 0.31 150 | 9.95 360 | 6 | 59 |
| 2 | 9.64 236 | 26 | 9.68 882 | 32 | 0.31 118 | 9.95 354 | 6 | 58 |
| 3 | 9.64 262 | 26 | 9.68 914 | 32 | 0.31 086 | 9.95 348 | 6 | 57 |
| 4 | 9.64 288 | 26 | 9.68 946 | 32 | 0.31 054 | 9.95 341 | 7 | 56 |
| 5 | 9.64 313 | 25 | 9.68 978 | 32 | 0.31 022 | 9.95 335 | 6 | 55 |
| 6 | 9.64 339 | 26 | 9.69 010 | 32 | 0.30 990 | 9.95 329 | 6 | 54 |
| 7 | 9.64 365 | 26 | 9.69 042 | 32 | 0.30 958 | 9.95 323 | 6 | 53 |
| 8 | 9.64 391 | 26 | 9.69 074 | 32 | 0.30 926 | 9.95 317 | 6 | 52 |
| 9 | 9.64 417 | 26 | 9.69 106 | 32 | 0.30 894 | 9.95 310 | 7 | 51 |
| 10 | 9.64 442 | 25 | 9.69 138 | 32 | 0.30 862 | 9.95 304 | 6 | 50 |
| 11 | 9.64 468 | 26 | 9.69 170 | 32 | 0.30 830 | 9.95 298 | 6 | 49 |
| 12 | 9.64 494 | 26 | 9.69 202 | 32 | 0.30 798 | 9.95 292 | 6 | 48 |
| 13 | 9.64 519 | 25 | 9.69 234 | 32 | 0.30 766 | 9.95 286 | 6 | 47 |
| 14 | 9.64 545 | 26 | 9.69 266 | 32 | 0.30 734 | 9.95 279 | 7 | 46 |
| 15 | 9.64 571 | 25 | 9.69 298 | 31 | 0.30 702 | 9.95 273 | 6 | 45 |
| 16 | 9.64 596 | 25 | 9.69 329 | 32 | 0.30 671 | 9.95 267 | 6 | 44 |
| 17 | 9.64 622 | 26 | 9.69 361 | 32 | 0.30 639 | 9.95 261 | 6 | 43 |
| 18 | 9.64 647 | 25 | 9.69 393 | 32 | 0.30 607 | 9.95 254 | 7 | 42 |
| 19 | 9.64 673 | 26 | 9.69 425 | 32 | 0.30 575 | 9.95 248 | 6 | 41 |
| 20 | 9.64 698 | 26 | 9.69 457 | 31 | 0.30 543 | 9.95 242 | 6 | 40 |
| 21 | 9.64 724 | 25 | 9.69 488 | 32 | 0.30 512 | 9.95 236 | 7 | 39 |
| 22 | 9.64 749 | 26 | 9.69 520 | 32 | 0.30 480 | 9.95 229 | 6 | 38 |
| 23 | 9.64 775 | 25 | 9.69 552 | 32 | 0.30 448 | 9.95 223 | 6 | 37 |
| 24 | 9.64 800 | 26 | 9.69 584 | 31 | 0.30 416 | 9.95 217 | 6 | 36 |
| 25 | 9.64 826 | 25 | 9.69 615 | 32 | 0.30 385 | 9.95 211 | 7 | 35 |
| 26 | 9.64 851 | 26 | 9.69 647 | 32 | 0.30 353 | 9.95 204 | 6 | 34 |
| 27 | 9.64 877 | 25 | 9.69 679 | 31 | 0.30 321 | 9.95 198 | 6 | 33 |
| 28 | 9.64 902 | 25 | 9.69 710 | 32 | 0.30 290 | 9.95 192 | 7 | 32 |
| 29 | 9.64 927 | 26 | 9.69 742 | 32 | 0.30 258 | 9.95 185 | 6 | 31 |
| 30 | 9.64 953 | 25 | 9.69 774 | 31 | 0.30 226 | 9.95 179 | 6 | 30 |
| 31 | 9.64 978 | 25 | 9.69 805 | 32 | 0.30 195 | 9.95 173 | 6 | 29 |
| 32 | 9.65 003 | 26 | 9.69 837 | 31 | 0.30 163 | 9.95 167 | 7 | 28 |
| 33 | 9.65 029 | 25 | 9.69 868 | 32 | 0.30 132 | 9.95 160 | 6 | 27 |
| 34 | 9.65 054 | 25 | 9.69 900 | 32 | 0.30 100 | 9.95 154 | 6 | 26 |
| 35 | 9.65 079 | 25 | 9.69 932 | 31 | 0.30 068 | 9.95 148 | 7 | 25 |
| 36 | 9.65 104 | 26 | 9.69 963 | 32 | 0.30 037 | 9.95 141 | 6 | 24 |
| 37 | 9.65 130 | 25 | 9.69 995 | 31 | 0.30 005 | 9.95 135 | 6 | 23 |
| 38 | 9.65 155 | 25 | 9.70 026 | 32 | 0.29 974 | 9.95 129 | 7 | 22 |
| 39 | 9.65 180 | 25 | 9.70 058 | 31 | 0.29 942 | 9.95 122 | 6 | 21 |
| 40 | 9.65 205 | 25 | 9.70 089 | 32 | 0.29 911 | 9.95 116 | 6 | 20 |
| 41 | 9.65 230 | 25 | 9.70 121 | 31 | 0.29 879 | 9.95 110 | 7 | 19 |
| 42 | 9.65 255 | 26 | 9.70 152 | 32 | 0.29 848 | 9.95 103 | 6 | 18 |
| 43 | 9.65 281 | 25 | 9.70 184 | 31 | 0.29 816 | 9.95 097 | 7 | 17 |
| 44 | 9.65 306 | 25 | 9.70 215 | 32 | 0.29 785 | 9.95 090 | 6 | 16 |
| 45 | 9.65 331 | 25 | 9.70 247 | 31 | 0.29 753 | 9.95 084 | 6 | 15 |
| 46 | 9.65 356 | 25 | 9.70 278 | 31 | 0.29 722 | 9.95 078 | 7 | 14 |
| 47 | 9.65 381 | 25 | 9.70 309 | 32 | 0.29 691 | 9.95 071 | 6 | 13 |
| 48 | 9.65 406 | 25 | 9.70 341 | 31 | 0.29 659 | 9.95 065 | 6 | 12 |
| 49 | 9.65 431 | 25 | 9.70 372 | 32 | 0.29 628 | 9.95 059 | 7 | 11 |
| 50 | 9.65 456 | 25 | 9.70 404 | 31 | 0.29 596 | 9.95 052 | 6 | 10 |
| 51 | 9.65 481 | 25 | 9.70 435 | 31 | 0.29 565 | 9.95 046 | 7 | 9 |
| 52 | 9.65 506 | 25 | 9.70 466 | 32 | 0.29 534 | 9.95 039 | 6 | 8 |
| 53 | 9.65 531 | 25 | 9.70 498 | 31 | 0.29 502 | 9.95 033 | 6 | 7 |
| 54 | 9.65 556 | 24 | 9.70 529 | 31 | 0.29 471 | 9.95 027 | 7 | 6 |
| 55 | 9.65 580 | 25 | 9.70 560 | 32 | 0.29 440 | 9.95 020 | 6 | 5 |
| 56 | 9.65 605 | 25 | 9.70 592 | 31 | 0.29 408 | 9.95 014 | 7 | 4 |
| 57 | 9.65 630 | 25 | 9.70 623 | 31 | 0.29 377 | 9.95 007 | 6 | 3 |
| 58 | 9.65 655 | 25 | 9.70 654 | 31 | 0.29 346 | 9.95 001 | 6 | 2 |
| 59 | 9.65 680 | 25 | 9.70 685 | 32 | 0.29 315 | 9.94 995 | 7 | 1 |
| 60 | 9.65 705 |    | 9.70 717 |    | 0.29 283 | 9.94 988 |   | 0 |
|   | L. Cos. | d. | L. Cot. | c.d. | L. Tan. | L. Sin. | d. | ' |

**P.P.**

| | 32 | 31 |
|---|----|----|
| 1 | 0.5 | 0.5 |
| 2 | 1.1 | 1.0 |
| 3 | 1.6 | 1.6 |
| 4 | 2.1 | 2.1 |
| 5 | 2.7 | 2.6 |
| 6 | 3.2 | 3.1 |
| 7 | 3.7 | 3 6 |
| 8 | 4.3 | 4.1 |
| 9 | 4.8 | 4.6 |
| 10 | 5.3 | 5.2 |
| 20 | 10.7 | 10.3 |
| 30 | 16.0 | 15.5 |
| 40 | 21.3 | 20.7 |
| 50 | 26.7 | 25.8 |

| | 26 | 25 | 26 |
|---|----|----|----|
| 1 | 0.4 | 0.4 | 0.4 |
| 2 | 0.9 | 0.8 | 0.8 |
| 3 | 1.3 | 1.2 | 1.2 |
| 4 | 1.7 | 1.7 | 1.6 |
| 5 | 2.2 | 2.1 | 2.0 |
| 6 | 2.6 | 2.5 | 2.4 |
| 7 | 3.0 | 2.9 | 2.8 |
| 8 | 3.5 | 3.3 | 3.2 |
| 9 | 3.9 | 3.8 | 3.6 |
| 10 | 4.3 | 4.2 | 4.0 |
| 20 | 8.7 | 8.3 | 8.0 |
| 30 | 13.0 | 12.5 | 12.0 |
| 40 | 17.3 | 16.7 | 16.0 |
| 50 | 21.7 | 20.8 | 20.0 |

| | 7 | 6 |
|---|----|----|
| 1 | 0.1 | 0.1 |
| 2 | 0.2 | 0.2 |
| 3 | 0.4 | 0.3 |
| 4 | 0.5 | 0.4 |
| 5 | 0.6 | 0.5 |
| 6 | 0.7 | 0.6 |
| 7 | 0.8 | 0.7 |
| 8 | 0.9 | 0.8 |
| 9 | 1.0 | 0.9 |
| 10 | 1.2 | 1.0 |
| 20 | 2.3 | 2.0 |
| 30 | 3.5 | 3.0 |
| 40 | 4.7 | 4.0 |
| 50 | 5.8 | 5.0 |

| | $\frac{7}{32}$ | $\frac{7}{31}$ | $\frac{6}{33}$ |
|---|----|----|----|
| 0 | | | |
| 1 | 2.3 | 2.2 | 2.7 |
| 2 | 6.9 | 6.6 | 8.0 |
| 3 | 11.4 | 11.1 | 13.3 |
| 4 | 16.0 | 15.5 | 18.7 |
| 5 | 20.6 | 19.9 | 24.0 |
| 6 | 25.1 | 24.4 | 29.3 |
| 7 | 29.7 | 28.8 | — |

| ' | L. Sin. | d. | L. Tan. | c.d. | L. Cot. | L. Cos. | d. | ' |
|---|---------|----|---------|------|---------|---------|----|---|
| 0 | 9.65 705̄ | | 9.70 717 | | 0.29 283 | 9.94 988 | | 60 |
| 1 | 9.65 729 | 24 | 9.70 748 | 31 | 0.29 252 | 9.94 982 | 6 | 59 |
| 2 | 9.65 754 | 25 | 9.70 779 | 31 | 0.29 221 | 9.94 975̄ | 7 | 58 |
| 3 | 9.65 779 | 25 | 9.70 810 | 31 | 0.29 190 | 9.94 969 | 6 | 57 |
| 4 | 9.65 804 | 25 | 9.70 841 | 31 | 0.29 159 | 9.94 962 | 7 | 56 |
| | | 24 | | 32 | | | 6 | |
| 5 | 9.65 828 | | 9.70 873 | | 0.29 127 | 9.94 956 | | 55 |
| 6 | 9.65 853 | 25 | 9.70 904 | 31 | 0.29 096 | 9.94 949 | 7 | 54 |
| 7 | 9.65 878 | 25 | 9.70 935̄ | 31 | 0.29 065̄ | 9.94 943 | 6 | 53 |
| 8 | 9.65 902 | 24 | 9.70 966 | 31 | 0.29 034 | 9.94 936 | 7 | 52 |
| 9 | 9.65 927 | 25 | 9.70 997 | 31 | 0.29 003 | 9.94 930 | 6 | 51 |
| | | 25 | | 31 | | | 7 | |
| 10 | 9.65 952 | | 9.71 028 | | 0.28 972 | 9.94 923 | | 50 |
| 11 | 9.65 976 | 24 | 9.71 059 | 31 | 0.28 941 | 9.94 917 | 6 | 49 |
| 12 | 9.66 001 | 25 | 9.71 090 | 31 | 0.28 910 | 9.94 911 | 6 | 48 |
| 13 | 9.66 025̄ | 24 | 9.71 121 | 31 | 0.28 879 | 9.94 904 | 7 | 47 |
| 14 | 9.66 050 | 25 | 9.71 153 | 32 | 0.28 847 | 9.94 898 | 6 | 46 |
| | | 25 | | 31 | | | 7 | |
| 15 | 9.66 075̄ | | 9.71 184 | | 0.28 816 | 9.94 891 | | 45 |
| 16 | 9.66 099 | 24 | 9.71 215̄ | 31 | 0.28 785̄ | 9.94 885̄ | 6 | 44 |
| 17 | 9.66 124 | 25 | 9.71 246 | 31 | 0.28 754 | 9.94 878 | 7 | 43 |
| 18 | 9.66 148 | 24 | 9.71 277 | 31 | 0.28 723 | 9.94 871 | 7 | 42 |
| 19 | 9.66 173 | 25 | 9.71 308 | 31 | 0.28 692 | 9.94 865̄ | 6 | 41 |
| | | 24 | | 31 | | | 7 | |
| 20 | 9.66 197 | | 9.71 339 | | 0.28 661 | 9.94 858 | | 40 |
| 21 | 9.66 221 | 24 | 9.71 370 | 31 | 0.28 630 | 9.94 852 | 6 | 39 |
| 22 | 9.66 246 | 25 | 9.71 401 | 31 | 0.28 599 | 9.94 845̄ | 7 | 38 |
| 23 | 9.66 270 | 24 | 9.71 431 | 30 | 0.28 569 | 9.94 839 | 6 | 37 |
| 24 | 9.66 295 | 25 | 9.71 462 | 31 | 0.28 538 | 9.94 832 | 7 | 36 |
| | | 24 | | 31 | | | 6 | |
| 25 | 9.66 319 | | 9.71 493 | | 0.28 507 | 9.94 826 | | 35 |
| 26 | 9.66 343 | 24 | 9.71 524 | 31 | 0.28 476 | 9.94 819 | 7 | 34 |
| 27 | 9.66 368 | 25 | 9.71 555̄ | 31 | 0.28 445̄ | 9.94 813 | 6 | 33 |
| 28 | 9.66 392 | 24 | 9.71 586 | 31 | 0.28 414 | 9.94 806 | 7 | 32 |
| 29 | 9.66 416 | 25 | 9.71 617 | 31 | 0.28 383 | 9.94 799 | 7 | 31 |
| | | 24 | | 31 | | | 6 | |
| 30 | 9.66 441 | | 9.71 648 | | 0.28 352 | 9.94 793 | | 30 |
| 31 | 9.66 465̄ | 24 | 9.71 679 | 31 | 0.28 321 | 9.94 786 | 7 | 29 |
| 32 | 9.66 489 | 24 | 9.71 709 | 30 | 0.28 291 | 9.94 780 | 6 | 28 |
| 33 | 9.66 513 | 24 | 9.71 740 | 31 | 0.28 260 | 9.94 773 | 7 | 27 |
| 34 | 9.66 537 | 25 | 9.71 771 | 31 | 0.28 229 | 9.94 767 | 6 | 26 |
| | | 25 | | 31 | | | 7 | |
| 35 | 9.66 562 | | 9.71 802 | | 0.28 198 | 9.94 760 | | 25 |
| 36 | 9.66 586 | 24 | 9.71 833 | 31 | 0.28 167 | 9.94 753 | 7 | 24 |
| 37 | 9.66 610 | 24 | 9.71 863 | 30 | 0.28 137 | 9.94 747 | 6 | 23 |
| 38 | 9.66 634 | 24 | 9.71 894 | 31 | 0.28 106 | 9.94 740 | 7 | 22 |
| 39 | 9.66 658 | 24 | 9.71 925̄ | 31 | 0.28 075̄ | 9.94 734 | 6 | 21 |
| | | 24 | | 30 | | | 7 | |
| 40 | 9.66 682 | | 9.71 955̄ | | 0.28 045̄ | 9.94 727 | | 20 |
| 41 | 9.66 706 | 24 | 9.71 986 | 31 | 0.28 014 | 9.94 720 | 7 | 19 |
| 42 | 9.66 731 | 25 | 9.72 017 | 31 | 0.27 983 | 9.94 714 | 6 | 18 |
| 43 | 9.66 755̄ | 24 | 9.72 048 | 31 | 0.27 952 | 9.94 707 | 7 | 17 |
| 44 | 9.66 779 | 24 | 9.72 078 | 30 | 0.27 922 | 9.94 700 | 7 | 16 |
| | | 24 | | 31 | | | 6 | |
| 45 | 9.66 803 | | 9.72 109 | | 0.27 891 | 9.94 694 | | 15 |
| 46 | 9.66 827 | 24 | 9.72 140 | 31 | 0.27 860 | 9.94 687 | 7 | 14 |
| 47 | 9.66 851 | 24 | 9.72 170 | 30 | 0.27 830 | 9.94 680 | 7 | 13 |
| 48 | 9.66 875̄ | 24 | 9.72 201 | 31 | 0.27 799 | 9.94 674 | 6 | 12 |
| 49 | 9.66 899 | 24 | 9.72 231 | 30 | 0.27 769 | 9.94 667 | 7 | 11 |
| | | 23 | | 31 | | | 7 | |
| 50 | 9.66 922 | | 9.72 262 | | 0.27 738 | 9.94 660 | | 10 |
| 51 | 9.66 946 | 24 | 9.72 293 | 31 | 0.27 707 | 9.94 654 | 6 | 9 |
| 52 | 9.66 970 | 24 | 9.72 323 | 30 | 0.27 677 | 9.94 647 | 7 | 8 |
| 53 | 9.66 994 | 24 | 9.72 354 | 31 | 0.27 646 | 9.94 640 | 7 | 7 |
| 54 | 9.67 018 | 24 | 9.72 384 | 30 | 0.27 616 | 9.94 634 | 6 | 6 |
| | | 24 | | 31 | | | 7 | |
| 55 | 9.67 042 | | 9.72 415̄ | | 0.27 585̄ | 9.94 627 | | 5 |
| 56 | 9.67 066 | 24 | 9.72 445̄ | 30 | 0.27 555̄ | 9.94 620 | 7 | 4 |
| 57 | 9.67 090 | 24 | 9.72 476 | 31 | 0.27 524 | 9.94 614 | 6 | 3 |
| 58 | 9.67 113 | 23 | 9.72 506 | 30 | 0.27 494 | 9.94 607 | 7 | 2 |
| 59 | 9.67 137 | 24 | 9.72 537 | 31 | 0.27 463 | 9.94 600 | 7 | 1 |
| | | 24 | | 30 | | | 7 | |
| 60 | 9.67 161 | | 9.72 567 | | 0.27 433 | 9.94 593 | | 0 |
| ' | L. Cos. | d. | L. Cot. | c.d. | L. Tan. | L. Sin. | d. | ' |

P. P.

| " | 32 | 31 | 30 |
|---|----|----|----|
| 1 | 0.5 | 0.5 | 0.5 |
| 2 | 1.1 | 1.0 | 1.0 |
| 3 | 1.6 | 1.6 | 1.5 |
| 4 | 2.1 | 2.1 | 2.0 |
| 5 | 2.7 | 2.6 | 2.5 |
| 6 | 3.2 | 3.1 | 3.0 |
| 7 | 3.7 | 3.6 | 3.5 |
| 8 | 4.3 | 4.1 | 4.0 |
| 9 | 4.8 | 4.6 | 4.5 |
| 10 | 5.3 | 5.2 | 5.0 |
| 20 | 10.7 | 10.3 | 10.0 |
| 30 | 16.0 | 15.5 | 15.0 |
| 40 | 21.3 | 20.7 | 20.0 |
| 50 | 26.7 | 25.8 | 25.0 |

| " | 25 | 24 | 23 |
|---|----|----|----|
| 1 | 0.4 | 0.4 | 0.4 |
| 2 | 0.8 | 0.8 | 0.8 |
| 3 | 1.2 | 1.2 | 1.2 |
| 4 | 1.7 | 1.6 | 1.5 |
| 5 | 2.1 | 2.0 | 1.9 |
| 6 | 2.5 | 2.4 | 2.3 |
| 7 | 2.9 | 2.8 | 2.7 |
| 8 | 3.3 | 3.2 | 3.1 |
| 9 | 3.8 | 3.6 | 3.4 |
| 10 | 4.2 | 4.0 | 3.8 |
| 20 | 8.3 | 8.0 | 7.7 |
| 30 | 12.5 | 12.0 | 11.5 |
| 40 | 16.7 | 16.0 | 15.3 |
| 50 | 20.8 | 20.0 | 19.2 |

| " | 7 | 6 |
|---|---|---|
| 1 | 0.1 | 0.1 |
| 2 | 0.2 | 0.2 |
| 3 | 0.4 | 0.3 |
| 4 | 0.5 | 0.4 |
| 5 | 0.6 | 0.5 |
| 6 | 0.7 | 0.6 |
| 7 | 0.8 | 0.7 |
| 8 | 0.9 | 0.8 |
| 9 | 1.0 | 0.9 |
| 10 | 1.2 | 1.0 |
| 20 | 2.3 | 2.0 |
| 30 | 3.5 | 3.0 |
| 40 | 4.7 | 4.0 |
| 50 | 5.8 | 5.0 |

| | 7/30 | 6/31 | 6/30 |
|---|------|------|------|
| 0 | | | |
| 1 | 2.1 | 2.6 | 2.5 |
| 2 | 6.4 | 7.8 | 7.5 |
| 3 | 10.7 | 12.9 | 12.5 |
| 4 | 15.0 | 18.1 | 17.5 |
| 5 | 19.3 | 23.2 | 22.5 |
| 6 | 23.6 | 28.4 | 27.5 |
| 7 | 27.9 | | |

## LOGARITHMS OF THE FUNCTIONS (Continued)

| ′ | L. Sin. | d. | L. Tan. | c.d. | L. Cot. | L. Cos. | d. | ′ |
|---|---------|----|---------|------|---------|---------|----|---|
| 0 | 9.67 161 | 24 | 9.72 567 | 31 | 0.27 433 | 9.94 593 | 6 | 60 |
| 1 | 9.67 185 | 23 | 9.72 598 | 30 | 0.27 402 | 9.94 587 | 7 | 59 |
| 2 | 9.67 208 | 24 | 9.72 628 | 31 | 0.27 372 | 9.94 580 | 7 | 58 |
| 3 | 9.67 232 | 24 | 9.72 659 | 30 | 0.27 341 | 9.94 573 | 6 | 57 |
| 4 | 9.67 256 | 24 | 9.72 689 | 31 | 0.27 311 | 9.94 567 | 7 | 56 |
| 5 | 9.67 280 | 23 | 9.72 720 | 30 | 0.27 280 | 9.94 560 | 7 | 55 |
| 6 | 9.67 303 | 24 | 9.72 750 | 30 | 0.27 250 | 9.94 553 | 7 | 54 |
| 7 | 9.67 327 | 23 | 9.72 780 | 31 | 0.27 220 | 9.94 546 | 6 | 53 |
| 8 | 9.67 350 | 24 | 9.72 811 | 30 | 0.27 189 | 9.94 540 | 7 | 52 |
| 9 | 9.67 374 | 24 | 9.72 841 | 31 | 0.27 159 | 9.94 533 | 7 | 51 |
| 10 | 9.67 398 | 23 | 9.72 872 | 30 | 0.27 128 | 9.94 526 | 7 | 50 |
| 11 | 9.67 421 | 24 | 9.72 902 | 30 | 0.27 098 | 9.94 519 | 6 | 49 |
| 12 | 9.67 445 | 23 | 9.72 932 | 31 | 0.27 068 | 9.94 513 | 7 | 48 |
| 13 | 9.67 468 | 24 | 9.72 963 | 30 | 0.27 037 | 9.94 506 | 7 | 47 |
| 14 | 9.67 492 | 23 | 9.72 993 | 30 | 0.27 007 | 9.94 499 | 7 | 46 |
| 15 | 9.67 515 | 24 | 9.73 023 | 31 | 0.26 977 | 9.94 492 | 7 | 45 |
| 16 | 9.67 539 | 23 | 9.73 054 | 30 | 0.26 946 | 9.94 485 | 6 | 44 |
| 17 | 9.67 562 | 24 | 9.73 084 | 30 | 0.26 916 | 9.94 479 | 7 | 43 |
| 18 | 9.67 586 | 23 | 9.73 114 | 30 | 0.26 886 | 9.94 472 | 7 | 42 |
| 19 | 9.67 609 | 24 | 9.73 144 | 31 | 0.26 856 | 9.94 465 | 7 | 41 |
| 20 | 9.67 633 | 23 | 9.73 175 | 30 | 0.26 825 | 9.94 458 | 7 | 40 |
| 21 | 9.67 656 | 24 | 9.73 205 | 30 | 0.26 795 | 9.94 451 | 6 | 39 |
| 22 | 9.67 680 | 23 | 9.73 235 | 30 | 0.26 765 | 9.94 445 | 7 | 38 |
| 23 | 9.67 703 | 23 | 9.73 265 | 30 | 0.26 735 | 9.94 438 | 7 | 37 |
| 24 | 9.67 726 | 24 | 9.73 295 | 31 | 0.26 705 | 9.94 431 | 7 | 36 |
| 25 | 9.67 750 | 23 | 9.73 326 | 30 | 0.26 674 | 9.94 424 | 7 | 35 |
| 26 | 9.67 773 | 23 | 9.73 356 | 30 | 0.26 644 | 9.94 417 | 7 | 34 |
| 27 | 9.67 796 | 24 | 9.73 386 | 30 | 0.26 614 | 9.94 410 | 6 | 33 |
| 28 | 9.67 820 | 23 | 9.73 416 | 30 | 0.26 584 | 9.94 404 | 7 | 32 |
| 29 | 9.67 843 | 23 | 9.73 446 | 30 | 0.26 554 | 9.94 397 | 7 | 31 |
| 30 | 9.67 866 | 24 | 9.73 476 | 31 | 0.26 524 | 9.94 390 | 7 | 30 |
| 31 | 9.67 890 | 23 | 9.73 507 | 30 | 0.26 493 | 9.94 383 | 7 | 29 |
| 32 | 9.67 913 | 23 | 9.73 537 | 30 | 0.26 463 | 9.94 376 | 7 | 28 |
| 33 | 9.67 936 | 23 | 9.73 567 | 30 | 0.26 433 | 9.94 369 | 7 | 27 |
| 34 | 9.67 959 | 23 | 9.73 597 | 30 | 0.26 403 | 9.94 362 | 7 | 26 |
| 35 | 9.67 982 | 24 | 9.73 627 | 30 | 0.26 373 | 9.94 355 | 6 | 25 |
| 36 | 9.68 006 | 23 | 9.73 657 | 30 | 0.26 343 | 9.94 349 | 7 | 24 |
| 37 | 9.68 029 | 23 | 9.73 687 | 30 | 0.26 313 | 9.94 342 | 7 | 23 |
| 38 | 9.68 052 | 23 | 9.73 717 | 30 | 0.26 283 | 9.94 335 | 7 | 22 |
| 39 | 9.68 075 | 23 | 9.73 747 | 30 | 0.26 253 | 9.94 328 | 7 | 21 |
| 40 | 9.68 098 | 23 | 9.73 777 | 30 | 0.26 223 | 9.94 321 | 7 | 20 |
| 41 | 9.68 121 | 23 | 9.73 807 | 30 | 0.26 193 | 9.94 314 | 7 | 19 |
| 42 | 9.68 144 | 23 | 9.73 837 | 30 | 0.26 163 | 9.94 307 | 7 | 18 |
| 43 | 9.68 167 | 23 | 9.73 867 | 30 | 0.26 133 | 9.94 300 | 7 | 17 |
| 44 | 9.68 190 | 23 | 9.73 897 | 30 | 0.26 103 | 9.94 293 | 7 | 16 |
| 45 | 9.68 213 | 24 | 9.73 927 | 30 | 0.26 073 | 9.94 286 | 7 | 15 |
| 46 | 9.68 237 | 23 | 9.73 957 | 30 | 0.26 043 | 9.94 279 | 6 | 14 |
| 47 | 9.68 260 | 23 | 9.73 987 | 30 | 0.26 013 | 9.94 273 | 7 | 13 |
| 48 | 9.68 283 | 22 | 9.74 017 | 30 | 0.25 983 | 9.94 266 | 7 | 12 |
| 49 | 9.68 305 | 23 | 9.74 047 | 30 | 0.25 953 | 9.94 259 | 7 | 11 |
| 50 | 9.68 328 | 23 | 9.74 077 | 30 | 0.25 923 | 9.94 252 | 7 | 10 |
| 51 | 9.68 351 | 23 | 9.74 107 | 30 | 0.25 893 | 9.94 245 | 7 | 9 |
| 52 | 9.68 374 | 23 | 9.74 137 | 29 | 0.25 863 | 9.94 238 | 7 | 8 |
| 53 | 9.68 397 | 23 | 9.74 166 | 30 | 0.25 834 | 9.94 231 | 7 | 7 |
| 54 | 9.68 420 | 23 | 9.74 196 | 30 | 0.25 804 | 9.94 224 | 7 | 6 |
| 55 | 9.68 443 | 23 | 9.74 226 | 30 | 0.25 774 | 9.94 217 | 7 | 5 |
| 56 | 9.68 466 | 23 | 9.74 256 | 30 | 0.25 744 | 9.94 210 | 7 | 4 |
| 57 | 9.68 489 | 23 | 9.74 286 | 30 | 0.25 714 | 9.94 203 | 7 | 3 |
| 58 | 9.68 512 | 22 | 9.74 316 | 29 | 0.25 684 | 9.94 196 | 7 | 2 |
| 59 | 9.68 534 | 23 | 9.74 345 | 30 | 0.25 655 | 9.94 189 | 7 | 1 |
| 60 | 9.68 557 | | 9.74 375 | | 0.25 625 | 9.94 182 | | 0 |

| ′ | L. Cos. | d. | L. Cot. | c.d. | L. Tan. | L. Sin. | d | ′ |

### P. P.

|  | 31 | 30 | 29 |
|---|----|----|----|
| 1 | 0.5 | 0.5 | 0.5 |
| 2 | 1.0 | 1.0 | 1.0 |
| 3 | 1.6 | 1.5 | 1.4 |
| 4 | 2.1 | 2.0 | 1.9 |
| 5 | 2.6 | 2.5 | 2.4 |
| 6 | 3.1 | 3.0 | 2.9 |
| 7 | 3.6 | 3.5 | 3.4 |
| 8 | 4.1 | 4.0 | 3.9 |
| 9 | 4.6 | 4.5 | 4.4 |
| 10 | 5.2 | 5.0 | 4.8 |
| 20 | 10.3 | 10.0 | 9.7 |
| 30 | 15.5 | 15.0 | 14.5 |
| 40 | 20.7 | 20.0 | 19.3 |
| 50 | 25.8 | 25.0 | 24.2 |

|  | 24 | 23 | 22 |
|---|----|----|----|
| 1 | 0.4 | 0.4 | 0.4 |
| 2 | 0.8 | 0.8 | 0.7 |
| 3 | 1.2 | 1.2 | 1.1 |
| 4 | 1.6 | 1.5 | 1.5 |
| 5 | 2.0 | 1.9 | 1.8 |
| 6 | 2.4 | 2.3 | 2.2 |
| 7 | 2.8 | 2.7 | 2.6 |
| 8 | 3.2 | 3.1 | 2.9 |
| 9 | 3.6 | 3.4 | 3.3 |
| 10 | 4.0 | 3.8 | 3.7 |
| 20 | 8.0 | 7.7 | 7.3 |
| 30 | 12.0 | 11.5 | 11.0 |
| 40 | 16.0 | 15.3 | 14.7 |
| 50 | 20.0 | 19.2 | 18.3 |

|  | 7 | 6 |
|---|---|---|
| 1 | 0.1 | 0.1 |
| 2 | 0.2 | 0.2 |
| 3 | 0.4 | 0.3 |
| 4 | 0.5 | 0.4 |
| 5 | 0.6 | 0.5 |
| 6 | 0.7 | 0.6 |
| 7 | 0.8 | 0.7 |
| 8 | 0.9 | 0.8 |
| 9 | 1.0 | 0.9 |
| 10 | 1.2 | 1.0 |
| 20 | 2.3 | 2.0 |
| 30 | 3.5 | 3.0 |
| 40 | 4.7 | 4.0 |
| 50 | 5.8 | 5.0 |

|  | 7/31 | 6/31 | 6/30 |
|---|----|----|----|
| 0 | | | |
| 1 | 2.2 | 2.6 | 2.5 |
| 2 | 6.6 | 7.8 | 7.5 |
| 3 | 11.1 | 12.9 | 12.5 |
| 4 | 15.5 | 18.1 | 17.5 |
| 5 | 19.9 | 23.2 | 22.5 |
| 6 | 24.4 | 28.4 | 27.5 |
| 7 | 28.8 | — | — |

# LOGARITHMS OF THE FUNCTIONS (Continued)

| ′ | L. Sin. | d. | L. Tan. | c.d. | L. Cot. | L. Cos. | d. | ′ |
|---|---|---|---|---|---|---|---|---|
| 0 | 9.68 557 | | 9.74 375 | | 0.25 625 | 9.94 182 | 7 | 60 |
| 1 | 9.68 580 | 23 | 9.74 405 | 30 | 0.25 595 | 9.94 175 | 7 | 59 |
| 2 | 9.68 603 | 23 | 9.74 435 | 30 | 0.25 565 | 9.94 168 | 7 | 58 |
| 3 | 9.68 625 | 22 | 9.74 465 | 30 | 0.25 535 | 9.94 161 | 7 | 57 |
| 4 | 9.68 648 | 23 | 9.74 494 | 29 | 0.25 506 | 9.94 154 | 7 | 56 |
| 5 | 9.68 671 | 23 | 9.74 524 | 30 | 0.25 476 | 9.94 147 | 7 | 55 |
| 6 | 9.68 694 | 23 | 9.74 554 | 30 | 0.25 446 | 9.94 140 | 7 | 54 |
| 7 | 9.68 716 | 22 | 9.74 583 | 29 | 0.25 417 | 9.94 133 | 7 | 53 |
| 8 | 9.68 739 | 22 | 9.74 613 | 30 | 0.25 387 | 9.94 126 | 7 | 52 |
| 9 | 9.68 762 | 23 | 9.74 643 | 30 | 0.25 357 | 9.94 119 | 7 | 51 |
| 10 | 9.68 784 | 22 | 9.74 673 | 30 | 0.25 327 | 9.94 112 | 7 | 50 |
| 11 | 9.68 807 | 23 | 9.74 702 | 29 | 0.25 298 | 9.94 105 | 7 | 49 |
| 12 | 9.68 829 | 22 | 9.74 732 | 30 | 0.25 268 | 9.94 098 | 8 | 48 |
| 13 | 9.68 852 | 22 | 9.74 762 | 30 | 0.25 238 | 9.94 090 | 7 | 47 |
| 14 | 9.68 875 | 23 | 9.74 791 | 29 | 0.25 209 | 9.94 083 | 7 | 46 |
| 15 | 9.68 897 | 23 | 9.74 821 | 30 | 0.25 179 | 9.94 076 | 7 | 45 |
| 16 | 9.68 920 | 22 | 9.74 851 | 30 | 0.25 149 | 9.94 069 | 7 | 44 |
| 17 | 9.68 942 | 23 | 9.74 880 | 29 | 0.25 120 | 9.94 062 | 7 | 43 |
| 18 | 9.68 965 | 22 | 9.74 910 | 30 | 0.25 090 | 9.94 055 | 7 | 42 |
| 19 | 9.68 987 | 23 | 9.74 939 | 29 | 0.25 061 | 9.94 048 | 7 | 41 |
| 20 | 9.69 010 | 22 | 9.74 969 | 30 | 0.25 031 | 9 94 041 | 7 | 40 |
| 21 | 9.69 032 | 23 | 9.74 998 | 29 | 0.25 002 | 9.94 034 | 7 | 39 |
| 22 | 9.69 055 | 22 | 9.75 028 | 30 | 0.24 972 | 9.94 027 | 7 | 38 |
| 23 | 9.69 077 | 23 | 9.75 058 | 29 | 0.24 942 | 9.94 020 | 8 | 37 |
| 24 | 9.69 100 | 22 | 9.75 087 | 30 | 0.24 913 | 9.94 012 | 7 | 36 |
| 25 | 9.69 122 | 22 | 9.75 117 | 29 | 0.24 883 | 9.94 005 | 7 | 35 |
| 26 | 9.69 144 | 23 | 9.75 146 | 30 | 0.24 854 | 9.93 998 | 7 | 34 |
| 27 | 9.69 167 | 22 | 9.75 176 | 30 | 0.24 824 | 9.93 991 | 7 | 33 |
| 28 | 9.69 189 | 23 | 9.75 205 | 29 | 0.24 795 | 9.93 984 | 7 | 32 |
| 29 | 9.69 212 | 22 | 9.75 235 | 30 | 0.24 765 | 9.93 977 | 7 | 31 |
| 30 | 9.69 234 | 22 | 9.75 264 | 30 | 0.24 736 | 9.93 970 | 7 | 30 |
| 31 | 9.69 256 | 23 | 9.75 294 | 29 | 0.24 706 | 9.93 963 | 8 | 29 |
| 32 | 9.69 279 | 22 | 9.75 323 | 30 | 0.24 677 | 9.93 955 | 7 | 28 |
| 33 | 9.69 301 | 22 | 9.75 353 | 29 | 0.24 647 | 9.93 948 | 7 | 27 |
| 34 | 9.69 323 | 22 | 9.75 382 | 29 | 0.24 618 | 9.93 941 | 7 | 26 |
| 35 | 9.69 345 | 23 | 9.75 411 | 30 | 0.24 589 | 9.93 934 | 7 | 25 |
| 36 | 9.69 368 | 22 | 9.75 441 | 29 | 0.24 559 | 9.93 927 | 7 | 24 |
| 37 | 9.69 390 | 22 | 9.75 470 | 30 | 0.24 530 | 9.93 920 | 7 | 23 |
| 38 | 9.69 412 | 22 | 9.75 500 | 30 | 0.24 500 | 9.93 912 | 8 | 22 |
| 39 | 9.69 434 | 22 | 9.75 529 | 29 | 0.24 471 | 9.93 905 | 7 | 21 |
| 40 | 9.69 456 | 23 | 9.75 558 | 29 | 0.24 442 | 9.93 898 | 7 | 20 |
| 41 | 9.69 479 | 22 | 9.75 588 | 30 | 0.24 412 | 9.93 891 | 7 | 19 |
| 42 | 9.69 501 | 22 | 9.75 617 | 29 | 0.24 383 | 9.93 884 | 8 | 18 |
| 43 | 9.69 523 | 22 | 9.75 647 | 30 | 0.24 353 | 9.93 876 | 7 | 17 |
| 44 | 9.69 545 | 22 | 9.75 676 | 29 | 0.24 324 | 9.93 869 | 7 | 16 |
| 45 | 9.69 567 | 22 | 9.75 705 | 29 | 0.24 295 | 9.93 862 | 7 | 15 |
| 46 | 9.69 589 | 22 | 9.75 735 | 30 | 0.24 265 | 9.93 855 | 8 | 14 |
| 47 | 9.69 611 | 22 | 9.75 764 | 29 | 0.24 236 | 9.93 847 | 7 | 13 |
| 48 | 9.69 633 | 22 | 9.75 793 | 29 | 0.24 207 | 9.93 840 | 7 | 12 |
| 49 | 9.69 655 | 22 | 9.75 822 | 29 | 0.24 178 | 9.93 833 | 7 | 11 |
| 50 | 9.69 677 | 22 | 9.75 852 | 30 | 0.24 148 | 9.93 826 | 7 | 10 |
| 51 | 9.69 699 | 22 | 9.75 881 | 29 | 0.24 119 | 9.93 819 | 8 | 9 |
| 52 | 9.69 721 | 22 | 9.75 910 | 29 | 0.24 090 | 9.93 811 | 7 | 8 |
| 53 | 9.69 743 | 22 | 9.75 939 | 29 | 0.24 061 | 9.93 804 | 7 | 7 |
| 54 | 9.69 765 | 22 | 9.75 969 | 30 | 0.24 031 | 9.93 797 | 8 | 6 |
| 55 | 9.69 787 | 22 | 9.75 998 | 29 | 0.24 002 | 9.93 789 | 7 | 5 |
| 56 | 9.69 809 | 22 | 9.76 027 | 29 | 0.23 973 | 9.93 782 | 7 | 4 |
| 57 | 9.69 831 | 22 | 9.76 056 | 29 | 0.23 944 | 9.93 775 | 7 | 3 |
| 58 | 9.69 853 | 22 | 9.76 086 | 30 | 0.23 914 | 9.93 768 | 7 | 2 |
| 59 | 9.69 875 | 22 | 9.76 115 | 29 | 0.23 886 | 9.93 760 | 8 | 1 |
| 60 | 9.69 897 | | 9.76 144 | 29 | 0.23 856 | 9.93 753 | 7 | 0 |

## P. P.

| | 30 | 29 | 28 |
|---|---|---|---|
| 1 | 0.5 | 0.5 | 0.4 |
| 2 | 1.0 | 1.0 | 0.8 |
| 3 | 1.5 | 1.4 | 1.2 |
| 4 | 2.0 | 1.9 | 1.8 |
| 5 | 2.5 | 2.4 | 1.9 |
| 6 | 3.0 | 2.9 | 2.3 |
| 7 | 3.5 | 3.4 | 2.7 |
| 8 | 4.0 | 3.9 | 3.1 |
| 9 | 4.5 | 4.4 | 3.4 |
| 10 | 5.0 | 4.8 | 3.8 |
| 20 | 10.0 | 9.7 | 7.7 |
| 30 | 15.0 | 14.5 | 11.5 |
| 40 | 20.0 | 19.3 | 15.3 |
| 50 | 25.0 | 24.2 | 19.2 |

| | 22 | 8 | 7 |
|---|---|---|---|
| 1 | 0.4 | 0.1 | 0.1 |
| 2 | 0.7 | 0.3 | 0.2 |
| 3 | 1.1 | 0.4 | 0.4 |
| 4 | 1.5 | 0.5 | 0.5 |
| 5 | 1.8 | 0.7 | 0.6 |
| 6 | 2.2 | 0.8 | 0.7 |
| 7 | 2.6 | 0.9 | 0.8 |
| 8 | 2.9 | 1.1 | 0.9 |
| 9 | 3.3 | 1.2 | 1.0 |
| 10 | 3.7 | 1.3 | 1.2 |
| 20 | 7.3 | 2.7 | 2.3 |
| 30 | 11.0 | 4.0 | 3.5 |
| 40 | 14.7 | 5.3 | 4.7 |
| 50 | 18.3 | 6.7 | 5.8 |

| | 8/30 | 8/29 |
|---|---|---|
| 0 | | |
| 1 | 1.9 | 1.8 |
| 2 | 5.6 | 5.4 |
| 3 | 9.4 | 9.1 |
| 4 | 13.1 | 12.7 |
| 5 | 16.9 | 16.3 |
| 6 | 20.6 | 19.9 |
| 7 | 24.4 | 23.6 |
| 8 | 28.1 | 27.2 |

| | 7/30 | 7/29 |
|---|---|---|
| 0 | | |
| 1 | 2.1 | 2.1 |
| 2 | 6.4 | 6.2 |
| 3 | 10.7 | 10.4 |
| 4 | 15.0 | 14.5 |
| 5 | 19.3 | 18.6 |
| 6 | 23.6 | 22.8 |
| 7 | 27.9 | 26.9 |

| ° | L. Cos. | d. | L. Cot. | c.d. | L. Tan. | L. Sin. | d. | ′ | P. P. |
|---|---|---|---|---|---|---|---|---|---|

**30° (210°)**                              **(329°) 149°**

| ′ | L. Sin. | d. | L. Tan. | c.d. | L. Cot. | L. Cos. | d. | ′ | P.P. | | |
|---|---------|----|---------|------|---------|---------|----|----|------|---|---|
| 0 | 9.69 897 | 22 | 9.76 144 | 29 | 0.23 856 | 9.93 753 | 7 | 60 | | | |
| 1 | 9.69 919 | 22 | 9.76 173 | 29 | 0.23 827 | 9.93 746 | 7 | 59 | | **30** | **29** | **28** |
| 2 | 9.69 941 | 22 | 9.76 202 | 29 | 0.23 798 | 9.93 738 | 8 | 58 | 1 | 0.5 | 0.5 | 0.5 |
| 3 | 9.69 963 | 21 | 9.76 231 | 30 | 0.23 769 | 9.93 731 | 7 | 57 | 2 | 1.0 | 1.0 | 0.9 |
| 4 | 9.69 984 | 22 | 9.76 261 | 29 | 0.23 739 | 9.93 724 | 7 | 56 | 3 | 1.5 | 1.4 | 1.4 |
| 5 | 9.70 006 | 22 | 9.76 290 | 29 | 0.23 710 | 9.93 717 | 7 | 55 | 4 | 2.0 | 1.9 | 1.9 |
| 6 | 9.70 028 | 22 | 9.76 319 | 29 | 0.23 681 | 9.93 709 | 8 | 54 | 5 | 2.5 | 2.4 | 2.3 |
| 7 | 9.70 050 | 22 | 9.76 348 | 29 | 0.23 652 | 9.93 702 | 7 | 53 | 6 | 3.0 | 2.9 | 2.8 |
| 8 | 9.70 072 | 22 | 9.76 377 | 29 | 0.23 623 | 9.93 695 | 8 | 52 | 7 | 3.5 | 3.4 | 3.3 |
| 9 | 9.70 093 | 22 | 9.76 406 | 29 | 0.23 594 | 9.93 687 | 7 | 51 | 8 | 4.0 | 3.9 | 3.7 |
| 10 | 9.70 115 | 22 | 9.76 435 | 29 | 0.23 565 | 9.93 680 | 7 | 50 | 9 | 4.5 | 4.4 | 4.2 |
| 11 | 9.70 137 | 22 | 9.76 464 | 29 | 0.23 536 | 9.93 673 | 8 | 49 | 10 | 5.0 | 4.8 | 4.7 |
| 12 | 9.70 159 | 21 | 9.76 493 | 29 | 0.23 507 | 9.93 665 | 7 | 48 | 20 | 10.0 | 9.7 | 9.3 |
| 13 | 9.70 180 | 22 | 9.76 522 | 29 | 0.23 478 | 9.93 658 | 8 | 47 | 30 | 15.0 | 14.5 | 14.0 |
| 14 | 9.70 202 | 22 | 9.76 551 | 29 | 0.23 449 | 9.93 650 | 7 | 46 | 40 | 20.0 | 19.3 | 18.7 |
| 15 | 9.70 224 | 21 | 9.76 580 | 29 | 0.23 420 | 9.93 643 | 7 | 45 | 50 | 25.0 | 24.2 | 23.3 |
| 16 | 9.70 245 | 22 | 9.76 609 | 30 | 0.23 391 | 9.93 636 | 8 | 44 | | | |
| 17 | 9.70 267 | 21 | 9.76 639 | 29 | 0.23 361 | 9.93 628 | 7 | 43 | | **22** | **21** |
| 18 | 9.70 288 | 22 | 9.76 668 | 29 | 0.23 332 | 9.93 621 | 7 | 42 | 1 | 0.4 | 0.4 |
| 19 | 9.70 310 | 22 | 9.76 697 | 28 | 0.23 303 | 9.93 614 | 8 | 41 | 2 | 0.7 | 0.7 |
| 20 | 9.70 332 | 21 | 9.76 725 | 29 | 0.23 275 | 9.93 606 | 7 | 40 | 3 | 1.1 | 1.0 |
| 21 | 9.70 353 | 22 | 9.76 754 | 29 | 0.23 246 | 9.93 599 | 8 | 39 | 4 | 1.5 | 1.4 |
| 22 | 9.70 375 | 21 | 9.76 783 | 29 | 0.23 217 | 9.93 591 | 7 | 38 | 5 | 1.8 | 1.8 |
| 23 | 9.70 396 | 22 | 9.76 812 | 29 | 0.23 188 | 9.93 584 | 7 | 37 | 6 | 2.2 | 2.1 |
| 24 | 9.70 418 | 21 | 9.76 841 | 29 | 0.23 159 | 9.93 577 | 8 | 36 | 7 | 2.6 | 2.4 |
| 25 | 9.70 439 | 22 | 9.76 870 | 29 | 0.23 130 | 9.93 569 | 7 | 35 | 8 | 2.9 | 2.8 |
| 26 | 9.70 461 | 21 | 9.76 899 | 29 | 0.23 101 | 9.93 562 | 8 | 34 | 9 | 3.3 | 3.2 |
| 27 | 9.70 482 | 22 | 9.76 928 | 29 | 0.23 072 | 9.93 554 | 7 | 33 | 10 | 3.7 | 3.5 |
| 28 | 9.70 504 | 21 | 9.76 957 | 29 | 0.23 043 | 9.93 547 | 8 | 32 | 20 | 7.3 | 7.0 |
| 29 | 9.70 525 | 22 | 9.76 986 | 29 | 0.23 014 | 9.93 539 | 7 | 31 | 30 | 11.0 | 10.5 |
| 30 | 9.70 547 | 21 | 9.77 015 | 29 | 0.22 985 | 9.93 532 | 7 | 30 | 40 | 14.7 | 14.0 |
| 31 | 9.70 568 | 22 | 9.77 044 | 29 | 0.22 956 | 9.93 525 | 8 | 29 | 50 | 18.3 | 17.5 |
| 32 | 9.70 590 | 21 | 9.77 073 | 28 | 0.22 927 | 9.93 517 | 7 | 28 | | | |
| 33 | 9.70 611 | 22 | 9.77 101 | 29 | 0.22 899 | 9.93 510 | 8 | 27 | | **8** | **7** |
| 34 | 9.70 633 | 21 | 9.77 130 | 29 | 0.22 870 | 9.93 502 | 7 | 26 | 1 | 0.1 | 0.1 |
| 35 | 9.70 654 | 21 | 9.77 159 | 29 | 0.22 841 | 9.93 495 | 8 | 25 | 2 | 0.3 | 0.2 |
| 36 | 9.70 675 | 22 | 9.77 188 | 29 | 0.22 812 | 9.93 487 | 7 | 24 | 3 | 0.4 | 0.4 |
| 37 | 9.70 697 | 21 | 9.77 217 | 29 | 0.22 783 | 9.93 480 | 8 | 23 | 4 | 0.5 | 0.5 |
| 38 | 9.70 718 | 21 | 9.77 246 | 28 | 0.22 754 | 9.93 472 | 7 | 22 | 5 | 0.7 | 0.6 |
| 39 | 9.70 739 | 22 | 9.77 274 | 29 | 0.22 726 | 9.93 465 | 8 | 21 | 6 | 0.8 | 0.7 |
| 40 | 9.70 761 | 21 | 9.77 303 | 29 | 0.22 697 | 9.93 457 | 7 | 20 | 7 | 0.9 | 0.8 |
| 41 | 9.70 782 | 21 | 9.77 332 | 29 | 0.22 668 | 9.93 450 | 8 | 19 | 8 | 1.1 | 0.9 |
| 42 | 9.70 803 | 21 | 9.77 361 | 29 | 0.22 639 | 9.93 442 | 7 | 18 | 9 | 1.2 | 1.0 |
| 43 | 9.70 824 | 22 | 9.77 390 | 28 | 0.22 610 | 9.93 435 | 8 | 17 | 10 | 1.3 | 1.2 |
| 44 | 9.70 846 | 21 | 9.77 418 | 29 | 0.22 582 | 9.93 427 | 7 | 16 | 20 | 2.7 | 2.3 |
| 45 | 9.70 867 | 21 | 9.77 447 | 29 | 0.22 553 | 9.93 420 | 8 | 15 | 30 | 4.0 | 3.5 |
| 46 | 9.70 888 | 21 | 9.77 476 | 29 | 0.22 524 | 9.93 412 | 7 | 14 | 40 | 5.3 | 4.7 |
| 47 | 9.70 909 | 22 | 9.77 505 | 28 | 0.22 495 | 9.93 405 | 8 | 13 | 50 | 6.7 | 5.8 |
| 48 | 9.70 931 | 21 | 9.77 533 | 29 | 0.22 467 | 9.93 397 | 8 | 12 | | | |
| 49 | 9.70 952 | 21 | 9.77 562 | 29 | 0.22 438 | 9.93 390 | 8 | 11 | | | |
| 50 | 9.70 973 | 21 | 9.77 591 | 28 | 0.22 409 | 9.93 382 | 7 | 10 | | **7** | **7** | **7** |
| 51 | 9.70 994 | 21 | 9.77 619 | 29 | 0.22 381 | 9.93 375 | 8 | 9 | | **30** | **29** | **28** |
| 52 | 9.71 015 | 21 | 9.77 648 | 29 | 0.22 352 | 9.93 367 | 7 | 8 | 0 | | | |
| 53 | 9.71 036 | 22 | 9.77 677 | 29 | 0.22 323 | 9.93 360 | 8 | 7 | 1 | 2.1 | 2.1 | 2.0 |
| 54 | 9.71 058 | 21 | 9.77 706 | 28 | 0.22 294 | 9.93 352 | 8 | 6 | 2 | 6.4 | 6.2 | 6.0 |
| 55 | 9.71 079 | 21 | 9.77 734 | 29 | 0.22 266 | 9.93 344 | 7 | 5 | 3 | 10.7 | 10.4 | 10.0 |
| 56 | 9.71 100 | 21 | 9.77 763 | 28 | 0.22 237 | 9.93 337 | 8 | 4 | 4 | 15.0 | 14.5 | 14.0 |
| 57 | 9.71 121 | 21 | 9.77 791 | 29 | 0.22 209 | 9.93 329 | 7 | 3 | 5 | 19.3 | 18.6 | 18.0 |
| 58 | 9.71 142 | 21 | 9.77 820 | 29 | 0.22 180 | 9.93 322 | 8 | 2 | 6 | 23.6 | 22.8 | 22.0 |
| 59 | 9.71 163 | 21 | 9.77 849 | 28 | 0.22 151 | 9.93 314 | 7 | 1 | 7 | 27.9 | 26.9 | 26.0 |
| 60 | 9.71 184 | | 9.77 877 | | 0.22 123 | 9.93 307 | | 0 | | | |

| ′ | L. Cos. | d. | L. Cot. | c.d. | L. Tan. | L. Sin. | d. | ′ | P.P. |

# LOGARITHMS OF THE FUNCTIONS (Continued)

| ′ | L. Sin. | d. | L. Tan. | c.d. | L. Cot. | L. Cos. | d. | ′ |
|---|---|---|---|---|---|---|---|---|
| 0 | 9.71 184 | 21 | 9.77 877 | 29 | 0.22 123 | 9.93 307 | 8 | 60 |
| 1 | 9.71 205̄ | 21 | 9.77 906 | 29 | 0.22 094 | 9.93 299 | 8 | 59 |
| 2 | 0.71 226 | 21 | 9.77 935̄ | 28 | 0.22 065̄ | 9.93 291 | 7 | 58 |
| 3 | 9.71 247 | 21 | 9.77 963 | 29 | 0.22 037 | 9.93 284 | 8 | 57 |
| 4 | 9.71 268 | 21 | 9.77 992 | 28 | 0.22 008 | 9.93 276 | 7 | 56 |
| 5 | 9.71 289 | 21 | 9.78 020 | 29 | 0.21 980 | 9.93 269 | 8 | 55 |
| 6 | 9.71 310 | 21 | 9.78 049 | 28 | 0.21 951 | 9.93 261 | 8 | 54 |
| 7 | 9.71 331 | 21 | 9.78 077 | 29 | 0.21 923 | 9.93 253 | 7 | 53 |
| 8 | 9.71 352 | 21 | 9.78 106 | 29 | 0.21 894 | 9.93 246 | 8 | 52 |
| 9 | 9.71 373 | 20 | 9.78 135̄ | 28 | 0.21 865̄ | 9.93 238 | 8 | 51 |
| 10 | 9.71 393 | 21 | 9.78 163 | 29 | 0.21 837 | 9.93 230 | 7 | 50 |
| 11 | 9.71 414 | 21 | 9.78 192 | 28 | 0.21 808 | 9.93 223 | 8 | 49 |
| 12 | 9.71 435̄ | 21 | 9.78 220 | 29 | 0.21 780 | 9.93 215̄ | 8 | 48 |
| 13 | 9.71 456 | 21 | 9.78 249 | 28 | 0.21 751 | 9.93 207 | 7 | 47 |
| 14 | 9.71 477 | 21 | 9.78 277 | 29 | 0.21 723 | 9.93 200 | 8 | 46 |
| 15 | 9.71 498 | 21 | 9.78 306 | 28 | 0.21 694 | 9.93 192 | 8 | 45 |
| 16 | 9.71 519 | 20 | 9.78 334 | 29 | 0.21 666 | 9.93 184 | 7 | 44 |
| 17 | 9.71 539 | 21 | 9.78 363 | 28 | 0.21 637 | 9.93 177 | 8 | 43 |
| 18 | 9.71 560 | 21 | 9.78 391 | 28 | 0.21 609 | 9.93 169 | 8 | 42 |
| 19 | 9.71 581 | 21 | 9.78 419 | 29 | 0.21 581 | 9.93 161 | 7 | 41 |
| 20 | 9.71 602 | 20 | 9.78 448 | 28 | 0.21 552 | 9.93 154 | 8 | 40 |
| 21 | 9.71 622 | 21 | 9.78 476 | 29 | 0.21 524 | 9.93 146 | 8 | 39 |
| 22 | 9.71 643 | 21 | 9.78 505̄ | 28 | 0.21 495̄ | 9.93 138 | 7 | 38 |
| 23 | 9.71 664 | 21 | 9.78 533 | 29 | 0.21 467 | 9.93 131 | 8 | 37 |
| 24 | 9.71 685̄ | 20 | 9.78 562 | 28 | 0.21 438 | 9.93 123 | 8 | 36 |
| 25 | 9.71 705̄ | 21 | 9.78 590 | 28 | 0.21 410 | 9.93 115̄ | 7 | 35 |
| 26 | 9.71 726 | 21 | 9.78 618 | 29 | 0.21 382 | 9.93 108 | 8 | 34 |
| 27 | 9.71 747 | 20 | 9.78 647 | 28 | 0.21 353 | 9.93 100 | 8 | 33 |
| 28 | 9.71 767 | 21 | 9.78 675̄ | 29 | 0.21 325̄ | 9.93 092 | 8 | 32 |
| 29 | 9.71 788 | 21 | 9.78 704 | 28 | 0.21 296 | 9.93 084 | 7 | 31 |
| 30 | 9.71 809 | 20 | 9.78 732 | 28 | 0.21 268 | 9.93 077 | 8 | 30 |
| 31 | 9.71 829 | 21 | 9.78 760 | 29 | 0.21 240 | 9.93 069 | 8 | 29 |
| 32 | 9.71 850̄ | 20 | 9.78 789 | 28 | 0.21 211 | 9.93 061 | 8 | 28 |
| 33 | 9.71 870 | 21 | 9.78 817 | 28 | 0.21 183 | 9.93 053̄ | 7 | 27 |
| 34 | 9.71 891 | 20 | 9.78 845̄ | 29 | 0.21 155̄ | 9.93 046 | 8 | 26 |
| 35 | 9.71 911 | 21 | 9.78 874 | 28 | 0.21 126 | 9.93 038 | 8 | 25 |
| 36 | 9.71 932 | 20 | 9.78 902 | 28 | 0.21 098 | 9.93 030 | 8 | 24 |
| 37 | 9.71 952 | 21 | 9.78 930 | 29 | 0.21 070 | 9.93 022 | 8 | 23 |
| 38 | 9.71 973 | 21 | 9.78 959 | 28 | 0.21 041 | 9.93 014 | 7 | 22 |
| 39 | 9.71 994 | 20 | 9.78 987 | 28 | 0.21 013 | 9.93 007 | 8 | 21 |
| 40 | 9.72 014 | 20 | 9.79 015̄ | 28 | 0.20 985̄ | 9.92 999 | 8 | 20 |
| 41 | 9.72 034 | 21 | 9.79 043 | 29 | 0.20 957 | 9.92 991 | 8 | 19 |
| 42 | 9.72 055̄ | 20 | 9.79 072 | 28 | 0.20 928 | 9.92 983 | 7 | 18 |
| 43 | 9.72 075̄ | 21 | 9.79 100 | 28 | 0.20 900 | 9.92 976 | 8 | 17 |
| 44 | 9.72 096 | 20 | 9.79 128 | 28 | 0.20 872 | 9.92 968 | 8 | 16 |
| 45 | 9.72 116 | 21 | 9.79 156 | 29 | 0.20 844 | 9.92 960 | 8 | 15 |
| 46 | 9.72 137 | 20 | 9.79 185̄ | 28 | 0.20 815̄ | 9.92 952 | 8 | 14 |
| 47 | 9.72 157 | 20 | 9.79 213 | 28 | 0.20 787 | 9.92 944 | 8 | 13 |
| 48 | 9.72 177 | 21 | 9.79 241 | 28 | 0.20 759 | 9.92 936 | 7 | 12 |
| 49 | 9.72 198 | 20 | 9.79 269 | 28 | 0.20 731 | 9.92 929 | 8 | 11 |
| 50 | 9.72 218 | 20 | 9.79 297 | 29 | 0.20 703 | 9.92 921 | 8 | 10 |
| 51 | 9.72 238 | 21 | 9.79 326 | 28 | 0.20 674 | 9.92 913 | 8 | 9 |
| 52 | 9.72 259 | 20 | 9.79 354 | 28 | 0.20 646 | 9.92 905̄ | 8 | 8 |
| 53 | 9.72 279 | 20 | 9.79 382 | 28 | 0.20 618 | 9.92 897 | 8 | 7 |
| 54 | 9.72 299 | 21 | 9.79 410 | 28 | 0.20 590 | 9.92 889 | 8 | 6 |
| 55 | 9.72 320 | 20 | 9.79 438 | 28 | 0.20 562 | 9.92 881 | 7 | 5 |
| 56 | 9.72 340 | 20 | 9.79 466 | 29 | 0.20 534 | 9.92 874 | 8 | 4 |
| 57 | 9.72 360 | 21 | 9.79 495̄ | 28 | 0.20 505̄ | 9.92 866 | 8 | 3 |
| 58 | 9.72 381 | 20 | 9.79 523 | 28 | 0.20 477 | 9.92 858 | 8 | 2 |
| 59 | 9.72 401 | 20 | 9.79 551 | 28 | 0.20 449 | 9.92 850̄ | 8 | 1 |
| 60 | 9.72 421 | | 9.79 579 | | 0.20 421 | 9.92 842 | | 0 |

**P.P.**

|  | 29 | 28 |
|---|---|---|
| ″ | | |
| 1 | 0.5̄ | 0.5̄ |
| 2 | 1.0 | 0.9 |
| 3 | 1.4 | 1.4 |
| 4 | 1.9 | 1.9 |
| 5 | 2.4 | 2.3 |
| 6 | 2.9 | 2.8 |
| 7 | 3.4 | 3.3 |
| 8 | 3.9 | 3.7 |
| 9 | 4.4 | 4.2 |
| 10 | 4.8 | 4.7 |
| 20 | 9.7 | 9.3 |
| 30 | 14.5 | 14.0 |
| 40 | 19.3 | 18.7 |
| 50 | 24.2 | 23.3 |

|  | 21 | 20 |
|---|---|---|
| 1 | 0.4 | 0.3 |
| 2 | 0.7 | 0.7 |
| 3 | 1.0 | 1.0 |
| 4 | 1.4 | 1.3 |
| 5 | 1.8 | 1.7 |
| 6 | 2.1 | 2.0 |
| 7 | 2.4 | 2.3 |
| 8 | 2.8 | 2.7 |
| 9 | 3.2 | 3.0 |
| 10 | 3.5̄ | 3.3 |
| 20 | 7.0 | 6.7 |
| 30 | 10.5̄ | 10.0 |
| 40 | 14.0 | 13.3 |
| 50 | 17.5̄ | 16.7 |

|  | 8 | 7 |
|---|---|---|
| ″ | | |
| 1 | 0.1 | 0.1 |
| 2 | 0.3 | 0.2 |
| 3 | 0.4 | 0.4 |
| 4 | 0.5̄ | 0.5̄ |
| 5 | 0.7 | 0.6 |
| 6 | 0.8 | 0.7 |
| 7 | 0.9 | 0.8 |
| 8 | 1.1 | 0.9 |
| 9 | 1.2 | 1.0 |
| 10 | 1.3 | 1.2 |
| 20 | 2.7 | 2.3 |
| 30 | 4.0 | 3.5̄ |
| 40 | 5.3̄ | 4.7 |
| 50 | 6.7 | 5.8 |

|  | 8/30 | 8/29 | 8/28 |
|---|---|---|---|
| 0 | | | |
| 1 | 1.9 | 1.8 | 1.8 |
| 2 | 5.6 | 5.4 | 5.2 |
| 3 | 9.4 | 9.1 | 8.8 |
| 4 | 13.1 | 12.7 | 12.2 |
| 5 | 16.9 | 16.3 | 15.8 |
| 6 | 20.6 | 19.9 | 19.2 |
| 7 | 24.4 | 23.6 | 22.8 |
| 8 | 28.1 | 27.2 | 26.2 |

| ′ | L. Cos. | d. | L. Cot. | c.d. | L. Tan. | L. Sin. | d. | ′ | P.P. |
|---|---|---|---|---|---|---|---|---|---|

# LOGARITHMS OF THE FUNCTIONS (Continued)

| ′ | L. Sin. | d. | L. Tan. | c.d. | L. Cot. | L. Cos. | d. | ′ |
|---|---|---|---|---|---|---|---|---|
| 0 | 9.72 421 | 20 | 9.79 579 | 28 | 0.20 421 | 9.92 842 | 8 | 60 |
| 1 | 9.72 441 | 20 | 9.79 607 | 28 | 0.20 393 | 9.92 834 | 8 | 59 |
| 2 | 9.72 461 | 21 | 9.79 635 | 28 | 0.20 365 | 9.92 826 | 8 | 58 |
| 3 | 9.72 482 | 20 | 9.79 663 | 28 | 0.20 337 | 9.92 818 | 8 | 57 |
| 4 | 9.72 502 | 20 | 9.79 691 | 28 | 0.20 309 | 9.92 810 | 7 | 56 |
| 5 | 9.72 522 | 20 | 9.79 719 | 28 | 0.20 281 | 9.92 803 | 8 | 55 |
| 6 | 9.72 542 | 20 | 9.79 747 | 29 | 0.20 253 | 9.92 795 | 8 | 54 |
| 7 | 9.72 562 | 20 | 9.79 776 | 28 | 0.20 224 | 9.92 787 | 8 | 53 |
| 8 | 9.72 582 | 20 | 9.79 804 | 28 | 0.20 196 | 9.92 779 | 8 | 52 |
| 9 | 9.72 602 | 20 | 9.79 832 | 28 | 0.20 168 | 9.92 771 | 8 | 51 |
| 10 | 9.72 622 | 21 | 9.79 860 | 28 | 0.20 140 | 9.92 763 | 8 | 50 |
| 11 | 9.72 643 | 20 | 9.79 888 | 28 | 0.20 112 | 9.92 755 | 8 | 49 |
| 12 | 9.72 663 | 20 | 9.79 916 | 28 | 0.20 084 | 9.92 747 | 8 | 48 |
| 13 | 9.72 683 | 20 | 9.79 944 | 28 | 0.20 056 | 9.92 739 | 8 | 47 |
| 14 | 9.72 703 | 20 | 9.79 972 | 28 | 0.20 028 | 9.92 731 | 8 | 46 |
| 15 | 9.72 723 | 20 | 9.80 000 | 28 | 0.20 000 | 9.92 723 | 8 | 45 |
| 16 | 9.72 743 | 20 | 9.80 028 | 28 | 0.19 972 | 9.92 715 | 8 | 44 |
| 17 | 9.72 763 | 20 | 9.80 056 | 28 | 0.19 944 | 9.92 707 | 8 | 43 |
| 18 | 9.72 783 | 20 | 9.80 084 | 28 | 0.19 916 | 9.92 699 | 8 | 42 |
| 19 | 9.72 803 | 20 | 9.80 112 | 28 | 0.19 888 | 9.92 691 | 8 | 41 |
| 20 | 9.72 823 | 20 | 9.80 140 | 28 | 0.19 860 | 9.92 683 | 8 | 40 |
| 21 | 9.72 843 | 20 | 9.80 168 | 27 | 0.19 832 | 9.92 675 | 8 | 39 |
| 22 | 9.72 863 | 20 | 9.80 195 | 28 | 0.19 805 | 9.92 667 | 8 | 38 |
| 23 | 9.72 883 | 19 | 9.80 223 | 28 | 0.19 777 | 9.92 659 | 8 | 37 |
| 24 | 9.72 902 | 20 | 9.80 251 | 28 | 0.19 749 | 9.92 651 | 8 | 36 |
| 25 | 9.72 922 | 20 | 9.80 279 | 28 | 0.19 721 | 9.92 643 | 8 | 35 |
| 26 | 9.72 942 | 20 | 9.80 307 | 28 | 0.19 693 | 9.92 635 | 8 | 34 |
| 27 | 9.72 962 | 20 | 9.80 335 | 28 | 0.19 665 | 9.92 627 | 8 | 33 |
| 28 | 9.72 982 | 20 | 9.80 363 | 28 | 0.19 637 | 9.92 619 | 8 | 32 |
| 29 | 9.73 002 | 20 | 9.80 391 | 28 | 0.19 609 | 9.92 611 | 8 | 31 |
| 30 | 9.73 022 | 19 | 9.80 419 | 28 | 0.19 581 | 9.92 603 | 8 | 30 |
| 31 | 9.73 041 | 20 | 9.80 447 | 27 | 0.19 553 | 9.92 595 | 8 | 29 |
| 32 | 9.73 061 | 20 | 9.80 474 | 28 | 0.19 526 | 9.92 587 | 8 | 28 |
| 33 | 9.73 081 | 20 | 9.80 502 | 28 | 0.19 498 | 9.92 579 | 8 | 27 |
| 34 | 9.73 101 | 20 | 9.80 530 | 28 | 0.19 470 | 9.92 571 | 8 | 26 |
| 35 | 9.73 121 | 19 | 9.80 558 | 28 | 0.19 442 | 9.92 563 | 8 | 25 |
| 36 | 9.73 140 | 20 | 9.80 586 | 28 | 0.19 414 | 9.92 555 | 9 | 24 |
| 37 | 9.73 160 | 20 | 9.80 614 | 28 | 0.19 386 | 9.92 546 | 8 | 23 |
| 38 | 9.73 180 | 20 | 9.80 642 | 27 | 0.19 358 | 9.92 538 | 8 | 22 |
| 39 | 9.73 200 | 19 | 9.80 669 | 28 | 0.19 331 | 9.92 530 | 8 | 21 |
| 40 | 9.73 219 | 20 | 9.80 697 | 28 | 0.19 303 | 9.92 522 | 8 | 20 |
| 41 | 9.73 239 | 20 | 9.80 725 | 28 | 0.19 275 | 9.92 514 | 8 | 19 |
| 42 | 9.73 259 | 19 | 9.80 753 | 28 | 0.19 247 | 9.92 506 | 8 | 18 |
| 43 | 9.73 278 | 20 | 9.80 781 | 27 | 0.19 219 | 9.92 498 | 8 | 17 |
| 44 | 9.73 298 | 20 | 9.80 808 | 28 | 0.19 192 | 9.92 490 | 8 | 16 |
| 45 | 9.73 318 | 19 | 9.80 836 | 28 | 0.19 164 | 9.92 482 | 9 | 15 |
| 46 | 9.73 337 | 20 | 9.80 864 | 28 | 0.19 136 | 9.92 473 | 8 | 14 |
| 47 | 9.73 357 | 20 | 9.80 892 | 27 | 0.19 108 | 9.92 465 | 8 | 13 |
| 48 | 9.73 377 | 19 | 9.80 919 | 28 | 0.19 081 | 9.92 457 | 8 | 12 |
| 49 | 9.73 396 | 20 | 9.80 947 | 28 | 0.19 053 | 9.92 449 | 8 | 11 |
| 50 | 9.73 416 | 19 | 9.80 975 | 28 | 0.19 025 | 9.92 441 | 8 | 10 |
| 51 | 9.73 435 | 20 | 9.81 003 | 27 | 0.18 997 | 9.92 433 | 8 | 9 |
| 52 | 9.73 455 | 19 | 9.81 030 | 28 | 0.18 970 | 9.92 425 | 9 | 8 |
| 53 | 9.73 474 | 20 | 9.81 058 | 28 | 0.18 942 | 9.92 416 | 8 | 7 |
| 54 | 9.73 494 | 19 | 9.81 086 | 27 | 0.18 914 | 9.92 408 | 8 | 6 |
| 55 | 9.73 513 | 20 | 9.81 113 | 28 | 0.18 887 | 9.92 400 | 8 | 5 |
| 56 | 9.73 533 | 19 | 9.81 141 | 28 | 0.18 859 | 9.92 392 | 8 | 4 |
| 57 | 9.73 552 | 20 | 9.81 169 | 27 | 0.18 831 | 9.92 384 | 8 | 3 |
| 58 | 9.73 572 | 19 | 9.81 196 | 28 | 0.18 804 | 9.92 376 | 9 | 2 |
| 59 | 9.73 591 | 20 | 9.81 224 | 28 | 0.18 776 | 9.92 367 | 8 | 1 |
| 60 | 9.73 611 |  | 9.81 252 |  | 0.18 748 | 9.92 359 |  | 0 |

| L. Cos. | d. | L. Cot. | c.d. | L. Tan. | L. Sin. | d. | ′ |
|---|---|---|---|---|---|---|---|

## P. P.

| ″ | 29 | 28 | 27 |
|---|---|---|---|
| 1 | 0.5 | 0.5 | 0.4 |
| 2 | 1.0 | 0.9 | 0.9 |
| 3 | 1.4 | 1.4 | 1.4 |
| 4 | 1.9 | 1.9 | 1.8 |
| 5 | 2.4 | 2.3 | 2.2 |
| 6 | 2.9 | 2.8 | 2.7 |
| 7 | 3.4 | 3.3 | 3.2 |
| 8 | 3.9 | 3.7 | 3.6 |
| 9 | 4.4 | 4.2 | 4.0 |
| 10 | 4.8 | 4.7 | 4.5 |
| 20 | 9.7 | 9.3 | 9.0 |
| 30 | 14.5 | 14.0 | 13.5 |
| 40 | 19.3 | 18.7 | 18.0 |
| 50 | 24.2 | 23.3 | 22.5 |

| ″ | 21 | 20 | 19 |
|---|---|---|---|
| 1 | 0.4 | 0.3 | 0.3 |
| 2 | 0.7 | 0.7 | 0.6 |
| 3 | 1.0 | 1.0 | 1.0 |
| 4 | 1.4 | 1.3 | 1.3 |
| 5 | 1.8 | 1.7 | 1.6 |
| 6 | 2.1 | 2.0 | 1.9 |
| 7 | 2.4 | 2.3 | 2.2 |
| 8 | 2.8 | 2.7 | 2.5 |
| 9 | 3.2 | 3.0 | 2.8 |
| 10 | 3.5 | 3.3 | 3.2 |
| 20 | 7.0 | 6.7 | 6.3 |
| 30 | 10.5 | 10.0 | 9.5 |
| 40 | 14.0 | 13.3 | 12.7 |
| 50 | 17.5 | 16.7 | 15.8 |

| ″ | 9 | 8 | 7 |
|---|---|---|---|
| 1 | 0.2 | 0.1 | 0.1 |
| 2 | 0.3 | 0.3 | 0.2 |
| 3 | 0.4 | 0.4 | 0.4 |
| 4 | 0.6 | 0.5 | 0.5 |
| 5 | 0.8 | 0.7 | 0.6 |
| 6 | 0.9 | 0.8 | 0.7 |
| 7 | 1.0 | 0.9 | 0.8 |
| 8 | 1.2 | 1.1 | 0.9 |
| 9 | 1.4 | 1.2 | 1.0 |
| 10 | 1.5 | 1.3 | 1.2 |
| 20 | 3.0 | 2.7 | 2.3 |
| 30 | 4.5 | 4.0 | 3.5 |
| 40 | 6.0 | 5.3 | 4.7 |
| 50 | 7.5 | 6.7 | 5.8 |

| | 8 | 8 | 7 |
|---|---|---|---|
| | 29 | 28 | 28 |
| 0 | 1.8 | 1.8 | 2.0 |
| 1 | 5.4 | 5.2 | 6.0 |
| 2 | 9.1 | 8.8 | 10.0 |
| 3 | 12.7 | 12.2 | 14.0 |
| 4 | 16.3 | 15.8 | 18.0 |
| 5 | 19.9 | 19.2 | 22.0 |
| 6 | 23.6 | 22.8 | 26.0 |
| 7 | 27.2 | 26.2 | — |
| 8 | | | |

| ' | L. Sin. | d. | L. Tan. | c.d. | L. Cot. | L. Cos. | d. | ' |
|---|---------|----|---------|------|---------|---------|----|---|
| **0** | 9.73 611 | | 9.81 252 | | 0.18 748 | 9.92 359 | | **60** |
| 1 | 9.73 630 | 19 | 9.81 279 | 27 | 0.18 721 | 9.92 351 | 8 | 59 |
| 2 | 9.73 650 | 20 | 9.81 307 | 28 | 0.18 693 | 9.92 343 | 8 | 58 |
| 3 | 9.73 669 | 19 | 9.81 335 | 28 | 0.18 665 | 9.92 335 | 8 | 57 |
| 4 | 9.73 689 | 20 | 9.81 362 | 27 | 0.18 638 | 9.92 326 | 9 | 56 |
| **5** | 9.73 708 | 19 | 9.81 390 | 28 | 0.18 610 | 9.92 318 | 8 | **55** |
| 6 | 9.73 727 | 19 | 9.81 418 | 28 | 0.18 582 | 9.92 310 | 8 | 54 |
| 7 | 9.73 747 | 19 | 9.81 445 | 27 | 0.18 555 | 9.92 302 | 8 | 53 |
| 8 | 9.73 766 | 19 | 9.81 473 | 28 | 0.18 527 | 9.92 293 | 9 | 52 |
| 9 | 9.73 785 | 19 | 9.81 500 | 27 | 0.18 500 | 9.92 285 | 8 | 51 |
| **10** | 9.73 805 | 20 | 9.81 528 | 28 | 0.18 472 | 9.92 277 | 8 | **50** |
| 11 | 9.73 824 | 19 | 9.81 556 | 28 | 0.18 444 | 9.92 269 | 8 | 49 |
| 12 | 9.73 843 | 19 | 9.81 583 | 27 | 0.18 417 | 9.92 260 | 8 | 48 |
| 13 | 9.73 863 | 20 | 9.81 611 | 28 | 0.18 389 | 9.92 252 | 8 | 47 |
| 14 | 9.73 882 | 19 | 9.81 638 | 27 | 0.18 362 | 9.92 244 | 9 | 46 |
| **15** | 9.73 901 | 19 | 9.81 666 | 28 | 0.18 334 | 9.92 235 | 8 | **45** |
| 16 | 9.73 921 | 20 | 9.81 693 | 27 | 0.18 307 | 9.92 227 | 8 | 44 |
| 17 | 9.73 940 | 19 | 9.81 721 | 28 | 0.18 279 | 9.92 219 | 8 | 43 |
| 18 | 9.73 959 | 19 | 9.81 748 | 27 | 0.18 252 | 9.92 211 | 8 | 42 |
| 19 | 9.73 978 | 19 | 9.81 776 | 27 | 0.18 224 | 9.92 202 | 9 | 41 |
| **20** | 9.73 997 | 19 | 9.81 803 | 28 | 0.18 197 | 9.92 194 | 8 | **40** |
| 21 | 9.74 017 | 20 | 9.81 831 | 27 | 0.18 169 | 9.92 186 | 9 | 39 |
| 22 | 9.74 036 | 19 | 9.81 858 | 28 | 0.18 142 | 9.92 177 | 8 | 38 |
| 23 | 9.74 055 | 19 | 9.81 886 | 27 | 0.18 114 | 9.92 169 | 8 | 37 |
| 24 | 9.74 074 | 19 | 9.81 913 | 28 | 0.18 087 | 9.92 161 | 9 | 36 |
| **25** | 9.74 093 | 20 | 9.81 941 | 27 | 0.18 059 | 9.92 152 | 8 | **35** |
| 26 | 9.74 113 | 19 | 9.81 968 | 28 | 0.18 032 | 9.92 144 | 8 | 34 |
| 27 | 9.74 132 | 19 | 9.81 996 | 27 | 0.18 004 | 9.92 136 | 9 | 33 |
| 28 | 9.74 151 | 19 | 9.82 023 | 28 | 0.17 977 | 9.92 127 | 8 | 32 |
| 29 | 9.74 170 | 19 | 9.82 051 | 27 | 0.17 949 | 9.92 119 | 8 | 31 |
| **30** | 9.74 189 | 19 | 9.82 078 | 28 | 0.17 922 | 9.92 111 | 8 | **30** |
| 31 | 9.74 208 | 19 | 9.82 106 | 27 | 0.17 894 | 9.92 102 | 9 | 29 |
| 32 | 9.74 227 | 19 | 9.82 133 | 28 | 0.17 867 | 9.92 094 | 8 | 28 |
| 33 | 9.74 246 | 19 | 9.82 161 | 27 | 0.17 839 | 9.92 086 | 9 | 27 |
| 34 | 9.74 265 | 19 | 9.82 188 | 27 | 0.17 812 | 9.92 077 | 8 | 26 |
| **35** | 9.74 284 | 19 | 9.82 215 | 28 | 0.17 785 | 9.92 069 | 9 | **25** |
| 36 | 9.74 303 | 19 | 9.82 243 | 27 | 0.17 757 | 9.92 060 | 8 | 24 |
| 37 | 9.74 322 | 19 | 9.82 270 | 28 | 0.17 730 | 9.92 052 | 8 | 23 |
| 38 | 9.74 341 | 19 | 9.82 298 | 27 | 0.17 702 | 9.92 044 | 9 | 22 |
| 39 | 9.74 360 | 19 | 9.82 325 | 27 | 0.17 675 | 9.92 035 | 8 | 21 |
| **40** | 9.74 379 | 19 | 9.82 352 | 28 | 0.17 648 | 9.92 027 | 9 | **20** |
| 41 | 9.74 398 | 19 | 9.82 380 | 27 | 0.17 620 | 9.92 018 | 8 | 19 |
| 42 | 9.74 417 | 19 | 9.82 407 | 28 | 0.17 593 | 9.92 010 | 8 | 18 |
| 43 | 9.74 436 | 19 | 9.82 435 | 27 | 0.17 565 | 9.92 002 | 9 | 17 |
| 44 | 9.74 455 | 19 | 9.82 462 | 27 | 0.17 538 | 9.91 993 | 8 | 16 |
| **45** | 9.74 474 | 19 | 9.82 489 | 28 | 0.17 511 | 9.91 985 | 9 | **15** |
| 46 | 9.74 493 | 19 | 9.82 517 | 27 | 0.17 483 | 9.91 976 | 8 | 14 |
| 47 | 9.74 512 | 19 | 9.82 544 | 27 | 0.17 456 | 9.91 968 | 9 | 13 |
| 48 | 9.74 531 | 18 | 9.82 571 | 28 | 0.17 429 | 9.91 959 | 8 | 12 |
| 49 | 9.74 549 | 19 | 9.82 599 | 27 | 0.17 401 | 9.91 951 | 9 | 11 |
| **50** | 9.74 568 | 19 | 9.82 626 | 27 | 0.17 374 | 9.91 942 | 8 | **10** |
| 51 | 9.74 587 | 19 | 9.82 653 | 28 | 0.17 347 | 9.91 934 | 9 | 9 |
| 52 | 9.74 606 | 19 | 9.82 681 | 27 | 0.17 319 | 9.91 925 | 8 | 8 |
| 53 | 9.74 625 | 19 | 9.82 708 | 27 | 0.17 292 | 9.91 917 | 9 | 7 |
| 54 | 9.74 644 | 18 | 9.82 735 | 27 | 0.17 265 | 9.91 908 | 8 | 6 |
| **55** | 9.74 662 | 19 | 9.82 762 | 28 | 0.17 238 | 9.91 900 | 9 | **5** |
| 56 | 9.74 681 | 19 | 9.82 790 | 27 | 0.17 210 | 9.91 891 | 8 | 4 |
| 57 | 9.74 700 | 19 | 9.82 817 | 27 | 0.17 183 | 9.91 883 | 9 | 3 |
| 58 | 9.74 719 | 18 | 9.82 844 | 27 | 0.17 156 | 9.91 874 | 8 | 2 |
| 59 | 9.74 737 | 19 | 9.82 871 | 28 | 0.17 129 | 9.91 866 | 9 | 1 |
| **60** | 9.74 756 | | 9.82 899 | | 0.17 101 | 9.91 857 | | **0** |
| ' | L. Cos. | d. | L. Cot. | c.d. | L. Tan | L. Sin. | d. | ' |

**P. P.**

| '' | 28 | 27 |
|----|----|----|
| 1 | 0.5 | 0.4 |
| 2 | 0.9 | 0.9 |
| 3 | 1.4 | 1.4 |
| 4 | 1.9 | 1.8 |
| 5 | 2.3 | 2.2 |
| 6 | 2.8 | 2.7 |
| 7 | 3.3 | 3.2 |
| 8 | 3.7 | 3.6 |
| 9 | 4.2 | 4.0 |
| 10 | 4.7 | 4.5 |
| 20 | 9.3 | 9.0 |
| 30 | 14.0 | 13.5 |
| 40 | 18.7 | 18.0 |
| 50 | 23.3 | 22.5 |

| '' | 20 | 19 | 18 |
|----|----|----|----|
| 1 | 0.3 | 0.3 | 0.3 |
| 2 | 0.7 | 0.6 | 0.6 |
| 3 | 1.0 | 1.0 | 0.9 |
| 4 | 1.3 | 1.3 | 1.2 |
| 5 | 1.7 | 1.6 | 1.5 |
| 6 | 2.0 | 1.9 | 1.8 |
| 7 | 2.3 | 2.2 | 2.1 |
| 8 | 2.7 | 2.5 | 2.4 |
| 9 | 3.0 | 2.8 | 2.7 |
| 10 | 3.3 | 3.2 | 3.0 |
| 20 | 6.7 | 6.3 | 6.0 |
| 30 | 10.0 | 9.5 | 9.0 |
| 40 | 13.3 | 12.7 | 12.0 |
| 50 | 16.7 | 15.8 | 15.0 |

| '' | 9 | 8 |
|----|---|---|
| 1 | 0.2 | 0.1 |
| 2 | 0.3 | 0.3 |
| 3 | 0.4 | 0.4 |
| 4 | 0.6 | 0.5 |
| 5 | 0.8 | 0.7 |
| 6 | 0.9 | 0.8 |
| 7 | 1.0 | 0.9 |
| 8 | 1.2 | 1.1 |
| 9 | 1.4 | 1.2 |
| 10 | 1.5 | 1.3 |
| 20 | 3.0 | 2.7 |
| 30 | 4.5 | 4.0 |
| 40 | 6.0 | 5.3 |
| 50 | 7.5 | 6.7 |

| | 9/28 | 9/27 | 8/27 |
|---|------|------|------|
| 0 | | | |
| 1 | 1.6 | 1.5 | 1.7 |
| 2 | 4.7 | 4.5 | 5.1 |
| 3 | 7.8 | 7.5 | 8.4 |
| 4 | 10.9 | 10.5 | 11.8 |
| 5 | 14.0 | 13.5 | 15.2 |
| 6 | 17.1 | 16.5 | 18.6 |
| 7 | 20.2 | 19.5 | 21.9 |
| 8 | 23.3 | 22.5 | 25.3 |
| 9 | 26.4 | 25.5 | — |

| ′ | L. Sin. | d. | L. Tan. | c.d. | L. Cot. | L. Cos. | d. | ′ |
|---|---------|----|---------|------|---------|---------|----|----|
| 0 | 9.74 756 |    | 9.82 899 |    | 0.17 101 | 9.91 857 |   | 60 |
| 1 | 9.74 775 | 19 | 9.82 926 | 27 | 0.17 074 | 9.91 849 | 8 | 59 |
| 2 | 9.74 794 | 19 | 9.82 953 | 27 | 0.17 047 | 9.91 840 | 9 | 58 |
| 3 | 9.74 812 | 18 | 9.82 980 | 27 | 0.17 020 | 9.91 832 | 8 | 57 |
| 4 | 9.74 831 | 19 | 9.83 008 | 28 | 0.16 992 | 9.91 823 | 9 | 56 |
| 5 | 9.74 850 | 19 | 9.83 035 | 27 | 0.16 965 | 9.91 815 | 8 | 55 |
| 6 | 9.74 868 | 18 | 9.83 062 | 27 | 0.16 938 | 9.91 806 | 9 | 54 |
| 7 | 9.74 887 | 19 | 9.83 089 | 27 | 0.16 911 | 9.91 798 | 8 | 53 |
| 8 | 9.74 906 | 19 | 9.83 117 | 28 | 0.16 883 | 9.91 789 | 9 | 52 |
| 9 | 9.74 924 | 18 | 9.83 144 | 27 | 0.16 856 | 9.91 781 | 8 | 51 |
| 10 | 9.74 943 | 19 | 9.83 171 | 27 | 0.16 829 | 9.91 772 | 9 | 50 |
| 11 | 9.74 961 | 18 | 9.83 198 | 27 | 0.16 802 | 9.91 763 | 9 | 49 |
| 12 | 9.74 980 | 19 | 9.83 225 | 27 | 0.16 775 | 9.91 755 | 8 | 48 |
| 13 | 9.74 999 | 19 | 9.83 252 | 27 | 0.16 748 | 9.91 746 | 9 | 47 |
| 14 | 9.75 017 | 18 | 9.83 280 | 28 | 0.16 720 | 9.91 738 | 8 | 46 |
| 15 | 9.75 036 | 19 | 9.83 307 | 27 | 0.16 693 | 9.91 729 | 9 | 45 |
| 16 | 9.75 054 | 18 | 9.83 334 | 27 | 0.16 666 | 9.91 720 | 9 | 44 |
| 17 | 9.75 073 | 19 | 9.83 361 | 27 | 0.16 639 | 9.91 712 | 8 | 43 |
| 18 | 9.75 091 | 18 | 9.83 388 | 27 | 0.16 612 | 9.91 703 | 9 | 42 |
| 19 | 9.75 110 | 19 | 9.83 415 | 27 | 0.16 585 | 9.91 695 | 8 | 41 |
| 20 | 9.75 128 | 18 | 9.83 442 | 28 | 0.16 558 | 9.91 686 | 9 | 40 |
| 21 | 9.75 147 | 19 | 9.83 470 | 27 | 0.16 530 | 9.91 677 | 9 | 39 |
| 22 | 9.75 165 | 18 | 9.83 497 | 27 | 0.16 503 | 9.91 669 | 8 | 38 |
| 23 | 9.75 184 | 19 | 9.83 524 | 27 | 0.16 476 | 9.91 660 | 9 | 37 |
| 24 | 9.75 202 | 18 | 9.83 551 | 27 | 0.16 449 | 9.91 651 | 9 | 36 |
| 25 | 9.75 221 | 19 | 9.83 578 | 27 | 0.16 422 | 9.91 643 | 8 | 35 |
| 26 | 9.75 239 | 18 | 9.83 605 | 27 | 0.16 395 | 9.91 634 | 9 | 34 |
| 27 | 9.75 258 | 19 | 9.83 632 | 27 | 0.16 368 | 9.91 625 | 9 | 33 |
| 28 | 9.75 276 | 18 | 9.83 659 | 27 | 0.16 341 | 9.91 617 | 8 | 32 |
| 29 | 9.75 294 | 18 | 9.83 686 | 27 | 0.16 314 | 9.91 608 | 9 | 31 |
| 30 | 9.75 313 | 19 | 9.83 713 | 27 | 0.16 287 | 9.91 599 | 9 | 30 |
| 31 | 9.75 331 | 18 | 9.83 740 | 27 | 0.16 260 | 9.91 591 | 8 | 29 |
| 32 | 9.75 350 | 19 | 9.83 768 | 28 | 0.16 232 | 9.91 582 | 9 | 28 |
| 33 | 9.75 368 | 18 | 9.83 795 | 27 | 0.16 205 | 9.91 573 | 9 | 27 |
| 34 | 9.75 386 | 18 | 9.83 822 | 27 | 0.16 178 | 9.91 565 | 8 | 26 |
| 35 | 9.75 405 | 19 | 9.83 849 | 27 | 0.16 151 | 9.91 556 | 9 | 25 |
| 36 | 9.75 423 | 18 | 9.83 876 | 27 | 0.16 124 | 9.91 547 | 9 | 24 |
| 37 | 9.75 441 | 18 | 9.83 903 | 27 | 0.16 097 | 9.91 538 | 8 | 23 |
| 38 | 9.75 459 | 18 | 9.83 930 | 27 | 0.16 070 | 9.91 530 | 9 | 22 |
| 39 | 9.75 478 | 19 | 9.83 957 | 27 | 0.16 043 | 9.91 521 | 9 | 21 |
| 40 | 9.75 496 | 18 | 9.83 984 | 27 | 0.16 016 | 9.91 512 | 8 | 20 |
| 41 | 9.75 514 | 18 | 9.84 011 | 27 | 0.15 989 | 9.91 504 | 9 | 19 |
| 42 | 9.75 533 | 19 | 9.84 038 | 27 | 0.15 962 | 9.91 495 | 9 | 18 |
| 43 | 9.75 551 | 18 | 9.84 065 | 27 | 0.15 935 | 9.91 486 | 9 | 17 |
| 44 | 9.75 569 | 18 | 9.84 092 | 27 | 0.15 908 | 9.91 477 | 8 | 16 |
| 45 | 9.75 587 | 18 | 9.84 119 | 27 | 0.15 881 | 9.91 469 | 9 | 15 |
| 46 | 9.75 605 | 19 | 9.84 146 | 27 | 0.15 854 | 9.91 460 | 9 | 14 |
| 47 | 9.75 624 | 18 | 9.84 173 | 27 | 0.15 827 | 9.91 451 | 9 | 13 |
| 48 | 9.75 642 | 18 | 9.84 200 | 27 | 0.15 800 | 9.91 442 | 9 | 12 |
| 49 | 9.75 660 | 18 | 9.84 227 | 27 | 0.15 773 | 9.91 433 | 8 | 11 |
| 50 | 9.75 678 | 18 | 9.84 254 | 26 | 0.15 746 | 9.91 425 | 9 | 10 |
| 51 | 9.75 696 | 18 | 9.84 280 | 27 | 0.15 720 | 9.91 416 | 9 | 9 |
| 52 | 9.75 714 | 19 | 9.84 307 | 27 | 0.15 693 | 9.91 407 | 9 | 8 |
| 53 | 9.75 733 | 18 | 9.84 334 | 27 | 0.15 666 | 9.91 398 | 9 | 7 |
| 54 | 9.75 751 | 18 | 9.84 361 | 27 | 0.15 639 | 9.91 389 | 8 | 6 |
| 55 | 9.75 769 | 18 | 9.84 388 | 27 | 0.15 612 | 9.91 381 | 9 | 5 |
| 56 | 9.75 787 | 18 | 9.84 415 | 27 | 0.15 585 | 9.91 372 | 9 | 4 |
| 57 | 9.75 805 | 18 | 9.84 442 | 27 | 0.15 558 | 9.91 363 | 9 | 3 |
| 58 | 9.75 823 | 18 | 9.84 469 | 27 | 0.15 531 | 9.91 354 | 9 | 2 |
| 59 | 9.75 841 | 18 | 9.84 496 | 27 | 0.15 504 | 9.91 345 | 9 | 1 |
| 60 | 9.75 859 |    | 9.84 523 |    | 0.15 477 | 9.91 336 |   | 0 |
| ° | L. Cos. | d. | L. Cot. | c.d. | L. Tan. | L. Sin. | d. | ′ |

**P.P.**

| ″ | 28 | 27 | 26 |
|---|----|----|----|
| 1 | 0.5 | 0.4 | 0.4 |
| 2 | 0.9 | 0.9 | 0.9 |
| 3 | 1.4 | 1.4 | 1.3 |
| 4 | 1.9 | 1.8 | 1.7 |
| 5 | 2.3 | 2.2 | 2.2 |
| 6 | 2.8 | 2.7 | 2.6 |
| 7 | 3.3 | 3.2 | 3.0 |
| 8 | 3.7 | 3.6 | 3.5 |
| 9 | 4.2 | 4.0 | 3.9 |
| 10 | 4.7 | 4.5 | 4.3 |
| 20 | 9.3 | 9.0 | 8.7 |
| 30 | 14.0 | 13.5 | 13.0 |
| 40 | 18.7 | 18.0 | 17.3 |
| 50 | 23.3 | 22.5 | 21.7 |

| ″ | 19 | 18 |
|---|----|----|
| 1 | 0.3 | 0.3 |
| 2 | 0.6 | 0.6 |
| 3 | 1.0 | 0.9 |
| 4 | 1.3 | 1.2 |
| 5 | 1.6 | 1.5 |
| 6 | 1.9 | 1.8 |
| 7 | 2.2 | 2.1 |
| 8 | 2.5 | 2.4 |
| 9 | 2.8 | 2.7 |
| 10 | 3.2 | 3.0 |
| 20 | 6.3 | 6.0 |
| 30 | 9.5 | 9.0 |
| 40 | 12.7 | 12.0 |
| 50 | 15.8 | 15.0 |

| ″ | 9 | 8 |
|---|----|----|
| 1 | 0.2 | 0.1 |
| 2 | 0.3 | 0.3 |
| 3 | 0.4 | 0.4 |
| 4 | 0.6 | 0.5 |
| 5 | 0.8 | 0.7 |
| 6 | 0.9 | 0.8 |
| 7 | 1.0 | 0.9 |
| 8 | 1.2 | 1.1 |
| 9 | 1.4 | 1.2 |
| 10 | 1.5 | 1.3 |
| 20 | 3.0 | 2.7 |
| 30 | 4.5 | 4.0 |
| 40 | 6.0 | 5.3 |
| 50 | 7.5 | 6.7 |

| | 9/28 | 8/28 | 8/27 |
|---|----|----|----|
| 0 |  |  |  |
| 1 | 1.6 | 1.8 | 1.7 |
| 2 | 4.7 | 5.2 | 5.1 |
| 3 | 7.8 | 8.8 | 8.4 |
| 4 | 10.9 | 12.2 | 11.8 |
| 5 | 14.0 | 15.8 | 15.2 |
| 6 | 17.1 | 19.2 | 18.6 |
| 7 | 20.2 | 22.8 | 21.9 |
| 8 | 23.3 | 26.2 | 25.3 |
| 9 | 26.4 | — | — |

# LOGARITHMS OF THE FUNCTIONS (Continued)

| ′ | L. Sin. | d. | L. Tan. | c.d. | L. Cot. | L. Cos. | d. | ′ |
|---|---------|----|---------|------|---------|---------|----|---|
| 0 | 9.75 859 | 18 | 9.84 523 | 27 | 0.15 477 | 9.91 336 | 8 | 60 |
| 1 | 9.75 877 | 18 | 9.84 550 | 26 | 0.15 450 | 9.91 328 | 9 | 59 |
| 2 | 9.75 895 | 18 | 9.84 576 | 27 | 0.15 424 | 9.91 319 | 9 | 58 |
| 3 | 9.75 913 | 18 | 9.84 603 | 27 | 0.15 397 | 9.91 310 | 9 | 57 |
| 4 | 9.75 931 | 18 | 9.84 630 | 27 | 0.15 370 | 9.91 301 | 9 | 56 |
| 5 | 9.75 949 | 18 | 9.84 657 | 27 | 0.15 343 | 9.91 292 | 9 | 55 |
| 6 | 9.75 967 | 18 | 9.84 684 | 27 | 0.15 316 | 9.91 283 | 9 | 54 |
| 7 | 9.75 985 | 18 | 9.84 711 | 27 | 0.15 289 | 9.91 274 | 8 | 53 |
| 8 | 9.76 003 | 18 | 9.84 738 | 27 | 0.15 262 | 9.91 266 | 9 | 52 |
| 9 | 9.76 021 | 18 | 9.84 764 | 26 | 0.15 236 | 9.91 257 | 9 | 51 |
| 10 | 9.76 039 | 18 | 9.84 791 | 27 | 0.15 209 | 9.91 248 | 9 | 50 |
| 11 | 9.76 057 | 18 | 9.84 818 | 27 | 0.15 182 | 9.91 239 | 9 | 49 |
| 12 | 9.76 075 | 18 | 9.84 845 | 27 | 0.15 155 | 9.91 230 | 9 | 48 |
| 13 | 9.76 093 | 18 | 9.84 872 | 27 | 0.15 128 | 9.91 221 | 9 | 47 |
| 14 | 9.76 111 | 18 | 9.84 899 | 26 | 0.15 101 | 9.91 212 | 9 | 46 |
| 15 | 9.76 129 | 17 | 9.84 925 | 27 | 0.15 075 | 9.91 203 | 9 | 45 |
| 16 | 9.76 146 | 18 | 9.84 952 | 27 | 0.15 048 | 9.91 194 | 9 | 44 |
| 17 | 9.76 164 | 18 | 9.84 979 | 27 | 0.15 021 | 9.91 185 | 9 | 43 |
| 18 | 9.76 182 | 18 | 9.85 006 | 27 | 0.14 994 | 9.91 176 | 9 | 42 |
| 19 | 9.76 200 | 18 | 9.85 033 | 26 | 0.14 967 | 9.91 167 | 9 | 41 |
| 20 | 9.76 218 | 18 | 9.85 059 | 27 | 0.14 941 | 9.91 158 | 9 | 40 |
| 21 | 9.76 236 | 17 | 9.85 086 | 27 | 0.14 914 | 9.91 149 | 8 | 39 |
| 22 | 9.76 253 | 18 | 9.85 113 | 27 | 0.14 887 | 9.91 141 | 9 | 38 |
| 23 | 9.76 271 | 18 | 9.85 140 | 26 | 0.14 860 | 9.91 132 | 9 | 37 |
| 24 | 9.76 289 | 18 | 9.85 166 | 27 | 0.14 834 | 9.91 123 | 9 | 36 |
| 25 | 9.76 307 | 17 | 9.85 193 | 27 | 0.14 807 | 9.91 114 | 9 | 35 |
| 26 | 9.76 324 | 18 | 9.85 220 | 27 | 0.14 780 | 9.91 105 | 9 | 34 |
| 27 | 9.76 342 | 18 | 9.85 247 | 26 | 0.14 753 | 9.91 096 | 9 | 33 |
| 28 | 9.76 360 | 18 | 9.85 273 | 27 | 0.14 727 | 9.91 087 | 9 | 32 |
| 29 | 9.76 378 | 17 | 9.85 300 | 27 | 0.14 700 | 9.91 078 | 9 | 31 |
| 30 | 9.76 395 | 18 | 9.85 327 | 27 | 0.14 673 | 9.91 069 | 9 | 30 |
| 31 | 9.76 413 | 18 | 9.85 354 | 26 | 0.14 646 | 9.91 060 | 9 | 29 |
| 32 | 9.76 431 | 17 | 9.85 380 | 27 | 0.14 620 | 9.91 051 | 9 | 28 |
| 33 | 9.76 448 | 18 | 9.85 407 | 27 | 0.14 593 | 9.91 042 | 9 | 27 |
| 34 | 9.76 466 | 18 | 9.85 434 | 26 | 0.14 566 | 9.91 033 | 10 | 26 |
| 35 | 9.76 484 | 17 | 9.85 460 | 27 | 0.14 540 | 9.91 023 | 9 | 25 |
| 36 | 9.76 501 | 18 | 9.85 487 | 27 | 0.14 513 | 9.91 014 | 9 | 24 |
| 37 | 9.76 519 | 18 | 9.85 514 | 26 | 0.14 486 | 9.91 005 | 9 | 23 |
| 38 | 9.76 537 | 17 | 9.85 540 | 27 | 0.14 460 | 9.90 996 | 9 | 22 |
| 39 | 9.76 554 | 18 | 9.85 567 | 27 | 0.14 433 | 9.90 987 | 9 | 21 |
| 40 | 9.76 572 | 18 | 9.85 594 | 26 | 0.14 406 | 9.90 978 | 9 | 20 |
| 41 | 9.76 590 | 17 | 9.85 620 | 27 | 0.14 380 | 9.90 969 | 9 | 19 |
| 42 | 9.76 607 | 18 | 9.85 647 | 27 | 0.14 353 | 9.90 960 | 9 | 18 |
| 43 | 9.76 625 | 17 | 9.85 674 | 26 | 0.14 326 | 9.90 951 | 9 | 17 |
| 44 | 9.76 642 | 18 | 9.85 700 | 27 | 0.14 300 | 9.90 942 | 9 | 16 |
| 45 | 9.76 660 | 17 | 9.85 727 | 27 | 0.14 273 | 9.90 933 | 9 | 15 |
| 46 | 9.76 677 | 18 | 9.85 754 | 26 | 0.14 246 | 9.90 924 | 9 | 14 |
| 47 | 9.76 695 | 17 | 9.85 780 | 27 | 0.14 220 | 9.90 915 | 9 | 13 |
| 48 | 9.76 712 | 18 | 9.85 807 | 27 | 0.14 193 | 9.90 906 | 10 | 12 |
| 49 | 9.76 730 | 17 | 9.85 834 | 26 | 0.14 166 | 9.90 896 | 9 | 11 |
| 50 | 9.76 747 | 18 | 9.85 860 | 27 | 0.14 140 | 9.90 887 | 9 | 10 |
| 51 | 9.76 765 | 17 | 9.85 887 | 27 | 0.14 113 | 9.90 878 | 9 | 9 |
| 52 | 9.76 782 | 18 | 9.85 913 | 26 | 0.14 087 | 9.90 869 | 9 | 8 |
| 53 | 9.76 800 | 17 | 9.85 940 | 27 | 0.14 060 | 9.90 860 | 9 | 7 |
| 54 | 9.76 817 | 18 | 9.85 967 | 26 | 0.14 033 | 9.90 851 | 9 | 6 |
| 55 | 9.76 835 | 17 | 9.85 993 | 27 | 0.14 007 | 9.90 842 | 10 | 5 |
| 56 | 9.76 852 | 18 | 9.86 020 | 26 | 0.13 980 | 9.90 832 | 9 | 4 |
| 57 | 9.76 870 | 17 | 9.86 046 | 27 | 0.13 954 | 9.90 823 | 9 | 3 |
| 58 | 9.76 887 | 17 | 9.86 073 | 27 | 0.13 927 | 9.90 814 | 9 | 2 |
| 59 | 9.76 904 | 18 | 9.86 100 | 26 | 0.13 900 | 9.90 805 | 9 | 1 |
| 60 | 9.76 922 |  | 9.86 126 |  | 0.13 874 | 9.90 796 |  | 0 |

**P.P.**

| ″ | 27 | 26 | 19 |
|---|----|----|----|
| 1 | 0.4 | 0.4 | 0.2 |
| 2 | 0.9 | 0.9 | 0.6 |
| 3 | 1.4 | 1.3 | 0.9 |
| 4 | 1.8 | 1.7 | 1.2 |
| 5 | 2.2 | 2.2 | 1.5 |
| 6 | 2.7 | 2.6 | 1.8 |
| 7 | 3.2 | 3.0 | 2.1 |
| 8 | 3.6 | 3.5 | 2.4 |
| 9 | 4.0 | 3.9 | 2.7 |
| 10 | 4.5 | 4.3 | 3.0 |
| 20 | 9.0 | 8.7 | 6.0 |
| 30 | 13.5 | 13.0 | 9.0 |
| 40 | 18.0 | 17.3 | 12.0 |
| 50 | 22.5 | 21.7 | 15.0 |

| ″ | 17 | 10 | 9 | 8 |
|---|----|----|----|----|
| 1 | 0.3 | 0.2 | 0.2 | 0.1 |
| 2 | 0.6 | 0.3 | 0.3 | 0.2 |
| 3 | 0.8 | 0.5 | 0.4 | 0.4 |
| 4 | 1.1 | 0.7 | 0.6 | 0.8 |
| 5 | 1.4 | 0.8 | 0.8 | 0.7 |
| 6 | 1.7 | 1.0 | 0.9 | 0.8 |
| 7 | 2.0 | 1.2 | 1.0 | 0.9 |
| 8 | 2.3 | 1.3 | 1.2 | 1.1 |
| 9 | 2.6 | 1.5 | 1.4 | 1.2 |
| 10 | 2.8 | 1.7 | 1.5 | 1.3 |
| 20 | 5.7 | 3.3 | 3.0 | 2.7 |
| 30 | 8.5 | 5.0 | 4.5 | 4.0 |
| 40 | 11.3 | 6.7 | 6.0 | 5.3 |
| 50 | 14.2 | 8.3 | 7.5 | 6.7 |

| | 10/27 | 10/26 |
|---|----|----|
| 0 | | |
| 1 | 1.4 | 1.3 |
| 2 | 4.1 | 3.9 |
| 3 | 6.8 | 6.5 |
| 4 | 9.4 | 9.1 |
| 5 | 12.2 | 11.7 |
| 6 | 14.8 | 14.3 |
| 7 | 17.6 | 16.9 |
| 8 | 20.2 | 19.5 |
| 9 | 22.9 | 22.1 |
| 10 | 25.6 | 24.7 |

| | 9/27 | 9/26 |
|---|----|----|
| 0 | | |
| 1 | 1.5 | 1.4 |
| 2 | 4.5 | 4.3 |
| 3 | 7.5 | 7.2 |
| 4 | 10.5 | 10.1 |
| 5 | 13.5 | 13.0 |
| 6 | 16.5 | 15.9 |
| 7 | 19.5 | 18.8 |
| 8 | 22.5 | 21.7 |
| 9 | 25.5 | 24.6 |

| ′ | L. Cos. | d. | L. Cot. | c.d. | L. Tan. | L. Sin. | d. | ′ | P.P. |
|---|---------|----|---------|------|---------|---------|----|---|------|

# LOGARITHMS OF THE FUNCTIONS (Continued)

| ' | L. Sin. | d. | L. Tan. | c.d. | L. Cot. | L. Cos. | d. | ' |
|---|---|---|---|---|---|---|---|---|
| 0 | 9.76 922 | 17 | 9.86 126 | 27 | 0.13 874 | 9.90 796 | 9 | 60 |
| 1 | 9.76 939 | 18 | 9.86 153 | 26 | 0.13 847 | 9.90 787 | 10 | 59 |
| 2 | 9.76 957 | 17 | 9.86 179 | 27 | 0.13 821 | 9.90 777 | 9 | 58 |
| 3 | 9.76 974 | 17 | 9.86 206 | 26 | 0.13 794 | 9.90 768 | 9 | 57 |
| 4 | 9.76 991 | 18 | 9.86 232 | 27 | 0.13 768 | 9.90 759 | 9 | 56 |
| 5 | 9.77 009 | 17 | 9.86 259 | 26 | 0.13 741 | 9.90 750 | 9 | 55 |
| 6 | 9.77 026 | 17 | 9.86 285 | 27 | 0.13 715 | 9.90 741 | 10 | 54 |
| 7 | 9.77 043 | 18 | 9.86 312 | 26 | 0.13 688 | 9.90 731 | 9 | 53 |
| 8 | 9.77 061 | 17 | 9.86 338 | 27 | 0.13 662 | 9.90 722 | 9 | 52 |
| 9 | 9.77 078 | 17 | 9.86 365 | 27 | 0.13 635 | 9.90 713 | 9 | 51 |
| 10 | 9.77 095 | 17 | 9.86 392 | 26 | 0.13 608 | 9.90 704 | 10 | 50 |
| 11 | 9.77 112 | 18 | 9.86 418 | 27 | 0.13 582 | 9.90 694 | 9 | 49 |
| 12 | 9.77 130 | 17 | 9.86 445 | 26 | 0.13 555 | 9.90 685 | 9 | 48 |
| 13 | 9.77 147 | 17 | 9.86 471 | 27 | 0.13 529 | 9.90 676 | 9 | 47 |
| 14 | 9.77 164 | 17 | 9.86 498 | 26 | 0.13 502 | 9.90 667 | 10 | 46 |
| 15 | 9.77 181 | 18 | 9.86 524 | 27 | 0.13 476 | 9.90 657 | 9 | 45 |
| 16 | 9.77 199 | 17 | 9.86 551 | 26 | 0.13 449 | 9.90 648 | 9 | 44 |
| 17 | 9.77 216 | 17 | 9.86 577 | 26 | 0.13 423 | 9.90 639 | 9 | 43 |
| 18 | 9.77 233 | 17 | 9.86 603 | 27 | 0.13 397 | 9.90 630 | 10 | 42 |
| 19 | 9.77 250 | 18 | 9.86 630 | 26 | 0.13 370 | 9.90 620 | 9 | 41 |
| 20 | 9.77 268 | 17 | 9.86 656 | 27 | 0.13 344 | 9.90 611 | 9 | 40 |
| 21 | 9.77 285 | 17 | 9.86 683 | 26 | 0.13 317 | 9.90 602 | 10 | 39 |
| 22 | 9.77 302 | 17 | 9.86 709 | 27 | 0.13 291 | 9.90 592 | 9 | 38 |
| 23 | 9.77 319 | 17 | 9.86 736 | 26 | 0.13 264 | 9.90 583 | 9 | 37 |
| 24 | 9.77 336 | 17 | 9.86 762 | 27 | 0.13 238 | 9.90 574 | 9 | 36 |
| 25 | 9.77 353 | 17 | 9.86 789 | 26 | 0.13 211 | 9.90 565 | 10 | 35 |
| 26 | 9.77 370 | 17 | 9.86 815 | 27 | 0.13 185 | 9.90 555 | 9 | 34 |
| 27 | 9.77 387 | 18 | 9.86 842 | 26 | 0.13 158 | 9.90 546 | 9 | 33 |
| 28 | 9.77 405 | 17 | 9.86 868 | 26 | 0.13 132 | 9.90 537 | 10 | 32 |
| 29 | 9.77 422 | 17 | 9.86 894 | 27 | 0.13 106 | 9.90 527 | 9 | 31 |
| 30 | 9.77 439 | 17 | 9.86 921 | 26 | 0.13 079 | 9.90 518 | 9 | 30 |
| 31 | 9.77 456 | 17 | 9.86 947 | 27 | 0.13 053 | 9.90 509 | 10 | 29 |
| 32 | 9.77 473 | 17 | 9.86 974 | 26 | 0.13 026 | 9.90 499 | 9 | 28 |
| 33 | 9.77 490 | 17 | 9.87 000 | 27 | 0.13 000 | 9.90 490 | 10 | 27 |
| 34 | 9.77 507 | 17 | 9.87 027 | 26 | 0.12 973 | 9.90 480 | 9 | 26 |
| 35 | 9.77 524 | 17 | 9.87 053 | 26 | 0.12 947 | 9.90 471 | 9 | 25 |
| 36 | 9.77 541 | 17 | 9.87 079 | 27 | 0.12 921 | 9.90 462 | 10 | 24 |
| 37 | 9.77 558 | 17 | 9.87 106 | 26 | 0.12 894 | 9.90 452 | 9 | 23 |
| 38 | 9.77 575 | 17 | 9.87 132 | 26 | 0.12 868 | 9.90 443 | 9 | 22 |
| 39 | 9.77 592 | 17 | 9.87 158 | 27 | 0.12 842 | 9.90 434 | 10 | 21 |
| 40 | 9.77 609 | 17 | 9.87 185 | 26 | 0.12 815 | 9.90 424 | 9 | 20 |
| 41 | 9.77 626 | 17 | 9.87 211 | 27 | 0.12 789 | 9.90 415 | 10 | 19 |
| 42 | 9.77 643 | 17 | 9.87 238 | 26 | 0.12 762 | 9.90 405 | 9 | 18 |
| 43 | 9.77 660 | 17 | 9.87 264 | 26 | 0.12 736 | 9.90 396 | 10 | 17 |
| 44 | 9.77 677 | 17 | 9.87 290 | 27 | 0.12 710 | 9.90 386 | 9 | 16 |
| 45 | 9.77 694 | 17 | 9.87 317 | 26 | 0.12 683 | 9.90 377 | 9 | 15 |
| 46 | 9.77 711 | 17 | 9.87 343 | 26 | 0.12 657 | 9.90 368 | 10 | 14 |
| 47 | 9.77 728 | 16 | 9.87 369 | 27 | 0.12 631 | 9.90 358 | 9 | 13 |
| 48 | 9.77 744 | 17 | 9.87 396 | 26 | 0.12 604 | 9.90 349 | 10 | 12 |
| 49 | 9.77 761 | 17 | 9.87 422 | 26 | 0.12 578 | 9.90 339 | 9 | 11 |
| 50 | 9.77 778 | 17 | 9.87 448 | 27 | 0.12 552 | 9.90 330 | 10 | 10 |
| 51 | 9.77 795 | 17 | 9.87 475 | 26 | 0.12 525 | 9.90 320 | 9 | 9 |
| 52 | 9.77 812 | 17 | 9.87 501 | 26 | 0.12 499 | 9.90 311 | 10 | 8 |
| 53 | 9.77 829 | 17 | 9.87 527 | 27 | 0.12 473 | 9.90 301 | 9 | 7 |
| 54 | 9.77 846 | 16 | 9.87 554 | 26 | 0.12 446 | 9.90 292 | 10 | 6 |
| 55 | 9.77 862 | 17 | 9.87 580 | 26 | 0.12 420 | 9.90 282 | 9 | 5 |
| 56 | 9.77 879 | 17 | 9.87 606 | 27 | 0.12 394 | 9.90 273 | 10 | 4 |
| 57 | 9.77 896 | 17 | 9.87 633 | 26 | 0.12 367 | 9.90 263 | 9 | 3 |
| 58 | 9.77 913 | 17 | 9.87 659 | 26 | 0.12 341 | 9.90 254 | 10 | 2 |
| 59 | 9.77 930 | 16 | 9.87 685 | 26 | 0.12 315 | 9.90 244 | 9 | 1 |
| 60 | 9.77 946 | | 9.87 711 | | 0.12 289 | 9.90 235 | | 0 |
| | L. Cos. | d. | L. Cot. | c.d. | L. Tan. | L. Sin. | d. | ' |

## P. P.

| " | 27 | 26 |
|---|---|---|
| 1 | 0.4 | 0.4 |
| 2 | 0.9 | 0.9 |
| 3 | 1.4 | 1.3 |
| 4 | 1.8 | 1.7 |
| 5 | 2.2 | 2.2 |
| 6 | 2.7 | 2.6 |
| 7 | 3.2 | 3.0 |
| 8 | 3.6 | 3.5 |
| 9 | 4.0 | 3.9 |
| 10 | 4.5 | 4.3 |
| 20 | 9.0 | 8.7 |
| 30 | 13.5 | 13.0 |
| 40 | 18.0 | 17.3 |
| 50 | 22.5 | 21.7 |

| " | 18 | 17 | 16 |
|---|---|---|---|
| 1 | 0.3 | 0.3 | 0.3 |
| 2 | 0.6 | 0.6 | 0.5 |
| 3 | 0.9 | 0.8 | 0.8 |
| 4 | 1.2 | 1.1 | 1.1 |
| 5 | 1.5 | 1.4 | 1.3 |
| 6 | 1.8 | 1.7 | 1.6 |
| 7 | 2.1 | 2.0 | 1.9 |
| 8 | 2.4 | 2.3 | 2.1 |
| 9 | 2.7 | 2.6 | 2.4 |
| 10 | 3.0 | 2.8 | 2.7 |
| 20 | 6.0 | 5.7 | 5.3 |
| 30 | 9.0 | 8.5 | 8.0 |
| 40 | 12.0 | 11.3 | 10.7 |
| 50 | 15.0 | 14.2 | 13.3 |

| " | 10 | 9 |
|---|---|---|
| 1 | 0.2 | 0.2 |
| 2 | 0.3 | 0.3 |
| 3 | 0.5 | 0.4 |
| 4 | 0.7 | 0.6 |
| 5 | 0.8 | 0.8 |
| 6 | 1.0 | 0.9 |
| 7 | 1.2 | 1.0 |
| 8 | 1.3 | 1.2 |
| 9 | 1.5 | 1.4 |
| 10 | 1.7 | 1.5 |
| 20 | 3.3 | 3.0 |
| 30 | 5.0 | 4.5 |
| 40 | 6.7 | 6.0 |
| 50 | 8.3 | 7.5 |

| | 9/27 | 9/26 |
|---|---|---|
| 0 | | |
| 1 | 1.5 | 1.4 |
| 2 | 4.5 | 4.3 |
| 3 | 7.5 | 7.2 |
| 4 | 10.5 | 10.1 |
| 5 | 13.5 | 13.0 |
| 6 | 16.5 | 15.9 |
| 7 | 19.5 | 18.8 |
| 8 | 22.5 | 21.7 |
| 9 | 25.5 | 24.6 |

# LOGARITHMS OF THE FUNCTIONS (Continued)

| ′ | L. Sin | d. | L. Tan. | c.d. | L. Cot. | L. Cos. | d. | ′ |
|---|--------|----|---------|------|---------|---------|----|---|
| 0 | 9.77 946 | 17 | 9.87 711 | 27 | 0.12 289 | 9.90 235̄ | 10 | 60 |
| 1 | 9.77 963 | 17 | 9.87 738 | 26 | 0.12 262 | 9.90 225̄ | 9 | 59 |
| 2 | 9.77 980 | 17 | 9.87 764 | 26 | 0.12 236 | 9.90 216 | 10 | 58 |
| 3 | 9.77 997 | 16 | 9.87 790 | 27 | 0.12 210 | 9.90 206 | 10 | 57 |
| 4 | 9.78 013 | 17 | 9.87 817 | 26 | 0.12 183 | 9.90 197 | 10 | 56 |
| 5 | 9.78 030 | 17 | 9.87 843 | 26 | 0.12 157 | 9.90 187 | 9 | 55 |
| 6 | 9.78 047 | 16 | 9.87 869 | 26 | 0.12 131 | 9.90 178 | 10 | 54 |
| 7 | 9.78 063 | 17 | 9.87 895̄ | 27 | 0.12 105̄ | 9.90 168 | 9 | 53 |
| 8 | 9.78 080 | 17 | 9.87 922 | 26 | 0.12 078 | 9.90 159 | 10 | 52 |
| 9 | 9.78 097 | 16 | 9.87 948 | 26 | 0.12 052 | 9.90 149 | 10 | 51 |
| 10 | 9.78 113 | 17 | 9.87 974 | 26 | 0.12 026 | 9.90 139 | 9 | 50 |
| 11 | 9.78 130 | 17 | 9.88 000 | 27 | 0.12 000 | 9.90 130 | 10 | 49 |
| 12 | 9.78 147 | 16 | 9.88 027 | 26 | 0.11 973 | 9.90 120 | 9 | 48 |
| 13 | 9.78 163 | 17 | 9.88 053 | 26 | 0.11 947 | 9.90 111 | 10 | 47 |
| 14 | 9.78 180 | 17 | 9.88 079 | 26 | 0.11 921 | 9.90 101 | 10 | 46 |
| 15 | 9.78 197 | 16 | 9.88 105̄ | 26 | 0.11 895̄ | 9.90 091 | 9 | 45 |
| 16 | 9.78 213 | 17 | 9.88 131 | 27 | 0.11 869 | 9.90 082 | 10 | 44 |
| 17 | 0.78 230 | 16 | 9.88 158 | 26 | 0.11 842 | 9.90 072 | 9 | 43 |
| 18 | 9.78 246 | 17 | 9.88 184 | 26 | 0.11 816 | 9.90 063 | 10 | 42 |
| 19 | 9.78 263 | 17 | 9.88 210 | 26 | 0.11 790 | 9.90 053 | 10 | 41 |
| 20 | 9.78 280 | 16 | 9.88 236 | 26 | 0.11 764 | 9.90 043 | 9 | 40 |
| 21 | 9.78 296 | 17 | 9.88 262 | 27 | 0.11 738 | 9.90 034 | 10 | 39 |
| 22 | 9.78 313 | 16 | 9.88 289 | 26 | 0.11 711 | 9.90 024 | 10 | 38 |
| 23 | 9.78 329 | 17 | 9.88 315̄ | 26 | 0.11 685̄ | 9.90 014 | 9 | 37 |
| 24 | 9.78 346 | 16 | 9.88 341 | 26 | 0.11 659 | 9.90 005̄ | 10 | 36 |
| 25 | 9.78 362 | 17 | 9.88 367 | 26 | 0.11 633 | 9.89 995̄ | 10 | 35 |
| 26 | 9.78 379 | 16 | 9.88 393 | 27 | 0.11 607 | 9.89 985̄ | 9 | 34 |
| 27 | 9.78 395̄ | 17 | 9.88 420 | 26 | 0.11 580 | 9.89 976 | 10 | 33 |
| 28 | 9.78 412 | 16 | 9.88 446 | 26 | 0.11 554 | 9.89 966 | 10 | 32 |
| 29 | 9.78 428 | 17 | 9.88 472 | 26 | 0.11 528 | 9.89 956 | 9 | 31 |
| 30 | 9.78 445̄ | 16 | 9.88 498 | 26 | 0.11 502 | 9.89 947 | 10 | 30 |
| 31 | 9.78 461 | 17 | 9.88 524 | 26 | 0.11 476 | 9.89 937 | 10 | 29 |
| 32 | 9.78 478 | 16 | 9.88 550̄ | 27 | 0.11 450 | 9.89 927 | 9 | 28 |
| 33 | 9.78 494 | 16 | 9.88 577 | 26 | 0.11 423 | 9.89 918 | 10 | 27 |
| 34 | 9.78 510 | 17 | 9.88 603 | 26 | 0.11 397 | 9.89 908 | 10 | 26 |
| 35 | 9.78 527 | 16 | 9.88 629 | 26 | 0.11 371 | 9.89 898 | 10 | 25 |
| 36 | 9.78 543 | 17 | 9.88 655̄ | 26 | 0.11 345̄ | 9.89 888 | 9 | 24 |
| 37 | 9.78 560 | 16 | 9.88 681 | 26 | 0.11 319 | 9.89 879 | 10 | 23 |
| 38 | 9.78 576 | 16 | 9.88 707 | 26 | 0.11 293 | 9.89 869 | 10 | 22 |
| 39 | 9.78 592 | 17 | 9.88 733 | 26 | 0.11 267 | 9.89 859 | 10 | 21 |
| 40 | 9.78 609 | 16 | 9.88 759 | 27 | 0.11 241 | 9.89 849 | 9 | 20 |
| 41 | 9.78 625̄ | 17 | 9.88 786 | 26 | 0.11 214 | 9.89 840 | 10 | 19 |
| 42 | 9.78 642 | 16 | 9.88 812 | 26 | 0.11 188 | 9.89 830 | 10 | 18 |
| 43 | 9.78 658 | 16 | 9.88 838 | 26 | 0.11 162 | 9.89 820 | 10 | 17 |
| 44 | 9.78 674 | 17 | 9.88 864 | 26 | 0.11 136 | 9.80 810 | 9 | 16 |
| 45 | 9.78 691 | 16 | 9.88 890 | 26 | 0.11 110 | 9.89 801 | 10 | 15 |
| 46 | 9.78 707 | 16 | 9.88 916 | 26 | 0.11 084 | 9.89 791 | 10 | 14 |
| 47 | 9.78 723 | 16 | 9.88 942 | 26 | 0.11 058 | 9.89 781 | 10 | 13 |
| 48 | 9.78 739 | 17 | 9.88 968 | 26 | 0.11 032 | 9.89 771 | 10 | 12 |
| 49 | 9.78 756 | 16 | 9.88 994 | 26 | 0.11 006 | 9.89 761 | 9 | 11 |
| 50 | 9.78 772 | 16 | 9.89 020 | 26 | 0.10 980 | 9.89 752 | 10 | 10 |
| 51 | 9.78 788 | 17 | 9.89 046 | 27 | 0.10 954 | 9.89 742 | 10 | 9 |
| 52 | 9.78 805̄ | 16 | 9.89 073 | 26 | 0.10 927 | 9.89 732 | 10 | 8 |
| 53 | 9.78 821 | 16 | 9.89 099 | 26 | 0.10 901 | 9.89 722 | 10 | 7 |
| 54 | 9.78 837 | 16 | 9.89 125̄ | 26 | 0.10 875̄ | 9.89 712 | 10 | 6 |
| 55 | 9.78 853 | 16 | 9.89 151 | 26 | 0.10 849 | 9.89 702 | 9 | 5 |
| 56 | 9.78 869 | 17 | 9.89 177 | 26 | 0.10 823 | 9.89 693 | 10 | 4 |
| 57 | 9.78 886 | 16 | 9.89 203 | 26 | 0.10 797 | 9.89 683 | 10 | 3 |
| 58 | 9.78 902 | 16 | 9.89 229 | 26 | 0.10 771 | 9.89 673 | 10 | 2 |
| 59 | 9.78 918 | 16 | 9.89 255̄ | 26 | 0.10 745̄ | 9.89 663 | 10 | 1 |
| 60 | 9.78 934 |  | 9.89 281 |  | 0.10 719 | 9.89 653 |  | 0 |
| ′ | L. Cos. | d. | L. Cot. | c.d. | L. Tan. | L. Sin. | d. | ′ |

## P. P.

| ″ | 27 | 26 |
|---|----|----|
| 1 | 0.4 | 0.4 |
| 2 | 0.9 | 0.9 |
| 3 | 1.4 | 1.3 |
| 4 | 1.8 | 1.7 |
| 5 | 2.2 | 2.2 |
| 6 | 2.7 | 2.6 |
| 7 | 3.2 | 3.0 |
| 8 | 3.6 | 3.5̄ |
| 9 | 4.0 | 3.9 |
| 10 | 4.5 | 4.3 |
| 20 | 9.0 | 8.7 |
| 30 | 13.5 | 13.0 |
| 40 | 18.0 | 17.3 |
| 50 | 22.5 | 21.7 |

| ″ | 17 | 16 |
|---|----|----|
| 1 | 0.3 | 0.3 |
| 1 | 0.6 | 0.5̄ |
| 3 | 0.8 | 0.8 |
| 4 | 1.1 | 1.1 |
| 5 | 1.4 | 1.3 |
| 6 | 1.7 | 1.6 |
| 7 | 2.0 | 1.9 |
| 8 | 2.3 | 2.1 |
| 9 | 2.6 | 2.4 |
| 10 | 2.8 | 2.7 |
| 20 | 5.7 | 5.3 |
| 30 | 8.5 | 8.0 |
| 40 | 11.3 | 10.7 |
| 50 | 14.2 | 13.3 |

| ″ | 10 | 9 |
|---|----|----|
| 1 | 0.2 | 0.2 |
| 2 | 0.3 | 0.3 |
| 3 | 0.5̄ | 0.4 |
| 4 | 0.7 | 0.6 |
| 5 | 0.8 | 0.8 |
| 6 | 1.0 | 0.9 |
| 7 | 1.2 | 1.0 |
| 8 | 1.3 | 1.2 |
| 9 | 1.5 | 1.4 |
| 10 | 1.7 | 1.5̄ |
| 20 | 3.3 | 3.0 |
| 30 | 5.0 | 4.5̄ |
| 40 | 6.7 | 6.0 |
| 50 | 8.3 | 7.5̄ |

| | 10 | 10 |
|---|----|----|
| | 27 | 26 |
| 0 | 1.4 | 1.3 |
| 1 | 4.1 | 3.9 |
| 2 | 6.8 | 6.5̄ |
| 3 | 9.4 | 9.1 |
| 4 | 12.2 | 11.7 |
| 5 | 14.8 | 14.3 |
| 6 | 17.6 | 16.9 |
| 7 | 20.2 | 19.5̄ |
| 8 | 22.9 | 22.1 |
| 9 | 25.6 | 24.7 |
| 10 | | |

| ´ | L. Sin. | d. | L. Tan. | c.d. | L. Cot. | L. Cos. | d. | ´ |
|---|---|---|---|---|---|---|---|---|
| 0 | 9.78 934 | 16 | 9.89 281 | 26 | 0.10 719 | 9.89 653 | 10 | 60 |
| 1 | 9.78 950 | 16 | 9.89 307 | 26 | 0.10 693 | 9.89 643 | 10 | 59 |
| 2 | 9.78 967 | 17 | 9.89 333 | 26 | 0.10 667 | 9.89 633 | 10 | 58 |
| 3 | 9.78 983 | 16 | 9.89 359 | 26 | 0.10 641 | 9.89 624 | 9 | 57 |
| 4 | 9.78 999 | 16 | 9.89 385 | 26 | 0.10 615 | 9.89 614 | 10 | 56 |
| 5 | 9.79 015 | 16 | 9.89 411 | 26 | 0.10 589 | 9.89 604 | 10 | 55 |
| 6 | 9.79 031 | 16 | 9.89 437 | 26 | 0.10 563 | 9.89 594 | 10 | 54 |
| 7 | 9.79 047 | 16 | 9.89 463 | 26 | 0.10 537 | 9.89 584 | 10 | 53 |
| 8 | 9.79 063 | 16 | 9.89 489 | 26 | 0.10 511 | 9.89 574 | 10 | 52 |
| 9 | 9.79 079 | 16 | 9.89 515 | 26 | 0.10 485 | 9.89 564 | 10 | 51 |
| 10 | 9.79 095 | 16 | 9.89 541 | 26 | 0.10 459 | 9.89 554 | 10 | 50 |
| 11 | 9.79 111 | 17 | 9.89 567 | 26 | 0.10 433 | 9.89 544 | 10 | 49 |
| 12 | 9.79 128 | 16 | 9.89 593 | 26 | 0.10 407 | 9.89 534 | 10 | 48 |
| 13 | 9.79 144 | 16 | 9.89 619 | 26 | 0.10 381 | 9.89 524 | 10 | 47 |
| 14 | 9.79 160 | 16 | 9.89 645 | 26 | 0.10 355 | 9.89 514 | 10 | 46 |
| 15 | 9.79 176 | 16 | 9.89 671 | 26 | 0.10 329 | 9.89 504 | 9 | 45 |
| 16 | 9.79 192 | 16 | 9.89 697 | 26 | 0.10 303 | 9.89 495 | 10 | 44 |
| 17 | 9.79 208 | 16 | 9.89 723 | 26 | 0.10 277 | 9.89 485 | 10 | 43 |
| 18 | 9.79 224 | 16 | 9.89 749 | 26 | 0.10 251 | 9.89 475 | 10 | 42 |
| 19 | 9.79 240 | 16 | 9.89 775 | 26 | 0.10 225 | 9.89 465 | 10 | 41 |
| 20 | 9.79 256 | 16 | 9.89 801 | 26 | 0.10 199 | 9.89 455 | 10 | 40 |
| 21 | 9.79 272 | 16 | 9.89 827 | 26 | 0.10 173 | 9.89 445 | 10 | 39 |
| 22 | 9.79 288 | 16 | 9.89 853 | 26 | 0.10 147 | 9.89 435 | 10 | 38 |
| 23 | 9.79 304 | 15 | 9.89 879 | 26 | 0.10 121 | 9.89 425 | 10 | 37 |
| 24 | 9.79 319 | 16 | 9.89 905 | 26 | 0.10 095 | 9.89 415 | 10 | 36 |
| 25 | 9.79 335 | 16 | 9.89 931 | 26 | 0.10 069 | 9.89 405 | 10 | 35 |
| 26 | 9.79 351 | 16 | 9.89 957 | 26 | 0.10 043 | 9.89 395 | 10 | 34 |
| 27 | 9.79 367 | 16 | 9.89 983 | 26 | 0.10 017 | 9.89 385 | 10 | 33 |
| 28 | 9.79 383 | 16 | 9.90 009 | 26 | 0.09 991 | 9.89 375 | 11 | 32 |
| 29 | 9.79 399 | 16 | 9.90 035 | 26 | 0.09 965 | 9.89 364 | 10 | 31 |
| 30 | 9.79 415 | 16 | 9.90 061 | 25 | 0.09 939 | 9.89 354 | 10 | 30 |
| 31 | 9.79 431 | 16 | 9.90 086 | 26 | 0.09 914 | 9.89 344 | 10 | 29 |
| 32 | 9.79 447 | 16 | 9.90 112 | 26 | 0.09 888 | 9.89 334 | 10 | 28 |
| 33 | 9.79 463 | 15 | 9.90 138 | 26 | 0.09 862 | 9.89 324 | 10 | 27 |
| 34 | 9.79 478 | 16 | 9.90 164 | 26 | 0.09 836 | 9.89 314 | 10 | 26 |
| 35 | 9.79 494 | 16 | 9.90 190 | 26 | 0.09 810 | 9.89 304 | 10 | 25 |
| 36 | 9.79 510 | 16 | 9.90 216 | 26 | 0.09 784 | 9.89 294 | 10 | 24 |
| 37 | 9.79 526 | 16 | 9.90 242 | 26 | 0.09 758 | 9.89 284 | 10 | 23 |
| 38 | 9.79 542 | 16 | 9.90 268 | 26 | 0.09 732 | 9.89 274 | 10 | 22 |
| 39 | 9.79 558 | 16 | 9.90 294 | 26 | 0.09 706 | 9.89 264 | 10 | 21 |
| 40 | 9.79 573 | 16 | 9.90 320 | 26 | 0.09 680 | 9.89 254 | 10 | 20 |
| 41 | 9.79 589 | 16 | 9.90 346 | 25 | 0.09 654 | 9.89 244 | 11 | 19 |
| 42 | 9.79 605 | 16 | 9.90 371 | 26 | 0.09 629 | 9.89 233 | 10 | 18 |
| 43 | 9.79 621 | 15 | 9.90 397 | 26 | 0.09 603 | 9.89 223 | 10 | 17 |
| 44 | 9.79 636 | 16 | 9.90 423 | 26 | 0.09 577 | 9.89 213 | 10 | 16 |
| 45 | 9.79 652 | 16 | 9.90 449 | 26 | 0.09 551 | 9.89 203 | 10 | 15 |
| 46 | 9.79 668 | 16 | 9.90 475 | 26 | 0.09 525 | 9.89 193 | 10 | 14 |
| 47 | 9.79 684 | 15 | 9.90 501 | 26 | 0.09 499 | 9.89 183 | 10 | 13 |
| 48 | 9.79 699 | 16 | 9.90 527 | 26 | 0.09 473 | 9.89 173 | 11 | 12 |
| 49 | 9.79 715 | 16 | 9.90 553 | 25 | 0.09 447 | 9.89 162 | 10 | 11 |
| 50 | 9.79 731 | 15 | 9.90 578 | 26 | 0.09 422 | 9.89 152 | 10 | 10 |
| 51 | 9.79 746 | 16 | 9.90 604 | 26 | 0.09 396 | 9.89 142 | 10 | 9 |
| 52 | 9.79 762 | 16 | 9.90 630 | 26 | 0.09 370 | 9.89 132 | 10 | 8 |
| 53 | 9.79 778 | 15 | 9.90 656 | 26 | 0.09 344 | 9.89 122 | 10 | 7 |
| 54 | 9.79 793 | 16 | 9.90 682 | 26 | 0.09 318 | 9.89 112 | 11 | 6 |
| 55 | 9.79 809 | 16 | 9.90 708 | 26 | 0.09 292 | 9.89 101 | 10 | 5 |
| 56 | 9.79 825 | 15 | 9.90 734 | 25 | 0.09 266 | 9.89 091 | 10 | 4 |
| 57 | 9.79 840 | 16 | 9.90 759 | 26 | 0.09 241 | 9.89 081 | 10 | 3 |
| 58 | 9.79 856 | 16 | 9.90 785 | 26 | 0.09 215 | 9.89 071 | 11 | 2 |
| 59 | 9.79 872 | 15 | 9.90 811 | 26 | 0.09 189 | 9.89 060 | 10 | 1 |
| 60 | 9.79 887 | | 9.90 837 | | 0.09 163 | 9.89 050 | | 0 |
| ´ | L. Cos. | d. | L. Cot. | c.d. | L. Tan. | L. Sin. | d. | ´ |

**P. P.**

| | 26 | 25 |
|---|---|---|
| 1 | 0.4 | 0.4 |
| 2 | 0.9 | 0.8 |
| 3 | 1.3 | 1.2 |
| 4 | 1.7 | 1.7 |
| 5 | 2.2 | 2.1 |
| 6 | 2.6 | 2.5 |
| 7 | 3.0 | 2.9 |
| 8 | 3.5 | 3.3 |
| 9 | 3.9 | 3.8 |
| 10 | 4.3 | 4.2 |
| 20 | 8.7 | 8.3 |
| 30 | 13.0 | 12.5 |
| 40 | 17.3 | 16.7 |
| 50 | 21.7 | 20.8 |

| | 17 | 16 | 15 |
|---|---|---|---|
| 1 | 0.3 | 0.3 | 0.2 |
| 2 | 0.6 | 0.5 | 0.5 |
| 3 | 0.8 | 0.8 | 0.8 |
| 4 | 1.1 | 1.1 | 1.0 |
| 5 | 1.4 | 1.3 | 1.3 |
| 6 | 1.7 | 1.6 | 1.5 |
| 7 | 2.0 | 1.9 | 1.8 |
| 8 | 2.3 | 2.1 | 2.0 |
| 9 | 2.6 | 2.4 | 2.3 |
| 10 | 2.8 | 2.7 | 2.5 |
| 20 | 5.7 | 5.3 | 5.0 |
| 30 | 8.5 | 8.0 | 7.5 |
| 40 | 11.3 | 10.7 | 10.0 |
| 50 | 14.2 | 13.3 | 12.5 |

| | 11 | 10 | 9 |
|---|---|---|---|
| 1 | 0.2 | 0.2 | 0.2 |
| 2 | 0.4 | 0.3 | 0.3 |
| 3 | 0.6 | 0.5 | 0.4 |
| 4 | 0.7 | 0.7 | 0.6 |
| 5 | 0.9 | 0.8 | 0.8 |
| 6 | 1.1 | 1.0 | 0.9 |
| 7 | 1.3 | 1.2 | 1.0 |
| 8 | 1.5 | 1.3 | 1.2 |
| 9 | 1.6 | 1.5 | 1.4 |
| 10 | 1.8 | 1.7 | 1.5 |
| 20 | 3.7 | 3.3 | 3.0 |
| 30 | 5.5 | 5.0 | 4.5 |
| 40 | 7.3 | 6.7 | 6.0 |
| 50 | 9.2 | 8.3 | 7.5 |

| | $\frac{10}{26}$ | $\frac{10}{25}$ | $\frac{9}{26}$ |
|---|---|---|---|
| 1 | 1.3 | 1.2 | 1.0 |
| 2 | 3.9 | 3.8 | 4.2 |
| 3 | 6.5 | 6.2 | 7.2 |
| 4 | 9.1 | 8.8 | 10.1 |
| 5 | 11.7 | 11.2 | 13.0 |
| 6 | 14.3 | 13.8 | 15.9 |
| 7 | 16.9 | 16.2 | 18.8 |
| 8 | 19.5 | 18.8 | 21.7 |
| 9 | 22.1 | 21.2 | 24.6 |
| 10 | 24.7 | 23.8 | |

# LOGARITHMS OF THE FUNCTIONS (Continued)

| ′ | L. Sin. | d. | L. Tan. | c.d. | L. Cot. | L. Cos. | d. | ′ |
|---|---------|----|---------|------|---------|---------|----|----|
| 0 | 9.79 887 | 16 | 9.90 837 | 26 | 0.09 163 | 9.89 050 | 10 | 60 |
| 1 | 9.79 903 | 16 | 9.90 863 | 26 | 0.09 137 | 9.89 040 | 10 | 59 |
| 2 | 9.79 918 | 15 | 9.90 889 | 26 | 0.09 111 | 9.89 030 | 10 | 58 |
| 3 | 9.79 934 | 16 | 9.90 914 | 25 | 0.09 086 | 9.89 020 | 10 | 57 |
| 4 | 9.79 950 | 16 | 9.90 940 | 26 | 0.09 060 | 9.89 009 | 11 | 56 |
| 5 | 9.79 965 | 15 | 9.90 966 | 26 | 0.09 034 | 9.88 999 | 10 | 55 |
| 6 | 9.79 981 | 16 | 9.90 992 | 26 | 0.09 008 | 9.88 989 | 10 | 54 |
| 7 | 9.79 996 | 16 | 9.91 018 | 26 | 0.08 982 | 9.88 978 | 11 | 53 |
| 8 | 9.80 012 | 16 | 9.91 043 | 25 | 0.08 957 | 9.88 968 | 10 | 52 |
| 9 | 9.80 027 | 16 | 9.91 069 | 26 | 0.08 931 | 9.88 958 | 10 | 51 |
| 10 | 9.80 043 | 16 | 9.91 095 | 26 | 0.08 905 | 9.88 948 | 10 | 50 |
| 11 | 9.80 058 | 15 | 9.91 121 | 26 | 0.08 879 | 9.88 937 | 11 | 49 |
| 12 | 9.80 074 | 16 | 9.91 147 | 26 | 0.08 853 | 9.88 927 | 10 | 48 |
| 13 | 9.80 089 | 15 | 9.91 172 | 25 | 0.08 828 | 9.88 917 | 10 | 47 |
| 14 | 9.80 105 | 16 | 9.91 198 | 26 | 0.08 802 | 9.88 906 | 11 | 46 |
| 15 | 9.80 120 | 15 | 9.91 224 | 26 | 0.08 776 | 9.88 896 | 10 | 45 |
| 16 | 9.80 136 | 16 | 9.91 250 | 26 | 0.08 750 | 9.88 886 | 10 | 44 |
| 17 | 9.80 151 | 15 | 9.91 276 | 26 | 0.08 724 | 9.88 875 | 11 | 43 |
| 18 | 9.80 166 | 16 | 9.91 301 | 25 | 0.08 699 | 9.88 865 | 10 | 42 |
| 19 | 9.80 182 | 15 | 9.91 327 | 26 | 0.08 673 | 9.88 855 | 10 | 41 |
| 20 | 9.80 197 | 16 | 9.91 353 | 26 | 0.08 647 | 9.88 844 | 11 | 40 |
| 21 | 9.80 213 | 15 | 9.91 379 | 25 | 0.08 621 | 9.88 834 | 10 | 39 |
| 22 | 9.80 228 | 16 | 9.91 404 | 26 | 0.08 596 | 9.88 824 | 11 | 38 |
| 23 | 9.80 244 | 15 | 9.91 430 | 26 | 0.08 570 | 9.88 813 | 10 | 37 |
| 24 | 9.80 259 | 15 | 9.91 456 | 26 | 0.08 544 | 9.88 803 | 10 | 36 |
| 25 | 9.80 274 | 16 | 9.91 482 | 25 | 0.08 518 | 9.88 793 | 11 | 35 |
| 26 | 9.80 290 | 15 | 9.91 507 | 26 | 0.08 493 | 9.88 782 | 10 | 34 |
| 27 | 9.80 305 | 15 | 9.91 533 | 26 | 0.08 467 | 9.88 772 | 11 | 33 |
| 28 | 9.80 320 | 16 | 9.91 559 | 26 | 0.08 441 | 9.88 761 | 10 | 32 |
| 29 | 9.80 336 | 15 | 9.91 585 | 25 | 0.08 415 | 9.88 751 | 10 | 31 |
| 30 | 9.80 351 | 15 | 9.91 610 | 26 | 0.08 390 | 9.88 741 | 11 | 30 |
| 31 | 9.80 366 | 16 | 9.91 636 | 26 | 0.08 364 | 9.88 730 | 10 | 29 |
| 32 | 9.80 382 | 15 | 9.91 662 | 26 | 0.08 338 | 9.88 720 | 11 | 28 |
| 33 | 9.80 397 | 15 | 9.91 688 | 25 | 0.08 312 | 9.88 709 | 10 | 27 |
| 34 | 9.80 412 | 16 | 9.91 713 | 26 | 0.08 287 | 9.88 699 | 11 | 26 |
| 35 | 9.80 428 | 15 | 9.91 739 | 26 | 0.08 261 | 9.88 688 | 10 | 25 |
| 36 | 9.80 443 | 15 | 9.91 765 | 26 | 0.08 235 | 9.88 678 | 10 | 24 |
| 37 | 9.80 458 | 15 | 9.91 791 | 25 | 0.08 209 | 9.88 668 | 11 | 23 |
| 38 | 9.80 473 | 16 | 9.91 816 | 26 | 0.08 184 | 9.88 657 | 10 | 22 |
| 39 | 9.80 489 | 15 | 9.91 842 | 26 | 0.08 158 | 9.88 647 | 11 | 21 |
| 40 | 9.80 504 | 15 | 9.91 868 | 25 | 0.08 132 | 9.88 636 | 10 | 20 |
| 41 | 9.80 519 | 15 | 9.91 893 | 26 | 0.08 107 | 9.88 626 | 11 | 19 |
| 42 | 9.80 534 | 16 | 9.91 919 | 26 | 0.08 081 | 9.88 615 | 10 | 18 |
| 43 | 9.80 550 | 15 | 9.91 945 | 26 | 0.08 055 | 9.88 605 | 11 | 17 |
| 44 | 9.80 565 | 15 | 9.91 971 | 25 | 0.08 029 | 9.88 594 | 10 | 16 |
| 45 | 9.80 580 | 15 | 9.91 996 | 26 | 0.08 004 | 9.88 584 | 11 | 15 |
| 46 | 9.80 595 | 15 | 9.92 022 | 26 | 0.07 978 | 9.88 573 | 10 | 14 |
| 47 | 9.80 610 | 15 | 9.92 048 | 25 | 0.07 952 | 9.88 563 | 11 | 13 |
| 48 | 9.80 625 | 16 | 9.92 073 | 26 | 0.07 927 | 9.88 552 | 10 | 12 |
| 49 | 9.80 641 | 15 | 9.92 099 | 26 | 0.07 901 | 9.88 542 | 11 | 11 |
| 50 | 9.80 656 | 15 | 9.92 125 | 25 | 0.07 875 | 9.88 531 | 10 | 10 |
| 51 | 9.80 671 | 15 | 9.92 150 | 26 | 0.07 850 | 9.88 521 | 11 | 9 |
| 52 | 9.80 686 | 15 | 9.92 176 | 26 | 0.07 824 | 9.88 510 | 11 | 8 |
| 53 | 9.80 701 | 15 | 9.92 202 | 25 | 0.07 798 | 9.88 499 | 10 | 7 |
| 54 | 9.80 716 | 15 | 9.92 227 | 26 | 0.07 773 | 9.88 489 | 11 | 6 |
| 55 | 9.80 731 | 15 | 9.92 253 | 26 | 0.07 747 | 9.88 478 | 10 | 5 |
| 56 | 9.80 746 | 16 | 9.92 279 | 25 | 0.07 721 | 9.88 468 | 11 | 4 |
| 57 | 9.80 762 | 15 | 9.92 304 | 26 | 0.07 696 | 9.88 457 | 11 | 3 |
| 58 | 9.80 777 | 15 | 9.92 330 | 26 | 0.07 670 | 9.88 447 | 11 | 2 |
| 59 | 9.80 792 | 15 | 9.92 356 | 25 | 0.07 644 | 9.88 436 | 11 | 1 |
| 60 | 9.80 807 | | 9.92 381 | | 0.07 619 | 9.88 425 | | 0 |
| ° | L. Cos. | d. | L. Cot. | c.d. | L. Tan. | L. Sin. | d. | ′ |

## P. P.

| ″ | 26 | 25 |
|---|----|----|
| 1 | 0.4 | 0.4 |
| 2 | 0.9 | 0.8 |
| 3 | 1.3 | 1.2 |
| 4 | 1.7 | 1.7 |
| 5 | 2.2 | 2.1 |
| 6 | 2.6 | 2.5 |
| 7 | 3.0 | 2.9 |
| 8 | 3.5 | 3.3 |
| 9 | 3.9 | 3.8 |
| 10 | 4.3 | 4.2 |
| 20 | 8.7 | 8.3 |
| 30 | 13.0 | 12.5 |
| 40 | 17.3 | 16.7 |
| 50 | 21.7 | 20.8 |

| ″ | 16 | 15 |
|---|----|----|
| 1 | 0.3 | 0.2 |
| 2 | 0.5 | 0.5 |
| 3 | 0.8 | 0.8 |
| 4 | 1.1 | 1.0 |
| 5 | 1.3 | 1.2 |
| 6 | 1.6 | 1.5 |
| 7 | 1.9 | 1.8 |
| 8 | 2.1 | 2.0 |
| 9 | 2.4 | 2.2 |
| 10 | 2.7 | 2.5 |
| 20 | 5.3 | 5.0 |
| 30 | 8.0 | 7.5 |
| 40 | 10.7 | 10.0 |
| 50 | 13.3 | 12.5 |

| ″ | 11 | 10 |
|---|----|----|
| 1 | 0.2 | 0.2 |
| 2 | 0.4 | 0.3 |
| 3 | 0.6 | 0.5 |
| 4 | 0.7 | 0.7 |
| 5 | 0.9 | 0.8 |
| 6 | 1.1 | 1.0 |
| 7 | 1.3 | 1.2 |
| 8 | 1.5 | 1.3 |
| 9 | 1.6 | 1.5 |
| 10 | 1.8 | 1.7 |
| 20 | 3.7 | 3.3 |
| 30 | 5.5 | 5.0 |
| 40 | 7.3 | 6.7 |
| 50 | 9.2 | 8.3 |

| | 11/26 | 11/25 |
|---|----|----|
| 1 | 1.2 | 1.1 |
| 2 | 3.5 | 3.4 |
| 3 | 5.9 | 5.7 |
| 4 | 8.3 | 7.9 |
| 5 | 10.6 | 10.2 |
| 6 | 13.0 | 12.5 |
| 7 | 15.4 | 14.8 |
| 8 | 17.7 | 17.1 |
| 9 | 20.1 | 19.3 |
| 10 | 22.5 | 21.6 |
| 11 | 24.8 | 23.9 |

| ′ | L. Sin. | d. | L. Tan. | c.d. | L. Cot. | L. Cos. | d. | ′ |
|---|---------|----|---------|------|---------|---------|----|---|
| 0 | 9.80 807 | 15 | 9.92 381 | 26 | 0.07 619 | 9.88 425 | 10 | 60 |
| 1 | 9.80 822 | 15 | 9.92 407 | 26 | 0.07 593 | 9.88 415 | 10 | 59 |
| 2 | 9.80 837 | 15 | 9.92 433 | 26 | 0.07 567 | 9.88 404 | 10 | 58 |
| 3 | 9.80 852 | 15 | 9.92 458 | 25 | 0.07 542 | 9.88 394 | 10 | 57 |
| 4 | 9.80 867 | 15 | 9.92 484 | 26 | 0.07 516 | 9.88 383 | 11 | 56 |
| 5 | 9.80 882 | 15 | 9.92 510 | 25 | 0.07 490 | 9.88 372 | 10 | 55 |
| 6 | 9.80 897 | 15 | 9.92 535 | 26 | 0.07 465 | 9.88 362 | 10 | 54 |
| 7 | 9.80 912 | 15 | 9.92 561 | 26 | 0.07 439 | 9.88 351 | 11 | 53 |
| 8 | 9.80 927 | 15 | 9.92 587 | 25 | 0.07 413 | 9.88 340 | 11 | 52 |
| 9 | 9.80 942 | 15 | 9.92 612 | 26 | 0.07 388 | 9.88 330 | 11 | 51 |
| 10 | 9.80 957 | 15 | 9.92 638 | 26 | 0.07 362 | 9.88 319 | 11 | 50 |
| 11 | 9.80 972 | 15 | 9.92 663 | 26 | 0.07 337 | 9.88 308 | 11 | 49 |
| 12 | 9.80 987 | 15 | 9.92 689 | 26 | 0.07 311 | 9.88 298 | 11 | 48 |
| 13 | 9.81 002 | 15 | 9.92 715 | 25 | 0.07 285 | 9.88 287 | 11 | 47 |
| 14 | 9.81 017 | 15 | 9.92 740 | 26 | 0.07 260 | 9.88 276 | 10 | 46 |
| 15 | 9.81 032 | 15 | 9.92 766 | 26 | 0.07 234 | 9.88 266 | 11 | 45 |
| 16 | 9.81 047 | 14 | 9.92 792 | 25 | 0.07 208 | 9.88 255 | 11 | 44 |
| 17 | 9.81 061 | 15 | 9.92 817 | 26 | 0.07 183 | 9.88 244 | 10 | 43 |
| 18 | 9.81 076 | 15 | 9.92 843 | 25 | 0.07 157 | 9.88 234 | 11 | 42 |
| 19 | 9.81 091 | 15 | 9.92 868 | 26 | 0.07 132 | 9.88 223 | 11 | 41 |
| 20 | 9.81 106 | 15 | 9.92 894 | 26 | 0.07 106 | 9.88 212 | 11 | 40 |
| 21 | 9.81 121 | 15 | 9.92 920 | 25 | 0.07 080 | 9.88 201 | 10 | 39 |
| 22 | 9.81 136 | 15 | 9.92 945 | 26 | 0.07 055 | 9.88 191 | 11 | 38 |
| 23 | 9.81 151 | 15 | 9.92 971 | 25 | 0.07 029 | 9.88 180 | 11 | 37 |
| 24 | 9.81 166 | 14 | 9.92 996 | 26 | 0.07 004 | 9.88 169 | 11 | 36 |
| 25 | 9.81 180 | 15 | 9.93 022 | 26 | 0.06 978 | 9.88 158 | 10 | 35 |
| 26 | 9.81 195 | 15 | 9.93 048 | 25 | 0.06 952 | 9.88 148 | 11 | 34 |
| 27 | 9.81 210 | 15 | 9.93 073 | 26 | 0.06 927 | 9.88 137 | 11 | 33 |
| 28 | 9.81 225 | 15 | 9.93 099 | 25 | 0.06 901 | 9.88 126 | 11 | 32 |
| 29 | 9.81 240 | 14 | 9.93 124 | 26 | 0.06 876 | 9.88 115 | 10 | 31 |
| 30 | 9.81 254 | 15 | 9.93 150 | 25 | 0.06 850 | 9.88 105 | 11 | 30 |
| 31 | 9.81 269 | 15 | 9.93 175 | 26 | 0.06 825 | 9.88 094 | 11 | 29 |
| 32 | 9.81 284 | 15 | 9.93 201 | 26 | 0.06 799 | 9.88 083 | 11 | 28 |
| 33 | 9.81 299 | 15 | 9.93 227 | 25 | 0.06 773 | 9.88 072 | 11 | 27 |
| 34 | 9.81 314 | 14 | 9.93 252 | 26 | 0.06 748 | 9.88 061 | 10 | 26 |
| 35 | 9.81 328 | 15 | 9.93 278 | 25 | 0.06 722 | 9.88 051 | 11 | 25 |
| 36 | 9.81 343 | 15 | 9.93 303 | 26 | 0.06 697 | 9.88 040 | 11 | 24 |
| 37 | 9.81 358 | 14 | 9.93 329 | 25 | 0.06 671 | 9.88 029 | 11 | 23 |
| 38 | 9.81 372 | 15 | 9.93 354 | 26 | 0.06 646 | 9.88 018 | 11 | 22 |
| 39 | 9.81 387 | 15 | 9.93 380 | 26 | 0.06 620 | 9.88 007 | 11 | 21 |
| 40 | 9.81 402 | 15 | 9.93 406 | 25 | 0.06 594 | 9.87 996 | 11 | 20 |
| 41 | 9.81 417 | 14 | 9.93 431 | 26 | 0.06 569 | 9.87 985 | 10 | 19 |
| 42 | 9.81 431 | 15 | 9.93 457 | 25 | 0.06 543 | 9.87 975 | 11 | 18 |
| 43 | 9.81 446 | 15 | 9.93 482 | 26 | 0.06 518 | 9.87 964 | 11 | 17 |
| 44 | 9.81 461 | 14 | 9.93 508 | 25 | 0.06 492 | 9.87 953 | 11 | 16 |
| 45 | 9.81 475 | 15 | 9.93 533 | 26 | 0.06 467 | 9.87 942 | 11 | 15 |
| 46 | 9.81 490 | 15 | 9.93 559 | 25 | 0.06 441 | 9.87 931 | 11 | 14 |
| 47 | 9.81 505 | 14 | 9.93 584 | 26 | 0.06 416 | 9.87 920 | 11 | 13 |
| 48 | 9.81 519 | 15 | 9.93 610 | 26 | 0.06 390 | 9.87 909 | 11 | 12 |
| 49 | 9.81 534 | 15 | 9.93 636 | 25 | 0.06 364 | 9.87 898 | 11 | 11 |
| 50 | 9.81 549 | 14 | 9.93 661 | 26 | 0.06 339 | 9.87 887 | 10 | 10 |
| 51 | 9.81 563 | 15 | 9.93 687 | 25 | 0.06 313 | 9.87 877 | 11 | 9 |
| 52 | 9.81 578 | 14 | 9.93 712 | 26 | 0.06 288 | 9.87 866 | 11 | 8 |
| 53 | 9.81 592 | 15 | 9.93 738 | 25 | 0.06 262 | 9.87 855 | 11 | 7 |
| 54 | 9.81 607 | 15 | 9.93 763 | 26 | 0.06 237 | 9.87 844 | 11 | 6 |
| 55 | 9.81 622 | 14 | 9.93 789 | 25 | 0.06 211 | 9.87 833 | 11 | 5 |
| 56 | 9.81 636 | 15 | 9.93 814 | 26 | 0.06 186 | 9.87 822 | 11 | 4 |
| 57 | 9.81 651 | 14 | 9.93 840 | 25 | 0.06 160 | 9.87 811 | 11 | 3 |
| 58 | 9.81 665 | 15 | 9.93 865 | 26 | 0.06 135 | 9.87 800 | 11 | 2 |
| 59 | 9.81 680 | 14 | 9.93 891 | 25 | 0.06 109 | 9.87 789 | 11 | 1 |
| 60 | 9.81 694 |  | 9.93 916 |  | 0.06 084 | 9.87 778 |  | 0 |

| ′ | L. Cos. | d. | L. Cot. | c.d. | L. Tan. | L. Sin. | d. | ′ |

**P. P.**

| ″ | 26 | 25 |
|---|----|----|
| 1 | 0.4 | 0.4 |
| 2 | 0.9 | 0.8 |
| 3 | 1.3 | 1.2 |
| 4 | 1.7 | 1.7 |
| 5 | 2.2 | 2.1 |
| 6 | 2.6 | 2.5 |
| 7 | 3.0 | 2.9 |
| 8 | 3.5 | 3.3 |
| 9 | 3.9 | 3.8 |
| 10 | 4.3 | 4.2 |
| 20 | 8.7 | 8.3 |
| 30 | 13.0 | 12.5 |
| 40 | 17.3 | 16.7 |
| 50 | 21.7 | 20.8 |

| ″ | 15 | 14 |
|---|----|----|
| 1 | 0.2 | 0.2 |
| 2 | 0.5 | 0.5 |
| 3 | 0.8 | 0.7 |
| 4 | 1.0 | 0.9 |
| 5 | 1.2 | 1.2 |
| 6 | 1.5 | 1.4 |
| 7 | 1.8 | 1.6 |
| 8 | 2.0 | 1.9 |
| 9 | 2.2 | 2.1 |
| 10 | 2.5 | 2.3 |
| 20 | 5.0 | 4.7 |
| 30 | 7.5 | 7.0 |
| 40 | 10.0 | 9.3 |
| 50 | 12.5 | 11.7 |

| ″ | 11 | 10 |
|---|----|----|
| 1 | 0.2 | 0.2 |
| 2 | 0.4 | 0.3 |
| 3 | 0.6 | 0.5 |
| 4 | 0.7 | 0.7 |
| 5 | 0.9 | 0.8 |
| 6 | 1.1 | 1.0 |
| 7 | 1.3 | 1.2 |
| 8 | 1.5 | 1.3 |
| 9 | 1.6 | 1.5 |
| 10 | 1.8 | 1.7 |
| 20 | 3.7 | 3.3 |
| 30 | 5.5 | 5.0 |
| 40 | 7.3 | 6.7 |
| 50 | 9.2 | 8.3 |

| | 11 / 26 | 10 / 26 | 10 / 25 |
|---|---------|---------|---------|
| 0 | 1.2 | 1.3 | 1.2 |
| 1 | 3.5 | 3.9 | 3.8 |
| 2 | 5.9 | 6.5 | 6.2 |
| 3 | 8.3 | 9.1 | 8.8 |
| 4 | 10.6 | 11.7 | 11.2 |
| 5 | 13.0 | 14.3 | 13.8 |
| 6 | 15.4 | 16.9 | 16.2 |
| 7 | 17.7 | 19.5 | 18.8 |
| 8 | 20.1 | 22.1 | 21.2 |
| 9 | 22.5 | 24.7 | 23.8 |
| 10 | 24.8 | — | — |
| 11 | | | |

| ' | L. Sin. | d. | L. Tan. | c.d. | L. Cot. | L. Cos. | d. | ' |
|---|---------|----|---------|------|---------|---------|----|----|
| **0** | 9.81 694 | 15 | 9.93 916 | 26 | 0.06 084 | 9.87 778 | 11 | **60** |
| 1 | 9.81 709 | 14 | 9.93 942 | 25 | 0.06 058 | 9.87 767 | 11 | 59 |
| 2 | 9.81 723 | 15 | 9.93 967 | 26 | 0.06 033 | 9.87 756 | 11 | 58 |
| 3 | 9.81 738 | 14 | 9.93 993 | 25 | 0.06 007 | 9.87 745 | 11 | 57 |
| 4 | 9.81 752 | 15 | 9.94 018 | 26 | 0.05 982 | 9.87 734 | 11 | 56 |
| **5** | 9.81 767 | 14 | 9.94 044 | 25 | 0.05 956 | 9.87 723 | 11 | **55** |
| 6 | 9.81 781 | 15 | 9.94 069 | 26 | 0.05 931 | 9.87 712 | 11 | 54 |
| 7 | 9.81 796 | 14 | 9.94 095 | 25 | 0.05 905 | 9.87 701 | 11 | 53 |
| 8 | 9.81 810 | 15 | 9.94 120 | 26 | 0.05 880 | 9.87 690 | 11 | 52 |
| 9 | 9.81 825 | 14 | 9.94 146 | 25 | 0.05 854 | 9.87 679 | 11 | 51 |
| **10** | 9.81 839 | 15 | 9.94 171 | 26 | 0.05 829 | 9.87 668 | 11 | **50** |
| 11 | 9.81 854 | 14 | 9.94 197 | 25 | 0.05 803 | 9.87 657 | 11 | 49 |
| 12 | 9.81 868 | 14 | 9.94 222 | 26 | 0.05 778 | 9.87 646 | 11 | 48 |
| 13 | 9.81 882 | 15 | 9.94 248 | 25 | 0.05 752 | 9.87 635 | 11 | 47 |
| 14 | 9.81 897 | 14 | 9.94 273 | 26 | 0.05 727 | 9.87 624 | 11 | 46 |
| **15** | 9.81 911 | 15 | 9.94 299 | 25 | 0.05 701 | 9.87 613 | 12 | **45** |
| 16 | 9.81 926 | 14 | 9.94 324 | 26 | 0.05 676 | 9.87 601 | 11 | 44 |
| 17 | 9.81 940 | 15 | 9.94 350 | 25 | 0.05 650 | 9.87 590 | 11 | 43 |
| 18 | 9.81 955 | 14 | 9.94 375 | 26 | 0.05 625 | 9.87 579 | 11 | 42 |
| 19 | 9.81 969 | 14 | 9.94 401 | 25 | 0.05 599 | 9.87 568 | 11 | 41 |
| **20** | 9.81 983 | 15 | 9.94 426 | 26 | 0.05 574 | 9.87 557 | 11 | **40** |
| 21 | 9.81 998 | 14 | 9.94 452 | 25 | 0.05 548 | 9.87 546 | 11 | 39 |
| 22 | 9.82 012 | 14 | 9.94 477 | 26 | 0.05 523 | 9.87 535 | 11 | 38 |
| 23 | 9.82 026 | 15 | 9.94 503 | 25 | 0.05 497 | 9.87 524 | 11 | 37 |
| 24 | 9.82 041 | 14 | 9.94 528 | 26 | 0.05 472 | 9.87 513 | 12 | 36 |
| **25** | 9.82 055 | 14 | 9.94 554 | 25 | 0.05 446 | 9.87 501 | 11 | **35** |
| 26 | 9.82 069 | 15 | 9.94 579 | 25 | 0.05 421 | 9.87 490 | 11 | 34 |
| 27 | 9.82 084 | 14 | 9.94 604 | 26 | 0.05 396 | 9.87 479 | 11 | 33 |
| 28 | 9.82 098 | 14 | 9.94 630 | 25 | 0.05 370 | 9.87 468 | 11 | 32 |
| 29 | 9.82 112 | 14 | 9.94 655 | 26 | 0.05 345 | 9.87 457 | 11 | 31 |
| **30** | 9.82 126 | 15 | 9.94 681 | 25 | 0.05 319 | 9.87 446 | 12 | **30** |
| 31 | 9.82 141 | 14 | 9.94 706 | 26 | 0.05 294 | 9.87 434 | 11 | 29 |
| 32 | 9.82 155 | 14 | 9.94 732 | 25 | 0.05 268 | 9.87 423 | 11 | 28 |
| 33 | 9.82 169 | 15 | 9.94 757 | 26 | 0.05 243 | 9.87 412 | 11 | 27 |
| 34 | 9.82 184 | 14 | 9.94 783 | 25 | 0.05 217 | 9.87 401 | 11 | 26 |
| **35** | 9.82 198 | 14 | 9.94 808 | 26 | 0.05 192 | 9.87 390 | 12 | **25** |
| 36 | 9.82 212 | 14 | 9.94 834 | 25 | 0.05 166 | 9.87 378 | 11 | 24 |
| 37 | 9.82 226 | 14 | 9.94 859 | 25 | 0.05 141 | 9.87 367 | 11 | 23 |
| 38 | 9.82 240 | 15 | 9.94 884 | 26 | 0.05 116 | 9.87 356 | 11 | 22 |
| 39 | 9.82 255 | 14 | 9.94 910 | 25 | 0.05 090 | 9.87 345 | 11 | 21 |
| **40** | 9.82 269 | 14 | 9.94 935 | 26 | 0.05 065 | 9.87 334 | 12 | **20** |
| 41 | 9.82 283 | 14 | 9.94 961 | 25 | 0.05 039 | 9.87 322 | 11 | 19 |
| 42 | 9.82 297 | 14 | 9.94 986 | 26 | 0.05 014 | 9.87 311 | 11 | 18 |
| 43 | 9.82 311 | 15 | 9.95 012 | 25 | 0.04 988 | 9.87 300 | 12 | 17 |
| 44 | 9.82 326 | 14 | 9.95 037 | 25 | 0.04 963 | 9.87 288 | 11 | 16 |
| **45** | 9.82 340 | 14 | 9.95 062 | 26 | 0.04 938 | 9.87 277 | 11 | **15** |
| 46 | 9.82 354 | 14 | 9.95 088 | 25 | 0.04 912 | 9.87 266 | 11 | 14 |
| 47 | 9.82 368 | 14 | 9.95 113 | 26 | 0.04 887 | 9.87 255 | 12 | 13 |
| 48 | 9.82 382 | 14 | 9.95 139 | 25 | 0.04 861 | 9.87 243 | 11 | 12 |
| 49 | 9.82 396 | 14 | 9.95 164 | 26 | 0.04 836 | 9.87 232 | 11 | 11 |
| **50** | 9.82 410 | 14 | 9.95 190 | 25 | 0.04 810 | 9.87 221 | 12 | **10** |
| 51 | 9.82 424 | 15 | 9.95 215 | 25 | 0.04 785 | 9.87 209 | 11 | 9 |
| 52 | 9.82 439 | 14 | 9.95 240 | 26 | 0.04 760 | 9.87 198 | 11 | 8 |
| 53 | 9.82 453 | 14 | 9.95 266 | 25 | 0.04 734 | 9.87 187 | 12 | 7 |
| 54 | 9.82 467 | 14 | 9.95 291 | 26 | 0.04 709 | 9.87 175 | 11 | 6 |
| **55** | 9.82 481 | 14 | 9.95 317 | 25 | 0.04 683 | 9.87 164 | 11 | **5** |
| 56 | 9.82 495 | 14 | 9.95 342 | 26 | 0.04 658 | 9.87 153 | 12 | 4 |
| 57 | 9.82 509 | 14 | 9.95 368 | 25 | 0.04 632 | 9.87 141 | 11 | 3 |
| 58 | 9.82 523 | 14 | 9.95 393 | 25 | 0.04 607 | 9.87 130 | 11 | 2 |
| 59 | 9.82 537 | 14 | 9.95 418 | 26 | 0.04 582 | 9.87 119 | 12 | 1 |
| **60** | 9.82 551 | | 9.95 444 | | 0.04 556 | 9.87 107 | | **0** |

## P. P.

| '' | 26 | 25 |
|----|----|----|
| 1 | 0.4 | 0.4 |
| 2 | 0.9 | 0.8 |
| 3 | 1.3 | 1.2 |
| 4 | 1.7 | 1.7 |
| 5 | 2.2 | 2.1 |
| 6 | 2.6 | 2.5 |
| 7 | 3.0 | 2.9 |
| 8 | 3.5 | 3.3 |
| 9 | 3.9 | 3.8 |
| 10 | 4.3 | 4.2 |
| 20 | 8.7 | 8.3 |
| 30 | 13.0 | 12.5 |
| 40 | 17.3 | 16.7 |
| 50 | 21.7 | 20.8 |

| '' | 15 | 14 |
|----|----|----|
| 1 | 0.2 | 0.2 |
| 2 | 0.5 | 0.5 |
| 3 | 0.8 | 0.7 |
| 4 | 1.0 | 0.9 |
| 5 | 1.2 | 1.2 |
| 6 | 1.5 | 1.4 |
| 7 | 1.8 | 1.6 |
| 8 | 2.0 | 1.9 |
| 9 | 2.2 | 2.1 |
| 10 | 2.5 | 2.3 |
| 20 | 5.0 | 4.7 |
| 30 | 7.5 | 7.0 |
| 40 | 10.0 | 9.3 |
| 50 | 12.5 | 11.7 |

| '' | 12 | 11 |
|----|----|----|
| 1 | 0.2 | 0.2 |
| 2 | 0.4 | 0.4 |
| 3 | 0.6 | 0.6 |
| 4 | 0.8 | 0.7 |
| 5 | 1.0 | 0.9 |
| 6 | 1.2 | 1.1 |
| 7 | 1.4 | 1.3 |
| 8 | 1.6 | 1.5 |
| 9 | 1.8 | 1.6 |
| 10 | 2.0 | 1.8 |
| 20 | 4.0 | 3.7 |
| 30 | 6.0 | 5.5 |
| 40 | 8.0 | 7.3 |
| 50 | 10.0 | 9.2 |

| | $\frac{12}{26}$ | $\frac{12}{25}$ | $\frac{11}{25}$ |
|----|----|----|----|
| 0 | 1.1 | 1.1 | 1.1 |
| 1 | 3.2 | 3.1 | 3.4 |
| 2 | 5.4 | 5.2 | 5.7 |
| 3 | 7.6 | 7.3 | 7.9 |
| 4 | 9.8 | 9.4 | 10.2 |
| 5 | 11.9 | 11.5 | 12.5 |
| 6 | 14.1 | 13.5 | 14.8 |
| 7 | 16.2 | 15.6 | 17.1 |
| 8 | 18.4 | 17.7 | 19.3 |
| 9 | 20.6 | 19.8 | 21.6 |
| 10 | 22.8 | 21.9 | 23.9 |
| 11 | 24.9 | 23.9 | |

| ' | L. Cos. | d. | L. Cot. | c.d. | L. Tan. | L. Sin. | P. P. |
|---|---------|----|---------|------|---------|---------|-------|

| ʹ | L. Sin. | d. | L. Tan. | c.d. | L. Cot. | L. Cos. | d. | ʹ |
|---|---|---|---|---|---|---|---|---|
| 0 | 9.82 551 | 14 | 9.95 444 | 25 | 0.04 556 | 9.87 107 | 11 | 60 |
| 1 | 9.82 565 | 14 | 9.95 469 | 26 | 0.04 531 | 9.87 096 | 11 | 59 |
| 2 | 9.82 579 | 14 | 9.95 495 | 25 | 0.04 505 | 9.87 085 | 11 | 58 |
| 3 | 9.82 593 | 14 | 9.95 520 | 25 | 0.04 480 | 9.87 073 | 12 | 57 |
| 4 | 9.82 607 | 14 | 9.95 545 | 26 | 0.04 455 | 9.87 062 | 11 | 56 |
| 5 | 9.82 621 | 14 | 9.95 571 | 25 | 0.04 429 | 9.87 050 | 12 | 55 |
| 6 | 9.82 635 | 14 | 9.95 596 | 26 | 0.04 404 | 9.87 039 | 11 | 54 |
| 7 | 9.82 649 | 14 | 9.95 622 | 25 | 0.04 378 | 9.87 028 | 11 | 53 |
| 8 | 9.82 663 | 14 | 9.95 647 | 25 | 0.04 353 | 9.87 016 | 12 | 52 |
| 9 | 9.82 677 | 14 | 9.95 672 | 26 | 0.04 328 | 9.87 005 | 11 | 51 |
| 10 | 9.82 691 | 14 | 9.95 698 | 25 | 0.04 302 | 9.86 993 | 12 | 50 |
| 11 | 9.82 705 | 14 | 9.95 723 | 25 | 0.04 277 | 9.86 982 | 11 | 49 |
| 12 | 9.82 719 | 14 | 9.95 748 | 26 | 0.04 252 | 9.86 970 | 12 | 48 |
| 13 | 9.82 733 | 14 | 9.95 774 | 25 | 0.04 226 | 9.86 959 | 11 | 47 |
| 14 | 9.82 747 | 14 | 9.95 799 | 26 | 0.04 201 | 9.86 947 | 11 | 46 |
| 15 | 9.82 761 | 14 | 9.95 825 | 25 | 0.04 175 | 9.86 936 | 11 | 45 |
| 16 | 9.82 775 | 13 | 9.95 850 | 25 | 0.04 150 | 9.86 924 | 12 | 44 |
| 17 | 9.82 788 | 14 | 9.95 875 | 26 | 0.04 125 | 9.86 913 | 11 | 43 |
| 18 | 9.82 802 | 14 | 9.95 901 | 25 | 0.04 099 | 9.86 902 | 11 | 42 |
| 19 | 9.82 816 | 14 | 9.95 926 | 26 | 0.04 074 | 9.86 890 | 12 | 41 |
| 20 | 9.82 830 | 14 | 9.95 952 | 25 | 0.04 048 | 9.86 879 | 11 | 40 |
| 21 | 9.82 844 | 14 | 9.95 977 | 25 | 0.04 023 | 9.86 867 | 12 | 39 |
| 22 | 9.82 858 | 14 | 9.96 002 | 26 | 0.03 998 | 9.86 855 | 11 | 38 |
| 23 | 9.82 872 | 13 | 9.96 028 | 25 | 0.03 972 | 9.86 844 | 11 | 37 |
| 24 | 9.82 885 | 14 | 9.96 053 | 25 | 0.03 947 | 9.86 832 | 12 | 36 |
| 25 | 9.82 899 | 14 | 9.96 078 | 26 | 0.03 922 | 9.86 821 | 11 | 35 |
| 26 | 9.82 913 | 14 | 9.96 104 | 25 | 0.03 896 | 9.86 809 | 12 | 34 |
| 27 | 9.82 927 | 14 | 9.96 129 | 26 | 0.03 871 | 9.86 798 | 11 | 33 |
| 28 | 9.82 941 | 14 | 9.96 155 | 25 | 0.03 845 | 9.86 786 | 12 | 32 |
| 29 | 9.82 955 | 13 | 9.96 180 | 25 | 0.03 820 | 9.86 775 | 11 | 31 |
| 30 | 9.82 968 | 14 | 9.96 205 | 26 | 0.03 795 | 9.86 763 | 12 | 30 |
| 31 | 9.82 982 | 14 | 9.96 231 | 25 | 0.03 769 | 9.86 752 | 11 | 29 |
| 32 | 9.82 996 | 14 | 9.96 256 | 25 | 0.03 744 | 9.86 740 | 12 | 28 |
| 33 | 9.83 010 | 14 | 9.96 281 | 26 | 0.03 719 | 9.86 728 | 11 | 27 |
| 34 | 9.83 023 | 14 | 9.96 307 | 25 | 0.03 693 | 9.86 717 | 12 | 26 |
| 35 | 9.83 037 | 14 | 9.96 332 | 25 | 0.03 668 | 9.86 705 | 11 | 25 |
| 36 | 9.83 051 | 14 | 9.96 357 | 26 | 0.03 643 | 9.86 694 | 12 | 24 |
| 37 | 9.83 065 | 13 | 9.96 383 | 25 | 0.03 617 | 9.86 682 | 12 | 23 |
| 38 | 9.83 078 | 14 | 9.96 408 | 25 | 0.03 592 | 9.86 670 | 11 | 22 |
| 39 | 9.83 092 | 14 | 9.96 433 | 26 | 0.03 567 | 9.86 659 | 12 | 21 |
| 40 | 9.83 106 | 14 | 9.96 459 | 25 | 0.03 541 | 9.86 647 | 11 | 20 |
| 41 | 9.83 120 | 13 | 9.96 484 | 26 | 0.03 516 | 9.86 635 | 12 | 19 |
| 42 | 9.83 133 | 14 | 9.96 510 | 25 | 0.03 490 | 9.86 624 | 11 | 18 |
| 43 | 9.83 147 | 14 | 9.96 535 | 25 | 0.03 465 | 9.86 612 | 12 | 17 |
| 44 | 9.83 161 | 13 | 9.96 560 | 26 | 0.03 440 | 9.86 600 | 11 | 16 |
| 45 | 9.83 174 | 14 | 9.96 586 | 25 | 0.03 414 | 9.86 589 | 12 | 15 |
| 46 | 9.83 188 | 14 | 9.96 611 | 25 | 0.03 389 | 9.86 577 | 12 | 14 |
| 47 | 9.83 202 | 13 | 9.96 636 | 26 | 0.03 364 | 9.86 565 | 11 | 13 |
| 48 | 9.83 215 | 14 | 9.96 662 | 25 | 0.03 338 | 9.86 554 | 12 | 12 |
| 49 | 9.83 229 | 13 | 9.96 687 | 25 | 0.03 313 | 9.86 542 | 12 | 11 |
| 50 | 9.83 242 | 14 | 9.96 712 | 26 | 0.03 288 | 9.86 530 | 12 | 10 |
| 51 | 9.83 256 | 14 | 9.96 738 | 25 | 0.03 262 | 9.86 518 | 11 | 9 |
| 52 | 9.83 270 | 13 | 9.96 763 | 25 | 0.03 237 | 9.86 507 | 12 | 8 |
| 53 | 9.83 283 | 14 | 9.96 788 | 26 | 0.03 212 | 9.86 495 | 12 | 7 |
| 54 | 9.83 297 | 13 | 9.96 814 | 25 | 0.03 186 | 9.86 483 | 11 | 6 |
| 55 | 9.83 310 | 14 | 9.96 839 | 25 | 0.03 161 | 9.86 472 | 12 | 5 |
| 56 | 9.83 324 | 14 | 9.96 864 | 26 | 0.03 136 | 9.86 460 | 12 | 4 |
| 57 | 9.83 338 | 13 | 9.96 890 | 25 | 0.03 110 | 9.86 448 | 12 | 3 |
| 58 | 9.83 351 | 14 | 9.96 915 | 25 | 0.03 085 | 9.86 436 | 12 | 2 |
| 59 | 9.83 365 | 13 | 9.96 940 | 26 | 0.03 060 | 9.86 425 | 12 | 1 |
| 60 | 9.83 378 | | 9.96 966 | | 0.03 034 | 9.86 413 | 12 | 0 |
| ʺ | L. Cos. | d. | L. Cot. | c.d. | L. Tan. | L. Sin. | d. | ʹ |

## P. P.

| | 26 | 25 |
|---|---|---|
| 1 | 0.4 | 0.4 |
| 2 | 0.9 | 0.8 |
| 3 | 1.3 | 1.2 |
| 4 | 1.7 | 1.7 |
| 5 | 2.2 | 2.1 |
| 6 | 2.6 | 2.5 |
| 7 | 3.0 | 2.9 |
| 8 | 3.5 | 3.3 |
| 9 | 3.9 | 3.8 |
| 10 | 4.3 | 4.2 |
| 20 | 8.7 | 8.3 |
| 30 | 13.0 | 12.5 |
| 40 | 17.3 | 16.7 |
| 50 | 21.7 | 20.8 |

| | 14 | 13 |
|---|---|---|
| 1 | 0.2 | 0.2 |
| 2 | 0.5 | 0.4 |
| 3 | 0.7 | 0.6 |
| 4 | 0.9 | 0.9 |
| 5 | 1.2 | 1.1 |
| 6 | 1.4 | 1.3 |
| 7 | 1.6 | 1.5 |
| 8 | 1.9 | 1.7 |
| 9 | 2.1 | 2.0 |
| 10 | 2.3 | 2.2 |
| 20 | 4.7 | 4.3 |
| 30 | 7.0 | 6.5 |
| 40 | 9.3 | 8.7 |
| 50 | 11.7 | 10.8 |

| | 12 | 11 |
|---|---|---|
| 1 | 0.2 | 0.2 |
| 2 | 0.4 | 0.4 |
| 3 | 0.6 | 0.6 |
| 4 | 0.8 | 0.7 |
| 5 | 1.0 | 0.9 |
| 6 | 1.2 | 1.1 |
| 7 | 1.4 | 1.3 |
| 8 | 1.6 | 1.5 |
| 9 | 1.8 | 1.6 |
| 10 | 2.0 | 1.8 |
| 20 | 4.0 | 3.7 |
| 30 | 6.0 | 5.5 |
| 40 | 8.0 | 7.3 |
| 50 | 10.0 | 9.2 |

| | 12 / 26 | 11 / 26 | 11 / 25 |
|---|---|---|---|
| 0 | | | |
| 1 | 1.1 | 1.2 | 1.1 |
| 2 | 3.2 | 3.5 | 3.4 |
| 3 | 5.4 | 5.9 | 5.7 |
| 4 | 7.6 | 8.3 | 7.9 |
| 5 | 9.8 | 10.6 | 10.2 |
| 6 | 11.9 | 13.0 | 12.5 |
| 7 | 14.1 | 15.4 | 14.8 |
| 8 | 16.2 | 17.7 | 17.1 |
| 9 | 18.4 | 20.1 | 19.3 |
| 10 | 20.6 | 22.5 | 21.6 |
| 11 | 22.8 | 24.8 | 23.0 |
| 12 | 24.9 | — | — |

# LOGARITHMS OF THE FUNCTIONS (Continued)

43° (223°)   (316°) 136°

| ′ | L. Sin. | d. | L. Tan. | c.d. | L. Cot. | L. Cos. | d. | ′ |
|---|---------|----|---------|------|---------|---------|----|---|
| 0 | 9.83 378 | 14 | 9.96 966 | 25 | 0.03 034 | 9.86 413 | 12 | 60 |
| 1 | 9.83 392 | 13 | 9.96 991 | 25 | 0.03 009 | 9.86 401 | 12 | 59 |
| 2 | 9.83 405 | 14 | 9.97 016 | 25 | 0.02 984 | 9.86 389 | 12 | 58 |
| 3 | 9.83 419 | 13 | 9.97 042 | 26 | 0.02 958 | 9.86 377 | 11 | 57 |
| 4 | 9.83 432 | 14 | 9.97 067 | 25 | 0.02 933 | 9.86 366 | 12 | 56 |
| 5 | 9.83 446 | 13 | 9.97 092 | 26 | 0.02 908 | 9.86 354 | 12 | 55 |
| 6 | 9.83 459 | 14 | 9.97 118 | 25 | 0.02 882 | 9.86 342 | 12 | 54 |
| 7 | 9.83 473 | 13 | 9.97 143 | 25 | 0.02 857 | 9.86 330 | 12 | 53 |
| 8 | 9.83 486 | 14 | 9.97 168 | 25 | 0.02 832 | 9.86 318 | 12 | 52 |
| 9 | 9.83 500 | 13 | 9.97 193 | 26 | 0.02 807 | 9.86 306 | 12 | 51 |
| 10 | 9.83 513 | 14 | 9.97 219 | 25 | 0.02 781 | 9.86 295 | 11 | 50 |
| 11 | 9.83 527 | 13 | 9.97 244 | 25 | 0.02 756 | 9.86 283 | 12 | 49 |
| 12 | 9.83 540 | 14 | 9.97 269 | 26 | 0.02 731 | 9.86 271 | 12 | 48 |
| 13 | 9.83 554 | 13 | 9.97 295 | 25 | 0.02 705 | 9.86 259 | 12 | 47 |
| 14 | 9.83 567 | 14 | 9.97 320 | 25 | 0.02 680 | 9.86 247 | 12 | 46 |
| 15 | 9.83 581 | 13 | 9.97 345 | 26 | 0.02 655 | 9.86 235 | 12 | 45 |
| 16 | 9.83 594 | 14 | 9.97 371 | 25 | 0.02 629 | 9.86 223 | 12 | 44 |
| 17 | 9.83 608 | 13 | 9.97 396 | 25 | 0.02 604 | 9.86 211 | 11 | 43 |
| 18 | 9.83 621 | 13 | 9.97 421 | 26 | 0.02 579 | 9.86 200 | 12 | 42 |
| 19 | 9.83 634 | 14 | 9.97 447 | 25 | 0.02 553 | 9.86 188 | 12 | 41 |
| 20 | 9.83 648 | 13 | 9.97 472 | 25 | 0.02 528 | 9.86 176 | 12 | 40 |
| 21 | 9.83 661 | 13 | 9.97 497 | 26 | 0.02 503 | 9.86 164 | 12 | 39 |
| 22 | 9.83 674 | 14 | 9.97 523 | 25 | 0.02 477 | 9.86 152 | 12 | 38 |
| 23 | 9.83 688 | 13 | 9.97 548 | 25 | 0.02 452 | 9.86 140 | 12 | 37 |
| 24 | 9.83 701 | 14 | 9.97 573 | 25 | 0.02 427 | 9.86 128 | 12 | 36 |
| 25 | 9.83 715 | 13 | 9.97 598 | 26 | 0.02 402 | 9.86 116 | 12 | 35 |
| 26 | 9.83 728 | 13 | 9.97 624 | 25 | 0.02 376 | 9.86 104 | 12 | 34 |
| 27 | 9.83 741 | 14 | 9.97 649 | 25 | 0.02 351 | 9.86 092 | 12 | 33 |
| 28 | 9.83 755 | 13 | 9.97 674 | 26 | 0.02 326 | 9.86 080 | 12 | 32 |
| 29 | 9.83 768 | 13 | 9.97 700 | 25 | 0.02 300 | 9.86 068 | 12 | 31 |
| 30 | 9.83 781 | 14 | 9.97 725 | 25 | 0.02 275 | 9.86 056 | 12 | 30 |
| 31 | 9.83 795 | 13 | 9.97 750 | 26 | 0.02 250 | 9.86 044 | 12 | 29 |
| 32 | 9.83 808 | 13 | 9.97 776 | 25 | 0.02 224 | 9.86 032 | 12 | 28 |
| 33 | 9.83 821 | 13 | 9.97 801 | 25 | 0.02 199 | 9.86 020 | 12 | 27 |
| 34 | 9.83 834 | 14 | 9.97 826 | 25 | 0.02 174 | 9.86 008 | 12 | 26 |
| 35 | 9.83 848 | 13 | 9.97 851 | 26 | 0.02 149 | 9.85 996 | 12 | 25 |
| 36 | 9.83 861 | 13 | 9.97 877 | 25 | 0.02 123 | 9.85 984 | 12 | 24 |
| 37 | 9.83 874 | 13 | 9.97 902 | 25 | 0.02 098 | 9.85 972 | 12 | 23 |
| 38 | 9.83 887 | 13 | 9.97 927 | 26 | 0.02 073 | 9.85 960 | 12 | 22 |
| 39 | 9.83 901 | 14 | 9.97 953 | 25 | 0.02 047 | 9.85 948 | 12 | 21 |
| 40 | 9.83 914 | 13 | 9.97 978 | 25 | 0.02 022 | 9.85 936 | 12 | 20 |
| 41 | 9.83 927 | 13 | 9.98 003 | 26 | 0.01 997 | 9.85 924 | 12 | 19 |
| 42 | 9.83 940 | 13 | 9.98 029 | 25 | 0.01 971 | 9.85 912 | 12 | 18 |
| 43 | 9.83 954 | 14 | 9.98 054 | 25 | 0.01 946 | 9.85 900 | 12 | 17 |
| 44 | 9.83 967 | 13 | 9.98 079 | 25 | 0.01 921 | 9.85 888 | 12 | 16 |
| 45 | 9.83 980 | 13 | 9.98 104 | 26 | 0.01 896 | 9.85 876 | 12 | 15 |
| 46 | 9.83 993 | 13 | 9.98 130 | 25 | 0.01 870 | 9.85 864 | 13 | 14 |
| 47 | 9.84 006 | 13 | 9.98 155 | 25 | 0.01 845 | 9.85 851 | 12 | 13 |
| 48 | 9.84 020 | 14 | 9.98 180 | 26 | 0.01 820 | 9.85 839 | 12 | 12 |
| 49 | 9.84 033 | 13 | 9.98 206 | 25 | 0.01 794 | 9.85 827 | 12 | 11 |
| 50 | 9.84 046 | 13 | 9.98 231 | 25 | 0.01 769 | 9.85 815 | 12 | 10 |
| 51 | 9.84 059 | 13 | 9.98 256 | 25 | 0.01 744 | 9.85 803 | 12 | 9 |
| 52 | 9.84 072 | 13 | 9.98 281 | 26 | 0.01 719 | 9.85 791 | 12 | 8 |
| 53 | 9.84 085 | 13 | 9.98 307 | 25 | 0.01 693 | 9.85 779 | 13 | 7 |
| 54 | 9.84 098 | 14 | 9.98 332 | 25 | 0.01 668 | 9.85 766 | 12 | 6 |
| 55 | 9.84 112 | 13 | 9.98 357 | 26 | 0.01 643 | 9.85 754 | 12 | 5 |
| 56 | 9.84 125 | 13 | 9.98 383 | 25 | 0.01 617 | 9.85 742 | 12 | 4 |
| 57 | 9.84 138 | 13 | 9.98 408 | 25 | 0.01 592 | 9.85 730 | 12 | 3 |
| 58 | 9.84 151 | 13 | 9.98 433 | 25 | 0.01 567 | 9.85 718 | 12 | 2 |
| 59 | 9.84 164 | 13 | 9.98 458 | 26 | 0.01 542 | 9.85 706 | 13 | 1 |
| 60 | 9.84 177 |    | 9.98 484 |    | 0.01 516 | 9.85 693 |    | 0 |

|   | L. Cos. | d. | L. Cot. | c.d. | L. Tan. | L. Sin. | d. | ′ |

## P. P.

| ″ | 26 | 25 |
|---|----|----|
| 1 | 0.4 | 0.4 |
| 2 | 0.9 | 0.8 |
| 3 | 1.3 | 1.2 |
| 4 | 1.7 | 1.7 |
| 5 | 2.2 | 2.1 |
| 6 | 2.6 | 2.5 |
| 7 | 3.0 | 2.9 |
| 8 | 3.5 | 3.3 |
| 9 | 3.9 | 3.8 |
| 10 | 4.3 | 4.2 |
| 20 | 8.7 | 8.3 |
| 30 | 13.0 | 12.5 |
| 40 | 17.3 | 16.7 |
| 50 | 21.7 | 20.8 |

| ″ | 14 | 13 |
|---|----|----|
| 1 | 0.2 | 0.2 |
| 2 | 0.5 | 0.4 |
| 3 | 0.7 | 0.6 |
| 4 | 0.9 | 0.9 |
| 5 | 1.2 | 1.1 |
| 6 | 1.4 | 1.3 |
| 7 | 1.6 | 1.5 |
| 8 | 1.9 | 1.7 |
| 9 | 2.1 | 2.0 |
| 10 | 2.3 | 2.2 |
| 20 | 4.7 | 4.3 |
| 30 | 7.0 | 6.5 |
| 40 | 9.3 | 8.7 |
| 50 | 11.7 | 10.8 |

| ″ | 12 | 11 |
|---|----|----|
| 1 | 0.2 | 0.2 |
| 2 | 0.4 | 0.4 |
| 3 | 0.6 | 0.6 |
| 4 | 0.8 | 0.7 |
| 5 | 1.0 | 0.9 |
| 6 | 1.2 | 1.1 |
| 7 | 1.4 | 1.3 |
| 8 | 1.6 | 1.5 |
| 9 | 1.8 | 1.6 |
| 10 | 2.0 | 1.8 |
| 20 | 4.0 | 3.7 |
| 30 | 6.0 | 5.5 |
| 40 | 8.0 | 7.3 |
| 50 | 10.0 | 9.2 |

|    | 13 | 13 | 12 |
|----|----|----|----|
|    | 26 | 25 | 25 |
| 0 | 1.0 | 0.9 | 1.1 |
| 1 | 3.0 | 2.9 | 3.1 |
| 2 | 5.0 | 4.8 | 5.2 |
| 3 | 7.0 | 6.7 | 7.3 |
| 4 | 9.0 | 8.7 | 9.4 |
| 5 | 11.0 | 10.6 | 11.5 |
| 6 | 13.0 | 12.5 | 13.5 |
| 7 | 15.0 | 14.4 | 15.6 |
| 8 | 17.0 | 16.3 | 17.7 |
| 9 | 19.0 | 18.3 | 19.8 |
| 10 | 21.0 | 20.2 | 21.9 |
| 11 | 23.0 | 22.1 | 23.9 |
| 12 | 25.0 | 24.1 | — |

133° (313°)   (226°) 46°

# LOGARITHMS OF THE FUNCTIONS (Continued)

| ' | L. Sin. | d. | L. Tan. | c.d. | L. Cot. | L. Cos. | d. | ' |
|---|---------|----|---------|------|---------|---------|----|---|
| 0 | 9.84 177 | 13 | 9.98 484 | 25 | 0.01 516 | 9.85 693 | 12 | 60 |
| 1 | 9.84 190 | 13 | 9.98 509 | 25 | 0.01 491 | 9.85 681 | 12 | 59 |
| 2 | 9.84 203 | 13 | 9.98 534 | 26 | 0.01 466 | 9.85 669 | 12 | 58 |
| 3 | 9.84 216 | 13 | 9.98 560 | 25 | 0.01 440 | 9.85 657 | 12 | 57 |
| 4 | 9.84 229 | 13 | 9.98 585 | 25 | 0.01 415 | 9.85 645 | 13/12 | 56 |
| 5 | 9.84 242 | 13 | 9.98 610 | 25 | 0.01 390 | 9.85 632 | 12 | 55 |
| 6 | 9.84 255 | 14 | 9.98 635 | 26 | 0.01 365 | 9.85 620 | 12 | 54 |
| 7 | 9.84 269 | 13 | 9.98 661 | 25 | 0.01 339 | 9.85 608 | 12 | 53 |
| 8 | 9.84 282 | 13 | 9.98 686 | 25 | 0.01 314 | 9.85 596 | 13 | 52 |
| 9 | 9.84 295 | 13 | 9.98 711 | 26 | 0.01 289 | 9.85 583 | 12 | 51 |
| 10 | 9.84 308 | 13 | 9.98 737 | 25 | 0.01 263 | 9.85 571 | 12 | 50 |
| 11 | 9.84 321 | 13 | 9.98 762 | 25 | 0.01 238 | 9.85 559 | 12 | 49 |
| 12 | 9.84 334 | 13 | 9.98 787 | 25 | 0.01 213 | 9.85 547 | 13 | 48 |
| 13 | 9.84 347 | 13 | 9.98 812 | 26 | 0.01 188 | 9.85 534 | 12 | 47 |
| 14 | 9.84 360 | 13 | 9.98 838 | 25 | 0.01 162 | 9.85 522 | 12 | 46 |
| 15 | 9.84 373 | 12 | 9.98 863 | 25 | 0.01 137 | 9.85 510 | 13 | 45 |
| 16 | 9.84 385 | 13 | 9.98 888 | 25 | 0.01 112 | 9.85 497 | 12 | 44 |
| 17 | 9.84 398 | 13 | 9.98 913 | 26 | 0.01 087 | 9.85 485 | 12 | 43 |
| 18 | 9.84 411 | 13 | 9.98 939 | 25 | 0.01 061 | 9.85 473 | 13 | 42 |
| 19 | 9.84 424 | 13 | 9.98 964 | 25 | 0.01 036 | 9.85 460 | 12 | 41 |
| 20 | 9.84 437 | 13 | 9.98 989 | 26 | 0.01 011 | 9.85 448 | 12 | 40 |
| 21 | 9.84 450 | 13 | 9.99 015 | 25 | 0.00 985 | 9.85 436 | 13 | 39 |
| 22 | 9.84 463 | 13 | 9.99 040 | 25 | 0.00 960 | 9.85 423 | 12 | 38 |
| 23 | 9.84 476 | 13 | 9.99 065 | 25 | 0.00 935 | 9.85 411 | 12 | 37 |
| 24 | 9.84 489 | 13 | 9.99 090 | 26 | 0.00 910 | 9.85 399 | 13 | 36 |
| 25 | 9.84 502 | 13 | 9.99 116 | 25 | 0.00 884 | 9.85 386 | 12 | 35 |
| 26 | 9.84 515 | 13 | 9.99 141 | 25 | 0.00 859 | 9.85 374 | 13 | 34 |
| 27 | 9.84 528 | 12 | 9.99 166 | 25 | 0.00 834 | 9.85 361 | 12 | 33 |
| 28 | 9.84 540 | 13 | 9.99 191 | 26 | 0.00 809 | 9.85 349 | 12 | 32 |
| 29 | 9.84 553 | 13 | 9.99 217 | 25 | 0.00 783 | 9.85 337 | 13 | 31 |
| 30 | 9.84 566 | 13 | 9.99 242 | 25 | 0.00 758 | 9.85 324 | 12 | 30 |
| 31 | 9.84 579 | 13 | 9.99 267 | 26 | 0.00 733 | 9.85 312 | 13 | 29 |
| 32 | 9.84 592 | 13 | 9.99 293 | 25 | 0.00 707 | 9.85 299 | 12 | 28 |
| 33 | 9.84 605 | 13 | 9.99 318 | 25 | 0.00 682 | 9.85 287 | 13 | 27 |
| 34 | 9.84 618 | 12 | 9.99 343 | 25 | 0.00 657 | 9.85 274 | 12 | 26 |
| 35 | 9.84 630 | 13 | 9.99 368 | 26 | 0.00 632 | 9.85 262 | 12 | 25 |
| 36 | 9.84 643 | 13 | 9.99 394 | 25 | 0.00 606 | 9.85 250 | 13 | 24 |
| 37 | 9.84 656 | 13 | 9.99 419 | 25 | 0.00 581 | 9.85 237 | 12 | 23 |
| 38 | 9.84 669 | 13 | 9.99 444 | 25 | 0.00 556 | 9.85 225 | 13 | 22 |
| 39 | 9.84 682 | 12 | 9.99 469 | 26 | 0.00 531 | 9.85 212 | 12 | 21 |
| 40 | 9.84 694 | 13 | 9.99 495 | 25 | 0.00 505 | 9.85 200 | 13 | 20 |
| 41 | 9.84 707 | 13 | 9.99 520 | 25 | 0.00 480 | 9.85 187 | 12 | 19 |
| 42 | 9.84 720 | 13 | 9.99 545 | 25 | 0.00 455 | 9.85 175 | 13 | 18 |
| 43 | 9.84 733 | 12 | 9.99 570 | 26 | 0.00 430 | 9.85 162 | 12 | 17 |
| 44 | 9.84 745 | 13 | 9.99 596 | 25 | 0.00 404 | 9.85 150 | 13 | 16 |
| 45 | 9.84 758 | 13 | 9.99 621 | 25 | 0.00 379 | 9.85 137 | 12 | 15 |
| 46 | 9.84 771 | 13 | 9.99 646 | 26 | 0.00 354 | 9.85 125 | 13 | 14 |
| 47 | 9.84 784 | 12 | 9.99 672 | 25 | 0.00 328 | 9.85 112 | 12 | 13 |
| 48 | 9.84 796 | 13 | 9.99 697 | 25 | 0.00 303 | 9.85 100 | 13 | 12 |
| 49 | 9.84 809 | 13 | 9.99 722 | 25 | 0.00 278 | 9.85 087 | 13 | 11 |
| 50 | 9.84 822 | 13 | 9.99 747 | 26 | 0.00 253 | 9.85 074 | 12 | 10 |
| 51 | 9.84 835 | 12 | 9.99 773 | 25 | 0.00 227 | 9.85 062 | 13 | 9 |
| 52 | 9.84 847 | 13 | 9.99 798 | 25 | 0.00 202 | 9.85 049 | 12 | 8 |
| 53 | 9.84 860 | 13 | 9.99 823 | 25 | 0.00 177 | 9.85 037 | 13 | 7 |
| 54 | 9.84 873 | 12 | 9.99 848 | 26 | 0.00 152 | 9.85 024 | 12 | 6 |
| 55 | 9.84 885 | 13 | 9.99 874 | 25 | 0.00 126 | 9.85 012 | 13 | 5 |
| 56 | 9.84 898 | 13 | 9.99 899 | 25 | 0.00 101 | 9.84 999 | 13 | 4 |
| 57 | 9.84 911 | 12 | 9.99 924 | 25 | 0.00 076 | 9.84 986 | 12 | 3 |
| 58 | 9.84 923 | 13 | 9.99 949 | 26 | 0.00 051 | 9.84 974 | 13 | 2 |
| 59 | 9.84 936 | 13 | 9.99 975 | 25 | 0.00 025 | 9.84 961 | 12 | 1 |
| 60 | 9.84 949 |  | 0.00 000 |  | 0.00 000 | 9.84 949 |  | 0 |

| ' | L. Cos. | d. | L. Cot. | c.d. | L. Tan. | L. Sin. | d. | ' |

**P. P.**

| | 26 | 25 |
|---|---|---|
| 1 | 0.4 | 0.4 |
| 2 | 0.9 | 0.8 |
| 3 | 1.3 | 1.2 |
| 4 | 1.7 | 1.7 |
| 5 | 2.2 | 2.1 |
| 6 | 2.6 | 2.5 |
| 7 | 3.0 | 2.9 |
| 8 | 3.5 | 3.3 |
| 9 | 3.9 | 3.8 |
| 10 | 4.3 | 4.2 |
| 20 | 8.7 | 8.3 |
| 30 | 13.0 | 12.5 |
| 40 | 17.3 | 16.7 |
| 50 | 21.7 | 20.8 |

| | 14 | 13 | 12 |
|---|---|---|---|
| 1 | 0.2 | 0.2 | 0.2 |
| 2 | 0.5 | 0.4 | 0.4 |
| 3 | 0.7 | 0.6 | 0.6 |
| 4 | 0.9 | 0.9 | 0.8 |
| 5 | 1.2 | 1.1 | 1.0 |
| 6 | 1.4 | 1.3 | 1.2 |
| 7 | 1.6 | 1.5 | 1.4 |
| 8 | 1.9 | 1.7 | 1.6 |
| 9 | 2.1 | 2.0 | 1.8 |
| 10 | 2.3 | 2.2 | 2.0 |
| 20 | 4.7 | 4.3 | 4.0 |
| 30 | 7.0 | 6.5 | 6.0 |
| 40 | 9.3 | 8.7 | 8.0 |
| 50 | 11.7 | 10.8 | 10.0 |

| | 13/26 | 13/25 |
|---|---|---|
| 0 | 1.0 | 0.9 |
| 1 | 3.0 | 2.9 |
| 2 | 5.0 | 4.8 |
| 3 | 7.0 | 6.7 |
| 4 | 9.0 | 8.7 |
| 5 | 11.0 | 10.6 |
| 6 | 13.0 | 12.5 |
| 7 | 15.0 | 14.4 |
| 8 | 17.0 | 16.3 |
| 9 | 19.0 | 18.3 |
| 10 | 21.0 | 20.2 |
| 11 | 23.0 | 22.1 |
| 12 | 25.0 | 24.1 |
| 13 | | |

| | 12/26 | 12/25 |
|---|---|---|
| 0 | 1.1 | 1.1 |
| 1 | 3.2 | 3.1 |
| 2 | 5.4 | 5.2 |
| 3 | 7.6 | 7.3 |
| 4 | 9.8 | 9.4 |
| 5 | 11.9 | 11.5 |
| 6 | 14.1 | 13.5 |
| 7 | 16.2 | 15.6 |
| 8 | 18.4 | 17.7 |
| 9 | 20.6 | 19.8 |
| 10 | 22.8 | 21.9 |
| 11 | 24.9 | 23.9 |
| 12 | | |

# NATURAL FUNCTIONS

| ′ | Sin | Tan | Cot | Cos | ′ | | ′ | Sin | Tan | Cot | Cos | ′ |
|---|---|---|---|---|---|---|---|---|---|---|---|---|
| **0** | .00000 | .00000 | ——— | 1.0000 | **60** | | **0** | .01745 | .01746 | 57.290 | .99985 | **60** |
| 1 | .00029 | .00029 | 3437.7 | 1.0000 | 59 | | 1 | .01774 | .01775 | 56.351 | .99984 | 59 |
| 2 | .00058 | .00058 | 1718.9 | 1.0000 | 58 | | 2 | .01803 | .01804 | 55.442 | .99984 | 58 |
| 3 | .00087 | .00087 | 1145.9 | 1.0000 | 57 | | 3 | .01832 | .01833 | 54.561 | .99983 | 57 |
| 4 | .00116 | .00116 | 859.44 | 1.0000 | 56 | | 4 | .01862 | .01862 | 53.709 | .99983 | 56 |
| **5** | .00145 | .00145 | 687.55 | 1.0000 | **55** | | **5** | .01891 | .01891 | 52.882 | .99982 | **55** |
| 6 | .00175 | .00175 | 572.96 | 1.0000 | 54 | | 6 | .01920 | .01920 | 52.081 | .99982 | 54 |
| 7 | .00204 | .00204 | 491.11 | 1.0000 | 53 | | 7 | .01949 | .01949 | 51.303 | .99981 | 53 |
| 8 | .00233 | .00233 | 429.72 | 1.0000 | 52 | | 8 | .01978 | .01978 | 50.549 | .99980 | 52 |
| 9 | .00262 | .00262 | 381.97 | 1.0000 | 51 | | 9 | .02007 | .02007 | 49.816 | .99980 | 51 |
| **10** | .00291 | .00291 | 343.77 | 1.0000 | **50** | | **10** | .02036 | .02036 | 49.104 | .99979 | **50** |
| 11 | .00320 | .00320 | 312.52 | .99999 | 49 | | 11 | .02065 | .02066 | 48.312 | .99979 | 49 |
| 12 | .00349 | .00349 | 286.48 | .99999 | 48 | | 12 | .02094 | .02095 | 47.740 | .99978 | 48 |
| 13 | .00378 | .00378 | 264.44 | .99999 | 47 | | 13 | .02123 | .02124 | 47.085 | .99977 | 47 |
| 14 | .00407 | .00407 | 245.55 | .99999 | 46 | | 14 | .02152 | .02153 | 46.449 | .99977 | 46 |
| **15** | .00436 | .00436 | 229.18 | .99999 | **45** | | **15** | .02181 | .02182 | 45.829 | .99976 | **45** |
| 16 | .00465 | .00465 | 214.86 | .99999 | 44 | | 16 | .02211 | .02211 | 45.226 | .99976 | 44 |
| 17 | .00495 | .00495 | 202.22 | .99999 | 43 | | 17 | .02240 | .02240 | 44.639 | .99975 | 43 |
| 18 | .00524 | .00524 | 190.98 | .99999 | 42 | | 18 | .02269 | .02269 | 44.066 | .99974 | 42 |
| 19 | .00553 | .00553 | 180.93 | .99998 | 41 | | 19 | .02298 | .02298 | 43.508 | .99974 | 41 |
| **20** | .00582 | .00582 | 171.89 | .99998 | **40** | | **20** | .02327 | .02328 | 42.964 | .99973 | **40** |
| 21 | .00611 | .00611 | 163.70 | .99998 | 39 | | 21 | .02356 | .02357 | 42.433 | .99972 | 39 |
| 22 | .00640 | .00640 | 156.26 | .99998 | 38 | | 22 | .02385 | .02386 | 41.916 | .99972 | 38 |
| 23 | .00669 | .00669 | 149.47 | .99998 | 37 | | 23 | .02414 | .02415 | 41.411 | .99971 | 37 |
| 24 | .00698 | .00698 | 143.24 | .99998 | 36 | | 24 | .02443 | .02444 | 40.917 | .99970 | 36 |
| **25** | .00727 | .00727 | 137.51 | .99997 | **35** | | **25** | .02472 | .02473 | 40.436 | .99969 | **35** |
| 26 | .00756 | .00756 | 132.22 | .99997 | 34 | | 26 | .02501 | .02502 | 39.965 | .99969 | 34 |
| 27 | .00785 | .00785 | 127.32 | .99997 | 33 | | 27 | .02530 | .02531 | 39.506 | .99968 | 33 |
| 28 | .00814 | .00815 | 122.77 | .99997 | 32 | | 28 | .02560 | .02560 | 39.057 | .99967 | 32 |
| 29 | .00844 | .00844 | 118.54 | .99996 | 31 | | 29 | .02589 | .02589 | 38.618 | .99966 | 31 |
| **30** | .00873 | .00873 | 114.59 | .99996 | **30** | | **30** | .02618 | .02619 | 38.188 | .99966 | **30** |
| 31 | .00902 | .00902 | 110.89 | .99996 | 29 | | 31 | .02647 | .02648 | 37.769 | .99965 | 29 |
| 32 | .00931 | .00931 | 107.43 | .99996 | 28 | | 32 | .02676 | .02677 | 37.358 | .99964 | 28 |
| 33 | .00960 | .00960 | 104.17 | .99995 | 27 | | 33 | .02705 | .02706 | 36.956 | .99963 | 27 |
| 34 | .00989 | .00989 | 101.11 | .99995 | 26 | | 34 | .02734 | .02735 | 36.563 | .99963 | 26 |
| **35** | .01018 | .01018 | 98.218 | .99995 | **25** | | **35** | .02763 | .02764 | 36.178 | .99962 | **25** |
| 36 | .01047 | .01047 | 95.489 | .99995 | 24 | | 36 | .02792 | .02793 | 35.801 | .99961 | 24 |
| 37 | .01076 | .01076 | 92.908 | .99994 | 23 | | 37 | .02821 | .02822 | 35.431 | .99960 | 23 |
| 38 | .01105 | .01105 | 90.463 | .99994 | 22 | | 38 | .02850 | .02851 | 35.070 | .99959 | 22 |
| 39 | .01134 | .01135 | 88.144 | .99994 | 21 | | 39 | .02879 | .02881 | 34.715 | .99959 | 21 |
| **40** | .01164 | .01164 | 85.940 | .99993 | **20** | | **40** | .02908 | .02910 | 34.368 | .99958 | **20** |
| 41 | .01193 | .01193 | 83.844 | .99993 | 19 | | 41 | .02938 | .02939 | 34.027 | .99957 | 19 |
| 42 | .01222 | .01222 | 81.847 | .99993 | 18 | | 42 | .02967 | .02968 | 33.694 | .99956 | 18 |
| 43 | .01251 | .01251 | 79.943 | .99992 | 17 | | 43 | .02996 | .02997 | 33.366 | .99955 | 17 |
| 44 | .01280 | .01280 | 78.126 | .99992 | 16 | | 44 | .03025 | .03026 | 33.045 | .99954 | 16 |
| **45** | .01309 | .01309 | 76.390 | .99991 | **15** | | **45** | .03054 | .03055 | 32.730 | .99953 | **15** |
| 46 | .01338 | .01338 | 74.729 | .99991 | 14 | | 46 | .03083 | .03084 | 32.421 | .99952 | 14 |
| 47 | .01367 | .01367 | 73.139 | .99991 | 13 | | 47 | .03112 | .03114 | 32.118 | .99952 | 13 |
| 48 | .01396 | .01396 | 71.615 | .99990 | 12 | | 48 | .03141 | .03143 | 31.821 | .99951 | 12 |
| 49 | .01425 | .01425 | 70.153 | .99990 | 11 | | 49 | .03170 | .03172 | 31.528 | .99950 | 11 |
| **50** | .01454 | .01455 | 68.750 | .99989 | **10** | | **50** | .03199 | .03201 | 31.242 | .99949 | **10** |
| 51 | .01483 | .01484 | 67.402 | .99989 | 9 | | 51 | .03228 | .03230 | 30.960 | .99948 | 9 |
| 52 | .01513 | .01513 | 66.105 | .99989 | 8 | | 52 | .03257 | .03259 | 30.683 | .99947 | 8 |
| 53 | .01542 | .01542 | 64.858 | .99988 | 7 | | 53 | .03286 | .03288 | 30.412 | .99946 | 7 |
| 54 | .01571 | .01571 | 63.657 | .99988 | 6 | | 54 | .03316 | .03317 | 30.145 | .99945 | 6 |
| **55** | .01600 | .01600 | 62.499 | .99987 | **5** | | **55** | .03345 | .03346 | 29.882 | .99944 | **5** |
| 56 | .01629 | .01629 | 61.383 | .99987 | 4 | | 56 | .03374 | .03376 | 29.624 | .99943 | 4 |
| 57 | .01658 | .01658 | 60.306 | .99986 | 3 | | 57 | .03403 | .03405 | 29.371 | .99942 | 3 |
| 58 | .01687 | .01687 | 59.266 | .99986 | 2 | | 58 | .03432 | .03434 | 29.122 | .99941 | 2 |
| 59 | .01716 | .01716 | 58.261 | .99985 | 1 | | 59 | .03461 | .03463 | 28.877 | .99940 | 1 |
| **60** | .01745 | .01746 | 57.290 | .99985 | **0** | | **60** | .03490 | .03492 | 28.636 | .99939 | **0** |
| ′ | Cos | Cot | Tan | Sin | ′ | | ′ | Cos | Cot | Tan | Sin | ′ |

# NATURAL FUNCTIONS (Continued)

| ′ | Sin | Tan | Cot | Cos | ′ | ′ | Sin | Tan | Cot | Cos | ′ |
|---|-----|-----|-----|-----|---|---|-----|-----|-----|-----|---|
| 0 | .03490 | .03492 | 28.636 | .99939 | 60 | 0 | .05234 | .05241 | 19.081 | .99863 | 60 |
| 1 | .03519 | .03521 | 28.399 | .99938 | 59 | 1 | .05263 | .05270 | 18.976 | .99861 | 59 |
| 2 | .03548 | .03550 | 28.166 | .99937 | 58 | 2 | .05292 | .05299 | 18.871 | .99860 | 58 |
| 3 | .03577 | .03579 | 27.937 | .99936 | 57 | 3 | .05321 | .05328 | 18.768 | .99858 | 57 |
| 4 | .03606 | .03609 | 27.712 | .99935 | 56 | 4 | .05350 | .05357 | 18.666 | .99857 | 56 |
| 5 | .03635 | .03638 | 27.490 | .99934 | 55 | 5 | .05379 | .05387 | 18.564 | .99855 | 55 |
| 6 | .03664 | .03667 | 27.271 | .99933 | 54 | 6 | .05408 | .05416 | 18.464 | .99854 | 54 |
| 7 | .03693 | .03696 | 27.057 | .99932 | 53 | 7 | .05437 | .05445 | 18.366 | .99852 | 53 |
| 8 | .03723 | .03725 | 26.845 | .99931 | 52 | 8 | .05466 | .05474 | 18.268 | .99851 | 52 |
| 9 | .03752 | .03754 | 26.637 | .99930 | 51 | 9 | .05495 | .05503 | 18.171 | .99849 | 51 |
| 10 | .03781 | .03783 | 26.432 | .99929 | 50 | 10 | .05524 | .05533 | 18.075 | .99847 | 50 |
| 11 | .03810 | .03812 | 26.230 | .99927 | 49 | 11 | .05553 | .05562 | 17.980 | .99846 | 49 |
| 12 | .03839 | .03842 | 26.031 | .99926 | 48 | 12 | .05582 | .05591 | 17.886 | .99844 | 48 |
| 13 | .03868 | .03871 | 25.835 | .99925 | 47 | 13 | .05611 | .05620 | 17.793 | .99842 | 47 |
| 14 | .03897 | .03900 | 25.642 | .99924 | 46 | 14 | .05640 | .05649 | 17.702 | .99841 | 46 |
| 15 | .03926 | .03929 | 25.452 | .99923 | 45 | 15 | .05669 | .05678 | 17.611 | .99839 | 45 |
| 16 | .03955 | .03958 | 25.264 | .99922 | 44 | 16 | .05698 | .05708 | 17.521 | .99838 | 44 |
| 17 | .03984 | .03987 | 25.080 | .99921 | 43 | 17 | .05727 | .05737 | 17.431 | .99836 | 43 |
| 18 | .04013 | .04016 | 24.898 | .99919 | 42 | 18 | .05756 | .05766 | 17.343 | .99834 | 42 |
| 19 | .04042 | .04046 | 24.719 | .99918 | 41 | 19 | .05785 | .05795 | 17.256 | .99833 | 41 |
| 20 | .04071 | .04075 | 24.542 | .99917 | 40 | 20 | .05814 | .05824 | 17.169 | .99831 | 40 |
| 21 | .04104 | .04104 | 24.368 | .99916 | 39 | 21 | .05844 | .05854 | 17.084 | .99829 | 39 |
| 22 | .04129 | .04133 | 24.196 | .99915 | 38 | 22 | .05873 | .05883 | 16.999 | .99827 | 38 |
| 23 | .04159 | .04162 | 24.026 | .99913 | 37 | 23 | .05902 | .05912 | 16.915 | .99826 | 37 |
| 24 | .04188 | .04191 | 23.859 | .99912 | 36 | 24 | .05931 | .05941 | 16.832 | .99824 | 36 |
| 25 | .04217 | .04220 | 23.695 | .99911 | 35 | 25 | .05960 | .05970 | 16.750 | .99822 | 35 |
| 26 | .04246 | .04250 | 23.532 | .99910 | 34 | 26 | .05989 | .05999 | 16.668 | .99821 | 34 |
| 27 | .04275 | .04279 | 23.372 | .99909 | 33 | 27 | .06018 | .06029 | 16.587 | .99819 | 33 |
| 28 | .04304 | .04308 | 23.214 | .99907 | 32 | 28 | .06047 | .06058 | 16.507 | .99817 | 32 |
| 29 | .04333 | .04337 | 23.058 | .99906 | 31 | 29 | .06076 | .06087 | 16.428 | .99815 | 31 |
| 30 | .04362 | .04366 | 22.904 | .99905 | 30 | 30 | .06105 | .06116 | 16.350 | .99813 | 30 |
| 31 | .04391 | .04395 | 22.752 | .99904 | 29 | 31 | .06134 | .06145 | 16.272 | .99812 | 29 |
| 32 | .04420 | .04424 | 22.602 | .99902 | 28 | 32 | .06163 | .06175 | 16.195 | .99810 | 28 |
| 33 | .04449 | .04454 | 22.454 | .99901 | 27 | 33 | .06192 | .06204 | 16.119 | .99808 | 27 |
| 34 | .04478 | .04483 | 22.308 | .99900 | 26 | 34 | .06221 | .06233 | 16.043 | .99806 | 26 |
| 35 | .04507 | .04512 | 22.164 | .99898 | 25 | 35 | .06250 | .06262 | 15.969 | .99804 | 25 |
| 36 | .04536 | .04541 | 22.022 | .99897 | 24 | 36 | .06279 | .06291 | 15.895 | .99803 | 24 |
| 37 | .04565 | .04570 | 21.881 | .99896 | 23 | 37 | .06308 | .06321 | 15.821 | .99801 | 23 |
| 38 | .04594 | .04599 | 21.743 | .99894 | 22 | 38 | .06337 | .06350 | 15.748 | .99799 | 22 |
| 39 | .04623 | .04628 | 21.606 | .99893 | 21 | 39 | .06366 | .06379 | 15.676 | .99797 | 21 |
| 40 | .04653 | .04658 | 21.470 | .99892 | 20 | 40 | .06395 | .06408 | 15.605 | .99795 | 20 |
| 41 | .04682 | .04687 | 21.337 | .99890 | 19 | 41 | .06424 | .06438 | 15.534 | .99793 | 19 |
| 42 | .04711 | .04716 | 21.205 | .99889 | 18 | 42 | .06453 | .06467 | 15.464 | .99792 | 18 |
| 43 | .04740 | .04745 | 21.075 | .99888 | 17 | 43 | .06482 | .06496 | 15.394 | .99790 | 17 |
| 44 | .04769 | .04774 | 20.946 | .99886 | 16 | 44 | .06511 | .06525 | 15.325 | .99788 | 16 |
| 45 | .04798 | .04803 | 20.819 | .99885 | 15 | 45 | .06540 | .06554 | 15.257 | .99786 | 15 |
| 46 | .04827 | .04833 | 20.693 | .99883 | 14 | 46 | .06569 | .06584 | 15.189 | .99784 | 14 |
| 47 | .04856 | .04862 | 20.569 | .99882 | 13 | 47 | .06598 | .06613 | 15.122 | .99782 | 13 |
| 48 | .04885 | .04891 | 20.446 | .99881 | 12 | 48 | .06627 | .06642 | 15.056 | .99780 | 12 |
| 49 | .04914 | .04920 | 20.325 | .99879 | 11 | 49 | .06656 | .06671 | 14.990 | .99778 | 11 |
| 50 | .04943 | .04949 | 20.206 | .99876 | 10 | 50 | .06685 | .06700 | 14.924 | .99776 | 10 |
| 51 | .04972 | .04978 | 20.087 | .99876 | 9 | 51 | .06714 | .06730 | 14.860 | .99774 | 9 |
| 52 | .05001 | .05007 | 19.970 | .99875 | 8 | 52 | .06743 | .06759 | 14.795 | .99772 | 8 |
| 53 | .05030 | .05037 | 19.855 | .99873 | 7 | 53 | .06773 | .06788 | 14.732 | .99770 | 7 |
| 54 | .05059 | .05066 | 19.740 | .99872 | 6 | 54 | .06802 | .06817 | 14.669 | .99768 | 6 |
| 55 | .05088 | .05095 | 19.627 | .99870 | 5 | 55 | .06831 | .06847 | 14.606 | .99766 | 5 |
| 56 | .05117 | .05124 | 19.516 | .99869 | 4 | 56 | .06860 | .06876 | 14.544 | .99764 | 4 |
| 57 | .05146 | .05153 | 19.405 | .99867 | 3 | 57 | .06889 | .06905 | 14.482 | .99762 | 3 |
| 58 | .05175 | .05182 | 19.296 | .99866 | 2 | 58 | .06918 | .06934 | 14.421 | .99760 | 2 |
| 59 | .05205 | .05212 | 19.188 | .99864 | 1 | 59 | .06947 | .06963 | 14.361 | .99758 | 1 |
| 60 | .05234 | .05241 | 19.081 | .99863 | 0 | 60 | .06976 | .06993 | 14.301 | .99756 | 0 |
| ′ | Cos | Cot | Tan | Sin | ′ | ′ | Cos | Cot | Tan | Sin | ′ |

## NATURAL FUNCTIONS (Continued)

| ′ | Sin | Tan | Cot | Cos | ′ | ′ | Sin | Tan | Cot | Cos | ′ |
|---|-----|-----|-----|-----|---|---|-----|-----|-----|-----|---|
| **0** | .06976 | .06993 | 14.301 | .99756 | **60** | **0** | .08716 | .08749 | 11.430 | .99619 | **60** |
| 1 | .07005 | .07022 | 14.241 | .99754 | 59 | 1 | .08745 | .08778 | 11.392 | .99617 | 59 |
| 2 | .07034 | .07051 | 14.182 | .99752 | 58 | 2 | .08774 | .08807 | 11.354 | .99614 | 58 |
| 3 | .07063 | .07080 | 14.124 | .99750 | 57 | 3 | .08803 | .08837 | 11.316 | .99612 | 57 |
| 4 | .07092 | .07110 | 14.065 | .99748 | 56 | 4 | .08831 | .08866 | 11.279 | .99609 | 56 |
| **5** | .07121 | .07139 | 14.008 | .99746 | **55** | **5** | .08860 | .08895 | 11.242 | .99607 | **55** |
| 6 | .07150 | .07168 | 13.951 | .99744 | 54 | 6 | .08889 | .08925 | 11.205 | .99604 | 54 |
| 7 | .07179 | .07197 | 13.894 | .99742 | 53 | 7 | .08918 | .08954 | 11.168 | .99602 | 53 |
| 8 | .07208 | .07227 | 13.838 | .99740 | 52 | 8 | .08947 | .08983 | 11.132 | .99599 | 52 |
| 9 | .07237 | .07256 | 13.782 | .99738 | 51 | 9 | .08976 | .09013 | 11.095 | .99596 | 51 |
| **10** | .07266 | .07285 | 13.727 | .99736 | **50** | **10** | .09005 | .09042 | 11.059 | .99594 | **50** |
| 11 | .07295 | .07314 | 13.672 | .99734 | 49 | 11 | .09034 | .09071 | 11.024 | .99591 | 49 |
| 12 | .07324 | .07344 | 13.617 | .99731 | 48 | 12 | .09063 | .09101 | 10.988 | .99588 | 48 |
| 13 | .07353 | .07373 | 13.563 | .99729 | 47 | 13 | .09092 | .09130 | 10.953 | .99586 | 47 |
| 14 | .07382 | .07402 | 13.510 | .99727 | 46 | 14 | .09121 | .09159 | 10.918 | .99583 | 46 |
| **15** | .07411 | .07431 | 13.457 | .99725 | **45** | **15** | .09150 | .09189 | 10.883 | .99580 | **45** |
| 16 | .07440 | .07461 | 13.404 | .99723 | 44 | 16 | .09179 | .09218 | 10.848 | .99578 | 44 |
| 17 | .07469 | .07490 | 13.352 | .99721 | 43 | 17 | .09208 | .09247 | 10.814 | .99575 | 43 |
| 18 | .07498 | .07519 | 13.300 | .99719 | 42 | 18 | .09237 | .09277 | 10.780 | .99572 | 42 |
| 19 | .07527 | .07548 | 13.248 | .99716 | 41 | 19 | .09266 | .09306 | 10.746 | .99570 | 41 |
| **20** | .07556 | .07578 | 13.197 | .99714 | **40** | **20** | .09295 | .09335 | 10.712 | .99567 | **40** |
| 21 | .07585 | .07607 | 13.146 | .99712 | 39 | 21 | .09324 | .09365 | 10.678 | .99564 | 39 |
| 22 | .07614 | .07636 | 13.096 | .99710 | 38 | 22 | .09353 | .09394 | 10.645 | .99562 | 38 |
| 23 | .07643 | .07665 | 13.046 | .99708 | 37 | 23 | .09382 | .09423 | 10.612 | .99559 | 37 |
| 24 | .07672 | .07695 | 12.996 | .99705 | 36 | 24 | .09411 | .09453 | 10.579 | .99556 | 36 |
| **25** | .07701 | .07724 | 12.947 | .99703 | **35** | **25** | .09440 | .09482 | 10.546 | .99553 | **35** |
| 26 | .07730 | .07753 | 12.898 | .99701 | 34 | 26 | .09469 | .09511 | 10.514 | .99551 | 34 |
| 27 | .07759 | .07782 | 12.850 | .99699 | 33 | 27 | .09498 | .09541 | 10.481 | .99548 | 33 |
| 28 | .07788 | .07812 | 12.801 | .99696 | 32 | 28 | .09527 | .09570 | 10.449 | .99545 | 32 |
| 29 | .07817 | .07841 | 12.754 | .99694 | 31 | 29 | .09556 | .09600 | 10.417 | .99542 | 31 |
| **30** | .07846 | .07870 | 12.706 | .99692 | **30** | **30** | .09585 | .09629 | 10.385 | .99540 | **30** |
| 31 | .07875 | .07899 | 12.659 | .99689 | 29 | 31 | .09614 | .09658 | 10.354 | .99537 | 29 |
| 32 | .07904 | .07929 | 12.612 | .99687 | 28 | 32 | .09642 | .09688 | 10.322 | .99534 | 28 |
| 33 | .07933 | .07958 | 12.566 | .99685 | 27 | 33 | .09671 | .09717 | 10.291 | .99531 | 27 |
| 34 | .07962 | .07987 | 12.520 | .99683 | 26 | 34 | .09700 | .09746 | 10.260 | .99528 | 26 |
| **35** | .07991 | .08017 | 12.474 | .99680 | **25** | **35** | .09729 | .09776 | 10.229 | .99526 | **25** |
| 36 | .08020 | .08046 | 12.429 | .99678 | 24 | 36 | .09758 | .09805 | 10.199 | .99523 | 24 |
| 37 | .08049 | .08075 | 12.384 | .99676 | 23 | 37 | .09787 | .09834 | 10.168 | .99520 | 23 |
| 38 | .08078 | .08104 | 12.339 | .99673 | 22 | 38 | .09816 | .09864 | 10.138 | .99517 | 22 |
| 39 | .08107 | .08134 | 12.295 | .99671 | 21 | 39 | .09845 | .09893 | 10.108 | .99514 | 21 |
| **40** | .08136 | .08163 | 12.251 | .99668 | **20** | **40** | .09874 | .09923 | 10.078 | .99511 | **20** |
| 41 | .08165 | .08192 | 12.207 | .99666 | 19 | 41 | .09903 | .09952 | 10.048 | .99508 | 19 |
| 42 | .08194 | .08221 | 12.163 | .99664 | 18 | 42 | .09932 | .09981 | 10.019 | .99506 | 18 |
| 43 | .08223 | .08251 | 12.120 | .99661 | 17 | 43 | .09961 | .10011 | 9.9893 | .99503 | 17 |
| 44 | .08252 | .08280 | 12.077 | .99659 | 16 | 44 | .09990 | .10040 | 9.9601 | .99500 | 16 |
| **45** | .08281 | .08309 | 12.035 | .99657 | **15** | **45** | .10019 | .10069 | 9.9310 | .99497 | **15** |
| 46 | .08310 | .08339 | 11.992 | .99654 | 14 | 46 | .10048 | .10099 | 9.9021 | .99494 | 14 |
| 47 | .08339 | .08368 | 11.950 | .99652 | 13 | 47 | .10077 | .10128 | 9.8734 | .99491 | 13 |
| 48 | .08368 | .08397 | 11.909 | .99649 | 12 | 48 | .10106 | .10158 | 9.8448 | .99488 | 12 |
| 49 | .08397 | .08427 | 11.867 | .99647 | 11 | 49 | .10135 | .10187 | 9.8164 | .99485 | 11 |
| **50** | .08426 | .08456 | 11.826 | .99644 | **10** | **50** | .10164 | .10216 | 9.7882 | .99482 | **10** |
| 51 | .08455 | .08485 | 11.785 | .99642 | 9 | 51 | .10192 | .10246 | 9.7601 | .99479 | 9 |
| 52 | .08484 | .08514 | 11.745 | .99639 | 8 | 52 | .10221 | .10275 | 9.7322 | .99476 | 8 |
| 53 | .08513 | .08544 | 11.705 | .99637 | 7 | 53 | .10250 | .10305 | 9.7044 | .99473 | 7 |
| 54 | .08542 | .08573 | 11.664 | .99635 | 6 | 54 | .10279 | .10334 | 9.6768 | .99470 | 6 |
| **55** | .08571 | .08602 | 11.625 | .99632 | **5** | **55** | .10308 | .10363 | 9.6493 | .99467 | **5** |
| 56 | .08600 | .08632 | 11.585 | .99630 | 4 | 56 | .10337 | .10393 | 9.6220 | .99464 | 4 |
| 57 | .08629 | .08661 | 11.546 | .99627 | 3 | 57 | .10366 | .10422 | 9.5949 | .99461 | 3 |
| 58 | .08658 | .08690 | 11.507 | .99625 | 2 | 58 | .10395 | .10452 | 9.5679 | .99458 | 2 |
| 59 | .08687 | .08720 | 11.468 | .99622 | 1 | 59 | .10424 | .10481 | 9.5411 | .99455 | 1 |
| **60** | .08716 | .08749 | 11.430 | .99619 | **0** | **60** | .10453 | .10510 | 9.5144 | .99452 | **0** |
| ′ | Cos | Cot | Tan | Sin | ′ | ′ | Cos | Cot | Tan | Sin | ′ |

6° (186°)  (353°) 173°  7° (187°)  (352°) 172°

| ′ | Sin | Tan | Cot | Cos | ′ | ′ | Sin | Tan | Cot | Cos | ′ |
|---|-----|-----|-----|-----|---|---|-----|-----|-----|-----|---|
| **0** | .10453 | .10510 | 9.5144 | .99452 | **60** | **0** | .12187 | .12278 | 8.1443 | .99255 | **60** |
| 1 | .10482 | .10540 | 9.4878 | .99449 | 59 | 1 | .12216 | .12308 | 8.1248 | .99251 | 59 |
| 2 | .10511 | .10569 | 9.4614 | .99446 | 58 | 2 | .12245 | .12338 | 8.1054 | .99248 | 58 |
| 3 | .10540 | .10599 | 9.4352 | .99443 | 57 | 3 | .12274 | .12367 | 8.0860 | .99244 | 57 |
| 4 | .10569 | .10628 | 9.4090 | .99440 | 56 | 4 | .12302 | .12397 | 8.0667 | .99240 | 56 |
| **5** | .10597 | .10657 | 9.3831 | .99437 | **55** | **5** | .12331 | .12426 | 8.0476 | .99237 | **55** |
| 6 | .10626 | .10687 | 9.3572 | .99434 | 54 | 6 | .12360 | .12456 | 8.0285 | .99233 | 54 |
| 7 | .10655 | .10716 | 9.3315 | .99431 | 53 | 7 | .12389 | .12485 | 8.0095 | .99230 | 53 |
| 8 | .10684 | .10746 | 9.3060 | .99428 | 52 | 8 | .12418 | .12515 | 7.9906 | .99226 | 52 |
| 9 | .10713 | .10775 | 9.2806 | .99424 | 51 | 9 | .12447 | .12544 | 7.9718 | .99222 | 51 |
| **10** | .10742 | .10805 | 9.2553 | .99421 | **50** | **10** | .12476 | .12574 | 7.9530 | .99219 | **50** |
| 11 | .10771 | .10834 | 9.2302 | .99418 | 49 | 11 | .12504 | .12603 | 7.9344 | .99215 | 49 |
| 12 | .10800 | .10863 | 9.2052 | .99415 | 48 | 12 | .12533 | .12633 | 7.9158 | .99211 | 48 |
| 13 | .10829 | .10893 | 9.1803 | .99412 | 47 | 13 | .12562 | .12662 | 7.8973 | .99208 | 47 |
| 14 | .10858 | .10922 | 9.1555 | .99409 | 56 | 14 | .12591 | .12692 | 7.8789 | .99204 | 46 |
| **15** | .10887 | .10952 | 9.1309 | .99406 | **45** | **15** | .12620 | .12722 | 7.8606 | .99200 | **45** |
| 16 | .10916 | .10981 | 9.1065 | .99402 | 44 | 16 | .12649 | .12751 | 7.8424 | .99197 | 44 |
| 17 | .10945 | .11011 | 9.0821 | .99399 | 43 | 17 | .12678 | .12781 | 7.8243 | .99193 | 43 |
| 18 | .10973 | .11040 | 9.0579 | .99396 | 42 | 18 | .12706 | .12810 | 7.8062 | .99189 | 42 |
| 19 | .11002 | .11070 | 9.0338 | .99393 | 41 | 19 | .12735 | .12840 | 7.7882 | .99186 | 41 |
| **20** | .11031 | .11099 | 9.0098 | .99390 | **40** | **20** | .12764 | .12869 | 7.7704 | .99182 | **40** |
| 21 | .11060 | .11128 | 8.9860 | .99386 | 39 | 21 | .12793 | .12899 | 7.7525 | .99178 | 39 |
| 22 | .11089 | .11158 | 8.9623 | .99383 | 38 | 22 | .12822 | .12929 | 7.7348 | .99175 | 38 |
| 23 | .11118 | .11187 | 8.9387 | .99380 | 37 | 23 | .12851 | .12958 | 7.7171 | .99171 | 37 |
| 24 | .11147 | .11217 | 8.9152 | .99377 | 36 | 24 | .12880 | .12988 | 7.6996 | .99167 | 36 |
| **25** | .11176 | .11246 | 8.8919 | .99374 | **35** | **25** | .12908 | .13017 | 7.6821 | .99163 | **35** |
| 26 | .11205 | .11276 | 8.8686 | .99370 | 34 | 26 | .12937 | .13047 | 7.6647 | .99160 | 34 |
| 27 | .11234 | .11305 | 8.8455 | .99367 | 33 | 27 | .12966 | .13076 | 7.6473 | .99156 | 33 |
| 28 | .11263 | .11335 | 8.8225 | .99364 | 32 | 28 | .12995 | .13106 | 7.6301 | .99152 | 32 |
| 29 | .11291 | .11364 | 8.7996 | .99360 | 31 | 29 | .13024 | .13136 | 7.6129 | .99148 | 31 |
| **30** | .11320 | .11394 | 8.7769 | .99357 | **30** | **30** | .13053 | .13165 | 7.5958 | .99144 | **30** |
| 31 | .11349 | .11423 | 8.7542 | .99354 | 29 | 31 | .13081 | .13195 | 7.5787 | .99141 | 29 |
| 32 | .11378 | .11452 | 8.7317 | .99351 | 28 | 32 | .13110 | .13224 | 7.5618 | .99137 | 28 |
| 33 | .11407 | .11482 | 8.7093 | .99347 | 27 | 33 | .13139 | .13254 | 7.5449 | .99133 | 27 |
| 34 | .11436 | .11511 | 8.6870 | .99344 | 26 | 34 | .13168 | .13284 | 7.5281 | .99129 | 26 |
| **35** | .11465 | .11541 | 8.6648 | .99341 | **25** | **35** | .13197 | .13313 | 7.5113 | .99125 | **25** |
| 36 | .11494 | .11570 | 8.6427 | .99337 | 24 | 36 | .13226 | .13343 | 7.4947 | .99122 | 24 |
| 37 | .11523 | .11600 | 8.6208 | .99334 | 23 | 37 | .13254 | .13372 | 7.4781 | .99118 | 23 |
| 38 | .11552 | .11629 | 8.5989 | .99331 | 22 | 38 | .13283 | .13402 | 7.4615 | .99114 | 22 |
| 39 | .11580 | .11659 | 8.5772 | .99327 | 21 | 39 | .13312 | .13432 | 7.4451 | .99110 | 21 |
| **40** | .11609 | .11688 | 8.5555 | .99324 | **20** | **40** | .13341 | .13461 | 7.4287 | .99106 | **20** |
| 41 | .11638 | .11718 | 8.5340 | .99320 | 19 | 41 | .13370 | .13491 | 7.4124 | .99102 | 19 |
| 42 | .11667 | .11747 | 8.5126 | .99317 | 18 | 42 | .13399 | .13521 | 7.3962 | .99098 | 18 |
| 43 | .11696 | .11777 | 8.4913 | .99314 | 17 | 43 | .13427 | .13550 | 7.3800 | .99094 | 17 |
| 44 | .11725 | .11806 | 8.4701 | .99310 | 16 | 44 | .13456 | .13580 | 7.3639 | .99091 | 16 |
| **45** | .11754 | .11836 | 8.4490 | .99307 | **15** | **45** | .13485 | .13609 | 7.3479 | .99087 | **15** |
| 46 | .11783 | .11865 | 8.4280 | .99303 | 14 | 46 | .13514 | .13639 | 7.3319 | .99083 | 14 |
| 47 | .11812 | .11895 | 8.4071 | .99300 | 13 | 47 | .13543 | .13669 | 7.3160 | .99079 | 13 |
| 48 | .11840 | .11924 | 8.3863 | .99297 | 12 | 48 | .13572 | .13698 | 7.3002 | .99075 | 12 |
| 49 | .11869 | .11954 | 8.3656 | .99293 | 11 | 49 | .13600 | .13728 | 7.2844 | .99071 | 11 |
| **50** | .11898 | .11983 | 8.3450 | .99290 | **10** | **50** | .13629 | .13758 | 7.2687 | .99067 | **10** |
| 51 | .11927 | .12013 | 8.3245 | .99286 | 9 | 51 | .13658 | .13787 | 7.2531 | .99063 | 9 |
| 52 | .11956 | .12042 | 8.3041 | .99283 | 8 | 52 | .13687 | .13817 | 7.2375 | .99059 | 8 |
| 53 | .11985 | .12072 | 8.2838 | .99279 | 7 | 53 | .13716 | .13846 | 7.2220 | .99055 | 7 |
| 54 | .12014 | .12101 | 8.2636 | .99276 | 6 | 54 | .13744 | .13876 | 7.2066 | .99051 | 6 |
| **55** | .12043 | .12131 | 8.2434 | .99272 | **5** | **55** | .13773 | .13906 | 7.1912 | .99047 | **5** |
| 56 | .12071 | .12160 | 8.2234 | .99269 | 4 | 56 | .13802 | .13935 | 7.1759 | .99043 | 4 |
| 57 | .12100 | .12190 | 8.2035 | .99265 | 3 | 57 | .13831 | .13965 | 7.1607 | .99039 | 3 |
| 58 | .12129 | .12219 | 8.1837 | .99262 | 2 | 58 | .13860 | .13995 | 7.1455 | .99035 | 2 |
| 59 | .12158 | .12249 | 8.1640 | .99258 | 1 | 59 | .13889 | .14024 | 7.1304 | .99031 | 1 |
| **60** | .12187 | .12278 | 8.1443 | .99255 | **0** | **60** | .13917 | .14054 | 7.1154 | .99027 | **0** |
| ′ | Cos | Cot | Tan | Sin | ′ | ′ | Cos | Cot | Tan | Sin | ′ |

96° (276°)  (263°) 83°  97° (277°)  (262°) 82°

| ' | Sin | Tan | Cot | Cos | ' |
|---|-----|-----|-----|-----|---|
| 0 | .13917 | .14054 | 7.1154 | .99027 | 60 |
| 1 | .13946 | .14084 | 7.1004 | .99023 | 59 |
| 2 | .13975 | .14113 | 7.0855 | .99019 | 58 |
| 3 | .14004 | .14143 | 7.0706 | .99015 | 57 |
| 4 | .14033 | .14173 | 7.0558 | .99011 | 56 |
| 5 | .14061 | .14202 | 7.0410 | .99006 | 55 |
| 6 | .14090 | .14232 | 7.0264 | .99002 | 54 |
| 7 | .14119 | .14262 | 7.0117 | .98998 | 53 |
| 8 | .14148 | .14291 | 6.9972 | .98994 | 52 |
| 9 | .14177 | .14321 | 6.9827 | .98990 | 51 |
| 10 | .14205 | .14351 | 6.9682 | .98986 | 50 |
| 11 | .14234 | .14381 | 6.9538 | .98982 | 49 |
| 12 | .14263 | .14410 | 6.9395 | .98978 | 48 |
| 13 | .14292 | .14440 | 6.9252 | .98973 | 47 |
| 14 | .14320 | .14470 | 6.9110 | .98969 | 46 |
| 15 | .14349 | .14499 | 6.8969 | .98965 | 45 |
| 16 | .14378 | .14529 | 6.8828 | .98961 | 44 |
| 17 | .14407 | .14559 | 6.8687 | .98957 | 43 |
| 18 | .14436 | .14588 | 6.8548 | .98953 | 42 |
| 19 | .14464 | .14618 | 6.8408 | .98948 | 41 |
| 20 | .14493 | .14648 | 6.8269 | .98944 | 40 |
| 21 | .14522 | .14678 | 6.8131 | .98940 | 39 |
| 22 | .14551 | .14707 | 6.7994 | .98936 | 38 |
| 23 | .14580 | .14737 | 6.7856 | .98931 | 37 |
| 24 | .14608 | .14767 | 6.7720 | .98927 | 36 |
| 25 | .14637 | .14796 | 6.7584 | .98923 | 35 |
| 26 | .14666 | .14826 | 6.7448 | .98919 | 34 |
| 27 | .14695 | .14856 | 6.7313 | .98914 | 33 |
| 28 | .14723 | .14886 | 6.7179 | .98910 | 32 |
| 29 | .14752 | .14915 | 6.7045 | .98906 | 31 |
| 30 | .14781 | .14945 | 6.6912 | .98902 | 30 |
| 31 | .14810 | .14975 | 6.6779 | .98897 | 29 |
| 32 | .14838 | .15005 | 6.6646 | .98893 | 28 |
| 33 | .14867 | .15034 | 6.6514 | .98889 | 27 |
| 34 | .14896 | .15064 | 6.6383 | .98884 | 26 |
| 35 | .14925 | .15094 | 6.6252 | .98880 | 25 |
| 36 | .14954 | .15124 | 6.6122 | .98876 | 24 |
| 37 | .14982 | .15153 | 6.5992 | .98871 | 23 |
| 38 | .15011 | .15183 | 6.5863 | .98867 | 22 |
| 39 | .15040 | .15213 | 6.5734 | .98863 | 21 |
| 40 | .15069 | .15243 | 6.5606 | .98858 | 20 |
| 41 | .15097 | .15272 | 6.5478 | .98854 | 19 |
| 42 | .15126 | .15302 | 6.5350 | .98849 | 18 |
| 43 | .15155 | .15332 | 6.5223 | .98845 | 17 |
| 44 | .15184 | .15362 | 6.5097 | .98841 | 16 |
| 45 | .15212 | .15391 | 6.4971 | .98836 | 15 |
| 46 | .15241 | .15421 | 6.4846 | .98832 | 14 |
| 47 | .15270 | .15451 | 6.4721 | .98827 | 13 |
| 48 | .15299 | .15481 | 6.4596 | .98823 | 12 |
| 49 | .15327 | .15511 | 6.4472 | .98818 | 11 |
| 50 | .15356 | .15540 | 6.4348 | .98814 | 10 |
| 51 | .15385 | .15570 | 6.4225 | .98809 | 9 |
| 52 | .15414 | .15600 | 6.4103 | .98805 | 8 |
| 53 | .15442 | .15630 | 6.3980 | .98800 | 7 |
| 54 | .15471 | .15660 | 6.3859 | .98796 | 6 |
| 55 | .15500 | .15689 | 6.3737 | .98791 | 5 |
| 56 | .15529 | .15719 | 6.3617 | .98787 | 4 |
| 57 | .15557 | .15749 | 6.3496 | .98782 | 3 |
| 58 | .15586 | .15779 | 6.3376 | .98778 | 2 |
| 59 | .15615 | .15809 | 6.3257 | .98773 | 1 |
| 60 | .15643 | .15838 | 6.3138 | .98769 | 0 |

| ' | Sin | Tan | Cot | Cos | ' |
|---|-----|-----|-----|-----|---|
| 0 | .15643 | .15838 | 6.3138 | .98769 | 60 |
| 1 | .15672 | .15868 | 6.3019 | .98764 | 59 |
| 2 | .15701 | .15898 | 6.2901 | .98760 | 58 |
| 3 | .15730 | .15928 | 6.2783 | .98755 | 57 |
| 4 | .15758 | .15958 | 6.2666 | .98751 | 56 |
| 5 | .15787 | .15988 | 6.2549 | .98746 | 55 |
| 6 | .15816 | .16017 | 6.2432 | .98741 | 54 |
| 7 | .15845 | .16047 | 6.2316 | .98737 | 53 |
| 8 | .15873 | .16077 | 6.2200 | .98732 | 52 |
| 9 | .15902 | .16107 | 6.2085 | .98728 | 51 |
| 10 | .15931 | .16137 | 6.1970 | .98723 | 50 |
| 11 | .15959 | .16167 | 6.1856 | .98718 | 49 |
| 12 | .15988 | .16196 | 6.1742 | .98714 | 48 |
| 13 | .16017 | .16226 | 6.1628 | .98709 | 47 |
| 14 | .16046 | .16256 | 6.1515 | .98704 | 46 |
| 15 | .16074 | .16286 | 6.1402 | .98700 | 45 |
| 16 | .16103 | .16316 | 6.1290 | .98695 | 44 |
| 17 | .16132 | .16346 | 6.1178 | .98690 | 43 |
| 18 | .16160 | .16376 | 6.1066 | .98686 | 42 |
| 19 | .16189 | .16405 | 6.0955 | .98681 | 41 |
| 20 | .16218 | .16435 | 6.0844 | .98676 | 40 |
| 21 | .16246 | .16465 | 6.0734 | .98671 | 39 |
| 22 | .16275 | .16495 | 6.0624 | .98667 | 38 |
| 23 | .16304 | .16525 | 6.0514 | .98662 | 37 |
| 24 | .16333 | .16555 | 6.0405 | .98657 | 36 |
| 25 | .16361 | .16585 | 6.0296 | .98652 | 35 |
| 26 | .16390 | .16615 | 6.0188 | .98648 | 34 |
| 27 | .16419 | .16645 | 6.0080 | .98643 | 33 |
| 28 | .16447 | .16674 | 5.9972 | .98638 | 32 |
| 29 | .16476 | .16704 | 5.9865 | .98633 | 31 |
| 30 | .16505 | .16734 | 5.9758 | .98629 | 30 |
| 31 | .16533 | .16764 | 5.9651 | .98624 | 29 |
| 32 | .16562 | .16794 | 5.9545 | .98619 | 28 |
| 33 | .16591 | .16824 | 5.9439 | .98614 | 27 |
| 34 | .16620 | .16854 | 5.9333 | .98609 | 26 |
| 35 | .16648 | .16884 | 5.9228 | .98604 | 25 |
| 36 | .16677 | .16914 | 5.9124 | .98600 | 24 |
| 37 | .16706 | .16944 | 5.9019 | .98595 | 23 |
| 38 | .16734 | .16974 | 5.8915 | .98590 | 22 |
| 39 | .16763 | .17004 | 5.8811 | .98585 | 21 |
| 40 | .16792 | .17033 | 5.8708 | .98580 | 20 |
| 41 | .16820 | .17063 | 5.8605 | .98575 | 19 |
| 42 | .16849 | .17093 | 5.8502 | .98570 | 18 |
| 43 | .16878 | .17123 | 5.8400 | .98565 | 17 |
| 44 | .16906 | .17153 | 5.8298 | .98561 | 16 |
| 45 | .16935 | .17183 | 5.8197 | .98556 | 15 |
| 46 | .16964 | .17213 | 5.8095 | .98551 | 14 |
| 47 | .16992 | .17243 | 5.7994 | .98546 | 13 |
| 48 | .17021 | .17273 | 5.7894 | .98541 | 12 |
| 49 | .17050 | .17303 | 5.7794 | .98536 | 11 |
| 50 | .17078 | .17333 | 5.7694 | .98531 | 10 |
| 51 | .17107 | .17363 | 5.7594 | .98526 | 9 |
| 52 | .17136 | .17393 | 5.7495 | .98521 | 8 |
| 53 | .17164 | .17423 | 5.7396 | .98516 | 7 |
| 54 | .17193 | .17453 | 5.7297 | .98511 | 6 |
| 55 | .17222 | .17483 | 5.7199 | .98506 | 5 |
| 56 | .17250 | .17513 | 5.7101 | .98501 | 4 |
| 57 | .17279 | .17543 | 5.7004 | .98496 | 3 |
| 58 | .17308 | .17573 | 5.6906 | .98491 | 2 |
| 59 | .17336 | .17603 | 5.6809 | .98486 | 1 |
| 60 | .17365 | .17633 | 5.6713 | .98481 | 0 |

| ' | Cos | Cot | Tan | Sin | ' |
|---|-----|-----|-----|-----|---|

**10°** (190°)                 (349°) **169°**          **11°** (191°)                 (348°) **168°**

| ′ | Sin | Tan | Cot | Cos | ′ | ′ | Sin | Tan | Cot | Cos | ′ |
|---|-----|-----|-----|-----|---|---|-----|-----|-----|-----|---|
| **0** | .17365 | .17633 | 5.6713 | .98481 | **60** | **0** | .19081 | .19438 | 5.1446 | .98163 | **60** |
| 1 | .17393 | .17663 | 5.6617 | .98476 | 59 | 1 | .19109 | .19468 | 5.1366 | .98157 | 59 |
| 2 | .17422 | .17693 | 5.6521 | .98471 | 58 | 2 | .19138 | .19498 | 5.1286 | .98152 | 58 |
| 3 | .17451 | .17723 | 5.6425 | .98466 | 57 | 3 | .19167 | .19529 | 5.1207 | .98146 | 57 |
| 4 | .17479 | .17753 | 5.6329 | .98461 | 56 | 4 | .19195 | .19559 | 5.1128 | .98140 | 56 |
| **5** | .17508 | .17783 | 5.6234 | .98455 | **55** | **5** | .19224 | .19589 | 5.1049 | .98135 | **55** |
| 6 | .17537 | .17813 | 5.6140 | .98450 | 54 | 6 | .19252 | .19619 | 5.0970 | .98129 | 54 |
| 7 | .17565 | .17843 | 5.6045 | .98445 | 53 | 7 | .19281 | .19649 | 5.0892 | .98124 | 53 |
| 8 | .17594 | .17873 | 5.5951 | .98440 | 52 | 8 | .19309 | .19680 | 5.0814 | .98118 | 52 |
| 9 | .17623 | .17903 | 5.5857 | .98435 | 51 | 9 | .19338 | .19710 | 5.0736 | .98112 | 51 |
| **10** | .17651 | .17933 | 5.5764 | .98430 | **50** | **10** | .19366 | .19740 | 5.0658 | .98107 | **50** |
| 11 | .17680 | .17963 | 5.5671 | .98425 | 49 | 11 | .19395 | .19770 | 5.0581 | .98101 | 49 |
| 12 | .17708 | .17993 | 5.5578 | .98420 | 48 | 12 | .19423 | .19801 | 5.0504 | .98096 | 48 |
| 13 | .17737 | .18023 | 5.5485 | .98414 | 47 | 13 | .19452 | .19831 | 5.0427 | .98090 | 47 |
| 14 | .17766 | .18053 | 5.5393 | .98409 | 46 | 14 | .19481 | .19861 | 5.0350 | .98084 | 46 |
| **15** | .17794 | .18083 | 5.5301 | .98404 | **45** | **15** | .19509 | .19891 | 5.0273 | .98079 | **45** |
| 16 | .17823 | .18113 | 5.5209 | .98399 | 44 | 16 | .19538 | .19921 | 5.0197 | .98073 | 44 |
| 17 | .17852 | .18143 | 5.5118 | .98394 | 43 | 17 | .19566 | .19952 | 5.0121 | .98067 | 43 |
| 18 | .17880 | .18173 | 5.5026 | .98389 | 42 | 18 | .19595 | .19982 | 5.0045 | .98061 | 42 |
| 19 | .17909 | .18203 | 5.4936 | .98383 | 41 | 19 | .19623 | .20012 | 4.9969 | .98056 | 41 |
| **20** | .17937 | .18233 | 5.4845 | .98378 | **40** | **20** | .19652 | .20042 | 4.9894 | .98050 | **40** |
| 21 | .17966 | .18263 | 5.4755 | .98373 | 39 | 21 | .19680 | .20073 | 4.9819 | .98044 | 39 |
| 22 | .17995 | .18293 | 5.4665 | .98368 | 38 | 22 | .19709 | .20103 | 4.9744 | .98039 | 38 |
| 23 | .18023 | .18323 | 5.4575 | .98362 | 37 | 23 | .19737 | .20133 | 4.9669 | .98033 | 37 |
| 24 | .18052 | .18353 | 5.4486 | .98357 | 36 | 24 | .19766 | .20164 | 4.9594 | .98027 | 36 |
| **25** | .18081 | .18384 | 5.4397 | .98352 | **35** | **25** | .19794 | .20194 | 4.9520 | .98021 | **35** |
| 26 | .18109 | .18414 | 5.4308 | .98347 | 34 | 26 | .19823 | .20224 | 4.9446 | .98016 | 34 |
| 27 | .18138 | .18444 | 5.4219 | .98341 | 33 | 27 | .19851 | .20254 | 4.9372 | .98010 | 33 |
| 28 | .18166 | .18474 | 5.4131 | .98336 | 32 | 28 | .19880 | .20285 | 4.9298 | .98004 | 32 |
| 29 | .18195 | .18504 | 5.4043 | .98331 | 31 | 29 | .19908 | .20315 | 4.9225 | .97998 | 31 |
| **30** | .18224 | .18534 | 5.3955 | .98325 | **30** | **30** | .19937 | .20345 | 4.9152 | .97992 | **30** |
| 31 | .18252 | .18564 | 5.3868 | .98320 | 29 | 31 | .19965 | .20376 | 4.9078 | .97987 | 29 |
| 32 | .18281 | .18594 | 5.3781 | .98315 | 28 | 32 | .19994 | .20406 | 4.9006 | .97981 | 28 |
| 33 | .18309 | .18624 | 5.3694 | .98310 | 27 | 33 | .20022 | .20436 | 4.8933 | .97975 | 27 |
| 34 | .18338 | .18654 | 5.3607 | .98304 | 26 | 34 | .20051 | .20466 | 4.8860 | .97969 | 26 |
| **35** | .18367 | .18684 | 5.3521 | .98299 | **25** | **35** | .20079 | .20497 | 4.8788 | .97963 | **25** |
| 36 | .18395 | .18714 | 5.3435 | .98294 | 24 | 36 | .20108 | .20527 | 4.8716 | .97958 | 24 |
| 37 | .18424 | .18745 | 5.3349 | .98288 | 23 | 37 | .20136 | .20557 | 4.8644 | .97952 | 23 |
| 38 | .18452 | .18775 | 5.3263 | .98283 | 22 | 38 | .20165 | .20588 | 4.8573 | .97946 | 22 |
| 39 | .18481 | .18805 | 5.3178 | .98277 | 21 | 39 | .20193 | .20618 | 4.8501 | .97940 | 21 |
| **40** | .18509 | .18835 | 5.3093 | .98272 | **20** | **40** | .20222 | .20648 | 4.8430 | .97934 | **20** |
| 41 | .18538 | .18865 | 5.3008 | .98267 | 19 | 41 | .20250 | .20679 | 4.8359 | .97928 | 19 |
| 42 | .18567 | .18895 | 5.2924 | .98261 | 18 | 42 | .20279 | .20709 | 4.8288 | .97922 | 18 |
| 43 | .18595 | .18925 | 5.2839 | .98256 | 17 | 43 | .20307 | .20739 | 4.8218 | .97916 | 17 |
| 44 | .18624 | .18955 | 5.2755 | .98250 | 16 | 44 | .20336 | .20770 | 4.8147 | .97910 | 16 |
| **45** | .18652 | .18986 | 5.2672 | .98245 | **15** | **45** | .20364 | .20800 | 4.8077 | .97905 | **15** |
| 46 | .18681 | .19016 | 5.2588 | .98240 | 14 | 46 | .20393 | .20830 | 4.8007 | .97899 | 14 |
| 47 | .18710 | .19046 | 5.2505 | .98234 | 13 | 47 | .20421 | .20861 | 4.7937 | .97893 | 13 |
| 48 | .18738 | .19076 | 5.2422 | .98229 | 12 | 48 | .20450 | .20891 | 4.7867 | .97887 | 12 |
| 49 | .18767 | .19106 | 5.2339 | .98223 | 11 | 49 | .20478 | .20921 | 4.7798 | .97881 | 11 |
| **50** | .18795 | .19136 | 5.2257 | .98218 | **10** | **50** | .20507 | .20952 | 4.7729 | .97875 | **10** |
| 51 | .18824 | .19166 | 5.2174 | .98212 | 9 | 51 | .20535 | .20982 | 4.7659 | .97869 | 9 |
| 52 | .18852 | .19197 | 5.2092 | .98207 | 8 | 52 | .20563 | .21013 | 4.7591 | .97863 | 8 |
| 53 | .18881 | .19227 | 5.2011 | .98201 | 7 | 53 | .20592 | .21043 | 4.7522 | .97857 | 7 |
| 54 | .18910 | .19257 | 5.1929 | .98196 | 6 | 54 | .20620 | .21073 | 4.7453 | .97851 | 6 |
| **55** | .18938 | .19287 | 5.1848 | .98190 | **5** | **55** | .20649 | .21104 | 4.7385 | .97845 | **5** |
| 56 | .18967 | .19317 | 5.1767 | .98185 | 4 | 56 | .20677 | .21134 | 4.7317 | .97839 | 4 |
| 57 | .18995 | .19347 | 5.1686 | .98179 | 3 | 57 | .20706 | .21164 | 4.7249 | .97833 | 3 |
| 58 | .19024 | .19378 | 5.1606 | .98174 | 2 | 58 | .20734 | .21195 | 4.7181 | .97827 | 2 |
| 59 | .19052 | .19408 | 5.1526 | .98168 | 1 | 59 | .20763 | .21225 | 4.7114 | .97821 | 1 |
| **60** | .19081 | .19438 | 5.1446 | .98163 | **0** | **60** | .20791 | .21256 | 4.7046 | .97815 | **0** |
| ′ | Cos | Cot | Tan | Sin | ′ | ′ | Cos | Cot | Tan | Sin | ′ |

**100°** (280°)                 (259°) **79°**          **101°** (281°)                 (258°) **78°**

# NATURAL FUNCTIONS (Continued)

| ′ | Sin | Tan | Cot | Cos | ′ | | ′ | Sin | Tan | Cot | Cos | ′ |
|---|---|---|---|---|---|---|---|---|---|---|---|---|
| **0** | .20791 | .21256 | 4.7046 | .97815 | **60** | | **0** | .22495 | .23087 | 4.3315 | .97437 | **60** |
| 1 | .20820 | .21286 | 4.6979 | .97809 | 59 | | 1 | .22523 | .23117 | 4.3257 | .97430 | 59 |
| 2 | .20848 | .21316 | 4.6912 | .97803 | 58 | | 2 | .22552 | .23148 | 4.3200 | .97424 | 58 |
| 3 | .20877 | .21347 | 4.6845 | .97797 | 57 | | 3 | .22580 | .23179 | 4.3143 | .97417 | 57 |
| 4 | .20905 | .21377 | 4.6779 | .97791 | 56 | | 4 | .22608 | .23209 | 4.3086 | .97411 | 56 |
| **5** | .20933 | .21408 | 4.6712 | .97784 | **55** | | **5** | .22637 | .23240 | 4.3029 | .97404 | **55** |
| 6 | .20962 | .21438 | 4.6646 | .97778 | 54 | | 6 | .22665 | .23271 | 4.2972 | .97398 | 54 |
| 7 | .20990 | .21469 | 4.6580 | .97772 | 53 | | 7 | .22693 | .23301 | 4.2916 | .97391 | 53 |
| 8 | .21019 | .21499 | 4.6514 | .97766 | 52 | | 8 | .22722 | .23332 | 4.2859 | .97384 | 52 |
| 9 | .21047 | .21529 | 4.6448 | .97760 | 51 | | 9 | .22750 | .23363 | 4.2803 | .97378 | 51 |
| **10** | .21076 | .21560 | 4.6382 | .97754 | **50** | | **10** | .22778 | .23393 | 4.2747 | .97371 | **50** |
| 11 | .21104 | .21590 | 4.6317 | .97748 | 49 | | 11 | .22807 | .23424 | 4.2691 | .97365 | 49 |
| 12 | .21132 | .21621 | 4.6252 | .97742 | 48 | | 12 | .22835 | .23455 | 4.2635 | .97358 | 48 |
| 13 | .21161 | .21651 | 4.6187 | .97735 | 47 | | 13 | .22863 | .23485 | 4.2580 | .97351 | 47 |
| 14 | .21189 | .21682 | 4.6122 | .97729 | 46 | | 14 | .22892 | .23516 | 4.2524 | .97345 | 46 |
| **15** | .21218 | .21712 | 4.6057 | .97723 | **45** | | **15** | .22920 | .23547 | 4.2468 | .97338 | **45** |
| 16 | .21246 | .21743 | 4.5993 | .97717 | 44 | | 16 | .22948 | .23578 | 4.2413 | .97331 | 44 |
| 17 | .21275 | .21773 | 4.5928 | .97711 | 43 | | 17 | .22977 | .23608 | 4.2358 | .97325 | 43 |
| 18 | .21303 | .21804 | 4.5864 | .97705 | 42 | | 18 | .23005 | .23639 | 4.2303 | .97318 | 42 |
| 19 | .21331 | .21834 | 4.5800 | .97698 | 41 | | 19 | .23033 | .23670 | 4.2248 | .97311 | 41 |
| **20** | .21360 | .21864 | 4.5736 | .97692 | **40** | | **20** | .23062 | .23700 | 4.2193 | .97304 | **40** |
| 21 | .21388 | .21895 | 4.5673 | .97686 | 39 | | 21 | .23090 | .23731 | 4.2139 | .97298 | 39 |
| 22 | .21417 | .21925 | 4.5609 | .97680 | 38 | | 22 | .23118 | .23762 | 4.2084 | .97291 | 38 |
| 23 | .21445 | .21956 | 4.5546 | .97673 | 37 | | 23 | .23146 | .23793 | 4.2030 | .97284 | 37 |
| 24 | .21474 | .21986 | 4.5483 | .97667 | 36 | | 24 | .23175 | .23823 | 4.1976 | .97278 | 36 |
| **25** | .21502 | .22017 | 4.5420 | .97661 | **35** | | **25** | .23203 | .23854 | 4.1922 | .97271 | **35** |
| 26 | .21530 | .22047 | 4.5357 | .97655 | 34 | | 26 | .23231 | .23885 | 4.1868 | .97264 | 34 |
| 27 | .21559 | .22078 | 4.5294 | .97648 | 33 | | 27 | .23260 | .23916 | 4.1814 | .97257 | 33 |
| 28 | .21587 | .22108 | 4.5232 | .97642 | 32 | | 28 | .23288 | .23946 | 4.1760 | .97251 | 32 |
| 29 | .21616 | .22139 | 4.5169 | .97636 | 31 | | 29 | .23316 | .23977 | 4.1706 | .97244 | 31 |
| **30** | .21644 | .22169 | 4.5107 | .97630 | **30** | | **30** | .23345 | .24008 | 4.1653 | .97237 | **30** |
| 31 | .21672 | .22200 | 4.5045 | .97623 | 29 | | 31 | .23373 | .24039 | 4.1600 | .97230 | 29 |
| 32 | .21701 | .22231 | 4.4983 | .97617 | 28 | | 32 | .23401 | .24069 | 4.1547 | .97223 | 28 |
| 33 | .21729 | .22261 | 4.4922 | .97611 | 27 | | 33 | .23429 | .24100 | 4.1493 | .97217 | 27 |
| 34 | .21758 | .22292 | 4.4860 | .97604 | 26 | | 34 | .23458 | .24131 | 4.1441 | .97210 | 26 |
| **35** | .21786 | .22322 | 4.4799 | .97598 | **25** | | **35** | .23486 | .24162 | 4.1388 | .97203 | **25** |
| 36 | .21814 | .22353 | 4.4737 | .97592 | 24 | | 36 | .23514 | .24193 | 4.1335 | .97196 | 24 |
| 37 | .21843 | .22383 | 4.4676 | .97585 | 23 | | 37 | .23542 | .24223 | 4.1282 | .97189 | 23 |
| 38 | .21871 | .22414 | 4.4615 | .97579 | 22 | | 38 | .23571 | .24254 | 4.1230 | .97182 | 22 |
| 39 | .21899 | .22444 | 4.4555 | .97573 | 21 | | 39 | .23599 | .24285 | 4.1178 | .97176 | 21 |
| **40** | .21928 | .22475 | 4.4494 | .97566 | **20** | | **40** | .23627 | .24316 | 4.1126 | .97169 | **20** |
| 41 | .21956 | .22505 | 4.4434 | .97560 | 19 | | 41 | .23656 | .24347 | 4.1074 | .97162 | 19 |
| 42 | .21985 | .22536 | 4.4373 | .97553 | 18 | | 42 | .23684 | .24377 | 4.1022 | .97155 | 18 |
| 43 | .22013 | .22567 | 4.4313 | .97547 | 17 | | 43 | .23712 | .24408 | 4.0970 | .97148 | 17 |
| 44 | .22041 | .22597 | 4.4253 | .97541 | 16 | | 44 | .23740 | .24439 | 4.0918 | .97141 | 16 |
| **45** | .22070 | .22628 | 4.4194 | .97534 | **15** | | **45** | .23769 | .24470 | 4.0867 | .97134 | **15** |
| 46 | .22098 | .22658 | 4.4134 | .97528 | 14 | | 46 | .23797 | .24501 | 4.0815 | .97127 | 14 |
| 47 | .22126 | .22689 | 4.4075 | .97521 | 13 | | 47 | .23825 | .24532 | 4.0764 | .97120 | 13 |
| 48 | .22155 | .22719 | 4.4015 | .97515 | 12 | | 48 | .23853 | .24562 | 4.0713 | .97113 | 12 |
| 49 | .22183 | .22750 | 4.3956 | .97508 | 11 | | 49 | .23882 | .24593 | 4.0662 | .97106 | 11 |
| **50** | .22212 | .22781 | 4.3897 | .97502 | **10** | | **50** | .23910 | .24624 | 4.0611 | .97100 | **10** |
| 51 | .22240 | .22811 | 4.3838 | .97496 | 9 | | 51 | .23938 | .24655 | 4.0560 | .97093 | 9 |
| 52 | .22268 | .22842 | 4.3779 | .97489 | 8 | | 52 | .23966 | .24686 | 4.0509 | .97086 | 8 |
| 53 | .22297 | .22872 | 4.3721 | .97483 | 7 | | 53 | .23995 | .24717 | 4.0459 | .97079 | 7 |
| 54 | .22325 | .22903 | 4.3662 | .97476 | 6 | | 54 | .24023 | .24747 | 4.0408 | .97072 | 6 |
| **55** | .22353 | .22934 | 4.3604 | .97470 | **5** | | **55** | .24051 | .24778 | 4.0358 | .97065 | **5** |
| 56 | .22382 | .22964 | 4.3546 | .97463 | 4 | | 56 | .24079 | .24809 | 4.0308 | .97058 | 4 |
| 57 | .22410 | .22995 | 4.3488 | .97457 | 3 | | 57 | .24108 | .24840 | 4.0257 | .97051 | 3 |
| 58 | .22438 | .23026 | 4.3430 | .97450 | 2 | | 58 | .24136 | .24871 | 4.0207 | .97044 | 2 |
| 59 | .22467 | .23056 | 4.3372 | .97444 | 1 | | 59 | .24164 | .24902 | 4.0158 | .97037 | 1 |
| **60** | .22495 | .23087 | 4.3315 | .97437 | **0** | | **60** | .24192 | .24933 | 4.0108 | .97030 | **0** |
| ′ | Cos | Cot | Tan | Sin | ′ | | ′ | Cos | Cot | Tan | Sin | ′ |

14° (194°)  (345°) 165°  15° (195°)  (344°) 164°

| ′ | Sin | Tan | Cot | Cos | ′ | | ′ | Sin | Tan | Cot | Cos | ′ |
|---|-----|-----|-----|-----|---|---|---|-----|-----|-----|-----|---|
| **0** | .24192 | .24933 | 4.0108 | .97030 | **60** | | **0** | .25882 | .26795 | 3.7321 | .96593 | **60** |
| 1 | .24220 | .24964 | 4.0058 | .97023 | 59 | | 1 | .25910 | .26826 | 3.7277 | .96585 | 59 |
| 2 | .24249 | .24995 | 4.0009 | .97015 | 58 | | 2 | .25938 | .26857 | 3.7234 | .96578 | 58 |
| 3 | .24277 | .25026 | 3.9959 | .97008 | 57 | | 3 | .25966 | .26888 | 3.7191 | .96570 | 57 |
| 4 | .24305 | .25056 | 3.9910 | .97001 | 56 | | 4 | .25994 | .26920 | 3.7148 | .96562 | 56 |
| **5** | .24333 | .25087 | 3.9861 | .96994 | **55** | | **5** | .26022 | .26951 | 3.7105 | .96555 | **55** |
| 6 | .24362 | .25118 | 3.9812 | .96987 | 54 | | 6 | .26050 | .26982 | 3.7062 | .96547 | 54 |
| 7 | .24390 | .25149 | 3.9763 | .96980 | 53 | | 7 | .26079 | .27013 | 3.7019 | .96540 | 53 |
| 8 | .24418 | .25180 | 3.9714 | .96973 | 52 | | 8 | .26107 | .27044 | 3.6976 | .96532 | 52 |
| 9 | .24446 | .25211 | 3.9665 | .96966 | 51 | | 9 | .26135 | .27076 | 3.6933 | .96524 | 51 |
| **10** | .24474 | .25242 | 3.9617 | .96959 | **50** | | **10** | .26163 | .27107 | 3.6891 | .96517 | **50** |
| 11 | .24503 | .25273 | 3.9568 | .96952 | 49 | | 11 | .26191 | .27138 | 3.6848 | .96509 | 49 |
| 12 | .24531 | .25304 | 3.9520 | .96945 | 48 | | 12 | .26219 | .27169 | 3.6806 | .96502 | 48 |
| 13 | .24559 | .25335 | 3.9471 | .96937 | 47 | | 13 | .26247 | .27201 | 3.6764 | .96494 | 47 |
| 14 | .24587 | .25366 | 3.9423 | .96930 | 46 | | 14 | .26275 | .27232 | 3.6722 | .96486 | 46 |
| **15** | .24615 | .25397 | 3.9375 | .96923 | **45** | | **15** | .26303 | .27263 | 3.6680 | .96479 | **45** |
| 16 | .24644 | .25428 | 3.9327 | .96916 | 44 | | 16 | .26331 | .27294 | 3.6638 | .96471 | 44 |
| 17 | .24672 | .25459 | 3.9279 | .96909 | 43 | | 17 | .26359 | .27326 | 3.6596 | .96463 | 43 |
| 18 | .24700 | .25490 | 3.9232 | .96902 | 42 | | 18 | .26387 | .27357 | 3.6554 | .96456 | 42 |
| 19 | .24728 | .25521 | 3.9184 | .96894 | 41 | | 19 | .26415 | .27388 | 3.6512 | .96448 | 41 |
| **20** | .24756 | .25552 | 3.9136 | .96887 | **40** | | **20** | .26443 | .27419 | 3.6470 | .96440 | **40** |
| 21 | .24784 | .25583 | 3.9089 | .96880 | 39 | | 21 | .26471 | .27451 | 3.6429 | .96433 | 39 |
| 22 | .24813 | .25614 | 3.9042 | .96873 | 38 | | 22 | .26500 | .27482 | 3.6387 | .96425 | 38 |
| 23 | .24841 | .25645 | 3.8995 | .96866 | 37 | | 23 | .26528 | .27513 | 3.6346 | .96417 | 37 |
| 24 | .24869 | .25676 | 3.8947 | .96858 | 36 | | 24 | .26556 | .27545 | 3.6305 | .96410 | 36 |
| **25** | .24897 | .25707 | 3.8900 | .96851 | **35** | | **25** | .26584 | .27576 | 3.6264 | .96402 | **35** |
| 26 | .24925 | .25738 | 3.8854 | .96844 | 34 | | 26 | .26612 | .27607 | 3.6222 | .96394 | 34 |
| 27 | .24954 | .25769 | 3.8807 | .96837 | 33 | | 27 | .26640 | .27638 | 3.6181 | .96386 | 33 |
| 28 | .24982 | .25800 | 3.8760 | .96829 | 32 | | 28 | .26668 | .27670 | 3.6140 | .96379 | 32 |
| 29 | .25010 | .25831 | 3.8714 | .96822 | 31 | | 29 | .26696 | .27701 | 3.6100 | .96371 | 31 |
| **30** | .25038 | .25862 | 3.8667 | .96815 | **30** | | **30** | .26724 | .27732 | 3.6059 | .96363 | **30** |
| 31 | .25066 | .25893 | 3.8621 | .96807 | 29 | | 31 | .26752 | .27764 | 3.6018 | .96355 | 29 |
| 32 | .25094 | .25924 | 3.8575 | .96800 | 28 | | 32 | .26780 | .27795 | 3.5978 | .96347 | 28 |
| 33 | .25122 | .25955 | 3.8528 | .96793 | 27 | | 33 | .26808 | .27826 | 3.5937 | .96340 | 27 |
| 34 | .25151 | .25986 | 3.8482 | .96786 | 26 | | 34 | .26836 | .27858 | 3.5897 | .96332 | 26 |
| **35** | .25179 | .26017 | 3.8436 | .96778 | **25** | | **35** | .26864 | .27889 | 3.5856 | .96324 | **25** |
| 36 | .25207 | .26048 | 3.8391 | .96771 | 24 | | 36 | .26892 | .27921 | 3.5816 | .96316 | 24 |
| 37 | .25235 | .26079 | 3.8345 | .96764 | 23 | | 37 | .26920 | .27952 | 3.5776 | .96308 | 23 |
| 38 | .25263 | .26110 | 3.8299 | .96756 | 22 | | 38 | .26948 | .27983 | 3.5736 | .96301 | 22 |
| 39 | .25291 | .26141 | 3.8254 | .96749 | 21 | | 39 | .26976 | .28015 | 3.5696 | .96293 | 21 |
| **40** | .25320 | .26172 | 3.8208 | .96742 | **20** | | **40** | .27004 | .28046 | 3.5656 | .96285 | **20** |
| 41 | .25348 | .26203 | 3.8163 | .96734 | 19 | | 41 | .27032 | .28077 | 3.5616 | .96277 | 19 |
| 42 | .25376 | .26235 | 3.8118 | .96727 | 18 | | 42 | .27060 | .28109 | 3.5576 | .96269 | 18 |
| 43 | .25404 | .26266 | 3.8073 | .96719 | 17 | | 43 | .27088 | .28140 | 3.5536 | .96261 | 17 |
| 44 | .25432 | .26297 | 3.8028 | .96712 | 16 | | 44 | .27116 | .28172 | 3.5497 | .96253 | 16 |
| **45** | .25460 | .26328 | 3.7983 | .96705 | **15** | | **45** | .27144 | .28203 | 3.5457 | .96246 | **15** |
| 46 | .25488 | .26359 | 3.7938 | .96697 | 14 | | 46 | .27172 | .28234 | 3.5418 | .96238 | 14 |
| 47 | .25516 | .26390 | 3.7893 | .96690 | 13 | | 47 | .27200 | .28266 | 3.5379 | .96230 | 13 |
| 48 | .25545 | .26421 | 3.7848 | .96682 | 12 | | 48 | .27228 | .28297 | 3.5339 | .96222 | 12 |
| 49 | .25573 | .26452 | 3.7804 | .96675 | 11 | | 49 | .27256 | .28329 | 3.5300 | .96214 | 11 |
| **50** | .25601 | .26483 | 3.7760 | .96667 | **10** | | **50** | .27284 | .28360 | 3.5261 | .96206 | **10** |
| 51 | .25629 | .26515 | 3.7715 | .96660 | 9 | | 51 | .27312 | .28391 | 3.5222 | .96198 | 9 |
| 52 | .25657 | .26546 | 3.7671 | .96653 | 8 | | 52 | .27340 | .28423 | 3.5183 | .96190 | 8 |
| 53 | .25685 | .26577 | 3.7627 | .96645 | 7 | | 53 | .27368 | .28454 | 3.5144 | .96182 | 7 |
| 54 | .25713 | .26608 | 3.7583 | .96638 | 6 | | 54 | .27396 | .28486 | 3.5105 | .96174 | 6 |
| **55** | .25741 | .26639 | 3.7539 | .96630 | **5** | | **55** | .27424 | .28517 | 3.5067 | .96166 | **5** |
| 56 | .25769 | .26670 | 3.7495 | .96623 | 4 | | 56 | .27452 | .28549 | 3.5028 | .96158 | 4 |
| 57 | .25798 | .26701 | 3.7451 | .96615 | 3 | | 57 | .27480 | .28580 | 3.4989 | .96150 | 3 |
| 58 | .25826 | .26733 | 3.7408 | .96608 | 2 | | 58 | .27508 | .28612 | 3.4951 | .96142 | 2 |
| 59 | .25854 | .26764 | 3.7364 | .96600 | 1 | | 59 | .27536 | .28643 | 3.4912 | .96134 | 1 |
| **60** | .25882 | .26795 | 3.7321 | .96593 | **0** | | **60** | .27564 | .28675 | 3.4874 | .96126 | **0** |
| ′ | Cos | Cot | Tan | Sin | ′ | | ′ | Cos | Cot | Tan | Sin | ′ |

| ′ | Sin | Tan | Cot | Cos | ′ | | ′ | Sin | Tan | Cot | Cos | ′ |
|---|-----|-----|-----|-----|---|---|---|-----|-----|-----|-----|---|
| 0 | .27564 | .28675 | 3.4874 | .96126 | 60 | | 0 | .29237 | .30573 | 3.2709 | .95630 | 60 |
| 1 | .27592 | .28706 | 3.4836 | .96118 | 59 | | 1 | .29265 | .30605 | 3.2675 | .95622 | 59 |
| 2 | .27620 | .28738 | 3.4798 | .96110 | 58 | | 2 | .29293 | .30637 | 3.2641 | .95613 | 58 |
| 3 | .27648 | .28769 | 3.4760 | .96102 | 57 | | 3 | .29321 | .30669 | 3.2607 | .95605 | 57 |
| 4 | .27676 | .28801 | 3.4722 | .96094 | 56 | | 4 | .29348 | .30700 | 3.2573 | .95596 | 56 |
| 5 | .27704 | .28832 | 3.4684 | .96086 | 55 | | 5 | .29376 | .30732 | 3.2539 | .95588 | 55 |
| 6 | .27731 | .28864 | 3.4646 | .96078 | 54 | | 6 | .29404 | .30764 | 3.2506 | .95579 | 54 |
| 7 | .27759 | .28895 | 3.4608 | .96070 | 53 | | 7 | .29432 | .30796 | 3.2472 | .95571 | 53 |
| 8 | .27787 | .28927 | 3.4570 | .96062 | 52 | | 8 | .29460 | .30828 | 3.2438 | .95562 | 52 |
| 9 | .27815 | .28958 | 3.4533 | .96054 | 51 | | 9 | .29487 | .30860 | 3.2405 | .95554 | 51 |
| 10 | .27843 | .28990 | 3.4495 | .96046 | 50 | | 10 | .29515 | .30891 | 3.2371 | .95545 | 50 |
| 11 | .27871 | .29021 | 3.4458 | .96037 | 49 | | 11 | .29543 | .30923 | 3.2338 | .95536 | 49 |
| 12 | .27899 | .29053 | 3.4420 | .96029 | 48 | | 12 | .29571 | .30955 | 3.2305 | .95528 | 48 |
| 13 | .27927 | .29084 | 3.4383 | .96021 | 47 | | 13 | .29599 | .30987 | 3.2272 | .95519 | 47 |
| 14 | .27955 | .29116 | 3.4346 | .96013 | 46 | | 14 | .29626 | .31019 | 3.2238 | .95511 | 46 |
| 15 | .27983 | .29147 | 3.4308 | .96005 | 45 | | 15 | .29654 | .31051 | 3.2205 | .95502 | 45 |
| 16 | .28011 | .29179 | 3.4271 | .95997 | 44 | | 16 | .29682 | .31083 | 3.2172 | .95493 | 44 |
| 17 | .28039 | .29210 | 3.4234 | .95989 | 43 | | 17 | .29710 | .31115 | 3.2139 | .95485 | 43 |
| 18 | .28067 | .29242 | 3.4197 | .95981 | 42 | | 18 | .29737 | .31147 | 3.2106 | .95476 | 42 |
| 19 | .28095 | .29274 | 3.4160 | .95972 | 41 | | 19 | .29765 | .31178 | 3.2073 | .95467 | 41 |
| 20 | .28123 | .29305 | 3.4124 | .95964 | 40 | | 20 | .29793 | .31210 | 3.2041 | .95459 | 40 |
| 21 | .28150 | .29337 | 3.4087 | .95956 | 39 | | 21 | .29821 | .31242 | 3.2008 | .95450 | 39 |
| 22 | .28178 | .29368 | 3.4050 | .95948 | 38 | | 22 | .29849 | .31274 | 3.1975 | .95441 | 38 |
| 23 | .28206 | .29400 | 3.4014 | .95940 | 37 | | 23 | .29876 | .31306 | 3.1943 | .95433 | 37 |
| 24 | .28234 | .29432 | 3.3977 | .95931 | 36 | | 24 | .29904 | .31338 | 3.1910 | .95424 | 36 |
| 25 | .28262 | .29463 | 3.3941 | .95923 | 35 | | 25 | .29932 | .31370 | 3.1878 | .95415 | 35 |
| 26 | .28290 | .29495 | 3.3904 | .95915 | 34 | | 26 | .29960 | .31402 | 3.1845 | .95407 | 34 |
| 27 | .28318 | .29526 | 3.3868 | .95907 | 33 | | 27 | .29987 | .31434 | 3.1813 | .95398 | 33 |
| 28 | .28346 | .29558 | 3.3832 | .95898 | 32 | | 28 | .30015 | .31466 | 3.1780 | .95389 | 32 |
| 29 | .28374 | .29590 | 3.3796 | .95890 | 31 | | 29 | .30043 | .31498 | 3.1748 | .95380 | 31 |
| 30 | .28402 | .29621 | 3.3759 | .95882 | 30 | | 30 | .30071 | .31530 | 3.1716 | .95372 | 30 |
| 31 | .28429 | .29653 | 3.3723 | .95874 | 29 | | 31 | .30098 | .31562 | 3.1684 | .95363 | 29 |
| 32 | .28457 | .29685 | 3.3687 | .95865 | 28 | | 32 | .30126 | .31594 | 3.1652 | .95354 | 28 |
| 33 | .28485 | .29716 | 3.3652 | .95857 | 27 | | 33 | .30154 | .31626 | 3.1620 | .95345 | 27 |
| 34 | .28513 | .29748 | 3.3616 | .95849 | 26 | | 34 | .30182 | .31658 | 3.1588 | .95337 | 26 |
| 35 | .28541 | .29780 | 3.3580 | .95841 | 25 | | 35 | .30209 | .31690 | 3.1556 | .95328 | 25 |
| 36 | .28569 | .29811 | 3.3544 | .95832 | 24 | | 36 | .30237 | .31722 | 3.1524 | .95319 | 24 |
| 37 | .28597 | .29843 | 3.3509 | .95824 | 23 | | 37 | .30265 | .31754 | 3.1492 | .95310 | 23 |
| 38 | .28625 | .29875 | 3.3473 | .95816 | 22 | | 38 | .30292 | .31786 | 3.1460 | .95301 | 22 |
| 39 | .28652 | .29906 | 3.3438 | .95807 | 21 | | 39 | .30320 | .31818 | 3.1429 | .95293 | 21 |
| 40 | .28680 | .29938 | 3.3402 | .95799 | 20 | | 40 | .30348 | .31850 | 3.1397 | .95284 | 20 |
| 41 | .28708 | .29970 | 3.3367 | .95791 | 19 | | 41 | .30376 | .31882 | 3.1366 | .95275 | 19 |
| 42 | .28736 | .30001 | 3.3332 | .95782 | 18 | | 42 | .30403 | .31914 | 3.1334 | .95266 | 18 |
| 43 | .28764 | .30033 | 3.3297 | .95774 | 17 | | 43 | .30431 | .31946 | 3.1303 | .95257 | 17 |
| 44 | .28792 | .30065 | 3.3261 | .95766 | 16 | | 44 | .30459 | .31978 | 3.1271 | .95248 | 16 |
| 45 | .28820 | .30097 | 3.3226 | .95757 | 15 | | 45 | .30486 | .32010 | 3.1240 | .95240 | 15 |
| 46 | .28847 | .30128 | 3.3191 | .95749 | 14 | | 46 | .30514 | .32042 | 3.1209 | .95231 | 14 |
| 47 | .28875 | .30160 | 3.3156 | .05740 | 13 | | 47 | .30542 | .32074 | 3.1178 | .95222 | 13 |
| 48 | .28903 | .30192 | 3.3122 | .95732 | 12 | | 48 | .30570 | .32106 | 3.1146 | .95213 | 12 |
| 49 | .28931 | .30224 | 3.3087 | .95724 | 11 | | 49 | .30597 | .32139 | 3.1115 | .95204 | 11 |
| 50 | .28959 | .30255 | 3.3052 | .95715 | 10 | | 50 | .30625 | .32171 | 3.1084 | .95195 | 10 |
| 51 | .28987 | .30287 | 3.3017 | .95707 | 9 | | 51 | .30653 | .32203 | 3.1053 | .95186 | 9 |
| 52 | .29015 | .30319 | 3.2983 | .95698 | 8 | | 52 | .30680 | .32235 | 3.1022 | .95177 | 8 |
| 53 | .29042 | .30351 | 3.2948 | .95690 | 7 | | 53 | .30708 | .32267 | 3.0991 | .95168 | 7 |
| 54 | .29070 | .30382 | 3.2914 | .95681 | 6 | | 54 | .30736 | .32299 | 3.0961 | .95159 | 6 |
| 55 | .29098 | .30414 | 3.2879 | .95673 | 5 | | 55 | .30763 | .32331 | 3.0930 | .95150 | 5 |
| 56 | .29126 | .30446 | 3.2845 | .95664 | 4 | | 56 | .30791 | .32363 | 3.0899 | .95142 | 4 |
| 57 | .29154 | .30478 | 3.2811 | .95656 | 3 | | 57 | .30819 | .32396 | 3.0868 | .95133 | 3 |
| 58 | .29182 | .30509 | 3.2777 | .95647 | 2 | | 58 | .30846 | .32428 | 3.0838 | .95124 | 2 |
| 59 | .29209 | .30541 | 3.2743 | .95639 | 1 | | 59 | .30874 | .32460 | 3.0807 | .95115 | 1 |
| 60 | .29237 | .30573 | 3.2709 | .95630 | 0 | | 60 | .30902 | .32492 | 3.0777 | .95106 | 0 |
| ′ | Cos | Cot | Tan | Sin | ′ | | ′ | Cos | Cot | Tan | Sin | ′ |

# NATURAL FUNCTIONS (Continued)

18° (198°) (341°) **161°**　　19° (199°) (340°) **160°**

| ′ | Sin | Tan | Cot | Cos | ′ | ′ | Sin | Tan | Cot | Cos | ′ |
|---|-----|-----|-----|-----|---|---|-----|-----|-----|-----|---|
| **0** | .30902 | .32492 | 3.0777 | .95106 | **60** | **0** | .32557 | .34433 | 2.9042 | .94552 | **60** |
| 1 | .30929 | .32524 | 3.0746 | .95097 | 59 | 1 | .32584 | .34465 | 2.9015 | .94542 | 59 |
| 2 | .30957 | .32556 | 3.0716 | .95088 | 58 | 2 | .32612 | .34498 | 2.8987 | .94533 | 58 |
| 3 | .30985 | .32588 | 3.0686 | .95079 | 57 | 3 | .32639 | .34530 | 2.8960 | .94523 | 57 |
| 4 | .31012 | .32621 | 3.0655 | .95070 | 56 | 4 | .32667 | .34563 | 2.8933 | .94514 | 56 |
| **5** | .31040 | .32653 | 3.0625 | .95061 | **55** | **5** | .32694 | .34596 | 2.8905 | .94504 | **55** |
| 6 | .31068 | .32685 | 3.0595 | .95052 | 54 | 6 | .32722 | .34628 | 2.8878 | .94495 | 54 |
| 7 | .31095 | .32717 | 3.0565 | .95043 | 53 | 7 | .32749 | .34661 | 2.8851 | .94485 | 53 |
| 8 | .31123 | .32749 | 3.0535 | .95033 | 52 | 8 | .32777 | .34693 | 2.8824 | .94476 | 52 |
| 9 | .31151 | .32782 | 3.0505 | .95024 | 51 | 9 | .32804 | .34726 | 2.8797 | .94466 | 51 |
| **10** | .31178 | .32814 | 3.0475 | .95015 | **50** | **10** | .32832 | .34758 | 2.8770 | .94457 | **50** |
| 11 | .31206 | .32846 | 3.0445 | .95006 | 49 | 11 | .32859 | .34791 | 2.8743 | .94447 | 49 |
| 12 | .31233 | .32878 | 3.0415 | .94997 | 48 | 12 | .32887 | .34824 | 2.8716 | .94438 | 48 |
| 13 | .31261 | .32911 | 3.0385 | .94988 | 47 | 13 | .32914 | .34856 | 2.8689 | .94428 | 47 |
| 14 | .31289 | .32943 | 3.0356 | .94979 | 46 | 14 | .32942 | .34889 | 2.8662 | .94418 | 46 |
| **15** | .31316 | .32975 | 3.0326 | .94970 | **45** | **15** | .32969 | .34922 | 2.8636 | .94409 | **45** |
| 16 | .31344 | .33007 | 3.0296 | .94961 | 44 | 16 | .32997 | .34954 | 2.8609 | .94399 | 44 |
| 17 | .31372 | .33040 | 3.0267 | .94952 | 43 | 17 | .33024 | .34987 | 2.8582 | .94390 | 43 |
| 18 | .31399 | .33072 | 3.0237 | .94943 | 42 | 18 | .33051 | .35020 | 2.8556 | .94380 | 42 |
| 19 | .31427 | .33104 | 3.0208 | .94933 | 41 | 19 | .33079 | .35052 | 2.8529 | .94370 | 41 |
| **20** | .31454 | .33136 | 3.0178 | .94924 | **40** | **20** | .33106 | .35085 | 2.8502 | .94361 | **40** |
| 21 | .31482 | .33169 | 3.0149 | .94915 | 39 | 21 | .33134 | .35118 | 2.8476 | .94351 | 39 |
| 22 | .31510 | .33201 | 3.0120 | .94906 | 38 | 22 | .33161 | .35150 | 2.8449 | .94342 | 38 |
| 23 | .31537 | .33233 | 3.0090 | .94897 | 37 | 23 | .33189 | .35183 | 2.8423 | .94332 | 37 |
| 24 | .31565 | .33266 | 3.0061 | .94888 | 36 | 24 | .33216 | .35216 | 2.8397 | .94322 | 36 |
| **25** | .31593 | .33298 | 3.0032 | .94878 | **35** | **25** | .33244 | .35248 | 2.8370 | .94313 | **35** |
| 26 | .31620 | .33330 | 3.0003 | .94869 | 34 | 26 | .33271 | .35281 | 2.8344 | .94303 | 34 |
| 27 | .31648 | .33363 | 2.9974 | .94860 | 33 | 27 | .33298 | .35314 | 2.8318 | .94293 | 33 |
| 28 | .31675 | .33395 | 2.9945 | .94851 | 32 | 28 | .33326 | .35346 | 2.8291 | .94284 | 32 |
| 29 | .31703 | .33427 | 2.9916 | .94842 | 31 | 29 | .33353 | .35379 | 2.8265 | .94274 | 31 |
| **30** | .31730 | .33460 | 2.9887 | .94832 | **30** | **30** | .33381 | .35412 | 2.8239 | .94264 | **30** |
| 31 | .31758 | .33492 | 2.9858 | .94823 | 29 | 31 | .33408 | .35445 | 2.8213 | .94254 | 29 |
| 32 | .31786 | .33524 | 2.9829 | .94814 | 28 | 32 | .33436 | .35477 | 2.8187 | .94245 | 28 |
| 33 | .31813 | .33557 | 2.9800 | .94805 | 27 | 33 | .33463 | .35510 | 2.8161 | .94235 | 27 |
| 34 | .31841 | .33589 | 2.9772 | .94795 | 26 | 34 | .33490 | .35543 | 2.8135 | .94225 | 26 |
| **35** | .31868 | .33621 | 2.9743 | .94786 | **25** | **35** | .33518 | .35576 | 2.8109 | .94215 | **25** |
| 36 | .31896 | .33654 | 2.9714 | .94777 | 24 | 36 | .33545 | .35608 | 2.8083 | .94206 | 24 |
| 37 | .31923 | .33686 | 2.9686 | .94768 | 23 | 37 | .33573 | .35641 | 2.8057 | .94196 | 23 |
| 38 | .31951 | .33718 | 2.9657 | .94758 | 22 | 38 | .33600 | .35674 | 2.8032 | .94186 | 22 |
| 39 | .31979 | .33751 | 2.9629 | .94749 | 21 | 39 | .33627 | .35707 | 2.8006 | .94176 | 21 |
| **40** | .32006 | .33783 | 2.9600 | .94740 | **20** | **40** | .33655 | .35740 | 2.7980 | .94167 | **20** |
| 41 | .32034 | .33816 | 2.9572 | .94730 | 19 | 41 | .33682 | .35772 | 2.7955 | .94157 | 19 |
| 42 | .32061 | .33848 | 2.9544 | .94721 | 18 | 42 | .33710 | .35805 | 2.7929 | .94147 | 18 |
| 43 | .32089 | .33881 | 2.9515 | .94712 | 17 | 43 | .33737 | .35838 | 2.7903 | .94137 | 17 |
| 44 | .32116 | .33913 | 2.9487 | .94702 | 16 | 44 | .33764 | .35871 | 2.7878 | .94127 | 16 |
| **45** | .32144 | .33945 | 2.9459 | .94693 | **15** | **45** | .33792 | .35904 | 2.7852 | .94118 | **15** |
| 46 | .32171 | .33978 | 2.9431 | .94684 | 14 | 46 | .33819 | .35937 | 2.7827 | .94108 | 14 |
| 47 | .32199 | .34010 | 2.9403 | .94674 | 13 | 47 | .33846 | .35969 | 2.7801 | .94098 | 13 |
| 48 | .32227 | .34043 | 2.9375 | .94665 | 12 | 48 | .33874 | .36002 | 2.7776 | .94088 | 12 |
| 49 | .32254 | .34075 | 2.9347 | .94656 | 11 | 49 | .33901 | .36035 | 2.7751 | .94078 | 11 |
| **50** | .32282 | .34108 | 2.9319 | .94646 | **10** | **50** | .33929 | .36068 | 2.7725 | .94068 | **10** |
| 51 | .32309 | .34140 | 2.9291 | .94637 | 9 | 51 | .33956 | .36101 | 2.7700 | .94058 | 9 |
| 52 | .32337 | .34173 | 2.9263 | .94627 | 8 | 52 | .33983 | .36134 | 2.7675 | .94049 | 8 |
| 53 | .32364 | .34205 | 2.9235 | .94618 | 7 | 53 | .34011 | .36167 | 2.7650 | .94039 | 7 |
| 54 | .32392 | .34238 | 2.9208 | .94609 | 6 | 54 | .34038 | .36199 | 2.7625 | .94029 | 6 |
| **55** | .32419 | .34270 | 2.9180 | .94599 | **5** | **55** | .34065 | .36232 | 2.7600 | .94019 | **5** |
| 56 | .32447 | .34303 | 2.9152 | .94590 | 4 | 56 | .34093 | .36265 | 2.7575 | .94009 | 4 |
| 57 | .32474 | .34335 | 2.9125 | .94580 | 3 | 57 | .34120 | .36298 | 2.7550 | .93999 | 3 |
| 58 | .32502 | .34368 | 2.9097 | .94571 | 2 | 58 | .34147 | .36331 | 2.7525 | .93989 | 2 |
| 59 | .32529 | .34400 | 2.9070 | .94561 | 1 | 59 | .34175 | .36364 | 2.7500 | .93979 | 1 |
| **60** | .32557 | .34433 | 2.9042 | .94552 | **0** | **60** | .34202 | .36397 | 2.7475 | .93969 | **0** |
| ′ | Cos | Cot | Tan | Sin | ′ | ′ | Cos | Cot | Tan | Sin | ′ |

**20° (200°)**                    (339°) **159°**    **21° (201°)**                    (338°) **158°**

| ′ | Sin | Tan | Cot | Cos | ′ | ′ | Sin | Tan | Cot | Cos | ′ |
|---|-----|-----|-----|-----|---|---|-----|-----|-----|-----|---|
| **0** | .34202 | .36397 | 2.7475 | .93969 | **60** | **0** | .35837 | .38386 | 2.6051 | .93358 | **60** |
| 1 | .34229 | .36430 | 2.7450 | .93959 | 59 | 1 | .35864 | .38420 | 2.6028 | .93348 | 59 |
| 2 | .34257 | .36463 | 2.7425 | .93949 | 58 | 2 | .35891 | .38453 | 2.6006 | .93337 | 58 |
| 3 | .34284 | .36496 | 2.7400 | .93939 | 57 | 3 | .35918 | .38487 | 2.5983 | .93327 | 57 |
| 4 | .34311 | .36529 | 2.7376 | .93929 | 56 | 4 | .35945 | .38520 | 2.5961 | .93316 | 56 |
| **5** | .34339 | .36562 | 2.7351 | .93919 | **55** | **5** | .35973 | .38553 | 2.5938 | .93306 | **55** |
| 6 | .34366 | .36595 | 2.7326 | .93909 | 54 | 6 | .36000 | .38587 | 2.5916 | .93295 | 54 |
| 7 | .34393 | .36628 | 2.7302 | .93899 | 53 | 7 | .36027 | .38620 | 2.5893 | .93285 | 53 |
| 8 | .34421 | .36661 | 2.7277 | .93889 | 52 | 8 | .36054 | .38654 | 2.5871 | .93274 | 52 |
| 9 | .34448 | .36694 | 2.7253 | .93879 | 51 | 9 | .36081 | .38687 | 2.5848 | .93264 | 51 |
| **10** | .34475 | .36727 | 2.7228 | .93869 | **50** | **10** | .36108 | .38721 | 2.5826 | .93253 | **50** |
| 11 | .34503 | .36760 | 2.7204 | .93859 | 49 | 11 | .36135 | .38754 | 2.5804 | .93243 | 49 |
| 12 | .34530 | .36793 | 2.7179 | .93849 | 48 | 12 | .36162 | .38787 | 2.5782 | .93232 | 48 |
| 13 | .34557 | .36826 | 2.7155 | .93839 | 47 | 13 | .36190 | .38821 | 2.5759 | .93222 | 47 |
| 14 | .34584 | .36859 | 2.7130 | .93829 | 46 | 14 | .36217 | .38854 | 2.5737 | .93211 | 46 |
| **15** | .34612 | .36892 | 2.7106 | .93819 | **45** | **15** | .36244 | .38888 | 2.5715 | .93201 | **45** |
| 16 | .34639 | .36925 | 2.7082 | .93809 | 44 | 16 | .36271 | .38921 | 2.5693 | .93190 | 44 |
| 17 | .34666 | .36958 | 2.7058 | .93799 | 43 | 17 | .36298 | .38955 | 2.5671 | .93180 | 43 |
| 18 | .34694 | .36991 | 2.7034 | .93789 | 42 | 18 | .36325 | .38988 | 2.5649 | .93169 | 42 |
| 19 | .34721 | .37024 | 2.7009 | .93779 | 41 | 19 | .36352 | .39022 | 2.5627 | .93159 | 41 |
| **20** | .34748 | .37057 | 2.6985 | .93769 | **40** | **20** | .36379 | .39055 | 2.5605 | .93148 | **40** |
| 21 | .34775 | .37090 | 2.6961 | .93759 | 39 | 21 | .36406 | .39089 | 2.5583 | .93137 | 39 |
| 22 | .34803 | .37123 | 2.6937 | .93748 | 38 | 22 | .36434 | .39122 | 2.5561 | .93127 | 38 |
| 23 | .34830 | .37157 | 2.6913 | .93738 | 37 | 23 | .36461 | .39156 | 2.5539 | .93116 | 37 |
| 24 | .34857 | .37190 | 2.6889 | .93728 | 36 | 24 | .36488 | .39190 | 2.5517 | .93106 | 36 |
| **25** | .34884 | .37223 | 2.6865 | .93718 | **35** | **25** | .36515 | .39223 | 2.5495 | .93095 | **35** |
| 26 | .34912 | .37256 | 2.6841 | .93708 | 34 | 26 | .36542 | .39257 | 2.5473 | .93084 | 34 |
| 27 | .34939 | .37289 | 2.6818 | .93698 | 33 | 27 | .36569 | .39290 | 2.5452 | .93074 | 33 |
| 28 | .34966 | .37322 | 2.6794 | .93688 | 32 | 28 | .36596 | .39324 | 2.5430 | .93063 | 32 |
| 29 | .34993 | .37355 | 2.6770 | .93677 | 31 | 29 | .36623 | .39357 | 2.5408 | .93052 | 31 |
| **30** | .35021 | .37388 | 2.6746 | .93667 | **30** | **30** | .36650 | .39391 | 2.5386 | .93042 | **30** |
| 31 | .35048 | .37422 | 2.6723 | .93657 | 29 | 31 | .36677 | .39425 | 2.5365 | .93031 | 29 |
| 32 | .35075 | .37455 | 2.6699 | .93647 | 28 | 32 | .36704 | .39458 | 2.5343 | .93020 | 28 |
| 33 | .35102 | .37488 | 2.6675 | .93637 | 27 | 33 | .36731 | .39492 | 2.5322 | .93010 | 27 |
| 34 | .35130 | .37521 | 2.6652 | .93626 | 26 | 34 | .36758 | .39526 | 2.5300 | .92999 | 26 |
| **35** | .35157 | .37554 | 2.6628 | .93616 | **25** | **35** | .36785 | .39559 | 2.5279 | .92988 | **25** |
| 36 | .35184 | .37588 | 2.6605 | .93606 | 24 | 36 | .36812 | .39593 | 2.5257 | .92978 | 24 |
| 37 | .35211 | .37621 | 2.6581 | .93596 | 23 | 37 | .36839 | .39626 | 2.5236 | .92967 | 23 |
| 38 | .35239 | .37654 | 2.6558 | .93585 | 22 | 38 | .36867 | .39660 | 2.5214 | .92956 | 22 |
| 39 | .35266 | .37687 | 2.6534 | .93575 | 21 | 39 | .36894 | .39694 | 2.5193 | .92945 | 21 |
| **40** | .35293 | .37720 | 2.6511 | .93565 | **20** | **40** | .36921 | .39727 | 2.5172 | .92935 | **20** |
| 41 | .35320 | .37754 | 2.6488 | .93555 | 19 | 41 | .36948 | .39761 | 2.5150 | .92924 | 19 |
| 42 | .35347 | .37787 | 2.6464 | .93544 | 18 | 42 | .36975 | .39795 | 2.5129 | .92913 | 18 |
| 43 | .35375 | .37820 | 2.6441 | .93534 | 17 | 43 | .37002 | .39829 | 2.5108 | .92902 | 17 |
| 44 | .35402 | .37853 | 2.6418 | .93524 | 16 | 44 | .37029 | .39862 | 2.5086 | .92892 | 16 |
| **45** | .35429 | .37887 | 2.6395 | .93514 | **15** | **45** | .37056 | .39896 | 2.5065 | .92881 | **15** |
| 46 | .35456 | .37920 | 2.6371 | .93503 | 14 | 46 | .37083 | .39930 | 2.5044 | .92870 | 14 |
| 47 | .35484 | .37953 | 2.6348 | .93493 | 13 | 47 | .37110 | .39963 | 2.5023 | .92859 | 13 |
| 48 | .35511 | .37986 | 2.6325 | .93483 | 12 | 48 | .37137 | .39997 | 2.5002 | .92849 | 12 |
| 49 | .35538 | .38020 | 2.6302 | .93472 | 11 | 49 | .37164 | .40031 | 2.4981 | .92838 | 11 |
| **50** | .35565 | .38053 | 2.6279 | .93462 | **10** | **50** | .37191 | .40065 | 2.4960 | .92827 | **10** |
| 51 | .35592 | .38086 | 2.6256 | .93452 | 9 | 51 | .37218 | .40098 | 2.4939 | .92816 | 9 |
| 52 | .35619 | .38120 | 2.6233 | .93441 | 8 | 52 | .37245 | .40132 | 2.4918 | .92805 | 8 |
| 53 | .35647 | .38153 | 2.6210 | .93431 | 7 | 53 | .37272 | .40166 | 2.4897 | .92794 | 7 |
| 54 | .35674 | .38186 | 2.6187 | .93420 | 6 | 54 | .37299 | .40200 | 2.4876 | .92784 | 6 |
| **55** | .35701 | .38220 | 2.6165 | .93410 | **5** | **55** | .37326 | .40234 | 2.4855 | .92773 | **5** |
| 56 | .35728 | .38253 | 2.6142 | .93400 | 4 | 56 | .37353 | .40267 | 2.4834 | .92762 | 4 |
| 57 | .35755 | .38286 | 2.6119 | .93389 | 3 | 57 | .37380 | .40301 | 2.4813 | .92751 | 3 |
| 58 | .35782 | .38320 | 2.6096 | .93379 | 2 | 58 | .37407 | .40335 | 2.4792 | .92740 | 2 |
| 59 | .35810 | .38353 | 2.6074 | .93368 | 1 | 59 | .37434 | .40369 | 2.4772 | .92729 | 1 |
| **60** | .35837 | .38386 | 2.6051 | .93358 | **0** | **60** | .37461 | .40403 | 2.4751 | .92718 | **0** |
| ′ | Cos | Cot | Tan | Sin | ′ | ′ | Cos | Cot | Tan | Sin | ′ |

| ' | Sin | Tan | Cot | Cos | ' | | ' | Sin | Tan | Cot | Cos | ' |
|---|---|---|---|---|---|---|---|---|---|---|---|---|
| 0 | .37461 | .40403 | 2.4751 | .92718 | 60 | | 0 | .39073 | .42447 | 2.3559 | .92050 | 60 |
| 1 | .37488 | .40436 | 2.4730 | .92707 | 59 | | 1 | .39100 | .42482 | 2.3539 | .92039 | 59 |
| 2 | .37515 | .40470 | 2.4709 | .92697 | 58 | | 2 | .39127 | .42516 | 2.3520 | .92028 | 58 |
| 3 | .37542 | .40504 | 2.4689 | .92686 | 57 | | 3 | .39153 | .42551 | 2.3501 | .92016 | 57 |
| 4 | .37569 | .40538 | 2.4668 | .92675 | 56 | | 4 | .39180 | .42585 | 2.3483 | .92005 | 56 |
| 5 | .37595 | .40572 | 2.4648 | .92664 | 55 | | 5 | .39207 | .42619 | 2.3464 | .91994 | 55 |
| 6 | .37622 | .40606 | 2.4627 | .92653 | 54 | | 6 | .39234 | .42654 | 2.3445 | .91982 | 54 |
| 7 | .37649 | .40640 | 2.4606 | .92642 | 53 | | 7 | .39260 | .42688 | 2.3426 | .91971 | 53 |
| 8 | .37676 | .40674 | 2.4586 | .92631 | 52 | | 8 | .39287 | .42722 | 2.3407 | .91959 | 52 |
| 9 | .37703 | .40707 | 2.4566 | .92620 | 51 | | 9 | .39314 | .42757 | 2.3388 | .91948 | 51 |
| 10 | .37730 | .40741 | 2.4545 | .92609 | 50 | | 10 | .39341 | .42791 | 2.3369 | .91936 | 50 |
| 11 | .37757 | .40775 | 2.4525 | .92598 | 49 | | 11 | .39367 | .42826 | 2.3351 | .91925 | 49 |
| 12 | .37784 | .40809 | 2.4504 | .92587 | 48 | | 12 | .39394 | .42860 | 2.3332 | .91914 | 48 |
| 13 | .37811 | .40843 | 2.4484 | .92576 | 47 | | 13 | .39421 | .42894 | 2.3313 | .91902 | 47 |
| 14 | .37838 | .40877 | 2.4464 | .92565 | 46 | | 14 | .39448 | .42929 | 2.3294 | .91891 | 46 |
| 15 | .37865 | .40911 | 2.4443 | .92554 | 45 | | 15 | .39474 | .42963 | 2.3276 | .91879 | 45 |
| 16 | .37892 | .40945 | 2.4423 | .92543 | 44 | | 16 | .39501 | .42998 | 2.3257 | .91868 | 44 |
| 17 | .37919 | .40979 | 2.4403 | .92532 | 43 | | 17 | .39528 | .43032 | 2.3238 | .91856 | 43 |
| 18 | .37946 | .41013 | 2.4383 | .92521 | 42 | | 18 | .39555 | .43067 | 2.3220 | .91845 | 42 |
| 19 | .37973 | .41047 | 2.4362 | .92510 | 41 | | 19 | .39581 | .43101 | 2.3201 | .91833 | 41 |
| 20 | .37999 | .41081 | 2.4342 | .92499 | 40 | | 20 | .39608 | .43136 | 2.3183 | .91822 | 40 |
| 21 | .38026 | .41115 | 2.4322 | .92488 | 39 | | 21 | .39635 | .43170 | 2.3164 | .91810 | 39 |
| 22 | .38053 | .41149 | 2.4302 | .92477 | 38 | | 22 | .39661 | .43205 | 2.3146 | .91799 | 38 |
| 23 | .38080 | .41183 | 2.4282 | .92466 | 37 | | 23 | .39688 | .43239 | 2.3127 | .91787 | 37 |
| 24 | .38107 | .41217 | 2.4262 | .92455 | 36 | | 24 | .39715 | .43274 | 2.3109 | .91775 | 36 |
| 25 | .38134 | .41251 | 2.4242 | .92444 | 35 | | 25 | .39741 | .43308 | 2.3090 | .91764 | 35 |
| 26 | .38161 | .41285 | 2.4222 | .92432 | 34 | | 26 | .39768 | .43343 | 2.3072 | .91752 | 34 |
| 27 | .38188 | .41319 | 2.4202 | .92421 | 33 | | 27 | .39795 | .43378 | 2.3053 | .91741 | 33 |
| 28 | .38215 | .41353 | 2.4182 | .92410 | 32 | | 28 | .39822 | .43412 | 2.3035 | .91729 | 32 |
| 29 | .38241 | .41387 | 2.4162 | .92399 | 31 | | 29 | .39848 | .43447 | 2.3017 | .91718 | 31 |
| 30 | .38268 | .41421 | 2.4142 | .92388 | 30 | | 30 | .39875 | .43481 | 2.2998 | .91706 | 30 |
| 31 | .38295 | .41455 | 2.4122 | .92377 | 29 | | 31 | .39902 | .43516 | 2.2980 | .91694 | 29 |
| 32 | .38322 | .41490 | 2.4102 | .92366 | 28 | | 32 | .39928 | .43550 | 2.2962 | .91683 | 28 |
| 33 | .38349 | .41524 | 2.4083 | .92355 | 27 | | 33 | .39955 | .43585 | 2.2944 | .91671 | 27 |
| 34 | .38376 | .41558 | 2.4063 | .92343 | 26 | | 34 | .39982 | .43620 | 2.2925 | .91660 | 26 |
| 35 | .38403 | .41592 | 2.4043 | .92332 | 25 | | 35 | .40008 | .43654 | 2.2907 | .91648 | 25 |
| 36 | .38430 | .41626 | 2.4023 | .92321 | 24 | | 36 | .40035 | .43689 | 2.2889 | .91636 | 24 |
| 37 | .38456 | .41660 | 2.4004 | .92310 | 23 | | 37 | .40062 | .43724 | 2.2871 | .91625 | 23 |
| 38 | .38483 | .41694 | 2.3984 | .92299 | 22 | | 38 | .40088 | .43758 | 2.2853 | .91613 | 22 |
| 39 | .38510 | .41728 | 2.3964 | .92287 | 21 | | 39 | .40115 | .43793 | 2.2835 | .91601 | 21 |
| 40 | .38537 | .41763 | 2.3945 | .92276 | 20 | | 40 | .40141 | .43828 | 2.2817 | .91590 | 20 |
| 41 | .38564 | .41797 | 2.3925 | .92265 | 19 | | 41 | .40168 | .43862 | 2.2799 | .91578 | 19 |
| 42 | .38591 | .41831 | 2.3906 | .92254 | 18 | | 42 | .40195 | .43897 | 2.2781 | .91566 | 18 |
| 43 | .38617 | .41865 | 2.3886 | .92243 | 17 | | 43 | .40221 | .43932 | 2.2763 | .91555 | 17 |
| 44 | .38644 | .41899 | 2.3867 | .92231 | 16 | | 44 | .40248 | .43966 | 2.2745 | .91543 | 16 |
| 45 | .38671 | .41933 | 2.3847 | .92220 | 15 | | 45 | .40275 | .44001 | 2.2727 | .91531 | 15 |
| 46 | .38698 | .41968 | 2.3828 | .92209 | 14 | | 46 | .40301 | .44036 | 2.2709 | .91519 | 14 |
| 47 | .38725 | .42002 | 2.3808 | .92198 | 13 | | 47 | .40328 | .44071 | 2.2691 | .91508 | 13 |
| 48 | .38752 | .42036 | 2.3789 | .92186 | 12 | | 48 | .40355 | .44105 | 2.2673 | .91496 | 12 |
| 49 | .38778 | .42070 | 2.3770 | .92175 | 11 | | 49 | .40381 | .44140 | 2.2655 | .91484 | 11 |
| 50 | .38805 | .42105 | 2.3750 | .92164 | 10 | | 50 | .40408 | .44175 | 2.2637 | .91472 | 10 |
| 51 | .38832 | .42139 | 2.3731 | .92152 | 9 | | 51 | .40434 | .44210 | 2.2620 | .91461 | 9 |
| 52 | .38859 | .42173 | 2.3712 | .92141 | 8 | | 52 | .40461 | .44244 | 2.2602 | .91449 | 8 |
| 53 | .38886 | .42207 | 2.3693 | .92130 | 7 | | 53 | .40488 | .44279 | 2.2584 | .91437 | 7 |
| 54 | .38912 | .42242 | 2.3673 | .92119 | 6 | | 54 | .40514 | .44314 | 2.2566 | .91425 | 6 |
| 55 | .38939 | .42276 | 2.3654 | .92107 | 5 | | 55 | .40541 | .44349 | 2.2549 | .91414 | 5 |
| 56 | .38966 | .42310 | 2.3635 | .92096 | 4 | | 56 | .40567 | .44384 | 2.2531 | .91402 | 4 |
| 57 | .38993 | .42345 | 2.3616 | .92085 | 3 | | 57 | .40594 | .44418 | 2.2513 | .91390 | 3 |
| 58 | .39020 | .42379 | 2.3597 | .92073 | 2 | | 58 | .40621 | .44453 | 2.2496 | .91378 | 2 |
| 59 | .39046 | .42413 | 2.3578 | .92062 | 1 | | 59 | .40647 | .44488 | 2.2478 | .91366 | 1 |
| 60 | .39073 | .42447 | 2.3559 | .92050 | 0 | | 60 | .40674 | .44523 | 2.2460 | .91355 | 0 |
| ' | Cos | Cot | Tan | Sin | ' | | ' | Cos | Cot | Tan | Sin | ' |

## NATURAL FUNCTIONS (Continued)

24° (204°)        (335°) **155°**        25° (205°)        (334°) **154°**

| ′ | Sin | Tan | Cot | Cos | ′ | | ′ | Sin | Tan | Cot | Cos | ′ |
|---|-----|-----|-----|-----|---|---|---|-----|-----|-----|-----|---|
| **0** | .40674 | .44523 | 2.2460 | .91355 | **60** | | **0** | .42262 | .46631 | 2.1445 | .90631 | **60** |
| 1 | .40700 | .44558 | 2.2443 | .91343 | 59 | | 1 | .42288 | .46666 | 2.1429 | .90618 | 59 |
| 2 | .40727 | .44593 | 2.2425 | .91331 | 58 | | 2 | .42315 | .46702 | 2.1413 | .90606 | 58 |
| 3 | .40753 | .44627 | 2.2408 | .91319 | 57 | | 3 | .42341 | .46737 | 2.1396 | .90594 | 57 |
| 4 | .40780 | .44662 | 2.2390 | .91307 | 56 | | 4 | .42367 | .46772 | 2.1380 | .90582 | 56 |
| **5** | .40806 | .44697 | 2.2373 | .91295 | **55** | | **5** | .42394 | .46808 | 2.1364 | .90569 | **55** |
| 6 | .40833 | .44732 | 2.2355 | .91283 | 54 | | 6 | .42420 | .46843 | 2.1348 | .90557 | 54 |
| 7 | .40860 | .44767 | 2.2338 | .91272 | 53 | | 7 | .42446 | .46879 | 2.1332 | .90545 | 53 |
| 8 | .40886 | .44802 | 2.2320 | .91260 | 52 | | 8 | .42473 | .46914 | 2.1315 | .90532 | 52 |
| 9 | .40913 | .44837 | 2.2303 | .91248 | 51 | | 9 | .42499 | .46950 | 2.1299 | .90520 | 51 |
| **10** | .40939 | .44872 | 2.2286 | .91236 | **50** | | **10** | .42525 | .46985 | 2.1283 | .90507 | **50** |
| 11 | .40966 | .44907 | 2.2268 | .91224 | 49 | | 11 | .42552 | .47021 | 2.1267 | .90495 | 49 |
| 12 | .40992 | .44942 | 2.2251 | .91212 | 48 | | 12 | .42578 | .47056 | 2.1251 | .90483 | 48 |
| 13 | .41019 | .44977 | 2.2234 | .91200 | 47 | | 13 | .42604 | .47092 | 2.1235 | .90470 | 47 |
| 14 | .41045 | .45012 | 2.2216 | .91188 | 46 | | 14 | .42631 | .47128 | 2.1219 | .90458 | 46 |
| **15** | .41072 | .45047 | 2.2199 | .91176 | **45** | | **15** | .42657 | .47163 | 2.1203 | .90446 | **45** |
| 16 | .41098 | .45082 | 2.2182 | .91164 | 44 | | 16 | .42683 | .47199 | 2.1187 | .90433 | 44 |
| 17 | .41125 | .45117 | 2.2165 | .91152 | 43 | | 17 | .42709 | .47234 | 2.1171 | .90421 | 43 |
| 18 | .41151 | .45152 | 2.2148 | .91140 | 42 | | 18 | .42736 | .47270 | 2.1155 | .90408 | 42 |
| 19 | .41178 | .45187 | 2.2130 | .91128 | 41 | | 19 | .42762 | .47305 | 2.1139 | .90396 | 41 |
| **20** | .41204 | .45222 | 2.2113 | .91116 | **40** | | **20** | .42788 | .47341 | 2.1123 | .90383 | **40** |
| 21 | .41231 | .45257 | 2.2096 | .91104 | 39 | | 21 | .42815 | .47377 | 2.1107 | .90371 | 39 |
| 22 | .41257 | .45292 | 2.2079 | .91092 | 38 | | 22 | .42841 | .47412 | 2.1092 | .90358 | 38 |
| 23 | .41284 | .45327 | 2.2062 | .91080 | 37 | | 23 | .42867 | .47448 | 2.1076 | .90346 | 37 |
| 24 | .41310 | .45362 | 2.2045 | .91068 | 36 | | 24 | .42894 | .47483 | 2.1060 | .90334 | 36 |
| **25** | .41337 | .45397 | 2.2028 | .91056 | **35** | | **25** | .42920 | .47519 | 2.1044 | .90321 | **35** |
| 26 | .41363 | .45432 | 2.2011 | .91044 | 34 | | 26 | .42946 | .47555 | 2.1028 | .90309 | 34 |
| 27 | .41390 | .45467 | 2.1994 | .91032 | 33 | | 27 | .42972 | .47590 | 2.1013 | .90296 | 33 |
| 28 | .41416 | .45502 | 2.1977 | .91020 | 32 | | 28 | .42999 | .47626 | 2.0997 | .90284 | 32 |
| 29 | .41443 | .45538 | 2.1960 | .91008 | 31 | | 29 | .43025 | .47662 | 2.0981 | .90271 | 31 |
| **30** | .41469 | .45573 | 2.1943 | .90996 | **30** | | **30** | .43051 | .47698 | 2.0965 | .90259 | **30** |
| 31 | .41496 | .45608 | 2.1926 | .90984 | 29 | | 31 | .43077 | .47733 | 2.0950 | .90246 | 29 |
| 32 | .41522 | .45643 | 2.1909 | .90972 | 28 | | 32 | .43104 | .47769 | 2.0934 | .90233 | 28 |
| 33 | .41549 | .45678 | 2.1892 | .90960 | 27 | | 33 | .43130 | .47805 | 2.0918 | .90221 | 27 |
| 34 | .41575 | .45713 | 2.1876 | .90948 | 26 | | 34 | .43156 | .47840 | 2.0903 | .90208 | 26 |
| **35** | .41602 | .45748 | 2.1859 | .90936 | **25** | | **35** | .43182 | .47876 | 2.0887 | .90196 | **25** |
| 36 | .41628 | .45784 | 2.1842 | .90924 | 24 | | 36 | .43209 | .47912 | 2.0872 | .90183 | 24 |
| 37 | .41655 | .45819 | 2.1825 | .90911 | 23 | | 37 | .43235 | .47948 | 2.0856 | .90171 | 23 |
| 38 | .41681 | .45854 | 2.1808 | .90899 | 22 | | 38 | .43261 | .47984 | 2.0840 | .90158 | 22 |
| 39 | .41707 | .45889 | 2.1792 | .90887 | 21 | | 39 | .43287 | .48019 | 2.0825 | .90146 | 21 |
| **40** | .41734 | .45924 | 2.1775 | .90875 | **20** | | **40** | .43313 | .48055 | 2.0809 | .90133 | **20** |
| 41 | .41760 | .45960 | 2.1758 | .90863 | 19 | | 41 | .43340 | .48091 | 2.0794 | .90120 | 19 |
| 42 | .41787 | .45995 | 2.1742 | .90851 | 18 | | 42 | .43366 | .48127 | 2.0778 | .90108 | 18 |
| 43 | .41813 | .46030 | 2.1725 | .90839 | 17 | | 43 | .43392 | .48163 | 2.0763 | .90095 | 17 |
| 44 | .41840 | .46065 | 2.1708 | .90826 | 16 | | 44 | .43418 | .48198 | 2.0748 | .90082 | 16 |
| **45** | .41866 | .46101 | 2.1692 | .90814 | **15** | | **45** | .43445 | .48234 | 2.0732 | .90070 | **15** |
| 46 | .41892 | .46136 | 2.1675 | .90802 | 14 | | 46 | .43471 | .48270 | 2.0717 | .90057 | 14 |
| 47 | .41919 | .46171 | 2.1659 | .90790 | 13 | | 47 | .43497 | .48306 | 2.0701 | .90045 | 13 |
| 48 | .41945 | .46206 | 2.1642 | .90778 | 12 | | 48 | .43523 | .48342 | 2.0686 | .90032 | 12 |
| 49 | .41972 | .46242 | 2.1625 | .90766 | 11 | | 49 | .43549 | .48378 | 2.0671 | .90019 | 11 |
| **50** | .41998 | .46277 | 2.1609 | .90753 | **10** | | **50** | .43575 | .48414 | 2.0655 | .90007 | **10** |
| 51 | .42024 | .46312 | 2.1592 | .90741 | 9 | | 51 | .43602 | .48450 | 2.0640 | .89994 | 9 |
| 52 | .42051 | .46348 | 2.1576 | .90729 | 8 | | 52 | .43628 | .48486 | 2.0625 | .89981 | 8 |
| 53 | .42077 | .46383 | 2.1560 | .90717 | 7 | | 53 | .43654 | .48521 | 2.0609 | .89968 | 7 |
| 54 | .42104 | .46418 | 2.1543 | .90704 | 6 | | 54 | .43680 | .48557 | 2.0594 | .89956 | 6 |
| **55** | .42130 | .46454 | 2.1527 | .90692 | **5** | | **55** | .43706 | .48593 | 2.0579 | .89943 | **5** |
| 56 | .42156 | .46489 | 2.1510 | .90680 | 4 | | 56 | .43733 | .48629 | 2.0564 | .89930 | 4 |
| 57 | .42183 | .46525 | 2.1494 | .90668 | 3 | | 57 | .43759 | .48665 | 2.0549 | .89918 | 3 |
| 58 | .42209 | .46560 | 2.1478 | .90655 | 2 | | 58 | .43785 | .48701 | 2.0533 | .89905 | 2 |
| 59 | .42235 | .46595 | 2.1461 | .90643 | 1 | | 59 | .43811 | .48737 | 2.0518 | .89892 | 1 |
| **60** | .42262 | .46631 | 2.1445 | .90631 | **0** | | **60** | .43837 | .48773 | 2.0503 | .89879 | **0** |
| ′ | Cos | Cot | Tan | Sin | ′ | | ′ | Cos | Cot | Tan | Sin | ′ |

114° (294°)        (245°) **65°**        115° (295°)        (244°) **64°**

# NATURAL FUNCTIONS (Continued)

| ′ | Sin | Tan | Cot | Cos | ′ | ′ | Sin | Tan | Cot | Cos | ′ |
|---|-----|-----|-----|-----|---|---|-----|-----|-----|-----|---|
| 0 | .43837 | .48773 | 2.0503 | .89879 | 60 | 0 | .45399 | .50953 | 1.9626 | .89101 | 60 |
| 1 | .43863 | .48809 | 2.0488 | .89867 | 59 | 1 | .45425 | .50989 | 1.9612 | .89087 | 59 |
| 2 | .43889 | .48845 | 2.0473 | .89854 | 58 | 2 | .45451 | .51026 | 1.9598 | .89074 | 58 |
| 3 | .43916 | .48881 | 2.0458 | .89841 | 57 | 3 | .45477 | .51063 | 1.9584 | .89061 | 57 |
| 4 | .43942 | .48917 | 2.0443 | .89828 | 56 | 4 | .45503 | .51099 | 1.9570 | .89048 | 56 |
| 5 | .43968 | .48953 | 2.0428 | .89816 | 55 | 5 | .45529 | .51136 | 1.9556 | .89035 | 55 |
| 6 | .43994 | .48989 | 2.0413 | .89803 | 54 | 6 | .45554 | .51173 | 1.9542 | .89021 | 54 |
| 7 | .44020 | .49026 | 2.0398 | .89790 | 53 | 7 | .45580 | .51209 | 1.9528 | .89008 | 53 |
| 8 | .44046 | .49062 | 2.0383 | .89777 | 52 | 8 | .45606 | .51246 | 1.9514 | .88995 | 52 |
| 9 | .44072 | .49098 | 2.0368 | .89764 | 51 | 9 | .45632 | .51283 | 1.9500 | .88981 | 51 |
| 10 | .44098 | .49134 | 2.0353 | .89752 | 50 | 10 | .45658 | .51319 | 1.9486 | .88968 | 50 |
| 11 | .44124 | .49170 | 2.0338 | .89739 | 49 | 11 | .45684 | .51356 | 1.9472 | .88955 | 49 |
| 12 | .44151 | .49206 | 2.0323 | .89726 | 48 | 12 | .45710 | .51393 | 1.9458 | .88942 | 48 |
| 13 | .44177 | .49242 | 2.0308 | .89713 | 47 | 13 | .45736 | .51430 | 1.9444 | .88928 | 47 |
| 14 | .44203 | .49278 | 2.0293 | .89700 | 46 | 14 | .45762 | .51467 | 1.9430 | .88915 | 46 |
| 15 | .44229 | .49315 | 2.0278 | .89687 | 45 | 15 | .45787 | .51503 | 1.9416 | .88902 | 45 |
| 16 | .44255 | .49351 | 2.0263 | .89674 | 44 | 16 | .45813 | .51540 | 1.9402 | .88888 | 44 |
| 17 | .44281 | .49387 | 2.0248 | .89662 | 43 | 17 | .45839 | .51577 | 1.9388 | .88875 | 43 |
| 18 | .44307 | .49423 | 2.0233 | .89649 | 42 | 18 | .45865 | .51614 | 1.9375 | .88862 | 42 |
| 19 | .44333 | .49459 | 2.0219 | .89636 | 41 | 19 | .45891 | .51651 | 1.9361 | .88848 | 41 |
| 20 | .44359 | .49495 | 2.0204 | .89623 | 40 | 20 | .45917 | .51688 | 1.9347 | .88835 | 40 |
| 21 | .44385 | .49532 | 2.0189 | .89610 | 39 | 21 | .45942 | .51724 | 1.9333 | .88822 | 39 |
| 22 | .44411 | .49568 | 2.0174 | .89597 | 38 | 22 | .45968 | .51761 | 1.9319 | .88808 | 38 |
| 23 | .44437 | .49604 | 2.0160 | .89584 | 37 | 23 | .45994 | .51798 | 1.9306 | .88795 | 37 |
| 24 | .44464 | .49640 | 2.0145 | .89571 | 36 | 24 | .46020 | .51835 | 1.9292 | .88782 | 36 |
| 25 | .44490 | .49677 | 2.0130 | .89558 | 35 | 25 | .46046 | .51872 | 1.9278 | .88768 | 35 |
| 26 | .44516 | .49713 | 2.0115 | .89545 | 34 | 26 | .46072 | .51909 | 1.9265 | .88755 | 34 |
| 27 | .44542 | .49749 | 2.0101 | .89532 | 33 | 27 | .46097 | .51946 | 1.9251 | .88741 | 33 |
| 28 | .44568 | .49786 | 2.0086 | .89519 | 32 | 28 | .46123 | .51983 | 1.9237 | .88728 | 32 |
| 29 | .44594 | .49822 | 2.0072 | .89506 | 31 | 29 | .46149 | .52020 | 1.9223 | .88715 | 31 |
| 30 | .44620 | .49858 | 2.0057 | .89493 | 30 | 30 | .46175 | .52057 | 1.9210 | .88701 | 30 |
| 31 | .44646 | .49894 | 2.0042 | .89480 | 29 | 31 | .46201 | .52094 | 1.9196 | .88688 | 29 |
| 32 | .44672 | .49931 | 2.0028 | .89467 | 28 | 32 | .46226 | .52131 | 1.9183 | .88674 | 28 |
| 33 | .44698 | .49967 | 2.0013 | .89454 | 27 | 33 | .46252 | .52168 | 1.9169 | .88661 | 27 |
| 34 | .44724 | .50004 | 1.9999 | .89441 | 26 | 34 | .46278 | .52205 | 1.9155 | .88647 | 26 |
| 35 | .44750 | .50040 | 1.9984 | .89428 | 25 | 35 | .46304 | .52242 | 1.9142 | .88634 | 25 |
| 36 | .44776 | .50076 | 1.9970 | .89415 | 24 | 36 | .46330 | .52279 | 1.9128 | .88620 | 24 |
| 37 | .44802 | .50113 | 1.9955 | .89402 | 23 | 37 | .46355 | .52316 | 1.9115 | .88607 | 23 |
| 38 | .44828 | .50149 | 1.9941 | .89389 | 22 | 38 | .46381 | .52353 | 1.9101 | .88593 | 22 |
| 39 | .44854 | .50185 | 1.9926 | .89376 | 21 | 39 | .46407 | .52390 | 1.9088 | .88580 | 21 |
| 40 | .44880 | .50222 | 1.9912 | .89363 | 20 | 40 | .46433 | .52427 | 1.9074 | .88566 | 20 |
| 41 | .44906 | .50258 | 1.9897 | .89350 | 19 | 41 | .46458 | .52464 | 1.9061 | .88553 | 19 |
| 42 | .44932 | .50295 | 1.9883 | .89337 | 18 | 42 | .46484 | .52501 | 1.9047 | .88539 | 18 |
| 43 | .44958 | .50331 | 1.9868 | .89324 | 17 | 43 | .46510 | .52538 | 1.9034 | .88526 | 17 |
| 44 | .44984 | .50368 | 1.9854 | .89311 | 16 | 44 | .46536 | .52575 | 1.9020 | .88512 | 16 |
| 45 | .45010 | .50404 | 1.9840 | .89298 | 15 | 45 | .46561 | .52613 | 1.9007 | .88499 | 15 |
| 46 | .45036 | .50441 | 1.9825 | .89285 | 14 | 46 | .46587 | .52650 | 1.8993 | .88485 | 14 |
| 47 | .45062 | .50477 | 1.9811 | .89272 | 13 | 47 | .46613 | .52687 | 1.8980 | .88472 | 13 |
| 48 | .45088 | .50514 | 1.9797 | .89259 | 12 | 48 | .46639 | .52724 | 1.8967 | .88458 | 12 |
| 49 | .45114 | .50550 | 1.9782 | .89245 | 11 | 49 | .46664 | .52761 | 1.8953 | .88445 | 11 |
| 50 | .45140 | .50587 | 1.9768 | .89232 | 10 | 50 | .46690 | .52798 | 1.8940 | .88431 | 10 |
| 51 | .45166 | .50623 | 1.9754 | .89219 | 9 | 51 | .46716 | .52836 | 1.8927 | .88417 | 9 |
| 52 | .45192 | .50660 | 1.9740 | .89206 | 8 | 52 | .46742 | .52873 | 1.8913 | .88404 | 8 |
| 53 | .45218 | .50696 | 1.9725 | .89193 | 7 | 53 | .46767 | .52910 | 1.8900 | .88390 | 7 |
| 54 | .45243 | .50733 | 1.9711 | .89180 | 6 | 54 | .46793 | .52947 | 1.8887 | .88377 | 6 |
| 55 | .45269 | .50769 | 1.9697 | .89167 | 5 | 55 | .46819 | .52985 | 1.8873 | .88363 | 5 |
| 56 | .45295 | .50806 | 1.9683 | .89153 | 4 | 56 | .46844 | .53022 | 1.8860 | .88349 | 4 |
| 57 | .45321 | .50843 | 1.9669 | .89140 | 3 | 57 | .46870 | .53059 | 1.8847 | .88336 | 3 |
| 58 | .45347 | .50879 | 1.9654 | .89127 | 2 | 58 | .46896 | .53096 | 1.8834 | .88322 | 2 |
| 59 | .45373 | .50916 | 1.9640 | .89114 | 1 | 59 | .46921 | .53134 | 1.8820 | .88308 | 1 |
| 60 | .45399 | .50953 | 1.9626 | .89101 | 0 | 60 | .46947 | .53171 | 1.8807 | .88295 | 0 |
| ′ | Cos | Cot | Tan | Sin | ′ | ′ | Cos | Cot | Tan | Sin | ′ |

28° (208°)                    (331°) 151°    29°(209°)                    (330°) 150°

| ' | Sin | Tan | Cot | Cos | ' | ' | Sin | Tan | Cot | Cos | ' |
|---|-----|-----|-----|-----|---|---|-----|-----|-----|-----|---|
| 0 | .46947 | .53171 | 1.8807 | .88295 | 60 | 0 | .48481 | .55431 | 1.8040 | .87462 | 60 |
| 1 | .46973 | .53208 | 1.8794 | .88281 | 59 | 1 | .48506 | .55469 | 1.8028 | .87448 | 59 |
| 2 | .46999 | .53246 | 1.8781 | .88267 | 58 | 2 | .48532 | .55507 | 1.8016 | .87434 | 58 |
| 3 | .47024 | .53283 | 1.8768 | .88254 | 57 | 3 | .48557 | .55545 | 1.8003 | .87420 | 57 |
| 4 | .47050 | .53320 | 1.8755 | .88240 | 56 | 4 | .48583 | .55583 | 1.7991 | .87406 | 56 |
| 5 | .47076 | .53358 | 1.8741 | .88226 | 55 | 5 | .48608 | .55621 | 1.7979 | .87391 | 55 |
| 6 | .47101 | .53395 | 1.8728 | .88213 | 54 | 6 | .48634 | .55659 | 1.7966 | .87377 | 54 |
| 7 | .47127 | .53432 | 1.8715 | .88199 | 53 | 7 | .48659 | .55697 | 1.7954 | .87363 | 53 |
| 8 | .47153 | .53470 | 1.8702 | .88185 | 52 | 8 | .48684 | .55736 | 1.7942 | .87349 | 52 |
| 9 | .47178 | .53507 | 1.8689 | .88172 | 51 | 9 | .48710 | .55774 | 1.7930 | .87335 | 51 |
| 10 | .47204 | .53545 | 1.8676 | .88158 | 50 | 10 | .48735 | .55812 | 1.7917 | .87321 | 50 |
| 11 | .47229 | .53582 | 1.8663 | .88144 | 49 | 11 | .48761 | .55850 | 1.7905 | .87306 | 49 |
| 12 | .47255 | .53620 | 1.8650 | .88130 | 48 | 12 | .48786 | .55888 | 1.7893 | .87292 | 48 |
| 13 | .47281 | .53657 | 1.8637 | .88117 | 47 | 13 | .48811 | .55926 | 1.7881 | .87278 | 47 |
| 14 | .47306 | .53694 | 1.8624 | .88103 | 46 | 14 | .48837 | .55964 | 1.7868 | .87264 | 46 |
| 15 | .47332 | .53732 | 1.8611 | .88089 | 45 | 15 | .48862 | .56003 | 1.7856 | .87250 | 45 |
| 16 | .47358 | .53769 | 1.8598 | .88075 | 44 | 16 | .48888 | .56041 | 1.7844 | .87235 | 44 |
| 17 | .47383 | .53807 | 1.8585 | .88062 | 43 | 17 | .48913 | .56079 | 1.7832 | .87221 | 43 |
| 18 | .47409 | .53844 | 1.8572 | .88048 | 42 | 18 | .48938 | .56117 | 1.7820 | .87207 | 42 |
| 19 | .47434 | .53882 | 1.8559 | .88034 | 41 | 19 | .48964 | .56156 | 1.7808 | .87193 | 41 |
| 20 | .47460 | .53920 | 1.8546 | .88020 | 40 | 20 | .48989 | .56194 | 1.7796 | .87178 | 40 |
| 21 | .47486 | .53957 | 1.8533 | .88006 | 39 | 21 | .49014 | .56232 | 1.7783 | .87164 | 39 |
| 22 | .47511 | .53995 | 1.8520 | .87993 | 38 | 22 | .49040 | .56270 | 1.7771 | .87150 | 38 |
| 23 | .47537 | .54032 | 1.8507 | .87979 | 37 | 23 | .49065 | .56309 | 1.7759 | .87136 | 37 |
| 24 | .47562 | .54070 | 1.8495 | .87965 | 36 | 24 | .49090 | .56347 | 1.7747 | .87121 | 36 |
| 25 | .47588 | .54107 | 1.8482 | .87951 | 35 | 25 | .49116 | .56385 | 1.7735 | .87107 | 35 |
| 26 | .47614 | .54145 | 1.8469 | .87937 | 34 | 26 | .49141 | .56424 | 1.7723 | .87093 | 34 |
| 27 | .47639 | .54183 | 1.8456 | .87923 | 33 | 27 | .49166 | .56462 | 1.7711 | .87079 | 33 |
| 28 | .47665 | .54220 | 1.8443 | .87909 | 32 | 28 | .49192 | .56501 | 1.7699 | .87064 | 32 |
| 29 | .47690 | .54258 | 1.8430 | .87896 | 31 | 29 | .49217 | .56539 | 1.7687 | .87050 | 31 |
| 30 | .47716 | .54296 | 1.8418 | .87882 | 30 | 30 | .49242 | .56577 | 1.7675 | .87036 | 30 |
| 31 | .47741 | .54333 | 1.8405 | .87868 | 29 | 31 | .49268 | .56616 | 1.7663 | .87021 | 29 |
| 32 | .47767 | .54371 | 1.8392 | .87854 | 28 | 32 | .49293 | .56654 | 1.7651 | .87007 | 28 |
| 33 | .47793 | .54409 | 1.8379 | .87840 | 27 | 33 | .49318 | .56693 | 1.7639 | .86993 | 27 |
| 34 | .47818 | .54446 | 1.8367 | .87826 | 26 | 34 | .49344 | .56731 | 1.7627 | .86978 | 26 |
| 35 | .47844 | .54484 | 1.8354 | .87812 | 25 | 35 | .49369 | .56769 | 1.7615 | .86964 | 25 |
| 36 | .47869 | .54522 | 1.8341 | .87798 | 24 | 36 | .49394 | .56808 | 1.7603 | .86949 | 24 |
| 37 | .47895 | .54560 | 1.8329 | .87784 | 23 | 37 | .49419 | .56846 | 1.7591 | .86935 | 23 |
| 38 | .47920 | .54597 | 1.8316 | .87770 | 22 | 38 | .49445 | .56885 | 1.7579 | .86921 | 22 |
| 39 | .47946 | .54635 | 1.8303 | .87756 | 21 | 39 | .49470 | .56923 | 1.7567 | .86906 | 21 |
| 40 | .47971 | .54673 | 1.8291 | .87743 | 20 | 40 | .49495 | .56962 | 1.7556 | .86892 | 20 |
| 41 | .47997 | .54711 | 1.8278 | .87729 | 19 | 41 | .49521 | .57000 | 1.7544 | .86878 | 19 |
| 42 | .48022 | .54748 | 1.8265 | .87715 | 18 | 42 | .49546 | .57039 | 1.7532 | .86863 | 18 |
| 43 | .48048 | .54786 | 1.8253 | .87701 | 17 | 43 | .49571 | .57078 | 1.7520 | .86849 | 17 |
| 44 | .48073 | .54824 | 1.8240 | .87687 | 16 | 44 | .49596 | .57116 | 1.7508 | .86834 | 16 |
| 45 | .48099 | .54862 | 1.8228 | .87673 | 15 | 45 | .49622 | .57155 | 1.7496 | .86820 | 15 |
| 46 | .48124 | .54900 | 1.8215 | .87659 | 14 | 46 | .49647 | .57193 | 1.7485 | .86805 | 14 |
| 47 | .48150 | .54938 | 1.8202 | .87645 | 13 | 47 | .49672 | .57232 | 1.7473 | .86791 | 13 |
| 48 | .48175 | .54975 | 1.8190 | .87631 | 12 | 48 | .49697 | .57271 | 1.7461 | .86777 | 12 |
| 49 | .48201 | .55013 | 1.8177 | .87617 | 11 | 49 | .49723 | .57309 | 1.7449 | .86762 | 11 |
| 50 | .48226 | .55051 | 1.8165 | .87603 | 10 | 50 | .49748 | .57348 | 1.7437 | .86748 | 10 |
| 51 | .48252 | .55089 | 1.8152 | .87589 | 9 | 51 | .49773 | .57386 | 1.7426 | .86733 | 9 |
| 52 | .48277 | .55127 | 1.8140 | .87575 | 8 | 52 | .49798 | .57425 | 1.7414 | .86719 | 8 |
| 53 | .48303 | .55165 | 1.8127 | .87561 | 7 | 53 | .49824 | .57464 | 1.7402 | .86704 | 7 |
| 54 | .48328 | .55203 | 1.8115 | .87546 | 6 | 54 | .49849 | .57503 | 1.7391 | .86690 | 6 |
| 55 | .48354 | .55241 | 1.8103 | .87532 | 5 | 55 | .49874 | .57541 | 1.7379 | .86675 | 5 |
| 56 | .48379 | .55279 | 1.8090 | .87518 | 4 | 56 | .49899 | .57580 | 1.7367 | .86661 | 4 |
| 57 | .48405 | .55317 | 1.8078 | .87504 | 3 | 57 | .49924 | .57619 | 1.7355 | .86646 | 3 |
| 58 | .48430 | .55355 | 1.8065 | .87490 | 2 | 58 | .49950 | .57657 | 1.7344 | .86632 | 2 |
| 59 | .48456 | .55393 | 1.8053 | .87476 | 1 | 59 | .49975 | .57696 | 1.7332 | .86617 | 1 |
| 60 | .48481 | .55431 | 1.8040 | .87462 | 0 | 60 | .50000 | .57735 | 1.7321 | .86603 | 0 |
| ' | Cos | Cot | Tan | Sin | ' | ' | Cos | Cot | Tan | Sin | ' |

| ′ | Sin | Tan | Cot | Cos | ′ | ′ | Sin | Tan | Cot | Cos | ′ |
|---|-----|-----|-----|-----|---|---|-----|-----|-----|-----|---|
| 0 | .50000 | .57735 | 1.7321 | .86603 | 60 | 0 | .51504 | .60086 | 1.6643 | .85717 | 60 |
| 1 | .50025 | .57774 | 1.7309 | .86588 | 59 | 1 | .51529 | .60126 | 1.6632 | .85702 | 59 |
| 2 | .50050 | .57813 | 1.7297 | .86573 | 58 | 2 | .51554 | .60165 | 1.6621 | .85687 | 58 |
| 3 | .50076 | .57851 | 1.7286 | .86559 | 57 | 3 | .51579 | .60205 | 1.6610 | .85672 | 57 |
| 4 | .50101 | .57890 | 1.7274 | .86544 | 56 | 4 | .51604 | .60245 | 1.6599 | .85657 | 56 |
| 5 | .50126 | .57929 | 1.7262 | .86530 | 55 | 5 | .51628 | .60284 | 1.6588 | .85642 | 55 |
| 6 | .50151 | .57968 | 1.7251 | .86515 | 54 | 6 | .51653 | .60324 | 1.6577 | .85627 | 54 |
| 7 | .50176 | .58007 | 1.7239 | .86501 | 53 | 7 | .51678 | .60364 | 1.6566 | .85612 | 53 |
| 8 | .50201 | .58046 | 1.7228 | .86486 | 52 | 8 | .51703 | .60403 | 1.6555 | .85597 | 52 |
| 9 | .50227 | .58085 | 1.7216 | .86471 | 51 | 9 | .51728 | .60443 | 1.6545 | .85582 | 51 |
| 10 | .50252 | .58124 | 1.7205 | .86457 | 50 | 10 | .51753 | .60483 | 1.6534 | .85567 | 50 |
| 11 | .50277 | .58162 | 1.7193 | .86442 | 49 | 11 | .51778 | .60522 | 1.6523 | .85551 | 49 |
| 12 | .50302 | .58201 | 1.7182 | .86427 | 48 | 12 | .51803 | .60562 | 1.6512 | .85536 | 48 |
| 13 | .50327 | .58240 | 1.7170 | .86413 | 47 | 13 | .51828 | .60602 | 1.6501 | .85521 | 47 |
| 14 | .50352 | .58279 | 1.7159 | .86398 | 46 | 14 | .51852 | .60642 | 1.6490 | .85506 | 46 |
| 15 | .50377 | .58318 | 1.7147 | .86384 | 45 | 15 | .51877 | .60681 | 1.6479 | .85491 | 45 |
| 16 | .50403 | .58357 | 1.7136 | .86369 | 44 | 16 | .51902 | .60721 | 1.6469 | .85476 | 44 |
| 17 | .50428 | .58396 | 1.7124 | .86354 | 43 | 17 | .51927 | .60761 | 1.6458 | .85461 | 43 |
| 18 | .50453 | .58435 | 1.7113 | .86340 | 42 | 18 | .51952 | .60801 | 1.6447 | .85446 | 42 |
| 19 | .50478 | .58474 | 1.7102 | .86325 | 41 | 19 | .51977 | .60841 | 1.6436 | .85431 | 41 |
| 20 | .50503 | .58513 | 1.7090 | .86310 | 40 | 20 | .52002 | .60881 | 1.6426 | .85416 | 40 |
| 21 | .50528 | .58552 | 1.7079 | .86295 | 39 | 21 | .52026 | .60921 | 1.6415 | .85401 | 39 |
| 22 | .50553 | .58591 | 1.7067 | .86281 | 38 | 22 | .52051 | .60960 | 1.6404 | .85385 | 38 |
| 23 | .50578 | .58631 | 1.7056 | .86266 | 37 | 23 | .52076 | .61000 | 1.6393 | .85370 | 37 |
| 24 | .50603 | .58670 | 1.7045 | .86251 | 36 | 24 | .52101 | .61040 | 1.6383 | .85355 | 36 |
| 25 | .50628 | .58709 | 1.7033 | .86237 | 35 | 25 | .52126 | .61080 | 1.6372 | .85340 | 35 |
| 26 | .50654 | .58748 | 1.7022 | .86222 | 34 | 26 | .52151 | .61120 | 1.6361 | .85325 | 34 |
| 27 | .50679 | .58787 | 1.7011 | .86207 | 33 | 27 | .52175 | .61160 | 1.6351 | .85310 | 33 |
| 28 | .50704 | .58826 | 1.6999 | .86192 | 32 | 28 | .52200 | .61200 | 1.6340 | .85294 | 32 |
| 29 | .50729 | .58865 | 1.6988 | .86178 | 31 | 29 | .52225 | .61240 | 1.6329 | .85279 | 31 |
| 30 | .50754 | .58905 | 1.6977 | .86163 | 30 | 30 | .52250 | .61280 | 1.6319 | .85264 | 30 |
| 31 | .50779 | .58944 | 1.6965 | .86148 | 29 | 31 | .52275 | .61320 | 1.6308 | .85249 | 29 |
| 32 | .50804 | .58983 | 1.6954 | .86133 | 28 | 32 | .52299 | .61360 | 1.6297 | .85234 | 28 |
| 33 | .50829 | .59022 | 1.6943 | .86119 | 27 | 33 | .52324 | .61400 | 1.6287 | .85218 | 27 |
| 34 | .50854 | .59061 | 1.6932 | .86104 | 26 | 34 | .52349 | .61440 | 1.6276 | .85203 | 26 |
| 35 | .50879 | .59101 | 1.6920 | .86089 | 25 | 35 | .52374 | .61480 | 1.6265 | .85188 | 25 |
| 36 | .50904 | .59140 | 1.6909 | .86074 | 24 | 36 | .52399 | .61520 | 1.6255 | .85173 | 24 |
| 37 | .50929 | .59179 | 1.6898 | .86059 | 23 | 37 | .52423 | .61561 | 1.6244 | .85157 | 23 |
| 38 | .50954 | .59218 | 1.6887 | .86045 | 22 | 38 | .52448 | .61601 | 1.6234 | .85142 | 22 |
| 39 | .50979 | .59258 | 1.6875 | .86030 | 21 | 39 | .52473 | .61641 | 1.6223 | .85127 | 21 |
| 40 | .51004 | .59297 | 1.6864 | .86015 | 20 | 40 | .52498 | .61681 | 1.6212 | .85112 | 20 |
| 41 | .51029 | .59336 | 1.6853 | .86000 | 19 | 41 | .52522 | .61721 | 1.6202 | .85096 | 19 |
| 42 | .51054 | .59376 | 1.6842 | .85985 | 18 | 42 | .52547 | .61761 | 1.6191 | .85081 | 18 |
| 43 | .51079 | .59415 | 1.6831 | .85970 | 17 | 43 | .52572 | .61801 | 1.6181 | .85066 | 17 |
| 44 | .51104 | .59454 | 1.6820 | .85956 | 16 | 44 | .52597 | .61842 | 1.6170 | .85051 | 16 |
| 45 | .51129 | .59494 | 1.6808 | .85941 | 15 | 45 | .52621 | .61882 | 1.6160 | .85035 | 15 |
| 46 | .51154 | .59533 | 1.6797 | .85926 | 14 | 46 | .52646 | .61922 | 1.6149 | .85020 | 14 |
| 47 | .51179 | .59573 | 1.6786 | .85911 | 13 | 47 | .52671 | .61962 | 1.6139 | .85005 | 13 |
| 48 | .51204 | .59612 | 1.6775 | .85896 | 12 | 48 | .52696 | .62003 | 1.6128 | .84989 | 12 |
| 49 | .51229 | .59651 | 1.6764 | .85881 | 11 | 49 | .52720 | .62043 | 1.6118 | .84974 | 11 |
| 50 | .51254 | .59691 | 1.6753 | .85866 | 10 | 50 | .52745 | .62083 | 1.6107 | .84959 | 10 |
| 51 | .51279 | .59730 | 1.6742 | .85851 | 9 | 51 | .52770 | .62124 | 1.6097 | .84943 | 9 |
| 52 | .51304 | .59770 | 1.6731 | .85836 | 8 | 52 | .52794 | .62164 | 1.6087 | .84928 | 8 |
| 53 | .51329 | .59809 | 1.6720 | .85821 | 7 | 53 | .52819 | .62204 | 1.6076 | .84913 | 7 |
| 54 | .51354 | .59849 | 1.6709 | .85806 | 6 | 54 | .52844 | .62245 | 1.6066 | .84897 | 6 |
| 55 | .51379 | .59888 | 1.6698 | .85792 | 5 | 55 | .52869 | .62285 | 1.6055 | .84882 | 5 |
| 56 | .51404 | .59928 | 1.6687 | .85777 | 4 | 56 | .52893 | .62325 | 1.6045 | .84866 | 4 |
| 57 | .51429 | .59967 | 1.6676 | .85762 | 3 | 57 | .52918 | .62366 | 1.6034 | .84851 | 3 |
| 58 | .51454 | .60007 | 1.6665 | .85747 | 2 | 58 | .52943 | .62406 | 1.6024 | .84836 | 2 |
| 59 | .51479 | .60046 | 1.6654 | .85732 | 1 | 59 | .52967 | .62446 | 1.6014 | .84820 | 1 |
| 60 | .51504 | .60086 | 1.6643 | .85717 | 0 | 60 | .52992 | .62487 | 1.6003 | .84805 | 0 |
| ′ | Cos | Cot | Tan | Sin | ′ | ′ | Cos | Cot | Tan | Sin | ′ |

## NATURAL FUNCTIONS (Continued)

| ′ | Sin | Tan | Cot | Cos | ′ | ′ | Sin | Tan | Cot | Cos | ′ |
|---|-----|-----|-----|-----|---|---|-----|-----|-----|-----|---|
| **0** | .52992 | .62487 | 1.6003 | .84805 | **60** | **0** | .54464 | .64941 | 1.5399 | .83867 | **60** |
| 1 | .53017 | .62527 | 1.5993 | .84789 | 59 | 1 | .54488 | .64982 | 1.5389 | .83851 | 59 |
| 2 | .53041 | .62568 | 1.5983 | .84774 | 58 | 2 | .54513 | .65024 | 1.5379 | .83835 | 58 |
| 3 | .53066 | .62608 | 1.5972 | .84759 | 57 | 3 | .54537 | .65065 | 1.5369 | .83819 | 57 |
| 4 | .53091 | .62649 | 1.5962 | .84743 | 56 | 4 | .54561 | .65106 | 1.5359 | .83804 | 56 |
| **5** | .53115 | .62689 | 1.5952 | .84728 | **55** | **5** | .54586 | .65148 | 1.5350 | .83788 | **55** |
| 6 | .53140 | .62730 | 1.5941 | .84712 | 54 | 6 | .54610 | .65189 | 1.5340 | .83772 | 54 |
| 7 | .53164 | .62770 | 1.5931 | .84697 | 53 | 7 | .54635 | .65231 | 1.5330 | .83756 | 53 |
| 8 | .53189 | .62811 | 1.5921 | .84681 | 52 | 8 | .54659 | .65272 | 1.5320 | .83740 | 52 |
| 9 | .53214 | .62852 | 1.5911 | .84666 | 51 | 9 | .54683 | .65314 | 1.5311 | .83724 | 51 |
| **10** | .53238 | .62892 | 1.5900 | .84650 | **50** | **10** | .54708 | .65355 | 1.5301 | .83708 | **50** |
| 11 | .53263 | .62933 | 1.5890 | .84635 | 49 | 11 | .54732 | .65397 | 1.5291 | .83692 | 49 |
| 12 | .53288 | .62973 | 1.5880 | .84619 | 48 | 12 | .54756 | .65438 | 1.5282 | .83676 | 48 |
| 13 | .53312 | .63014 | 1.5869 | .84604 | 47 | 13 | .54781 | .65480 | 1.5272 | .83660 | 47 |
| 14 | .53337 | .63055 | 1.5859 | .84588 | 46 | 14 | .54805 | .65521 | 1.5262 | .83645 | 46 |
| **15** | .53361 | .63095 | 1.5849 | .84573 | **45** | **15** | .54829 | .65563 | 1.5253 | .83629 | **45** |
| 16 | .53386 | .63136 | 1.5839 | .84557 | 44 | 16 | .54854 | .65604 | 1.5243 | .83613 | 44 |
| 17 | .53411 | .63177 | 1.5829 | .84542 | 43 | 17 | .54878 | .65646 | 1.5233 | .83597 | 43 |
| 18 | .53435 | .63217 | 1.5818 | .84526 | 42 | 18 | .54902 | .65688 | 1.5224 | .83581 | 42 |
| 19 | .53460 | .63258 | 1.5808 | .84511 | 41 | 19 | .54927 | .65729 | 1.5214 | .83565 | 41 |
| **20** | .53484 | .63299 | 1.5798 | .84495 | **40** | **20** | .54951 | .65771 | 1.5204 | .83549 | **40** |
| 21 | .53509 | .63340 | 1.5788 | .84480 | 39 | 21 | .54975 | .65813 | 1.5195 | .83533 | 39 |
| 22 | .53534 | .63380 | 1.5778 | .84464 | 38 | 22 | .54999 | .65854 | 1.5185 | .83517 | 38 |
| 23 | .53558 | .63421 | 1.5768 | .84448 | 37 | 23 | .55024 | .65896 | 1.5175 | .83501 | 37 |
| 24 | .53583 | .63462 | 1.5757 | .84433 | 36 | 24 | .55048 | .65938 | 1.5166 | .83485 | 36 |
| **25** | .53607 | .63503 | 1.5747 | .84417 | **35** | **25** | .55072 | .65980 | 1.5156 | .83469 | **35** |
| 26 | .53632 | .63544 | 1.5737 | .84402 | 34 | 26 | .55097 | .66021 | 1.5147 | .83453 | 34 |
| 27 | .53656 | .63584 | 1.5727 | .84386 | 33 | 27 | .55121 | .66063 | 1.5137 | .83437 | 33 |
| 28 | .53681 | .63625 | 1.5717 | .84370 | 32 | 28 | .55145 | .66105 | 1.5127 | .83421 | 32 |
| 29 | .53705 | .63666 | 1.5707 | .84355 | 31 | 29 | .55169 | .66147 | 1.5118 | .83405 | 31 |
| **30** | .53730 | .63707 | 1.5697 | .84339 | **30** | **30** | .55194 | .66189 | 1.5108 | .83389 | **30** |
| 31 | .53754 | .63748 | 1.5687 | .84324 | 29 | 31 | .55218 | .66230 | 1.5099 | .83373 | 29 |
| 32 | .53779 | .63789 | 1.5677 | .84308 | 28 | 32 | .55242 | .66272 | 1.5089 | .83356 | 28 |
| 33 | .53804 | .63830 | 1.5667 | .84292 | 27 | 33 | .55266 | .66314 | 1.5080 | .83340 | 27 |
| 34 | .53828 | .63871 | 1.5657 | .84277 | 26 | 34 | .55291 | .66356 | 1.5070 | .83324 | 26 |
| **35** | .53853 | .63912 | 1.5647 | .84261 | **25** | **35** | .55315 | .66398 | 1.5061 | .83308 | **25** |
| 36 | .53877 | .63953 | 1.5637 | .84245 | 24 | 36 | .55339 | .66440 | 1.5051 | .83292 | 24 |
| 37 | .53902 | .63994 | 1.5627 | .84230 | 23 | 37 | .55363 | .66482 | 1.5042 | .83276 | 23 |
| 38 | .53926 | .64035 | 1.5617 | .84214 | 22 | 38 | .55388 | .66524 | 1.5032 | .83260 | 22 |
| 39 | .53951 | .64076 | 1.5607 | .84198 | 21 | 39 | .55412 | .66566 | 1.5023 | .83244 | 21 |
| **40** | .53975 | .64117 | 1.5597 | .84182 | **20** | **40** | .55436 | .66608 | 1.5013 | .83228 | **20** |
| 41 | .54000 | .64158 | 1.5587 | .84167 | 19 | 41 | .55460 | .66650 | 1.5004 | .83212 | 19 |
| 42 | .54024 | .64199 | 1.5577 | .84151 | 18 | 42 | .55484 | .66692 | 1.4994 | .83195 | 18 |
| 43 | .54049 | .64240 | 1.5567 | .84135 | 17 | 43 | .55509 | .66734 | 1.4985 | .83179 | 17 |
| 44 | .54073 | .64281 | 1.5557 | .84120 | 16 | 44 | .55533 | .66776 | 1.4975 | .83163 | 16 |
| **45** | .54097 | .64322 | 1.5547 | .84104 | **15** | **45** | .55557 | .66818 | 1.4966 | .83147 | **15** |
| 46 | .54122 | .64363 | 1.5537 | .84088 | 14 | 46 | .55581 | .66860 | 1.4957 | .83131 | 14 |
| 47 | .54146 | .64404 | 1.5527 | .84072 | 13 | 47 | .55605 | .66902 | 1.4947 | .83115 | 13 |
| 48 | .54171 | .64446 | 1.5517 | .84057 | 12 | 48 | .55630 | .66944 | 1.4938 | .83098 | 12 |
| 49 | .54195 | .64487 | 1.5507 | .84041 | 11 | 49 | .55654 | .66986 | 1.4928 | .83082 | 11 |
| **50** | .54220 | .64528 | 1.5497 | .84025 | **10** | **50** | .55678 | .67028 | 1.4919 | .83066 | **10** |
| 51 | .54244 | .64569 | 1.5487 | .84009 | 9 | 51 | .55702 | .67071 | 1.4910 | .83050 | 9 |
| 52 | .54269 | .64610 | 1.5477 | .83994 | 8 | 52 | .55726 | .67113 | 1.4900 | .83034 | 8 |
| 53 | .54293 | .64652 | 1.5468 | .83978 | 7 | 53 | .55750 | .67155 | 1.4891 | .83017 | 7 |
| 54 | .54317 | .64693 | 1.5458 | .83962 | 6 | 54 | .55775 | .67197 | 1.4882 | .83001 | 6 |
| **55** | .54342 | .64734 | 1.5448 | .83946 | **5** | **55** | .55799 | .67239 | 1.4872 | .82985 | **5** |
| 56 | .54366 | .64775 | 1.5438 | .83930 | 4 | 56 | .55823 | .67282 | 1.4863 | .82969 | 4 |
| 57 | .54391 | .64817 | 1.5428 | .83915 | 3 | 57 | .55847 | .67324 | 1.4854 | .82953 | 3 |
| 58 | .54415 | .64858 | 1.5418 | .83899 | 2 | 58 | .55871 | .67366 | 1.4844 | .82936 | 2 |
| 59 | .54440 | .64899 | 1.5408 | .83883 | 1 | 59 | .55895 | .67409 | 1.4835 | .82920 | 1 |
| **60** | .54464 | .64941 | 1.5399 | .83867 | **0** | **60** | .55919 | .67451 | 1.4826 | .82904 | **0** |
| ′ | Cos | Cot | Tan | Sin | ′ | ′ | Cos | Cot | Tan | Sin | ′ |

**34° (214°)**      (325°) **145°**      **35° (215°)**      (324°) **144°**

| ′ | Sin | Tan | Cot | Cos | ′ | | ′ | Sin | Tan | Cot | Cos | ′ |
|---|-----|-----|-----|-----|---|---|---|-----|-----|-----|-----|---|
| **0** | .55919 | .67451 | 1.4826 | .82904 | **60** | | **0** | .57358 | .70021 | 1.4281 | .81915 | **60** |
| 1 | .55943 | .67493 | 1.4816 | .82887 | 59 | | 1 | .57381 | .70064 | 1.4273 | .81899 | 59 |
| 2 | .55968 | .67536 | 1.4807 | .82871 | 58 | | 2 | .57405 | .70107 | 1.4264 | .81882 | 58 |
| 3 | .55992 | .67578 | 1.4798 | .82855 | 57 | | 3 | .57429 | .70151 | 1.4255 | .81865 | 57 |
| 4 | .56016 | .67620 | 1.4788 | .82839 | 56 | | 4 | .57453 | .70194 | 1.4246 | .81848 | 56 |
| **5** | .56040 | .67663 | 1.4779 | .82822 | **55** | | **5** | .57477 | .70238 | 1.4237 | .81832 | **55** |
| 6 | .56064 | .67705 | 1.4770 | .82806 | 54 | | 6 | .57501 | .70281 | 1.4229 | .81815 | 54 |
| 7 | .56088 | .67748 | 1.4761 | .82790 | 53 | | 7 | .57524 | .70325 | 1.4220 | .81798 | 53 |
| 8 | .56112 | .67790 | 1.4751 | .82773 | 52 | | 8 | .57548 | .70368 | 1.4211 | .81782 | 52 |
| 9 | .56136 | .67832 | 1.4742 | .82757 | 51 | | 9 | .57572 | .70412 | 1.4202 | .81765 | 51 |
| **10** | .56160 | .67875 | 1.4733 | .82741 | **50** | | **10** | .57596 | .70455 | 1.4193 | .81748 | **50** |
| 11 | .56184 | .67917 | 1.4724 | .82724 | 49 | | 11 | .57619 | .70499 | 1.4185 | .81731 | 49 |
| 12 | .56208 | .67960 | 1.4715 | .82708 | 48 | | 12 | .57643 | .70542 | 1.4176 | .81714 | 48 |
| 13 | .56232 | .68002 | 1.4705 | .82692 | 47 | | 13 | .57667 | .70586 | 1.4167 | .81698 | 47 |
| 14 | .56256 | .68045 | 1.4696 | .82675 | 46 | | 14 | .57691 | .70629 | 1.4158 | .81681 | 46 |
| **15** | .56280 | .68088 | 1.4687 | .82659 | **45** | | **15** | .57715 | .70673 | 1.4150 | .81664 | **45** |
| 16 | .56305 | .68130 | 1.4678 | .82643 | 44 | | 16 | .57738 | .70717 | 1.4141 | .81647 | 44 |
| 17 | .56329 | .68173 | 1.4669 | .82626 | 43 | | 17 | .57762 | .70760 | 1.4132 | .81631 | 43 |
| 18 | .56353 | .68215 | 1.4659 | .82610 | 42 | | 18 | .57786 | .70804 | 1.4124 | .81614 | 42 |
| 19 | .56377 | .68258 | 1.4650 | .82593 | 41 | | 19 | .57810 | .70848 | 1.4115 | .81597 | 41 |
| **20** | .56401 | .68301 | 1.4641 | .82577 | **40** | | **20** | .57833 | .70891 | 1.4106 | .81580 | **40** |
| 21 | .56425 | .68343 | 1.4632 | .82561 | 39 | | 21 | .57857 | .70935 | 1.4097 | .81563 | 39 |
| 22 | .56449 | .68386 | 1.4623 | .82544 | 38 | | 22 | .57881 | .70979 | 1.4089 | .81546 | 38 |
| 23 | .56473 | .68429 | 1.4614 | .82528 | 37 | | 23 | .57904 | .71023 | 1.4080 | .81530 | 37 |
| 24 | .56497 | .68471 | 1.4605 | .82511 | 36 | | 24 | .57928 | .71066 | 1.4071 | .81513 | 36 |
| **25** | .56521 | .68514 | 1.4596 | .82495 | **35** | | **25** | .57952 | .71110 | 1.4063 | .81496 | **35** |
| 26 | .56545 | .68557 | 1.4586 | .82478 | 34 | | 26 | .57976 | .71154 | 1.4054 | .81479 | 34 |
| 27 | .56569 | .68600 | 1.4577 | .82462 | 33 | | 27 | .57999 | .71198 | 1.4045 | .81462 | 33 |
| 28 | .56593 | .68642 | 1.4568 | .82446 | 32 | | 28 | .58023 | .71242 | 1.4037 | .81445 | 32 |
| 29 | .56617 | .68685 | 1.4559 | .82429 | 31 | | 29 | .58047 | .71285 | 1.4028 | .81428 | 31 |
| **30** | .56641 | .68728 | 1.4550 | .82413 | **30** | | **30** | .58070 | .71329 | 1.4019 | .81412 | **30** |
| 31 | .56665 | .68771 | 1.4541 | .82396 | 29 | | 31 | .58094 | .71373 | 1.4011 | .81395 | 29 |
| 32 | .56689 | .68814 | 1.4532 | .82380 | 28 | | 32 | .58118 | .71417 | 1.4002 | .81378 | 28 |
| 33 | .56713 | .68857 | 1.4523 | .82363 | 27 | | 33 | .58141 | .71461 | 1.3994 | .81361 | 27 |
| 34 | .56736 | .68900 | 1.4514 | .82347 | 26 | | 34 | .58165 | .71505 | 1.3985 | .81344 | 26 |
| **35** | .56760 | .68942 | 1.4505 | .82330 | **25** | | **35** | .58189 | .71549 | 1.3976 | .81327 | **25** |
| 36 | .56784 | .68985 | 1.4496 | .82314 | 24 | | 36 | .58212 | .71593 | 1.3968 | .81310 | 24 |
| 37 | .56808 | .69028 | 1.4487 | .82297 | 23 | | 37 | .58236 | .71637 | 1.3959 | .81293 | 23 |
| 38 | .56832 | .69071 | 1.4478 | .82281 | 22 | | 38 | .58260 | .71681 | 1.3951 | .81276 | 22 |
| 39 | .56856 | .69114 | 1.4469 | .82264 | 21 | | 39 | .58283 | .71725 | 1.3942 | .81259 | 21 |
| **40** | .56880 | .69157 | 1.4460 | .82248 | **20** | | **40** | .58307 | .71769 | 1.3934 | .81242 | **20** |
| 41 | .56904 | .69200 | 1.4451 | .82231 | 19 | | 41 | .58330 | .71813 | 1.3925 | .81225 | 19 |
| 42 | .56928 | .69243 | 1.4442 | .82214 | 18 | | 42 | .58354 | .71857 | 1.3916 | .81208 | 18 |
| 43 | .56952 | .69286 | 1.4433 | .82198 | 17 | | 43 | .58378 | .71901 | 1.3908 | .81191 | 17 |
| 44 | .56976 | .69329 | 1.4424 | .82181 | 16 | | 44 | .58401 | .71946 | 1.3899 | .81174 | 16 |
| **45** | .57000 | .69372 | 1.4415 | .82165 | **15** | | **45** | .58425 | .71990 | 1.3891 | .81157 | **15** |
| 46 | .57024 | .69416 | 1.4406 | .82148 | 14 | | 46 | .58449 | .72034 | 1.3882 | .81140 | 14 |
| 47 | .57047 | .69459 | 1.4397 | .82132 | 13 | | 47 | .58472 | .72078 | 1.3874 | .81123 | 13 |
| 48 | .57071 | .69502 | 1.4388 | .82115 | 12 | | 48 | .58496 | .72122 | 1.3865 | .81106 | 12 |
| 49 | .57095 | .69545 | 1.4379 | .82098 | 11 | | 49 | .58519 | .72167 | 1.3857 | .81089 | 11 |
| **50** | .57119 | .69588 | 1.4370 | .82082 | **10** | | **50** | .58543 | .72211 | 1.3848 | .81072 | **10** |
| 51 | .57143 | .69631 | 1.4361 | .82065 | 9 | | 51 | .58567 | .72255 | 1.3840 | .81055 | 9 |
| 52 | .57167 | .69675 | 1.4352 | .82048 | 8 | | 52 | .58590 | .72299 | 1.3831 | .81038 | 8 |
| 53 | .57191 | .69718 | 1.4344 | .82032 | 7 | | 53 | .58614 | .72344 | 1.3823 | .81021 | 7 |
| 54 | .57215 | .69761 | 1.4335 | .82015 | 6 | | 54 | .58637 | .72388 | 1.3814 | .81004 | 6 |
| **55** | .57238 | .69804 | 1.4326 | .81999 | **5** | | **55** | .58661 | .72432 | 1.3806 | .80987 | **5** |
| 56 | .57262 | .69847 | 1.4317 | .81982 | 4 | | 56 | .58684 | .72477 | 1.3798 | .80970 | 4 |
| 57 | .57286 | .69891 | 1.4308 | .81965 | 3 | | 57 | .58708 | .72521 | 1.3789 | .80953 | 3 |
| 58 | .57310 | .69934 | 1.4299 | .81949 | 2 | | 58 | .58731 | .72565 | 1.3781 | .80936 | 2 |
| 59 | .57334 | .69977 | 1.4290 | .81932 | 1 | | 59 | .58755 | .72610 | 1.3772 | .80919 | 1 |
| **60** | .57358 | .70021 | 1.4281 | .81915 | **0** | | **60** | .58779 | .72654 | 1.3764 | .80902 | **0** |
| ′ | Cos | Cot | Tan | Sin | ′ | | ′ | Cos | Cot | Tan | Sin | ′ |

**124° (304°)**      (235°) **55°**      **125° (305°)**      (234°) **54°**

## NATURAL FUNCTIONS (Continued)

36° (216°)      (323°) 143°      37° (217°)      (322°) 142°

| ′ | Sin | Tan | Cot | Cos | ′ | ′ | Sin | Tan | Cot | Cos | ′ |
|---|---|---|---|---|---|---|---|---|---|---|---|
| 0 | .58779 | .72654 | 1.3764 | .80902 | 60 | 0 | .60182 | .75355 | 1.3270 | .79864 | 60 |
| 1 | .58802 | .72699 | 1.3755 | .80885 | 59 | 1 | .60205 | .75401 | 1.3262 | .79846 | 59 |
| 2 | .58826 | .72743 | 1.3747 | .80867 | 58 | 2 | .60228 | .75447 | 1.3254 | .79829 | 58 |
| 3 | .58849 | .72788 | 1.3739 | .80850 | 57 | 3 | .60251 | .75492 | 1.3246 | .79811 | 57 |
| 4 | .58873 | .72832 | 1.3730 | .80833 | 56 | 4 | .60274 | .75538 | 1.3238 | .79793 | 56 |
| 5 | .58896 | .72877 | 1.3722 | .80816 | 55 | 5 | .60298 | .75584 | 1.3230 | .79776 | 55 |
| 6 | .58920 | .72921 | 1.3713 | .80799 | 54 | 6 | .60321 | .75629 | 1.3222 | .79758 | 54 |
| 7 | .58943 | .72966 | 1.3705 | .80782 | 53 | 7 | .60344 | .75675 | 1.3214 | .79741 | 53 |
| 8 | .58967 | .73010 | 1.3697 | .80765 | 52 | 8 | .60367 | .75721 | 1.3206 | .79723 | 52 |
| 9 | .58990 | .73055 | 1.3688 | .80748 | 51 | 9 | .60390 | .75767 | 1.3198 | .79706 | 51 |
| 10 | .59014 | .73100 | 1.3680 | .80730 | 50 | 10 | .60414 | .75812 | 1.3190 | .79688 | 50 |
| 11 | .59037 | .73144 | 1.3672 | .80713 | 49 | 11 | .60437 | .75858 | 1.3182 | .79671 | 49 |
| 12 | .59061 | .73189 | 1.3663 | .80696 | 48 | 12 | .60460 | .75904 | 1.3175 | .79653 | 48 |
| 13 | .59084 | .73234 | 1.3655 | .80679 | 47 | 13 | .60483 | .75950 | 1.3167 | .79635 | 47 |
| 14 | .59108 | .73278 | 1.3647 | .80662 | 46 | 14 | .60506 | .75996 | 1.3159 | .79618 | 46 |
| 15 | .59131 | .73323 | 1.3638 | .80644 | 45 | 15 | .60529 | .76042 | 1.3151 | .79600 | 45 |
| 16 | .59154 | .73368 | 1.3630 | .80627 | 44 | 16 | .60553 | .76088 | 1.3143 | .79583 | 44 |
| 17 | .59178 | .73413 | 1.3622 | .80610 | 43 | 17 | .60576 | .76134 | 1.3135 | .79565 | 43 |
| 18 | .59201 | .73457 | 1.3613 | .80593 | 42 | 18 | .60599 | .76180 | 1.3127 | .79547 | 42 |
| 19 | .59225 | .73502 | 1.3605 | .80576 | 41 | 19 | .60622 | .76226 | 1.3119 | .79530 | 41 |
| 20 | .59248 | .73547 | 1.3597 | .80558 | 40 | 20 | .60645 | .76272 | 1.3111 | .79512 | 40 |
| 21 | .59272 | .73592 | 1.3588 | .80541 | 39 | 21 | .60668 | .76318 | 1.3103 | .79494 | 39 |
| 22 | .59295 | .73637 | 1.3580 | .80524 | 38 | 22 | .60691 | .76364 | 1.3095 | .79477 | 38 |
| 23 | .59318 | .73681 | 1.3572 | .80507 | 37 | 23 | .60714 | .76410 | 1.3087 | .79459 | 37 |
| 24 | .59342 | .73726 | 1.3564 | .80489 | 36 | 24 | .60738 | .76456 | 1.3079 | .79441 | 36 |
| 25 | .59365 | .73771 | 1.3555 | .80472 | 35 | 25 | .60761 | .76502 | 1.3072 | .79424 | 35 |
| 26 | .59389 | .73816 | 1.3547 | .80455 | 34 | 26 | .60784 | .76548 | 1.3064 | .79406 | 34 |
| 27 | .59412 | .73861 | 1.3539 | .80438 | 33 | 27 | .60807 | .76594 | 1.3056 | .79388 | 33 |
| 28 | .59436 | .73906 | 1.3531 | .80420 | 32 | 28 | .60830 | .76640 | 1.3048 | .79371 | 32 |
| 29 | .59459 | .73951 | 1.3522 | .80403 | 31 | 29 | .60853 | .76686 | 1.3040 | .79353 | 31 |
| 30 | .59482 | .73996 | 1.3514 | .80386 | 30 | 30 | .60876 | .76733 | 1.3032 | .79335 | 30 |
| 31 | .59506 | .74041 | 1.3506 | .80368 | 29 | 31 | .60899 | .76779 | 1.3024 | .79318 | 29 |
| 32 | .59529 | .74086 | 1.3498 | .80351 | 28 | 32 | .60922 | .76825 | 1.3017 | .79300 | 28 |
| 33 | .59552 | .74131 | 1.3490 | .80334 | 27 | 33 | .60945 | .76871 | 1.3009 | .79282 | 27 |
| 34 | .59576 | .74176 | 1.3481 | .80316 | 26 | 34 | .60968 | .76918 | 1.3001 | .79264 | 26 |
| 35 | .59599 | .74221 | 1.3473 | .80299 | 25 | 35 | .60991 | .76964 | 1.2993 | .79247 | 25 |
| 36 | .59622 | .74267 | 1.3465 | .80282 | 24 | 36 | .61015 | .77010 | 1.2985 | .79229 | 24 |
| 37 | .59646 | .74312 | 1.3457 | .80264 | 23 | 37 | .61038 | .77057 | 1.2977 | .79211 | 23 |
| 38 | .59669 | .74357 | 1.3449 | .80247 | 22 | 38 | .61061 | .77103 | 1.2970 | .79193 | 22 |
| 39 | .59693 | .74402 | 1.3440 | .80230 | 21 | 39 | .61084 | .77149 | 1.2962 | .79176 | 21 |
| 40 | .59716 | .74447 | 1.3432 | .80212 | 20 | 40 | .61107 | .77196 | 1.2954 | .79158 | 20 |
| 41 | .59739 | .74492 | 1.3424 | .80195 | 19 | 41 | .61130 | .77242 | 1.2946 | .79140 | 19 |
| 42 | .59763 | .74538 | 1.3416 | .80178 | 18 | 42 | .61153 | .77289 | 1.2938 | .79122 | 18 |
| 43 | .59786 | .74583 | 1.3408 | .80160 | 17 | 43 | .61176 | .77335 | 1.2931 | .79105 | 17 |
| 44 | .59809 | .74628 | 1.3400 | .80143 | 16 | 44 | .61199 | .77382 | 1.2923 | .79087 | 16 |
| 45 | .59832 | .74674 | 1.3392 | .80125 | 15 | 45 | .61222 | .77428 | 1.2915 | .79069 | 15 |
| 46 | .59856 | .74719 | 1.3384 | .80108 | 14 | 46 | .61245 | .77475 | 1.2907 | .79051 | 14 |
| 47 | .59879 | .74764 | 1.3375 | .80091 | 13 | 47 | .61268 | .77521 | 1.2900 | .79033 | 13 |
| 48 | .59902 | .74810 | 1.3367 | .80073 | 12 | 48 | .61291 | .77568 | 1.2892 | .79016 | 12 |
| 49 | .59926 | .74855 | 1.3359 | .80056 | 11 | 49 | .61314 | .77615 | 1.2884 | .78998 | 11 |
| 50 | .59949 | .74900 | 1.3351 | .80038 | 10 | 50 | .61337 | .77661 | 1.2876 | .78980 | 10 |
| 51 | .59972 | .74946 | 1.3343 | .80021 | 9 | 51 | .61360 | .77708 | 1.2869 | .78962 | 9 |
| 52 | .59995 | .74991 | 1.3335 | .80003 | 8 | 52 | .61383 | .77754 | 1.2861 | .78944 | 8 |
| 53 | .60019 | .75037 | 1.3327 | .79986 | 7 | 53 | .61406 | .77801 | 1.2853 | .78926 | 7 |
| 54 | .60042 | .75082 | 1.3319 | .79968 | 6 | 54 | .61429 | .77848 | 1.2846 | .78908 | 6 |
| 55 | .60065 | .75128 | 1.3311 | .79951 | 5 | 55 | .61451 | .77895 | 1.2838 | .78891 | 5 |
| 56 | .60089 | .75173 | 1.3303 | .79934 | 4 | 56 | .61474 | .77941 | 1.2830 | .78873 | 4 |
| 57 | .60112 | .75219 | 1.3295 | .79916 | 3 | 57 | .61497 | .77988 | 1.2322 | .78855 | 3 |
| 58 | .60135 | .75264 | 1.3287 | .79899 | 2 | 58 | .61520 | .78035 | 1.2815 | .78837 | 2 |
| 59 | .60158 | .75310 | 1.3278 | .79881 | 1 | 59 | .61543 | .78082 | 1.2807 | .78819 | 1 |
| 60 | .60182 | .75355 | 1.3270 | .79864 | 0 | 60 | .61566 | .78129 | 1.2799 | .78801 | 0 |
| ′ | Cos | Cot | Tan | Sin | ′ | ′ | Cos | Cot | Tan | Sin | ′ |

126° (306°)      (233°) 53°      127° (307°)      (232°) 52°

| ′ | Sin | Tan | Cot | Cos | ′ | ′ | Sin | Tan | Cot | Cos | ′ |
|---|---|---|---|---|---|---|---|---|---|---|---|
| **0** | .61566 | .78129 | 1.2799 | .78801 | **60** | **0** | .62932 | .80978 | 1.2349 | .77715 | **60** |
| 1 | .61589 | .78175 | 1.2792 | .78783 | 59 | 1 | .62955 | .81027 | 1.2342 | .77696 | 59 |
| 2 | .61612 | .78222 | 1.2784 | .78765 | 58 | 2 | .62977 | .81075 | 1.2334 | .77678 | 58 |
| 3 | .61635 | .78269 | 1.2776 | .78747 | 57 | 3 | .63000 | .81123 | 1.2327 | .77660 | 57 |
| 4 | .61658 | .78316 | 1.2769 | .78729 | 56 | 4 | .63022 | .81171 | 1.2320 | .77641 | 56 |
| **5** | .61681 | .78363 | 1.2761 | .78711 | **55** | **5** | .63045 | .81220 | 1.2312 | .77623 | **55** |
| 6 | .61704 | .78410 | 1.2753 | .78694 | 54 | 6 | .63068 | .81268 | 1.2305 | .77605 | 54 |
| 7 | .61726 | .78457 | 1.2746 | .78676 | 53 | 7 | .63090 | .81316 | 1.2298 | .77586 | 53 |
| 8 | .61749 | .78504 | 1.2738 | .78658 | 52 | 8 | .63113 | .81364 | 1.2290 | .77568 | 52 |
| 9 | .61772 | .78551 | 1.2731 | .78640 | 51 | 9 | .63135 | .81413 | 1.2283 | .77550 | 51 |
| **10** | .61795 | .78598 | 1.2723 | .78622 | **50** | **10** | .63158 | .81461 | 1.2276 | .77531 | **50** |
| 11 | .61818 | .78645 | 1.2715 | .78604 | 49 | 11 | .63180 | .81510 | 1.2268 | .77513 | 49 |
| 12 | .61841 | .78692 | 1.2708 | .78586 | 48 | 12 | .63203 | .81558 | 1.2261 | .77494 | 48 |
| 13 | .61864 | .78739 | 1.2700 | .78568 | 47 | 13 | .63225 | .81606 | 1.2254 | .77476 | 47 |
| 14 | .61887 | .78786 | 1.2693 | .78550 | 46 | 14 | .63248 | .81655 | 1.2247 | .77458 | 46 |
| **15** | .61909 | .78834 | 1.2685 | .78532 | **45** | **15** | .63271 | .81703 | 1.2239 | .77439 | **45** |
| 16 | .61932 | .78881 | 1.2677 | .78514 | 44 | 16 | .63293 | .81752 | 1.2232 | .77421 | 44 |
| 17 | .61955 | .78928 | 1.2670 | .78496 | 43 | 17 | .63316 | .81800 | 1.2225 | .77402 | 43 |
| 18 | .61978 | .78975 | 1.2662 | .78478 | 42 | 18 | .63338 | .81849 | 1.2218 | .77384 | 42 |
| 19 | .62001 | .79022 | 1.2655 | .78460 | 41 | 19 | .63361 | .81898 | 1.2210 | .77366 | 41 |
| **20** | .62024 | .79070 | 1.2647 | .78442 | **40** | **20** | .63383 | .81946 | 1.2203 | .77347 | **40** |
| 21 | .62046 | .79117 | 1.2640 | .78424 | 39 | 21 | .63406 | .81995 | 1.2196 | .77329 | 39 |
| 22 | .62069 | .79164 | 1.2632 | .78405 | 38 | 22 | .63428 | .82044 | 1.2189 | .77310 | 38 |
| 23 | .62092 | .79212 | 1.2624 | .78387 | 37 | 23 | .63451 | .82092 | 1.2181 | .77292 | 37 |
| 24 | .62115 | .79259 | 1.2617 | .78369 | 36 | 24 | .63473 | .82141 | 1.2174 | .77273 | 36 |
| **25** | .62138 | .79306 | 1.2609 | .78351 | **35** | **25** | .63496 | .82190 | 1.2167 | .77255 | **35** |
| 26 | .62160 | .79354 | 1.2602 | .78333 | 34 | 26 | .63518 | .82238 | 1.2160 | .77236 | 34 |
| 27 | .62183 | .79401 | 1.2594 | .78315 | 33 | 27 | .63540 | .82287 | 1.2153 | .77218 | 33 |
| 28 | .62206 | .79449 | 1.2587 | .78297 | 32 | 28 | .63563 | .82336 | 1.2145 | .77199 | 32 |
| 29 | .62229 | .79496 | 1.2579 | .78279 | 31 | 29 | .63585 | .82385 | 1.2138 | .77181 | 31 |
| **30** | .62251 | .79544 | 1.2572 | .78261 | **30** | **30** | .63608 | .82434 | 1.2131 | .77162 | **30** |
| 31 | .62274 | .79591 | 1.2564 | .78243 | 29 | 31 | .63630 | .82483 | 1.2124 | .77144 | 29 |
| 32 | .62297 | .79639 | 1.2557 | .78225 | 28 | 32 | .63653 | .82531 | 1.2117 | .77125 | 28 |
| 33 | .62320 | .79686 | 1.2549 | .78206 | 27 | 33 | .63675 | .82580 | 1.2109 | .77107 | 27 |
| 34 | .62342 | .79734 | 1.2542 | .78188 | 26 | 34 | .63698 | .82629 | 1.2102 | .77088 | 26 |
| **35** | .62365 | .79781 | 1.2534 | .78170 | **25** | **35** | .63720 | .82678 | 1.2095 | .77070 | **25** |
| 36 | .62388 | .79829 | 1.2527 | .78152 | 24 | 36 | .63742 | .82727 | 1.2088 | .77051 | 24 |
| 37 | .62411 | .79877 | 1.2519 | .78134 | 23 | 37 | .63765 | .82776 | 1.2081 | .77033 | 23 |
| 38 | .62433 | .79924 | 1.2512 | .78116 | 22 | 38 | .63787 | .82825 | 1.2074 | .77014 | 22 |
| 39 | .62456 | .79972 | 1.2504 | .78098 | 21 | 39 | .63810 | .82874 | 1.2066 | .76996 | 21 |
| **40** | .62479 | .80020 | 1.2497 | .78079 | **20** | **40** | .63832 | .82923 | 1.2059 | .76977 | **20** |
| 41 | .62502 | .80067 | 1.2489 | .78061 | 19 | 41 | .63854 | .82972 | 1.2052 | .76959 | 19 |
| 42 | .62524 | .80115 | 1.2482 | .78043 | 18 | 42 | .63877 | .83022 | 1.2045 | .76940 | 18 |
| 43 | .62547 | .80163 | 1.2475 | .78025 | 17 | 43 | .63899 | .83071 | 1.2038 | .76921 | 17 |
| 44 | .62570 | .80211 | 1.2467 | .78007 | 16 | 44 | .63922 | .83120 | 1.2031 | .76903 | 16 |
| **45** | .62592 | .80258 | 1.2460 | .77988 | **15** | **45** | .63944 | .83169 | 1.2024 | .76884 | **15** |
| 46 | .62615 | .80306 | 1.2452 | .77970 | 14 | 46 | .63966 | .83218 | 1.2017 | .76866 | 14 |
| 47 | .62638 | .80354 | 1.2445 | .77952 | 13 | 47 | .63989 | .83268 | 1.2009 | .76847 | 13 |
| 48 | .62660 | .80402 | 1.2437 | .77934 | 12 | 48 | .64011 | .83317 | 1.2002 | .76828 | 12 |
| 49 | .62683 | .80450 | 1.2430 | .77916 | 11 | 49 | .64033 | .83366 | 1.1995 | .76810 | 11 |
| **50** | .62706 | .80498 | 1.2423 | .77897 | **10** | **50** | .64056 | .83415 | 1.1988 | .76791 | **10** |
| 51 | .62728 | .80546 | 1.2415 | .77879 | 9 | 51 | .64078 | .83465 | 1.1981 | .76772 | 9 |
| 52 | .62751 | .80594 | 1.2408 | .77861 | 8 | 52 | .64100 | .83514 | 1.1974 | .76754 | 8 |
| 53 | .62774 | .80642 | 1.2401 | .77843 | 7 | 53 | .64123 | .83564 | 1.1967 | .76735 | 7 |
| 54 | .62796 | .80690 | 1.2393 | .77824 | 6 | 54 | .64145 | .83613 | 1.1960 | .76717 | 6 |
| **55** | .62819 | .80738 | 1.2386 | .77806 | **5** | **55** | .64167 | .83662 | 1.1953 | .76698 | **5** |
| 56 | .62842 | .80786 | 1.2378 | .77788 | 4 | 56 | .64190 | .83712 | 1.1946 | .76679 | 4 |
| 57 | .62864 | .80834 | 1.2371 | .77769 | 3 | 57 | .64212 | .83761 | 1.1939 | .76661 | 3 |
| 58 | .62887 | .80882 | 1.2364 | .77751 | 2 | 58 | .64234 | .83811 | 1.1932 | .76642 | 2 |
| 59 | .62909 | .80930 | 1.2356 | .77733 | 1 | 59 | .64256 | .83860 | 1.1925 | .76623 | 1 |
| **60** | .62932 | .80978 | 1.2349 | .77715 | **0** | **60** | .64279 | .83910 | 1.1918 | .76604 | **0** |
| ′ | Cos | Cot | Tan | Sin | ′ | ′ | Cos | Cot | Tan | Sin | ′ |

| ′ | Sin | Tan | Cot | Cos | ′ |
|---|-----|-----|-----|-----|---|
| **0** | .64279 | .83910 | 1.1918 | .76604 | **60** |
| 1 | .64301 | .83960 | 1.1910 | .76586 | 59 |
| 2 | .64323 | .84009 | 1.1903 | .76567 | 58 |
| 3 | .64346 | .84059 | 1.1896 | .76548 | 57 |
| 4 | .64368 | .84108 | 1.1889 | .76530 | 56 |
| **5** | .64390 | .84158 | 1.1882 | .76511 | **55** |
| 6 | .64412 | .84208 | 1.1875 | .76492 | 54 |
| 7 | .64435 | .84258 | 1.1868 | .73473 | 53 |
| 8 | .64457 | .84307 | 1.1861 | .76455 | 52 |
| 9 | .64479 | .84357 | 1.1854 | .76436 | 51 |
| **10** | .64501 | .84407 | 1.1847 | .76417 | **50** |
| 11 | .64524 | .84457 | 1.1840 | .76398 | 49 |
| 12 | .64546 | .84507 | 1.1833 | .76380 | 48 |
| 13 | .64568 | .84556 | 1.1826 | .76361 | 47 |
| 14 | .64590 | .84606 | 1.1819 | .76342 | 46 |
| **15** | .64612 | .84656 | 1.1812 | .76323 | **45** |
| 16 | .64635 | .84706 | 1.1806 | .76304 | 44 |
| 17 | .64657 | .84756 | 1.1799 | .76286 | 43 |
| 18 | .64679 | .84806 | 1.1792 | .76267 | 42 |
| 19 | .64701 | .84856 | 1.1785 | .76248 | 41 |
| **20** | .64723 | .84906 | 1.1778 | .76229 | **40** |
| 21 | .64746 | .84956 | 1.1771 | .76210 | 39 |
| 22 | .64768 | .85006 | 1.1764 | .76192 | 38 |
| 23 | .64790 | .85057 | 1.1757 | .76173 | 37 |
| 24 | .64812 | .85107 | 1.1750 | .76154 | 36 |
| **25** | .64834 | .85157 | 1.1743 | .76135 | **35** |
| 26 | .64856 | .85207 | 1.1736 | .76116 | 34 |
| 27 | .64878 | .85257 | 1.1729 | .76097 | 33 |
| 28 | .64901 | .85308 | 1.1722 | .76078 | 32 |
| 29 | .64923 | .85358 | 1.1715 | .76059 | 31 |
| **30** | .64945 | .85408 | 1.1708 | .76041 | **30** |
| 31 | .64967 | .85458 | 1.1702 | .76022 | 29 |
| 32 | .64989 | .85509 | 1.1695 | .76003 | 28 |
| 33 | .65011 | .85559 | 1.1688 | .75984 | 27 |
| 34 | .65033 | .85609 | 1.1681 | .75965 | 26 |
| **35** | .65055 | .85660 | 1.1674 | .75946 | **25** |
| 36 | .65077 | .85710 | 1.1667 | .75927 | 24 |
| 37 | .65100 | .85761 | 1.1660 | .75908 | 23 |
| 38 | .65122 | .85811 | 1.1653 | .75889 | 22 |
| 39 | .65144 | .85862 | 1.1647 | .75870 | 21 |
| **40** | .65166 | .85912 | 1.1640 | .75851 | **20** |
| 41 | .65188 | .85963 | 1.1633 | .75832 | 19 |
| 42 | .65210 | .86014 | 1.1626 | .75813 | 18 |
| 43 | .65232 | .86064 | 1.1619 | .75794 | 17 |
| 44 | .65254 | .86115 | 1.1612 | .75775 | 16 |
| **45** | .65276 | .86166 | 1.1606 | .75756 | **15** |
| 46 | .65298 | .86216 | 1.1599 | .75738 | 14 |
| 47 | .65320 | .86267 | 1.1592 | .75719 | 13 |
| 48 | .65342 | .86318 | 1.1585 | .75700 | 12 |
| 49 | .65364 | .86368 | 1.1578 | .75680 | 11 |
| **50** | .65386 | .86419 | 1.1571 | .75661 | **10** |
| 51 | .65408 | .86470 | 1.1565 | .75642 | 9 |
| 52 | .65430 | .86521 | 1.1558 | .75623 | 8 |
| 53 | .65452 | .86572 | 1.1551 | .75604 | 7 |
| 54 | .65474 | .86623 | 1.1544 | .75585 | 6 |
| **55** | .65496 | .86674 | 1.1538 | .75566 | **5** |
| 56 | .65518 | .86725 | 1.1531 | .75547 | 4 |
| 57 | .65540 | .86776 | 1.1524 | .75528 | 3 |
| 58 | .65562 | .86827 | 1.1517 | .75509 | 2 |
| 59 | .65584 | .86878 | 1.1510 | .75490 | 1 |
| **60** | .65606 | .86929 | 1.1504 | .75471 | **0** |
| ′ | Cos | Cot | Tan | Sin | ′ |

| ′ | Sin | Tan | Cot | Cos | ′ |
|---|-----|-----|-----|-----|---|
| **0** | .65606 | .86929 | 1.1504 | .75471 | **60** |
| 1 | .65628 | .86980 | 1.1497 | .75452 | 59 |
| 2 | .65650 | .87031 | 1.1490 | .75433 | 58 |
| 3 | .65672 | .87082 | 1.1483 | .75414 | 57 |
| 4 | .65694 | .87133 | 1.1477 | .75395 | 56 |
| **5** | .65716 | .87184 | 1.1470 | .75375 | **55** |
| 6 | .65738 | .87236 | 1.1463 | .75356 | 54 |
| 7 | .65759 | .87287 | 1.1456 | .75337 | 53 |
| 8 | .65781 | .87338 | 1.1450 | .75318 | 52 |
| 9 | .65803 | .87389 | 1.1443 | .75299 | 51 |
| **10** | .65825 | .87441 | 1.1436 | .75280 | **50** |
| 11 | .65847 | .87492 | 1.1430 | .75261 | 49 |
| 12 | .65869 | .87543 | 1.1423 | .75241 | 48 |
| 13 | .65891 | .87595 | 1.1416 | .75222 | 47 |
| 14 | .65913 | .87646 | 1.1410 | .75203 | 46 |
| **15** | .65935 | .87698 | 1.1403 | .75184 | **45** |
| 16 | .65956 | .87749 | 1.1396 | .75165 | 44 |
| 17 | .65978 | .87801 | 1.1389 | .75146 | 43 |
| 18 | .66000 | .87852 | 1.1383 | .75126 | 42 |
| 19 | .66022 | .87904 | 1.1376 | .75107 | 41 |
| **20** | .66044 | .87955 | 1.1369 | .75088 | **40** |
| 21 | .66066 | .88007 | 1.1363 | .75069 | 39 |
| 22 | .66088 | .88059 | 1.1356 | .75050 | 38 |
| 23 | .66109 | .88110 | 1.1349 | .75030 | 37 |
| 24 | .66131 | .88162 | 1.1343 | .75011 | 36 |
| **25** | .66153 | .88214 | 1.1336 | .74992 | **35** |
| 26 | .66175 | .88265 | 1.1329 | .74973 | 34 |
| 27 | .66197 | .88317 | 1.1323 | .74953 | 33 |
| 28 | .66218 | .88369 | 1.1316 | .74934 | 32 |
| 29 | .66240 | .88421 | 1.1310 | .74915 | 31 |
| **30** | .66262 | .88473 | 1.1303 | .74896 | **30** |
| 31 | .66284 | .88524 | 1.1296 | .74876 | 29 |
| 32 | .66306 | .88576 | 1.1290 | .74857 | 28 |
| 33 | .66327 | .88628 | 1.1283 | .74838 | 27 |
| 34 | .66349 | .88680 | 1.1276 | .74818 | 26 |
| **35** | .66371 | .88732 | 1.1270 | .74799 | **25** |
| 36 | .66393 | .88748 | 1.1263 | .74780 | 24 |
| 37 | .66414 | .88836 | 1.1257 | .74760 | 23 |
| 38 | .66436 | .88888 | 1.1250 | .74741 | 22 |
| 39 | .66458 | .88940 | 1.1243 | .74722 | 21 |
| **40** | .66480 | .88992 | 1.1237 | .74703 | **20** |
| 41 | .66501 | .89045 | 1.1230 | .74683 | 19 |
| 42 | .66523 | .89097 | 1.1224 | .74664 | 18 |
| 43 | .66545 | .89149 | 1.1217 | .74644 | 17 |
| 44 | .66566 | .89201 | 1.1211 | .74625 | 16 |
| **45** | .66588 | .89253 | 1.1204 | .74606 | **15** |
| 46 | .66610 | .89306 | 1.1197 | .74586 | 14 |
| 47 | .66632 | .89358 | 1.1191 | .74567 | 13 |
| 48 | .66653 | .89410 | 1.1184 | .74548 | 12 |
| 49 | .66675 | .89463 | 1.1178 | .74528 | 11 |
| **50** | .66697 | .89515 | 1.1171 | .74509 | **10** |
| 51 | .66718 | .89567 | 1.1165 | .74489 | 9 |
| 52 | .66740 | .89620 | 1.1158 | .74470 | 8 |
| 53 | .66762 | .89672 | 1.1152 | .74451 | 7 |
| 54 | .66783 | .89725 | 1.1145 | .74431 | 6 |
| **55** | .66805 | .89777 | 1.1139 | .74412 | **5** |
| 56 | .66827 | .89830 | 1.1132 | .74392 | 4 |
| 57 | .66848 | .89883 | 1.1126 | .74373 | 3 |
| 58 | .66870 | .89935 | 1.1119 | .74353 | 2 |
| 59 | .66891 | .89988 | 1.1113 | .74334 | 1 |
| **60** | .66913 | .90040 | 1.1106 | .74314 | **0** |
| ′ | Cos | Cot | Tan | Sin | ′ |

**42°** (222°)      (317°) **137°**      **43°** (223°)      (316°) **136°**

| ′ | Sin | Tan | Cot | Cos | ′ | | ′ | Sin | Tan | Cot | Cos | ′ |
|---|-----|-----|-----|-----|---|---|---|-----|-----|-----|-----|---|
| **0** | .66913 | .90040 | 1.1106 | .74314 | **60** | | **0** | .68200 | .93252 | 1.0724 | .73135 | **60** |
| 1 | .66935 | .90093 | 1.1100 | .74295 | 59 | | 1 | .68221 | .93306 | 1.0717 | .73116 | 59 |
| 2 | .66956 | .90146 | 1.1093 | .74276 | 58 | | 2 | .68242 | .93360 | 1.0711 | .73096 | 58 |
| 3 | .66978 | .90199 | 1.1087 | .74256 | 57 | | 3 | .68264 | .93415 | 1.0705 | .73076 | 57 |
| 4 | .66999 | .90251 | 1.1080 | .74237 | 56 | | 4 | .68285 | .93469 | 1.0699 | .73056 | 56 |
| **5** | .67021 | .90304 | 1.1074 | .74217 | **55** | | **5** | .68306 | .93524 | 1.0692 | .73036 | **55** |
| 6 | .67043 | .90357 | 1.1067 | .74198 | 54 | | 6 | .68327 | .93578 | 1.0686 | .73016 | 54 |
| 7 | .67064 | .90410 | 1.1061 | .74178 | 53 | | 7 | .68349 | .93633 | 1.0680 | .72996 | 53 |
| 8 | .67086 | .90463 | 1.1054 | .74159 | 52 | | 8 | .68370 | .93688 | 1.0674 | .72976 | 52 |
| 9 | .67107 | .90516 | 1.1048 | .74139 | 51 | | 9 | .68391 | .93742 | 1.0668 | .72957 | 51 |
| **10** | .67129 | .90569 | 1.1041 | .74120 | **50** | | **10** | .68412 | .93796 | 1.0661 | .72937 | **50** |
| 11 | .67151 | .90621 | 1.1035 | .74100 | 49 | | 11 | .68434 | .93852 | 1.0655 | .72917 | 49 |
| 12 | .67172 | .90674 | 1.1028 | .74080 | 48 | | 12 | .68455 | .93906 | 1.0649 | .72897 | 48 |
| 13 | .67194 | .90727 | 1.1022 | .74061 | 47 | | 13 | .68476 | .93961 | 1.0643 | .72877 | 47 |
| 14 | .67215 | .90781 | 1.1016 | .74041 | 46 | | 14 | .68497 | .94016 | 1.0637 | .72857 | 46 |
| **15** | .67237 | .90834 | 1.1009 | .74022 | **45** | | **15** | .68518 | .94071 | 1.0630 | .72837 | **45** |
| 16 | .67258 | .90887 | 1.1003 | .74002 | 44 | | 16 | .68539 | .94125 | 1.0624 | .72817 | 44 |
| 17 | .67280 | .90940 | 1.0996 | .73983 | 43 | | 17 | .68561 | .94180 | 1.0618 | .72797 | 43 |
| 18 | .67301 | .90993 | 1.0990 | .73963 | 42 | | 18 | .68582 | .94235 | 1.0612 | .72777 | 42 |
| 19 | .67323 | .91046 | 1.0983 | .73944 | 41 | | 19 | .68603 | .94290 | 1.0606 | .72757 | 41 |
| **20** | .67344 | .91099 | 1.0977 | .73924 | **40** | | **20** | .68624 | .94345 | 1.0599 | .72737 | **40** |
| 21 | .67366 | .91153 | 1.0971 | .73904 | 39 | | 21 | .68645 | .94400 | 1.0593 | .72717 | 39 |
| 22 | .67387 | .91206 | 1.0964 | .73885 | 38 | | 22 | .68666 | .94455 | 1.0587 | .72697 | 38 |
| 23 | .67409 | .91259 | 1.0958 | .73865 | 37 | | 23 | .68688 | .94510 | 1.0581 | .72677 | 37 |
| 24 | .67430 | .91313 | 1.0951 | .73846 | 36 | | 24 | .68709 | .94565 | 1.0575 | .72657 | 36 |
| **25** | .67452 | .91366 | 1.0945 | .73826 | **35** | | **25** | .68730 | .94620 | 1.0569 | .72637 | **35** |
| 26 | .67473 | .91419 | 1.0939 | .73806 | 34 | | 26 | .68751 | .94676 | 1.0562 | .72617 | 34 |
| 27 | .67495 | .91473 | 1.0932 | .73787 | 33 | | 27 | .68772 | .94731 | 1.0556 | .72597 | 33 |
| 28 | .67516 | .91526 | 1.0926 | .73767 | 32 | | 28 | .68793 | .94786 | 1.0550 | .72577 | 32 |
| 29 | .67538 | .91580 | 1.0919 | .73747 | 31 | | 29 | .68814 | .94841 | 1.0544 | .72557 | 31 |
| **30** | .67559 | .91633 | 1.0913 | .73728 | **30** | | **30** | .68835 | .94896 | 1.0538 | .72537 | **30** |
| 31 | .67580 | .91687 | 1.0907 | .73708 | 29 | | 31 | .68857 | .94952 | 1.0532 | .72517 | 29 |
| 32 | .67602 | .91740 | 1.0900 | .73688 | 28 | | 32 | .68878 | .95007 | 1.0526 | .72497 | 28 |
| 33 | .67623 | .91794 | 1.0894 | .73669 | 27 | | 33 | .68899 | .95062 | 1.0519 | .72477 | 27 |
| 34 | .67645 | .91847 | 1.0888 | .73649 | 26 | | 34 | .68920 | .95118 | 1.0513 | .72457 | 26 |
| **35** | .67666 | .91901 | 1.0881 | .73629 | **25** | | **35** | .68941 | .95173 | 1.0507 | .72437 | **25** |
| 36 | .67688 | .91955 | 1.0875 | .73610 | 24 | | 36 | .68962 | .95229 | 1.0501 | .72417 | 24 |
| 37 | .67709 | .92008 | 1.0869 | .73590 | 23 | | 37 | .68983 | .95284 | 1.0495 | .72397 | 23 |
| 38 | .67730 | .92062 | 1.0862 | .73570 | 22 | | 38 | .69004 | .95340 | 1.0489 | .72377 | 22 |
| 39 | .67752 | .92116 | 1.0856 | .73551 | 21 | | 39 | .69025 | .95395 | 1.0483 | .72357 | 21 |
| **40** | .67773 | .92170 | 1.0850 | .73531 | **20** | | **40** | .69046 | .95451 | 1.0477 | .72337 | **20** |
| 41 | .67795 | .92224 | 1.0843 | .73511 | 19 | | 41 | .69067 | .95506 | 1.0470 | .72317 | 19 |
| 42 | .67816 | .92277 | 1.0837 | .73491 | 18 | | 42 | .69088 | .95562 | 1.0464 | .72297 | 18 |
| 43 | .67837 | .92331 | 1.0831 | .73472 | 17 | | 43 | .69109 | .95618 | 1.0458 | .72277 | 17 |
| 44 | .67859 | .92385 | 1.0824 | .73452 | 16 | | 44 | .69130 | .95673 | 1.0452 | .72257 | 16 |
| **45** | .67880 | .92439 | 1.0818 | .73432 | **15** | | **45** | .69151 | .95729 | 1.0446 | .72236 | **15** |
| 46 | .67901 | .92493 | 1.0812 | .73413 | 14 | | 46 | .69172 | .95785 | 1.0440 | .72216 | 14 |
| 47 | .67923 | .92547 | 1.0805 | .73393 | 13 | | 47 | .69193 | .95841 | 1.0434 | .72196 | 13 |
| 48 | .67944 | .92601 | 1.0799 | .73373 | 12 | | 48 | .69214 | .95897 | 1.0428 | .72176 | 12 |
| 49 | .67965 | .92655 | 1.0793 | .73353 | 11 | | 49 | .69235 | .95952 | 1.0422 | .72156 | 11 |
| **50** | .67987 | .92709 | 1.0786 | .73333 | **10** | | **50** | .69256 | .96008 | 1.0416 | .72136 | **10** |
| 51 | .68008 | .92763 | 1.0780 | .73314 | 9 | | 51 | .69277 | .96064 | 1.0410 | .72116 | 9 |
| 52 | .68029 | .92817 | 1.0774 | .73294 | 8 | | 52 | .69298 | .96120 | 1.0404 | .72095 | 8 |
| 53 | .68051 | .92872 | 1.0768 | .73274 | 7 | | 53 | .69319 | .96176 | 1.0398 | .72075 | 7 |
| 54 | .68072 | .92926 | 1.0761 | .73254 | 6 | | 54 | .69340 | .96232 | 1.0392 | .72055 | 6 |
| **55** | .68093 | .92980 | 1.0755 | .73234 | **5** | | **55** | .69361 | .96288 | 1.0385 | .72035 | **5** |
| 56 | .68115 | .93034 | 1.0749 | .73215 | 4 | | 56 | .69382 | .96344 | 1.0379 | .72015 | 4 |
| 57 | .68136 | .93088 | 1.0742 | .73195 | 3 | | 57 | .69403 | .96400 | 1.0373 | .71995 | 3 |
| 58 | .68157 | .93143 | 1.0736 | .73175 | 2 | | 58 | .69424 | .96457 | 1.0367 | .71974 | 2 |
| 59 | .68179 | .93197 | 1.0730 | .73155 | 1 | | 59 | .69445 | .96513 | 1.0361 | .71954 | 1 |
| **60** | .68200 | .93252 | 1.0724 | .73135 | **0** | | **60** | .69466 | .96569 | 1.0355 | .71934 | **0** |
| ′ | Cos | Cot | Tan | Sin | ′ | | ′ | Cos | Cot | Tan | Sin | ′ |

## NATURAL FUNCTIONS (Continued)

| ′ | Sin | Tan | Cot | Cos | ′ |
|---|---|---|---|---|---|
| 0 | .69466 | .96569 | 1.0355 | .71934 | 60 |
| 1 | .69487 | .96625 | 1.0349 | .71914 | 59 |
| 2 | .69508 | .96681 | 1.0343 | .71894 | 58 |
| 3 | .69529 | .96738 | 1.0337 | .71873 | 57 |
| 4 | .69549 | .96794 | 1.0331 | .71853 | 56 |
| 5 | .69570 | .96850 | 1.0325 | .71833 | 55 |
| 6 | .69591 | .96907 | 1.0319 | .71813 | 54 |
| 7 | .69612 | .96963 | 1.0313 | .71792 | 53 |
| 8 | .69633 | .97020 | 1.0307 | .71772 | 52 |
| 9 | .69654 | .97076 | 1.0301 | .71752 | 51 |
| 10 | .69675 | .97133 | 1.0295 | .71732 | 50 |
| 11 | .69696 | .97189 | 1.0289 | .71711 | 49 |
| 12 | .69717 | .97246 | 1.0283 | .71691 | 48 |
| 13 | .69737 | .97302 | 1.0277 | .71671 | 47 |
| 14 | .69758 | .97359 | 1.0271 | .71650 | 46 |
| 15 | .69779 | .97416 | 1.0265 | .71630 | 45 |
| 16 | .69800 | .97472 | 1.0259 | .71610 | 44 |
| 17 | .69821 | .97529 | 1.0253 | .71590 | 43 |
| 18 | .69842 | .97586 | 1.0247 | .71569 | 42 |
| 19 | .69862 | .97643 | 1.0241 | .71549 | 41 |
| 20 | .69883 | .97700 | 1.0235 | .71529 | 40 |
| 21 | .69904 | .97756 | 1.0230 | .71508 | 39 |
| 22 | .69925 | .97813 | 1.0224 | .71488 | 38 |
| 23 | .69946 | .97870 | 1.0218 | .71468 | 37 |
| 24 | .69966 | .97927 | 1.0212 | .71447 | 36 |
| 25 | .69987 | .97984 | 1.0206 | .71427 | 35 |
| 26 | .70008 | .98041 | 1.0200 | .71407 | 34 |
| 27 | .70029 | .98098 | 1.0194 | .71386 | 33 |
| 28 | .70049 | .98155 | 1.0188 | .71366 | 32 |
| 29 | .70070 | .98213 | 1.0182 | .71345 | 31 |
| 30 | .70091 | .98270 | 1.0176 | .71325 | 30 |
| 31 | .70112 | .98327 | 1.0170 | .71305 | 29 |
| 32 | .70132 | .98384 | 1.0164 | .71284 | 28 |
| 33 | .70153 | .98441 | 1.0158 | .71264 | 27 |
| 34 | .70174 | .98499 | 1.0152 | .71243 | 26 |
| 35 | .70195 | .98556 | 1.0147 | .71223 | 25 |
| 36 | .70215 | .98613 | 1.0141 | .71203 | 24 |
| 37 | .70236 | .98671 | 1.0135 | .71182 | 23 |
| 38 | .70257 | .98728 | 1.0129 | .71162 | 22 |
| 39 | .70277 | .98786 | 1.0123 | .71141 | 21 |
| 40 | .70298 | .98843 | 1.0117 | .71121 | 20 |
| 41 | .70319 | .98901 | 1.0111 | .71100 | 19 |
| 42 | .70339 | .98958 | 1.0105 | .71080 | 18 |
| 43 | .70360 | .99016 | 1.0099 | .71059 | 17 |
| 44 | .70381 | .99073 | 1.0094 | .71039 | 16 |
| 45 | .70401 | .99131 | 1.0088 | .71019 | 15 |
| 46 | .70422 | .99189 | 1.0082 | .70998 | 14 |
| 47 | .70443 | .99247 | 1.0076 | .70978 | 13 |
| 48 | .70463 | .99304 | 1.0070 | .70957 | 12 |
| 49 | .70484 | .99362 | 1.0064 | .70937 | 11 |
| 50 | .70505 | .99420 | 1.0058 | .70916 | 10 |
| 51 | .70525 | .99478 | 1.0052 | .70896 | 9 |
| 52 | .70546 | .99536 | 1.0047 | .70875 | 8 |
| 53 | .70567 | .99594 | 1.0041 | .70855 | 7 |
| 54 | .70587 | .99652 | 1.0035 | .70834 | 6 |
| 55 | .70608 | .99710 | 1.0029 | .70813 | 5 |
| 56 | .70628 | .99768 | 1.0023 | .70793 | 4 |
| 57 | .70649 | .99826 | 1.0017 | .70772 | 3 |
| 58 | .70670 | .99884 | 1.0012 | .70752 | 2 |
| 59 | .70690 | .99942 | 1.0006 | .70731 | 1 |
| 60 | .70711 | 1.0000 | 1.0000 | .70711 | 0 |
| ′ | Cos | Cot | Tan | Sin | ′ |

**0° (180°)**  (359°) **179°**  **1° (181°)**  (358°) **178°**  **2° (182°)**  (357°) **177°**

| ' | Sec | Csc | ' | ' | Sec | Csc | ' | ' | Sec | Csc | ' |
|---|-----|-----|---|---|-----|-----|---|---|-----|-----|---|
| 0 | 1.0000 | — | 60 | 0 | 1.0002 | 57.299 | 60 | 0 | 1.0006 | 28.654 | 60 |
| 1 | 1.0000 | 3437.7 | 59 | 1 | 1.0002 | 56.359 | 59 | 1 | 1.0006 | 28.417 | 59 |
| 2 | 1.0000 | 1718.9 | 58 | 2 | 1.0002 | 55.451 | 58 | 2 | 1.0006 | 28.184 | 58 |
| 3 | 1.0000 | 1145.9 | 57 | 3 | 1.0002 | 54.570 | 57 | 3 | 1.0006 | 27.955 | 57 |
| 4 | 1.0000 | 859.44 | 56 | 4 | 1.0002 | 53.718 | 56 | 4 | 1.0007 | 27.730 | 56 |
| 5 | 1.0000 | 687.55 | 55 | 5 | 1.0002 | 52.892 | 55 | 5 | 1.0007 | 27.508 | 55 |
| 6 | 1.0000 | 572.96 | 54 | 6 | 1.0002 | 52.090 | 54 | 6 | 1.0007 | 27.290 | 54 |
| 7 | 1.0000 | 491.11 | 53 | 7 | 1.0002 | 51.313 | 53 | 7 | 1.0007 | 27.075 | 53 |
| 8 | 1.0000 | 429.72 | 52 | 8 | 1.0002 | 50.558 | 52 | 8 | 1.0007 | 26.864 | 52 |
| 9 | 1.0000 | 381.97 | 51 | 9 | 1.0002 | 49.826 | 51 | 9 | 1.0007 | 26.655 | 51 |
| 10 | 1.0000 | 343.78 | 50 | 10 | 1.0002 | 49.114 | 50 | 10 | 1.0007 | 26.451 | 50 |
| 11 | 1.0000 | 312.52 | 49 | 11 | 1.0002 | 48.422 | 49 | 11 | 1.0007 | 26.249 | 49 |
| 12 | 1.0000 | 286.48 | 48 | 12 | 1.0002 | 47.750 | 48 | 12 | 1.0007 | 26.050 | 48 |
| 13 | 1.0000 | 264.44 | 47 | 13 | 1.0002 | 47.096 | 47 | 13 | 1.0007 | 25.854 | 47 |
| 14 | 1.0000 | 245.55 | 46 | 14 | 1.0002 | 46.460 | 46 | 14 | 1.0008 | 25.661 | 46 |
| 15 | 1.0000 | 229.18 | 45 | 15 | 1.0002 | 45.840 | 45 | 15 | 1.0008 | 25.471 | 45 |
| 16 | 1.0000 | 214.86 | 44 | 16 | 1.0002 | 45.237 | 44 | 16 | 1.0008 | 25.284 | 44 |
| 17 | 1.0000 | 202.22 | 43 | 17 | 1.0003 | 44.650 | 43 | 17 | 1.0008 | 25.100 | 43 |
| 18 | 1.0000 | 190.99 | 42 | 18 | 1.0003 | 44.077 | 42 | 18 | 1.0008 | 24.918 | 42 |
| 19 | 1.0000 | 180.93 | 41 | 19 | 1.0003 | 43.520 | 41 | 19 | 1.0008 | 24.739 | 41 |
| 20 | 1.0000 | 171.89 | 40 | 20 | 1.0003 | 42.976 | 40 | 20 | 1.0008 | 24.562 | 40 |
| 21 | 1.0000 | 163.70 | 39 | 21 | 1.0003 | 42.445 | 39 | 21 | 1.0008 | 24.388 | 39 |
| 22 | 1.0000 | 156.26 | 38 | 22 | 1.0003 | 41.928 | 38 | 22 | 1.0009 | 24.216 | 38 |
| 23 | 1.0000 | 149.47 | 37 | 23 | 1.0003 | 41.423 | 37 | 23 | 1.0009 | 24.047 | 37 |
| 24 | 1.0000 | 143.24 | 36 | 24 | 1.0003 | 40.930 | 36 | 24 | 1.0009 | 23.880 | 36 |
| 25 | 1.0000 | 137.51 | 35 | 25 | 1.0003 | 40.448 | 35 | 25 | 1.0009 | 23.716 | 35 |
| 26 | 1.0000 | 132.22 | 34 | 26 | 1.0003 | 39.978 | 34 | 26 | 1.0009 | 23.553 | 34 |
| 27 | 1.0000 | 127.33 | 33 | 27 | 1.0003 | 39.519 | 33 | 27 | 1.0009 | 23.393 | 33 |
| 28 | 1.0000 | 122.78 | 32 | 28 | 1.0003 | 39.070 | 32 | 28 | 1.0009 | 23.235 | 32 |
| 29 | 1.0000 | 118.54 | 31 | 29 | 1.0003 | 38.631 | 31 | 29 | 1.0009 | 23.079 | 31 |
| 30 | 1.0000 | 114.59 | 30 | 30 | 1.0003 | 38.202 | 30 | 30 | 1.0010 | 22.926 | 30 |
| 31 | 1.0000 | 110.90 | 29 | 31 | 1.0004 | 37.782 | 29 | 31 | 1.0010 | 22.774 | 29 |
| 32 | 1.0000 | 107.43 | 28 | 32 | 1.0004 | 37.371 | 28 | 32 | 1.0010 | 22.624 | 28 |
| 33 | 1.0000 | 104.18 | 27 | 33 | 1.0004 | 36.970 | 27 | 33 | 1.0010 | 22.476 | 27 |
| 34 | 1.0000 | 101.11 | 26 | 34 | 1.0004 | 36.576 | 26 | 34 | 1.0010 | 22.330 | 26 |
| 35 | 1.0001 | 98.223 | 25 | 35 | 1.0004 | 36.191 | 25 | 35 | 1.0010 | 22.187 | 25 |
| 36 | 1.0001 | 95.495 | 24 | 36 | 1.0004 | 35.815 | 24 | 36 | 1.0010 | 22.044 | 24 |
| 37 | 1.0001 | 92.914 | 23 | 37 | 1.0004 | 35.445 | 23 | 37 | 1.0010 | 21.904 | 23 |
| 38 | 1.0001 | 90.469 | 22 | 38 | 1.0004 | 35.084 | 22 | 38 | 1.0011 | 21.766 | 22 |
| 39 | 1.0001 | 88.149 | 21 | 39 | 1.0004 | 34.730 | 21 | 39 | 1.0011 | 21.629 | 21 |
| 40 | 1.0001 | 85.946 | 20 | 40 | 1.0004 | 34.382 | 20 | 40 | 1.0011 | 21.494 | 20 |
| 41 | 1.0001 | 83.849 | 19 | 41 | 1.0004 | 34.042 | 19 | 41 | 1.0011 | 21.360 | 19 |
| 42 | 1.0001 | 81.853 | 18 | 42 | 1.0004 | 33.708 | 18 | 42 | 1.0011 | 21.229 | 18 |
| 43 | 1.0001 | 79.950 | 17 | 43 | 1.0004 | 33.381 | 17 | 43 | 1.0011 | 21.098 | 17 |
| 44 | 1.0001 | 78.133 | 16 | 44 | 1.0005 | 33.060 | 16 | 44 | 1.0011 | 20.970 | 16 |
| 45 | 1.0001 | 76.397 | 15 | 45 | 1.0005 | 32.746 | 15 | 45 | 1.0012 | 20.843 | 15 |
| 46 | 1.0001 | 74.736 | 14 | 46 | 1.0005 | 32.437 | 14 | 46 | 1.0012 | 20.717 | 14 |
| 47 | 1.0001 | 73.146 | 13 | 47 | 1.0005 | 32.134 | 13 | 47 | 1.0012 | 20.593 | 13 |
| 48 | 1.0001 | 71.622 | 12 | 48 | 1.0005 | 31.836 | 12 | 48 | 1.0012 | 20.471 | 12 |
| 49 | 1.0001 | 70.160 | 11 | 49 | 1.0005 | 31.544 | 11 | 49 | 1.0012 | 20.350 | 11 |
| 50 | 1.0001 | 68.757 | 10 | 50 | 1.0005 | 31.258 | 10 | 50 | 1.0012 | 20.230 | 10 |
| 51 | 1.0001 | 67.409 | 9 | 51 | 1.0005 | 30.976 | 9 | 51 | 1.0012 | 20.112 | 9 |
| 52 | 1.0001 | 66.113 | 8 | 52 | 1.0005 | 30.700 | 8 | 52 | 1.0013 | 19.995 | 8 |
| 53 | 1.0001 | 64.866 | 7 | 53 | 1.0005 | 30.428 | 7 | 53 | 1.0013 | 19.880 | 7 |
| 54 | 1.0001 | 63.665 | 6 | 54 | 1.0006 | 30.161 | 6 | 54 | 1.0013 | 19.766 | 6 |
| 55 | 1.0001 | 62.507 | 5 | 55 | 1.0006 | 29.899 | 5 | 55 | 1.0013 | 19.653 | 5 |
| 56 | 1.0001 | 61.391 | 4 | 56 | 1.0006 | 29.641 | 4 | 56 | 1.0013 | 19.541 | 4 |
| 57 | 1.0001 | 60.314 | 3 | 57 | 1.0006 | 29.388 | 3 | 57 | 1.0013 | 19.431 | 3 |
| 58 | 1.0001 | 59.274 | 2 | 58 | 1.0006 | 29.139 | 2 | 58 | 1.0013 | 19.322 | 2 |
| 59 | 1.0001 | 58.270 | 1 | 59 | 1.0006 | 28.894 | 1 | 59 | 1.0014 | 19.214 | 1 |
| 60 | 1.0002 | 57.299 | 0 | 60 | 1.0006 | 28 654 | 0 | 60 | 1.0014 | 19.107 | 0 |
| ' | Csc | Sec | ' | ' | Csc | Sec | ' | ' | Csc | Sec | ' |

**3° (183°)**          (356°) **176°**          **4° (18₊°)**          (355°) **175°**          **5° (185°)**          (354°) **174°**

| ′ | Sec | Csc | ′ | ′ | Sec | Csc | ′ | ′ | Sec | Csc | ′ |
|---|-----|-----|---|---|-----|-----|---|---|-----|-----|---|
| 0 | 1.0014 | 19.107 | 60 | 0 | 1.0024 | 14.336 | 60 | 0 | 1.0038 | 11.474 | 60 |
| 1 | 1.0014 | 19.002 | 59 | 1 | 1.0025 | 14.276 | 59 | 1 | 1.0038 | 11.436 | 59 |
| 2 | 1.0014 | 18.898 | 58 | 2 | 1.0025 | 14.217 | 58 | 2 | 1.0039 | 11.398 | 58 |
| 3 | 1.0014 | 18.794 | 57 | 3 | 1.0025 | 14.159 | 57 | 3 | 1.0039 | 11.360 | 57 |
| 4 | 1.0014 | 18.692 | 56 | 4 | 1.0025 | 14.101 | 56 | 4 | 1.0039 | 11.323 | 56 |
| 5 | 1.0014 | 18.591 | 55 | 5 | 1.0025 | 14.044 | 55 | 5 | 1.0039 | 11.286 | 55 |
| 6 | 1.0015 | 18.492 | 54 | 6 | 1.0026 | 13.987 | 54 | 6 | 1.0040 | 11.249 | 54 |
| 7 | 1.0015 | 18.393 | 53 | 7 | 1.0026 | 13.930 | 53 | 7 | 1.0040 | 11.213 | 53 |
| 8 | 1.0015 | 18.295 | 52 | 8 | 1.0026 | 13.874 | 52 | 8 | 1.0040 | 11.176 | 52 |
| 9 | 1.0015 | 18.198 | 51 | 9 | 1.0026 | 13.818 | 51 | 9 | 1.0041 | 11.140 | 51 |
| 10 | 1.0015 | 18.103 | 50 | 10 | 1.0027 | 13.763 | 50 | 10 | 1.0041 | 11.105 | 50 |
| 11 | 1.0015 | 18.008 | 49 | 11 | 1.0027 | 13.708 | 49 | 11 | 1.0041 | 11.069 | 49 |
| 12 | 1.0016 | 17.914 | 48 | 12 | 1.0027 | 13.654 | 48 | 12 | 1.0041 | 11.034 | 48 |
| 13 | 1.0016 | 17.822 | 47 | 13 | 1.0027 | 13.600 | 47 | 13 | 1.0042 | 10.998 | 47 |
| 14 | 1.0016 | 17.730 | 46 | 14 | 1.0027 | 13.547 | 46 | 14 | 1.0042 | 10.963 | 46 |
| 15 | 1.0016 | 17.639 | 45 | 15 | 1.0028 | 13.494 | 45 | 15 | 1.0042 | 10.929 | 45 |
| 16 | 1.0016 | 17.549 | 44 | 16 | 1.0028 | 13.441 | 44 | 16 | 1.0042 | 10.894 | 44 |
| 17 | 1.0016 | 17.460 | 43 | 17 | 1.0028 | 13.389 | 43 | 17 | 1.0043 | 10.860 | 43 |
| 18 | 1.0017 | 17.372 | 42 | 18 | 1.0028 | 13.337 | 42 | 18 | 1.0043 | 10.826 | 42 |
| 19 | 1.0017 | 17.285 | 41 | 19 | 1.0028 | 13.286 | 41 | 19 | 1.0043 | 10.792 | 41 |
| 20 | 1.0017 | 17.198 | 40 | 20 | 1.0029 | 13.235 | 40 | 20 | 1.0043 | 10.758 | 40 |
| 21 | 1.0017 | 17.113 | 39 | 21 | 1.0029 | 13.184 | 39 | 21 | 1.0044 | 10.725 | 39 |
| 22 | 1.0017 | 17.028 | 38 | 22 | 1.0029 | 13.134 | 38 | 22 | 1.0044 | 10.692 | 38 |
| 23 | 1.0017 | 16.945 | 37 | 23 | 1.0029 | 13.084 | 37 | 23 | 1.0044 | 10.659 | 37 |
| 24 | 1.0018 | 16.862 | 36 | 24 | 1.0030 | 13.035 | 36 | 24 | 1.0045 | 10.626 | 36 |
| 25 | 1.0018 | 16.779 | 35 | 25 | 1.0030 | 12.985 | 35 | 25 | 1.0045 | 10.593 | 35 |
| 26 | 1.0018 | 16.698 | 34 | 26 | 1.0030 | 12.937 | 34 | 26 | 1.0045 | 10.561 | 34 |
| 27 | 1.0018 | 16.618 | 33 | 27 | 1.0030 | 12.888 | 33 | 27 | 1.0045 | 10.529 | 33 |
| 28 | 1.0018 | 16.538 | 32 | 28 | 1.0030 | 12.840 | 32 | 28 | 1.0046 | 10.497 | 32 |
| 29 | 1.0019 | 16.459 | 31 | 29 | 1.0031 | 12.793 | 31 | 29 | 1.0046 | 10.465 | 31 |
| 30 | 1.0019 | 16.380 | 30 | 30 | 1.0031 | 12.745 | 30 | 30 | 1.0046 | 10.433 | 30 |
| 31 | 1.0019 | 16.303 | 29 | 31 | 1.0031 | 12.699 | 29 | 31 | 1.0047 | 10.402 | 29 |
| 32 | 1.0019 | 16.226 | 28 | 32 | 1.0031 | 12.652 | 28 | 32 | 1.0047 | 10.371 | 28 |
| 33 | 1.0019 | 16.150 | 27 | 33 | 1.0032 | 12.606 | 27 | 33 | 1.0047 | 10.340 | 27 |
| 34 | 1.0019 | 16.075 | 26 | 34 | 1.0032 | 12.560 | 26 | 34 | 1.0047 | 10.309 | 26 |
| 35 | 1.0020 | 16.000 | 25 | 35 | 1.0032 | 12.514 | 25 | 35 | 1.0048 | 10.278 | 25 |
| 36 | 1.0020 | 15.926 | 24 | 36 | 1.0032 | 12.469 | 24 | 36 | 1.0048 | 10.248 | 24 |
| 37 | 1.0020 | 15.853 | 23 | 37 | 1.0033 | 12.424 | 23 | 37 | 1.0048 | 10.217 | 23 |
| 38 | 1.0020 | 15.780 | 22 | 38 | 1.0033 | 12.379 | 22 | 38 | 1.0049 | 10.187 | 22 |
| 39 | 1.0020 | 15.708 | 21 | 39 | 1.0033 | 12.335 | 21 | 39 | 1.0049 | 10.157 | 21 |
| 40 | 1.0021 | 15.637 | 20 | 40 | 1.0033 | 12.291 | 20 | 40 | 1.0049 | 10.128 | 20 |
| 41 | 1.0021 | 15.566 | 19 | 41 | 1.0034 | 12.248 | 19 | 41 | 1.0049 | 10.098 | 19 |
| 42 | 1.0021 | 15.496 | 18 | 42 | 1.0034 | 12.204 | 18 | 42 | 1.0050 | 10.068 | 18 |
| 43 | 1.0021 | 15.427 | 17 | 43 | 1.0034 | 12.161 | 17 | 43 | 1.0050 | 10.039 | 17 |
| 44 | 1.0021 | 15.358 | 16 | 44 | 1.0034 | 12.119 | 16 | 44 | 1.0050 | 10.010 | 16 |
| 45 | 1.0021 | 15.290 | 15 | 45 | 1.0034 | 12.076 | 15 | 45 | 1.0051 | 9.9812 | 15 |
| 46 | 1.0022 | 15.222 | 14 | 46 | 1.0035 | 12.034 | 14 | 46 | 1.0051 | 9.9525 | 14 |
| 47 | 1.0022 | 15.155 | 13 | 47 | 1.0035 | 11.992 | 13 | 47 | 1.0051 | 9.9239 | 13 |
| 48 | 1.0022 | 15.089 | 12 | 48 | 1.0035 | 11.951 | 12 | 48 | 1.0051 | 9.8955 | 12 |
| 49 | 1.0022 | 15.023 | 11 | 49 | 1.0035 | 11.909 | 11 | 49 | 1.0052 | 9.8672 | 11 |
| 50 | 1.0022 | 14.958 | 10 | 50 | 1.0036 | 11.868 | 10 | 50 | 1.0052 | 9.8391 | 10 |
| 51 | 1.0023 | 14.893 | 9 | 51 | 1.0036 | 11.828 | 9 | 51 | 1.0052 | 9.8112 | 9 |
| 52 | 1.0023 | 14.829 | 8 | 52 | 1.0036 | 11.787 | 8 | 52 | 1.0053 | 9.7834 | 8 |
| 53 | 1.0023 | 14.766 | 7 | 53 | 1.0036 | 11.747 | 7 | 53 | 1.0053 | 9.7558 | 7 |
| 54 | 1.0023 | 14.703 | 6 | 54 | 1.0037 | 11.707 | 6 | 54 | 1.0053 | 9.7283 | 6 |
| 55 | 1.0023 | 14.640 | 5 | 55 | 1.0037 | 11.668 | 5 | 55 | 1.0054 | 9.7010 | 5 |
| 56 | 1.0024 | 14.581 | 4 | 56 | 1.0037 | 11.628 | 4 | 56 | 1.0054 | 9.6739 | 4 |
| 57 | 1.0024 | 14.517 | 3 | 57 | 1.0037 | 11.589 | 3 | 57 | 1.0054 | 9.6469 | 3 |
| 58 | 1.0024 | 14.456 | 2 | 58 | 1.0038 | 11.551 | 2 | 58 | 1.0054 | 9.6200 | 2 |
| 59 | 1.0024 | 14.395 | 1 | 59 | 1.0038 | 11.512 | 1 | 59 | 1.0055 | 9.5933 | 1 |
| 60 | 1.0024 | 14.336 | 0 | 60 | 1.0038 | 11.474 | 0 | 60 | 1.0055 | 9.5668 | 0 |
| ′ | Csc | Sec | ′ | ′ | Csc | Sec | ′ | ′ | Csc | Sec | ′ |

**6° (186°)**      (353°) **173°**      **7° (187°)**      (352°) **172°**      **8° (188°)**      (351°) **171°**

| ′ | Sec | Csc | ′ | ′ | Sec | Csc | ′ | ′ | Sec | Csc | ′ |
|---|---|---|---|---|---|---|---|---|---|---|---|
| 0 | 1.0055 | 9.5668 | 60 | 0 | 1.0075 | 8.2055 | 60 | 0 | 1.0098 | 7.1853 | 60 |
| 1 | 1.0055 | 9.5404 | 59 | 1 | 1.0075 | 8.1861 | 59 | 1 | 1.0099 | 7.1705 | 59 |
| 2 | 1.0056 | 9.5141 | 58 | 2 | 1.0076 | 8.1668 | 58 | 2 | 1.0099 | 7.1557 | 58 |
| 3 | 1.0056 | 9.4880 | 57 | 3 | 1.0076 | 8.1476 | 57 | 3 | 1.0100 | 7.1410 | 57 |
| 4 | 1.0056 | 9.4620 | 56 | 4 | 1.0077 | 8.1285 | 56 | 4 | 1.0100 | 7.1263 | 56 |
| 5 | 1.0057 | 9.4362 | 55 | 5 | 1.0077 | 8.1095 | 55 | 5 | 1.0100 | 7.1117 | 55 |
| 6 | 1.0057 | 9.4105 | 54 | 6 | 1.0077 | 8.0905 | 54 | 6 | 1.0101 | 7.0972 | 54 |
| 7 | 1.0057 | 9.3850 | 53 | 7 | 1.0078 | 8.0717 | 53 | 7 | 1.0101 | 7.0827 | 53 |
| 8 | 1.0058 | 9.3596 | 52 | 8 | 1.0078 | 8.0529 | 52 | 8 | 1.0102 | 7.0683 | 52 |
| 9 | 1.0058 | 9.3343 | 51 | 9 | 1.0078 | 8.0342 | 51 | 9 | 1.0102 | 7.0539 | 51 |
| 10 | 1.0058 | 9.3092 | 50 | 10 | 1.0079 | 8.0156 | 50 | 10 | 1.0102 | 7.0396 | 50 |
| 11 | 1.0059 | 9.2842 | 49 | 11 | 1.0079 | 7.9971 | 49 | 11 | 1.0103 | 7.0254 | 49 |
| 12 | 1.0059 | 9.2593 | 48 | 12 | 1.0079 | 7.9787 | 48 | 12 | 1.0103 | 7.0112 | 48 |
| 13 | 1.0059 | 9.2346 | 47 | 13 | 1.0080 | 7.9604 | 47 | 13 | 1.0104 | 6.9971 | 47 |
| 14 | 1.0059 | 9.2100 | 46 | 14 | 1.0080 | 7.9422 | 46 | 14 | 1.0104 | 6.9830 | 46 |
| 15 | 1.0060 | 9.1855 | 45 | 15 | 1.0081 | 7.9240 | 45 | 15 | 1.0105 | 6.9690 | 45 |
| 16 | 1.0060 | 9.1612 | 44 | 16 | 1.0081 | 7.9059 | 44 | 16 | 1.0105 | 6.9550 | 44 |
| 17 | 1.0060 | 9.1370 | 43 | 17 | 1.0081 | 7.8879 | 43 | 17 | 1.0105 | 6.9411 | 43 |
| 18 | 1.0061 | 9.1129 | 42 | 18 | 1.0082 | 7.8700 | 42 | 18 | 1.0106 | 6.9273 | 42 |
| 19 | 1.0061 | 9.0890 | 41 | 19 | 1.0082 | 7.8522 | 41 | 19 | 1.0106 | 6.9135 | 41 |
| 20 | 1.0061 | 9.0652 | 40 | 20 | 1.0082 | 7.8344 | 40 | 20 | 1.0107 | 6.8998 | 40 |
| 21 | 1.0062 | 9.0415 | 39 | 21 | 1.0083 | 7.8168 | 39 | 21 | 1.0107 | 6.8861 | 39 |
| 22 | 1.0062 | 9.0179 | 38 | 22 | 1.0083 | 7.7992 | 38 | 22 | 1.0108 | 6.8725 | 38 |
| 23 | 1.0062 | 8.9944 | 37 | 23 | 1.0083 | 7.7817 | 37 | 23 | 1.0108 | 6.8589 | 37 |
| 24 | 1.0063 | 8.9711 | 36 | 24 | 1.0084 | 7.7642 | 36 | 24 | 1.0108 | 6.8454 | 36 |
| 25 | 1.0063 | 8.9479 | 35 | 25 | 1.0084 | 7.7469 | 35 | 25 | 1.0109 | 6.8320 | 35 |
| 26 | 1.0063 | 8.9248 | 34 | 26 | 1.0085 | 7.7296 | 34 | 26 | 1.0109 | 6.8186 | 34 |
| 27 | 1.0064 | 8.9019 | 33 | 27 | 1.0085 | 7.7124 | 33 | 27 | 1.0110 | 6.8052 | 33 |
| 28 | 1.0064 | 8.8790 | 32 | 28 | 1.0086 | 7.6953 | 32 | 28 | 1.0110 | 6.7919 | 32 |
| 29 | 1.0064 | 8.8563 | 31 | 29 | 1.0086 | 7.6783 | 31 | 29 | 1.0111 | 6.7787 | 31 |
| 30 | 1.0065 | 8.8337 | 30 | 30 | 1.0086 | 7.6613 | 30 | 30 | 1.0111 | 6.7655 | 30 |
| 31 | 1.0065 | 8.8112 | 29 | 31 | 1.0087 | 7.6444 | 29 | 31 | 1.0112 | 6.7523 | 29 |
| 32 | 1.0065 | 8.7888 | 28 | 32 | 1.0087 | 7.6276 | 28 | 32 | 1.0112 | 6.7392 | 28 |
| 33 | 1.0066 | 8.7665 | 27 | 33 | 1.0087 | 7.6109 | 27 | 33 | 1.0112 | 6.7262 | 27 |
| 34 | 1.0066 | 8.7444 | 26 | 34 | 1.0088 | 7.5942 | 26 | 34 | 1.0113 | 6.7132 | 26 |
| 35 | 1.0066 | 8.7223 | 25 | 35 | 1.0088 | 7.5776 | 25 | 35 | 1.0113 | 6.7003 | 25 |
| 36 | 1.0067 | 8.7004 | 24 | 36 | 1.0089 | 7.5611 | 24 | 36 | 1.0114 | 6.6874 | 24 |
| 37 | 1.0067 | 8.6786 | 23 | 37 | 1.0089 | 7.5446 | 23 | 37 | 1.0114 | 6.6745 | 23 |
| 38 | 1.0067 | 8.6569 | 22 | 38 | 1.0089 | 7.5282 | 22 | 38 | 1.0115 | 6.6618 | 22 |
| 39 | 1.0068 | 8.6353 | 21 | 39 | 1.0090 | 7.5119 | 21 | 39 | 1.0115 | 6.6490 | 21 |
| 40 | 1.0068 | 8.6138 | 20 | 40 | 1.0090 | 7.4957 | 20 | 40 | 1.0116 | 6.6363 | 20 |
| 41 | 1.0068 | 8.5924 | 19 | 41 | 1.0091 | 7.4795 | 19 | 41 | 1.0116 | 6.6237 | 19 |
| 42 | 1.0069 | 8.5711 | 18 | 42 | 1.0091 | 7.4635 | 18 | 42 | 1.0116 | 6.6111 | 18 |
| 43 | 1.0069 | 8.5500 | 17 | 43 | 1.0091 | 7.4474 | 17 | 43 | 1.0117 | 6.5986 | 17 |
| 44 | 1.0069 | 8.5289 | 16 | 44 | 1.0092 | 7.4315 | 16 | 44 | 1.0117 | 6.5861 | 16 |
| 45 | 1.0070 | 8.5079 | 15 | 45 | 1.0092 | 7.4156 | 15 | 45 | 1.0118 | 6.5736 | 15 |
| 46 | 1.0070 | 8.4871 | 14 | 46 | 1.0093 | 7.3998 | 14 | 46 | 1.0118 | 6.5612 | 14 |
| 47 | 1.0070 | 8.4663 | 13 | 47 | 1.0093 | 7.3840 | 13 | 47 | 1.0119 | 6.5489 | 13 |
| 48 | 1.0071 | 8.4457 | 12 | 48 | 1.0093 | 7.3684 | 12 | 48 | 1.0119 | 6.5366 | 12 |
| 49 | 1.0071 | 8.4251 | 11 | 49 | 1.0094 | 7.3527 | 11 | 49 | 1.0120 | 6.5243 | 11 |
| 50 | 1.0072 | 8.4047 | 10 | 50 | 1.0094 | 7.3372 | 10 | 50 | 1.0120 | 6.5121 | 10 |
| 51 | 1.0072 | 8.3843 | 9 | 51 | 1.0095 | 7.3217 | 9 | 51 | 1.0120 | 6.4999 | 9 |
| 52 | 1.0072 | 8.3641 | 8 | 52 | 1.0095 | 7.3063 | 8 | 52 | 1.0121 | 6.4878 | 8 |
| 53 | 1.0073 | 8.3439 | 7 | 53 | 1.0095 | 7.2909 | 7 | 53 | 1.0121 | 6.4757 | 7 |
| 54 | 1.0073 | 8.3238 | 6 | 54 | 1.0096 | 7.2757 | 6 | 54 | 1.0122 | 6.4637 | 6 |
| 55 | 1.0073 | 8.3039 | 5 | 55 | 1.0096 | 7.2604 | 5 | 55 | 1.0122 | 6.4517 | 5 |
| 56 | 1.0074 | 8.2840 | 4 | 56 | 1.0097 | 7.2453 | 4 | 56 | 1.0123 | 6.4398 | 4 |
| 57 | 1.0074 | 8.2642 | 3 | 57 | 1.0097 | 7.2302 | 3 | 57 | 1.0123 | 6.4279 | 3 |
| 58 | 1.0074 | 8.2446 | 2 | 58 | 1.0097 | 7.2152 | 2 | 58 | 1.0124 | 6.4160 | 2 |
| 59 | 1.0075 | 8.2250 | 1 | 59 | 1.0098 | 7.2002 | 1 | 59 | 1.0124 | 6.4042 | 1 |
| 60 | 1.0075 | 8.2055 | 0 | 60 | 1.0098 | 7.1853 | 0 | 60 | 1.0125 | 6.3925 | 0 |
| ′ | Csc | Sec | ′ | ′ | Csc | Sec | ′ | ′ | Csc | Sec | ′ |

**96° (276°)**      (263°) **83°**      **97° (277°)**      (262°) **82°**      **98° (278°)**      (261°) **81°**

**9° (189°) (350°) 170°**

| ′ | Sec | Csc | ′ |
|---|---|---|---|
| 0 | 1.0125 | 6.3925 | 60 |
| 1 | 1.0125 | 6.3807 | 59 |
| 2 | 1.0126 | 6.3691 | 58 |
| 3 | 1.0126 | 6.3574 | 57 |
| 4 | 1.0127 | 6.3458 | 56 |
| 5 | 1.0127 | 6.3343 | 55 |
| 6 | 1.0127 | 6.3228 | 54 |
| 7 | 1.0128 | 6.3113 | 53 |
| 8 | 1.0128 | 6.2999 | 52 |
| 9 | 1.0129 | 6.2885 | 51 |
| 10 | 1.0129 | 6.2772 | 50 |
| 11 | 1.0130 | 6.2659 | 49 |
| 12 | 1.0130 | 6.2546 | 48 |
| 13 | 1.0131 | 6.2434 | 47 |
| 14 | 1.0131 | 6.2323 | 46 |
| 15 | 1.0132 | 6.2211 | 45 |
| 16 | 1.0132 | 6.2100 | 44 |
| 17 | 1.0133 | 6.1990 | 43 |
| 18 | 1.0133 | 6.1880 | 42 |
| 19 | 1.0134 | 6.1770 | 41 |
| 20 | 1.0134 | 6.1661 | 40 |
| 21 | 1.0135 | 6.1552 | 39 |
| 22 | 1.0135 | 6.1443 | 38 |
| 23 | 1.0136 | 6.1335 | 37 |
| 24 | 1.0136 | 6.1227 | 36 |
| 25 | 1.0137 | 6.1120 | 35 |
| 26 | 1.0137 | 6.1013 | 34 |
| 27 | 1.0138 | 6.0906 | 33 |
| 28 | 1.0138 | 6.0800 | 32 |
| 29 | 1.0139 | 6.0694 | 31 |
| 30 | 1.0139 | 6.0589 | 30 |
| 31 | 1.0140 | 6.0483 | 29 |
| 32 | 1.0140 | 6.0379 | 28 |
| 33 | 1.0141 | 6.0274 | 27 |
| 34 | 1.0141 | 6.0170 | 26 |
| 35 | 1.0142 | 6.0067 | 25 |
| 36 | 1.0142 | 5.9963 | 24 |
| 37 | 1.0143 | 5.9860 | 23 |
| 38 | 1.0143 | 5.9758 | 22 |
| 39 | 1.0144 | 5.9656 | 21 |
| 40 | 1.0144 | 5.9554 | 20 |
| 41 | 1.0145 | 5.9452 | 19 |
| 42 | 1.0145 | 5.9351 | 18 |
| 43 | 1.0146 | 5.9250 | 17 |
| 44 | 1.0146 | 5.9150 | 16 |
| 45 | 1.0147 | 5.9049 | 15 |
| 46 | 1.0147 | 5.8950 | 14 |
| 47 | 1.0148 | 5.8850 | 13 |
| 48 | 1.0148 | 5.8751 | 12 |
| 49 | 1.0149 | 5.8652 | 11 |
| 50 | 1.0149 | 5.8554 | 10 |
| 51 | 1.0150 | 5.8456 | 9 |
| 52 | 1.0150 | 5.8358 | 8 |
| 53 | 1.0151 | 5.8261 | 7 |
| 54 | 1.0151 | 5.8164 | 6 |
| 55 | 1.0152 | 5.8067 | 5 |
| 56 | 1.0152 | 5.7970 | 4 |
| 57 | 1.0153 | 5.7874 | 3 |
| 58 | 1.0153 | 5.7778 | 2 |
| 59 | 1.0154 | 5.7683 | 1 |
| 60 | 1.0154 | 5.7588 | 0 |
| ′ | Csc | Sec | ′ |

**10° (190°) (349°) 169°**

| ′ | Sec | Csc | ′ |
|---|---|---|---|
| 0 | 1.0154 | 5.7588 | 60 |
| 1 | 1.0155 | 5.7493 | 59 |
| 2 | 1.0155 | 5.7398 | 58 |
| 3 | 1.0156 | 5.7304 | 57 |
| 4 | 1.0156 | 5.7210 | 56 |
| 5 | 1.0157 | 5.7117 | 55 |
| 6 | 1.0157 | 5.7023 | 54 |
| 7 | 1.0158 | 5.6930 | 53 |
| 8 | 1.0158 | 5.6838 | 52 |
| 9 | 1.0159 | 5.6745 | 51 |
| 10 | 1.0160 | 5.6653 | 50 |
| 11 | 1.0160 | 5.6562 | 49 |
| 12 | 1.0161 | 5.6470 | 48 |
| 13 | 1.0161 | 5.6379 | 47 |
| 14 | 1.0162 | 5.6288 | 46 |
| 15 | 1.0162 | 5.6198 | 45 |
| 16 | 1.0163 | 5.6107 | 44 |
| 17 | 1.0163 | 5.6017 | 43 |
| 18 | 1.0164 | 5.5928 | 42 |
| 19 | 1.0164 | 5.5838 | 41 |
| 20 | 1.0165 | 5.5749 | 40 |
| 21 | 1.0165 | 5.5660 | 39 |
| 22 | 1.0166 | 5.5572 | 38 |
| 23 | 1.0166 | 5.5484 | 37 |
| 24 | 1.0167 | 5.5396 | 36 |
| 25 | 1.0168 | 5.5308 | 35 |
| 26 | 1.0168 | 5.5221 | 34 |
| 27 | 1.0169 | 5.5134 | 33 |
| 28 | 1.0169 | 5.5047 | 32 |
| 29 | 1.0170 | 5.4960 | 31 |
| 30 | 1.0170 | 5.4874 | 30 |
| 31 | 1.0171 | 5.4788 | 29 |
| 32 | 1.0171 | 5.4702 | 28 |
| 33 | 1.0172 | 5.4617 | 27 |
| 34 | 1.0173 | 5.4532 | 26 |
| 35 | 1.0173 | 5.4447 | 25 |
| 36 | 1.0174 | 5.4362 | 24 |
| 37 | 1.0174 | 5.4278 | 23 |
| 38 | 1.0175 | 5.4194 | 22 |
| 39 | 1.0175 | 5.4110 | 21 |
| 40 | 1.0176 | 5.4026 | 20 |
| 41 | 1.0176 | 5.3943 | 19 |
| 42 | 1.0177 | 5.3860 | 18 |
| 43 | 1.0178 | 5.3777 | 17 |
| 44 | 1.0178 | 5.3695 | 16 |
| 45 | 1.0179 | 5.3612 | 15 |
| 46 | 1.0179 | 5.3530 | 14 |
| 47 | 1.0180 | 5.3449 | 13 |
| 48 | 1.0180 | 5.3367 | 12 |
| 49 | 1.0181 | 5.3286 | 11 |
| 50 | 1.0181 | 5.3205 | 10 |
| 51 | 1.0182 | 5.3124 | 9 |
| 52 | 1.0183 | 5.3044 | 8 |
| 53 | 1.0183 | 5.2963 | 7 |
| 54 | 1.0184 | 5.2883 | 6 |
| 55 | 1.0184 | 5.2804 | 5 |
| 56 | 1.0185 | 5.2724 | 4 |
| 57 | 1.0185 | 5.2645 | 3 |
| 58 | 1.0186 | 5.2566 | 2 |
| 59 | 1.0187 | 5.2487 | 1 |
| 60 | 1.0187 | 5.2408 | 0 |
| ′ | Csc | Sec | ′ |

**11° (191°) (348°) 168°**

| ′ | Sec | Csc | ′ |
|---|---|---|---|
| 0 | 1.0187 | 5.2408 | 60 |
| 1 | 1.0188 | 5.2330 | 59 |
| 2 | 1.0188 | 5.2252 | 58 |
| 3 | 1.0189 | 5.2174 | 57 |
| 4 | 1.0189 | 5.2097 | 56 |
| 5 | 1.0190 | 5.2019 | 55 |
| 6 | 1.0191 | 5.1942 | 54 |
| 7 | 1.0191 | 5.1865 | 53 |
| 8 | 1.0192 | 5.1789 | 52 |
| 9 | 1.0192 | 5.1712 | 51 |
| 10 | 1.0193 | 5.1636 | 50 |
| 11 | 1.0194 | 5.1560 | 49 |
| 12 | 1.0194 | 5.1484 | 48 |
| 13 | 1.0195 | 5.1409 | 47 |
| 14 | 1.0195 | 5.1333 | 46 |
| 15 | 1.0196 | 5.1258 | 45 |
| 16 | 1.0197 | 5.1183 | 44 |
| 17 | 1.0197 | 5.1109 | 43 |
| 18 | 1.0198 | 5.1034 | 42 |
| 19 | 1.0198 | 5.0960 | 41 |
| 20 | 1.0199 | 5.0886 | 40 |
| 21 | 1.0199 | 5.0813 | 39 |
| 22 | 1.0200 | 5.0739 | 38 |
| 23 | 1.0201 | 5.0666 | 37 |
| 24 | 1.0201 | 5.0593 | 36 |
| 25 | 1.0202 | 5.0520 | 35 |
| 26 | 1.0202 | 5.0447 | 34 |
| 27 | 1.0203 | 5.0375 | 33 |
| 28 | 1.0204 | 5.0302 | 32 |
| 29 | 1.0204 | 5.0230 | 31 |
| 30 | 1.0205 | 5.0159 | 30 |
| 31 | 1.0205 | 5.0087 | 29 |
| 32 | 1.0206 | 5.0016 | 28 |
| 33 | 1.0207 | 4.9944 | 27 |
| 34 | 1.0207 | 4.9873 | 26 |
| 35 | 1.0208 | 4.9803 | 25 |
| 36 | 1.0209 | 4.9732 | 24 |
| 37 | 1.0209 | 4.9662 | 23 |
| 38 | 1.0210 | 4.9591 | 22 |
| 39 | 1.0210 | 4.9521 | 21 |
| 40 | 1.0211 | 4.9452 | 20 |
| 41 | 1.0212 | 4.9382 | 19 |
| 42 | 1.0212 | 4.9313 | 18 |
| 43 | 1.0213 | 4.9244 | 17 |
| 44 | 1.0213 | 4.9175 | 16 |
| 45 | 1.0214 | 4.9106 | 15 |
| 46 | 1.0215 | 4.9037 | 14 |
| 47 | 1.0215 | 4.8969 | 13 |
| 48 | 1.0216 | 4.8901 | 12 |
| 49 | 1.0217 | 4.8833 | 11 |
| 50 | 1.0217 | 4.8765 | 10 |
| 51 | 1.0218 | 4.8697 | 9 |
| 52 | 1.0218 | 4.8630 | 8 |
| 53 | 1.0219 | 4.8563 | 7 |
| 54 | 1.0220 | 4.8496 | 6 |
| 55 | 1.0220 | 4.8429 | 5 |
| 56 | 1.0221 | 4.8362 | 4 |
| 57 | 1.0222 | 4.8296 | 3 |
| 58 | 1.0222 | 4.8229 | 2 |
| 59 | 1.0223 | 4.8163 | 1 |
| 60 | 1.0223 | 4.8097 | 0 |
| ′ | Csc | Sec | ′ |

# NATURAL FUNCTIONS—SECANTS AND COSECANTS (Continued)

| ′ | Sec | Csc | ′ | ′ | Sec | Csc | ′ | ′ | Sec | Csc | ′ |
|---|-----|-----|---|---|-----|-----|---|---|-----|-----|---|
| 0 | 1.0223 | 4.8097 | 60 | 0 | 1.0263 | 4.4454 | 60 | 0 | 1.0306 | 4.1336 | 60 |
| 1 | 1.0224 | 4.8032 | 59 | 1 | 1.0264 | 4.4398 | 59 | 1 | 1.0307 | 4.1287 | 59 |
| 2 | 1.0225 | 4.7966 | 58 | 2 | 1.0264 | 4.4342 | 58 | 2 | 1.0308 | 4.1239 | 58 |
| 3 | 1.0225 | 4.7901 | 57 | 3 | 1.0265 | 4.4287 | 57 | 3 | 1.0308 | 4.1191 | 57 |
| 4 | 1.0226 | 4.7836 | 56 | 4 | 1.0266 | 4.4231 | 56 | 4 | 1.0309 | 4.1144 | 56 |
| 5 | 1.0227 | 4.7771 | 55 | 5 | 1.0266 | 4.4176 | 55 | 5 | 1.0310 | 4.1096 | 55 |
| 6 | 1.0227 | 4.7706 | 54 | 6 | 1.0267 | 4.4121 | 54 | 6 | 1.0311 | 4.1048 | 54 |
| 7 | 1.0228 | 4.7641 | 53 | 7 | 1.0268 | 4.4066 | 53 | 7 | 1.0311 | 4.1001 | 53 |
| 8 | 1.0228 | 4.7577 | 52 | 8 | 1.0269 | 4.4011 | 52 | 8 | 1.0312 | 4.0954 | 52 |
| 9 | 1.0229 | 4.7512 | 51 | 9 | 1.0269 | 4.3956 | 51 | 9 | 1.0313 | 4.0906 | 51 |
| 10 | 1.0230 | 4.7448 | 50 | 10 | 1.0270 | 4.3901 | 50 | 10 | 1.0314 | 4.0859 | 50 |
| 11 | 1.0230 | 4.7384 | 49 | 11 | 1.0271 | 4.3847 | 49 | 11 | 1.0314 | 4.0812 | 49 |
| 12 | 1.0231 | 4.7321 | 48 | 12 | 1.0271 | 4.3792 | 48 | 12 | 1.0315 | 4.0765 | 48 |
| 13 | 1.0232 | 4.7257 | 47 | 13 | 1.0272 | 4.3738 | 47 | 13 | 1.0316 | 4.0718 | 47 |
| 14 | 1.0232 | 4.7194 | 46 | 14 | 1.0273 | 4.3684 | 46 | 14 | 1.0317 | 4.0672 | 46 |
| 15 | 1.0233 | 4.7130 | 45 | 15 | 1.0273 | 4.3630 | 45 | 15 | 1.0317 | 4.0625 | 45 |
| 16 | 1.0234 | 4.7067 | 44 | 16 | 1.0274 | 4.3576 | 44 | 16 | 1.0318 | 4.0579 | 44 |
| 17 | 1.0234 | 4.7004 | 43 | 17 | 1.0275 | 4.3522 | 43 | 17 | 1.0319 | 4.0532 | 43 |
| 18 | 1.0235 | 4.6942 | 42 | 18 | 1.0276 | 4.3469 | 42 | 18 | 1.0320 | 4.0486 | 42 |
| 19 | 1.0236 | 4.6879 | 41 | 19 | 1.0276 | 4.3415 | 41 | 19 | 1.0321 | 4.0440 | 41 |
| 20 | 1.0236 | 4.6817 | 40 | 20 | 1.0277 | 4.3362 | 40 | 20 | 1.0321 | 4.0394 | 40 |
| 21 | 1.0237 | 4.6755 | 39 | 21 | 1.0278 | 4.3309 | 39 | 21 | 1.0322 | 4.0348 | 39 |
| 22 | 1.0238 | 4.6693 | 38 | 22 | 1.0278 | 4.3256 | 38 | 22 | 1.0823 | 4.0302 | 38 |
| 23 | 1.0238 | 4.6631 | 37 | 23 | 1.0279 | 4.3203 | 37 | 23 | 1.0324 | 4.0256 | 37 |
| 24 | 1.0239 | 4.6569 | 36 | 24 | 1.0280 | 4.3150 | 36 | 24 | 1.0324 | 4.0211 | 36 |
| 25 | 1.0240 | 4.6507 | 35 | 25 | 1.0281 | 4.3098 | 35 | 25 | 1.0325 | 4.0165 | 35 |
| 26 | 1.0240 | 4.6446 | 34 | 26 | 1.0281 | 4.3045 | 34 | 26 | 1.0326 | 4.0120 | 34 |
| 27 | 1.0241 | 4.6385 | 33 | 27 | 1.0282 | 4.2993 | 33 | 27 | 1.0327 | 4.0075 | 33 |
| 28 | 1.0241 | 4.6324 | 32 | 28 | 1.0283 | 4.2941 | 32 | 28 | 1.0327 | 4.0029 | 32 |
| 29 | 1.0242 | 4.6263 | 31 | 29 | 1.0283 | 4.2889 | 31 | 29 | 1.0328 | 3.9984 | 31 |
| 30 | 1.0243 | 4.6202 | 30 | 30 | 1.0284 | 4.2837 | 30 | 30 | 1.0329 | 3.9939 | 30 |
| 31 | 1.0243 | 4.6142 | 29 | 31 | 1.0285 | 4.2785 | 29 | 31 | 1.0330 | 3.9894 | 29 |
| 32 | 1.0244 | 4.6081 | 28 | 32 | 1.0286 | 4.2733 | 28 | 32 | 1.0331 | 3.9850 | 28 |
| 33 | 1.0245 | 4.6021 | 27 | 33 | 1.0286 | 4.2681 | 27 | 33 | 1.0331 | 3.9805 | 27 |
| 34 | 1.0245 | 4.5961 | 26 | 34 | 1.0287 | 4.2630 | 26 | 34 | 1.0332 | 3.9760 | 26 |
| 35 | 1.0246 | 4.5901 | 25 | 35 | 1.0288 | 4.2579 | 25 | 35 | 1.0333 | 3.9716 | 25 |
| 36 | 1.0247 | 4.5841 | 24 | 36 | 1.0288 | 4.2527 | 24 | 36 | 1.0334 | 3.9672 | 24 |
| 37 | 1.0247 | 4.5782 | 23 | 37 | 1.0289 | 4.2476 | 23 | 37 | 1.0334 | 3.9627 | 23 |
| 38 | 1.0248 | 4.5722 | 22 | 38 | 1.0290 | 4.2425 | 22 | 38 | 1.0335 | 3.9583 | 22 |
| 39 | 1.0249 | 4.5663 | 21 | 39 | 1.0291 | 4.2375 | 21 | 39 | 1.0336 | 3.9539 | 21 |
| 40 | 1.0249 | 4.5604 | 20 | 40 | 1.0291 | 4.2324 | 20 | 40 | 1.0337 | 3.9495 | 20 |
| 41 | 1.0250 | 4.5545 | 19 | 41 | 1.0292 | 4.2273 | 19 | 41 | 1.0338 | 3.9451 | 19 |
| 42 | 1.0251 | 4.5486 | 18 | 42 | 1.0293 | 4.2223 | 18 | 42 | 1.0338 | 3.9408 | 18 |
| 43 | 1.0251 | 4.5428 | 17 | 43 | 1.0294 | 4.2173 | 17 | 43 | 1.0339 | 3.9364 | 17 |
| 44 | 1.0252 | 4.5369 | 16 | 44 | 1.0294 | 4.2122 | 16 | 44 | 1.0340 | 3.9320 | 16 |
| 45 | 1.0253 | 4.5311 | 15 | 45 | 1.0295 | 4.2072 | 15 | 45 | 1.0341 | 3.9277 | 15 |
| 46 | 1.0253 | 4.5253 | 14 | 46 | 1.0296 | 4.2022 | 14 | 46 | 1.0342 | 3.9234 | 14 |
| 47 | 1.0254 | 4.5195 | 13 | 47 | 1.0297 | 4.1973 | 13 | 47 | 1.0342 | 3.9190 | 13 |
| 48 | 1.0255 | 4.5137 | 12 | 48 | 1.0297 | 4.1923 | 12 | 48 | 1.0343 | 3.9147 | 12 |
| 49 | 1.0256 | 4.5079 | 11 | 49 | 1.0298 | 4.1873 | 11 | 49 | 1.0344 | 3.9104 | 11 |
| 50 | 1.0256 | 4.5022 | 10 | 50 | 1.0299 | 4.1824 | 10 | 50 | 1.0345 | 3.9061 | 10 |
| 51 | 1.0257 | 4.4964 | 9 | 51 | 1.0299 | 4.1774 | 9 | 51 | 1.0346 | 3.9018 | 9 |
| 52 | 1.0258 | 4.4907 | 8 | 52 | 1.0300 | 4.1725 | 8 | 52 | 1.0346 | 3.8976 | 8 |
| 53 | 1.0258 | 4.4850 | 7 | 53 | 1.0301 | 4.1676 | 7 | 53 | 1.0347 | 3.8933 | 7 |
| 54 | 1.0259 | 4.4793 | 6 | 54 | 1.0302 | 4.1627 | 6 | 54 | 1.0348 | 3.8890 | 6 |
| 55 | 1.0260 | 4.4736 | 5 | 55 | 1.0302 | 4.1578 | 5 | 55 | 1.0349 | 3.8848 | 5 |
| 56 | 1.0260 | 4.4679 | 4 | 56 | 1.0303 | 4.1529 | 4 | 56 | 1.0350 | 3.8806 | 4 |
| 57 | 1.0261 | 4.4623 | 3 | 57 | 1.0304 | 4.1481 | 3 | 57 | 1.0350 | 3.8763 | 3 |
| 58 | 1.0262 | 4.4566 | 2 | 58 | 1.0305 | 4.1432 | 2 | 58 | 1.0351 | 3.8721 | 2 |
| 59 | 1.0262 | 4.4510 | 1 | 59 | 1.0305 | 4.1384 | 1 | 59 | 1.0352 | 3.8679 | 1 |
| 60 | 1.0263 | 4.4454 | 0 | 60 | 1.0306 | 4.1336 | 0 | 60 | 1.0353 | 3.8637 | 0 |
| ′ | Csc | Sec | ′ | ′ | Csc | Sec | ′ | ′ | Csc | Sec | ′ |

**15° (195°)**          (344°) **164°**     **16° (196°)**          (343°) **163°**     **17° (197°)**          (342°) **162°**

| ′ | Sec | Csc | ′ | ′ | Sec | Csc | ′ | ′ | Sec | Csc | ′ |
|---|-----|-----|---|---|-----|-----|---|---|-----|-----|---|
| 0 | 1.0353 | 3.8637 | 60 | 0 | 1.0403 | 3.6280 | 60 | 0 | 1.0457 | 3.4203 | 60 |
| 1 | 1.0354 | 3.8595 | 59 | 1 | 1.0404 | 3.6243 | 59 | 1 | 1.0458 | 3.4171 | 59 |
| 2 | 1.0354 | 3.8553 | 58 | 2 | 1.0405 | 3.6206 | 58 | 2 | 1.0459 | 3.4138 | 58 |
| 3 | 1.0355 | 3.8512 | 57 | 3 | 1.0406 | 3.6169 | 57 | 3 | 1.0460 | 3.4106 | 57 |
| 4 | 1:0356 | 3.8470 | 56 | 4 | 1.0406 | 3.6133 | 56 | 4 | 1.0461 | 3.4073 | 56 |
| 5 | 1.0357 | 3.8428 | 55 | 5 | 1.0407 | 3.6097 | 55 | 5 | 1.0462 | 3.4041 | 55 |
| 6 | 1.0358 | 3.8387 | 54 | 6 | 1.0408 | 3.6060 | 54 | 6 | 1.0463 | 3.4009 | 54 |
| 7 | 1.0358 | 3.8346 | 53 | 7 | 1.0409 | 3.6024 | 53 | 7 | 1.0463 | 3.3977 | 53 |
| 8 | 1.0359 | 3.8304 | 52 | 8 | 1.0410 | 3.5988 | 52 | 8 | 1.0464 | 3.3945 | 52 |
| 9 | 1.0360 | 3.8263 | 51 | 9 | 1.0411 | 3.5951 | 51 | 9 | 1.0465 | 3.3913 | 51 |
| 10 | 1.0361 | 3.8222 | 50 | 10 | 1.0412 | 3.5915 | 50 | 10 | 1.0466 | 3.3881 | 50 |
| 11 | 1.0362 | 3.8181 | 49 | 11 | 1.0413 | 3.5879 | 49 | 11 | 1.0467 | 3.3849 | 49 |
| 12 | 1.0363 | 3.8140 | 48 | 12 | 1.0413 | 3.5843 | 48 | 12 | 1.0468 | 3.3817 | 48 |
| 13 | 1.0363 | 3.8100 | 47 | 13 | 1.0414 | 3.5808 | 47 | 13 | 1.0469 | 3.3785 | 47 |
| 14 | 1.0364 | 3.8059 | 46 | 14 | 1.0415 | 3.5772 | 46 | 14 | 1.0470 | 3.3754 | 46 |
| 15 | 1.0365 | 3.8018 | 45 | 15 | 1.0416 | 3.5736 | 45 | 15 | 1.0471 | 3.3722 | 45 |
| 16 | 1.0366 | 3.7978 | 44 | 16 | 1.0417 | 3.5700 | 44 | 16 | 1.0472 | 3.3691 | 44 |
| 17 | 1.0367 | 3.7937 | 43 | 17 | 1.0418 | 3.5665 | 43 | 17 | 1.0473 | 3.3659 | 43 |
| 18 | 1.0367 | 3.7897 | 42 | 18 | 1.0419 | 3.5629 | 42 | 18 | 1.0474 | 3.3628 | 42 |
| 19 | 1.0368 | 3.7857 | 41 | 19 | 1.0420 | 3.5594 | 41 | 19 | 1.0475 | 3.3596 | 41 |
| 20 | 1.0369 | 3.7817 | 40 | 20 | 1.0421 | 3.5559 | 40 | 20 | 1.0476 | 3.3565 | 40 |
| 21 | 1.0370 | 3.7777 | 39 | 21 | 1.0421 | 3.5523 | 39 | 21 | 1.0477 | 3.3534 | 39 |
| 22 | 1.0371 | 3.7737 | 38 | 22 | 1.0422 | 3.5488 | 38 | 22 | 1.0478 | 3.3502 | 38 |
| 23 | 1.0372 | 3.7697 | 37 | 23 | 1.0423 | 3.5453 | 37 | 23 | 1.0479 | 3.3471 | 37 |
| 24 | 1.0372 | 3.7657 | 36 | 24 | 1.0424 | 3.5418 | 36 | 24 | 1.0480 | 3.3440 | 36 |
| 25 | 1.0373 | 3.7617 | 35 | 25 | 1.0425 | 3.5383 | 35 | 25 | 1.0480 | 3.3409 | 35 |
| 26 | 1.0374 | 3.7577 | 34 | 26 | 1.0426 | 3.5348 | 34 | 26 | 1.0481 | 3.3378 | 34 |
| 27 | 1.0375 | 3.7538 | 33 | 27 | 1.0427 | 3.5313 | 33 | 27 | 1.0482 | 3.3347 | 33 |
| 28 | 1.0376 | 3.7498 | 32 | 28 | 1.0428 | 3.5279 | 32 | 28 | 1.0483 | 3.3317 | 32 |
| 29 | 1.0377 | 3.7459 | 31 | 29 | 1.0429 | 3.5244 | 31 | 29 | 1.0484 | 3.3286 | 31 |
| 30 | 1.0377 | 3.7420 | 30 | 30 | 1.0429 | 3.5209 | 30 | 30 | 1.0485 | 3.3255 | 30 |
| 31 | 1.0378 | 3.7381 | 29 | 31 | 1.0430 | 3.5175 | 29 | 31 | 1.0486 | 3.3224 | 29 |
| 32 | 1.0379 | 3.7341 | 28 | 32 | 1.0431 | 3.5140 | 28 | 32 | 1.0487 | 3.3194 | 28 |
| 33 | 1.0380 | 3.7302 | 27 | 33 | 1.0432 | 3.5106 | 27 | 33 | 1.0488 | 3.3163 | 27 |
| 34 | 1.0381 | 3.7263 | 26 | 34 | 1.0433 | 3.5072 | 26 | 34 | 1.0489 | 3.3133 | 26 |
| 35 | 1.0382 | 3.7225 | 25 | 35 | 1.0434 | 3.5037 | 25 | 35 | 1.0490 | 3.3102 | 25 |
| 36 | 1.0382 | 3.7186 | 24 | 36 | 1.0435 | 3.5003 | 24 | 36 | 1.0491 | 3.3072 | 24 |
| 37 | 1.0383 | 3.7147 | 23 | 37 | 1.0436 | 3.4969 | 23 | 37 | 1.0492 | 3.3042 | 23 |
| 38 | 1.0384 | 3.7108 | 22 | 38 | 1.0437 | 3.4935 | 22 | 38 | 1.0493 | 3.3012 | 22 |
| 39 | 1.0385 | 3.7070 | 21 | 39 | 1.0438 | 3.4901 | 21 | 39 | 1.0494 | 3.2981 | 21 |
| 40 | 1.0386 | 3.7032 | 20 | 40 | 1.0439 | 3.4867 | 20 | 40 | 1.0495 | 3.2951 | 20 |
| 41 | 1.0387 | 3.6993 | 19 | 41 | 1.0439 | 3.4833 | 19 | 41 | 1.0496 | 3.2921 | 19 |
| 42 | 1.0388 | 3.6955 | 18 | 42 | 1.0440 | 3.4799 | 18 | 42 | 1.0497 | 3.2891 | 18 |
| 43 | 1.0388 | 3.6917 | 17 | 43 | 1.0441 | 3.4766 | 17 | 43 | 1.0498 | 3.2861 | 17 |
| 44 | 1.0389 | 3.6879 | 16 | 44 | 1.0442 | 3.4732 | 16 | 44 | 1.0499 | 3.2831 | 16 |
| 45 | 1.0390 | 3.6840 | 15 | 45 | 1.0443 | 3.4699 | 15 | 45 | 1.0500 | 3.2801 | 15 |
| 46 | 1.0391 | 3.6803 | 14 | 46 | 1.0444 | 3.4665 | 14 | 46 | 1.0501 | 3.2772 | 14 |
| 47 | 1.0392 | 3.6765 | 13 | 47 | 1.0445 | 3.4632 | 13 | 47 | 1.0502 | 3.2742 | 13 |
| 48 | 1.0393 | 3.6727 | 12 | 48 | 1.0446 | 3.4598 | 12 | 48 | 1.0503 | 3.2712 | 12 |
| 49 | 1.0394 | 3.6689 | 11 | 49 | 1.0447 | 3.4565 | 11 | 49 | 1.0504 | 3.2683 | 11 |
| 50 | 1.0394 | 3.6652 | 10 | 50 | 1.0448 | 3.4532 | 10 | 50 | 1.0505 | 3.2653 | 10 |
| 51 | 1.0395 | 3.6614 | 9 | 51 | 1.0449 | 3.4499 | 9 | 51 | 1.0506 | 3.2624 | 9 |
| 52 | 1.0396 | 3.6576 | 8 | 52 | 1.0450 | 3.4465 | 8 | 52 | 1.0507 | 3.2594 | 8 |
| 53 | 1.0397 | 3.6539 | 7 | 53 | 1.0450 | 3.4432 | 7 | 53 | 1.0508 | 3.2565 | 7 |
| 54 | 1.0398 | 3.6502 | 6 | 54 | 1.0451 | 3.4399 | 6 | 54 | 1.0509 | 3.2535 | 6 |
| 55 | 1.0399 | 3.6465 | 5 | 55 | 1.0452 | 3.4367 | 5 | 55 | 1.0510 | 3.2506 | 5 |
| 56 | 1.0400 | 3.6427 | 4 | 56 | 1.0453 | 3.4334 | 4 | 56 | 1.0511 | 3.2477 | 4 |
| 57 | 1.0400 | 3.6390 | 3 | 57 | 1.0454 | 3.4301 | 3 | 57 | 1.0512 | 3.2448 | 3 |
| 58 | 1.0401 | 3.6353 | 2 | 58 | 1.0455 | 3.4268 | 2 | 58 | 1.0513 | 3.2419 | 2 |
| 59 | 1.0402 | 3.6316 | 1 | 59 | 1.0456 | 3.4236 | 1 | 59 | 1.0514 | 3.2390 | 1 |
| 60 | 1.0403 | 3.6280 | 0 | 60 | 1.0457 | 3.4203 | 0 | 60 | 1.0515 | 3.2361 | 0 |
| ′ | Csc | Sec | ′ | ′ | Csc | Sec | ′ | ′ | Csc | Sec | ′ |

**18° (198°)**     **(341°) 161°**     **19° (199°)**     **(340°) 160°**     **20° (200°)**     **(339°) 159°**

| ′ | Sec | Csc | ′ | ′ | Sec | Csc | ′ | ′ | Sec | Csc | ′ |
|---|-----|-----|---|---|-----|-----|---|---|-----|-----|---|
| 0 | 1.0515 | 3.2361 | 60 | 0 | 1.0576 | 3.0716 | 60 | 0 | 1.0642 | 2.9238 | 60 |
| 1 | 1.0516 | 3.2332 | 59 | 1 | 1.0577 | 3.0690 | 59 | 1 | 1.0643 | 2.9215 | 59 |
| 2 | 1.0517 | 3.2303 | 58 | 2 | 1.0578 | 3.0664 | 58 | 2 | 1.0644 | 2.9191 | 58 |
| 3 | 1.0518 | 3.2274 | 57 | 3 | 1.0579 | 3.0638 | 57 | 3 | 1.0645 | 2.9168 | 57 |
| 4 | 1.0519 | 3.2245 | 56 | 4 | 1.0580 | 3.0612 | 56 | 4 | 1.0646 | 2.9145 | 56 |
| 5 | 1.0520 | 3.2217 | 55 | 5 | 1.0582 | 3.0586 | 55 | 5 | 1.0647 | 2.9122 | 55 |
| 6 | 1.0521 | 3.2188 | 54 | 6 | 1.0583 | 3.0561 | 54 | 6 | 1.0649 | 2.9099 | 54 |
| 7 | 1.0522 | 3.2159 | 53 | 7 | 1.0584 | 3.0535 | 53 | 7 | 1.0650 | 2.9075 | 53 |
| 8 | 1.0523 | 3.2131 | 52 | 8 | 1.0585 | 3.0509 | 52 | 8 | 1.0651 | 2.9052 | 52 |
| 9 | 1.0524 | 3.2102 | 51 | 9 | 1.0586 | 3.0484 | 51 | 9 | 1.0652 | 2.9029 | 51 |
| 10 | 1.0525 | 3.2074 | 50 | 10 | 1.0587 | 3.0458 | 50 | 10 | 1.0653 | 2.9006 | 50 |
| 11 | 1.0526 | 3.2045 | 49 | 11 | 1.0588 | 3.0433 | 49 | 11 | 1.0654 | 2.8983 | 49 |
| 12 | 1.0527 | 3.2017 | 48 | 12 | 1.0589 | 3.0407 | 48 | 12 | 1.0655 | 2.8960 | 48 |
| 13 | 1.0528 | 3.1989 | 47 | 13 | 1.0590 | 3.0382 | 47 | 13 | 1.0657 | 2.8938 | 47 |
| 14 | 1.0529 | 3.1960 | 46 | 14 | 1.0591 | 3.0357 | 46 | 14 | 1.0658 | 2.8915 | 46 |
| 15 | 1.0530 | 3.1932 | 45 | 15 | 1.0592 | 3.0331 | 45 | 15 | 1.0659 | 2.8892 | 45 |
| 16 | 1.0531 | 3.1904 | 44 | 16 | 1.0593 | 3.0306 | 44 | 16 | 1.0660 | 2.8869 | 44 |
| 17 | 1.0532 | 3.1876 | 43 | 17 | 1.0594 | 3.0281 | 43 | 17 | 1.0661 | 2.8846 | 43 |
| 18 | 1.0533 | 3.1848 | 42 | 18 | 1.0595 | 3.0256 | 42 | 18 | 1.0662 | 2.8824 | 42 |
| 19 | 1.0534 | 3.1820 | 41 | 19 | 1.0597 | 3.0231 | 41 | 19 | 1.0663 | 2.8801 | 41 |
| 20 | 1.0535 | 3.1792 | 40 | 20 | 1.0598 | 3.0206 | 40 | 20 | 1.0665 | 2.8779 | 40 |
| 21 | 1.0536 | 3.1764 | 39 | 21 | 1.0599 | 3.0181 | 39 | 21 | 1.0666 | 2.8756 | 39 |
| 22 | 1.0537 | 3.1736 | 38 | 22 | 1.0600 | 3.0156 | 38 | 22 | 1.0667 | 2.8733 | 38 |
| 23 | 1.0538 | 3.1708 | 37 | 23 | 1.0601 | 3.0131 | 37 | 23 | 1.0668 | 2.8711 | 37 |
| 24 | 1.0539 | 3.1681 | 36 | 24 | 1.0602 | 3.0106 | 36 | 24 | 1.0669 | 2.8688 | 36 |
| 25 | 1.0540 | 3.1653 | 35 | 25 | 1.0603 | 3.0081 | 35 | 25 | 1.0670 | 2.8666 | 35 |
| 26 | 1.0541 | 3.1625 | 34 | 26 | 1.0604 | 3.0056 | 34 | 26 | 1.0671 | 2.8644 | 34 |
| 27 | 1.0542 | 3.1598 | 33 | 27 | 1.0605 | 3.0031 | 33 | 27 | 1.0673 | 2.8621 | 33 |
| 28 | 1.0543 | 3.1570 | 32 | 28 | 1.0606 | 3.0007 | 32 | 28 | 1.0674 | 2.8599 | 32 |
| 29 | 1.0544 | 3.1543 | 31 | 29 | 1.0607 | 2.9982 | 31 | 29 | 1.0675 | 2.8577 | 31 |
| 30 | 1.0545 | 3.1515 | 30 | 30 | 1.0608 | 2.9957 | 30 | 30 | 1.0676 | 2.8555 | 30 |
| 31 | 1.0546 | 3.1488 | 29 | 31 | 1.0610 | 2.9933 | 29 | 31 | 1.0677 | 2.8532 | 29 |
| 32 | 1.0547 | 3.1461 | 28 | 32 | 1.0611 | 2.9908 | 28 | 32 | 1.0678 | 2.8510 | 28 |
| 33 | 1.0548 | 3.1433 | 27 | 33 | 1.0612 | 2.9884 | 27 | 33 | 1.0680 | 2.8488 | 27 |
| 34 | 1.0549 | 3.1406 | 26 | 34 | 1.0613 | 2.9859 | 26 | 34 | 1.0681 | 2.8466 | 26 |
| 35 | 1.0550 | 3.1379 | 25 | 35 | 1.0614 | 2.9835 | 25 | 35 | 1.0682 | 2.8444 | 25 |
| 36 | 1.0551 | 3.1352 | 24 | 36 | 1.0615 | 2.9811 | 24 | 36 | 1.0683 | 2.8422 | 24 |
| 37 | 1.0552 | 3.1325 | 23 | 37 | 1.0616 | 2.9786 | 23 | 37 | 1.0684 | 2.8400 | 23 |
| 38 | 1.0553 | 3.1298 | 22 | 38 | 1.0617 | 2.9762 | 22 | 38 | 1.0685 | 2.8378 | 22 |
| 39 | 1.0554 | 3.1271 | 21 | 39 | 1.0618 | 2.9738 | 21 | 39 | 1.0687 | 2.8356 | 21 |
| 40 | 1.0555 | 3.1244 | 20 | 40 | 1.0619 | 2.9713 | 20 | 40 | 1.0688 | 2.8334 | 20 |
| 41 | 1.0556 | 3.1217 | 19 | 41 | 1.0621 | 2.9689 | 19 | 41 | 1.0689 | 2.8312 | 19 |
| 42 | 1.0557 | 3.1190 | 18 | 42 | 1.0622 | 2.9665 | 18 | 42 | 1.0690 | 2.8291 | 18 |
| 43 | 1.0558 | 3.1163 | 17 | 43 | 1.0623 | 2.9641 | 17 | 43 | 1.0691 | 2.8269 | 17 |
| 44 | 1.0559 | 3.1137 | 16 | 44 | 1.0624 | 2.9617 | 16 | 44 | 1.0692 | 2.8247 | 16 |
| 45 | 1.0560 | 3.1110 | 15 | 45 | 1.0625 | 2.9593 | 15 | 45 | 1.0694 | 2.8225 | 15 |
| 46 | 1.0561 | 3.1083 | 14 | 46 | 1.0626 | 2.9569 | 14 | 46 | 1.0695 | 2.8204 | 14 |
| 47 | 1.0563 | 3.1057 | 13 | 47 | 1.0627 | 2.9545 | 13 | 47 | 1.0696 | 2.8182 | 13 |
| 48 | 1.0564 | 3.1030 | 12 | 48 | 1.0628 | 2.9521 | 12 | 48 | 1.0697 | 2.8161 | 12 |
| 49 | 1.0565 | 3.1004 | 11 | 49 | 1.0629 | 2.9498 | 11 | 49 | 1.0698 | 2.8139 | 11 |
| 50 | 1.0566 | 3.0977 | 10 | 50 | 1.0631 | 2.9474 | 10 | 50 | 1.0700 | 2.8117 | 10 |
| 51 | 1.0567 | 3.0951 | 9 | 51 | 1.0632 | 2.9450 | 9 | 51 | 1.0701 | 2.8096 | 9 |
| 52 | 1.0568 | 3.0925 | 8 | 52 | 1.0633 | 2.9426 | 8 | 52 | 1.0702 | 2.8075 | 8 |
| 53 | 1.0569 | 3.0898 | 7 | 53 | 1.0634 | 2.9403 | 7 | 53 | 1.0703 | 2.8053 | 7 |
| 54 | 1.0570 | 3.0872 | 6 | 54 | 1.0635 | 2.9379 | 6 | 54 | 1.0704 | 2.8032 | 6 |
| 55 | 1.0571 | 3.0846 | 5 | 55 | 1.0636 | 2.9355 | 5 | 55 | 1.0705 | 2.8010 | 5 |
| 56 | 1.0572 | 3.0820 | 4 | 56 | 1.0637 | 2.9332 | 4 | 56 | 1.0707 | 2.7989 | 4 |
| 57 | 1.0573 | 3.0794 | 3 | 57 | 1.0638 | 2.9308 | 3 | 57 | 1.0708 | 2.7968 | 3 |
| 58 | 1.0574 | 3.0768 | 2 | 58 | 1.0640 | 2.9285 | 2 | 58 | 1.0709 | 2.7947 | 2 |
| 59 | 1.0575 | 3.0742 | 1 | 59 | 1.0641 | 2.9261 | 1 | 59 | 1.0710 | 2.7925 | 1 |
| 60 | 1.0576 | 3.0716 | 0 | 60 | 1.0642 | 2.9238 | 0 | 60 | 1.0711 | 2.7904 | 0 |
| ′ | Csc | Sec | ′ | ′ | Csc | Sec | ′ | ′ | Csc | Sec | ′ |

**21° (201°)**　　　(338°) **158°**　　　**22° (202°)**　　　(337°) **157°**　　　**23° (203°)**　　　(336°) **156°**

| ′ | Sec | Csc | ′ | ′ | Sec | Csc | ′ | ′ | Sec | Csc | ′ |
|---|---|---|---|---|---|---|---|---|---|---|---|
| 0 | 1.0711 | 2.7904 | 60 | 0 | 1.0785 | 2.6695 | 60 | 0 | 1.0864 | 2.5593 | 60 |
| 1 | 1.0713 | 2.7883 | 59 | 1 | 1.0787 | 2.6675 | 59 | 1 | 1.0865 | 2.5576 | 59 |
| 2 | 1.0714 | 2.7862 | 58 | 2 | 1.0788 | 2.6656 | 58 | 2 | 1.0866 | 2.5558 | 58 |
| 3 | 1.0715 | 2.7841 | 57 | 3 | 1.0789 | 2.6637 | 57 | 3 | 1.0868 | 2.5541 | 57 |
| 4 | 1.0716 | 2.7820 | 56 | 4 | 1.0790 | 2.6618 | 56 | 4 | 1.0869 | 2.5523 | 56 |
| 5 | 1.0717 | 2.7799 | 55 | 5 | 1.0792 | 2.6599 | 55 | 5 | 1.0870 | 2.5506 | 55 |
| 6 | 1.0719 | 2.7778 | 54 | 6 | 1.0793 | 2.6580 | 54 | 6 | 1.0872 | 2.5488 | 54 |
| 7 | 1.0720 | 2.7757 | 53 | 7 | 1.0794 | 2.6561 | 53 | 7 | 1.0873 | 2.5471 | 53 |
| 8 | 1.0721 | 2.7736 | 52 | 8 | 1.0796 | 2.6542 | 52 | 8 | 1.0874 | 2.5454 | 52 |
| 9 | 1.0722 | 2.7715 | 51 | 9 | 1.0797 | 2.6523 | 51 | 9 | 1.0876 | 2.5436 | 51 |
| 10 | 1.0723 | 2.7695 | 50 | 10 | 1.0798 | 2.6504 | 50 | 10 | 1.0877 | 2.5419 | 50 |
| 11 | 1.0725 | 2.7674 | 49 | 11 | 1.0799 | 2.6485 | 49 | 11 | 1.0878 | 2.5402 | 49 |
| 12 | 1.0726 | 2.7653 | 48 | 12 | 1.0801 | 2.6466 | 48 | 12 | 1.0880 | 2.5384 | 48 |
| 13 | 1.0727 | 2.7632 | 47 | 13 | 1.0802 | 2.6447 | 47 | 13 | 1.0881 | 2.5367 | 47 |
| 14 | 1.0728 | 2.7612 | 46 | 14 | 1.0803 | 2.6429 | 46 | 14 | 1.0883 | 2.5350 | 46 |
| 15 | 1.0730 | 2.7591 | 45 | 15 | 1.0804 | 2.6410 | 45 | 15 | 1.0884 | 2.5333 | 45 |
| 16 | 1.0731 | 2.7570 | 44 | 16 | 1.0806 | 2.6391 | 44 | 16 | 1.0885 | 2.5316 | 44 |
| 17 | 1.0732 | 2.7550 | 43 | 17 | 1.0807 | 2.6372 | 43 | 17 | 1.0887 | 2.5299 | 43 |
| 18 | 1.0733 | 2.7529 | 42 | 18 | 1.0808 | 2.6354 | 42 | 18 | 1.0888 | 2.5282 | 42 |
| 19 | 1.0734 | 2.7509 | 41 | 19 | 1.0810 | 2.6335 | 41 | 19 | 1.0889 | 2.5264 | 41 |
| 20 | 1.0736 | 2.7488 | 40 | 20 | 1.0811 | 2.6316 | 40 | 20 | 1.0891 | 2.5247 | 40 |
| 21 | 1.0737 | 2.7468 | 39 | 21 | 1.0812 | 2.6298 | 39 | 21 | 1.0892 | 2.5230 | 39 |
| 22 | 1.0738 | 2.7447 | 38 | 22 | 1.0814 | 2.6279 | 38 | 22 | 1.0893 | 2.5213 | 38 |
| 23 | 1.0739 | 2.7427 | 37 | 23 | 1.0815 | 2.6260 | 37 | 23 | 1.0895 | 2.5196 | 37 |
| 24 | 1.0740 | 2.7407 | 36 | 24 | 1.0816 | 2.6242 | 36 | 24 | 1.0896 | 2.5180 | 36 |
| 25 | 1.0742 | 2.7386 | 35 | 25 | 1.0817 | 2.6223 | 35 | 25 | 1.0898 | 2.5163 | 35 |
| 26 | 1.0743 | 2.7366 | 34 | 26 | 1.0819 | 2.6205 | 34 | 26 | 1.0899 | 2.5146 | 34 |
| 27 | 1.0744 | 2.7346 | 33 | 27 | 1.0820 | 2.6186 | 33 | 27 | 1.0900 | 2.5129 | 33 |
| 28 | 1.0745 | 2.7325 | 32 | 28 | 1.0821 | 2.6168 | 32 | 28 | 1.0902 | 2.5112 | 32 |
| 29 | 1.0747 | 2.7305 | 31 | 29 | 1.0823 | 2.6150 | 31 | 29 | 1.0903 | 2.5095 | 31 |
| 30 | 1.0748 | 2.7285 | 30 | 30 | 1.0824 | 2.6131 | 30 | 30 | 1.0904 | 2.5078 | 30 |
| 31 | 1.0749 | 2.7265 | 29 | 31 | 1.0825 | 2.6113 | 29 | 31 | 1.0906 | 2.5062 | 29 |
| 32 | 1.0750 | 2.7245 | 28 | 32 | 1.0827 | 2.6095 | 28 | 32 | 1.0907 | 2.5045 | 28 |
| 33 | 1.0752 | 2.7225 | 27 | 33 | 1.0828 | 2.6076 | 27 | 33 | 1.0909 | 2.5028 | 27 |
| 34 | 1.0753 | 2.7205 | 26 | 34 | 1.0829 | 2.6058 | 26 | 34 | 1.0910 | 2.5012 | 26 |
| 35 | 1.0754 | 2.7185 | 25 | 35 | 1.0830 | 2.6040 | 25 | 35 | 1.0911 | 2.4995 | 25 |
| 36 | 1.0755 | 2.7165 | 24 | 36 | 1.0832 | 2.6022 | 24 | 36 | 1.0913 | 2.4978 | 24 |
| 37 | 1.0757 | 2.7145 | 23 | 37 | 1.0833 | 2.6003 | 23 | 37 | 1.0914 | 2.4962 | 23 |
| 38 | 1.0758 | 2.7125 | 22 | 38 | 1.0834 | 2.5985 | 22 | 38 | 1.0915 | 2.4945 | 22 |
| 39 | 1.0759 | 2.7105 | 21 | 39 | 1.0836 | 2.5967 | 21 | 39 | 1.0917 | 2.4928 | 21 |
| 40 | 1.0760 | 2.7085 | 20 | 40 | 1.0837 | 2.5949 | 20 | 40 | 1.0918 | 2.4912 | 20 |
| 41 | 1.0761 | 2.7065 | 19 | 41 | 1.0838 | 2.5931 | 19 | 41 | 1.0920 | 2.4895 | 19 |
| 42 | 1.0763 | 2.7046 | 18 | 42 | 1.0840 | 2.5913 | 18 | 42 | 1.0921 | 2.4879 | 18 |
| 43 | 1.0764 | 2.7026 | 17 | 43 | 1.0841 | 2.5895 | 17 | 43 | 1.0922 | 2.4862 | 17 |
| 44 | 1.0765 | 2.7006 | 16 | 44 | 1.0842 | 2.5877 | 16 | 44 | 1.0924 | 2.4846 | 16 |
| 45 | 1.0766 | 2.6986 | 15 | 45 | 1.0844 | 2.5859 | 15 | 45 | 1.0925 | 2.4830 | 15 |
| 46 | 1.0768 | 2.6967 | 14 | 46 | 1.0845 | 2.5841 | 14 | 46 | 1.0927 | 2.4813 | 14 |
| 47 | 1.0769 | 2.6947 | 13 | 47 | 1.0846 | 2.5823 | 13 | 47 | 1.0928 | 2.4797 | 13 |
| 48 | 1.0770 | 2.6927 | 12 | 48 | 1.0848 | 2.5805 | 12 | 48 | 1.0929 | 2.4780 | 12 |
| 49 | 1.0771 | 2.6908 | 11 | 49 | 1.0849 | 2.5788 | 11 | 49 | 1.0931 | 2.4764 | 11 |
| 50 | 1.0773 | 2.6888 | 10 | 50 | 1.0850 | 2.5770 | 10 | 50 | 1.0932 | 2.4748 | 10 |
| 51 | 1.0774 | 2.6869 | 9 | 51 | 1.0852 | 2.5752 | 9 | 51 | 1.0934 | 2.4731 | 9 |
| 52 | 1.0775 | 2.6849 | 8 | 52 | 1.0853 | 2.5734 | 8 | 52 | 1.0935 | 2.4715 | 8 |
| 53 | 1.0777 | 2.6830 | 7 | 53 | 1.0854 | 2.5716 | 7 | 53 | 1.0936 | 2.4699 | 7 |
| 54 | 1.0778 | 2.6811 | 6 | 54 | 1.0856 | 2.5699 | 6 | 54 | 1.0938 | 2.4683 | 6 |
| 55 | 1.0779 | 2.6791 | 5 | 55 | 1.0857 | 2.5681 | 5 | 55 | 1.0939 | 2.4667 | 5 |
| 56 | 1.0780 | 2.6772 | 4 | 56 | 1.0858 | 2.5663 | 4 | 56 | 1.0941 | 2.4650 | 4 |
| 57 | 1.0782 | 2.6752 | 3 | 57 | 1.0860 | 2.5646 | 3 | 57 | 1.0942 | 2.4634 | 3 |
| 58 | 1.0783 | 2.6733 | 2 | 58 | 1.0861 | 2.5628 | 2 | 58 | 1.0944 | 2.4618 | 2 |
| 59 | 1.0784 | 2.6714 | 1 | 59 | 1.0862 | 2.5611 | 1 | 59 | 1.0945 | 2.4602 | 1 |
| 60 | 1.0785 | 2.6695 | 0 | 60 | 1.0864 | 2.5593 | 0 | 60 | 1.0946 | 2.4586 | 0 |
| ′ | Csc | Sec | ′ | ′ | Csc | Sec | ′ | ′ | Csc | Sec | ′ |

**24°** (204°)    (335°) **155°**        **25°** (205°)    (334°) **154°**        **26°** (206°)    (333°) **153°**

| ′ | Sec | Csc | ′ | ′ | Sec | Csc | ′ | ′ | Sec | Csc | ′ |
|---|-----|-----|---|---|-----|-----|---|---|-----|-----|---|
| 0 | 1.0946 | 2.4586 | 60 | 0 | 1.1034 | 2.3662 | 60 | 0 | 1.1126 | 2.2812 | 60 |
| 1 | 1.0948 | 2.4570 | 59 | 1 | 1.1035 | 2.3647 | 59 | 1 | 1.1128 | 2.2798 | 59 |
| 2 | 1.0949 | 2.4554 | 58 | 2 | 1.1037 | 2.3633 | 58 | 2 | 1.1129 | 2.2785 | 58 |
| 3 | 1.0951 | 2.4538 | 57 | 3 | 1.1038 | 2.3618 | 57 | 3 | 1.1131 | 2.2771 | 57 |
| 4 | 1.0952 | 2.4522 | 56 | 4 | 1.1040 | 2.3603 | 56 | 4 | 1.1132 | 2.2757 | 56 |
| 5 | 1.0953 | 2.4506 | 55 | 5 | 1.1041 | 2.3588 | 55 | 5 | 1.1134 | 2.2744 | 55 |
| 6 | 1.0955 | 2.4490 | 54 | 6 | 1.1043 | 2.3574 | 54 | 6 | 1.1136 | 2.2730 | 54 |
| 7 | 1.0956 | 2.4474 | 53 | 7 | 1.1044 | 2.3559 | 53 | 7 | 1.1137 | 2.2717 | 53 |
| 8 | 1.0958 | 2.4458 | 52 | 8 | 1.1046 | 2.3545 | 52 | 8 | 1.1139 | 2.2703 | 52 |
| 9 | 1.0959 | 2.4442 | 51 | 9 | 1.1047 | 2.3530 | 51 | 9 | 1.1140 | 2.2690 | 51 |
| 10 | 1.0961 | 2.4426 | 50 | 10 | 1.1049 | 2.3515 | 50 | 10 | 1.1142 | 2.2677 | 50 |
| 11 | 1.0962 | 2.4411 | 49 | 11 | 1.1050 | 2.3501 | 49 | 11 | 1.1143 | 2.2663 | 49 |
| 12 | 1.0963 | 2.4395 | 48 | 12 | 1.1052 | 2.3486 | 48 | 12 | 1.1145 | 2.2650 | 48 |
| 13 | 1.0965 | 2.4379 | 47 | 13 | 1.1053 | 2.3472 | 47 | 13 | 1.1147 | 2.2636 | 47 |
| 14 | 1.0966 | 2.4363 | 46 | 14 | 1.1055 | 2.3457 | 46 | 14 | 1.1148 | 2.2623 | 46 |
| 15 | 1.0968 | 2.4348 | 45 | 15 | 1.1056 | 2.3443 | 45 | 15 | 1.1150 | 2.2610 | 45 |
| 16 | 1.0969 | 2.4332 | 44 | 16 | 1.1058 | 2.3428 | 44 | 16 | 1.1151 | 2.2596 | 44 |
| 17 | 1.0971 | 2.4316 | 43 | 17 | 1.1059 | 2.3414 | 43 | 17 | 1.1153 | 2.2583 | 43 |
| 18 | 1.0972 | 2.4300 | 42 | 18 | 1.1061 | 2.3400 | 42 | 18 | 1.1155 | 2.2570 | 42 |
| 19 | 1.0974 | 2.4285 | 41 | 19 | 1.1062 | 2.3385 | 41 | 19 | 1.1156 | 2.2556 | 41 |
| 20 | 1.0975 | 2.4269 | 40 | 20 | 1.1064 | 2.3371 | 40 | 20 | 1.1158 | 2.2543 | 40 |
| 21 | 1.0976 | 2.4254 | 39 | 21 | 1.1066 | 2.3356 | 39 | 21 | 1.1159 | 2.2530 | 39 |
| 22 | 1.0978 | 2.4238 | 38 | 22 | 1.1067 | 2.3342 | 38 | 22 | 1.1161 | 2.2517 | 38 |
| 23 | 1.0979 | 2.4222 | 37 | 23 | 1.1069 | 2.3328 | 37 | 23 | 1.1163 | 2.2504 | 37 |
| 24 | 1.0981 | 2.4207 | 36 | 24 | 1.1070 | 2.3314 | 36 | 24 | 1.1164 | 2.2490 | 36 |
| 25 | 1.0982 | 2.4191 | 35 | 25 | 1.1072 | 2.3299 | 35 | 25 | 1.1166 | 2.2477 | 35 |
| 26 | 1.0984 | 2.4176 | 34 | 26 | 1.1073 | 2.3285 | 34 | 26 | 1.1168 | 2.2464 | 34 |
| 27 | 1.0985 | 2.4160 | 33 | 27 | 1.1075 | 2.3271 | 33 | 27 | 1.1169 | 2.2451 | 33 |
| 28 | 1.0987 | 2.4145 | 32 | 28 | 1.1076 | 2.3257 | 32 | 28 | 1.1171 | 2.2438 | 32 |
| 29 | 1.0988 | 2.4130 | 31 | 29 | 1.1078 | 2.3242 | 31 | 29 | 1.1172 | 2.2425 | 31 |
| 30 | 1.0989 | 2.4114 | 30 | 30 | 1.1079 | 2.3228 | 30 | 30 | 1.1174 | 2.2412 | 30 |
| 31 | 1.0991 | 2.4099 | 29 | 31 | 1.1081 | 2.3214 | 29 | 31 | 1.1176 | 2.2399 | 29 |
| 32 | 1.0992 | 2.4083 | 28 | 32 | 1.1082 | 2.3200 | 28 | 32 | 1.1177 | 2.2385 | 28 |
| 33 | 1.0994 | 2.4068 | 27 | 33 | 1.1084 | 2.3186 | 27 | 33 | 1.1179 | 2.2372 | 27 |
| 34 | 1.0995 | 2.4053 | 26 | 34 | 1.1085 | 2.3172 | 26 | 34 | 1.1180 | 2.2359 | 26 |
| 35 | 1.0997 | 2.4038 | 25 | 35 | 1.1087 | 2.3158 | 25 | 35 | 1.1182 | 2.2346 | 25 |
| 36 | 1.0998 | 2.4022 | 24 | 36 | 1.1089 | 2.3144 | 24 | 36 | 1.1184 | 2.2333 | 24 |
| 37 | 1.1000 | 2.4007 | 23 | 37 | 1.1090 | 2.3130 | 23 | 37 | 1.1185 | 2.2320 | 23 |
| 38 | 1.1001 | 2.3992 | 22 | 38 | 1.1092 | 2.3115 | 22 | 38 | 1.1187 | 2.2308 | 22 |
| 39 | 1.1003 | 2.3977 | 21 | 39 | 1.1093 | 2.3101 | 21 | 39 | 1.1189 | 2.2295 | 21 |
| 40 | 1.1004 | 2.3961 | 20 | 40 | 1.1095 | 2.3088 | 20 | 40 | 1.1190 | 2.2282 | 20 |
| 41 | 1.1006 | 2.3946 | 19 | 41 | 1.1096 | 2.3074 | 19 | 41 | 1.1192 | 2.2269 | 19 |
| 42 | 1.1007 | 2.3931 | 18 | 42 | 1.1098 | 2.3060 | 18 | 42 | 1.1194 | 2.2256 | 18 |
| 43 | 1.1009 | 2.3916 | 17 | 43 | 1.1099 | 2.3046 | 17 | 43 | 1.1195 | 2.2243 | 17 |
| 44 | 1.1010 | 2.3901 | 16 | 44 | 1.1101 | 2.3032 | 16 | 44 | 1.1197 | 2.2230 | 16 |
| 45 | 1.1011 | 2.3886 | 15 | 45 | 1.1102 | 2.3018 | 15 | 45 | 1.1198 | 2.2217 | 15 |
| 46 | 1.1013 | 2.3871 | 14 | 46 | 1.1104 | 2.3004 | 14 | 46 | 1.1200 | 2.2205 | 14 |
| 47 | 1.1014 | 2.3856 | 13 | 47 | 1.1106 | 2.2990 | 13 | 47 | 1.1202 | 2.2192 | 13 |
| 48 | 1.1016 | 2.3841 | 12 | 48 | 1.1107 | 2.2976 | 12 | 48 | 1.1203 | 2.2179 | 12 |
| 49 | 1.1017 | 2.3826 | 11 | 49 | 1.1109 | 2.2962 | 11 | 49 | 1.1205 | 2.2166 | 11 |
| 50 | 1.1019 | 2.3811 | 10 | 50 | 1.1110 | 2.2949 | 10 | 50 | 1.1207 | 2.2153 | 10 |
| 51 | 1.1020 | 2.3796 | 9 | 51 | 1.1112 | 2.2935 | 9 | 51 | 1.1208 | 2.2141 | 9 |
| 52 | 1.1022 | 2.3781 | 8 | 52 | 1.1113 | 2.2921 | 8 | 52 | 1.1210 | 2.2128 | 8 |
| 53 | 1.1023 | 2.3766 | 7 | 53 | 1.1115 | 2.2907 | 7 | 53 | 1.1212 | 2.2115 | 7 |
| 54 | 1.1025 | 2.3751 | 6 | 54 | 1.1117 | 2.2894 | 6 | 54 | 1.1213 | 2.2103 | 6 |
| 55 | 1.1026 | 2.3736 | 5 | 55 | 1.1118 | 2.2880 | 5 | 55 | 1.1215 | 2.2090 | 5 |
| 56 | 1.1028 | 2.3721 | 4 | 56 | 1.1120 | 2.2866 | 4 | 56 | 1.1217 | 2.2077 | 4 |
| 57 | 1.1029 | 2.3706 | 3 | 57 | 1.1121 | 2.2853 | 3 | 57 | 1.1218 | 2.2065 | 3 |
| 58 | 1.1031 | 2.3692 | 2 | 58 | 1.1123 | 2.2839 | 2 | 58 | 1.1220 | 2.2052 | 2 |
| 59 | 1.1032 | 2.3677 | 1 | 59 | 1.1124 | 2.2825 | 1 | 59 | 1.1222 | 2.2039 | 1 |
| 60 | 1.1034 | 2.3662 | 0 | 60 | 1.1126 | 2.2812 | 0 | 60 | 1.1223 | 2.2027 | 0 |
| ′ | Csc | Sec | ′ | ′ | Csc | Sec | ′ | ′ | Csc | Sec | ′ |

**114°** (294°)    (245°) **65°**        **115°** (295°)    (244°) **64°**        **116°** (296°)    (243°) **63°**

**27° (207°)**      (332°) **152°**       **28° (208°)**      (331°) **151°**       **29° (209°)**      (330°) **150°**

| ′ | Sec | Csc | ′ | ′ | Sec | Csc | ′ | ′ | Sec | Csc | ′ |
|---|-----|-----|---|---|-----|-----|---|---|-----|-----|---|
| 0 | 1.1223 | 2.2027 | 60 | 0 | 1.1326 | 2.1301 | 60 | 0 | 1.1434 | 2.0627 | 60 |
| 1 | 1.1225 | 2.2014 | 59 | 1 | 1.1327 | 2.1289 | 59 | 1 | 1.1435 | 2.0616 | 59 |
| 2 | 1.1227 | 2.2002 | 58 | 2 | 1.1329 | 2.1277 | 58 | 2 | 1.1437 | 2.0605 | 58 |
| 3 | 1.1228 | 2.1989 | 57 | 3 | 1.1331 | 2.1266 | 57 | 3 | 1.1439 | 2.0594 | 57 |
| 4 | 1.1230 | 2.1977 | 56 | 4 | 1.1333 | 2.1254 | 56 | 4 | 1.1441 | 2.0583 | 56 |
| 5 | 1.1232 | 2.1964 | 55 | 5 | 1.1334 | 2.1242 | 55 | 5 | 1.1443 | 2.0573 | 55 |
| 6 | 1.1233 | 2.1952 | 54 | 6 | 1.1336 | 2.1231 | 54 | 6 | 1.1445 | 2.0562 | 54 |
| 7 | 1.1235 | 2.1939 | 53 | 7 | 1.1338 | 2.1219 | 53 | 7 | 1.1446 | 2.0551 | 53 |
| 8 | 1.1237 | 2.1927 | 52 | 8 | 1.1340 | 2.1208 | 52 | 8 | 1.1448 | 2.0540 | 52 |
| 9 | 1.1238 | 2.1914 | 51 | 9 | 1.1342 | 2.1196 | 51 | 9 | 1.1450 | 2.0530 | 51 |
| 10 | 1.1240 | 2.1902 | 50 | 10 | 1.1343 | 2.1185 | 50 | 10 | 1.1452 | 2.0519 | 50 |
| 11 | 1.1242 | 2.1890 | 49 | 11 | 1.1345 | 2.1173 | 49 | 11 | 1.1454 | 2.0508 | 49 |
| 12 | 1.1243 | 2.1877 | 48 | 12 | 1.1347 | 2.1162 | 48 | 12 | 1.1456 | 2.0498 | 48 |
| 13 | 1.1245 | 2.1865 | 47 | 13 | 1.1349 | 2.1150 | 47 | 13 | 1.1458 | 2.0487 | 47 |
| 14 | 1.1247 | 2.1852 | 46 | 14 | 1.1350 | 2.1139 | 46 | 14 | 1.1460 | 2.0476 | 46 |
| 15 | 1.1248 | 2.1840 | 45 | 15 | 1.1352 | 2.1127 | 45 | 15 | 1.1461 | 2.0466 | 45 |
| 16 | 1.1250 | 2.1828 | 44 | 16 | 1.1354 | 2.1116 | 44 | 16 | 1.1463 | 2.0455 | 44 |
| 17 | 1.1252 | 2.1815 | 43 | 17 | 1.1356 | 2.1105 | 43 | 17 | 1.1465 | 2.0445 | 43 |
| 18 | 1.1253 | 2.1803 | 42 | 18 | 1.1357 | 2.1093 | 42 | 18 | 1.1467 | 2.0434 | 42 |
| 19 | 1.1255 | 2.1791 | 41 | 19 | 1.1359 | 2.1082 | 41 | 19 | 1.1469 | 2.0423 | 41 |
| 20 | 1.1257 | 2.1779 | 40 | 20 | 1.1361 | 2.1070 | 40 | 20 | 1.1471 | 2.0413 | 40 |
| 21 | 1.1259 | 2.1766 | 39 | 21 | 1.1363 | 2.1059 | 39 | 21 | 1.1473 | 2.0402 | 39 |
| 22 | 1.1260 | 2.1754 | 38 | 22 | 1.1365 | 2.1048 | 38 | 22 | 1.1474 | 2.0392 | 38 |
| 23 | 1.1262 | 2.1742 | 37 | 23 | 1.1366 | 2.1036 | 37 | 23 | 1.1476 | 2.0381 | 37 |
| 24 | 1.1264 | 2.1730 | 36 | 24 | 1.1368 | 2.1025 | 36 | 24 | 1.1478 | 2.0371 | 36 |
| 25 | 1.1265 | 2.1718 | 35 | 25 | 1.1370 | 2.1014 | 35 | 25 | 1.1480 | 2.0360 | 35 |
| 26 | 1.1267 | 2.1705 | 34 | 26 | 1.1372 | 2.1002 | 34 | 26 | 1.1482 | 2.0350 | 34 |
| 27 | 1.1269 | 2.1693 | 33 | 27 | 1.1374 | 2.0991 | 33 | 27 | 1.1484 | 2.0339 | 33 |
| 28 | 1.1270 | 2.1681 | 32 | 28 | 1.1375 | 2.0980 | 32 | 28 | 1.1486 | 2.0329 | 32 |
| 29 | 1.1272 | 2.1669 | 31 | 29 | 1.1377 | 2.0969 | 31 | 29 | 1.1488 | 2.0318 | 31 |
| 30 | 1.1274 | 2.1657 | 30 | 30 | 1.1379 | 2.0957 | 30 | 30 | 1.1490 | 2.0308 | 30 |
| 31 | 1.1276 | 2.1645 | 29 | 31 | 1.1381 | 2.0946 | 29 | 31 | 1.1491 | 2.0297 | 29 |
| 32 | 1.1277 | 2.1633 | 28 | 32 | 1.1383 | 2.0935 | 28 | 32 | 1.1493 | 2.0287 | 28 |
| 33 | 1.1279 | 2.1621 | 27 | 33 | 1.1384 | 2.0924 | 27 | 33 | 1.1495 | 2.0276 | 27 |
| 34 | 1.1281 | 2.1609 | 26 | 34 | 1.1386 | 2.0913 | 26 | 34 | 1.1497 | 2.0266 | 26 |
| 35 | 1.1282 | 2.1596 | 25 | 35 | 1.1388 | 2.0901 | 25 | 35 | 1.1499 | 2.0256 | 25 |
| 36 | 1.1284 | 2.1584 | 24 | 36 | 1.1390 | 2.0890 | 24 | 36 | 1.1501 | 2.0245 | 24 |
| 37 | 1.1286 | 2.1572 | 23 | 37 | 1.1392 | 2.0879 | 23 | 37 | 1.1503 | 2.0235 | 23 |
| 38 | 1.1288 | 2.1560 | 22 | 38 | 1.1393 | 2.0868 | 22 | 38 | 1.1505 | 2.0225 | 22 |
| 39 | 1.1289 | 2.1549 | 21 | 39 | 1.1395 | 2.0857 | 21 | 39 | 1.1507 | 2.0214 | 21 |
| 40 | 1.1291 | 2.1537 | 20 | 40 | 1.1397 | 2.0846 | 20 | 40 | 1.1509 | 2.0204 | 20 |
| 41 | 1.1293 | 2.1525 | 19 | 41 | 1.1399 | 2.0835 | 19 | 41 | 1.1510 | 2.0194 | 19 |
| 42 | 1.1294 | 2.1513 | 18 | 42 | 1.1401 | 2.0824 | 18 | 42 | 1.1512 | 2.0183 | 18 |
| 43 | 1.1296 | 2.1501 | 17 | 43 | 1.1402 | 2.0813 | 17 | 43 | 1.1514 | 2.0173 | 17 |
| 44 | 1.1298 | 2.1489 | 16 | 44 | 1.1404 | 2.0802 | 16 | 44 | 1.1516 | 2.0163 | 16 |
| 45 | 1.1300 | 2.1477 | 15 | 45 | 1.1406 | 2.0791 | 15 | 45 | 1.1518 | 2.0152 | 15 |
| 46 | 1.1301 | 2.1465 | 14 | 46 | 1.1408 | 2.0779 | 14 | 46 | 1.1520 | 2.0142 | 14 |
| 47 | 1.1303 | 2.1453 | 13 | 47 | 1.1410 | 2.0768 | 13 | 47 | 1.1522 | 2.0132 | 13 |
| 48 | 1.1305 | 2.1441 | 12 | 48 | 1.1412 | 2.0757 | 12 | 48 | 1.1524 | 2.0122 | 12 |
| 49 | 1.1307 | 2.1430 | 11 | 49 | 1.1413 | 2.0747 | 11 | 49 | 1.1526 | 2.0112 | 11 |
| 50 | 1.1308 | 2.1418 | 10 | 50 | 1.1415 | 2.0736 | 10 | 50 | 1.1528 | 2.0101 | 10 |
| 51 | 1.1310 | 2.1406 | 9 | 51 | 1.1417 | 2.0725 | 9 | 51 | 1.1530 | 2.0091 | 9 |
| 52 | 1.1312 | 2.1394 | 8 | 52 | 1.1419 | 2.0714 | 8 | 52 | 1.1532 | 2.0081 | 8 |
| 53 | 1.1313 | 2.1382 | 7 | 53 | 1.1421 | 2.0703 | 7 | 53 | 1.1533 | 2.0071 | 7 |
| 54 | 1.1315 | 2.1371 | 6 | 54 | 1.1423 | 2.0692 | 6 | 54 | 1.1535 | 2.0061 | 6 |
| 55 | 1.1317 | 2.1359 | 5 | 55 | 1.1424 | 2.0681 | 5 | 55 | 1.1537 | 2.0051 | 5 |
| 56 | 1.1319 | 2.1347 | 4 | 56 | 1.1426 | 2.0670 | 4 | 56 | 1.1539 | 2.0040 | 4 |
| 57 | 1.1320 | 2.1336 | 3 | 57 | 1.1428 | 2.0659 | 3 | 57 | 1.1541 | 2.0030 | 3 |
| 58 | 1.1322 | 2.1324 | 2 | 58 | 1.1430 | 2.0648 | 2 | 58 | 1.1543 | 2.0020 | 2 |
| 59 | 1.1324 | 2.1312 | 1 | 59 | 1.1432 | 2.0637 | 1 | 59 | 1.1545 | 2.0010 | 1 |
| 60 | 1.1326 | 2.1301 | 0 | 60 | 1.1434 | 2.0627 | 0 | 60 | 1.1547 | 2.0000 | 0 |
| ′ | Csc | Sec | ′ | ′ | Csc | Sec | ′ | ′ | Csc | Sec | ′ |

# NATURAL FUNCTIONS—SECANTS AND COSECANTS (Continued)

| ′ | Sec | Csc | ′ | ′ | Sec | Csc | ′ | ′ | Sec | Csc | ′ |
|---|-----|-----|---|---|-----|-----|---|---|-----|-----|---|
| **0** | 1.1547 | 2.0000 | **60** | **0** | 1.1666 | 1.9416 | **60** | **0** | 1.1792 | 1.8871 | **60** |
| 1 | 1.1549 | 1.9990 | 59 | 1 | 1.1668 | 1.9407 | 59 | 1 | 1.1794 | 1.8862 | 59 |
| 2 | 1.1551 | 1.9980 | 58 | 2 | 1.1670 | 1.9397 | 58 | 2 | 1.1796 | 1.8853 | 58 |
| 3 | 1.1553 | 1.9970 | 57 | 3 | 1.1672 | 1.9388 | 57 | 3 | 1.1798 | 1.8844 | 57 |
| 4 | 1.1555 | 1.9960 | 56 | 4 | 1.1675 | 1.9379 | 56 | 4 | 1.1800 | 1.8836 | 56 |
| **5** | 1.1557 | 1.9950 | **55** | **5** | 1.1677 | 1.9369 | **55** | **5** | 1.1803 | 1.8827 | **55** |
| 6 | 1.1559 | 1.9940 | 54 | 6 | 1.1679 | 1.9360 | 54 | 6 | 1.1805 | 1.8818 | 54 |
| 7 | 1.1561 | 1.9930 | 53 | 7 | 1.1681 | 1.9351 | 53 | 7 | 1.1807 | 1.8810 | 53 |
| 8 | 1.1563 | 1.9920 | 52 | 8 | 1.1683 | 1.9341 | 52 | 8 | 1.1809 | 1.8801 | 52 |
| 9 | 1.1565 | 1.9910 | 51 | 9 | 1.1685 | 1.9332 | 51 | 9 | 1.1811 | 1.8792 | 51 |
| **10** | 1.1566 | 1.9900 | **50** | **10** | 1.1687 | 1.9323 | **50** | **10** | 1.1813 | 1.8783 | **50** |
| 11 | 1.1568 | 1.9890 | 49 | 11 | 1.1689 | 1.9313 | 49 | 11 | 1.1815 | 1.8775 | 49 |
| 12 | 1.1570 | 1.9880 | 48 | 12 | 1.1691 | 1.9304 | 48 | 12 | 1.1818 | 1.8766 | 48 |
| 13 | 1.1572 | 1.9870 | 47 | 13 | 1.1693 | 1.9295 | 47 | 13 | 1.1820 | 1.8757 | 47 |
| 14 | 1.1574 | 1.9860 | 46 | 14 | 1.1695 | 1.9285 | 46 | 14 | 1.1822 | 1.8749 | 46 |
| **15** | 1.1576 | 1.9850 | **45** | **15** | 1.1697 | 1.9276 | **45** | **15** | 1.1824 | 1.8740 | **45** |
| 16 | 1.1578 | 1.9840 | 44 | 16 | 1.1699 | 1.9267 | 44 | 16 | 1.1826 | 1.8731 | 44 |
| 17 | 1.1580 | 1.9830 | 43 | 17 | 1.1701 | 1.9258 | 43 | 17 | 1.1828 | 1.8723 | 43 |
| 18 | 1.1582 | 1.9821 | 42 | 18 | 1.1703 | 1.9249 | 42 | 18 | 1.1831 | 1.8714 | 42 |
| 19 | 1.1584 | 1.9811 | 41 | 19 | 1.1705 | 1.9239 | 41 | 19 | 1.1833 | 1.8706 | 41 |
| **20** | 1.1586 | 1.9801 | **40** | **20** | 1.1707 | 1.9230 | **40** | **20** | 1.1835 | 1.8697 | **40** |
| 21 | 1.1588 | 1.9791 | 39 | 21 | 1.1710 | 1.9221 | 39 | 21 | 1.1837 | 1.8688 | 39 |
| 22 | 1.1590 | 1.9781 | 38 | 22 | 1.1712 | 1.9212 | 38 | 22 | 1.1839 | 1.8680 | 38 |
| 23 | 1.1592 | 1.9771 | 37 | 23 | 1.1714 | 1.9203 | 37 | 23 | 1.1842 | 1.8671 | 37 |
| 24 | 1.1594 | 1.9762 | 36 | 24 | 1.1716 | 1.9194 | 36 | 24 | 1.1844 | 1.8663 | 36 |
| **25** | 1.1596 | 1.9752 | **35** | **25** | 1.1718 | 1.9184 | **35** | **25** | 1.1846 | 1.8654 | **35** |
| 26 | 1.1598 | 1.9742 | 34 | 26 | 1.1720 | 1.9175 | 34 | 26 | 1.1848 | 1.8646 | 34 |
| 27 | 1.1600 | 1.9732 | 33 | 27 | 1.1722 | 1.9166 | 33 | 27 | 1.1850 | 1.8637 | 33 |
| 28 | 1.1602 | 1.9722 | 32 | 28 | 1.1724 | 1.9157 | 32 | 28 | 1.1852 | 1.8629 | 32 |
| 29 | 1.1604 | 1.9713 | 31 | 29 | 1.1726 | 1.9148 | 31 | 29 | 1.1855 | 1.8620 | 31 |
| **30** | 1.1606 | 1.9703 | **30** | **30** | 1.1728 | 1.9139 | **30** | **30** | 1.1857 | 1.8612 | **30** |
| 31 | 1.1608 | 1.9693 | 29 | 31 | 1.1730 | 1.9130 | 29 | 31 | 1.1859 | 1.8603 | 29 |
| 32 | 1.1610 | 1.9684 | 28 | 32 | 1.1732 | 1.9121 | 28 | 32 | 1.1861 | 1.8595 | 28 |
| 33 | 1.1612 | 1.9674 | 27 | 33 | 1.1735 | 1.9112 | 27 | 33 | 1.1863 | 1.8586 | 27 |
| 34 | 1.1614 | 1.9664 | 26 | 34 | 1.1737 | 1.9103 | 26 | 34 | 1.1866 | 1.8578 | 26 |
| **35** | 1.1616 | 1.9654 | **25** | **35** | 1.1739 | 1.9094 | **25** | **35** | 1.1868 | 1.8569 | **25** |
| 36 | 1.1618 | 1.9645 | 24 | 36 | 1.1741 | 1.9084 | 24 | 36 | 1.1870 | 1.8561 | 24 |
| 37 | 1.1620 | 1.9635 | 23 | 37 | 1.1743 | 1.9075 | 23 | 37 | 1.1872 | 1.8552 | 23 |
| 38 | 1.1622 | 1.9625 | 22 | 38 | 1.1745 | 1.9066 | 22 | 38 | 1.1875 | 1.8544 | 22 |
| 39 | 1.1624 | 1.9616 | 21 | 39 | 1.1747 | 1.9057 | 21 | 39 | 1.1877 | 1.8535 | 21 |
| **40** | 1.1626 | 1.9606 | **20** | **40** | 1.1749 | 1.9048 | **20** | **40** | 1.1879 | 1.8527 | **20** |
| 41 | 1.1628 | 1.9597 | 19 | 41 | 1.1751 | 1.9039 | 19 | 41 | 1.1881 | 1.8519 | 19 |
| 42 | 1.1630 | 1.9587 | 18 | 42 | 1.1753 | 1.9031 | 18 | 42 | 1.1883 | 1.8510 | 18 |
| 43 | 1.1632 | 1.9577 | 17 | 43 | 1.1756 | 1.9022 | 17 | 43 | 1.1886 | 1.8502 | 17 |
| 44 | 1.1634 | 1.9568 | 16 | 44 | 1.1758 | 1.9013 | 16 | 44 | 1.1888 | 1.8494 | 16 |
| **45** | 1.1636 | 1.9558 | **15** | **45** | 1.1760 | 1.9004 | **15** | **45** | 1.1890 | 1.8485 | **15** |
| 46 | 1.1638 | 1.9549 | 14 | 46 | 1.1762 | 1.8995 | 14 | 46 | 1.1892 | 1.8477 | 14 |
| 47 | 1.1640 | 1.9539 | 13 | 47 | 1.1764 | 1.8986 | 13 | 47 | 1.1895 | 1.8468 | 13 |
| 48 | 1.1642 | 1.9530 | 12 | 48 | 1.1766 | 1.8977 | 12 | 48 | 1.1897 | 1.8460 | 12 |
| 49 | 1.1644 | 1.9520 | 11 | 49 | 1.1768 | 1.8968 | 11 | 49 | 1.1899 | 1.8452 | 11 |
| **50** | 1.1646 | 1.9511 | **10** | **50** | 1.1770 | 1.8959 | **10** | **50** | 1.1901 | 1.8443 | **10** |
| 51 | 1.1648 | 1.9501 | 9 | 51 | 1.1773 | 1.8950 | 9 | 51 | 1.1903 | 1.8435 | 9 |
| 52 | 1.1650 | 1.9492 | 8 | 52 | 1.1775 | 1.8941 | 8 | 52 | 1.1906 | 1.8427 | 8 |
| 53 | 1.1652 | 1.9482 | 7 | 53 | 1.1777 | 1.8933 | 7 | 53 | 1.1908 | 1.8419 | 7 |
| 54 | 1.1654 | 1.9473 | 6 | 54 | 1.1779 | 1.8924 | 6 | 54 | 1.1910 | 1.8410 | 6 |
| **55** | 1.1656 | 1.9463 | **5** | **55** | 1.1781 | 1.8915 | **5** | **55** | 1.1912 | 1.8402 | **5** |
| 56 | 1.1658 | 1.9454 | 4 | 56 | 1.1783 | 1.8906 | 4 | 56 | 1.1915 | 1.8394 | 4 |
| 57 | 1.1660 | 1.9444 | 3 | 57 | 1.1785 | 1.8897 | 3 | 57 | 1.1917 | 1.8385 | 3 |
| 58 | 1.1662 | 1.9435 | 2 | 58 | 1.1788 | 1.8888 | 2 | 58 | 1.1919 | 1.8377 | 2 |
| 59 | 1.1664 | 1.9425 | 1 | 59 | 1.1790 | 1.8880 | 1 | 59 | 1.1921 | 1.8369 | 1 |
| **60** | 1.1666 | 1.9416 | **0** | **60** | 1.1792 | 1.8871 | **0** | **60** | 1.1924 | 1.8361 | **0** |
| ′ | Csc | Sec | ′ | ′ | Csc | Sec | ′ | ′ | Csc | Sec | ′ |

**33° (213°)**  (326°) **146°**   **34° (214°)**  (325°) **145°**   **35° (215°)**  (324°) **144°**

| ′ | Sec | Csc | ′ | ′ | Sec | Csc | ′ | ′ | Sec | Csc | ′ |
|---|-----|-----|---|---|-----|-----|---|---|-----|-----|---|
| 0 | 1.1924 | 1.8361 | 60 | 0 | 1.2062 | 1.7883 | 60 | 0 | 1.2208 | 1.7434 | 60 |
| 1 | 1.1926 | 1.8353 | 59 | 1 | 1.2065 | 1.7875 | 59 | 1 | 1.2210 | 1.7427 | 59 |
| 2 | 1.1928 | 1.8344 | 58 | 2 | 1.2067 | 1.7868 | 58 | 2 | 1.2213 | 1.7420 | 58 |
| 3 | 1.1930 | 1.8336 | 57 | 3 | 1.2069 | 1.7860 | 57 | 3 | 1.2215 | 1.7413 | 57 |
| 4 | 1.1933 | 1.8328 | 56 | 4 | 1.2072 | 1.7852 | 56 | 4 | 1 2218 | 1.7406 | 56 |
| 5 | 1.1935 | 1.8320 | 55 | 5 | 1.2074 | 1.7844 | 55 | 5 | 1.2220 | 1.7398 | 55 |
| 6 | 1.1937 | 1.8312 | 54 | 6 | 1.2076 | 1.7837 | 54 | 6 | 1.2223 | 1.7391 | 54 |
| 7 | 1.1939 | 1.8303 | 53 | 7 | 1.2079 | 1.7829 | 53 | 7 | 1.2225 | 1.7384 | 53 |
| 8 | 1.1942 | 1.8295 | 52 | 8 | 1.2081 | 1.7821 | 52 | 8 | 1.2228 | 1.7377 | 52 |
| 9 | 1.1944 | 1.8287 | 51 | 9 | 1.2084 | 1.7814 | 51 | 9 | 1.2230 | 1.7370 | 51 |
| 10 | 1.1946 | 1.8279 | 50 | 10 | 1.2086 | 1.7806 | 50 | 10 | 1.2233 | 1.7362 | 50 |
| 11 | 1.1949 | 1.8271 | 49 | 11 | 1.2088 | 1.7799 | 49 | 11 | 1.2235 | 1.7355 | 49 |
| 12 | 1.1951 | 1.8263 | 48 | 12 | 1.2091 | 1.7791 | 48 | 12 | 1.2238 | 1.7348 | 48 |
| 13 | 1.1953 | 1.8255 | 47 | 13 | 1.2093 | 1.7783 | 47 | 13 | 1.2240 | 1.7341 | 47 |
| 14 | 1.1955 | 1.8247 | 46 | 14 | 1.2096 | 1.7776 | 46 | 14 | 1.2243 | 1.7334 | 46 |
| 15 | 1.1958 | 1.8238 | 45 | 15 | 1.2098 | 1.7768 | 45 | 15 | 1.2245 | 1.7327 | 45 |
| 16 | 1.1960 | 1.8230 | 44 | 16 | 1.2100 | 1.7761 | 44 | 16 | 1.2248 | 1.7320 | 44 |
| 17 | 1.1962 | 1.8222 | 43 | 17 | 1.2103 | 1.7753 | 43 | 17 | 1.2250 | 1.7312 | 43 |
| 18 | 1.1964 | 1.8214 | 42 | 18 | 1.2105 | 1.7745 | 42 | 18 | 1.2253 | 1.7305 | 42 |
| 19 | 1.1967 | 1.8206 | 41 | 19 | 1.2108 | 1.7738 | 41 | 19 | 1.2255 | 1.7298 | 41 |
| 20 | 1.1969 | 1.8198 | 40 | 20 | 1.2110 | 1.7730 | 40 | 20 | 1.2258 | 1.7291 | 40 |
| 21 | 1.1971 | 1.8190 | 39 | 21 | 1.2112 | 1.7723 | 39 | 21 | 1.2260 | 1.7284 | 39 |
| 22 | 1.1974 | 1.8182 | 38 | 22 | 1.2115 | 1.7715 | 38 | 22 | 1.2263 | 1.7277 | 38 |
| 23 | 1.1976 | 1.8174 | 37 | 23 | 1.2117 | 1.7708 | 37 | 23 | 1.2265 | 1.7270 | 37 |
| 24 | 1.1978 | 1.8166 | 36 | 24 | 1.2120 | 1.7700 | 36 | 24 | 1.2268 | 1.7263 | 36 |
| 25 | 1.1981 | 1.8158 | 35 | 25 | 1.2122 | 1.7693 | 35 | 25 | 1.2271 | 1.7256 | 35 |
| 26 | 1.1983 | 1.8150 | 34 | 26 | 1.2124 | 1.7685 | 34 | 26 | 1.2273 | 1.7249 | 34 |
| 27 | 1.1985 | 1.8142 | 33 | 27 | 1.2127 | 1.7678 | 33 | 27 | 1.2276 | 1.7242 | 33 |
| 28 | 1.1987 | 1.8134 | 32 | 28 | 1.2129 | 1.7670 | 32 | 28 | 1.2278 | 1.7235 | 32 |
| 29 | 1.1990 | 1.8126 | 31 | 29 | 1.2132 | 1.7663 | 31 | 29 | 1.2281 | 1.7228 | 31 |
| 30 | 1.1992 | 1.8118 | 30 | 30 | 1.2134 | 1.7655 | 30 | 30 | 1.2283 | 1.7221 | 30 |
| 31 | 1.1994 | 1.8110 | 29 | 31 | 1.2136 | 1.7648 | 29 | 31 | 1.2286 | 1.7213 | 29 |
| 32 | 1.1997 | 1.8102 | 28 | 32 | 1.2139 | 1.7640 | 28 | 32 | 1.2288 | 1.7206 | 28 |
| 33 | 1.1999 | 1.8094 | 27 | 33 | 1.2141 | 1.7633 | 27 | 33 | 1.2291 | 1.7199 | 27 |
| 34 | 1.2001 | 1.8086 | 26 | 34 | 1.2144 | 1.7625 | 26 | 34 | 1.2293 | 1.7192 | 26 |
| 35 | 1.2004 | 1.8078 | 25 | 35 | 1.2146 | 1.7618 | 25 | 35 | 1.2296 | 1.7185 | 25 |
| 36 | 1.2006 | 1.8070 | 24 | 36 | 1.2149 | 1.7610 | 24 | 36 | 1.2299 | 1.7179 | 24 |
| 37 | 1.2008 | 1.8062 | 23 | 37 | 1.2151 | 1.7603 | 23 | 37 | 1.2301 | 1.7172 | 23 |
| 38 | 1.2011 | 1.8055 | 22 | 38 | 1.2154 | 1.7596 | 22 | 38 | 1.2304 | 1.7165 | 22 |
| 39 | 1.2013 | 1.8047 | 21 | 39 | 1.2156 | 1.7588 | 21 | 39 | 1.2306 | 1.7158 | 21 |
| 40 | 1.2015 | 1.8039 | 20 | 40 | 1.2158 | 1.7581 | 20 | 40 | 1.2309 | 1.7151 | 20 |
| 41 | 1.2018 | 1.8031 | 19 | 41 | 1.2161 | 1.7573 | 19 | 41 | 1.2311 | 1.7144 | 19 |
| 42 | 1.2020 | 1.8023 | 18 | 42 | 1.2163 | 1.7566 | 18 | 42 | 1.2314 | 1.7137 | 18 |
| 43 | 1.2022 | 1.8015 | 17 | 43 | 1.2166 | 1.7559 | 17 | 43 | 1.2317 | 1.7130 | 17 |
| 44 | 1.2025 | 1.8007 | 16 | 44 | 1.2168 | 1.7551 | 16 | 44 | 1.2319 | 1.7123 | 16 |
| 45 | 1.2027 | 1.8000 | 15 | 45 | 1.2171 | 1.7544 | 15 | 45 | 1.2322 | 1.7116 | 15 |
| 46 | 1.2029 | 1.7992 | 14 | 46 | 1.2173 | 1.7537 | 14 | 46 | 1.2324 | 1.7109 | 14 |
| 47 | 1.2032 | 1.7984 | 13 | 47 | 1.2176 | 1.7529 | 13 | 47 | 1.2327 | 1.7102 | 13 |
| 48 | 1.2034 | 1.7976 | 12 | 48 | 1.2178 | 1.7522 | 12 | 48 | 1.2329 | 1.7095 | 12 |
| 49 | 1.2036 | 1.7968 | 11 | 49 | 1.2181 | 1.7515 | 11 | 49 | 1.2332 | 1.7088 | 11 |
| 50 | 1.2039 | 1.7960 | 10 | 50 | 1.2183 | 1.7507 | 10 | 50 | 1.2335 | 1.7081 | 10 |
| 51 | 1.2041 | 1.7953 | 9 | 51 | 1.2185 | 1.7500 | 9 | 51 | 1.2337 | 1.7075 | 9 |
| 52 | 1.2043 | 1.7945 | 8 | 52 | 1.2188 | 1.7493 | 8 | 52 | 1.2340 | 1.7068 | 8 |
| 53 | 1.2046 | 1.7937 | 7 | 53 | 1.2190 | 1.7485 | 7 | 53 | 1.2342 | 1.7061 | 7 |
| 54 | 1.2048 | 1.7929 | 6 | 54 | 1.2193 | 1.7478 | 6 | 54 | 1.2345 | 1.7054 | 6 |
| 55 | 1.2050 | 1.7922 | 5 | 55 | 1.2195 | 1.7471 | 5 | 55 | 1.2348 | 1.7047 | 5 |
| 56 | 1.2053 | 1.7914 | 4 | 56 | 1.2198 | 1.7463 | 4 | 56 | 1.2350 | 1.7040 | 4 |
| 57 | 1.2055 | 1.7906 | 3 | 57 | 1.2200 | 1.7456 | 3 | 57 | 1.2353 | 1.7033 | 3 |
| 58 | 1.2057 | 1.7898 | 2 | 58 | 1.2203 | 1.7449 | 2 | 58 | 1.2355 | 1.7027 | 2 |
| 59 | 1.2060 | 1.7891 | 1 | 59 | 1.2205 | 1.7442 | 1 | 59 | 1.2358 | 1.7020 | 1 |
| 60 | 1.2062 | 1.7883 | 0 | 60 | 1.2208 | 1.7434 | 0 | 60 | 1.2361 | 1.7013 | 0 |
| ′ | Csc | Sec | ′ | ′ | Csc | Sec | ′ | ′ | Csc | Sec | ′ |

**36° (216°)**　　　(323°) **143°**　　　**37° (217°)**　　　(322°) **142°**　　　**38° (218°)**　　　(321°) **141°**

| ′ | Sec | Csc | ′ | ′ | Sec | Csc | ′ | ′ | Sec | Csc | ′ |
|---|-----|-----|---|---|-----|-----|---|---|-----|-----|---|
| 0 | 1.2361 | 1.7013 | 60 | 0 | 1.2521 | 1.6616 | 60 | 0 | 1.2690 | 1.6243 | 60 |
| 1 | 1.2363 | 1.7006 | 59 | 1 | 1.2524 | 1.6610 | 59 | 1 | 1.2693 | 1.6237 | 59 |
| 2 | 1.2366 | 1.6999 | 58 | 2 | 1.2527 | 1.6604 | 58 | 2 | 1.2696 | 1.6231 | 58 |
| 3 | 1.2369 | 1.6993 | 57 | 3 | 1.2530 | 1.6597 | 57 | 3 | 1.2699 | 1.6225 | 57 |
| 4 | 1.2371 | 1.6986 | 56 | 4 | 1.2532 | 1.6591 | 56 | 4 | 1.2702 | 1.6219 | 56 |
| 5 | 1.2374 | 1.6979 | 55 | 5 | 1.2535 | 1.6584 | 55 | 5 | 1.2705 | 1.6213 | 55 |
| 6 | 1.2376 | 1.6972 | 54 | 6 | 1.2538 | 1.6578 | 54 | 6 | 1.2708 | 1.6207 | 54 |
| 7 | 1.2379 | 1.6966 | 53 | 7 | 1.2541 | 1.6572 | 53 | 7 | 1.2710 | 1.6201 | 53 |
| 8 | 1.2382 | 1.6959 | 52 | 8 | 1.2543 | 1.6565 | 52 | 8 | 1.2713 | 1.6195 | 52 |
| 9 | 1.2384 | 1.6952 | 51 | 9 | 1.2546 | 1.6559 | 51 | 9 | 1.2716 | 1.6189 | 51 |
| 10 | 1.2387 | 1.6945 | 50 | 10 | 1.2549 | 1.6553 | 50 | 10 | 1.2719 | 1.6183 | 50 |
| 11 | 1.2390 | 1.6939 | 49 | 11 | 1.2552 | 1.6546 | 49 | 11 | 1.2722 | 1.6177 | 49 |
| 12 | 1.2392 | 1.6932 | 48 | 12 | 1.2554 | 1.6540 | 48 | 12 | 1.2725 | 1.6171 | 48 |
| 13 | 1.2395 | 1.6925 | 47 | 13 | 1.2557 | 1.6534 | 47 | 13 | 1.2728 | 1.6165 | 47 |
| 14 | 1.2397 | 1.6918 | 46 | 14 | 1.2560 | 1.6527 | 46 | 14 | 1.2731 | 1.6159 | 46 |
| 15 | 1.2400 | 1.6912 | 45 | 15 | 1.2563 | 1.6521 | 45 | 15 | 1.2734 | 1.6153 | 45 |
| 16 | 1.2403 | 1.6905 | 44 | 16 | 1.2566 | 1.6515 | 44 | 16 | 1.2737 | 1.6147 | 44 |
| 17 | 1.2405 | 1.6898 | 43 | 17 | 1.2568 | 1.6508 | 43 | 17 | 1.2740 | 1.6141 | 43 |
| 18 | 1.2408 | 1.6892 | 42 | 18 | 1.2571 | 1.6502 | 42 | 18 | 1.2742 | 1.6135 | 42 |
| 19 | 1.2411 | 1.6885 | 41 | 19 | 1.2574 | 1.6496 | 41 | 19 | 1.2745 | 1.6129 | 41 |
| 20 | 1.2413 | 1.6878 | 40 | 20 | 1.2577 | 1.6489 | 40 | 20 | 1.2748 | 1.6123 | 40 |
| 21 | 1.2416 | 1.6871 | 39 | 21 | 1.2579 | 1.6483 | 39 | 21 | 1.2751 | 1.6117 | 39 |
| 22 | 1.2419 | 1.6865 | 38 | 22 | 1.2582 | 1.6477 | 38 | 22 | 1.2754 | 1.6111 | 38 |
| 23 | 1.2421 | 1.6858 | 37 | 23 | 1.2585 | 1.6471 | 37 | 23 | 1.2757 | 1.6105 | 37 |
| 24 | 1.2424 | 1.6852 | 36 | 24 | 1.2588 | 1.6464 | 36 | 24 | 1.2760 | 1.6099 | 36 |
| 25 | 1.2427 | 1.6845 | 35 | 25 | 1.2591 | 1.6458 | 35 | 25 | 1.2763 | 1.6093 | 35 |
| 26 | 1.2429 | 1.6838 | 34 | 26 | 1.2593 | 1.6452 | 34 | 26 | 1.2766 | 1.6087 | 34 |
| 27 | 1.2432 | 1.6832 | 33 | 27 | 1.2596 | 1.6446 | 33 | 27 | 1.2769 | 1.6082 | 33 |
| 28 | 1.2435 | 1.6825 | 32 | 28 | 1.2599 | 1.6439 | 32 | 28 | 1.2772 | 1.6076 | 32 |
| 29 | 1.2437 | 1.6818 | 31 | 29 | 1.2602 | 1.6433 | 31 | 29 | 1.2775 | 1.6070 | 31 |
| 30 | 1.2440 | 1.6812 | 30 | 30 | 1.2605 | 1.6427 | 30 | 30 | 1.2778 | 1.6064 | 30 |
| 31 | 1.2443 | 1.6805 | 29 | 31 | 1.2608 | 1.6421 | 29 | 31 | 1.2781 | 1.6058 | 29 |
| 32 | 1.2445 | 1.6799 | 28 | 32 | 1.2610 | 1.6414 | 28 | 32 | 1.2784 | 1.6052 | 28 |
| 33 | 1.2448 | 1.6792 | 27 | 33 | 1.2613 | 1.6408 | 27 | 33 | 1.2787 | 1.6046 | 27 |
| 34 | 1.2451 | 1.6785 | 26 | 34 | 1.2616 | 1.6402 | 26 | 34 | 1.2790 | 1.6040 | 26 |
| 35 | 1.2453 | 1.6779 | 25 | 35 | 1.2619 | 1.6396 | 25 | 35 | 1.2793 | 1.6035 | 25 |
| 36 | 1.2456 | 1.6772 | 24 | 36 | 1.2622 | 1.6390 | 24 | 36 | 1.2796 | 1.6029 | 24 |
| 37 | 1.2459 | 1.6766 | 23 | 37 | 1.2624 | 1.6383 | 23 | 37 | 1.2799 | 1.6023 | 23 |
| 38 | 1.2462 | 1.6759 | 22 | 38 | 1.2627 | 1.6377 | 22 | 38 | 1.2802 | 1.6017 | 22 |
| 39 | 1.2464 | 1.6753 | 21 | 39 | 1.2630 | 1.6371 | 21 | 39 | 1.2804 | 1.6011 | 21 |
| 40 | 1.2467 | 1.6746 | 20 | 40 | 1.2633 | 1.6365 | 20 | 40 | 1.2807 | 1.6005 | 20 |
| 41 | 1.2470 | 1.6739 | 19 | 41 | 1.2636 | 1.6359 | 19 | 41 | 1.2810 | 1.6000 | 19 |
| 42 | 1.2472 | 1.6733 | 18 | 42 | 1.2639 | 1.6353 | 18 | 42 | 1.2813 | 1.5994 | 18 |
| 43 | 1.2475 | 1.6726 | 17 | 43 | 1.2641 | 1.6346 | 17 | 43 | 1.2816 | 1.5988 | 17 |
| 44 | 1.2478 | 1.6720 | 16 | 44 | 1.2644 | 1.6340 | 16 | 44 | 1.2819 | 1.5982 | 16 |
| 45 | 1.2480 | 1.6713 | 15 | 45 | 1.2647 | 1.6334 | 15 | 45 | 1.2822 | 1.5976 | 15 |
| 46 | 1.2483 | 1.6707 | 14 | 46 | 1.2650 | 1.6328 | 14 | 46 | 1.2825 | 1.5971 | 14 |
| 47 | 1.2486 | 1.6700 | 13 | 47 | 1.2653 | 1.6322 | 13 | 47 | 1.2828 | 1.5965 | 13 |
| 48 | 1.2489 | 1.6694 | 12 | 48 | 1.2656 | 1.6316 | 12 | 48 | 1.2831 | 1.5959 | 12 |
| 49 | 1.2491 | 1.6687 | 11 | 49 | 1.2659 | 1.6310 | 11 | 49 | 1.2834 | 1.5953 | 11 |
| 50 | 1.2494 | 1.6681 | 10 | 50 | 1.2661 | 1.6303 | 10 | 50 | 1.2837 | 1.5948 | 10 |
| 51 | 1.2497 | 1.6674 | 9 | 51 | 1.2664 | 1.6297 | 9 | 51 | 1.2840 | 1.5942 | 9 |
| 52 | 1.2499 | 1.6668 | 8 | 52 | 1.2667 | 1.6291 | 8 | 52 | 1.2843 | 1.5936 | 8 |
| 53 | 1.2502 | 1.6661 | 7 | 53 | 1.2670 | 1.6285 | 7 | 53 | 1.2846 | 1.5930 | 7 |
| 54 | 1.2505 | 1.6655 | 6 | 54 | 1.2673 | 1.6279 | 6 | 54 | 1.2849 | 1.5925 | 6 |
| 55 | 1.2508 | 1.6649 | 5 | 55 | 1.2676 | 1.6273 | 5 | 55 | 1.2852 | 1.5919 | 5 |
| 56 | 1.2510 | 1.6642 | 4 | 56 | 1.2679 | 1.6267 | 4 | 56 | 1.2855 | 1.5913 | 4 |
| 57 | 1.2513 | 1.6636 | 3 | 57 | 1.2682 | 1.6261 | 3 | 57 | 1.2859 | 1.5907 | 3 |
| 58 | 1.2516 | 1.6629 | 2 | 58 | 1.2684 | 1.6255 | 2 | 58 | 1.2862 | 1.5902 | 2 |
| 59 | 1.2519 | 1.6623 | 1 | 59 | 1.2687 | 1.6249 | 1 | 59 | 1.2865 | 1.5896 | 1 |
| 60 | 1.2521 | 1.6616 | 0 | 60 | 1.2690 | 1.6243 | 0 | 60 | 1.2868 | 1.5890 | 0 |
| ′ | Csc | Sec | ′ | ′ | Csc | Sec | ′ | ′ | Cs c | Sec | ′ |

**39° (219°)**     (320°) **140°**     **40° (220°)**     (319°) **139°**     **41° (221°)**     (318°) **138°**

| ′ | Sec | Csc | ′ | ′ | Sec | Csc | ′ | ′ | Sec | Csc | ′ |
|---|---|---|---|---|---|---|---|---|---|---|---|
| 0 | 1.2868 | 1.5890 | 60 | 0 | 1.3054 | 1.5557 | 60 | 0 | 1.3250 | 1.5243 | 60 |
| 1 | 1.2871 | 1.5884 | 59 | 1 | 1.3057 | 1.5552 | 59 | 1 | 1.3253 | 1.5237 | 59 |
| 2 | 1.2874 | 1.5879 | 58 | 2 | 1.3060 | 1.5546 | 58 | 2 | 1.3257 | 1.5232 | 58 |
| 3 | 1.2877 | 1.5873 | 57 | 3 | 1.3064 | 1.5541 | 57 | 3 | 1.3260 | 1.5227 | 57 |
| 4 | 1.2880 | 1.5867 | 56 | 4 | 1.3067 | 1.5536 | 56 | 4 | 1.3264 | 1.5222 | 56 |
| 5 | 1.2883 | 1.5862 | 55 | 5 | 1.3070 | 1.5530 | 55 | 5 | 1.3267 | 1.5217 | 55 |
| 6 | 1.2886 | 1.5856 | 54 | 6 | 1.3076 | 1.5525 | 54 | 6 | 1.3270 | 1.5212 | 54 |
| 7 | 1.2889 | 1.5850 | 53 | 7 | 1.3076 | 1.5520 | 53 | 7 | 1.3274 | 1.5207 | 53 |
| 8 | 1.2892 | 1.5845 | 52 | 8 | 1.3080 | 1.5514 | 52 | 8 | 1.3277 | 1.5202 | 52 |
| 9 | 1.2895 | 1.5839 | 51 | 9 | 1.3083 | 1.5509 | 51 | 9 | 1.3280 | 1.5197 | 51 |
| 10 | 1.2898 | 1.5833 | 50 | 10 | 1.3086 | 1.5504 | 50 | 10 | 1.3284 | 1.5192 | 50 |
| 11 | 1.2901 | 1.5828 | 49 | 11 | 1.3089 | 1.5498 | 49 | 11 | 1.3287 | 1.5187 | 49 |
| 12 | 1.2904 | 1.5822 | 48 | 12 | 1.3093 | 1.5493 | 48 | 12 | 1.3291 | 1.5182 | 48 |
| 13 | 1.2907 | 1.5816 | 47 | 13 | 1.3096 | 1.5488 | 47 | 13 | 1.3294 | 1.5177 | 47 |
| 14 | 1.2910 | 1.5811 | 46 | 14 | 1.3099 | 1.5482 | 46 | 14 | 1.3297 | 1.5172 | 46 |
| 15 | 1.2913 | 1.5805 | 45 | 15 | 1.3102 | 1.5477 | 45 | 15 | 1.3301 | 1.5167 | 45 |
| 16 | 1.2916 | 1.5800 | 44 | 16 | 1.3105 | 1.5472 | 44 | 16 | 1.3304 | 1.5162 | 44 |
| 17 | 1.2919 | 1.5794 | 43 | 17 | 1.3109 | 1.5466 | 43 | 17 | 1.3307 | 1.5156 | 43 |
| 18 | 1.2923 | 1.5788 | 42 | 18 | 1.3112 | 1.5461 | 42 | 18 | 1.3311 | 1.5151 | 42 |
| 19 | 1.2926 | 1.5783 | 41 | 19 | 1.3115 | 1.5456 | 41 | 19 | 1.3314 | 1.5146 | 41 |
| 20 | 1.2929 | 1.5777 | 40 | 20 | 1.3118 | 1.5450 | 40 | 20 | 1.3318 | 1.5141 | 40 |
| 21 | 1.2932 | 1.5771 | 39 | 21 | 1.3122 | 1.5445 | 39 | 21 | 1.3321 | 1.5136 | 39 |
| 22 | 1.2935 | 1.5766 | 38 | 22 | 1.3125 | 1.5440 | 38 | 22 | 1.3325 | 1.5131 | 38 |
| 23 | 1.2938 | 1.5760 | 37 | 23 | 1.3128 | 1.5435 | 37 | 23 | 1.3328 | 1.5126 | 37 |
| 24 | 1.2941 | 1.5755 | 36 | 24 | 1.3131 | 1.5429 | 36 | 24 | 1.3331 | 1.5121 | 36 |
| 25 | 1.2944 | 1.5749 | 35 | 25 | 1.3135 | 1.5424 | 35 | 25 | 1.3335 | 1.5116 | 35 |
| 26 | 1.2947 | 1.5744 | 34 | 26 | 1.3138 | 1.5419 | 34 | 26 | 1.3338 | 1.5111 | 34 |
| 27 | 1.2950 | 1.5738 | 33 | 27 | 1.3141 | 1.5413 | 33 | 27 | 1.3342 | 1.5107 | 33 |
| 28 | 1.2953 | 1.5732 | 32 | 28 | 1.3144 | 1.5408 | 32 | 28 | 1.3345 | 1.5102 | 32 |
| 29 | 1.2957 | 1.5727 | 31 | 29 | 1.3148 | 1.5403 | 31 | 29 | 1.3348 | 1.5097 | 31 |
| 30 | 1.2960 | 1.5721 | 30 | 30 | 1.3151 | 1.5398 | 30 | 30 | 1.3352 | 1.5092 | 30 |
| 31 | 1.2963 | 1.5716 | 29 | 31 | 1.3154 | 1.5392 | 29 | 31 | 1.3355 | 1.5087 | 29 |
| 32 | 1.2966 | 1.5710 | 28 | 32 | 1.3157 | 1.5387 | 28 | 32 | 1.3359 | 1.5082 | 28 |
| 33 | 1.2969 | 1.5705 | 27 | 33 | 1.3161 | 1.5382 | 27 | 33 | 1.3362 | 1.5077 | 27 |
| 34 | 1.2972 | 1.5699 | 26 | 34 | 1.3164 | 1.5377 | 26 | 34 | 1.3366 | 1.5072 | 26 |
| 35 | 1.2975 | 1.5694 | 25 | 35 | 1.3167 | 1.5372 | 25 | 35 | 1.3369 | 1.5067 | 25 |
| 36 | 1.2978 | 1.5688 | 24 | 36 | 1.3171 | 1.5366 | 24 | 36 | 1.3373 | 1.5062 | 24 |
| 37 | 1.2981 | 1.5683 | 23 | 37 | 1.3174 | 1.5361 | 23 | 37 | 1.3376 | 1.5057 | 23 |
| 38 | 1.2985 | 1.5677 | 22 | 38 | 1.3177 | 1.5356 | 22 | 38 | 1.3380 | 1.5052 | 22 |
| 39 | 1.2988 | 1.5672 | 21 | 39 | 1.3180 | 1.5351 | 21 | 39 | 1.3383 | 1.5047 | 21 |
| 40 | 1.2991 | 1.5666 | 20 | 40 | 1.3184 | 1.5345 | 20 | 40 | 1.3386 | 1.5042 | 20 |
| 41 | 1.2994 | 1.5661 | 19 | 41 | 1.3187 | 1.5340 | 19 | 41 | 1.3390 | 1.5037 | 19 |
| 42 | 1.2997 | 1.5655 | 18 | 42 | 1.3190 | 1.5335 | 18 | 42 | 1.3393 | 1.5032 | 18 |
| 43 | 1.3000 | 1.5650 | 17 | 43 | 1.3194 | 1.5330 | 17 | 43 | 1.3397 | 1.5027 | 17 |
| 44 | 1.3003 | 1.5644 | 16 | 44 | 1.3197 | 1.5325 | 16 | 44 | 1.3400 | 1.5023 | 16 |
| 45 | 1.3007 | 1.5639 | 15 | 45 | 1.3200 | 1.5320 | 15 | 45 | 1.3404 | 1.5018 | 15 |
| 46 | 1.3010 | 1.5633 | 14 | 46 | 1.3203 | 1.5314 | 14 | 46 | 1.3407 | 1.5013 | 14 |
| 47 | 1.3013 | 1.5628 | 13 | 47 | 1.3207 | 1.5309 | 13 | 47 | 1.3411 | 1.5008 | 13 |
| 48 | 1.3016 | 1.5622 | 12 | 48 | 1.3210 | 1.5304 | 12 | 48 | 1.3414 | 1.5003 | 12 |
| 49 | 1.3019 | 1.5617 | 11 | 49 | 1.3213 | 1.5299 | 11 | 49 | 1.3418 | 1.4998 | 11 |
| 50 | 1.3022 | 1.5611 | 10 | 50 | 1.3217 | 1.5294 | 10 | 50 | 1.3421 | 1.4993 | 10 |
| 51 | 1.3026 | 1.5606 | 9 | 51 | 1.3220 | 1.5289 | 9 | 51 | 1.3425 | 1.4988 | 9 |
| 52 | 1.3029 | 1.5601 | 8 | 52 | 1.3223 | 1.5283 | 8 | 52 | 1.3428 | 1.4984 | 8 |
| 53 | 1.3032 | 1.5595 | 7 | 53 | 1.3227 | 1.5278 | 7 | 53 | 1.3432 | 1.4979 | 7 |
| 54 | 1.3035 | 1.5590 | 6 | 54 | 1.3230 | 1.5273 | 6 | 54 | 1.3435 | 1.4974 | 6 |
| 55 | 1.3038 | 1.5584 | 5 | 55 | 1.3233 | 1.5268 | 5 | 55 | 1.3439 | 1.4969 | 5 |
| 56 | 1.3041 | 1.5579 | 4 | 56 | 1.3237 | 1.5263 | 4 | 56 | 1.3442 | 1.4964 | 4 |
| 57 | 1.3045 | 1.5573 | 3 | 57 | 1.3240 | 1.5258 | 3 | 57 | 1.3446 | 1.4959 | 3 |
| 58 | 1.3048 | 1.5568 | 2 | 58 | 1.3243 | 1.5253 | 2 | 58 | 1.3449 | 1.4954 | 2 |
| 59 | 1.3051 | 1.5563 | 1 | 59 | 1.3247 | 1.5248 | 1 | 59 | 1.3453 | 1.4950 | 1 |
| 60 | 1.3054 | 1.5557 | 0 | 60 | 1.3250 | 1.5243 | 0 | 60 | 1.3456 | 1.4945 | 0 |
| ′ | Csc | Sec | ′ | ′ | Csc | Sec | ′ | ′ | Csc | Sec | ′ |

**42° (222°)   (317°) 137°   43° (223°)   (316°) 136°   44° (224°)   (315°) 135°**

| ′ | Sec | Csc | ′ | ′ | Sec | Csc | ′ | ′ | Sec | Csc | ′ |
|---|-----|-----|---|---|-----|-----|---|---|-----|-----|---|
| 0 | 1.3456 | 1.4945 | 60 | 0 | 1.3673 | 1.4663 | 60 | 0 | 1.3902 | 1.4396 | 60 |
| 1 | 1.3460 | 1.4940 | 59 | 1 | 1.3677 | 1.4658 | 59 | 1 | 1.3906 | 1.4391 | 59 |
| 2 | 1.3463 | 1.4935 | 58 | 2 | 1.3681 | 1.4654 | 58 | 2 | 1.3909 | 1.4387 | 58 |
| 3 | 1.3467 | 1.4930 | 57 | 3 | 1.3684 | 1.4649 | 57 | 3 | 1.3913 | 1.4383 | 57 |
| 4 | 1.3470 | 1.4925 | 56 | 4 | 1.3688 | 1.4645 | 56 | 4 | 1.3917 | 1.4378 | 56 |
| 5 | 1.3474 | 1.4921 | 55 | 5 | 1.3692 | 1.4640 | 55 | 5 | 1.3921 | 1.4374 | 55 |
| 6 | 1.3478 | 1.4916 | 54 | 6 | 1.3696 | 1.4635 | 54 | 6 | 1.3925 | 1.4370 | 54 |
| 7 | 1.3481 | 1.4911 | 53 | 7 | 1.3699 | 1.4631 | 53 | 7 | 1.3929 | 1.4365 | 53 |
| 8 | 1.3485 | 1.4906 | 52 | 8 | 1.3703 | 1.4626 | 52 | 8 | 1.3933 | 1.4361 | 52 |
| 9 | 1.3488 | 1.4901 | 51 | 9 | 1.3707 | 1.4622 | 51 | 9 | 1.3937 | 1.4357 | 51 |
| 10 | 1.3492 | 1.4897 | 50 | 10 | 1.3711 | 1.4617 | 50 | 10 | 1.3941 | 1.4352 | 50 |
| 11 | 1.3495 | 1.4892 | 49 | 11 | 1.3714 | 1.4613 | 49 | 11 | 1.3945 | 1.4348 | 49 |
| 12 | 1.3499 | 1.4887 | 48 | 12 | 1.3718 | 1.4608 | 48 | 12 | 1.3949 | 1.4344 | 48 |
| 13 | 1.3502 | 1.4882 | 47 | 13 | 1.3722 | 1.4604 | 47 | 13 | 1.3953 | 1.4340 | 47 |
| 14 | 1.3506 | 1.4878 | 46 | 14 | 1.3726 | 1.4599 | 46 | 14 | 1.3957 | 1.4335 | 46 |
| 15 | 1.3510 | 1.4873 | 45 | 15 | 1.3729 | 1.4595 | 45 | 15 | 1.3961 | 1.4331 | 45 |
| 16 | 1.3513 | 1.4868 | 44 | 16 | 1.3733 | 1.4590 | 44 | 16 | 1.3965 | 1.4327 | 44 |
| 17 | 1.3517 | 1.4863 | 43 | 17 | 1.3737 | 1.4586 | 43 | 17 | 1.3969 | 1.4322 | 43 |
| 18 | 1.3520 | 1.4859 | 42 | 18 | 1.3741 | 1.4581 | 42 | 18 | 1.3972 | 1.4318 | 42 |
| 19 | 1.3524 | 1.4854 | 41 | 19 | 1.3744 | 1.4577 | 41 | 19 | 1.3976 | 1.4314 | 41 |
| 20 | 1.3527 | 1.4849 | 40 | 20 | 1.3748 | 1.4572 | 40 | 20 | 1.3980 | 1.4310 | 40 |
| 21 | 1.3531 | 1.4844 | 39 | 21 | 1.3752 | 1.4568 | 39 | 21 | 1.3984 | 1.4305 | 39 |
| 22 | 1.3535 | 1.4840 | 38 | 22 | 1.3756 | 1.4563 | 38 | 22 | 1.3988 | 1.4301 | 38 |
| 23 | 1.3538 | 1.4835 | 37 | 23 | 1.3759 | 1.4559 | 37 | 23 | 1.3992 | 1.4297 | 37 |
| 24 | 1.3542 | 1.4830 | 36 | 24 | 1.3763 | 1.4554 | 36 | 24 | 1.3996 | 1.4293 | 36 |
| 25 | 1.3545 | 1.4825 | 35 | 25 | 1.3767 | 1.4550 | 35 | 25 | 1.4000 | 1.4288 | 35 |
| 26 | 1.3549 | 1.4821 | 34 | 26 | 1.3771 | 1.4545 | 34 | 26 | 1.4004 | 1.4284 | 34 |
| 27 | 1.3553 | 1.4816 | 33 | 27 | 1.3775 | 1.4541 | 33 | 27 | 1.4008 | 1.4280 | 33 |
| 28 | 1.3556 | 1.4811 | 32 | 28 | 1.3778 | 1.4536 | 32 | 28 | 1.4012 | 1.4276 | 32 |
| 29 | 1.3560 | 1.4807 | 31 | 29 | 1.3782 | 1.4532 | 31 | 29 | 1.4016 | 1.4271 | 31 |
| 30 | 1.3563 | 1.4802 | 30 | 30 | 1.3786 | 1.4527 | 30 | 30 | 1.4020 | 1.4267 | 30 |
| 31 | 1.3567 | 1.4797 | 29 | 31 | 1.3790 | 1.4523 | 29 | 31 | 1.4024 | 1.4263 | 29 |
| 32 | 1.3571 | 1.4792 | 28 | 32 | 1.3794 | 1.4518 | 28 | 32 | 1.4028 | 1.4259 | 28 |
| 33 | 1.3574 | 1.4788 | 27 | 33 | 1.3797 | 1.4514 | 27 | 33 | 1.4032 | 1.4255 | 27 |
| 34 | 1.3578 | 1.4783 | 26 | 34 | 1.3801 | 1.4510 | 26 | 34 | 1.4036 | 1.4250 | 26 |
| 35 | 1.3582 | 1.4778 | 25 | 35 | 1.3805 | 1.4505 | 25 | 35 | 1.4040 | 1.4246 | 25 |
| 36 | 1.3585 | 1.4774 | 24 | 36 | 1.3809 | 1.4501 | 24 | 36 | 1.4044 | 1.4242 | 24 |
| 37 | 1.3589 | 1.4769 | 23 | 37 | 1.3813 | 1.4496 | 23 | 37 | 1.4048 | 1.4238 | 23 |
| 38 | 1.3592 | 1.4764 | 22 | 38 | 1.3817 | 1.4492 | 22 | 38 | 1.4052 | 1.4234 | 22 |
| 39 | 1.3596 | 1.4760 | 21 | 39 | 1.3820 | 1.4487 | 21 | 39 | 1.4057 | 1.4229 | 21 |
| 40 | 1.3600 | 1.4755 | 20 | 40 | 1.3824 | 1.4483 | 20 | 40 | 1.4061 | 1.4225 | 20 |
| 41 | 1.3603 | 1.4750 | 19 | 41 | 1.3828 | 1.4479 | 19 | 41 | 1.4065 | 1.4221 | 19 |
| 42 | 1.3607 | 1.4746 | 18 | 42 | 1.3832 | 1.4474 | 18 | 42 | 1.4069 | 1.4217 | 18 |
| 43 | 1.3611 | 1.4741 | 17 | 43 | 1.3836 | 1.4470 | 17 | 43 | 1.4073 | 1.4213 | 17 |
| 44 | 1.3614 | 1.4737 | 16 | 44 | 1.3840 | 1.4465 | 16 | 44 | 1.4077 | 1.4208 | 16 |
| 45 | 1.3618 | 1.4732 | 15 | 45 | 1.3843 | 1.4461 | 15 | 45 | 1.4081 | 1.4204 | 15 |
| 46 | 1.3622 | 1.4727 | 14 | 46 | 1.3847 | 1.4457 | 14 | 46 | 1.4085 | 1.4200 | 14 |
| 47 | 1.3625 | 1.4723 | 13 | 47 | 1.3851 | 1.4452 | 13 | 47 | 1.4089 | 1.4196 | 13 |
| 48 | 1.3629 | 1.4718 | 12 | 48 | 1.3855 | 1.4448 | 12 | 48 | 1.4093 | 1.4192 | 12 |
| 49 | 1.3633 | 1.4713 | 11 | 49 | 1.3859 | 1.4443 | 11 | 49 | 1.4097 | 1.4188 | 11 |
| 50 | 1.3636 | 1.4709 | 10 | 50 | 1.3863 | 1.4439 | 10 | 50 | 1.4101 | 1.4183 | 10 |
| 51 | 1.3640 | 1.4704 | 9 | 51 | 1.3867 | 1.4435 | 9 | 51 | 1.4105 | 1.4179 | 9 |
| 52 | 1.3644 | 1.4700 | 8 | 52 | 1.3871 | 1.4430 | 8 | 52 | 1.4109 | 1.4175 | 8 |
| 53 | 1.3647 | 1.4695 | 7 | 53 | 1.3874 | 1.4426 | 7 | 53 | 1.4113 | 1.4171 | 7 |
| 54 | 1.3651 | 1.4690 | 6 | 54 | 1.3878 | 1.4422 | 6 | 54 | 1.4118 | 1.4167 | 6 |
| 55 | 1.3655 | 1.4686 | 5 | 55 | 1.3882 | 1.4417 | 5 | 55 | 1.4122 | 1.4163 | 5 |
| 56 | 1.3658 | 1.4681 | 4 | 56 | 1.3886 | 1.4413 | 4 | 56 | 1.4126 | 1.4159 | 4 |
| 57 | 1.3662 | 1.4677 | 3 | 57 | 1.3890 | 1.4409 | 3 | 57 | 1.4130 | 1.4154 | 3 |
| 58 | 1.3666 | 1.4672 | 2 | 58 | 1.3894 | 1.4404 | 2 | 58 | 1.4134 | 1.4150 | 2 |
| 59 | 1.3670 | 1.4667 | 1 | 59 | 1.3898 | 1.4400 | 1 | 59 | 1.4138 | 1.4146 | 1 |
| 60 | 1.3673 | 1.4663 | 0 | 60 | 1.3902 | 1.4396 | 0 | 60 | 1.4142 | 1.4142 | 0 |
| ′ | Csc | Sec | ′ | ′ | Csc | Sec | | | Csc | Sec | ′ |

**132° (312°)   (227°) 47°   133° (313°)   (226°) 46°   134° (314°)   (225°) 45°**

# NATURAL TRIGONOMETRIC FUNCTIONS FOR ANGLES IN DEGREES AND DECIMALS

| Deg. | Sin | *Tan | *Cot | Cos | Deg. |
|------|------|------|------|------|------|
| **0.0** | .00000 | .00000 | ∞ | 1.0000 | **90.0** |
| .1 | .00175 | .00175 | 573.0 | 1.0000 | 89.9 |
| .2 | .00349 | .00349 | 286.5 | 1.0000 | .8 |
| .3 | .00524 | .00524 | 191.0 | 1.0000 | .7 |
| .4 | .00698 | .00698 | 143.24 | 1.0000 | .6 |
| .5 | .00873 | .00873 | 114.59 | 1.0000 | .5 |
| .6 | .01047 | .01047 | 95.49 | 0.9999 | .4 |
| .7 | .01222 | .01222 | 81.85 | .9999 | .3 |
| .8 | .01396 | .01396 | 71.62 | .9999 | .2 |
| .9 | .01571 | .01571 | 63.66 | .9999 | 89.1 |
| **1.0** | .01745 | .01746 | 57.29 | 0.9998 | **89.0** |
| .1 | .01920 | .01920 | 52.08 | .9998 | 88.9 |
| .2 | .02094 | .02095 | 47.74 | .9998 | .8 |
| .3 | .02269 | .02269 | 44.07 | .9997 | .7 |
| .4 | .02443 | .02444 | 40.92 | .9997 | .6 |
| .5 | .02618 | .02619 | 38.19 | .9997 | .5 |
| .6 | .02792 | .02793 | 35.80 | .9996 | .4 |
| .7 | .02967 | .02968 | 33.69 | .9996 | .3 |
| .8 | .03141 | .03143 | 31.82 | .9995 | .2 |
| .9 | .03316 | .03317 | 30.14 | .9995 | 88.1 |
| **2.0** | .03490 | .03492 | 28.64 | 0.9994 | **88.0** |
| .1 | .03664 | .03667 | 27.27 | .9993 | 87.9 |
| .2 | .03839 | .03842 | 26.03 | .9993 | .8 |
| .3 | .04013 | .04016 | 24.90 | .9992 | .7 |
| .4 | .04188 | .04191 | 23.86 | .9991 | .6 |
| .5 | .04362 | .04366 | 22.90 | .9990 | .5 |
| .6 | .04536 | .04541 | 22.02 | .9990 | .4 |
| .7 | .04711 | .04716 | 21.20 | .9989 | .3 |
| .8 | .04885 | .04891 | 20.45 | .9988 | .2 |
| .9 | .05059 | .05066 | 19.74 | .9987 | 87 1 |
| **3.0** | .05234 | .05241 | 19.081 | 0.9986 | **87.0** |
| .1 | .05408 | .05416 | 18.464 | .9985 | 86.9 |
| .2 | .05582 | .05591 | 17.886 | .9984 | .8 |
| .3 | .05756 | .05766 | 17.343 | .9983 | .7 |
| .4 | .05931 | .05941 | 16.832 | .9982 | .6 |
| .5 | .06105 | .06116 | 16.350 | .9981 | .5 |
| .6 | .06279 | .06291 | 15.895 | .9980 | .4 |
| .7 | .06453 | .06467 | 15.464 | .9979 | .3 |
| .8 | .06627 | .06642 | 15.056 | .9978 | .2 |
| .9 | .06802 | .06817 | 14.669 | .9977 | 86.1 |
| **4.0** | .06976 | .06993 | 14.301 | 0.9976 | **86.0** |
| .1 | .07150 | .07168 | 13.951 | .9974 | 85.9 |
| .2 | .07324 | .07344 | 13.617 | .9973 | .8 |
| .3 | .07498 | .07519 | 13.300 | .9972 | .7 |
| .4 | .07672 | .07695 | 12.996 | .9971 | .6 |
| .5 | .07846 | .07870 | 12.706 | .9969 | .5 |
| .6 | .08020 | .08046 | 12.429 | .9968 | .4 |
| .7 | .08194 | .08221 | 12.163 | .9966 | .3 |
| .8 | .08368 | .08397 | 11.909 | .9965 | .2 |
| .9 | .08542 | .08573 | 11.664 | .9963 | 85.1 |
| **5.0** | .08716 | .08749 | 11.430 | 0.9962 | **85.0** |
| .1 | .08889 | .08925 | 11.205 | .9960 | 84.9 |
| .2 | .09063 | .09101 | 10.988 | .9959 | .8 |
| .3 | .09237 | .09277 | 10.780 | .9957 | .7 |
| .4 | .09411 | .09453 | 10.579 | .9956 | .6 |
| .5 | .09585 | .09629 | 10.385 | .9954 | .5 |
| .6 | .09758 | .09805 | 10.199 | .9952 | .4 |
| .7 | .09932 | .09981 | 10.019 | .9951 | .3 |
| .8 | .10106 | .10158 | 9.845 | .9949 | .2 |
| .9 | .10279 | .10334 | 9.677 | .9947 | 84.1 |
| **6.0** | .10453 | .10510 | 9.514 | 0.9945 | **84.0** |

| Deg. | Sin | Tan | Cot | Cos | Deg. |
|------|------|------|------|------|------|
| **6.0** | .10453 | .10510 | 9.514 | 0.9945 | **84.0** |
| .1 | .10626 | .10687 | 9.357 | .9943 | 83.9 |
| .2 | .1080 | .10863 | 9.205 | .9942 | .8 |
| .3 | .10973 | .11040 | 9.058 | .9940 | .7 |
| .4 | .11147 | .11217 | 8.915 | .9938 | .6 |
| .5 | .11320 | .11394 | 8.777 | .9936 | .5 |
| .6 | .11494 | .11570 | 8.643 | .9934 | .4 |
| .7 | .11667 | .11747 | 8.513 | .9932 | .3 |
| .8 | .11840 | .11924 | 8.386 | .9930 | .2 |
| .9 | .12014 | .12101 | 8.264 | .9928 | 83.1 |
| **7.0** | .12187 | .12278 | 8.144 | 0.9925 | **83.0** |
| .1 | .12360 | .12456 | 8.028 | .9923 | 82.9 |
| .2 | .12533 | .12633 | 7.916 | .9921 | .8 |
| .3 | .12706 | .12810 | 7.806 | .9919 | .7 |
| .4 | .12880 | .12988 | 7.700 | .9917 | .6 |
| .5 | .13053 | .13165 | 7.596 | .9914 | .5 |
| .6 | .13226 | .13343 | 7.495 | .9912 | .4 |
| .7 | .13399 | .13521 | 7.396 | .9910 | .3 |
| .8 | .13572 | .13698 | 7.300 | .9907 | .2 |
| .9 | .13744 | .13876 | 7.207 | .9905 | 82.1 |
| **8.0** | .13917 | .14054 | 7.115 | 0.9903 | **82.0** |
| .1 | .14090 | .14232 | 7.026 | .9900 | 81.9 |
| .2 | .14263 | .14410 | 6.940 | .9898 | .8 |
| .3 | .14436 | .14588 | 6.855 | .9895 | .7 |
| .4 | .14608 | .14767 | 6.772 | .9893 | .6 |
| .5 | .14781 | .14945 | 6.691 | .9890 | .5 |
| .6 | .14954 | .15124 | 6.612 | .9888 | .4 |
| .7 | .15126 | .15302 | 6.535 | .9885 | .3 |
| .8 | .15299 | .15481 | 6.460 | .9882 | .2 |
| .9 | .15471 | .15660 | 6.386 | .9880 | 81.1 |
| **9.0** | .15643 | .15838 | 6.314 | 0.9877 | **81.0** |
| .1 | .15816 | .16017 | 6.243 | .9874 | 80.9 |
| .2 | .15988 | .16196 | 6.174 | .9871 | .8 |
| .3 | .16160 | .16376 | 6.107 | .9869 | .7 |
| .4 | .16333 | .16555 | 6.041 | .9866 | .6 |
| .5 | .16505 | .16734 | 5.976 | .9863 | .5 |
| .6 | .16677 | .16914 | 5.912 | .9860 | .4 |
| .7 | .16849 | .17093 | 5.850 | .9857 | .3 |
| .8 | .17021 | .17273 | 5.789 | 9854 | .2 |
| .9 | .17193 | .17453 | 5.730 | .9851 | 80.1 |
| **10.0** | .1736 | .1763 | 5.671 | 0.9848 | **80.0** |
| .1 | .1754 | .1781 | 5.614 | .9845 | 79.9 |
| .2 | .1771 | .1799 | 5.558 | .9842 | .8 |
| .3 | .1788 | .1817 | 5.503 | .9839 | .7 |
| .4 | .1805 | .1835 | 5.449 | .9836 | .6 |
| .5 | .1822 | .1853 | 5.396 | .9833 | .5 |
| .6 | .1840 | .1871 | 5.343 | .9829 | .4 |
| .7 | .1857 | .1890 | 5.292 | .9826 | .3 |
| .8 | .1874 | .1908 | 5.242 | .9823 | .2 |
| .9 | .1891 | .1926 | 5.193 | .9820 | 79.1 |
| **11.0** | .1908 | .1944 | 5.145 | 0.9816 | **79.0** |
| .1 | .1925 | .1962 | 5.097 | .9813 | 78.9 |
| .2 | .1942 | .1980 | 5.050 | .9810 | .8 |
| .3 | .1959 | .1998 | 5.005 | .9806 | .7 |
| .4 | .1977 | .2016 | 4.959 | .9803 | .6 |
| .5 | .1994 | .2035 | 4.915 | .9799 | .5 |
| .6 | .2011 | .2053 | 4.872 | .9796 | .4 |
| .7 | .2028 | .2071 | 4.829 | .9792 | .3 |
| .8 | .2045 | .2089 | 4.787 | .9789 | .2 |
| .9 | .2062 | .2107 | 4.745 | .9785 | 78.1 |
| **12.0** | .2079 | .2126 | 4.705 | 0.9781 | **78.0** |

| Deg. | Cos | *Cot | *Tan | Sin | Deg. |
|------|------|------|------|------|------|

| Deg. | Cos | Cot | Tan | Sin | Deg. |
|------|------|------|------|------|------|

* Interpolation in this section of the table is inaccurate.

| Deg. | Sin | Tan | Cot | Cos | Deg. | Deg. | Sin | Tan | Cot | Cos | Deg. |
|---|---|---|---|---|---|---|---|---|---|---|---|
| 12.0 | 0.2079 | 0.2126 | 4.705 | 0.9781 | 78.0 | 18.0 | 0.3090 | 0.3249 | 3.078 | 0.9511 | 72.0 |
| .1 | .2096 | .2144 | 4.635 | .9778 | 77.9 | .1 | .3107 | .3269 | 3.060 | .9505 | 71.9 |
| .2 | .2113 | .2162 | 4.625 | .9774 | .8 | .2 | .3123 | .3288 | 3.042 | .9500 | .8 |
| .3 | .2130 | .2180 | 4.586 | .9770 | .7 | .3 | .3140 | .3307 | 3.024 | .9494 | .7 |
| .4 | .2147 | .2199 | 4.548 | .9767 | .6 | .4 | .3156 | .3327 | 3.006 | .9489 | .6 |
| .5 | .2164 | .2217 | 4.511 | .9763 | .5 | .5 | .3173 | .3346 | 2.989 | .9483 | .5 |
| .6 | .2181 | .2235 | 4.474 | .9759 | .4 | .6 | .3190 | .3365 | 2.971 | .9478 | .4 |
| 7 | .2198 | .2254 | 4.437 | .9755 | .3 | .7 | .3206 | .3385 | 2.954 | .9472 | .3 |
| .8 | .2215 | .2272 | 4.402 | .9751 | .2 | .8 | .3223 | .3404 | 2.937 | .9466 | .2 |
| .9 | .2233 | .2290 | 4.366 | .9748 | 77.1 | .9 | .3239 | .3424 | 2.921 | .9461 | 71.1 |
| 13.0 | 0.2250 | 0.2309 | 4.331 | 0.9744 | 77.0 | 19.0 | 0.3256 | 0.3443 | 2.904 | 0.9455 | 71.0 |
| .1 | .2267 | .2327 | 4.297 | .9740 | 76.9 | .1 | .3272 | .3463 | 2.888 | .9449 | 70.9 |
| .2 | .2284 | .2345 | 4.264 | .9736 | .8 | .2 | .3289 | .3482 | 2.872 | .9444 | .8 |
| .3 | .2300 | .2364 | 4.230 | .9732 | .7 | .3 | .3305 | .3502 | 2.856 | .9438 | .7 |
| .4 | .2317 | .2382 | 4.198 | .9728 | .6 | .4 | .3322 | .3522 | 2.840 | .9432 | .6 |
| .5 | .2334 | .2401 | 4.165 | .9724 | .5 | .5 | .3338 | .3541 | 2.824 | .9426 | .5 |
| .6 | .2351 | .2419 | 4.134 | .9720 | .4 | .6 | .3355 | .3561 | 2.808 | .9421 | .4 |
| .7 | .2368 | .2438 | 4.102 | .9715 | .3 | .7 | .3371 | .3581 | 2.793 | .9415 | .3 |
| .8 | .2385 | .2456 | 4.071 | .9711 | .2 | .8 | .3387 | .3600 | 2.778 | .9409 | .2 |
| .9 | .2402 | .2475 | 4.041 | .9707 | 76.1 | .9 | .3404 | .3620 | 2.762 | .9403 | 70.1 |
| 14.0 | 0.2419 | 0.2493 | 4.011 | 0.9703 | 76.0 | 20.0 | 0.3420 | 0.3640 | 2.747 | 0.9397 | 70.0 |
| .1 | .2436 | .2512 | 3.981 | .9699 | 75.9 | .1 | .3437 | .3659 | 2.733 | .9391 | 69.9 |
| .2 | .2453 | .2530 | 3.952 | .9694 | .8 | .2 | .3453 | .3679 | 2.718 | .9385 | .8 |
| .3 | .2470 | .2549 | 3.923 | .9690 | .7 | .3 | .3469 | .3699 | 2.703 | .9379 | .7 |
| .4 | .2487 | .2568 | 3.895 | .9686 | .6 | .4 | .3486 | .3719 | 2.689 | .9373 | .6 |
| .5 | .2504 | .2586 | 3.867 | .9681 | .5 | .5 | .3502 | .3739 | 2.675 | .9367 | .5 |
| .6 | .2521 | .2605 | 3.839 | .9677 | .4 | .6 | .3518 | .3759 | 2.660 | .9361 | .4 |
| .7 | .2538 | .2623 | 3.812 | .9673 | .3 | .7 | .3535 | .3779 | 2.646 | .9354 | .3 |
| .8 | .2554 | .2642 | 3.785 | .9668 | .2 | .8 | .3551 | .3799 | 2.633 | .9348 | .2 |
| .9 | .2571 | .2661 | 3.758 | .9664 | 75.1 | .9 | .3567 | .3819 | 2.619 | .9342 | 69.1 |
| 15.0 | 0.2588 | 0.2679 | 3.732 | 0.9659 | 75.0 | 21.0 | 0.3584 | 0.3839 | 2.605 | 0.9336 | 69.0 |
| .1 | .2605 | .2698 | 3.706 | .9655 | 74.9 | .1 | .3600 | .3859 | 2.592 | .9330 | 68.9 |
| .2 | .2622 | .2717 | 3.681 | .9650 | .8 | .2 | .3616 | .3879 | 2.578 | .9323 | .8 |
| .3 | .2639 | .2736 | 3.655 | .9646 | .7 | .3 | .3633 | .3899 | 2.565 | .9317 | .7 |
| .4 | .2656 | .2754 | 3.630 | .9641 | .6 | .4 | .3649 | .3919 | 2.552 | .9311 | .6 |
| .5 | .2672 | .2773 | 3.606 | .9636 | .5 | .5 | .3665 | .3939 | 2.539 | .9304 | .5 |
| .6 | .2689 | .2792 | 3.582 | .9632 | .4 | .6 | .3681 | .3959 | 2.526 | .9298 | .4 |
| .7 | .2706 | .2811 | 3.558 | .9627 | .3 | .7 | .3697 | .3979 | 2.513 | .9291 | .3 |
| .8 | .2723 | .2830 | 3.534 | .9622 | .2 | .8 | .3714 | .4000 | 2.500 | .9285 | .2 |
| .9 | .2740 | .2849 | 3.511 | .9617 | 74.1 | .9 | .3730 | .4020 | 2.488 | .9278 | 68.1 |
| 16.0 | 0.2756 | 0.2867 | 3.487 | 0.9613 | 74.0 | 22.0 | 0.3746 | 0.4040 | 2.475 | 0.9272 | 68.0 |
| .1 | .2773 | .2886 | 3.465 | .9608 | 73.9 | .1 | .3762 | .4061 | 2.463 | .9265 | 67.9 |
| .2 | .2790 | .2905 | 3.442 | .9603 | .8 | .2 | .3778 | .4081 | 2.450 | .9259 | .8 |
| .3 | .2807 | .2924 | 3.420 | .9598 | .7 | .3 | .3795 | .4101 | 2.438 | .9252 | .7 |
| .4 | .2823 | .2943 | 3.398 | .9593 | .6 | .4 | .3811 | .4122 | 2.426 | .9245 | .6 |
| .5 | .2840 | .2962 | 3.376 | .9588 | .5 | .5 | .3827 | .4142 | 2.414 | .9239 | .5 |
| .6 | .2857 | .2981 | 3.354 | .9583 | .4 | .6 | .3843 | .4163 | 2.402 | .9232 | .4 |
| .7 | .2874 | .3000 | 3.333 | .9578 | .3 | .7 | .3859 | .4183 | 2.391 | .9225 | .3 |
| .8 | .2890 | .3019 | 3.312 | .9573 | .2 | .8 | .3875 | .4204 | 2.379 | .9219 | .2 |
| .9 | .2907 | .3038 | 3.291 | .9568 | 73.1 | .9 | .3891 | .4224 | 2.367 | .9212 | 67.1 |
| 17.0 | 0.2924 | 0.3057 | 3.271 | 0.9563 | 73.0 | 23.0 | 0.3907 | 0.4245 | 2.356 | 0.9205 | 67.0 |
| .1 | .2940 | .3076 | 3.251 | .9558 | 72.9 | .1 | .3923 | .4265 | 2.344 | .9198 | 66.9 |
| .2 | .2957 | .3096 | 3.230 | .9553 | .8 | .2 | .3939 | .4286 | 2.333 | .9191 | .8 |
| .3 | .2974 | .3115 | 3.211 | .9548 | .7 | .3 | .3955 | .4307 | 2.322 | .9184 | .7 |
| .4 | .2990 | .3134 | 3.191 | .9542 | .6 | .4 | .3971 | .4327 | 2.311 | .9178 | .6 |
| .5 | .3007 | .3153 | 3.172 | .9537 | .5 | .5 | .3987 | .4348 | 2.300 | .9171 | .5 |
| .6 | .3024 | .3172 | 3.152 | .9532 | .4 | .6 | .4003 | .4369 | 2.289 | .9164 | .4 |
| .7 | .3040 | .3191 | 3.133 | .9527 | .3 | .7 | .4019 | .4390 | 2.278 | .9157 | .3 |
| .8 | .3057 | .3211 | 3.115 | .9521 | .2 | .8 | .4035 | .4411 | 2.267 | .9150 | .2 |
| .9 | .3074 | .3230 | 3.096 | .9516 | 72.1 | .9 | .4051 | .4431 | 2.257 | .9143 | 66.1 |
| 18.0 | 0.3090 | 0.3249 | 3.078 | 0.9511 | 72.0 | 24.0 | 0.4067 | 0.4452 | 2.246 | 0.9135 | 66.0 |
| Deg. | Cos | Cot | Tan | Sin | Deg. | Deg. | Cos | Cot | Tan | Sin | Deg. |

## NATURAL FUNCTIONS FOR DEGREES AND DECIMALS (Continued)

| Deg. | Sin | Tan | Cot | Cos | Deg. |
|---|---|---|---|---|---|
| **24.0** | 0.4067 | 0.4452 | 2.246 | 0.9135 | **66.0** |
| .1 | .4083 | .4473 | 2.236 | .9128 | 65.9 |
| .2 | .4099 | .4494 | 2.225 | .9121 | .8 |
| .3 | .4115 | .4515 | 2.215 | .9114 | .7 |
| .4 | .4131 | .4536 | 2.204 | .9107 | .6 |
| .5 | .4147 | .4557 | 2.194 | .9100 | .5 |
| .6 | .4163 | .4578 | 2.184 | .9092 | .4 |
| .7 | .4179 | .4599 | 2.174 | .9085 | .3 |
| .8 | .4195 | .4621 | 2.164 | 9078 | .2 |
| .9 | .4210 | .4642 | 2.154 | .9070 | 65.1 |
| **25.0** | 0.4226 | 0.4663 | 2.145 | 0.9063 | **65.0** |
| .1 | .4242 | .4684 | 2.135 | .9056 | 64.9 |
| .2 | .4258 | .4706 | 2.125 | .9048 | .8 |
| .3 | .4274 | .4727 | 2.116 | .9041 | .7 |
| .4 | .4289 | .4748 | 2.106 | .9033 | .6 |
| .5 | .4305 | .4770 | 2.097 | .9026 | .5 |
| .6 | .4321 | .4791 | 2.087 | .9018 | .4 |
| .7 | .4337 | .4813 | 2.078 | .9011 | .3 |
| .8 | .4352 | .4834 | 2.069 | .9003 | .2 |
| .9 | .4368 | .4856 | 2.059 | .8996 | 64.1 |
| **26.0** | 0.4384 | 0.4877 | 2.050 | 0.8988 | **64.0** |
| .1 | .4399 | .4899 | 2.041 | .8980 | 63.9 |
| .2 | .4415 | .4921 | 2.032 | .8973 | .8 |
| .3 | .4431 | .4942 | 2.023 | .8965 | .7 |
| .4 | .4446 | .4964 | 2.014 | .8957 | .6 |
| .5 | .4462 | .4986 | 2.006 | .8949 | .5 |
| .6 | .4478 | .5008 | 1.997 | .8942 | .4 |
| .7 | .4493 | .5029 | 1.988 | .8934 | .3 |
| .8 | .4509 | .5051 | 1.980 | .8926 | .2 |
| .9 | .4524 | .5073 | 1.971 | .8918 | 63.1 |
| **27.0** | 0.4540 | 0.5095 | 1.963 | 0.8910 | **63.0** |
| .1 | .4555 | .5117 | 1.954 | .8902 | 62.9 |
| .2 | .4571 | .5139 | 1.946 | .8894 | .8 |
| .3 | .4586 | .5161 | 1.937 | .8886 | .7 |
| .4 | .4602 | .5184 | 1.929 | .8878 | .6 |
| .5 | .4617 | .5206 | 1.921 | .8870 | .5 |
| .6 | .4633 | .5228 | 1.913 | .8862 | .4 |
| .7 | .4648 | .5250 | 1.905 | .8854 | .3 |
| .8 | .4664 | .5272 | 1.897 | .8846 | .2 |
| .9 | .4679 | .5295 | 1.889 | .8838 | 62.1 |
| **28.0** | 0.4695 | 0.5317 | 1.881 | 0.8829 | **62.0** |
| .1 | .4710 | .5340 | 1.873 | .8821 | 61.9 |
| .2 | .4726 | .5362 | 1.865 | .8813 | .8 |
| .3 | .4741 | .5384 | 1.857 | .8805 | .7 |
| .4 | .4756 | .5407 | 1.849 | .8796 | .6 |
| .5 | .4772 | .5430 | 1.842 | .8788 | .5 |
| .6 | .4787 | .5452 | 1.834 | .8780 | .4 |
| .7 | .4802 | .5475 | 1.827 | .8771 | .3 |
| .8 | .4818 | .5498 | 1.819 | 8763 | .2 |
| .9 | .4833 | .5520 | 1.811 | .8755 | 61.1 |
| **29.0** | 0.4848 | 0.5543 | 1.804 | 0.8746 | **61.0** |
| .1 | .4863 | .5566 | 1.797 | .8738 | 60.9 |
| .2 | .4879 | .5589 | 1.789 | .8729 | .8 |
| .3 | .4894 | .5612 | 1.782 | .8721 | .7 |
| .4 | .4909 | .5635 | 1.775 | .8712 | .6 |
| .5 | .4924 | .5658 | 1.767 | .8704 | .5 |
| .6 | .4939 | .5681 | 1.760 | .8695 | .4 |
| .7 | .4955 | .5704 | 1.753 | .8686 | .3 |
| .8 | .4970 | .5727 | 1.746 | .8678 | .2 |
| .9 | .4985 | .5750 | 1.739 | .8669 | 60.1 |
| **30.0** | 0.5000 | 0.5774 | 1.732 | 0.8660 | **60.0** |
| **Deg.** | Cos | Cot | Tan | Sin | **Deg.** |

| Deg. | Sin | Tan | Cot | Cos | Deg. |
|---|---|---|---|---|---|
| **30.0** | 0.5000 | 0.5774 | 1.7321 | 0.8660 | **60.0** |
| .1 | .5015 | .5797 | 1.7251 | .8652 | 59.9 |
| .2 | .5030 | .5820 | 1.7182 | .8643 | .8 |
| .3 | .5045 | .5844 | 1.7113 | .8634 | .7 |
| .4 | .5060 | .5867 | 1.7045 | .8625 | .6 |
| .5 | .5075 | .5890 | 1.6977 | .8616 | .5 |
| .6 | .5090 | .5914 | 1.6909 | .8607 | .4 |
| .7 | .5105 | .5938 | 1.6842 | .8599 | .3 |
| .8 | .5120 | .5961 | 1.6775 | .8590 | .2 |
| .9 | .5135 | .5985 | 1.6709 | .8581 | 59.1 |
| **31.0** | 0.5150 | 0.6009 | 1.6643 | 0.8572 | **59.0** |
| .1 | .5165 | .6032 | 1.6577 | .8563 | 58.9 |
| .2 | .5180 | .6056 | 1.6512 | .8554 | .8 |
| .3 | .5195 | .6080 | 1.6447 | .8545 | .7 |
| .4 | .5210 | .6104 | 1.6383 | .8536 | .6 |
| .5 | .5225 | .6128 | 1.6319 | .8526 | .5 |
| .6 | .5240 | .6152 | 1.6255 | .8517 | .4 |
| .7 | .5255 | .6176 | 1.6191 | .8508 | .3 |
| .8 | .5270 | .6200 | 1.6128 | .8499 | .2 |
| .9 | .5284 | .6224 | 1.6066 | .8490 | 58.1 |
| **32.0** | 0.5299 | 0.6249 | 1.6003 | 0.8480 | **58.0** |
| .1 | .5314 | .6273 | 1.5941 | .8471 | 57.9 |
| .2 | .5329 | .6297 | 1.5880 | .8462 | .8 |
| .3 | .5344 | .6322 | 1.5818 | .8453 | .7 |
| .4 | .5358 | .6346 | 1.5757 | .8443 | .6 |
| .5 | .5373 | .6371 | 1.5697 | .8434 | .5 |
| .6 | .5388 | .6395 | 1.5637 | .8425 | .4 |
| .7 | .5402 | .6420 | 1.5577 | .8415 | .3 |
| .8 | .5417 | .6445 | 1.5517 | .8406 | .2 |
| .9 | .5432 | .6469 | 1.5458 | .8396 | 57.1 |
| **33.0** | 0.5446 | 0.6494 | 1.5399 | 0.8387 | **57.0** |
| .1 | .5461 | .6519 | 1.5340 | .8377 | 56.9 |
| .2 | .5476 | .6544 | 1.5282 | .8368 | .8 |
| .3 | .5490 | .6569 | 1.5224 | .8358 | .7 |
| .4 | .5505 | .6594 | 1.5166 | .8348 | .6 |
| .5 | .5519 | .6619 | 1.5108 | .8339 | .5 |
| .6 | .5534 | .6644 | 1.5051 | .8329 | .4 |
| .7 | .5548 | .6669 | 1.4994 | .8320 | .3 |
| .8 | .5563 | .6694 | 1.4938 | .8310 | .2 |
| .9 | .5577 | .6720 | 1.4882 | .8300 | 56.1 |
| **34.0** | 0.5592 | 0.6745 | 1.4826 | 0.8290 | **56.0** |
| .1 | .5606 | .6771 | 1.4770 | .8281 | 55.9 |
| .2 | .5621 | .6796 | 1.4715 | .8271 | .8 |
| .3 | .5635 | .6822 | 1.4659 | .8261 | .7 |
| .4 | .5650 | .6847 | 1.4605 | .8251 | .6 |
| .5 | .5664 | .6873 | 1.4550 | .8241 | .5 |
| .6 | .5678 | .6899 | 1.4496 | .8231 | .4 |
| .7 | .5693 | .6924 | 1.4442 | .8221 | .3 |
| .8 | .5707 | .6950 | 1.4388 | .8211 | .2 |
| .9 | .5721 | .6976 | 1.4335 | .8202 | 55.1 |
| **35.0** | 0.5736 | 0.7002 | 1.4281 | 0.8192 | **55.0** |
| .1 | .5750 | .7028 | 1.4229 | .8181 | 54.9 |
| .2 | .5764 | .7054 | 1.4176 | .8171 | .8 |
| .3 | .5779 | .7080 | 1.4124 | .8161 | .7 |
| .4 | .5793 | .7107 | 1.4071 | .8151 | .6 |
| .5 | .5807 | .7133 | 1.4019 | .8141 | .5 |
| .6 | .5821 | .7159 | 1.3968 | .8131 | .4 |
| .7 | .5835 | .7186 | 1.3916 | .8121 | .3 |
| .8 | .5850 | .7212 | 1.3865 | .8111 | .2 |
| .9 | .5864 | .7239 | 1.3814 | .8100 | 54.1 |
| **36.0** | 0.5878 | 0.7265 | 1.3764 | 0.8090 | **54.0** |
| **Deg.** | Cos | Cot | Tan | Sin | **Deg.** |

| Deg. | Sin | Tan | Cot | Cos | Deg. | Deg. | Sin | Tan | Cot | Cos | Deg. |
|---|---|---|---|---|---|---|---|---|---|---|---|
| **36.0** | 0.5878 | 0.7265 | 1.3764 | 0.8090 | **54.0** | **40.5** | 0.6494 | 0.8541 | 1.1708 | 0.7604 | **49.5** |
| .1 | .5892 | .7292 | 1.3713 | .8080 | 53.9 | .6 | .6508 | .8571 | 1 1667 | .7593 | .4 |
| .2 | .5906 | .7319 | 1.3663 | .8070 | .8 | .7 | .6521 | .8601 | 1.1626 | .7581 | .3 |
| .3 | .5920 | .7346 | 1.3613 | .8059 | .7 | .8 | .6534 | .8632 | 1.1585 | .7570 | .2 |
| .4 | .5934 | .7373 | 1.3564 | .8049 | .6 | .9 | .6547 | .8662 | 1.1544 | .7559 | 49.1 |
| .5 | .5948 | .7400 | 1.3514 | .8039 | .5 | **41.0** | 0.6561 | 0.8693 | 1.1504 | 0.7547 | **49.0** |
| .6 | .5962 | .7427 | 1.3465 | .8028 | .4 | .1 | .6574 | .8724 | 1.1463 | .7536 | 48.9 |
| .7 | .5976 | .7454 | 1.3416 | .8018 | .3 | .2 | .6587 | .8754 | 1.1423 | .7524 | 8 |
| .8 | .5990 | .7481 | 1.3367 | .8007 | .2 | .3 | .6600 | .8785 | 1.1383 | .7513 | .7 |
| .9 | .6004 | .7508 | 1.3319 | .7997 | 53.1 | .4 | .6613 | .8816 | 1.1343 | .7501 | .6 |
| **37.0** | 0.6018 | 0.7536 | 1.3270 | 0.7986 | **53.0** | .5 | .6626 | .8847 | 1.1303 | .7490 | .5 |
| .1 | .6032 | .7563 | 1.3222 | .7976 | 52.9 | .6 | .6639 | .8878 | 1.1263 | .7478 | .4 |
| .2 | .6046 | .7590 | 1.3175 | .7965 | .8 | .7 | .6652 | .8910 | 1.1224 | .7466 | .3 |
| .3 | .6060 | .7618 | 1.3127 | .7955 | .7 | .8 | .6665 | .8941 | 1.1184 | .7455 | .2 |
| .4 | .6074 | .7646 | 1.3079 | .7944 | .6 | .9 | .6678 | .8972 | 1.1145 | .7443 | 48.1 |
| .5 | .6088 | .7673 | 1.3032 | .7934 | .5 | **42.0** | 0.6691 | 0.9004 | 1 1106 | 0.7431 | **48.0** |
| .6 | .6101 | .7701 | 1.2985 | .7923 | .4 | .1 | .6704 | .9036 | 1.1067 | .7420 | 47 9 |
| .7 | .6115 | .7729 | 1.2938 | .7912 | .3 | .2 | .6717 | .9067 | 1.1028 | .7408 | 8 |
| .8 | .6129 | .7757 | 1.2892 | .7902 | .2 | .3 | .6730 | .9099 | 1.0990 | .7396 | .7 |
| .9 | .6143 | .7785 | 1.2846 | .7891 | 52.1 | .4 | .6743 | .9131 | 1.0951 | .7385 | .6 |
| **38.0** | 0.6157 | 0.7813 | 1.2799 | 0.7880 | **52.0** | .5 | .6756 | .9163 | 1.0913 | .7373 | .5 |
| .1 | .6170 | .7841 | 1.2753 | .7869 | 51.9 | .6 | .6769 | .9195 | 1.0875 | .7361 | .4 |
| .2 | .6184 | .7869 | 1.2708 | .7859 | .8 | .7 | .6782 | .9228 | 1.0837 | .7349 | .3 |
| .3 | .6198 | .7898 | 1.2662 | .7848 | .7 | .8 | .6794 | .9260 | 1.0799 | .7337 | .2 |
| .4 | .6211 | .7926 | 1.2617 | .7837 | .6 | .9 | .6807 | .9293 | 1.0761 | .7325 | 47.1 |
| .5 | .6225 | .7954 | 1.2572 | .7826 | .5 | **43.0** | 0.6820 | 0.9325 | 1.0724 | 0.7314 | **47.0** |
| .6 | .6239 | .7983 | 1.2527 | .7815 | .4 | .1 | .6833 | .9358 | 1.0686 | .7302 | 46.9 |
| .7 | .6252 | .8012 | 1.2482 | .7804 | .3 | .2 | .6845 | .9391 | 1.0649 | .7290 | .8 |
| .8 | .6266 | .8040 | 1.2437 | .7793 | .2 | .3 | .6858 | .9424 | 1.0612 | .7278 | .7 |
| .9 | .6280 | .8069 | 1.2393 | .7782 | 51.1 | .4 | .6871 | .9457 | 1.0575 | .7266 | .6 |
| **39.0** | 0.6293 | 0.8098 | 1.2349 | 0.7771 | **51.0** | .5 | .6884 | .9490 | 1.0538 | .7254 | .5 |
| .1 | .6307 | .8127 | 1.2305 | .7760 | 50.9 | .6 | .6896 | .9523 | 1.0501 | .7242 | .4 |
| .2 | .6320 | .8156 | 1.2261 | .7749 | .8 | .7 | .6909 | .9556 | 1.0464 | .7230 | .3 |
| .3 | .6334 | .8185 | 1.2218 | .7738 | .7 | 8 | .6921 | .9590 | 1.0428 | .7218 | .2 |
| .4 | .6347 | .8214 | 1.2174 | .7727 | .6 | .9 | .6934 | .9623 | 1.0392 | .7206 | 46.1 |
| .5 | .6361 | .8243 | 1.2131 | .7716 | 5 | **44.0** | 0.6947 | 0.9657 | 1.0355 | 0.7193 | **46.0** |
| .6 | .6374 | .8273 | 1.2088 | .7705 | .4 | .1 | .6959 | .9691 | 1.0319 | .7181 | 45.9 |
| .7 | .6388 | .8302 | 1.2045 | .7694 | .3 | .2 | .6972 | .9725 | 1.0283 | .7169 | .8 |
| .8 | .6401 | .8332 | 1.2002 | .7683 | .2 | .3 | .6984 | .9759 | 1.0247 | .7157 | .7 |
| .9 | .6414 | .8361 | 1.1960 | .7672 | 50.1 | .4 | .6997 | .9793 | 1.0212 | .7145 | .6 |
| **40.0** | 0.6428 | 0.8391 | 1.1918 | 0.7660 | **50.0** | .5 | .7009 | .9827 | 1.0176 | .7133 | .5 |
| .1 | .6441 | .8421 | 1.1875 | .7649 | 49.9 | .6 | .7022 | .9861 | 1.0141 | .7120 | .4 |
| .2 | .6455 | .8451 | 1.1833 | .7638 | .8 | .7 | .7034 | .9896 | 1.0105 | .7108 | .3 |
| .3 | .6468 | .8481 | 1.1792 | .7627 | .7 | .8 | .7046 | .9930 | 1.0070 | .7096 | .2 |
| .4 | .6481 | .8511 | 1.1750 | .7615 | .6 | .9 | .7059 | .9965 | 1.0035 | .7083 | 45.1 |
| **40.5** | 0.6494 | 0.8541 | 1.1708 | 0.7604 | **49.5** | **45.0** | 0.7071 | 1.0000 | 1.0000 | 0.7071 | **45.0** |
| **Deg.** | Cos | Cot | Tan | Sin | **Deg.** | **Deg.** | Cos | Cot | Tan | Sin | **Deg.** |

# LOGARITHMS OF TRIGONOMETRIC FUNCTIONS FOR ANGLES IN DEGREES AND DECIMALS

| Deg. | L. Sin | *L. Tan | *L. Cot | L. Cos | Deg. |
|---|---|---|---|---|---|
| **0.0** | − ∞ | − ∞ | ∞ | 0.0000 | **90.0** |
| .1 | 7.2419 | 7.2419 | 2.7581 | 0.0000 | 89.9 |
| .2 | 7.5429 | 7.5429 | 2.4571 | 0.0000 | .8 |
| .3 | 7.7190 | 7.7190 | 2.2810 | 0.0000 | .7 |
| .4 | 7.8439 | 7.8439 | 2.1561 | 0.0000 | .6 |
| .5 | 7.9408 | 7.9409 | 2 0591 | 0.0000 | .5 |
| .6 | 8.0200 | 8.0200 | 1.9800 | 0.0000 | .4 |
| .7 | 8.0870 | 8.0870 | 1.9130 | 0.0000 | .3 |
| .8 | 8.1450 | 8 1450 | 1.8550 | 0.0000 | .2 |
| .9 | 8.1961 | 8.1962 | 1.8038 | 9.9999 | 89.1 |
| **1.0** | 8.2419 | 8.2419 | 1.7581 | 9.9999 | **89.0** |
| .1 | 8.2832 | 8.2833 | 1.7167 | 9.9999 | 88.9 |
| .2 | 8.3210 | 8.3211 | 1.6789 | 9.9999 | .8 |
| .3 | 8.3558 | 8.3559 | 1.6441 | 9.9999 | .7 |
| .4 | 8.3880 | 8.3881 | 1.6119 | 9.9999 | .6 |
| .5 | 8.4179 | 8.4181 | 1.5819 | 9.9999 | .5 |
| .6 | 8.4459 | 8.4461 | 1.5539 | 9.9998 | .4 |
| .7 | 8.4723 | 8.4725 | 1.5275 | 9.9998 | .3 |
| .8 | 8.4971 | 8.4973 | 1.5027 | 9.9998 | .2 |
| .9 | 8.5206 | 8.5208 | 1.4792 | 9.9998 | 88.1 |
| **2.0** | 8.5428 | 8.5431 | 1.4569 | 9.9997 | **88.0** |
| 1 | 8.5640 | 8.5643 | 1.4357 | 9.9997 | 87.9 |
| .2 | 8.5842 | 8.5845 | 1.4155 | 9.9997 | .8 |
| .3 | 8.6035 | 8.6038 | 1.3962 | 9.9996 | .7 |
| 4 | 8.6220 | 8.6223 | 1.3777 | 9.9996 | .6 |
| .5 | 8.6397 | 8.6401 | 1.3599 | 9.9996 | .5 |
| .6 | 8.6567 | 8 6571 | 1.3429 | 9.9996 | .4 |
| .7 | 8.6731 | 8.6736 | 1.3264 | 9.9995 | .3 |
| .8 | 8 6889 | 8.6894 | 1.3106 | 9.9995 | .2 |
| 9 | 8.7041 | 8.7046 | 1.2954 | 9.9994 | 87.1 |
| **3.0** | 8.7188 | 8.7194 | 1.2806 | 9.9994 | **87.0** |
| .1 | 8.7330 | 8.7337 | 1.2663 | 9.9994 | 86.9 |
| 2 | 8.7468 | 8.7475 | 1.2525 | 9.9993 | .8 |
| .3 | 8.7602 | 8.7609 | 1.2391 | 9.9993 | .7 |
| .4 | 8.7731 | 8.7739 | 1.2261 | 9.9992 | .6 |
| .5 | 8.7857 | 8.7865 | 1.2135 | 9.9992 | .5 |
| .6 | 8.7979 | 8 7988 | 1.2012 | 9.9991 | .4 |
| .7 | 8.8098 | 8.8107 | 1.1893 | 9.9991 | .3 |
| .8 | 8.8213 | 8.8223 | 1.1777 | 9.9990 | .2 |
| .9 | 8.8326 | 8.8336 | 1.1664 | 9.9990 | 86.1 |
| **4.0** | 8.8446 | 8.8446 | 1.1554 | 9.9989 | **86.0** |
| .1 | 8.8543 | 8.8554 | 1.1446 | 9.9989 | 85.9 |
| .2 | 8.8647 | 8.8659 | 1.1341 | 9.9988 | .8 |
| .3 | 8.8749 | 8.8762 | 1.1238 | 9.9988 | .7 |
| .4 | 8.8849 | 8.8862 | 1.1138 | 9.9987 | .6 |
| .5 | 8.8946 | 8.8960 | 1.1040 | 9.9987 | .5 |
| .6 | 8.9042 | 8.9056 | 1.0944 | 9.9986 | .4 |
| .7 | 8.9135 | 8.9150 | 1.0850 | 9.9985 | .3 |
| .8 | 8 9226 | 8.9241 | 1.0759 | 9.9985 | .2 |
| .9 | 8.9315 | 8.9331 | 1.0669 | 9.9984 | 85.1 |
| **5.0** | 8.9403 | 8.9420 | 1.0580 | 9.9983 | **85.0** |
| .1 | 8.9489 | 8.9506 | 1.0494 | 9.9983 | 84.9 |
| .2 | 8.9573 | 8.9591 | 1.0409 | 9.9982 | .8 |
| .3 | 8.9655 | 8.9674 | 1.0326 | 9.9981 | .7 |
| .4 | 8.9736 | 8.9756 | 1.0244 | 9.9981 | .6 |
| .5 | 8.9816 | 8.9836 | 1.0164 | 9.9980 | .5 |
| 6 | 8.9894 | 8.9915 | 1.0085 | 9.9979 | .4 |
| .7 | 8.9970 | 8.9992 | 1.0008 | 9.9978 | .3 |
| .8 | 9.0046 | 9.0068 | 0.9932 | 9.9978 | .2 |
| .9 | 9.0120 | 9.0143 | 0.9857 | 9.9977 | 84.1 |
| **6.0** | 9.0192 | 9.0216 | 0.9784 | 9.9976 | **84.0** |

| Deg. | L. Sin | L. Tan | L. Cot | L. Cos | Deg. |
|---|---|---|---|---|---|
| **6.0** | 9.0192 | 9.0216 | 0 9784 | 9.9976 | **84.0** |
| .1 | 9 0264 | 9.0289 | 0 9711 | 9.9975 | 83.9 |
| .2 | 9.0334 | 9.0360 | 0 9640 | 9.9975 | .8 |
| .3 | 9.0403 | 9.0430 | 0 9570 | 9.9974 | .7 |
| .4 | 9.0472 | 9.0499 | 0.9501 | 9.9973 | .6 |
| .5 | 9.0539 | 9.0567 | 0.9433 | 9.9972 | .5 |
| .6 | 9.0605 | 9.0633 | 0.9367 | 9.9971 | .4 |
| .7 | 9.0670 | 9.0699 | 0.9301 | 9.9970 | .3 |
| .8 | 9.0734 | 9.0764 | 0.9236 | 9.9969 | .2 |
| .9 | 9.0797 | 9.0828 | 0.9172 | 9.9968 | 83.1 |
| **7.0** | 9.0859 | 9.0891 | 0.9109 | 9.9968 | **83.0** |
| .1 | 9.0920 | 9.0954 | 0.9046 | 9.9967 | 82.9 |
| .2 | 9.0981 | 9.1015 | 0.8985 | 9.9966 | .8 |
| .3 | 9 1040 | 9.1076 | 0.8924 | 9.9965 | .7 |
| .4 | 9.1099 | 9.1135 | 0.8865 | 9.9964 | .6 |
| .5 | 9.1157 | 9.1194 | 0.8806 | 9.9963 | .5 |
| .6 | 9.1214 | 9.1252 | 0.8748 | 9.9962 | .4 |
| .7 | 9.1271 | 9.1310 | 0.8690 | 9.9961 | .3 |
| .8 | 9.1326 | 9.1367 | 0.8633 | 9.9960 | .2 |
| .9 | 9.1381 | 9.1423 | 0.8577 | 9.9959 | 82.1 |
| **8.0** | 9.1436 | 9.1478 | 0.8522 | 9.9958 | **82.0** |
| .1 | 9.1489 | 9.1533 | 0.8467 | 9.9956 | 81.9 |
| .2 | 9.1542 | 9.1587 | 0.8413 | 9.9955 | .8 |
| .3 | 9.1594 | 9.1640 | 0.8360 | 9.9954 | .7 |
| .4 | 9.1646 | 9.1693 | 0.8307 | 9.9953 | .6 |
| .5 | 9.1697 | 9.1745 | 0.8255 | 9.9952 | .5 |
| .6 | 9.1747 | 9.1797 | 0.8203 | 9.9951 | .4 |
| .7 | 9.1797 | 9.1848 | 0.8152 | 9.9950 | .3 |
| .8 | 9.1847 | 9.1898 | 0.8102 | 9.9949 | .2 |
| .9 | 9.1895 | 9.1948 | 0.8052 | 9.9947 | 81.1 |
| **9.0** | 9.1943 | 9.1997 | 0.8003 | 9.9946 | **81.0** |
| .1 | 9.1991 | 9.2046 | 0.7954 | 9.9945 | 80.9 |
| .2 | 9.2038 | 9.2094 | 0.7906 | 9.9944 | .8 |
| .3 | 9.2085 | 9.2142 | 0.7858 | 9.9943 | .7 |
| .4 | 9.2131 | 9.2189 | 0.7811 | 9.9941 | .6 |
| .5 | 9.2176 | 9.2236 | 0.7764 | 9.9940 | .5 |
| .6 | 9.2221 | 9.2282 | 0.7718 | 9.9939 | .4 |
| .7 | 9.2266 | 9.2328 | 0.7672 | 9.9937 | .3 |
| .8 | 9.2310 | 9.2374 | 0.7626 | 9.9936 | .2 |
| .9 | 9.2353 | 9.2419 | 0.7581 | 9.9935 | 80.1 |
| **10.0** | 9.2397 | 9.2463 | 0.7537 | 9.9934 | **80.0** |
| .1 | 9.2439 | 9.2507 | 0.7493 | 9.9932 | 79.9 |
| .2 | 9.2482 | 9.2551 | 0.7449 | 9.9931 | .8 |
| .3 | 9.2524 | 9.2594 | 0.7406 | 9.9929 | .7 |
| .4 | 9.2565 | 9.2637 | 0.7363 | 9.9928 | .6 |
| .5 | 9.2606 | 9.2680 | 0.7320 | 9.9927 | .5 |
| .6 | 9.2647 | 9.2722 | 0.7278 | 9.9925 | .4 |
| .7 | 9.2687 | 9.2764 | 0.7236 | 9.9924 | .3 |
| .8 | 9.2727 | 9.2805 | 0.7195 | 9.9922 | .2 |
| .9 | 9.2767 | 9.2846 | 0.7154 | 9.9921 | 79.1 |
| **11.0** | 9.2806 | 9.2887 | 0.7113 | 9.9919 | **79.0** |
| .1 | 9.2845 | 9.2927 | 0.7073 | 9.9918 | 78.9 |
| .2 | 9.2883 | 9.2967 | 0.7033 | 9.9916 | .8 |
| .3 | 9.2921 | 9.3006 | 0.6994 | 9.9915 | .7 |
| .4 | 9.2959 | 9.3046 | 0.6954 | 9.9913 | .6 |
| .5 | 9.2997 | 9.3085 | 0.6915 | 9.9912 | .5 |
| .6 | 9.3034 | 9.3123 | 0.6877 | 9.9910 | .4 |
| .7 | 9.3070 | 9.3162 | 0.6838 | 9.9909 | .3 |
| .8 | 9.3107 | 9.3200 | 0.6800 | 9.9907 | .2 |
| .9 | 9.3143 | 9.3237 | 0.6763 | 9.9906 | 78.1 |
| **12.0** | 9.3179 | 9.3275 | 0.6725 | 9.9904 | **78.0** |

| Deg. | L. Cos | *L. Cot | *L. Tan | L. Sin | Deg. |
|---|---|---|---|---|---|

* Interpolation in this section of the table is inaccurate.

| Deg | L. Sin | L. Tan | L. Cot | L. Cos | Deg |
|---|---|---|---|---|---|
| **12.0** | 9.3179 | 9.3275 | 0.6725 | 9.9904 | **78.0** |
| .1 | 9 3214 | 9.3312 | 0.6688 | 9 9902 | 77 9 |
| .2 | 9.3250 | 9.3349 | 0.6651 | 9.9901 | .8 |
| .3 | 9 3284 | 9.3385 | 0.6615 | 9 9899 | .7 |
| .4 | 9.3319 | 9.3422 | 0.6578 | 9.9897 | .6 |
| .5 | 9 3353 | 9.3458 | 0.6542 | 9.9896 | .5 |
| .6 | 9 3387 | 9.3493 | 0.6507 | 9.9894 | .4 |
| .7 | 9.3421 | 9.3529 | 0.6471 | 9 9892 | .3 |
| .8 | 9 3455 | 9.3564 | 0.6436 | 9 9891 | .2 |
| .9 | 9.3488 | 9.3599 | 0.6401 | 9.9889 | 77.1 |
| **13.0** | 9.3521 | 9.3634 | 0.6366 | 9.9887 | **77.0** |
| .1 | 9.3554 | 9.3668 | 0.6332 | 9.9885 | 76 9 |
| .2 | 9.3586 | 9.3702 | 0.6298 | 9.9884 | .8 |
| .3 | 9.3618 | 9 3736 | 0.6264 | 9 9882 | 7 |
| .4 | 9.3650 | 9.3770 | 0.6230 | 9.9880 | .6 |
| .5 | 9 3682 | 9.3804 | 0.6196 | 9.9878 | .5 |
| .6 | 9 3713 | 9.3837 | 0.6163 | 9.9876 | .4 |
| .7 | 9.3745 | 9.3870 | 0.6130 | 9.9875 | .3 |
| 8 | 9.3775 | 9.3903 | 0.6097 | 9.9873 | .2 |
| 9 | 9 3806 | 9.3935 | 0.6065 | 9.9871 | 76.1 |
| **14.0** | 9.3837 | 9.3968 | 0.6032 | 9.9869 | **76.0** |
| .1 | 9 3867 | 9.4000 | 0 6000 | 9 9867 | 75.9 |
| .2 | 9.3897 | 9.4032 | 0.5968 | 9.9865 | .8 |
| .3 | 9.3927 | 9.4064 | 0.5936 | 9 9863 | .7 |
| 4 | 9 3957 | 9.4095 | 0.5905 | 9.9861 | .6 |
| .5 | 9.3986 | 9.4127 | 0.5873 | 9.9859 | 5 |
| .6 | 9 4015 | 9.4158 | 0.5842 | 9.9857 | 4 |
| 7 | 9 4044 | 9.4189 | 0 5811 | 9.9855 | .3 |
| .8 | 9.4073 | 9.4220 | 0.5780 | 9.9853 | .2 |
| .9 | 9 4102 | 9.4250 | 0.5750 | 9.9851 | 75 1 |
| **15.0** | 9.4130 | 9.4281 | 0.5719 | 9.9849 | **75.0** |
| .1 | 9 4158 | 9.4311 | 0.5689 | 9.9847 | 74.9 |
| .2 | 9.4186 | 9.4341 | 0.5659 | 9.9845 | .8 |
| 3 | 9.4214 | 9.4371 | 0.5629 | 9 9843 | .7 |
| .4 | 9.4242 | 9.4400 | 0.5600 | 9.9841 | .6 |
| .5 | 9.4269 | 9.4430 | 0.5570 | 9.9839 | .5 |
| 6 | 9.4296 | 9.4459 | 0.5541 | 9.9837 | .4 |
| .7 | 9 4323 | 9.4488 | 0.5512 | 9.9835 | 3 |
| .8 | 9.4350 | 9.4517 | 0.5483 | 9.9833 | .2 |
| .9 | 9.4377 | 9.4546 | 0.5454 | 9.9831 | 74.1 |
| **16.0** | 9.4403 | 9.4575 | 0.5425 | 9.9828 | **74.0** |
| .1 | 9.4430 | 9.4603 | 0 5397 | 9.9826 | 73.9 |
| .2 | 9.4456 | 9.4632 | 0.5368 | 9.9824 | 8 |
| 3 | 9.4482 | 9.4660 | 0.5340 | 9.9822 | .7 |
| .4 | 9 4508 | 9.4688 | 0.5312 | 9.9820 | .6 |
| 5 | 9.4533 | 9.4716 | 0.5284 | 9.9817 | .5 |
| .6 | 9.4559 | 9.4744 | 0 5256 | 9.9815 | .4 |
| .7 | 9.4584 | 9.4771 | 0.5229 | 9.9813 | .3 |
| .8 | 9 4609 | 9.4799 | 0.5201 | 9.9811 | .2 |
| .9 | 9 4634 | 9.4826 | 0.5174 | 9.9808 | 73.1 |
| **17.0** | 9.4659 | 9.4853 | 0.5147 | 9.9806 | **73.0** |
| .1 | 9.4684 | 9.4880 | 0.5120 | 9.9804 | 72.9 |
| .2 | 9.4709 | 9.4907 | 0.5093 | 9.9801 | .8 |
| .3 | 9.4733 | 9.4934 | 0.5066 | 9.9799 | .7 |
| .4 | 9.4757 | 9.4961 | 0.5039 | 9.9797 | .6 |
| .5 | 9.4781 | 9.4987 | 0.5013 | 9.9794 | .5 |
| .6 | 9.4805 | 9.5014 | 0.4986 | 9.9792 | .4 |
| .7 | 9.4829 | 9.5040 | 0.4960 | 9 9789 | .3 |
| .8 | 9.4853 | 9.5066 | 0 4934 | 9.9787 | .2 |
| .9 | 9.4876 | 9.5092 | 0.4908 | 9.9785 | 72.1 |
| **18.0** | 9.4900 | 9.5118 | 0.4882 | 9.9782 | **72.0** |

| Deg. | L. Sin | L. Tan | L. Cot | L. Cos | Deg |
|---|---|---|---|---|---|
| **18.0** | 9.4900 | 9.5118 | 0.4882 | 9.9782 | **72.0** |
| .1 | 9 4923 | 9.5143 | 0.4857 | 9.9780 | 71.9 |
| .2 | 9.4946 | 9.5169 | 0 4831 | 9.9777 | .8 |
| .3 | 9.4969 | 9.5195 | 0.4805 | 9 9775 | .7 |
| .4 | 9.4992 | 9.5220 | 0.4780 | 9.9772 | .6 |
| .5 | 9.5015 | 9.5245 | 0.4755 | 9.9770 | .5 |
| .6 | 9.5037 | 9.5270 | 0 4730 | 9 9767 | .4 |
| .7 | 9.5060 | 9.5295 | 0.4705 | 9.9764 | 3 |
| .8 | 9.5082 | 9.5320 | 0.4680 | 9.9762 | .2 |
| .9 | 9.5104 | 9.5345 | 0.4655 | 9 9759 | 71.1 |
| **19.0** | 9 5126 | 9.5370 | 0.4630 | 9.9757 | **71.0** |
| .1 | 9.5148 | 9.5394 | 0.4606 | 9.9754 | 70.9 |
| .2 | 9.5170 | 9 5419 | 0.4581 | 9.9751 | .8 |
| .3 | 9.5192 | 9.5443 | 0.4557 | 9.9749 | .7 |
| .4 | 9.5213 | 9.5467 | 0 4533 | 9.9746 | 6 |
| .5 | 9.5235 | 9 5491 | 0.4509 | 9.9743 | .5 |
| .6 | 9 5256 | 9.5516 | 0.4484 | 9.9741 | 4 |
| .7 | 9.5278 | 9.5539 | 0.4461 | 9.9738 | .3 |
| .8 | 9.5299 | 9.5563 | 0 4437 | 9.9735 | .2 |
| .9 | 9.5320 | 9.5587 | 0.4413 | 9.9733 | 70.1 |
| **20.0** | 9.5341 | 9.5611 | 0.4389 | 9.9730 | **70.0** |
| .1 | 9.5361 | 9.5634 | 0.4366 | 9.9727 | 69 9 |
| .2 | 9.5382 | 9.5658 | 0.4342 | 9.9724 | .8 |
| .3 | 9.5402 | 9 5681 | 0.4319 | 9.9722 | .7 |
| .4 | 9.5423 | 9.5704 | 0.4296 | 9 9719 | .6 |
| .5 | 9.5443 | 9.5727 | 0.4273 | 9.9716 | .5 |
| .6 | 9 5463 | 9.5750 | 0.4250 | 9 9713 | .4 |
| .7 | 9.5484 | 9.5773 | 0.4227 | 9.9710 | .3 |
| .8 | 9.5504 | 9.5796 | 0.4204 | 9.9707 | 2 |
| .9 | 9.5523 | 9.5819 | 0.4181 | 9.9704 | 69.1 |
| **21.0** | 9.5543 | 9.5842 | 0.4158 | 9.9702 | **69.0** |
| .1 | 9.5563 | 9.5864 | 0.4136 | 9.9699 | 68.9 |
| .2 | 9.5583 | 9.5887 | 0.4113 | 9.9696 | .8 |
| .3 | 9.5602 | 9.5909 | 0.4091 | 9.9693 | .7 |
| .4 | 9.5621 | 9.5932 | 0.4068 | 9.9690 | .6 |
| .5 | 9.5641 | 9.5954 | 0.4046 | 9.9687 | .5 |
| .6 | 9.5660 | 9.5976 | 0.4024 | 9.9684 | .4 |
| .7 | 9.5679 | 9.5998 | 0.4002 | 9.9681 | .3 |
| .8 | 9.5698 | 9.6020 | 0.3980 | 9.9678 | .2 |
| .9 | 9.5717 | 9.6042 | 0.3958 | 9.9675 | 68.1 |
| **22.0** | 9.5736 | 9.6064 | 0.3936 | 9 9672 | **68.0** |
| .1 | 9.5754 | 9.6086 | 0.3914 | 9.9669 | 67.9 |
| .2 | 9.5773 | 9.6108 | 0.3892 | 9.9666 | .8 |
| .3 | 9.5792 | 9.6129 | 0.3871 | 9.9662 | .7 |
| .4 | 9.5810 | 9.6151 | 0.3849 | 9.9659 | .6 |
| .5 | 9.5828 | 9.6172 | 0.3828 | 9.9656 | .5 |
| .6 | 9.5847 | 9.6194 | 0.3806 | 9.9653 | 4 |
| .7 | 9.5865 | 9.6215 | 0.3785 | 9.9650 | .3 |
| .8 | 9.5883 | 9.6236 | 0.3764 | 9.9647 | .2 |
| .9 | 9.5901 | 9.6257 | 0.3743 | 9.9643 | 67.1 |
| **23.0** | 9.5919 | 9.6279 | 0.3721 | 9.9640 | **67.0** |
| .1 | 9.5937 | 9.6300 | 0.3700 | 9.9637 | 66.9 |
| .2 | 9.5954 | 9.6321 | 0.3679 | 9.9634 | .8 |
| .3 | 9.5972 | 9.6341 | 0.3659 | 9.9631 | .7 |
| .4 | 9.5990 | 9.6362 | 0.3638 | 9.9627 | .6 |
| .5 | 9.6007 | 9.6383 | 0.3617 | 9.9624 | .5 |
| .6 | 9.6024 | 9.6404 | 0.3596 | 9 9621 | .4 |
| .7 | 9.6042 | 9.6424 | 0.3576 | 9 9617 | .3 |
| .8 | 9.6059 | 9.6445 | 0.3555 | 9.9614 | .2 |
| .9 | 9.6076 | 9.6465 | 0.3535 | 9.9611 | 66.1 |
| **24.0** | 9.6093 | 9.6486 | 0.3514 | 9.9607 | **66.0** |

| Deg. | L. Cos | L. Cot | L. Tan | L. Sin | Deg. |
|---|---|---|---|---|---|

| Deg. | L. Sin | L. Tan | L. Cot | L. Cos | Deg. | Deg. | L. Sin | L. Tan | L. Cot | L. Cos | Deg. |
|---|---|---|---|---|---|---|---|---|---|---|---|
| 24.0 | 9.6093 | 9.6486 | 0.3514 | 9.9607 | 66.0 | 30.0 | 9.6990 | 9.7614 | 0.2386 | 9.9375 | 60.0 |
| .1 | 9 6110 | 9.6506 | 0.3494 | 9.9604 | 65.9 | .1 | 9.7003 | 9.7632 | 0.2368 | 9.9371 | 59.9 |
| .2 | 9.6127 | 9.6527 | 0.3473 | 9.9601 | .8 | .2 | 9.7016 | 9.7649 | 0.2351 | 9.9367 | .8 |
| .3 | 9.6144 | 9.6547 | 0.3453 | 9.9597 | .7 | 3 | 9.7029 | 9.7667 | 0.2333 | 9 9362 | .7 |
| .4 | 9.6161 | 9.6567 | 0.3433 | 9.9594 | .6 | .4 | 9.7042 | 9.7684 | 0.2316 | 9 9358 | .6 |
| .5 | 9.6177 | 9.6587 | 0.3413 | 9 9590 | .5 | .5 | 9.7055 | 9.7701 | 0.2299 | 9.9353 | .5 |
| .6 | 9 6194 | 9.6607 | 0.3393 | 9.9587 | .4 | .6 | 9.7068 | 9.7719 | 0.2281 | 9.9349 | .4 |
| .7 | 9 6210 | 9.6627 | 0.3373 | 9.9583 | .3 | .7 | 9.7080 | 9.7736 | 0.2264 | 9.9344 | .3 |
| .8 | 9.6227 | 9.6647 | 0.3353 | 9.9580 | .2 | .8 | 9.7093 | 9.7753 | 0.2247 | 9.9340 | .2 |
| .9 | 9.6243 | 9.6667 | 0.3333 | 9.9576 | 65.1 | .9 | 9.7106 | 9.7771 | 0.2229 | 9.9335 | 59.1 |
| 25.0 | 9.6259 | 9.6687 | 0.3313 | 9.9573 | 65.0 | 31.0 | 9.7118 | 9.7788 | 0.2212 | 9.9331 | 59.0 |
| .1 | 9.6276 | 9.6706 | 0.3294 | 9.9569 | 64.9 | .1 | 9.7131 | 9.7805 | 0.2195 | 9.9326 | 58.9 |
| .2 | 9.6292 | 9.6726 | 0 3274 | 9.9566 | .8 | .2 | 9.7144 | 9.7822 | 0.2178 | 9.9322 | .8 |
| .3 | 9.6308 | 9.6746 | 0.3254 | 9.9562 | .7 | .3 | 9.7156 | 9.7839 | 0.2161 | 9.9317 | .7 |
| .4 | 9.6324 | 9.6765 | 0.3235 | 9.9558 | .6 | .4 | 9.7168 | 9.7856 | 0.2144 | 9.9312 | .6 |
| .5 | 9.6340 | 9.6785 | 0 3215 | 9.9555 | .5 | .5 | 9.7181 | 9.7873 | 0.2127 | 9.9308 | .5 |
| .6 | 9.6356 | 9.6804 | 0.3196 | 9.9551 | .4 | .6 | 9.7193 | 9.7890 | 0.2110 | 9.9303 | .4 |
| .7 | 9.6371 | 9.6824 | 0.3176 | 9.9548 | .3 | .7 | 9.7205 | 9.7907 | 0.2093 | 9.9298 | .3 |
| .8 | 9.6387 | 9.6843 | 0.3157 | 9.9544 | .2 | .8 | 9.7218 | 9.7924 | 0.2076 | 9.9294 | .2 |
| .9 | 9 6403 | 9.6863 | 0.3137 | 9.9540 | 64.1 | .9 | 9.7230 | 9.7941 | 0 2059 | 9.9289 | 58.1 |
| 26.0 | 9.6418 | 9.6882 | 0.3118 | 9.9537 | 64.0 | 32.0 | 9.7242 | 9.7958 | 0.2042 | 9.9284 | 58.0 |
| .1 | 9.6434 | 9.6901 | 0.3099 | 9.9533 | 63.9 | .1 | 9.7254 | 9.7975 | 0.2025 | 9.9279 | 57.9 |
| .2 | 9.6449 | 9.6920 | 0.3080 | 9.9529 | .8 | .2 | 9.7266 | 9.7992 | 0.2008 | 9.9275 | .8 |
| .3 | 9.6465 | 9.6939 | 0.3061 | 9 9525 | .7 | .3 | 9.7278 | 9.8008 | 0.1992 | 9.9270 | .7 |
| .4 | 9.6480 | 9.6958 | 0.3042 | 9.9522 | .6 | .4 | 9.7290 | 9.8025 | 0.1975 | 9.9265 | .6 |
| .5 | 9.6495 | 9.6977 | 0.3023 | 9.9518 | .5 | .5 | 9 7302 | 9.8042 | 0.1958 | 9.9260 | .5 |
| .6 | 9.6510 | 9.6996 | 0 3004 | 9.9514 | .4 | .6 | 9.7314 | 9.8059 | 0.1941 | 9.9255 | .4 |
| .7 | 9.6526 | 9.7015 | 0.2985 | 9.9510 | .3 | .7 | 9.7326 | 9.8075 | 0.1925 | 9.9251 | .3 |
| .8 | 9.6541 | 9.7034 | 0.2966 | 9.9506 | .2 | .8 | 9.7338 | 9.8092 | 0.1908 | 9.9246 | .2 |
| .9 | 9.6556 | 9.7053 | 0.2947 | 9.9503 | 63.1 | .9 | 9.7349 | 9.8109 | 0.1891 | 9.9242 | 57.1 |
| 27.0 | 9.6570 | 9.7072 | 0.2928 | 9.9499 | 63.0 | 33.0 | 9.7361 | 9.8125 | 0.1875 | 9.9236 | 57.0 |
| .1 | 9.6585 | 9.7090 | 0.2910 | 9.9495 | 62.9 | .1 | 9.7373 | 9.8142 | 0.1858 | 9.9231 | 56.9 |
| .2 | 9.6600 | 9.7109 | 0.2891 | 9.9491 | .8 | .2 | 9.7384 | 9.8158 | 0.1842 | 9.9226 | .8 |
| .3 | 9.6615 | 9.7128 | 0.2872 | 9.9487 | .7 | .3 | 9.7396 | 9.8175 | 0.1825 | 9.9221 | .7 |
| .4 | 9.6629 | 9.7146 | 0.2854 | 9.9483 | .6 | .4 | 9.7407 | 9.8191 | 0.1809 | 9.9216 | .6 |
| .5 | 9.6644 | 9.7165 | 0.2835 | 9.9479 | .5 | .5 | 9.7419 | 9.8208 | 0.1792 | 9.9211 | .5 |
| .6 | 9.6659 | 9.7183 | 0.2817 | 9.9475 | .4 | .6 | 9.7430 | 9.8224 | 0.1776 | 9.9206 | .4 |
| .7 | 9.6673 | 9.7202 | 0.2798 | 9.9471 | .3 | .7 | 9.7442 | 9.8241 | 0.1759 | 9.9201 | .3 |
| .8 | 9.6687 | 9.7220 | 0.2780 | 9.9467 | .2 | .8 | 9.7453 | 9.8257 | 0.1743 | 9.9196 | .2 |
| .9 | 9.6702 | 9.7238 | 0.2762 | 9.9463 | 62.1 | .9 | 9.7464 | 9.8274 | 0.1726 | 9.9191 | 56.1 |
| 28.0 | 9.6716 | 9.7257 | 0.2743 | 9.9459 | 62.0 | 34.0 | 9.7476 | 9.8290 | 0.1710 | 9.9186 | 56.0 |
| .1 | 9.6730 | 9.7275 | 0.2725 | 9.9455 | 61.9 | .1 | 9.7487 | 9.8306 | 0.1694 | 9.9181 | 55.9 |
| .2 | 9.6744 | 9.7293 | 0.2707 | 9.9451 | .8 | .2 | 9.7498 | 9.8323 | 0.1677 | 9.9175 | .8 |
| .3 | 9.6759 | 9.7311 | 0.2689 | 9.9447 | .7 | .3 | 9.7509 | 9.8339 | 0.1661 | 9.9170 | .7 |
| .4 | 9.6773 | 9.7330 | 0.2670 | 9.9443 | .6 | .4 | 9.7520 | 9.8355 | 0.1645 | 9 9165 | 6 |
| .5 | 9.6787 | 9.7348 | 0.2652 | 9.9439 | .5 | .5 | 9.7531 | 9.8371 | 0.1629 | 9 9160 | .5 |
| .6 | 9.6801 | 9.7366 | 0.2634 | 9.9435 | .4 | .6 | 9.7542 | 9.8388 | 0.1612 | 9.9155 | .4 |
| .7 | 9.6814 | 9.7384 | 0.2616 | 9.9431 | .3 | .7 | 9.7553 | 9.8404 | 0.1596 | 9.3149 | .3 |
| .8 | 9.6828 | 9.7402 | 0.2598 | 9.9427 | .2 | .8 | 9.7564 | 9.8420 | 0.1580 | 9.9144 | .2 |
| .9 | 9.6842 | 9.7420 | 0.2580 | 9.9422 | 61.1 | .9 | 9.7575 | 9.8436 | 0.1564 | 9 9129 | 55.1 |
| 29.0 | 9.6856 | 9.7438 | 0.2562 | 9.9418 | 61.0 | 35.0 | 9.7586 | 9.8452 | 0 1548 | 9.9134 | 55.0 |
| .1 | 9.6869 | 9.7455 | 0.2545 | 9.9414 | 30.9 | .1 | 9.7597 | 9.8468 | 0.1532 | 9.0128 | 54.9 |
| .2 | 9.6883 | 9.7473 | 0.2527 | 9.9410 | .8 | .2 | 9.7607 | 9.8484 | 0.1516 | 9.9123 | .8 |
| .3 | 9.6896 | 9.7491 | 0.2509 | 9.9406 | .7 | .3 | 9 7618 | 9.8501 | 0.1499 | 9.9118 | .7 |
| .4 | 9.6910 | 9.7509 | 0.2491 | 9.9401 | .6 | .4 | 9.7629 | 9.8517 | 0.1483 | 9 9112 | 6 |
| .5 | 9.6923 | 9.7526 | 0.2474 | 9.9397 | .5 | .5 | 9.7640 | 9.8533 | 0.1467 | 9.9107 | .5 |
| .6 | 9.6937 | 9.7544 | 0.2456 | 9.9393 | .4 | .6 | 9.7650 | 9.8549 | 0.1451 | 9.9101 | .4 |
| .7 | 9.6950 | 9.7562 | 0.2438 | 9.9388 | .3 | .7 | 9.7661 | 9.8565 | 0.1435 | 9 9096 | .3 |
| .8 | 9.6963 | 9.7579 | 0.2421 | 9.9384 | .2 | .8 | 9.7671 | 9.8581 | 0.1419 | 9.9091 | .2 |
| .9 | 9.6977 | 9.7597 | 0.2403 | 9.9380 | 60.1 | .9 | 9.7682 | 9.8597 | 0 1403 | 9.9085 | 54.1 |
| 30.0 | 9.6990 | 9 7614 | 0.2386 | 9.9375 | 60.0 | 36.0 | 9.7692 | 9.8613 | 0 1387 | 9 9080 | 54.0 |
| Deg. | L. Cos | L. Cot | L. Tan | L. Sin | Deg. | Deg. | L. Cos | L. Cot | L. Tan | L. Sin | Deg. |

# LOGARITHMS OF FUNCTIONS FOR DEGREES AND DECIMALS (Continued)

| Deg. | L. Sin | L. Tan | L. Cot | L. Cos | Deg. | Deg. | L. Sin | L. Tan | L. Cot | L. Cos | Deg. |
|---|---|---|---|---|---|---|---|---|---|---|---|
| **36.0** | 9.7692 | 9.8613 | 0.1387 | 9.9080 | **54.0** | **41.0** | 9.8169 | 9.9392 | 0.0608 | 9.8778 | **49.0** |
| .1 | 9.7703 | 9.8629 | 0.1371 | 9.9074 | 53.9 | .1 | 9.8178 | 9.9407 | 0.0593 | 9.8771 | 48.9 |
| .2 | 9.7713 | 9.8644 | 0.1356 | 9.9069 | .8 | .2 | 9.8187 | 9.9422 | 0.0578 | 9.8765 | .8 |
| .3 | 9.7723 | 9.8660 | 0.1340 | 9.9063 | .7 | .3 | 9.8195 | 9.9438 | 0.0562 | 9.8758 | .7 |
| .4 | 9.7734 | 9.8676 | 0.1324 | 9.9057 | .6 | .4 | 9.8204 | 9.9453 | 0.0547 | 9.8751 | .6 |
| .5 | 9.7744 | 9.8692 | 0.1308 | 9.9052 | .5 | .5 | 9.8213 | 9.9468 | 0.0532 | 9.8745 | .5 |
| .6 | 9.7754 | 9.8708 | 0.1292 | 9.9046 | .4 | .6 | 9.8221 | 9.9483 | 0.0517 | 9.8738 | .4 |
| .7 | 9.7764 | 9.8724 | 0.1276 | 9.9041 | .3 | .7 | 9.8230 | 9.9499 | 0.0501 | 9.8731 | .3 |
| .8 | 9.7774 | 9.8740 | 0.1260 | 9.9035 | .2 | .8 | 9.8238 | 9.9514 | 0.0486 | 9.8724 | .2 |
| .9 | 9.7785 | 9.8755 | 0.1245 | 9.9029 | 53.1 | .9 | 9.8247 | 9.9529 | 0.0471 | 9.8718 | 48.1 |
| **37.0** | 9.7795 | 9.8771 | 0.1229 | 9.9023 | **53.0** | **42.0** | 9.8255 | 9.9544 | 0.0456 | 9.8711 | **48.0** |
| .1 | 9.7805 | 9.8787 | 0.1213 | 9.9018 | 52.9 | .1 | 9.8264 | 9.9560 | 0.0440 | 9.8704 | 47.9 |
| .2 | 9.7815 | 9.8803 | 0.1197 | 9.9012 | .8 | .2 | 9.8272 | 9.9575 | 0.0425 | 9.8697 | .8 |
| .3 | 9.7825 | 9.8818 | 0.1182 | 9.9006 | .7 | .3 | 9.8280 | 9.9590 | 0.0410 | 9.8690 | .7 |
| .4 | 9.7835 | 9.8834 | 0.1166 | 9.9000 | .6 | .4 | 9.8289 | 9.9605 | 0.0395 | 9.8683 | .6 |
| .5 | 9.7844 | 9.8850 | 0.1150 | 9.8995 | .5 | .5 | 9.8297 | 9.9621 | 0.0379 | 9.8676 | .5 |
| .6 | 9.7854 | 9.8865 | 0.1135 | 9.8989 | .4 | .6 | 9.8305 | 9.9636 | 0.0364 | 9.8669 | .4 |
| .7 | 9.7864 | 9.8881 | 0.1119 | 9.8983 | .3 | .7 | 9.8313 | 9.9651 | 0.0349 | 9.8662 | .3 |
| .8 | 9.7874 | 9.8897 | 0.1103 | 9.8977 | .2 | .8 | 9.8322 | 9.9666 | 0.0334 | 9.8655 | .2 |
| .9 | 9.7884 | 9.8912 | 0.1088 | 9.8971 | 52.1 | 9 | 9.8330 | 9.9681 | 0.0319 | 9.8648 | 47.1 |
| **38.0** | 9.7893 | 9.8928 | 0.1072 | 9.8965 | **52.0** | **43.0** | 9.8338 | 9.9697 | 0.0303 | 9.8641 | **47.0** |
| 1 | 9.7903 | 9.8944 | 0.1056 | 9.8959 | 51.9 | .1 | 9.8346 | 9.9712 | 0.0288 | 9.8634 | 46.9 |
| .2 | 9.7913 | 9.8959 | 0.1041 | 9.8953 | .8 | 2 | 9.8354 | 9.9727 | 0.0273 | 9.8627 | .8 |
| .3 | 9.7922 | 9.8975 | 0.1025 | 9.8947 | .7 | .3 | 9.8362 | 9.9742 | 0.0258 | 9.8620 | .7 |
| .4 | 9.7932 | 9.8990 | 0.1010 | 9.8941 | .6 | .4 | 9.8370 | 9.9757 | 0.0243 | 9.8613 | .6 |
| .5 | 9.7941 | 9.9006 | 0.0994 | 9.8935 | .5 | .5 | 9.8378 | 9.9772 | 0.0228 | 9.8606 | .5 |
| .6 | 9.7951 | 9.9022 | 0.0978 | 9.8929 | .4 | .6 | 9.8386 | 9.9788 | 0.0212 | 9.8598 | .4 |
| .7 | 9.7960 | 9.9037 | 0.0963 | 9.8923 | .3 | .7 | 9.8394 | 9.9803 | 0.0197 | 9.8591 | .3 |
| .8 | 9.7970 | 9.9053 | 0.0947 | 9.8917 | .2 | .8 | 9.8402 | 9.9818 | 0.0182 | 9.8584 | .2 |
| .9 | 9.7979 | 9.9068 | 0.0932 | 9.8911 | 51.1 | .9 | 9.8410 | 9.9833 | 0.0167 | 9.8577 | 46.1 |
| **39.0** | 9.7989 | 9.9084 | 0.0916 | 9.8905 | **51.0** | **44.0** | 9.8418 | 9.9848 | 0.0152 | 9.8569 | **46.0** |
| .1 | 9.7998 | 9.9099 | 0.0901 | 9.8899 | 50.9 | .1 | 9.8426 | 9.9864 | 0.0136 | 9.8562 | 45.9 |
| .2 | 9.8007 | 9.9115 | 0.0885 | 9.8893 | .8 | .2 | 9.8433 | 9.9879 | 0.0121 | 9.8555 | .8 |
| .3 | 9.8017 | 9.9130 | 0.0870 | 9.8887 | .7 | .3 | 9.8441 | 9.9894 | 0.0106 | 9.8547 | .7 |
| .4 | 9.8026 | 9.9146 | 0.0854 | 9.8880 | .6 | .4 | 9.8449 | 9.9909 | 0.0091 | 9.8540 | .6 |
| .5 | 9.8035 | 9.9161 | 0.0839 | 9.8874 | .5 | .5 | 9.8457 | 9.9924 | 0.0076 | 9.8532 | .5 |
| .6 | 9.8044 | 9.9176 | 0.0824 | 9.8868 | .4 | .6 | 9.8464 | 9.9939 | 0.0061 | 9.8525 | .4 |
| .7 | 9.8053 | 9.9192 | 0.0808 | 9.8862 | .3 | .7 | 9.8472 | 9.9955 | 0.0045 | 9.8517 | .3 |
| .8 | 9.8063 | 9.9207 | 0.0793 | 9.8855 | .2 | .8 | 9.8480 | 9.9970 | 0.0030 | 9.8510 | .2 |
| .9 | 9.8072 | 9.9223 | 0.0777 | 9.8849 | 50.1 | .9 | 9.8487 | 9.9985 | 0.0015 | 9.8502 | 45.1 |
| **40.0** | 9.8081 | 9.9238 | 0.0762 | 9.8843 | **50.0** | **45.0** | 9.8495 | 0.0000 | 0.0000 | 9.8495 | **45.0** |
| .1 | 9.8090 | 9.9254 | 0.0746 | 9.8836 | 49.9 | | | | | | |
| .2 | 9.8099 | 9.9269 | 0.0731 | 9.8830 | .8 | Deg. | L Cos | L. Cot | L. Tan | L. Sin | Deg. |
| .3 | 9.8108 | 9.9284 | 0.0716 | 9.8823 | .7 | | | | | | |
| .4 | 9.8117 | 9.9300 | 0.0700 | 9.8817 | .6 | | | | | | |
| .5 | 9.8125 | 9.9315 | 0.0685 | 9.8810 | .5 | | | | | | |
| .6 | 9.8134 | 9.9330 | 0.0670 | 9.8804 | .4 | | | | | | |
| .7 | 9.8143 | 9.9346 | 0.0654 | 9.8797 | .3 | | | | | | |
| 8 | 9.8152 | 9.9361 | 0.0639 | 9.8791 | 2 | | | | | | |
| .9 | 9.8161 | 9.9376 | 0.0624 | 9.8784 | 49.1 | | | | | | |
| **41.0** | 9.8169 | 9.9392 | 0.0608 | 9.8778 | **49.0** | | | | | | |
| Deg. | L. Cos | L. Cot | L. Tan | L. Sin | Deg. | | | | | | |

137

# NATURAL FUNCTIONS FOR ANGLES IN RADIANS

| Rad. | Sin | Tan | Cot | Cos | Rad. | Sin | Tan | Cot | Cos |
|------|------|------|------|------|------|------|------|------|------|
| **.00** | .00000 | .00000 | ∞ | 1.0000 | **.50** | .47943 | .54630 | 1.8305 | .87758 |
| .01 | .01000 | .01000 | 99.997 | .99995 | .51 | .48818 | .55936 | 1.7878 | .87274 |
| .02 | .02000 | .02000 | 49.993 | .99980 | .52 | .49688 | .57256 | 1.7465 | .86782 |
| .03 | .03000 | .03001 | 33.323 | .99955 | .53 | .50553 | .58592 | 1.7067 | .86281 |
| .04 | .03999 | .04002 | 24.987 | .99920 | .54 | .51414 | .59943 | 1.6683 | .85771 |
| .05 | .04998 | .05004 | 19.983 | .99875 | .55 | .52269 | .61311 | 1.6310 | .85252 |
| .06 | .05996 | .06007 | 16.647 | .99820 | .56 | .53119 | .62695 | 1.5950 | .84726 |
| .07 | .06994 | .07011 | 14.262 | .99755 | .57 | .53963 | .64097 | 1.5601 | .84190 |
| .08 | .07991 | .08017 | 12.473 | .99680 | .58 | .54802 | .65517 | 1.5263 | .83646 |
| .09 | .08988 | .09024 | 11.081 | .99595 | .59 | .55636 | .66956 | 1.4935 | .83094 |
| **.10** | .09983 | .10033 | 9.9666 | .99500 | **.60** | .56464 | .68414 | 1.4617 | .82534 |
| .11 | .10978 | .11045 | 9.0542 | .99396 | .61 | .57287 | .69892 | 1.4308 | .81965 |
| .12 | .11971 | .12058 | 8.2933 | .99281 | .62 | .58104 | .71391 | 1.4007 | .81388 |
| .13 | .12963 | .13074 | 7.6489 | .99156 | .63 | .58914 | .72911 | 1.3715 | .80803 |
| .14 | .13954 | .14092 | 7.0961 | .99022 | .64 | .59720 | .74454 | 1.3431 | .80210 |
| .15 | .14944 | .15114 | 6.6166 | .98877 | .65 | .60519 | .76020 | 1.3154 | .79608 |
| .16 | .15932 | .16138 | 6.1966 | .98723 | .66 | .61312 | .77610 | 1.2885 | .78999 |
| .17 | .16918 | .17166 | 5.8256 | .98558 | .67 | .62099 | .79225 | 1.2622 | .78382 |
| .18 | .17903 | .18197 | 5.4954 | .98384 | .68 | .62879 | .80866 | 1.2366 | .77757 |
| .19 | .18886 | .19232 | 5.1997 | .98200 | .69 | .63654 | .82534 | 1.2116 | .77125 |
| **.20** | .19867 | .20271 | 4.9332 | .98007 | **.70** | .64422 | .84229 | 1.1872 | .76484 |
| .21 | .20846 | .21314 | 4.6917 | .97803 | .71 | .65183 | .85953 | 1.1634 | .75836 |
| .22 | .21823 | .22362 | 4.4719 | .97590 | .72 | .65938 | .87707 | 1.1402 | .75181 |
| .23 | .22798 | .23414 | 4.2709 | .97367 | .73 | .66687 | .89492 | 1.1174 | .74517 |
| .24 | .23770 | .24472 | 4.0864 | .97134 | .74 | .67429 | .91309 | 1.0952 | .73847 |
| .25 | .24740 | .25534 | 3.9163 | .96891 | .75 | .68164 | .93160 | 1.0734 | .73169 |
| .26 | .25708 | .26602 | 3.7591 | .96639 | .76 | .68892 | .95045 | 1.0521 | .72484 |
| .27 | .26673 | .27676 | 3.6133 | .96377 | .77 | .69614 | .96967 | 1.0313 | .71791 |
| .28 | .27636 | .28755 | 3.4776 | .96106 | .78 | .70328 | .98926 | 1.0109 | .71091 |
| .29 | .28595 | .29841 | 3.3511 | .95824 | .79 | .71035 | 1.0092 | .99084 | .70385 |
| **.30** | .29552 | .30934 | 3.2327 | .95534 | **.80** | .71736 | 1.0296 | .97121 | .69671 |
| .31 | .30506 | .32033 | 3.1218 | .95233 | .81 | .72429 | 1.0505 | .95197 | .68950 |
| .32 | .31457 | .33139 | 3.0176 | .94924 | .82 | .73115 | 1.0717 | .93309 | .68222 |
| .33 | .32404 | .34252 | 2.9195 | .94604 | .83 | .73793 | 1.0934 | .91455 | .67488 |
| .34 | .33349 | .35374 | 2.8270 | .94275 | .84 | .74464 | 1.1156 | .89635 | .66746 |
| .35 | .34290 | .36503 | 2.7395 | .93937 | .85 | .75128 | 1.1383 | .87848 | .65998 |
| .36 | .35227 | .37640 | 2.6567 | .93590 | .86 | .75784 | 1.1616 | .86091 | .65244 |
| .37 | .36162 | .38786 | 2.5782 | .93233 | .87 | .76433 | 1.1853 | .84365 | .64483 |
| .38 | .37092 | .39941 | 2.5037 | .92866 | .88 | .77074 | 1.2097 | .82668 | .63715 |
| .39 | .38019 | .41105 | 2.4328 | .92491 | .89 | .77707 | 1.2346 | .80998 | .62941 |
| **.40** | .38942 | .42279 | 2.3652 | .92106 | **.90** | .78333 | 1.2602 | .79355 | .62161 |
| .41 | .39861 | .43463 | 2.3008 | .91712 | .91 | .78950 | 1.2864 | .77738 | .61375 |
| .42 | .40776 | .44657 | 2.2393 | .91309 | .92 | .79560 | 1.3133 | .76146 | .60582 |
| .43 | .41687 | .45862 | 2.1804 | .90897 | .93 | .80162 | 1.3409 | .74578 | .59783 |
| .44 | .42594 | .47078 | 2.1241 | .90475 | .94 | .80756 | 1.3692 | .73034 | .58979 |
| .45 | .43497 | .48306 | 2.0702 | .90045 | .95 | .81342 | 1.3984 | .71511 | .58168 |
| .46 | .44395 | .49545 | 2.0184 | .89605 | .96 | .81919 | 1.4284 | .70010 | .57352 |
| .47 | .45289 | .50797 | 1.9686 | .89157 | .97 | .82489 | 1.4592 | .68531 | .56530 |
| .48 | .46178 | .52061 | 1.9208 | .88699 | .98 | .83050 | 1.4910 | .67071 | .55702 |
| .49 | .47063 | .53339 | 1.8748 | .88233 | .99 | .83603 | 1.5237 | .65631 | .54869 |
| **.50** | .47943 | .54630 | 1.8305 | .87758 | **1.00** | .84147 | 1.5574 | .64209 | .54030 |
| Rad. | Sin | Tan | Cot | Cos | Rad. | Sin | Tan | Cot | Cos |

| Rad. | Sin | Tan | Cot | Cos | Rad. | Sin | Tan | Cot | Cos |
|---|---|---|---|---|---|---|---|---|---|
| **1.00** | .84147 | 1.5574 | .64209 | .54030 | **1.50** | .99749 | 14.101 | .07091 | .07074 |
| 1.01 | .84683 | 1.5922 | .62806 | .53186 | 1.51 | .99815 | 16.428 | .06087 | .06076 |
| 1.02 | .85211 | 1.6281 | .61420 | .52337 | 1.52 | .99871 | 19.670 | .05084 | .05077 |
| 1.03 | .85730 | 1.6652 | .60051 | .51482 | 1.53 | .99917 | 24.498 | .04082 | .04079 |
| 1.04 | .86240 | 1.7036 | .58699 | .50622 | 1.54 | .99953 | 32.461 | .03081 | .03079 |
| 1.05 | .86742 | 1.7433 | .57362 | .49757 | 1.55 | .99978 | 48.078 | .02080 | .02079 |
| 1.06 | .87236 | 1.7844 | .56040 | .48887 | 1.56 | .99994 | 92.621 | .01080 | .01080 |
| 1.07 | .87720 | 1.8270 | .54734 | .48012 | 1.57 | 1.0000 | 1255.8 | .00080 | .00080 |
| 1.08 | .88196 | 1.8712 | .53441 | .47133 | 1.58 | .99996 | −108.65 | −.00920 | −.00920 |
| 1.09 | .88663 | 1.9171 | .52162 | .46249 | 1.59 | .99982 | −52.067 | −.01921 | −.01921 |
| **1.10** | .89121 | 1.9648 | .50897 | .45360 | **1.60** | .99957 | −34.233 | −.02921 | −.02920 |
| 1.11 | .89570 | 2.0143 | .49644 | .44466 | 1.61 | .99923 | −25.495 | −.03922 | −.03919 |
| 1.12 | .90010 | 2.0660 | .48404 | .43568 | 1.62 | .99879 | −20.307 | −.04924 | −.04918 |
| 1.13 | .90441 | 2.1198 | .47175 | .42666 | 1.63 | .99825 | −16.871 | −.05927 | −.05917 |
| 1.14 | .90863 | 2.1759 | .45959 | .41759 | 1.64 | .99761 | −14.427 | −.06931 | −.06915 |
| 1.15 | .91276 | 2.2345 | .44753 | .40849 | 1.65 | .99687 | −12.599 | −.07937 | −.07912 |
| 1.16 | .91680 | 2.2958 | .43558 | .39934 | 1.66 | .99602 | −11.181 | −.08944 | −.08909 |
| 1.17 | .92075 | 2.3600 | .42373 | .39015 | 1.67 | .99508 | −10.047 | −.09953 | −.09904 |
| 1.18 | .92461 | 2.4273 | .41199 | .38092 | 1.68 | .99404 | −9.1208 | −.10964 | −.10899 |
| 1.19 | .92837 | 2.4979 | .40034 | .37166 | 1.69 | .99290 | −8.3492 | −.11977 | −.11892 |
| **1.20** | .93204 | 2.5722 | .38878 | .36236 | **1.70** | .99166 | −7.6966 | −.12993 | −.12884 |
| 1.21 | .93562 | 2.6503 | .37731 | .35302 | 1.71 | .99033 | −7.1373 | −.14011 | −.13875 |
| 1.22 | .93910 | 2.7328 | .36593 | .34365 | 1.72 | .98889 | −6.6524 | −.15032 | −.14865 |
| 1.23 | .94249 | 2.8198 | .35463 | .33424 | 1.73 | .98735 | −6.2281 | −.16056 | −.15853 |
| 1.24 | .94578 | 2.9119 | .34341 | .32480 | 1.74 | .98572 | −5.8535 | −.17084 | −.16840 |
| 1.25 | .94898 | 3.0096 | .33227 | .31532 | 1.75 | .98399 | −5.5204 | −.18115 | −.17825 |
| 1.26 | .95209 | 3.1133 | .32121 | .30582 | 1.76 | .98215 | −5.2221 | −.19149 | −.18808 |
| 1.27 | .95510 | 3.2236 | .31021 | .29628 | 1.77 | .98022 | −4.9534 | −.20188 | −.19789 |
| 1.28 | .95802 | 3.3413 | .29928 | .28672 | 1.78 | .97820 | −4.7101 | −.21231 | −.20768 |
| 1.29 | .96084 | 3.4672 | .28842 | .27712 | 1.79 | .97607 | −4.4887 | −.22278 | −.21745 |
| **1.30** | .96356 | 3.6021 | .27762 | .26750 | **1.80** | .97385 | −4.2863 | −.23339 | −.22720 |
| 1.31 | .96618 | 3.7471 | .26687 | .25785 | 1.81 | .97153 | −4.1005 | −.24387 | −.23693 |
| 1.32 | .96872 | 3.9033 | .25619 | .24818 | 1.82 | .96911 | −3.9294 | −.25449 | −.24663 |
| 1.33 | .97115 | 4.0723 | .24556 | .23848 | 1.83 | .96659 | −3.7712 | −.26517 | −.25631 |
| 1.34 | .97348 | 4.2556 | .23498 | .22875 | 1.84 | .96398 | −3.6245 | −.27590 | −.26596 |
| 1.35 | .97572 | 4.4552 | .22446 | .21901 | 1.85 | .96128 | −3.4881 | −.28669 | −.27559 |
| 1.36 | .97786 | 4.6734 | .21398 | .20924 | 1.86 | .95847 | −3.3608 | −.29755 | −.28519 |
| 1.37 | .97991 | 4.9131 | .20354 | .19945 | 1.87 | .95557 | −3.2419 | −.30846 | −.29476 |
| 1.38 | .98185 | 5.1774 | .19315 | .18964 | 1.88 | .95258 | −3.1304 | −.31945 | −.30430 |
| 1.39 | .98370 | 5.4707 | .18279 | .17981 | 1.89 | .94949 | −3.0257 | −.33051 | −.31381 |
| **1.40** | .98545 | 5.7979 | .17248 | .16997 | **1.90** | .94630 | −2.9271 | −.34164 | −.32329 |
| 1.41 | .98710 | 6.1654 | .16220 | .16010 | 1.91 | .94302 | −2.8341 | −.35284 | −.33274 |
| 1.42 | .98865 | 6.5811 | .15195 | .15023 | 1.92 | .93965 | −2.7463 | −.36413 | −.34215 |
| 1.43 | .99010 | 7.0555 | .14173 | .14033 | 1.93 | .93618 | −2.6632 | −.37549 | −.35153 |
| 1.44 | .99146 | 7.6018 | .13155 | .13042 | 1.94 | .93262 | −2.5843 | −.38695 | −.36087 |
| 1.45 | .99271 | 8.2381 | .12139 | .12050 | 1.95 | .92896 | −2.5095 | −.39849 | −.37018 |
| 1.46 | .99387 | 8.9886 | .11125 | .11057 | 1.96 | .92521 | −2.4383 | −.41012 | −.37945 |
| 1.47 | .99492 | 9.8874 | .10114 | .10063 | 1.97 | .92137 | −2.3705 | −.42185 | −.38868 |
| 1.48 | .99588 | 10.983 | .09105 | .09067 | 1.98 | .91744 | −2.3058 | −.43368 | −.39788 |
| 1.49 | .99674 | 12.350 | .08097 | .08071 | 1.99 | .91341 | −2.2441 | −.44562 | −.40703 |
| **1.50** | .99749 | 14.101 | .07091 | .07074 | **2.00** | .90930 | −2.1850 | −.45766 | −.41615 |
| Rad. | Sin | Tan | Cot | Cos | Rad. | Sin | Tan | Cot | Cos |

# LOGARITHMS OF THE FUNCTIONS FOR ANGLES IN RADIANS

| Rad. | L. Sin | L. Tan | L. Cot | L. Cos | Rad. | L. Sin | L. Tan | L. Cot | L. Cos |
|---|---|---|---|---|---|---|---|---|---|
| .00 | − ∞ | − ∞ | ∞ | 0.00000 | .50 | 9.68072 | 9.73743 | 0.26257 | 9.94329 |
| .01 | 7.99999 | 8.00001 | 1.99999 | 9.99998 | .51 | 9.68858 | 9.74769 | 0.25231 | 9.94089 |
| .02 | 8.30100 | 8.30109 | 1.69891 | 9.99991 | .52 | 9.69625 | 9.75782 | 0.24218 | 9.93843 |
| .03 | 8.47706 | 8.47725 | 1.52275 | 9.99980 | .53 | 9.70375 | 9.76784 | 0.23216 | 9.93591 |
| .04 | 8.60194 | 8.60229 | 1.39771 | 9.99965 | .54 | 9.71108 | 9.77774 | 0.22226 | 9.93334 |
| .05 | 8.69879 | 8.69933 | 1.30067 | 9.99946 | .55 | 9.71824 | 9.78754 | 0.21246 | 9.93071 |
| .06 | 8.77789 | 8.77867 | 1.22133 | 9.99922 | .56 | 9.72525 | 9.79723 | 0.20277 | 9.92801 |
| .07 | 8.84474 | 8.84581 | 1.15419 | 9.99894 | .57 | 9.73210 | 9.80684 | 0.19316 | 9.92526 |
| .08 | 8.90263 | 8.90402 | 1.09598 | 9.99861 | .58 | 9.73880 | 9.81635 | 0.18365 | 9.92245 |
| .09 | 8.95366 | 8.95542 | 1.04458 | 9.99824 | .59 | 9.74536 | 9.82579 | 0.17421 | 9.91957 |
| .10 | 8.99928 | 9.00145 | 0.99855 | 9.99782 | .60 | 9.75177 | 9.83514 | 0.16486 | 9.91663 |
| .11 | 9.04052 | 9.04315 | 0.95685 | 9.99737 | .61 | 9.75805 | 9.84443 | 0.15557 | 9.91363 |
| .12 | 9.07814 | 9.08127 | 0.91873 | 9.99687 | .62 | 9.76420 | 9.85364 | 0.14636 | 9.91056 |
| .13 | 9.11272 | 9.11640 | 0.88360 | 9.99632 | .63 | 9.77022 | 9.86280 | 0.13720 | 9.90743 |
| .14 | 9.14471 | 9.14898 | 0.85102 | 9.99573 | .64 | 9.77612 | 9.87189 | 0.12811 | 9 90423 |
| .15 | 9.17446 | 9.17937 | 0.82063 | 9.99510 | .65 | 9.78189 | 9.88093 | 0.11907 | 9.90096 |
| .16 | 9.20227 | 9.20785 | 0.79215 | 9.99442 | .66 | 9.78754 | 9.88992 | 0.11008 | 9.89762 |
| .17 | 9.22836 | 9.23466 | 0.76534 | 9.99369 | .67 | 9.79308 | 9.89886 | 0.10114 | 9.89422 |
| .18 | 9.25292 | 9.26000 | 0.74000 | 9.99293 | .68 | 9.79851 | 9.90777 | 0.09223 | 9.89074 |
| .19 | 9.27614 | 9.28402 | 0.71598 | 9.99211 | .69 | 9.80382 | 9.91663 | 0.08337 | 9.88719 |
| .20 | 9.29813 | 9.30688 | 0.69312 | 9.99126 | 70 | 9.80903 | 9.92546 | 0.07454 | 9.88357 |
| .21 | 9.31902 | 9.32867 | 0.67133 | 9.99035 | .71 | 9.81414 | 9.93426 | 0.06574 | 9.87988 |
| .22 | 9.33891 | 9.34951 | 0.65049 | 9.98940 | .72 | 9.81914 | 9.94303 | 0.05697 | 9.87611 |
| .23 | 9.35789 | 9.36948 | 0.63052 | 9.98841 | .73 | 9.82404 | 9.95178 | 0.04822 | 9.87226 |
| .24 | 9.37603 | 9.38866 | 0.61134 | 9.98737 | .74 | 9.82885 | 9.96051 | 0.03949 | 9.86833 |
| .25 | 9.39341 | 9.40712 | 0.59288 | 9.98628 | .75 | 9.83355 | 9 96923 | 0.03077 | 9.86433 |
| .26 | 9.41007 | 9.42492 | 0.57508 | 9.98515 | .76 | 9.83817 | 9.97793 | 0.02207 | 9.86024 |
| .27 | 9.42607 | 9.44210 | 0.55790 | 9.98397 | .77 | 9.84269 | 9.98662 | 0.01338 | 9.85607 |
| .28 | 9.44147 | 9.45872 | 0.54128 | 9.98275 | .78 | 9.84713 | 9.99531 | 0.00469 | 9.85182 |
| .29 | 9.45629 | 9.47482 | 0.52518 | 9.98148 | .79 | 9.85147 | 0.00400 | 9.99600 | 9.84748 |
| .30 | 9.47059 | 9.49043 | 0.50957 | 9.98016 | .80 | 9.85573 | 0.01268 | 9.98732 | 9.84305 |
| .31 | 9.48438 | 9.50559 | 0.49441 | 9.97879 | .81 | 9.85991 | 0.02138 | 9.97862 | 9.83853 |
| .32 | 9.49771 | 9.52034 | 0.47966 | 9.97737 | .82 | 9.86400 | 0.03008 | 9.96992 | 9.83393 |
| .33 | 9.51060 | 9.53469 | 0.46531 | 9.97591 | .83 | 9.86802 | 0.03879 | 9.96121 | 9.82922 |
| .34 | 9.52308 | 9.54868 | 0.45132 | 9.97440 | .84 | 9.87195 | 0.04752 | 9.95248 | 9.82443 |
| .35 | 9 53516 | 9.56233 | 0.43767 | 9.97284 | .85 | 9.87580 | 0.05627 | 9.94373 | 9.81953 |
| .36 | 9.54688 | 9.57565 | 0.42435 | 9.97123 | .86 | 9.87958 | 0.06504 | 9.93496 | 9.81454 |
| .37 | 9.55825 | 9.58868 | 0.41132 | 9.96957 | .87 | 9.88328 | 0.07384 | 9.92616 | 9.80944 |
| .38 | 9.56928 | 9.60142 | 0.39858 | 9.96786 | .88 | 9.88691 | 0.08266 | 9.91734 | 9.80424 |
| .39 | 9.58000 | 9.61390 | 0.38610 | 9.96610 | .89 | 9.89046 | 0.09153 | 9.90847 | 9.79894 |
| .40 | 9.59042 | 9.62613 | 0.37387 | 9.96429 | .90 | 9.89394 | 0.10043 | 9.89957 | 9.79352 |
| .41 | 9.60055 | 9.63812 | 0.36188 | 9.96243 | .91 | 9.89735 | 0.10937 | 9.89063 | 9.78799 |
| .42 | 9.61041 | 9.64989 | 0.35011 | 9.96051 | .92 | 9.90070 | 0.11835 | 9.88165 | 9.78234 |
| .43 | 9.62000 | 9.66145 | 0.33855 | 9.95855 | .93 | 9.90397 | 0.12739 | 9.87261 | 9.77658 |
| .44 | 9.62935 | 9.67282 | 0.32718 | 9.95653 | .94 | 9.90717 | 0.13648 | 9.86352 | 9.77070 |
| .45 | 9.63845 | 9.68400 | 0.31600 | 9.95446 | 95 | 9.91031 | 0.14563 | 9.85437 | 9.76469 |
| .46 | 9.64733 | 9.69500 | 0 30500 | 9.95233 | .96 | 9.91339 | 0.15484 | 9.84516 | 9.75855 |
| .47 | 9.65599 | 9.70583 | 0.29417 | 9.95015 | .97 | 9.91639 | 0.16412 | 9.83588 | 9.75228 |
| .48 | 9.66443 | 9.71651 | 0.28349 | 9 94792 | .98 | 9.91934 | 0.17347 | 9.82653 | 9.74587 |
| .49 | 9.67268 | 9.72704 | 0.27296 | 9.94563 | .99 | 9.92222 | 0.18289 | 9.81711 | 9.73933 |
| .50 | 9.68072 | 9.73743 | 0.26257 | 9.94329 | 1.00 | 9.92504 | 0.19240 | 9.80760 | 9.73264 |
| Rad | L. Sin | L. Tan | L. Cot | L. Cos | Rad. | L. Sin | L. Tan | L. Cot | L. Cos |

| Rad. | L. Sin | L. Tan | L. Cot | L. Cos | Rad | L. Sin | L. Tan | L. Cot | L. Cos |
|---|---|---|---|---|---|---|---|---|---|
| **1.00** | 9.92504 | 0.19240 | 9.80760 | 9.73264 | **1.50** | 9.99891 | 1.14926 | 8.85074 | 8 84965 |
| 1.01 | 9.92780 | 0.20200 | 9.79800 | 9.72580 | 1.51 | 9.99920 | 1.21559 | 8.78441 | 8.78361 |
| 1.02 | 9.93049 | 0.21169 | 9.78831 | 9.71881 | 1.52 | 9.99944 | 1.29379 | 8.70621 | 8.70565 |
| 1.03 | 9.93313 | 0.22148 | 9.77852 | 9.71165 | 1.53 | 9.99964 | 1.38914 | 8.61086 | 8.61050 |
| 1.04 | 9.93571 | 0.23137 | 9.76863 | 9.70434 | 1.54 | 9.99979 | 1.51136 | 8.48864 | 8 48843 |
| 1.05 | 9.93823 | 0.24138 | 9.75862 | 9.69686 | 1.55 | 9.99991 | 1.68195 | 8.31805 | 8.31796 |
| 1.06 | 9.94069 | 0.25150 | 9.74850 | 9.68920 | 1.56 | 9.99997 | 1.96671 | 8.03329 | 8.03327 |
| 1.07 | 9.94310 | 0.26175 | 9.73825 | 9.68135 | 1.57 | 0.00000 | 3.09891 | 6.90109 | 6.90109 |
| 1.08 | 9.94545 | 0.27212 | 9.72788 | 9.67332 | 1.58 | 9.99998 | 2.03603* | 7.96397* | 7 96396* |
| 1.09 | 9.94774 | 0.28264 | 9.71736 | 9.66510 | 1.59 | 9.99992 | 1.71656 | 8.28344 | 8.28336 |
| **1.10** | 9.94998 | 0.29331 | 9.70669 | 9.65667 | **1.60** | 9.99981 | 1.53444 | 8 46556 | 8.46538 |
| 1.11 | 9.95216 | 0.30413 | 9.69587 | 9.64803 | 1.61 | 9.99967 | 1.40645 | 8.59355 | 8.59323 |
| 1.12 | 9.95429 | 0.31512 | 9.68488 | 9.63917 | 1.62 | 9.99947 | 1.30765 | 8.69235 | 8.69182 |
| 1.13 | 9.95637 | 0.32628 | 9.67372 | 9 63008 | 1.63 | 9.99924 | 1.22714 | 8.77286 | 8.77209 |
| 1.14 | 9.95839 | 0.33763 | 9.66237 | 9.62075 | 1.64 | 9.99896 | 1.15918 | 8.84082 | 8.83978 |
| 1.15 | 9.96036 | 0 34918 | 9.65082 | 9.61118 | 1.65 | 9.99864 | 1.10035 | 8.89965 | 8.89829 |
| 1.16 | 9 96228 | 0.36093 | 9.63907 | 9.60134 | 1.66 | 9.99827 | 1.04847 | 8.95154 | 8.94981 |
| 1.17 | 9.96414 | 0.37291 | 9.62709 | 9 59123 | 1.67 | 9.99786 | 1.00204 | 8.99796 | 8.99582 |
| 1.18 | 9.96596 | 0.38512 | 9.61488 | 9.58084 | 1.68 | 9.99741 | 0.96003 | 9.03997 | 9.03737 |
| 1.19 | 9.96772 | 0.39757 | 9.60243 | 9.57015 | 1.69 | 9.99691 | 0.92165 | 9.07835 | 9.07526 |
| **1.20** | 9.96943 | 0.41030 | 9.58970 | 9.55914 | **1.70** | 9.99636 | 0 88630 | 9.11370 | 9.11007 |
| 1.21 | 9 97110 | 0.42330 | 9.57670 | 9.54780 | 1.71 | 9.99578 | 0.85353 | 9.14647 | 9.14225 |
| 1.22 | 9.97271 | 0.43660 | 9.56340 | 9.53611 | 1.72 | 9.99515 | 0.82298 | 9.17702 | 9.17217 |
| 1.23 | 9.97428 | 0.45022 | 9.54978 | 9.52406 | 1.73 | 9.99447 | 0.79436 | 9.20564 | 9.20012 |
| 1.24 | 9.97579 | 0.46418 | 9.53582 | 9.51161 | **1.74** | 9.99375 | 0.76742 | 9.23258 | 9.22634 |
| 1.25 | 9 97726 | 0.47850 | 9.52150 | 9 49875 | 1.75 | 9.99299 | 0.74197 | 9.25803 | 9.25102 |
| 1.26 | 9.97868 | 0.49322 | 9.50678 | 9.48546 | 1.76 | 9.99218 | 0.71784 | 9.28216 | 9.27434 |
| 1.27 | 9.98005 | 0.50835 | 9.49165 | 9.47170 | 1.77 | 9.99133 | 0.69490 | 9.30510 | 9.29642 |
| 1.28 | 9.98137 | 0.52392 | 9.47608 | 9.45745 | 1.78 | 9.99043 | 0.67303 | 9.32697 | 9.31740 |
| 1.29 | 9.98265 | 0.53998 | 9.46002 | 9.44267 | 1.79 | 9 98948 | 0.65212 | 9.34788 | 9.33736 |
| **1.30** | 9.98388 | 0.55656 | 9.44344 | 9.42732 | **1.80** | 9.98849 | 0.63208 | 9.36792 | 9.35641 |
| 1.31 | 9.98506 | 0.57369 | 9.42631 | 9.41137 | 1.81 | 9.98745 | 0.61284 | 9.38716 | 9.37462 |
| 1.32 | 9.98620 | 0.59144 | 9.40856 | 9.39476 | 1.82 | 9.98637 | 0.59432 | 9.40568 | 9.39205 |
| 1.33 | 9.98729 | 0.60984 | 9.39016 | 9.37744 | 1.83 | 9.98524 | 0.57648 | 9.42352 | 9.40877 |
| 1.34 | 9.98833 | 0.62896 | 9.37104 | 9.35937 | 1.84 | 9.98407 | 0.55925 | 9.44075 | 9.42482 |
| 1.35 | 9.98933 | 0.64887 | 9.35113 | 9.34046 | 1.85 | 9.98285 | 0.54258 | 9.45742 | 9.44026 |
| 1.36 | 9.99028 | 0.66964 | 9.33036 | 9.32064 | 1.86 | 9.98158 | 0.52645 | 9.47355 | 9.45513 |
| 1.37 | 9.99119 | 0.69135 | 9.30865 | 9.29983 | 1.87 | 9.98026 | 0.51080 | 9.48920 | 9.46947 |
| 1.38 | 9.99205 | 0.71411 | 9.28589 | 9.27793 | 1.88 | 9.97890 | 0.49560 | 9.50440 | 9.48330 |
| 1.39 | 9.99286 | 0.73804 | 9.26196 | 9.25482 | 1.89 | 9.97749 | 0.48082 | 9.51918 | 9.49667 |
| **1.40** | 9.99363 | 0.76327 | 9.23673 | 9.23036 | **1.90** | 9.97603 | 0.46644 | 9.53356 | 9.50959 |
| 1.41 | 9.99436 | 0.78996 | 9.21004 | 9.20440 | 1.91 | 9.97452 | 0.45242 | 9.54758 | 9.52210 |
| 1.42 | 9.99504 | 0.81839 | 9.18170 | 9.17674 | 1.92 | 9.97296 | 0.43875 | 9.56125 | 9.53422 |
| 1.43 | 9.99568 | 0.84853 | 9.15147 | 9.14716 | 1.93 | 9.97136 | 0.42540 | 9.57460 | 9.54597 |
| 1.44 | 9.99627 | 0.88092 | 9.11908 | 9.11536 | 1.94 | 9.96970 | 0.41235 | 9.58765 | 9.55735 |
| 1.45 | 9.99682 | 0.91583 | 9.08417 | 9.08100 | 1.95 | 9.96800 | 0.39958 | 9.60042 | 9.56841 |
| 1.46 | 9.99733 | 0.95369 | 9.04631 | 9.04364 | 1.96 | 9.96624 | 0.38708 | 9.61292 | 9.57916 |
| 1.47 | 9.99779 | 0.99508 | 9.00492 | 9.00271 | 1.97 | 9.96443 | 0.37484 | 9.62516 | 9.58960 |
| 1.48 | 9.99821 | 1.04074 | 8.95926 | 8.95747 | 1.98 | 9.96258 | 0.36283 | 9.63717 | 9.59975 |
| 1.49 | 9.99858 | 1.09166 | 8.90834 | 8.90692 | 1.99 | 9.96067 | 0.35104 | 9.64896 | 9.60963 |
| **1.50** | 9.99891 | 1.14926 | 8.85074 | 8.84965 | **2.00** | 9.95871 | 0.33946 | 9.66054 | 9.61925 |
| Rad. | L. Sin | L. Tan | L. Cot | L. Cos | Rad. | L. Sin | L. Tan | L. Cot | L. Cos |

* Values of the cosine, tangent and cotangent for angles in the table, 1.58 radians and above, are negative. As a consequence the logarithms of the functions involved are for their absolute values. For example log |cos 1.90| = 9.50959 − 10.

# NATURAL FUNCTIONS FOR ANGLES
## IN $\pi$ RADIANS

| $x\pi$ Radians | | Sin | Tan | Cot | Cos |
|---|---|---|---|---|---|
| $x =$ | | | | | |
| .00 or 1.00 | | .00000 | .00000 | inf | 1.00000 |
| .01 | .99 | .03141 | .03143 | 31.821 | .99951 |
| .02 | .98 | .06279 | .06291 | 15.895 | .99803 |
| .03 | .97 | .09411 | .09453 | 10.579 | .99556 |
| .04 | .96 | .12533 | .12633 | 7.9158 | .99211 |
| .05 | .95 | .15643 | .15838 | 6.3138 | .98769 |
| .06 | .94 | .18738 | .19076 | 5.2422 | .98229 |
| .07 | .93 | .21814 | .22353 | 4.4737 | .97592 |
| .08 | .92 | .24869 | .25676 | 3.8947 | .96858 |
| .09 | .91 | .27899 | .29053 | 3.4420 | .96029 |
| .10 | .90 | .30902 | .32492 | 3.0777 | .95106 |
| .11 | .89 | .33874 | .36002 | 2.7776 | .94088 |
| .12 | .88 | .36812 | .39593 | 2.5257 | .92978 |
| .13 | .87 | .39715 | .43274 | 2.3109 | .91775 |
| .14 | .86 | .42578 | .47056 | 2.1251 | .90483 |
| .15 | .85 | .45399 | .50953 | 1.9626 | .89101 |
| .16 | .84 | .48175 | .54975 | 1.8190 | .87631 |
| .17 | .83 | .50904 | .59140 | 1.6909 | .86074 |
| .18 | .82 | .53583 | .63462 | 1.5757 | .84433 |
| .19 | .81 | .56208 | .67960 | 1.4715 | .82708 |
| .20 | .80 | .58779 | .72654 | 1.3764 | .80902 |
| .21 | .79 | .61291 | .77568 | 1.2892 | .79016 |
| .22 | .78 | .63742 | .82727 | 1.2088 | .77051 |
| .23 | .77 | .66131 | .88162 | 1.1343 | .75011 |
| .24 | .76 | .68455 | .93906 | 1.0649 | .72897 |
| .25 | .75 | .70711 | 1.0000 | 1.0000 | .70711 |
| .26 | .74 | .72897 | 1.0649 | .93906 | .68455 |
| .27 | .73 | .75011 | 1.1343 | .88162 | .66131 |
| .28 | .72 | .77051 | 1.2088 | .82727 | .63742 |
| .29 | .71 | .79016 | 1.2892 | .77568 | .61291 |
| .30 | .70 | .80902 | 1.3764 | .72654 | .58779 |
| .31 | .69 | .82708 | 1.4715 | .67960 | .56208 |
| .32 | .68 | .84433 | 1.5757 | .63462 | .53583 |
| .33 | .67 | .86074 | 1.6909 | .59140 | .50904 |
| .34 | .66 | .87631 | 1.8190 | .54975 | .48175 |
| .35 | .65 | .89101 | 1.9626 | .50953 | .45399 |
| .36 | .64 | .90483 | 2.1251 | .47056 | .42578 |
| .37 | .63 | .91775 | 2.3109 | .43274 | .39715 |
| .38 | .62 | .92978 | 2.5257 | .39593 | .36812 |
| .39 | .61 | .94088 | 2.7776 | .36002 | .33874 |
| .40 | .60 | .95106 | 3.0777 | .32492 | .30902 |
| .41 | .59 | .96029 | 3.4420 | .29053 | .27899 |
| .42 | .58 | .96858 | 3.8947 | .25676 | .24869 |
| .43 | .57 | .97592 | 4.4737 | .22353 | .21814 |
| .44 | .56 | .98229 | 5.2422 | .19076 | .18738 |
| .45 | .55 | .98769 | 6.3138 | .15838 | .15643 |
| .46 | .54 | .99211 | 7.9158 | .12633 | .12533 |
| .47 | .53 | .99556 | 10.579 | .09453 | .09411 |
| .48 | .52 | .99803 | 15.895 | .06291 | .06279 |
| .49 | .51 | .99951 | 31.821 | .03143 | .03141 |
| .50 | .50 | 1.0000 | inf | .00000 | .00000 |

These functions are useful in the solution of wave equations such as the displacement equation of a sound wave in the form:

$$y = A \sin 2\pi nx$$

without the necessity of reducing the angular rotation either to radians or to degrees in order to find the value of the function.

The algebraic sign of the function follows the familiar Quadrant Law for the particular function desired. Thus a numerical value of $9.13\pi$ radians becomes (by the subtraction of the greatest multiple of $2\pi$ radians) $1.13\pi$ radians. This is the same as $.13\pi$ radians in the 3rd Quadrant, which would give, from the tables above, a value of the sine function of $-.39715$.

Submitted by J. A. Blythe Jr.

# HAVERSINES

hav $\theta = \frac{1}{2}$ vers $\theta = \frac{1}{2}(1 - \cos \theta) = \sin^2 \frac{1}{2}\theta$
hav $(-\theta) = $ hav $\theta$
hav $(180° - \theta) = $ hav $(180° + \theta) = 1 - $ hav $\theta$
Characteristics of the logarithms are omitted.

| $\theta°$ | 0′ Value | 0′ Log | 10′ Value | 10′ Log | 20′ Value | 20′ Log | 30′ Value | 30′ Log | 40′ Value | 40′ Log | 50′ Value | 50′ Log |
|---|---|---|---|---|---|---|---|---|---|---|---|---|
| 0 | .0000 | — | .0000 | $\bar{6}$.3254 | .0000 | $\bar{6}$.9275 | .0000 | $\bar{5}$.2796 | .0000 | $\bar{5}$.5295 | .0001 | $\bar{5}$.7233 |
| 1 | .0001 | $\bar{8}$.8817 | .0001 | .0156 | .0001 | .1316 | .0002 | .2339 | .0002 | .3254 | .0003 | .4081 |
| 2 | .0003 | .4837 | .0004 | .5532 | .0004 | .6176 | .0005 | .6775 | .0005 | .7336 | .0006 | .7862 |
| 3 | .0007 | .8358 | .0008 | .8828 | .0008 | .9273 | .0009 | .9697 | .0010 | .0101 | .0011 | .0487 |
| 4 | .0012 | .0856 | .0013 | .1211 | .0014 | .1551 | .0015 | .1879 | .0017 | .2195 | .0018 | .2499 |
| 5 | .0019 | .2794 | .0020 | .3078 | .0022 | .3354 | .0023 | .3621 | .0024 | .3880 | .0026 | .4132 |
| 6 | .0027 | .4376 | .0029 | .4614 | .0031 | .4845 | .0032 | .5071 | .0034 | .5290 | .0036 | .5504 |
| 7 | .0037 | .5714 | .0039 | .5918 | .0041 | .6117 | .0043 | .6312 | .0045 | .6503 | .0047 | .6689 |
| 8 | .0049 | .6872 | .0051 | 7051 | .0053 | .7226 | .0055 | .7397 | .0057 | .7566 | .0059 | .7731 |
| 9 | .0062 | .7893 | .0064 | .8052 | .0066 | .8208 | .0069 | .8361 | .0071 | .8512 | .0073 | .8660 |
| 10 | .0076 | .8806 | .0079 | .8949 | .0081 | .9090 | .0084 | .9229 | .0086 | .9365 | .0089 | .9495 |
| 11 | .0092 | .9631 | .0095 | .9762 | .0097 | .9890 | .0100 | .0016 | .0103 | .0141 | .0106 | .0265 |
| 12 | .0109 | .0385 | .0112 | .0504 | .0115 | .0622 | .0119 | .0738 | .0122 | .0852 | .0125 | .0966 |
| 13 | .0128 | .1077 | .0131 | .1187 | .0135 | .1296 | .0138 | .1404 | .0142 | .1510 | .0145 | .1614 |
| 14 | .0149 | .1718 | .0152 | .1820 | .0156 | .1921 | .0159 | .2021 | .0163 | .2120 | .0167 | .2217 |
| 15 | .0170 | .2314 | .0174 | .2409 | .0178 | .2504 | .0182 | .2597 | .0186 | .2689 | .0190 | .2781 |
| 16 | .0194 | .2871 | .0198 | .2961 | .0202 | .3049 | .0206 | .3137 | .0210 | .3223 | .0214 | .3309 |
| 17 | .0218 | .3394 | .0223 | .3478 | .0227 | .3561 | .0231 | .3644 | .0236 | .3726 | .0240 | .3807 |
| 18 | .0245 | .3887 | .0249 | .3966 | .0254 | .4045 | .0258 | .4123 | .0263 | .4200 | .0268 | .4276 |
| 19 | .0272 | .4352 | .0277 | .4427 | .0282 | .4502 | .0287 | .4576 | .0292 | .4649 | .0297 | .4721 |
| 20 | .0302 | .4793 | .0307 | .4865 | .0312 | .4935 | .0317 | .5006 | .0322 | .5075 | .0327 | .5144 |
| 21 | .0332 | .5213 | .0337 | .5281 | .0343 | .5348 | .0348 | .5415 | .0353 | .5481 | .0359 | .5547 |
| 22 | .0364 | .5612 | .0370 | .5677 | .0375 | .5741 | .0381 | .5805 | .0386 | .5868 | .0392 | .5931 |
| 23 | .0397 | .5993 | .0403 | .6055 | .0409 | .6116 | .0415 | .6177 | .0421 | .6238 | .0426 | .6298 |
| 24 | .0432 | .6358 | .0438 | .6417 | .0444 | .6476 | .0450 | .6534 | .0456 | .6592 | .0462 | .6650 |
| 25 | .0468 | .6707 | .0475 | .6764 | .0481 | .6820 | .0487 | .6876 | .0493 | .6932 | .0500 | .6987 |
| 26 | .0506 | .7042 | .0512 | .7096 | .0519 | .7150 | .0525 | .7204 | .0532 | .7258 | .0538 | .7311 |
| 27 | .0545 | .7364 | .0552 | .7416 | .0558 | .7468 | .0565 | .7520 | .0572 | .7572 | .0578 | .7623 |
| 28 | .0585 | .7674 | .0592 | .7724 | .0599 | .7774 | .0606 | .7824 | .0613 | .7874 | .0620 | .7923 |
| 29 | .0627 | .7972 | .0634 | .8021 | .0641 | .8069 | .0648 | .8117 | .0655 | .8165 | .0663 | .8213 |
| 30 | .0670 | .8260 | .0677 | .8307 | .0684 | .8354 | .0692 | .8400 | .0699 | .8446 | .0707 | .8492 |
| 31 | .0714 | .8538 | .0722 | .8583 | .0729 | .8629 | .0737 | .8673 | .0744 | .8718 | .0752 | .8763 |
| 32 | .0760 | .8807 | .0767 | .8851 | .0775 | .8894 | .0783 | .8938 | .0791 | .8981 | .0799 | .9024 |
| 33 | .0807 | .9067 | .0815 | .9109 | .0823 | .9152 | .0831 | .9194 | .0839 | .9236 | .0847 | .9277 |
| 34 | .0855 | .9319 | .0863 | .9360 | .0871 | .9401 | .0879 | .9442 | .0888 | .9482 | .0896 | .9523 |
| 35 | .0904 | .9563 | .0913 | .9603 | .0921 | .9643 | .0929 | .9682 | .0938 | .9721 | .0946 | .9761 |
| 36 | .0955 | .9800 | .0963 | .9838 | .0972 | .9877 | .0981 | .9915 | .0989 | .9954 | .0998 | .9992 |
| 37 | .1007 | .0030 | .1016 | .0067 | .1024 | .0105 | .1033 | .0142 | .1042 | .0179 | .1051 | .0216 |
| 38 | .1060 | .0253 | .1069 | .0289 | .1078 | .0326 | .1087 | .0362 | .1096 | .0398 | .1105 | .0434 |
| 39 | .1114 | .0470 | .1123 | .0505 | .1133 | .0541 | .1142 | .0576 | .1151 | .0611 | .1160 | .0646 |
| 40 | .1170 | .0681 | .1179 | .0716 | .1189 | .0750 | .1198 | .0784 | .1207 | .0819 | .1217 | .0853 |
| 41 | .1226 | .0887 | .1236 | .0920 | .1246 | .0954 | .1255 | .0987 | .1265 | .1020 | .1275 | .1054 |
| 42 | .1284 | .1087 | .1294 | .1119 | .1304 | .1152 | .1314 | .1185 | .1323 | .1217 | .1333 | .1249 |
| 43 | .1343 | .1282 | .1353 | .1314 | .1363 | .1345 | .1373 | .1377 | .1383 | .1409 | .1393 | .1440 |
| 44 | .1403 | .1472 | .1413 | .1503 | .1424 | .1534 | .1434 | .1565 | .1444 | .1596 | .1454 | .1626 |
| 45 | .1464 | .1657 | .1475 | .1687 | .1485 | .1718 | .1495 | .1748 | .1506 | .1778 | .1516 | .1808 |
| 46 | .1527 | .1838 | .1537 | .1867 | .1548 | .1897 | .1558 | .1926 | .1569 | .1956 | .1579 | .1985 |
| 47 | .1590 | .2014 | .1601 | .2043 | .1611 | .2072 | .1622 | .2101 | .1633 | .2129 | .1644 | .2158 |
| 48 | .1654 | .2186 | .1665 | .2215 | .1676 | .2243 | .1687 | .2271 | .1698 | .2299 | .1709 | .2327 |
| 49 | .1720 | .2355 | .1731 | .2382 | .1742 | .2410 | .1753 | .2437 | .1764 | .2465 | .1775 | .2492 |
| 50 | .1786 | .2519 | .1797 | .2546 | .1808 | .2573 | .1820 | .2600 | .1831 | .2627 | .1842 | .2653 |
| 51 | .1853 | .2680 | .1865 | .2706 | .1876 | .2732 | .1887 | .2759 | .1899 | .2785 | .1910 | .2811 |
| 52 | .1922 | .2837 | .1933 | .2863 | .1945 | .2888 | .1956 | .2914 | .1968 | .2940 | .1979 | .2965 |
| 53 | .1991 | .2991 | .2003 | .3016 | .2014 | .3041 | .2026 | .3066 | .2038 | .3091 | .2049 | .3116 |
| 54 | .2061 | .3141 | .2073 | .3166 | .2085 | .3190 | .2096 | .3215 | .2108 | .3239 | .2120 | .3264 |
| 55 | .2132 | .3288 | .2144 | .3312 | .2156 | .3336 | .2168 | .3361 | .2180 | .3384 | .2192 | .3408 |
| 56 | .2204 | .3432 | .2216 | .3456 | .2228 | .3480 | .2240 | .3503 | .2252 | .3527 | .2265 | .3550 |
| 57 | .2277 | .3573 | .2289 | .3596 | .2301 | .3620 | .2314 | .3643 | .2326 | .3666 | .2338 | .3689 |
| 58 | .2350 | .3711 | .2363 | .3734 | .2375 | .3757 | .2388 | .3779 | .2400 | .3802 | .2412 | .3824 |
| 59 | .2425 | .3847 | .2437 | .3869 | .2450 | .3891 | .2462 | .3913 | .2475 | .3935 | .2487 | .3957 |

# HAVERSINES (Continued)

Characteristics of the logarithms are omitted.

| θ° | 0' Value | 0' Log | 10' Value | 10' Log | 20' Value | 20' Log | 30' Value | 30' Log | 40' Value | 40' Log | 50' Value | 50' Log |
|---|---|---|---|---|---|---|---|---|---|---|---|---|
| 60 | .2500 | .3979 | .2513 | .4001 | .2525 | .4023 | .2538 | .4045 | .2551 | .4066 | .2563 | .4088 |
| 61 | .2576 | .4109 | .2589 | .4131 | .2601 | .4152 | .2614 | .4173 | .2627 | .4195 | .2640 | .4216 |
| 62 | .2653 | .4237 | .2665 | .4258 | .2678 | .4279 | .2691 | .4300 | .2704 | .4320 | .2717 | .4341 |
| 63 | .2730 | .4362 | .2743 | .4382 | .2756 | .4403 | .2769 | .4423 | .2782 | .4444 | .2795 | .4464 |
| 64 | .2808 | .4484 | .2821 | .4504 | .2834 | .4524 | .2847 | .4545 | .2861 | .4565 | .2874 | .4584 |
| 65 | .2887 | .4604 | .2900 | .4624 | .2913 | .4644 | .2927 | .4664 | .2940 | .4683 | .2953 | .4703 |
| 66 | .2966 | .4722 | .2980 | .4742 | .2993 | .4761 | .3006 | .4780 | .3020 | .4799 | .3033 | .4819 |
| 67 | .3046 | .4838 | .3060 | .4857 | .3073 | .4876 | .3087 | .4895 | .3100 | .4914 | .3113 | .4932 |
| 68 | .3127 | .4951 | .3140 | .4970 | .3154 | .4989 | .3167 | .5007 | .3181 | .5026 | .3195 | .5044 |
| 69 | .3208 | .5063 | .3222 | .5081 | .3235 | .5099 | .3249 | .5117 | .3263 | .5136 | .3276 | .5154 |
| 70 | .3290 | .5172 | .3304 | .5190 | .3317 | .5208 | .3331 | .5226 | .3345 | .5244 | .3358 | .5261 |
| 71 | .3372 | .5279 | .3386 | .5297 | .3400 | .5314 | .3413 | .5332 | .3427 | .5349 | .3441 | .5367 |
| 72 | .3455 | .5384 | .3469 | .5402 | .3483 | .5419 | .3496 | .5436 | .3510 | .5454 | .3524 | .5471 |
| 73 | .3538 | .5488 | .3552 | .5505 | .3566 | .5522 | .3580 | .5539 | .3594 | .5556 | .3608 | .5572 |
| 74 | .3622 | .5589 | .3636 | .5606 | .3650 | .5623 | .3664 | .5639 | .3678 | .5656 | .3692 | .5672 |
| 75 | .3706 | .5689 | .3720 | .5705 | .3734 | .5722 | .3748 | .5738 | .3762 | .5754 | .3776 | .5771 |
| 76 | .3790 | .5787 | .3805 | .5803 | .3819 | .5819 | .3833 | .5835 | .3847 | .5851 | .3861 | .5867 |
| 77 | .3875 | .5883 | .3889 | .5899 | .3904 | .5915 | .3918 | .5930 | .3932 | .5946 | .3946 | .5962 |
| 78 | .3960 | .5977 | .3975 | .5993 | .3989 | .6009 | .4003 | .6024 | .4017 | .6039 | .4032 | .6055 |
| 79 | .4046 | .6070 | .4060 | .6086 | .4075 | .6101 | .4089 | .6116 | .4103 | .6131 | .4117 | .6146 |
| 80 | .4132 | .6161 | .4146 | .6176 | .4160 | .6191 | .4175 | .6206 | .4189 | .6221 | .4203 | .6236 |
| 81 | .4218 | .6251 | .4232 | .6266 | .4247 | .6280 | .4261 | .6295 | .4275 | .6310 | .4290 | .6324 |
| 82 | .4304 | .6339 | .4319 | .6353 | .4333 | .6368 | .4347 | .6382 | .4362 | .6397 | .4376 | .6411 |
| 83 | .4391 | .6425 | .4405 | .6440 | .4420 | .6454 | .4434 | .6468 | .4448 | .6482 | .4463 | .6496 |
| 84 | .4477 | .6510 | .4492 | .6524 | .4506 | .6538 | .4521 | .6552 | .4535 | .6566 | .4550 | .6580 |
| 85 | .4564 | .6594 | .4579 | .6607 | .4593 | .6621 | .4608 | .6635 | .4622 | .6648 | .4637 | .6662 |
| 86 | .4651 | .6676 | .4666 | .6689 | .4680 | .6703 | .4695 | .6716 | .4709 | .6730 | .4724 | .6743 |
| 87 | .4738 | .6756 | .4753 | .6770 | .4767 | .6783 | .4782 | .6796 | .4796 | .6809 | .4811 | .6822 |
| 88 | .4826 | .6835 | .4840 | .6848 | .4855 | .6862 | .4869 | .6875 | .4884 | .6887 | .4898 | .6900 |
| 89 | .4913 | .6913 | .4927 | .6926 | .4942 | .6939 | .4956 | .6952 | .4971 | .6964 | .4985 | .6977 |
| 90 | .5000 | .6990 | .5015 | .7002 | .5029 | .7015 | .5044 | .7027 | .5058 | .7040 | .5073 | .7052 |
| 91 | .5087 | .7065 | .5102 | .7077 | .5116 | .7090 | .5131 | .7102 | .5145 | .7114 | .5160 | .7126 |
| 92 | .5174 | .7139 | .5189 | .7151 | .5204 | .7163 | .5218 | .7175 | .5233 | .7187 | .5247 | .7199 |
| 93 | .5262 | .7211 | .5276 | .7223 | .5291 | .7235 | .5305 | .7247 | .5320 | .7259 | .5334 | .7271 |
| 94 | .5349 | .7283 | .5363 | .7294 | .5378 | .7306 | .5392 | .7318 | .5407 | .7329 | .5421 | .7341 |
| 95 | .5436 | .7353 | .5450 | .7364 | .5465 | .7376 | .5479 | .7387 | .5494 | .7399 | .5508 | .7410 |
| 96 | .5523 | .7421 | .5537 | .7433 | .5552 | .7444 | .5566 | .7455 | .5580 | .7467 | .5595 | .7478 |
| 97 | .5609 | .7489 | .5624 | .7500 | .5638 | .7511 | .5653 | .7523 | .5667 | .7534 | .5681 | .7545 |
| 98 | .5696 | .7556 | .5710 | .7567 | .5725 | .7577 | .5739 | .7588 | .5753 | .7599 | .5768 | .7610 |
| 99 | .5782 | .7621 | .5797 | .7632 | .5811 | .7642 | .5825 | .7653 | .5840 | .7664 | .5854 | .7674 |
| 100 | .5868 | .7685 | .5883 | .7696 | .5897 | .7706 | .5911 | .7717 | .5925 | .7727 | .5940 | .7738 |
| 101 | .5954 | .7748 | .5968 | .7759 | .5983 | .7769 | .5997 | .7779 | .6011 | .7790 | .6025 | .7800 |
| 102 | .6040 | .7810 | .6054 | .7820 | .6068 | .7830 | .6082 | .7841 | .6096 | .7851 | .6111 | .7861 |
| 103 | .6125 | .7871 | .6139 | .7881 | .6153 | .7891 | .6167 | .7901 | .6181 | .7911 | .6195 | .7921 |
| 104 | .6210 | .7931 | .6224 | .7940 | .6238 | .7950 | .6252 | .7960 | .6266 | .7970 | .6280 | .7980 |
| 105 | .6294 | .7989 | .6308 | .7999 | .6322 | .8009 | .6336 | .8018 | .6350 | .8028 | .6364 | .8037 |
| 106 | .6378 | .8047 | .6392 | .8056 | .6406 | .8066 | .6420 | .8075 | .6434 | .8085 | .6448 | .8094 |
| 107 | .6462 | .8104 | .6476 | .8113 | .6490 | .8122 | .6504 | .8131 | .6517 | .8141 | .6531 | .8150 |
| 108 | .6545 | .8159 | .6559 | .8168 | .6573 | .8177 | .6587 | .8187 | .6600 | .8196 | .6614 | .8205 |
| 109 | .6628 | .8214 | .6642 | .8223 | .6655 | .8232 | .6669 | .8241 | .6683 | .8250 | .6696 | .8258 |
| 110 | .6710 | .8267 | .6724 | .8276 | .6737 | .8285 | .6751 | .8294 | .6765 | .8302 | .6778 | .8311 |
| 111 | .6792 | .8320 | .6805 | .8329 | .6819 | .8337 | .6833 | .8346 | .6846 | .8354 | .6860 | .8363 |
| 112 | .6873 | .8371 | .6887 | .8380 | .6900 | .8388 | .6913 | .8397 | .6927 | .8405 | .6940 | .8414 |
| 113 | .6954 | .8422 | .6967 | .8430 | .6980 | .8439 | .6994 | .8447 | .7007 | .8455 | .7020 | .8464 |
| 114 | .7034 | .8472 | .7047 | .8480 | .7060 | .8488 | .7073 | .8496 | .7087 | .8504 | .7100 | .8513 |
| 115 | .7113 | .8521 | .7126 | .8529 | .7139 | .8537 | .7153 | .8545 | .7166 | .8553 | .7179 | .8561 |
| 116 | .7192 | .8568 | .7205 | .8576 | .7218 | .8584 | .7231 | .8592 | .7244 | .8600 | .7257 | .8608 |
| 117 | .7270 | .8615 | .7283 | .8623 | .7296 | .8631 | .7309 | .8638 | .7322 | .8646 | .7335 | .8654 |
| 118 | .7347 | .8661 | .7360 | .8669 | .7373 | .8676 | .7386 | .8684 | .7399 | .8691 | .7411 | .8699 |
| 119 | .7424 | .8706 | .7437 | .8714 | .7449 | .8721 | .7462 | .8729 | .7475 | .8736 | .7487 | .8743 |

Characteristics of the logarithms are omitted.

| θ° | 0' Value | Log | 10' Value | Log | 20' Value | Log | 30' Value | Log | 40' Value | Log | 50' Value | Log |
|---|---|---|---|---|---|---|---|---|---|---|---|---|
| 120 | .7500 | .8751 | .7513 | .8758 | .7525 | .8765 | .7538 | .8772 | .7550 | .8780 | .7563 | .8787 |
| 121 | .7575 | .8794 | .7588 | .8801 | .7600 | .8808 | .7612 | .8815 | .7625 | .8822 | .7637 | .8829 |
| 122 | .7650 | .8836 | .7662 | .8843 | .7674 | .8850 | .7686 | .8857 | .7699 | .8864 | .7711 | .8871 |
| 123 | .7723 | .8878 | .7735 | .8885 | .7748 | .8892 | .7760 | .8898 | .7772 | .8905 | .7784 | .8912 |
| 124 | .7796 | .8919 | .7808 | .8925 | .7820 | .8932 | .7832 | .8939 | .7844 | .8945 | .7856 | .8952 |
| 125 | .7868 | .8959 | .7880 | .8965 | .7892 | .8972 | .7904 | .8978 | .7915 | .8985 | .7927 | .8991 |
| 126 | .7939 | .8998 | .7951 | .9004 | .7962 | .9010 | .7974 | .9017 | .7986 | .9023 | .7997 | .9030 |
| 127 | .8009 | .9036 | .8021 | .9042 | .8032 | .9048 | .8044 | .9055 | .8055 | .9061 | .8067 | .9067 |
| 128 | .8078 | .9073 | .8090 | .9079 | .8101 | .9085 | .8113 | .9092 | .8124 | .9098 | .8135 | .9104 |
| 129 | .8147 | .9110 | .8158 | .9116 | .8169 | .9122 | .8180 | .9128 | .8192 | .9134 | .8203 | .9140 |
| 130 | .8214 | .9146 | .8225 | .9151 | .8236 | .9157 | .8247 | .9163 | .8258 | .9169 | .8269 | .9175 |
| 131 | .8280 | .9180 | .8291 | .9186 | .8302 | .9192 | .8313 | .9198 | .8324 | .9203 | .8335 | .9209 |
| 132 | .8346 | .9215 | .8356 | .9220 | .8367 | .9226 | .8378 | .9231 | .8389 | .9237 | .8399 | .9242 |
| 133 | .8410 | .9248 | .8421 | .9253 | .8431 | .9259 | .8442 | .9264 | .8452 | .9270 | .8463 | .9275 |
| 134 | .8473 | .9281 | .8484 | .9286 | .8494 | .9291 | .8505 | .9297 | .8515 | .9302 | .8525 | .9307 |
| 135 | .8536 | .9312 | .8546 | .9318 | .8556 | .9323 | .8566 | .9328 | .8576 | .9333 | .8587 | .9338 |
| 136 | .8597 | .9343 | .8607 | .9348 | .8617 | .9353 | .8627 | .9359 | .8637 | .9364 | .8647 | .9369 |
| 137 | .8657 | .9374 | .8667 | .9379 | .8677 | .9383 | .8686 | .9388 | .8696 | .9393 | .8706 | .9398 |
| 138 | .8716 | .9403 | .8725 | .9408 | .8735 | .9413 | .8745 | .9417 | .8754 | .9422 | .8764 | .9427 |
| 139 | .8774 | .9432 | .8783 | .9436 | .8793 | .9441 | .8802 | .9446 | .8811 | .9450 | .8821 | .9455 |
| 140 | .8830 | .9460 | .8840 | .9464 | .8849 | .9469 | .8858 | .9473 | .8867 | .9478 | .8877 | .9482 |
| 141 | .8886 | .9487 | .8895 | .9491 | .8904 | .9496 | .8913 | .9500 | .8922 | .9505 | .8931 | .9509 |
| 142 | .8940 | .9513 | .8949 | .9518 | .8958 | .9522 | .8967 | .9526 | .8976 | .9531 | .8984 | .9535 |
| 143 | .8993 | .9539 | .9002 | .9543 | .9011 | .9548 | .9019 | .9552 | .9028 | .9556 | .9037 | .9560 |
| 144 | .9045 | .9564 | .9054 | .9568 | .9062 | .9572 | .9071 | .9576 | .9079 | .9580 | .9087 | .9584 |
| 145 | .9096 | .9588 | .9104 | .9592 | .9112 | .9596 | .9121 | .9600 | .9129 | .9604 | .9137 | .9608 |
| 146 | .9145 | .9612 | .9153 | .9616 | .9161 | .9620 | .9169 | .9623 | .9177 | .9627 | .9185 | .9631 |
| 147 | .9193 | .9635 | .9201 | .9638 | .9209 | .9642 | .9217 | .9646 | .9225 | .9650 | .9233 | .9653 |
| 148 | .9240 | .9657 | .9248 | .9660 | .9256 | .9664 | .9263 | .9668 | .9271 | .9671 | .9278 | .9675 |
| 149 | .9286 | .9678 | .9293 | .9682 | .9301 | .9685 | .9308 | .9689 | .9316 | .9692 | .9323 | .9695 |
| 150 | .9330 | .9699 | .9337 | .9702 | .9345 | .9706 | .9352 | .9709 | .9359 | .9712 | .9366 | .9716 |
| 151 | .9373 | .9719 | .9380 | .9722 | .9387 | .9725 | .9394 | .9729 | .9401 | .9732 | .9408 | .9735 |
| 152 | .9415 | .9738 | .9422 | .9741 | .9428 | .9744 | .9435 | .9747 | .9442 | .9751 | .9448 | .9754 |
| 153 | .9455 | .9757 | .9462 | .9760 | .9468 | .9763 | .9475 | .9766 | .9481 | .9769 | .9488 | .9772 |
| 154 | .9494 | .9774 | .9500 | .9777 | .9507 | .9780 | .9513 | .9783 | .9519 | .9786 | .9525 | .9789 |
| 155 | .9532 | .9792 | .9538 | .9794 | .9544 | .9797 | .9550 | .9800 | .9556 | .9803 | .9562 | .9805 |
| 156 | .9568 | .9808 | .9574 | .9811 | .9579 | .9813 | .9585 | .9816 | .9591 | .9819 | .9597 | .9821 |
| 157 | .9603 | .9824 | .9608 | .9826 | .9614 | .9829 | .9619 | .9831 | .9625 | .9834 | .9630 | .9836 |
| 158 | .9636 | .9839 | .9641 | .9841 | .9647 | .9844 | .9652 | .9846 | .9657 | .9849 | .9663 | .9851 |
| 159 | .9668 | .9853 | .9673 | .9856 | .9678 | .9858 | .9683 | .9860 | .9688 | .9863 | .9693 | .9865 |
| 160 | .9698 | .9867 | .9703 | .9869 | .9708 | .9871 | .9713 | .9874 | .9718 | .9876 | .9723 | .9878 |
| 161 | .9728 | .9880 | .9732 | .9882 | .9737 | .9884 | .9742 | .9886 | .9746 | .9888 | .9751 | .9890 |
| 162 | .9755 | .9892 | .9760 | .9894 | .9764 | .9896 | .9769 | .9898 | .9773 | .9900 | .9777 | .9902 |
| 163 | .9782 | .9904 | .9786 | .9906 | .9790 | .9908 | .9794 | .9910 | .9798 | .9911 | .9802 | .9913 |
| 164 | .9806 | .9915 | .9810 | .9917 | .9814 | .9919 | .9818 | .9920 | .9822 | .9922 | .9826 | .9924 |
| 165 | .9830 | .9925 | .9833 | .9927 | .9837 | .9929 | .9841 | .9930 | .9844 | .9932 | .9848 | .9933 |
| 166 | .9851 | .9935 | .9855 | .9937 | .9858 | .9938 | .9862 | .9940 | .9865 | .9941 | .9869 | .9943 |
| 167 | .9872 | .9944 | .9875 | .9945 | .9878 | .9947 | .9881 | .9948 | .9885 | .9950 | .9888 | .9951 |
| 168 | .9891 | .9952 | .9894 | .9954 | .9897 | .9955 | .9900 | .9956 | .9903 | .9957 | .9905 | .9959 |
| 169 | .9908 | .9960 | .9911 | .9961 | .9914 | .9962 | .9916 | .9963 | .9919 | .9965 | .9921 | .9966 |
| 170 | .9924 | .9967 | .9927 | .9968 | .9929 | .9969 | .9931 | .9970 | .9934 | .9971 | .9936 | .9972 |
| 171 | .9938 | .9973 | .9941 | .9974 | .9943 | .9975 | .9945 | .9976 | .9947 | .9977 | .9949 | .9978 |
| 172 | .9951 | .9979 | .9953 | .9980 | .9955 | .9981 | .9957 | .9981 | .9959 | .9982 | .9961 | .9983 |
| 173 | .9963 | .9984 | .9964 | .9985 | .9966 | .9985 | .9968 | .9986 | .9969 | .9987 | .9971 | .9987 |
| 174 | .9973 | .9988 | .9974 | .9989 | .9976 | .9989 | .9977 | .9990 | .9978 | .9991 | .9980 | .9991 |
| 175 | .9981 | .9992 | .9982 | .9992 | .9983 | .9993 | .9985 | .9993 | .9986 | .9994 | .9987 | .9994 |
| 176 | .9988 | .9995 | .9989 | .9995 | .9990 | .9996 | .9991 | .9996 | .9992 | .9997 | .9992 | .9997 |
| 177 | .9993 | .9997 | .9994 | .9997 | .9995 | .9998 | .9995 | .9998 | .9996 | .9998 | .9996 | .9998 |
| 178 | .9997 | .9999 | .9997 | .9999 | .9998 | .9999 | .9998 | .9999 | .9999 | .9999 | .9999 | .9999 |
| 179 | .9999 | .9999 | .9999 | .9999 | 1.0000 | .0000 | 1.0000 | .0000 | 1.0000 | .0000 | 1.0000 | .0000 |
| 180 | 1.0000 | .0000 | | | | | | | | | | |

# NATURAL OR NAPERIAN LOGARITHMS

## 0.000–0.499

| N | 0 | 1 | 2 | 3 | 4 | 5 | 6 | 7 | 8 | 9 |
|---|---|---|---|---|---|---|---|---|---|---|
| **0.00** | − ∞ | −6‡ .90776 | −6 .21461 | −5 .80914 | −5 .52146 | −5 .29832 | −5 .11600 | −4 .96185 | −4 .82831 | −4 .71053 |
| .01 | −4.60517 | .50986 | .42285 | .34281 | .26870 | .19971 | .13517 | .07454 | .01738 | *.96332 |
| .02 | −3.91202 | .86323 | .81671 | .77226 | .72970 | .68888 | .64966 | .61192 | .57555 | .54046 |
| .03 | .50656 | .47377 | .44202 | .41125 | .38139 | .35241 | .32424 | .29684 | .27017 | .24419 |
| .04 | .21888 | .19418 | .17009 | .14656 | .12357 | .10109 | .07911 | .05761 | .03655 | .01593 |
| .05 | −2.99573 | .97593 | .95651 | .93746 | .91877 | .90042 | .88240 | .86470 | .84731 | .83022 |
| .06 | .81341 | .79688 | .78062 | .76462 | .74887 | .73337 | .71810 | .70306 | .68825 | .67365 |
| .07 | .65926 | .64508 | .63109 | .61730 | .60369 | .59027 | .57702 | .56395 | .55105 | .53831 |
| .08 | .52573 | .51331 | .50104 | .48891 | .47694 | .46510 | .45341 | .44185 | .43042 | .41912 |
| .09 | .40795 | .39690 | .38597 | .37516 | .36446 | .35388 | .34341 | .33304 | .32279 | .31264 |
| **0.10** | −2.30259 | .29263 | .28278 | .27303 | .26336 | .25379 | .24432 | .23493 | .22562 | .21641 |
| .11 | .20727 | .19823 | .18926 | .18037 | .17156 | .16282 | .15417 | .14558 | .13707 | .12863 |
| .12 | .12026 | .11196 | .10373 | .09557 | .08747 | .07944 | .07147 | .06357 | .05573 | .04794 |
| .13 | .04022 | .03256 | .02495 | .01741 | .00992 | .00248 | *.99510 | *.98777 | *.98050 | *.97328 |
| .14 | −1.96611 | .95900 | .95193 | .94491 | .93794 | .93102 | .92415 | .91732 | .91054 | .90381 |
| .15 | .89712 | .89048 | .88387 | .87732 | .87080 | .86433 | .85790 | .85151 | .84516 | .83885 |
| .16 | .83258 | .82635 | .82016 | .81401 | .80789 | .80181 | .79577 | .78976 | .78379 | .77786 |
| .17 | .77196 | .76609 | .76026 | .75446 | .74870 | .74297 | .73727 | .73161 | .72597 | .72037 |
| .18 | .71480 | .70926 | .70375 | .69827 | .69282 | .68740 | .68201 | .67665 | .67131 | .66601 |
| .19 | .66073 | .65548 | .65026 | .64507 | .63990 | .63476 | .62964 | .62455 | .61949 | .61445 |
| **0.20** | −1.60944 | .60445 | .59949 | .59455 | .58964 | .58475 | .57988 | .57504 | .57022 | .56542 |
| .21 | .56065 | .55590 | .55117 | .54646 | .54178 | .53712 | .53248 | .52786 | .52326 | .51868 |
| .22 | .51413 | .50959 | .50508 | .50058 | .49611 | .49165 | .48722 | .48281 | .47841 | .47403 |
| .23 | .46968 | .46534 | .46102 | .45672 | .45243 | .44817 | .44392 | .43970 | .43548 | .43129 |
| .24 | .42712 | .42296 | .41882 | .41469 | .41059 | .40650 | .40242 | .39837 | .39433 | .39030 |
| .25 | .38629 | .38230 | .37833 | .37437 | .37042 | .36649 | .36258 | .35868 | .35480 | .35093 |
| .26 | .34707 | .34323 | .33941 | .33560 | .33181 | .32803 | .32426 | .32051 | .31677 | .31304 |
| .27 | .30933 | .30564 | .30195 | .29828 | .29463 | .29098 | .28735 | .28374 | .28013 | .27654 |
| .28 | .27297 | .26940 | .26585 | .26231 | .25878 | .25527 | .25176 | .24827 | .24479 | .24133 |
| .29 | .23787 | .23443 | .23100 | .22758 | .22418 | .22078 | .21740 | .21402 | .21066 | .20731 |
| **0.30** | −1.20397 | .20065 | .19733 | .19402 | .19073 | .18744 | .18417 | .18091 | .17766 | .17441 |
| .31 | .17118 | .16796 | .16475 | .16155 | .15836 | .15518 | .15201 | .14885 | .14570 | .14256 |
| .32 | .13943 | .13631 | .13320 | .13010 | .12701 | .12393 | .12086 | .11780 | .11474 | .11170 |
| .33 | .10866 | .10564 | .10262 | .09961 | .09661 | .09362 | .09064 | .08767 | .08471 | .08176 |
| .34 | .07881 | .07587 | .07294 | .07002 | .06711 | .06421 | .06132 | .05843 | .05555 | .05268 |
| .35 | −1.04982 | .04697 | .04412 | .04129 | .03846 | .03564 | .03282 | .03002 | .02722 | .02443 |
| .36 | .02165 | .01888 | .01611 | .01335 | .01060 | .00786 | .00512 | .00239 | *.99967 | *.99696 |
| .37 | −0.99425 | .99155 | .98886 | .98618 | .98351 | .98083 | .97817 | .97551 | .97286 | .97022 |
| .38 | .96758 | .96496 | .96233 | .95972 | .95711 | .95451 | .95192 | .94933 | .94675 | .94418 |
| .39 | .94161 | .93905 | .93649 | .93395 | .93140 | .92887 | .92634 | .92382 | .92130 | .91879 |
| **0.40** | −0.91629 | .91379 | .91130 | .90882 | .90634 | .90387 | .90140 | .89894 | .89649 | .89404 |
| .41 | .89160 | .88916 | .88673 | .88431 | .88189 | .87948 | .87707 | .87467 | .87227 | .86988 |
| .42 | .86750 | .86512 | .86275 | .86038 | .85802 | .85567 | .85332 | .85097 | .84863 | .84630 |
| .43 | .84397 | .84165 | .83933 | .83702 | .83471 | .83241 | .83011 | .82782 | .82554 | .82326 |
| .44 | .82098 | .81871 | .81645 | .81419 | .81193 | .80968 | .80744 | .80520 | .80296 | .80073 |
| .45 | .79851 | .79629 | .79407 | .79186 | .78966 | .78746 | .78526 | .78307 | .78089 | .77871 |
| .46 | .77653 | .77436 | .77219 | .77003 | .76787 | .76572 | .76357 | .76143 | .75929 | .75715 |
| .47 | .75502 | .75290 | .75078 | .74866 | .74655 | .74444 | .74234 | .74024 | .73814 | .73605 |
| .48 | .73397 | .73189 | .72981 | .72774 | .72567 | .72361 | .72155 | .71949 | .71744 | .71539 |
| .49 | .71335 | .71131 | .70928 | .70725 | .70522 | .70320 | .70118 | .69917 | .69716 | .69515 |

‡ Note that the whole number values are given above the decimal values for the first line. In the second and following lines they are given at the left. All decimal values are negative on this page.

**0.500-0.999**

| N | 0 | 1 | 2 | 3 | 4 | 5 | 6 | 7 | 8 | 9 |
|---|---|---|---|---|---|---|---|---|---|---|
| **0.50** | −0.69315 | .69115 | .68916 | .68717 | .68518 | .68320 | .68122 | .67924 | .67727 | .67531 |
| .51 | .67334 | .67139 | .66943 | .66748 | .66553 | .66359 | .66165 | .65971 | .65778 | .65585 |
| .52 | .65393 | .65201 | .65009 | .64817 | .64626 | .64436 | .64245 | .64055 | .63866 | .63677 |
| .53 | .63488 | .63299 | .63111 | .62923 | .62736 | .62549 | .62362 | .62176 | .61990 | .61804 |
| .54 | .61619 | .61434 | .61249 | .61065 | .60881 | .60697 | .60514 | .60331 | .60148 | .59966 |
| .55 | .59784 | .59602 | .59421 | .59240 | .59059 | .58879 | .58699 | .58519 | .58340 | .58161 |
| .56 | .57982 | .57803 | .57625 | .57448 | .57270 | .57093 | .56916 | .56740 | .56563 | .56387 |
| .57 | .56212 | .56037 | .55862 | .55687 | .55513 | .55339 | .55165 | .54991 | .54818 | .54645 |
| .58 | .54473 | .54300 | .54128 | .53957 | .53785 | .53614 | .53444 | .53273 | .53103 | .52933 |
| .59 | .52763 | .52594 | .52425 | .52256 | .52088 | .51919 | .51751 | .51584 | .51416 | .51249 |
| **0.60** | −0.51083 | .50916 | .50750 | .50584 | .50418 | .50253 | .50088 | .49923 | .49758 | .49594 |
| .61 | .49430 | .49266 | .49102 | .48939 | .48776 | .48613 | .48451 | .48289 | .48127 | .47965 |
| .62 | .47804 | .47642 | .47482 | .47321 | .47160 | .47000 | .46840 | .46681 | .46522 | .46362 |
| .63 | .46204 | .46045 | .45887 | .45728 | .45571 | .45413 | .45256 | .45099 | .44942 | .44785 |
| .64 | .44629 | .44473 | .44317 | .44161 | .44006 | .43850 | .43696 | .43541 | .43386 | .43232 |
| .65 | .43078 | .42925 | .42771 | .42618 | .42465 | .42312 | .42159 | .42007 | .41855 | .41703 |
| .66 | .41552 | .41400 | .41249 | .41098 | .40947 | .40797 | .40647 | .40497 | .40347 | .40197 |
| .67 | .40048 | .39899 | .39750 | .39601 | .39453 | .39304 | .39156 | .39008 | .38861 | .38713 |
| .68 | .38566 | .38419 | .38273 | .38126 | .37980 | .37834 | .37688 | .37542 | .37397 | .37251 |
| .69 | .37106 | .36962 | .36817 | .36673 | .36528 | .36384 | .36241 | .36097 | .35954 | .35810 |
| **0.70** | −0.35667 | .35525 | .35382 | .35240 | .35098 | .34956 | .34814 | .34672 | .34531 | .34390 |
| .71 | .34249 | .34108 | .33968 | .33827 | .33687 | .33547 | .33408 | .33268 | .33129 | .32989 |
| .72 | .32850 | .32712 | .32573 | .32435 | .32296 | .32158 | .32021 | .31883 | .31745 | .31608 |
| .73 | .31471 | .31334 | .31197 | .31061 | .30925 | .30788 | .30653 | .30517 | .30381 | .30246 |
| .74 | .30111 | .29975 | .29841 | .29706 | .29571 | .29437 | .29303 | .29169 | .29035 | .28902 |
| .75 | .28768 | .28635 | .28502 | .28369 | .28236 | .28104 | .27971 | .27839 | .27707 | .27575 |
| .76 | .27444 | .27312 | .27181 | .27050 | .26919 | .26788 | .26657 | .26527 | .26397 | .26266 |
| .77 | .26136 | .26007 | .25877 | .25748 | .25618 | .25489 | .25360 | .25231 | .25103 | .24974 |
| .78 | .24846 | .24718 | .24590 | .24462 | .24335 | .24207 | .24080 | .23953 | .23826 | .23699 |
| .79 | .23572 | .23446 | .23319 | .23193 | .23067 | .22941 | .22816 | .22690 | .22565 | .22439 |
| **0.80** | −0.22314 | .22189 | .22065 | .21940 | .21816 | .21691 | .21567 | .21443 | .21319 | .21196 |
| .81 | .21072 | .20949 | .20825 | .20702 | .20579 | .20457 | .20334 | .20212 | .20089 | .19967 |
| .82 | .19845 | .19723 | .19601 | .19480 | .19358 | .19237 | .19116 | .18995 | .18874 | .18754 |
| .83 | .18633 | .18513 | .18392 | .18272 | .18152 | .18032 | .17913 | .17793 | .17674 | .17554 |
| .84 | .17435 | .17316 | .17198 | .17079 | .16960 | .16842 | .16724 | .16605 | .16487 | .16370 |
| .85 | −0.16252 | .16134 | .16017 | .15900 | .15782 | .15665 | .15548 | .15432 | .15315 | .15199 |
| .86 | .15032 | .14966 | .14850 | .14734 | .14618 | .14503 | .14387 | .14272 | .14156 | .14041 |
| .87 | .13926 | .13811 | .13697 | .13582 | .13467 | .13353 | .13239 | .13125 | .13011 | .12897 |
| .88 | .12783 | .12670 | .12556 | .12443 | .12330 | .12217 | .12104 | .11991 | .11878 | .11766 |
| .89 | .11653 | .11541 | .11429 | .11317 | .11205 | .11093 | .10981 | .10870 | .10759 | .10647 |
| **0.90** | −0.10536 | .10425 | .10314 | .10203 | .10093 | .09982 | .09872 | .09761 | .09651 | .09541 |
| .91 | .09431 | .09321 | .09212 | .09102 | .08992 | .08883 | .08774 | .08665 | .08556 | .08447 |
| .92 | .08338 | .08230 | .08121 | .08013 | .07904 | .07796 | .07688 | .07580 | .07472 | .07365 |
| .93 | .07257 | .07150 | .07042 | .06935 | .06828 | .06721 | .06614 | .06507 | .06401 | .06294 |
| .94 | .06188 | .06081 | .05975 | .05869 | .05763 | .05657 | .05551 | .05446 | .05340 | .05235 |
| .95 | .05129 | .05024 | .04919 | .04814 | .04709 | .04604 | .04500 | .04395 | .04291 | .04186 |
| .96 | .04082 | .03978 | .03874 | .03770 | .03666 | .03563 | .03459 | .03356 | .03252 | .03149 |
| .97 | .03046 | .02943 | .02840 | .02737 | .02634 | .02532 | .02429 | .02327 | .02225 | .02122 |
| .98 | .02020 | .01918 | .01816 | .01715 | .01613 | .01511 | .01410 | .01309 | .01207 | .01106 |
| .99 | .01005 | .00904 | .00803 | .00702 | .00602 | .00501 | .00401 | .00300 | .00200 | .00100 |

# NATURAL OR NAPERIAN LOGARITHMS (Continued)

To find the natural logarithm of a number which is $\frac{1}{10}$, $\frac{1}{100}$, $\frac{1}{1000}$, etc. of a number whose logarithm is given, subtract from the given logarithm $\log_e 10$, $2\log_e 10$, $3\log_e 10$, etc.

To find the natural logarithm of a number which is 10, 100, 1000, etc. times a number whose logarithm is given, add to the given logarithm $\log_e 10$, $2\log_e 10$, $3\log_e 10$, etc.

| | |
|---|---|
| $\log_e 10 = 2.30258\ 50930$ | $6\log_e 10 = 13.81551\ 05580$ |
| $2\log_e 10 = 4.60517\ 01860$ | $7\log_e 10 = 16.11809\ 56510$ |
| $3\log_e 10 = 6.90775\ 52790$ | $8\log_e 10 = 18.42068\ 07440$ |
| $4\log_e 10 = 9.21034\ 03720$ | $9\log_e 10 = 20.72326\ 58369$ |
| $5\log_e 10 = 11.51292\ 54650$ | $10\log_e 10 = 23.02585\ 09299$ |

See preceding table for logarithms for numbers between 0.000 and 0.999.

### 1.00–4.99

| N | 0 | 1 | 2 | 3 | 4 | 5 | 6 | 7 | 8 | 9 |
|---|---|---|---|---|---|---|---|---|---|---|
| **1.0** | 0.00000 | .00995 | .01980 | .02956 | .03922 | .04879 | .05827 | .06766 | .07696 | .08618 |
| .1 | .09531 | .10436 | .11333 | .12222 | .13103 | .13976 | .14842 | .15700 | .16551 | .17395 |
| .2 | .18232 | .19062 | .19885 | .20701 | .21511 | .22314 | .23111 | .23902 | .24686 | .25464 |
| .3 | .26236 | .27003 | .27763 | .28518 | .29267 | .30010 | .30748 | .31481 | .32208 | .32930 |
| .4 | .33647 | .34359 | .35066 | .35767 | .36464 | .37156 | .37844 | .38526 | .39204 | .39878 |
| .5 | .40547 | .41211 | .41871 | .42527 | .43178 | .43825 | .44469 | .45108 | .45742 | .46373 |
| .6 | .47000 | .47623 | .48243 | .48858 | .49470 | .50078 | .50682 | .51282 | .51879 | .52473 |
| .7 | .53063 | .53649 | .54232 | .54812 | .55389 | .55962 | .56531 | .57098 | .57661 | .58222 |
| .8 | .58779 | .59333 | .59884 | .60432 | .60977 | .61519 | .62058 | .62594 | .63127 | .63658 |
| .9 | .64185 | .64710 | .65233 | .65752 | .66269 | .66783 | .67294 | .67803 | .68310 | .68813 |
| **2.0** | 0.69315 | .69813 | .70310 | .70804 | .71295 | .71784 | .72271 | .72755 | .73237 | .73716 |
| .1 | .74194 | .74669 | .75142 | .75612 | .76081 | .76547 | .77011 | .77473 | .77932 | .78390 |
| .2 | .78846 | .79299 | .79751 | .80200 | .80648 | .81093 | .81536 | .81978 | .82418 | .82855 |
| .3 | .83291 | .83725 | .84157 | .84587 | .85015 | .85442 | .85866 | .86289 | .86710 | .87129 |
| .4 | .87547 | .87963 | .88377 | .88789 | .89200 | .89609 | .90016 | .90422 | .90826 | .91228 |
| .5 | .91629 | .92028 | .92426 | .92822 | .93216 | .93609 | .94001 | .94391 | .94779 | .95166 |
| .6 | .95551 | .95935 | .96317 | .96698 | .97078 | .97456 | .97833 | .98208 | .98582 | .98954 |
| .7 | .99325 | .99695 | *.00063 | *.00430 | *.00796 | *.01160 | *.01523 | *.01885 | *.02245 | *.02604 |
| .8 | 1.02962 | .03318 | .03674 | .04028 | .04380 | .04732 | .05082 | .05431 | .05779 | .06126 |
| .9 | .06471 | .06815 | .07158 | .07500 | .07841 | .08181 | .08519 | .08856 | .09192 | .09527 |
| **3.0** | 1.09861 | .10194 | .10526 | .10856 | .11186 | .11514 | .11841 | .12168 | .12493 | .12817 |
| .1 | .13140 | .13462 | .13783 | .14103 | .14422 | .14740 | .15057 | .15373 | .15688 | .16002 |
| .2 | .16315 | .16627 | .16938 | .17248 | .17557 | .17865 | .18173 | .18479 | .18784 | .19089 |
| .3 | .19392 | .19695 | .19996 | .20297 | .20597 | .20896 | .21194 | .21491 | .21788 | .22083 |
| .4 | .22378 | .22671 | .22964 | .23256 | .23547 | .23837 | .24127 | .24415 | .24703 | .24990 |
| .5 | .25276 | .25562 | .25846 | .26130 | .26413 | .26695 | .26976 | .27257 | .27536 | .27815 |
| .6 | .28093 | .28371 | .28647 | .28923 | .29198 | .29473 | .29746 | .30019 | .30291 | .30563 |
| .7 | .30833 | .31103 | .31372 | .31641 | .31909 | .32176 | .32442 | .32708 | .32972 | .33237 |
| .8 | .33500 | .33763 | .34025 | .34286 | .34547 | .34807 | .35067 | .35325 | .35584 | .35841 |
| .9 | .36098 | .36354 | .36609 | .36864 | .37118 | .37372 | .37624 | .37877 | .38128 | .38379 |
| **4.0** | 1.38629 | .38879 | .39128 | .39377 | .39624 | .39872 | .40118 | .40364 | .40610 | .40854 |
| .1 | .41099 | .41342 | .41585 | .41828 | .42070 | .42311 | .42552 | .42792 | .43031 | .43270 |
| .2 | .43508 | .43746 | .43984 | .44220 | .44456 | .44692 | .44927 | .45161 | .45395 | .45629 |
| .3 | .45862 | .46094 | .46326 | .46557 | .46787 | .47018 | .47247 | .47476 | .47705 | .47933 |
| .4 | .48160 | .48387 | .48614 | .48840 | .49065 | .49290 | .49515 | .49739 | .49962 | .50185 |
| .5 | .50408 | .50630 | .50851 | .51072 | .51293 | .51513 | .51732 | .51951 | .52170 | .52388 |
| .6 | .52606 | .52823 | .53039 | .53256 | .53471 | .53687 | .53902 | .54116 | .54330 | .54543 |
| .7 | .54756 | .54969 | .55181 | .55393 | .55604 | .55814 | .56025 | .56235 | .56444 | .56653 |
| .8 | .56862 | .57070 | .57277 | .57485 | .57691 | .57898 | .58104 | .58309 | .58515 | .58719 |
| .9 | .58924 | .59127 | .59331 | .59534 | .59737 | .59939 | .60141 | .60342 | .60543 | .60744 |

**5.00–9.99**

| N | 0 | 1 | 2 | 3 | 4 | 5 | 6 | 7 | 8 | 9 |
|---|---|---|---|---|---|---|---|---|---|---|
| **5.0** | 1.60944 | .61144 | .61343 | .61542 | .61741 | .61939 | .62137 | .62334 | .62531 | .62728 |
| .1 | .62924 | .63120 | .63315 | .63511 | .63705 | .63900 | .64094 | .64287 | .64481 | .64673 |
| .2 | .64866 | .65058 | .65250 | .65441 | .65632 | .65823 | .66013 | .66203 | .66393 | .66582 |
| .3 | .66771 | .66959 | .67147 | .67335 | .67523 | .67710 | .67896 | .68083 | .68269 | .68455 |
| .4 | .68640 | .68825 | .69010 | .69194 | .69378 | .69562 | .69745 | .69928 | .70111 | .70293 |
| .5 | .70475 | .70656 | .70838 | .71019 | .71199 | .71380 | .71560 | .71740 | .71919 | .72098 |
| .6 | .72277 | .72455 | .72633 | .72811 | .72988 | .73166 | .73342 | .73519 | .73695 | .73871 |
| .7 | .74047 | .74222 | .74397 | .74572 | .74746 | .74920 | .75094 | .75267 | .75440 | .75613 |
| .8 | .75786 | .75958 | .76130 | .76302 | .76473 | .76644 | .76815 | .76985 | .77156 | .77326 |
| .9 | .77495 | .77665 | .77834 | .78002 | .78171 | .78339 | .78507 | .78675 | .78842 | .79009 |
| **6.0** | 1.79176 | .79342 | .79509 | .79675 | .79840 | .80006 | .80171 | .80336 | .80500 | .80665 |
| .1 | .80829 | .80993 | .81156 | .81319 | .81482 | .81645 | .81808 | .81970 | .82132 | .82294 |
| .2 | .82455 | .82616 | .82777 | .82938 | .83098 | .83258 | .83418 | .83578 | .83737 | .83896 |
| .3 | .84055 | .84214 | .84372 | .84530 | .84688 | .84845 | .85003 | .85160 | .85317 | .85473 |
| .4 | .85630 | .85786 | .85942 | .86097 | .86253 | .86408 | .86563 | .86718 | .86872 | .87026 |
| .5 | .87180 | .87334 | .87487 | .87641 | .87794 | .87947 | .88099 | .88251 | .88403 | .88555 |
| .6 | .88707 | .88858 | .89010 | .89160 | .89311 | .89462 | .89612 | .89762 | .89912 | .90061 |
| .7 | .90211 | .90360 | .90509 | .90658 | .90806 | .90954 | .91102 | .91250 | .91398 | .91545 |
| .8 | .91692 | .91839 | .91986 | .92132 | .92279 | .92425 | .92571 | .92716 | .92862 | .93007 |
| .9 | .93152 | .93297 | .93442 | .93586 | .93730 | .93874 | .94018 | .94162 | .94305 | .94448 |
| **7.0** | 1.94591 | .94734 | .94876 | .95019 | .95161 | .95303 | .95445 | .95586 | .95727 | .95869 |
| .1 | .96009 | .96150 | .96291 | .96431 | .96571 | .96711 | .96851 | .96991 | .97130 | .97269 |
| .2 | .97408 | .97547 | .97685 | .97824 | .97962 | .98100 | .98238 | .98376 | .98513 | .98650 |
| .3 | .98787 | .98924 | .99061 | .99198 | .99334 | .99470 | .99606 | .99742 | .99877 | *.00013 |
| .4 | 2.00148 | .00283 | .00418 | .00553 | .00687 | .00821 | .00956 | .01089 | .01223 | .01357 |
| .5 | .01490 | .01624 | .01757 | .01890 | .02022 | .02155 | .02287 | .02419 | .02551 | .02683 |
| .6 | .02815 | .02946 | .03078 | .03209 | .03340 | .03471 | .03601 | .03732 | .03862 | .03992 |
| .7 | .04122 | .04252 | .04381 | .04511 | .04640 | .04769 | .04898 | .05027 | .05156 | .05284 |
| .8 | .05412 | .05540 | .05668 | .05796 | .05924 | .06051 | .06179 | .06306 | .06433 | .06560 |
| .9 | .06686 | .06813 | .06939 | .07065 | .07191 | .07317 | .07443 | .07568 | .07694 | .07819 |
| **8.0** | 2.07944 | .08069 | .08194 | .08318 | .08443 | .08567 | .08691 | .08815 | .08939 | .09063 |
| .1 | .09186 | .09310 | .09433 | .09556 | .09679 | .09802 | .09924 | .10047 | .10169 | .10291 |
| .2 | .10413 | .10535 | .10657 | .10779 | .10900 | .11021 | .11142 | .11263 | .11384 | .11505 |
| .3 | .11626 | .11746 | .11866 | .11986 | .12106 | .12226 | .12346 | .12465 | .12585 | .12704 |
| .4 | .12823 | .12942 | .13061 | .13180 | .13298 | .13417 | .13535 | .13653 | .13771 | .13889 |
| .5 | .14007 | .14124 | .14242 | .14359 | .14476 | .14593 | .14710 | .14827 | .14943 | .15060 |
| .6 | .15176 | .15292 | .15409 | .15524 | .15640 | .15756 | .15871 | .15987 | .16102 | .16217 |
| .7 | .16332 | .16447 | .16562 | .16677 | .16791 | .16905 | .17020 | .17134 | .17248 | .17361 |
| .8 | .17475 | .17589 | .17702 | .17816 | .17929 | .18042 | .18155 | .18267 | .18380 | .18493 |
| .9 | .18605 | .18717 | .18830 | .18942 | .19054 | .19165 | .19277 | .19389 | .19500 | .19611 |
| **9.0** | 2.19722 | .19834 | .19944 | .20055 | .20166 | .20276 | .20387 | .20497 | .20607 | .20717 |
| .1 | .20827 | .20937 | .21047 | .21157 | .21266 | .21375 | .21485 | .21594 | .21703 | .21812 |
| .2 | .21920 | .22029 | .22138 | .22246 | .22354 | .22462 | .22570 | .22678 | .22786 | .22894 |
| .3 | .23001 | .23109 | .23216 | .23324 | .23431 | .23538 | .23645 | .23751 | .23858 | .23965 |
| .4 | .24071 | .24177 | .24284 | .24390 | .24496 | .24601 | .24707 | .24813 | .24918 | .25024 |
| .5 | .25129 | .25234 | .25339 | .25444 | .25549 | .25654 | .25759 | .25863 | .25968 | .26072 |
| .6 | .26176 | .26280 | .26384 | .26488 | .26592 | .26696 | .26799 | .26903 | .27006 | .27109 |
| .7 | .27213 | .27316 | .27419 | .27521 | .27624 | .27727 | .27829 | .27932 | .28034 | .28136 |
| .8 | .28238 | .28340 | .28442 | .28544 | .28646 | .28747 | .28849 | .28950 | .29051 | .29152 |
| .9 | .29253 | .29354 | .29455 | .29556 | .29657 | .29757 | .29858 | .29958 | .30058 | .30158 |

# NATURAL OR NAPERIAN LOGARITHMS (Continued)

Constants

$\log_e 10 = 2.30258\ 50930$  
$2\log_e 10 = 4.60517\ 01860$  
$3\log_e 10 = 6.90775\ 52790$  
$4\log_e 10 = 9.21034\ 03720$  
$5\log_e 10 = 11.51292\ 54650$

$6\log_e 10 = 13.81551\ 05580$  
$7\log_e 10 = 16.11809\ 56510$  
$8\log_e 10 = 18.42068\ 07440$  
$9\log_e 10 = 20.72326\ 58369$  
$10\log_e 10 = 23.02585\ 09299$

## 10.0–49.9

| N | 0 | 1 | 2 | 3 | 4 | 5 | 6 | 7 | 8 | 9 |
|---|---|---|---|---|---|---|---|---|---|---|
| **10.** | 2.30259 | .31254 | .32239 | .33214 | .34181 | .35138 | .36085 | .37024 | .37955 | .38876 |
| 11. | .39790 | .40695 | .41591 | .42480 | .43361 | .44235 | .45101 | .45959 | .46810 | .47654 |
| 12. | .48491 | .49321 | .50144 | .50960 | .51770 | .52573 | .53370 | .54160 | .54945 | .55723 |
| 13. | .56495 | .57261 | .58022 | .58776 | .59525 | .60269 | .61007 | .61740 | .62467 | .63189 |
| 14. | .63906 | .64617 | .65324 | .66026 | .66723 | .67415 | .68102 | .68785 | .69463 | .70136 |
| 15. | .70805 | .71469 | .72130 | .72785 | .73437 | .74084 | .74727 | .75366 | .76001 | .76632 |
| 16. | .77259 | .77882 | .78501 | .79117 | .79728 | .80336 | .80940 | .81541 | .82138 | .82731 |
| 17. | .83321 | .83908 | .84491 | .85071 | .85647 | .86220 | .86790 | .87356 | .87920 | .88480 |
| 18. | .89037 | .89591 | .90142 | .90690 | .91235 | .91777 | .92316 | .92852 | .93386 | .93916 |
| 19. | .94444 | .94969 | .95491 | .96011 | .96527 | .97041 | .97553 | .98062 | .98568 | .99072 |
| **20.** | 2.99573 | *.00072 | *.00568 | *.01062 | *.01553 | *.02042 | *.02529 | *.03013 | *.03495 | *.03975 |
| 21. | 3.04452 | .04927 | .05400 | .05871 | .06339 | .06805 | .07269 | .07731 | .08191 | .08649 |
| 22. | .09104 | .09558 | .10009 | .10459 | .10906 | .11352 | .11795 | .12236 | .12676 | .13114 |
| 23. | .13549 | .13983 | .14415 | .14845 | .15274 | .15700 | .16125 | .16548 | .16969 | .17388 |
| 24. | .17805 | .18221 | .18635 | .19048 | .19458 | .19867 | .20275 | .20680 | .21084 | .21487 |
| 25. | .21888 | .22287 | .22684 | .23080 | .23475 | .23868 | .24259 | .24649 | .25037 | .25424 |
| 26. | .25810 | .26194 | .26576 | .26957 | .27336 | .27714 | .28091 | .28466 | .28840 | .29213 |
| 27. | .29584 | .29953 | .30322 | .30689 | .31054 | .31419 | .31782 | .32143 | .32504 | .32863 |
| 28. | .33220 | .33577 | .33932 | .34286 | .34639 | .34990 | .35341 | .35690 | .36038 | .36384 |
| 29. | .36730 | .37074 | .37417 | .37759 | .38099 | .38439 | .38777 | .39115 | .39451 | .39786 |
| **30.** | 3.40120 | .40453 | .40784 | .41115 | .41444 | .41773 | .42100 | .42426 | .42751 | .43076 |
| 31. | .43399 | .43721 | .44042 | .44362 | .44681 | .44999 | .45316 | .45632 | .45947 | .46261 |
| 32. | .46574 | .46886 | .47197 | .47507 | .47816 | .48124 | .48431 | .48738 | .49043 | .49347 |
| 33. | .49651 | .49953 | .50255 | .50556 | .50856 | .51155 | .51453 | .51750 | .52046 | .52342 |
| 34. | .52636 | .52930 | .53223 | .53515 | .53806 | .54096 | .54385 | .54674 | .54962 | .55249 |
| 35. | .55535 | .55820 | .56105 | .56388 | .56671 | .56953 | .57235 | .57515 | .57795 | .58074 |
| 36. | .58352 | .58629 | .58906 | .59182 | .59457 | .59731 | .60005 | .60278 | .60550 | .60821 |
| 37. | .61092 | .61362 | .61631 | .61899 | .62167 | .62434 | .62700 | .62966 | .63231 | .63495 |
| 38. | .63759 | .64021 | .64284 | .64545 | .64806 | .65066 | .65325 | .65584 | .65842 | .66099 |
| 39. | .66356 | .66612 | .66868 | .67122 | .67377 | .67630 | .67883 | .68135 | .68387 | .68638 |
| **40.** | 3.68888 | .69138 | .69387 | .69635 | .69883 | .70130 | .70377 | .70623 | .70868 | .71113 |
| 41. | .71357 | .71601 | .71844 | .72086 | .72328 | .72569 | .72810 | .73050 | .73290 | .73529 |
| 42. | .73767 | .74005 | .74242 | .74479 | .74715 | .74950 | .75185 | .75420 | .75654 | .75887 |
| 43. | .76120 | .76352 | .76584 | .76815 | .77046 | .77276 | .77506 | .77735 | .77963 | .78191 |
| 44. | .78419 | .78646 | .78872 | .79098 | .79324 | .79549 | .79773 | .79997 | .80221 | .80444 |
| 45. | .80666 | .80888 | .81110 | .81331 | .81551 | .81771 | .81991 | .82210 | .82428 | .82647 |
| 46. | .82864 | .83081 | .83298 | .83514 | .83730 | .83945 | .84160 | .84374 | .84588 | .84802 |
| 47. | .85015 | .85227 | .85439 | .85651 | .85862 | .86073 | .86283 | .86493 | .86703 | .86912 |
| 48. | .87120 | .87328 | .87536 | .87743 | .87950 | .88156 | .88362 | .88568 | .88773 | .88978 |
| 49. | .89182 | .89386 | .89589 | .89792 | .89995 | .90197 | .90399 | .90600 | .90801 | .91002 |

# NATURAL OR NAPERIAN LOGARITHMS (Continued)

### 50.0-99.9

| N | 0 | 1 | 2 | 3 | 4 | 5 | 6 | 7 | 8 | 9 |
|---|---|---|---|---|---|---|---|---|---|---|
| **50.** | 3.91202 | .91402 | .91602 | .91801 | .91999 | .92197 | .92395 | .92593 | .92790 | .92986 |
| 51. | .93183 | .93378 | .93574 | .93769 | .93964 | .94158 | .94352 | .94546 | .94739 | .94932 |
| 52. | .95124 | .95316 | .95508 | .95700 | .95891 | .96081 | .96272 | .96462 | .96651 | .96840 |
| 53. | .97029 | .97218 | .97406 | .97594 | .97781 | .97968 | .98155 | .98341 | .98527 | .98713 |
| 54. | .98898 | .99083 | .99268 | .99452 | .99636 | .99820 | *.00003 | *.00186 | *.00369 | *.00551 |
| **55.** | 4.00733 | .00915 | .01096 | .01277 | .01458 | .01638 | .01818 | .01998 | .02177 | .02356 |
| 56. | .02535 | .02714 | .02892 | .03069 | .03247 | .03424 | .03603 | .03777 | .03954 | .04130 |
| 57. | .04305 | .04480 | .04655 | .04830 | .05004 | .05178 | .05352 | .05526 | .05699 | .05872 |
| 58. | .06044 | .06217 | .06389 | .06560 | .06772 | .06903 | .07073 | .07244 | .07414 | .07584 |
| 59. | .07754 | .07923 | .08092 | .08261 | .08429 | .08598 | .08766 | .08933 | .09101 | .09268 |
| **60.** | 4.09434 | .09601 | .09767 | .09933 | .10099 | .10264 | .10429 | .10594 | .10759 | .10923 |
| 61. | .11087 | .11251 | .11415 | .11578 | .11741 | .11904 | .12066 | .12228 | .12390 | .12552 |
| 62. | .12713 | .12875 | .13036 | .13196 | .13357 | .13517 | .13677 | .13836 | .13996 | .14155 |
| 63. | .14313 | .14472 | .14630 | .14789 | .14946 | .15104 | .15261 | .15418 | .15575 | .15732 |
| 64. | .15888 | .16044 | .16200 | .16356 | .16511 | .16667 | .16821 | .16976 | .17131 | .17285 |
| **65.** | .17439 | .17592 | .17746 | .17899 | .18052 | .18205 | .18358 | 18510 | .18662 | .18814 |
| 66. | .18965 | .19117 | .19268 | .19419 | .19570 | .19720 | .19870 | .20020 | .20170 | .20320 |
| 67. | .20469 | .20618 | .20767 | .20916 | .21065 | .21213 | .21361 | .21509 | .21656 | 21804 |
| 68. | .21951 | .22098 | .22244 | .22391 | .22537 | .22683 | .22829 | .22975 | .23120 | .23266 |
| 69. | .23411 | .23555 | .23700 | .23844 | .23989 | .24133 | .24276 | .24420 | .24563 | .24707 |
| **70.** | 4.24850 | .24992 | .25135 | .25277 | .25419 | .25561 | .25703 | .25845 | .25986 | .26127 |
| 71. | .26268 | .26409 | .26549 | .26690 | .26830 | .26970 | .27110 | .27249 | .27388 | .27528 |
| 72. | .27667 | .27805 | .27944 | .28082 | .28221 | .28359 | .28496 | .28634 | .28772 | .28909 |
| 73. | .29046 | .29183 | .29320 | .29456 | .29592 | .29729 | .29865 | .30000 | .30136 | .30271 |
| 74. | .30407 | .30542 | .30676 | .30811 | .30946 | .31080 | .31214 | .31348 | .31482 | .31615 |
| **75.** | .31749 | .31882 | .32015 | .32149 | .32281 | .32413 | .32546 | .32678 | .32810 | .32942 |
| 76. | .33073 | .33205 | .33336 | .33467 | .33598 | .33729 | .33860 | .33990 | .34120 | .34251 |
| 77. | .34381 | .34510 | .34640 | .34769 | .34899 | .35028 | .35157 | .35286 | .35414 | .35543 |
| 78. | .35671 | .35800 | .35927 | .36055 | .36182 | .36310 | .36437 | .36564 | .36691 | .36818 |
| 79. | .36945 | .37071 | .37198 | .37324 | .37450 | .37576 | .37701 | .37827 | .37952 | .38078 |
| **80.** | 4.38203 | .38328 | .38452 | .38577 | .38701 | .38826 | .38950 | .39074 | .39198 | .39321 |
| 81. | .39445 | .39568 | .39692 | .39815 | .39938 | .40060 | .40183 | .40305 | .40428 | .40550 |
| 82. | .40672 | .40794 | .40916 | .41037 | .41159 | .41280 | .41401 | .41522 | .41643 | 41764 |
| 83. | .41884 | .42004 | .42125 | .42245 | .42365 | .42485 | .42604 | .42724 | .42843 | .42963 |
| 84. | .43082 | .43201 | .43319 | .43438 | .43557 | .43675 | .43793 | .43912 | .44030 | .44147 |
| **85.** | .44265 | .44383 | .44500 | .44617 | .44735 | .44852 | .44969 | .45085 | .45202 | .45318 |
| 86. | .45435 | .45551 | .45667 | .45783 | .45899 | .46014 | .46130 | .46245 | .46361 | .46476 |
| 87. | .46591 | .46706 | .46820 | .46935 | .47050 | .47164 | .47278 | .47392 | .47506 | .47620 |
| 88. | .47734 | .47847 | .47961 | .48074 | .48187 | .48300 | .48413 | .48526 | .48639 | .48751 |
| 89. | .48864 | .48976 | .49088 | .49200 | .49312 | .49424 | .49536 | .49647 | .49758 | .49870 |
| **90.** | 4.49981 | .50092 | .50203 | .50314 | .50424 | .50535 | .50645 | .50756 | .50866 | .50976 |
| 91. | .51086 | .51196 | 51305 | .51415 | .51525 | .51634 | .51743 | 51852 | .51961 | .52070 |
| 92. | .52179 | 52287 | .52396 | .52504 | .52613 | .52721 | .52829 | 52937 | .53045 | .53152 |
| 93. | .53260 | .53367 | .53475 | .53552 | .53689 | .53796 | .53903 | .54010 | .54116 | .54223 |
| 94. | .54329 | .54436 | 54542 | .54648 | .54754 | .54860 | .54966 | .55071 | .55177 | .55282 |
| **95.** | .55388 | .55493 | .55598 | .55703 | .55808 | .55913 | .56017 | .56122 | .56226 | .56331 |
| 96. | .56435 | .56539 | .56643 | .56747 | .56851 | .56954 | .57058 | .57161 | .57265 | .57368 |
| 97. | .57471 | .57574 | .57677 | .57780 | .57883 | .57985 | .58088 | 58190 | .58292 | 58395 |
| 98. | .58497 | .58599 | .58701 | .58802 | .58904 | .59006 | 59107 | .59208 | .59310 | .59411 |
| 99. | .59512 | .59613 | 59714 | .59815 | .59915 | .60016 | .60116 | .60217 | .60317 | .60417 |

| N | 0 | 1 | 2 | 3 | 4 | 5 | 6 | 7 | 8 | 9 |
|---|---|---|---|---|---|---|---|---|---|---|
| 0 | − ∞ | 0.00000 | 0.69315 | 1.09861 | .38629 | .60944 | .79176 | .94591 | *.07944 | *.19722 |
| 1 | 2.30259 | .39790 | .48491 | .56495 | .63906 | .70805 | .77259 | .83321 | .89037 | .94444 |
| 2 | .99573 | *.04452 | *.09104 | *.13549 | *.17805 | *.21888 | .25810 | *.29584 | *.33220 | *.36730 |
| 3 | 3.40120 | .43399 | .46574 | .49651 | .52636 | .55535 | .58352 | .61092 | .63759 | .66356 |
| 4 | .68888 | .71357 | .73767 | .76120 | .78419 | .80666 | .82864 | .85015 | .87120 | .89182 |
| 5 | .91202 | .93183 | .95124 | .97029 | .98898 | *.00733 | *.02535 | *.04305 | *.06044 | *.07754 |
| 6 | 4.09434 | .11087 | .12713 | .14313 | .15888 | .17439 | .18965 | .20469 | .21951 | .23411 |
| 7 | .24850 | .26268 | .27667 | .29046 | .30407 | .31749 | .33073 | .34381 | .35671 | .36945 |
| 8 | .38203 | .39445 | .40672 | .41884 | .43082 | .44265 | .45435 | .46591 | .47734 | .48864 |
| 9 | .49981 | .51086 | .52179 | .53260 | .54329 | .55388 | .56435 | .57471 | .58497 | .59512 |
| 10 | 4.60517 | .61512 | .62497 | .63473 | .64439 | .65396 | .66344 | .67283 | .68213 | .69135 |
| 11 | .70048 | .70953 | .71850 | .72739 | .73620 | .74493 | .75359 | .76217 | .77068 | .77912 |
| 12 | .78749 | .79579 | .80402 | .81218 | .82028 | .82831 | .83628 | .84419 | .85203 | .85981 |
| 13 | .86753 | .87520 | .88280 | .89035 | .89784 | .90527 | .91265 | .91998 | .92725 | .93447 |
| 14 | .94164 | .94876 | .95583 | .96284 | .96981 | .97673 | .98361 | .99043 | .99721 | *.00395 |
| 15 | 5.01064 | .01728 | .02388 | .03044 | .03695 | .04343 | .04986 | .05625 | .06260 | .06890 |
| 16 | .07517 | .08140 | .08760 | .09375 | .09987 | .10595 | .11199 | .11799 | .12396 | .12990 |
| 17 | .13580 | .14166 | .14749 | .15329 | .15906 | .16479 | .17048 | .17615 | .18178 | .18739 |
| 18 | .19296 | .19850 | .20401 | .20949 | .21494 | .22036 | .22575 | .23111 | .23644 | .24175 |
| 19 | .24702 | .25227 | .25750 | .26269 | .26786 | .27300 | .27811 | .28320 | .28827 | .29330 |
| 20 | 5.29832 | .30330 | .30827 | .31321 | .31812 | .32301 | .32788 | .33272 | .33754 | .34233 |
| 21 | .34711 | .35186 | .35659 | .36129 | .36598 | .37064 | .37528 | .37990 | .38450 | .38907 |
| 22 | .39363 | .39816 | .40268 | .40717 | .41165 | .41610 | .42053 | .42495 | .42935 | .43372 |
| 23 | .43808 | .44242 | .44674 | .45104 | .45532 | .45959 | .46383 | .46806 | .47227 | .47646 |
| 24 | .48064 | .48480 | .48894 | .49306 | .49717 | .50126 | .50533 | .50939 | .51343 | .51745 |
| 25 | .52146 | .52545 | .52943 | .53339 | .53733 | .54126 | .54518 | .54908 | .55296 | .55683 |
| 26 | .56068 | .56452 | .56834 | .57215 | .57595 | .57973 | .58350 | .58725 | .59099 | .59471 |
| 27 | .59842 | .60212 | .60580 | .60947 | .61313 | .61677 | .62040 | .62402 | .62762 | .63121 |
| 28 | .63479 | .63835 | .64191 | .64545 | .64897 | .65249 | .65599 | .65948 | .66296 | .66643 |
| 29 | .66988 | .67332 | .67675 | .68017 | .68358 | .68698 | .69036 | .69373 | .69709 | .70044 |
| 30 | 5.70378 | .70711 | .71043 | .71373 | .71703 | .72031 | .72359 | .72685 | .73010 | .73334 |
| 31 | .73657 | .73979 | .74300 | .74620 | .74939 | .75257 | .75574 | .75890 | .76205 | .76519 |
| 32 | .76832 | .77144 | .77455 | .77765 | .78074 | .78383 | .78690 | .78996 | .79301 | .79606 |
| 33 | .79909 | .80212 | .80513 | .80814 | .81114 | .81413 | .81711 | .82008 | .82305 | .82600 |
| 34 | .82895 | .83188 | .83481 | .83773 | .84064 | .84354 | .84644 | .84932 | .85220 | .85507 |
| 35 | .85793 | .86079 | .86363 | .86647 | .86930 | .87212 | .87493 | .87774 | .88053 | .88332 |
| 36 | .88610 | .88888 | .89164 | .89440 | .89715 | .89990 | .90263 | .90536 | .90808 | .91080 |
| 37 | .91350 | .91620 | .91889 | .92158 | .92426 | .92693 | .92959 | .93225 | .93489 | .93754 |
| 38 | .94017 | .94280 | .94542 | .94803 | .95064 | .95324 | .95584 | .95842 | .96101 | .96358 |
| 39 | .96615 | .96871 | .97126 | .97381 | .97635 | .97889 | .98141 | .98394 | .98645 | .98896 |
| 40 | 5.99146 | .99396 | .99645 | .99894 | *.00141 | *.00389 | *.00635 | *.00881 | *.01127 | *.01372 |
| 41 | 6.01616 | .01859 | .02102 | .02345 | .02587 | .02828 | .03069 | .03309 | .03548 | .03787 |
| 42 | .04025 | .04263 | .04501 | .04737 | .04973 | .05209 | .05444 | .05678 | .05912 | .06146 |
| 43 | .06379 | .06611 | .06843 | .07074 | .07304 | .07535 | .07764 | .07993 | .08222 | .08450 |
| 44 | .08677 | .08904 | .09131 | .09357 | .09582 | .09807 | .10032 | .10256 | .10479 | .10702 |
| 45 | .10925 | .11147 | .11368 | .11589 | .11810 | .12030 | .12249 | .12468 | .12687 | .12905 |
| 46 | .13123 | .13340 | .13556 | .13773 | .13988 | .14204 | .14419 | .14633 | .14847 | .15060 |
| 47 | .15273 | .15486 | .15698 | .15910 | .16121 | .16331 | .16542 | .16752 | .16961 | .17170 |
| 48 | .17379 | .17587 | .17794 | .18002 | .18208 | .18415 | .18621 | .18826 | .19032 | .19236 |
| 49 | .19441 | .19644 | .19848 | .20051 | .20254 | .20456 | .20658 | .20859 | .21060 | .21261 |

**500-999**

| N | 0 | 1 | 2 | 3 | 4 | 5 | 6 | 7 | 8 | 9 |
|---|---|---|---|---|---|---|---|---|---|---|
| 50 | 6.21461 | .21661 | .21860 | .22059 | .22258 | .22456 | .22654 | .22851 | .23048 | .23245 |
| 51 | .23441 | .23637 | .23832 | .24028 | .24222 | .24417 | .24611 | .24804 | .24998 | .25190 |
| 52 | .25383 | .25575 | .25767 | .25958 | .26149 | .26340 | .26530 | .26720 | .26910 | .27099 |
| 53 | .27288 | .27476 | .27664 | .27852 | .28040 | .28227 | .28413 | .28600 | .28786 | .28972 |
| 54 | .29157 | .29342 | .29527 | .29711 | .29895 | .30079 | .30262 | .30445 | .30628 | .30810 |
| 55 | .30992 | .31173 | .31355 | .31536 | .31716 | .31897 | .32077 | .32257 | .32436 | .32615 |
| 56 | .32794 | .32972 | .33150 | .33328 | .33505 | .33683 | .33859 | .34036 | .34212 | .34388 |
| 57 | .34564 | .34739 | .34914 | .35089 | .35263 | .35437 | .35611 | .35784 | .35957 | .36130 |
| 58 | .36303 | .36475 | .36647 | .36819 | .36990 | .37161 | .37332 | .37502 | .37673 | .37843 |
| 59 | .38012 | .38182 | .38351 | .38519 | .38688 | .38856 | .39024 | .39192 | .39359 | .39526 |
| 60 | 6.39693 | .39859 | .40026 | .40192 | .40357 | .40523 | .40688 | .40853 | .41017 | .41182 |
| 61 | .41346 | .41510 | .41673 | .41836 | .41999 | .42162 | .42325 | .42487 | .42649 | .42811 |
| 62 | .42972 | .43133 | .43294 | .43455 | .43615 | .43775 | .43935 | .44095 | .44254 | .44412 |
| 63 | .44572 | .44731 | .44889 | .45047 | .45205 | .45362 | .45520 | .45677 | .45834 | .45990 |
| 64 | .46147 | .46303 | .46459 | .46614 | .46770 | .46925 | .47080 | .47235 | .47389 | .47543 |
| 65 | .47697 | .47851 | .48004 | .48158 | .48311 | .48464 | .48616 | .48768 | .48920 | .49072 |
| 66 | .49224 | .49375 | .49527 | .49677 | .49828 | .49979 | .50129 | .50279 | .50429 | .50578 |
| 67 | .50728 | .50877 | .51026 | .51175 | .51323 | .51471 | .51619 | .51767 | .51915 | .52062 |
| 68 | .52209 | .52356 | .52503 | .52649 | .52796 | .52942 | .53088 | .53233 | .53379 | .53524 |
| 69 | .53669 | .53814 | .53959 | .54103 | .54247 | .54391 | .54535 | .54679 | .54822 | .54965 |
| 70 | 6.55108 | .55251 | .55393 | .55536 | .55678 | .55820 | .55962 | .56103 | .56244 | .56386 |
| 71 | .56526 | .56667 | .56808 | .56948 | .57088 | .57228 | .57368 | .57508 | .57647 | .57786 |
| 72 | .57925 | .58064 | .58203 | .58341 | .58479 | .58617 | .58755 | .58893 | .59030 | .59167 |
| 73 | .59304 | .59441 | .59578 | .59715 | .59851 | .59987 | .60123 | .60259 | .60394 | .60530 |
| 74 | .60665 | .60800 | .60935 | .61070 | .61204 | .61338 | .61473 | .61607 | .61740 | .61874 |
| 75 | .62007 | .62141 | .62274 | .62407 | .62539 | .62672 | .62804 | .62936 | .63068 | .63200 |
| 76 | .63332 | .63463 | .63595 | .63726 | .63857 | .63988 | .64118 | .64249 | .64379 | .64509 |
| 77 | .64639 | .64769 | .64898 | .65028 | .65157 | .65286 | .65415 | .65544 | .65673 | .65801 |
| 78 | .65929 | .66058 | .66185 | .66313 | .66441 | .66568 | .66696 | .66823 | .66950 | .67077 |
| 79 | .67203 | .67330 | .67456 | .67582 | .67708 | .67834 | .67960 | .68085 | .68211 | .68336 |
| 80 | 6.68461 | .68586 | .68711 | .68835 | .68960 | .69084 | .69208 | .69332 | .69456 | .69580 |
| 81 | .69703 | .69827 | .69950 | .70073 | .70196 | .70319 | .70441 | .70564 | .70686 | .70808 |
| 82 | .70930 | .71052 | .71174 | .71296 | .71417 | .71538 | .71659 | .71780 | .71901 | .72022 |
| 83 | .72143 | .72263 | .72383 | .72503 | .72623 | .72743 | .72863 | .72982 | .73102 | .73221 |
| 84 | .73340 | .73459 | .73578 | .73697 | .73815 | .73934 | .74052 | .74170 | .74288 | .74406 |
| 85 | .74524 | .74641 | .74759 | .74876 | .74993 | .75110 | .75227 | .75344 | .75460 | .75577 |
| 86 | .75693 | .75809 | .75926 | .76041 | .76157 | .76273 | .76388 | .76504 | .76619 | .76734 |
| 87 | .76849 | .76964 | .77079 | .77194 | .77308 | .77422 | .77537 | .77651 | .77765 | .77878 |
| 88 | .77992 | .78106 | .78219 | .78333 | .78446 | .78559 | .78672 | .78784 | .78897 | .79010 |
| 89 | .79122 | .79234 | .79347 | .79459 | .79571 | .79682 | .79794 | .79906 | .80017 | .80128 |
| 90 | 6.80239 | .80351 | .80461 | .80572 | .80683 | .80793 | .80904 | .81014 | .81124 | .81235 |
| 91 | .81344 | .81454 | .81564 | .81674 | .81783 | .81892 | .82002 | .82111 | .82220 | .82329 |
| 92 | .82437 | .82546 | .82655 | .82763 | .82871 | .82979 | .83087 | .83195 | .83303 | .83411 |
| 93 | .83518 | .83626 | .83733 | .83841 | .83948 | .84055 | .84162 | .84268 | .84375 | .84482 |
| 94 | .84588 | .84694 | .84801 | .84907 | .85013 | .85118 | .85224 | .85330 | .85435 | .85541 |
| 95 | .85646 | .85751 | .85857 | .85961 | .86066 | .86171 | .86276 | .86380 | .86485 | .86589 |
| 96 | .86693 | .86797 | .86901 | .87005 | .87109 | .87213 | .87316 | .87420 | .87523 | .87626 |
| 97 | .87730 | .87833 | .87936 | .88038 | .88141 | .88244 | .88346 | .88449 | .88551 | .88653 |
| 98 | .88755 | .88857 | .88959 | .89061 | .89163 | .89264 | .89366 | .89467 | .89568 | .89669 |
| 99 | .89770 | .89871 | .89972 | .90073 | .90174 | .90274 | .90375 | .90475 | .90575 | .90675 |

# EXPONENTIAL FUNCTIONS

| $x$ | $e^x$ | $\text{Log}_{10}(e^x)$ | $e^{-x}$ | $x$ | $e^x$ | $\text{Log}_{10}(e^x)$ | $e^{-x}$ |
|---|---|---|---|---|---|---|---|
| **0.00** | 1.0000 | 0.00000 | 1.000000 | **0.50** | 1.6487 | 0.21715 | 0.606531 |
| 0.01 | 1.0101 | .00434 | 0.990050 | 0.51 | 1 6653 | .22149 | .600496 |
| 0.02 | 1.0202 | .00869 | .980199 | 0.52 | 1 6820 | 22583 | .594521 |
| 0.03 | 1.0305 | .01303 | .970446 | 0.53 | 1.6989 | .23018 | .588605 |
| 0.04 | 1.0408 | .01737 | .960789 | 0.54 | 1.7160 | .23452 | .582748 |
| **0.05** | 1.0513 | 0.02171 | 0.951229 | **0.55** | 1.7333 | 0.23886 | 0.576950 |
| 0.06 | 1.0618 | .02606 | .941765 | 0.56 | 1.7507 | .24320 | .571209 |
| 0.07 | 1.0725 | .03040 | .932394 | 0.57 | 1.7683 | .24755 | .565525 |
| 0.08 | 1 0833 | .03474 | .923116 | 0.58 | 1.7860 | .25189 | .559898 |
| 0.09 | 1.0942 | .03909 | .913931 | 0.59 | 1.8040 | .25623 | .554327 |
| **0.10** | 1.1052 | 0.04343 | 0.904837 | **0.60** | 1.8221 | 0.26058 | 0.548812 |
| 0.11 | 1.1163 | .04777 | .895834 | 0.61 | 1.8404 | .26492 | .543351 |
| 0.12 | 1.1275 | .05212 | .886920 | 0.62 | 1.8589 | .26926 | .537944 |
| 0.13 | 1.1388 | .05646 | .878095 | 0.63 | 1.8776 | .27361 | .532592 |
| 0.14 | 1.1503 | .06080 | .869358 | 0.64 | 1.8965 | .27795 | .527292 |
| **0.15** | 1.1618 | 0.06514 | 0.860708 | **0.65** | 1.9155 | 0.28229 | 0.522046 |
| 0.16 | 1.1735 | .06949 | .852144 | 0.66 | 1 9348 | .28663 | .516851 |
| 0.17 | 1.1853 | 07383 | .843665 | 0.67 | 1.9542 | .29098 | .511709 |
| 0.18 | 1.1972 | .07817 | .835270 | 0.68 | 1.9739 | .29532 | .506617 |
| 0.19 | 1.2092 | .08252 | .826959 | 0.69 | 1.9937 | .29966 | .501576 |
| **0.20** | 1.2214 | 0.08686 | 0.818731 | **0.70** | 2 0138 | 0.30401 | 0.496585 |
| 0.21 | 1.2337 | .09120 | .810584 | 0.71 | 2.0340 | .30835 | .491644 |
| 0.22 | 1 2461 | .09554 | .802519 | 0.72 | 2.0544 | .31269 | .486752 |
| 0.23 | 1.2586 | .09989 | .794534 | 0.73 | 2.0751 | .31703 | .481909 |
| 0.24 | 1.2712 | .10423 | .786628 | 0.74 | 2.0959 | .32138 | .477114 |
| **0.25** | 1.2840 | 0.10857 | 0.778801 | **0.75** | 2 1170 | 0.32572 | 0.472367 |
| 0.26 | 1 2969 | .11292 | .771052 | 0 76 | 2.1383 | .33006 | .467666 |
| 0.27 | 1 3100 | .11726 | .763379 | 0.77 | 2 1598 | .33441 | .463013 |
| 0.28 | 1 3231 | .12160 | .755784 | 0.78 | 2.1815 | .33875 | .458406 |
| 0.29 | 1.3364 | .12595 | .748264 | 0.79 | 2.2034 | .34309 | .453845 |
| **0.30** | 1 3499 | 0.13029 | 0.740818 | **0.80** | 2.2255 | 0.34744 | 0.449329 |
| 0.31 | 1.3634 | .13463 | .733447 | 0.81 | 2.2479 | 35178 | .444858 |
| 0.32 | 1.3771 | .13897 | .726149 | 0.82 | 2.2705 | .35612 | .440432 |
| 0.33 | 1 3910 | .14332 | .718924 | 0.83 | 2.2933 | .36046 | .436049 |
| 0.34 | 1.4049 | .14766 | .711770 | 0.84 | 2.3164 | .36481 | .431711 |
| **0.35** | 1.4191 | 0.15200 | 0.704688 | **0.85** | 2.3396 | 0.36915 | 0.427415 |
| 0.36 | 1 4333 | .15635 | .697676 | 0.86 | 2.3632 | .37349 | .423162 |
| 0.37 | 1.4477 | .16069 | .690734 | 0.87 | 2.3869 | .37784 | .418952 |
| 0.38 | 1 4623 | .16503 | .683861 | 0.88 | 2.4109 | .38218 | .414783 |
| 0.39 | 1.4770 | .16937 | .677057 | 0.89 | 2.4351 | .38652 | .410656 |
| **0.40** | 1.4918 | 0.17372 | 0.670320 | **0.90** | 2.4596 | 0.39087 | 0.406570 |
| 0.41 | 1.5068 | .17806 | .663650 | 0.91 | 2.4843 | .39521 | .402524 |
| 0.42 | 1.5220 | .18240 | .657047 | 0.92 | 2.5093 | .39955 | .398519 |
| 0.43 | 1.5373 | .18675 | .650509 | 0.93 | 2.5345 | .40389 | .394554 |
| 0.44 | 1.5527 | .19109 | .644036 | 0.94 | 2.5600 | .40824 | .390628 |
| **0.45** | 1.5683 | 0.19543 | 0.637628 | **0.95** | 2.5857 | 0.41258 | 0.386741 |
| 0.46 | 1.5841 | .19978 | .631284 | 0.96 | 2.6117 | .41692 | .382893 |
| 0.47 | 1.6000 | .20412 | .625002 | 0.97 | 2.6379 | .42127 | .379083 |
| 0.48 | 1.6161 | .20846 | .618783 | 0.98 | 2.6645 | .42561 | .375311 |
| 0.49 | 1.6323 | .21280 | .612626 | 0.99 | 2.6912 | .42995 | .371577 |
| **0.50** | 1.6487 | 0.21715 | 0.606531 | **1.00** | 2.7183 | 0.43429 | 0.367879 |

| $x$ | $e^x$ | $\mathrm{Log}_{10}(e^x)$ | $e^{-x}$ | $x$ | $e^x$ | $\mathrm{Log}_{10}(e^x)$ | $e^{-x}$ |
|---|---|---|---|---|---|---|---|
| **1.00** | 2.7183 | 0.43429 | 0.367879 | **1.50** | 4.4817 | 0.65144 | 0.223130 |
| 1.01 | 2.7456 | .43864 | .364219 | 1.51 | 4.5267 | .65578 | .220910 |
| 1.02 | 2.7732 | .44298 | .360595 | 1.52 | 4.5722 | .66013 | .218712 |
| 1.03 | 2.8011 | .44732 | .357007 | 1.53 | 4.6182 | .66447 | .216536 |
| 1.04 | 2.8292 | .45167 | .353455 | 1.54 | 4.6646 | .66881 | .214381 |
| **1.05** | 2.8577 | 0.45601 | 0.349938 | **1.55** | 4.7115 | 0.67316 | 0.212248 |
| 1.06 | 2.8864 | .46035 | .346456 | 1.56 | 4.7588 | .67750 | .210136 |
| 1.07 | 2.9154 | .46470 | .343009 | 1.57 | 4.8066 | .68184 | .208045 |
| 1.08 | 2.9447 | .46904 | .339596 | 1.58 | 4.8550 | .68619 | .205975 |
| 1.09 | 2.9743 | .47338 | .336216 | 1.59 | 4.9037 | .69053 | .203926 |
| **1.10** | 3.0042 | 0.47772 | 0.332871 | **1.60** | 4.9530 | 0.69487 | 0.201897 |
| 1.11 | 3.0344 | .48207 | .329559 | 1.61 | 5.0028 | .69921 | .199888 |
| 1.12 | 3.0649 | .48641 | .326280 | 1.62 | 5.0531 | .70356 | .197899 |
| 1.13 | 3.0957 | .49075 | .323033 | 1.63 | 5.1039 | .70790 | .195930 |
| 1.14 | 3.1268 | .49510 | .319819 | 1.64 | 5.1552 | .71224 | .193980 |
| **1.15** | 3.1582 | 0.49944 | 0.316637 | **1.65** | 5.2070 | 0.71659 | 0.192050 |
| 1.16 | 3.1899 | .50378 | .313486 | 1.66 | 5.2593 | .72093 | .190139 |
| 1.17 | 3.2220 | .50812 | .310367 | 1.67 | 5.3122 | .72527 | .188247 |
| 1.18 | 3.2544 | .51247 | .307279 | 1.68 | 5.3656 | .72961 | .186374 |
| 1.19 | 3.2871 | .51681 | .304221 | 1.69 | 5.4195 | .73396 | .184520 |
| **1.20** | 3.3201 | 0.52115 | 0.301194 | **1.70** | 5.4739 | 0.73830 | 0.182684 |
| 1.21 | 3.3535 | .52550 | .298197 | 1.71 | 5.5290 | .74264 | .180866 |
| 1.22 | 3.3872 | .52984 | .295230 | 1.72 | 5.5845 | .74699 | .179066 |
| 1.23 | 3.4212 | .53418 | .292293 | 1.73 | 5.6407 | .75133 | .177284 |
| 1.24 | 3.4556 | .53853 | .289384 | 1.74 | 5.6973 | .75567 | .175520 |
| **1.25** | 3.4903 | 0.54287 | 0.286505 | **1.75** | 5.7546 | 0.76002 | 0.173774 |
| 1.26 | 3.5254 | .54721 | .283654 | 1.76 | 5.8124 | .76436 | .172045 |
| 1.27 | 3.5609 | .55155 | .280832 | 1.77 | 5.8709 | .76870 | .170333 |
| 1.28 | 3.5966 | .55590 | .278037 | 1.78 | 5.9299 | .77304 | .168638 |
| 1.29 | 3.6328 | .56024 | .275271 | 1.79 | 5.9895 | .77739 | .166960 |
| **1.30** | 3.6693 | 0.56458 | 0.272532 | **1.80** | 6.0496 | 0.78173 | 0.165299 |
| 1.31 | 3.7062 | .56893 | .269820 | 1.81 | 6.1104 | .78607 | .163654 |
| 1.32 | 3.7434 | .57327 | .267135 | 1.82 | 6.1719 | .79042 | .162026 |
| 1.33 | 3.7810 | .57761 | .264477 | 1.83 | 6.2339 | .79476 | .160414 |
| 1.34 | 3.8190 | .58195 | .261846 | 1.84 | 6.2965 | .79910 | .158817 |
| **1.35** | 3.8574 | 0.58630 | 0.259240 | **1.85** | 6.3598 | 0.80344 | 0.157237 |
| 1.36 | 3.8962 | .59064 | .256661 | 1.86 | 6.4237 | .80779 | .155673 |
| 1.37 | 3.9354 | .59498 | .254107 | 1.87 | 6.4883 | .81213 | .154124 |
| 1.38 | 3.9749 | .59933 | .251579 | 1.88 | 6.5535 | .81647 | .152590 |
| 1.39 | 4.0149 | .60367 | .249075 | 1.89 | 6.6194 | .82082 | .151072 |
| **1.40** | 4.0552 | 0.60801 | 0.246597 | **1.90** | 6.6859 | 0.82516 | 0.149569 |
| 1.41 | 4.0960 | .61236 | .244143 | 1.91 | 6.7531 | .82950 | .148080 |
| 1.42 | 4.1371 | .61670 | .241714 | 1.92 | 6.8210 | .83385 | .146607 |
| 1.43 | 4.1787 | .62104 | .239309 | 1.93 | 6.8895 | .83819 | .145148 |
| 1.44 | 4.2207 | .62538 | .236928 | 1.94 | 6.9588 | .84253 | .143704 |
| **1.45** | 4.2631 | 0.62973 | 0.234570 | **1.95** | 7.0287 | 0.84687 | 0.142274 |
| 1.46 | 4.3060 | .63407 | .232236 | 1.96 | 7.0993 | .85122 | .140858 |
| 1.47 | 4.3492 | .63841 | .229925 | 1.97 | 7.1707 | .85556 | .139457 |
| 1.48 | 4.3929 | .64276 | .227638 | 1.98 | 7.2427 | .85990 | .138069 |
| 1.49 | 4.4371 | .64710 | .225373 | 1.99 | 7.3155 | .86425 | .136695 |
| **1.50** | 4.4817 | 0.65144 | 0.223130 | **2.00** | 7.3891 | 0.86859 | 0.135335 |

## EXPONENTIAL FUNCTIONS (Continued)

| $x$ | $e^x$ | $Log_{10}(e^x)$ | $e^{-x}$ | $x$ | $e^x$ | $Log_{10}(e^x)$ | $e^{-x}$ |
|---|---|---|---|---|---|---|---|
| **2.00** | 7.3891 | 0.86859 | 0.135335 | **2.50** | 12.182 | 1.08574 | 0.082085 |
| 2.01 | 7.4633 | .87293 | .133989 | 2.51 | 12.305 | 1.09008 | .081268 |
| 2.02 | 7.5383 | .87727 | .132655 | 2.52 | 12.429 | 1.09442 | .080460 |
| 2.03 | 7.6141 | .88162 | .131336 | 2.53 | 12.554 | 1.09877 | .079659 |
| 2.04 | 7.6906 | .88596 | .130029 | 2.54 | 12.680 | 1.10311 | .078866 |
| **2.05** | 7.7679 | 0.89030 | 0.128735 | **2.55** | 12.807 | 1.10745 | 0.078082 |
| 2.06 | 7.8460 | .89465 | .127454 | 2.56 | 12.936 | 1.11179 | .077305 |
| 2.07 | 7.9248 | .89899 | .126186 | 2.57 | 13.066 | 1.11614 | .076536 |
| 2.08 | 8.0045 | .90333 | .124930 | 2.58 | 13.197 | 1.12048 | .075774 |
| 2.09 | 8.0849 | .90768 | .123687 | 2.59 | 13.330 | 1.12482 | .075020 |
| **2.10** | 8.1662 | 0.91202 | 0.122456 | **2.60** | 13.464 | 1.12917 | 0.074274 |
| 2.11 | 8.2482 | .91636 | .121238 | 2.61 | 13.599 | 1.13351 | .073535 |
| 2.12 | 8.3311 | .92070 | .120032 | 2.62 | 13.736 | 1.13785 | .072803 |
| 2.13 | 8.4149 | .92505 | .118837 | 2.63 | 13.874 | 1.14219 | .072078 |
| 2.14 | 8.4994 | .92939 | .117655 | 2.64 | 14.013 | 1.14654 | .071361 |
| **2.15** | 8.5849 | 0.93373 | 0.116484 | **2.65** | 14.154 | 1.15088 | 0.070651 |
| 2.16 | 8.6711 | .93808 | .115325 | 2.66 | 14.296 | 1.15522 | .069948 |
| 2.17 | 8.7583 | .94242 | .114178 | 2.67 | 14.440 | 1.15957 | .069252 |
| 2.18 | 8.8463 | .94676 | .113042 | 2.68 | 14.585 | 1.16391 | .068563 |
| 2.19 | 8.9352 | .95110 | .111917 | 2.69 | 14.732 | 1.16825 | .067881 |
| **2.20** | 9.0250 | 0.95545 | 0.110803 | **2.70** | 14.880 | 1.17260 | 0.067206 |
| 2.21 | 9.1157 | .95979 | .109701 | 2.71 | 15.029 | 1.17694 | .066537 |
| 2.22 | 9.2073 | .96413 | .108609 | 2.72 | 15.180 | 1.18128 | .065875 |
| 2.23 | 9.2999 | .96848 | .107528 | 2.73 | 15.333 | 1.18562 | .065219 |
| 2.24 | 9.3933 | .97282 | .106459 | 2.74 | 15.487 | 1.18997 | .064570 |
| **2.25** | 9.4877 | 0.97716 | 0.105399 | **2.75** | 15.643 | 1.19431 | 0.063928 |
| 2.26 | 9.5831 | .98151 | .104350 | 2.76 | 15.800 | 1.19865 | .063292 |
| 2.27 | 9.6794 | .98585 | .103312 | 2.77 | 15.959 | 1.20300 | .062662 |
| 2.28 | 9.7767 | .99019 | .102284 | 2.78 | 16.119 | 1.20734 | .062039 |
| 2.29 | 9.8749 | .99453 | .101266 | 2.79 | 16.281 | 1.21168 | .061421 |
| **2.30** | 9.9742 | 0.99888 | 0.100259 | **2.80** | 16.445 | 1.21602 | 0.060810 |
| 2.31 | 10.074 | 1.00322 | .099261 | 2.81 | 16.610 | 1.22037 | .060205 |
| 2.32 | 10.176 | 1.00756 | .098274 | 2.82 | 16.777 | 1.22471 | .059606 |
| 2.33 | 10.278 | 1.01191 | .097296 | 2.83 | 16.945 | 1.22905 | .059013 |
| 2.34 | 10.381 | 1.01625 | .096328 | 2.84 | 17.116 | 1.23340 | .058426 |
| **2.35** | 10.486 | 1.02059 | 0.095369 | **2.85** | 17.288 | 1.23774 | 0.057844 |
| 2.36 | 10.591 | 1.02493 | .094420 | 2.86 | 17.462 | 1.24208 | .057269 |
| 2.37 | 10.697 | 1.02928 | .093481 | 2.87 | 17.637 | 1.24643 | .056699 |
| 2.38 | 10.805 | 1.03362 | .092551 | 2.88 | 17.814 | 1.25077 | .056135 |
| 2.39 | 10.913 | 1.03796 | .091630 | 2.89 | 17.993 | 1.25511 | .055576 |
| **2.40** | 11.023 | 1.04231 | 0.090718 | **2.90** | 18.174 | 1.25945 | 0.055023 |
| 2.41 | 11.134 | 1.04665 | .089815 | 2.91 | 18.357 | 1.26380 | .054476 |
| 2.42 | 11.246 | 1.05099 | .088922 | 2.92 | 18.541 | 1.26814 | .053934 |
| 2.43 | 11.359 | 1.05534 | .088037 | 2.93 | 18.728 | 1.27248 | .053397 |
| 2.44 | 11.473 | 1.05968 | .087161 | 2.94 | 18.916 | 1.27683 | .052866 |
| **2.45** | 11.588 | 1.06402 | 0.086294 | **2.95** | 19.106 | 1.28117 | 0.052340 |
| 2.46 | 11.705 | 1.06836 | .085435 | 2.96 | 19.298 | 1.28551 | .051819 |
| 2.47 | 11.822 | 1.07271 | .084585 | 2.97 | 19.492 | 1.28985 | .051303 |
| 2.48 | 11.941 | 1.07705 | .083743 | 2.98 | 19.688 | 1.29420 | .050793 |
| 2.49 | 12.061 | 1.08139 | .082910 | 2.99 | 19.886 | 1.29854 | .050287 |
| **2.50** | 12.182 | 1.08574 | 0.082085 | **3.00** | 20.086 | 1.30288 | 0.049787 |

# EXPONENTIAL FUNCTIONS (Continued)

| $x$ | $e^x$ | $\mathrm{Log}_{10}(e^x)$ | $e^{-x}$ | $x$ | $e^x$ | $\mathrm{Log}_{10}(e^x)$ | $e^{-x}$ |
|---|---|---|---|---|---|---|---|
| **3.00** | 20.086 | 1.30288 | 0.049787 | **3.50** | 33.115 | 1.52003 | 0.030197 |
| 3.01 | 20.287 | 1.30723 | .049292 | 3.51 | 33.448 | 1.52437 | .029897 |
| 3.02 | 20.491 | 1.31157 | .048801 | 3.52 | 33.784 | 1.52872 | .029599 |
| 3.03 | 20.697 | 1.31591 | .048316 | 3.53 | 34.124 | 1.53306 | .029305 |
| 3.04 | 20.905 | 1.32026 | .047835 | 3.54 | 34.467 | 1.53740 | .029013 |
| **3.05** | 21.115 | 1.32460 | 0.047359 | **3.55** | 34.813 | 1.54175 | 0.028725 |
| 3.06 | 21.328 | 1.32894 | .046888 | 3.56 | 35.163 | 1.54609 | .028439 |
| 3.07 | 21.542 | 1.33328 | .046421 | 3.57 | 35.517 | 1.55043 | .028156 |
| 3.08 | 21.758 | 1.33763 | .045959 | 3.58 | 35.874 | 1.55477 | .027876 |
| 3.09· | 21.977 | 1.34197 | .045502 | 3.59 | 36.234 | 1.55912 | .027598 |
| **3.10** | 22.198 | 1.34631 | 0.045049 | **3.60** | 36.598 | 1.56346 | 0.027324 |
| 3.11 | 22.421 | 1.35066 | .044601 | 3.61 | 36.966 | 1.56780 | .027052 |
| 3.12 | 22.646 | 1.35500 | .044157 | 3.62 | 37.338 | 1.57215 | .026783 |
| 3.13 | 22.874 | 1.35934 | .043718 | 3.63 | 37.713 | 1.57649 | .026516 |
| 3.14 | 23.104 | 1.36368 | .043283 | 3.64 | 38.092 | 1.58083 | .026252 |
| **3.15** | 23.336 | 1.36803 | 0.042852 | **3.65** | 38.475 | 1.58517 | 0.025991 |
| 3.16 | 23.571 | 1.37237 | .042426 | 3.66 | 38.861 | 1.58952 | .025733 |
| 3.17 | 23.807 | 1.37671 | .042004 | 3.67 | 39.252 | 1.59386 | .025476 |
| 3.18 | 24.047 | 1.38106 | .041586 | 3.68 | 39.646 | 1.59820 | .025223 |
| 3.19 | 24.288 | 1.38540 | .041172 | 3.69 | 40.045 | 1.60255 | .024972 |
| **3.20** | 24.533 | 1.38974 | 0 040762 | **3.70** | 40.447 | 1.60689 | 0.024724 |
| 3.21 | 24.779 | 1.39409 | .040357 | 3.71 | 40.854 | 1.61123 | .024478 |
| 3.22 | 25.028 | 1.39843 | .039955 | 3.72 | 41.264 | 1.61558 | .024234 |
| 3.23 | 25.280 | 1.40277 | .039557 | 3.73 | 41.679 | 1.61992 | .023993 |
| 3.24 | 25.534 | 1.40711 | .039164 | 3.74 | 42.098 | 1.62426 | .023754 |
| **3.25** | 25.790 | 1.41146 | 0.038774 | **3.75** | 42.521 | 1.62860 | 0.023518 |
| 3.26 | 26.050 | 1.41580 | .038388 | 3.76 | 42.948 | 1.63295 | .023284 |
| 3.27 | 26.311 | 1.42014 | .038006 | 3.77 | 43.380 | 1.63729 | .023052 |
| 3.28 | 26.576 | 1.42449 | .037628 | 3.78 | 43.816 | 1.64163 | .022823 |
| 3.29 | 26.843 | 1.42883 | .037254 | 3.79 | 44.256 | 1.64598 | .022596 |
| **3.30** | 27.113 | 1.43317 | 0.036883 | **3.80** | 44.701 | 1.65032 | 0.022371 |
| 3.31 | 27.385 | 1.43751 | .036516 | 3.81 | 45.150 | 1.65466 | .022148 |
| 3.32 | 27.660 | 1.44186 | .036153 | 3.82 | 45.604 | 1.65900 | .021928 |
| 3.33 | 27.938 | 1.44620 | .035793 | 3.83 | 46.063 | 1.66335 | .021710 |
| 3.34 | 28.219 | 1.45054 | .035437 | 3.84 | 46.525 | 1.66769 | .021494 |
| **3.35** | 28.503 | 1.45489 | 0.035084 | **3.85** | 46.993 | 1.67203 | 0.021280 |
| 3.36 | 28.789 | 1.45923 | .034735 | 3.86 | 47.465 | 1.67638 | .021068 |
| 3.37 | 29.079 | 1.46357 | .034390 | 3.87 | 47.942 | 1.68072 | .020858 |
| 3.38 | 29.371 | 1.46792 | .034047 | 3.88 | 48.424 | 1.68506 | .020651 |
| 3.39 | 29.666 | 1.47226 | .033709 | 3.89 | 48.911 | 1.68941 | .020445 |
| **3.40** | 29.964 | 1.47660 | 0.033373 | **3.90** | 49.402 | 1.69375 | 0.020242 |
| 3.41 | 30.265 | 1.48094 | .033041 | 3.91 | 49.899 | 1.69809 | .020041 |
| 3.42 | 30.569 | 1.48529 | .032712 | 3.92 | 50.400 | 1.70243 | .019841 |
| 3.43 | 30.877 | 1.48963 | .032387 | 3.93 | 50.907 | 1.70678 | .019644 |
| 3.44 | 31.187 | 1.49397 | .032065 | 3.94 | 51.419 | 1.71112 | .019448 |
| **3.45** | 31.500 | 1.49832 | 0.031746 | **3.95** | 51.935 | 1.71546 | 0.019255 |
| 3.46 | 31.817 | 1.50266 | .031430 | 3.96 | 52.457 | 1.71981 | .019063 |
| 3.47 | 32.137 | 1.50700 | .031117 | 3.97 | 52.985 | 1.72415 | .018873 |
| 3.48 | 32.460 | 1.51134 | .030807 | 3.98 | 53.517 | 1.72849 | .018686 |
| 3.49 | 32.786 | 1.51569 | .030501 | 3.99 | 54.055 | 1.73283 | .018500 |
| **3.50** | 33.115 | 1.52003 | 0.030197 | **4.00** | 54.598 | 1.73718 | 0.018316 |

## EXPONENTIAL FUNCTIONS (Continued)

| $x$ | $e^x$ | $\text{Log}_{10}(e^x)$ | $e^{-x}$ | $x$ | $e^x$ | $\text{Log}_{10}(e^x)$ | $e^{-x}$ |
|---|---|---|---|---|---|---|---|
| **4.00** | 54.598 | 1.73718 | 0.018316 | **4.50** | 90.017 | 1.95433 | 0.011109 |
| 4.01 | 55.147 | 1.74152 | .018133 | 4.51 | 90.922 | 1.95867 | .010998 |
| 4.02 | 55.701 | 1.74586 | .017953 | 4.52 | 91.836 | 1.96301 | .010889 |
| 4.03 | 56.261 | 1.75021 | .017774 | 4.53 | 92.759 | 1.96735 | .010781 |
| 4.04 | 56.826 | 1.75455 | .017597 | 4.54 | 93.691 | 1.97170 | .010673 |
| **4.05** | 57.397 | 1.75889 | 0.017422 | **4.55** | 94.632 | 1.97604 | 0.010567 |
| 4.06 | 57.974 | 1.76324 | .017249 | 4.56 | 95.583 | 1.98038 | .010462 |
| 4.07 | 58.557 | 1.76758 | .017077 | 4.57 | 96.544 | 1.98473 | .010358 |
| 4.08 | 59.145 | 1.77192 | .016907 | 4.58 | 97.514 | 1.98907 | .010255 |
| 4.09 | 59.740 | 1.77626 | .016739 | 4.59 | 98.494 | 1.99341 | .010153 |
| **4.10** | 60.340 | 1.78061 | 0.016573 | **4.60** | 99.484 | 1.99775 | 0.010052 |
| 4.11 | 60.947 | 1.78495 | .016408 | 4.61 | 100.48 | 2.00210 | .009952 |
| 4.12 | 61.559 | 1.78929 | .016245 | 4.62 | 101.49 | 2.00644 | .009853 |
| 4.13 | 62.178 | 1.79364 | .016083 | 4.63 | 102.51 | 2.01078 | .009755 |
| 4.14 | 62.803 | 1.79798 | .015923 | 4.64 | 103.54 | 2.01513 | .009658 |
| **4.15** | 63.434 | 1.80232 | 0.015764 | **4.65** | 104.58 | 2.01947 | 0.009562 |
| 4.16 | 64.072 | 1.80667 | .015608 | 4.66 | 105.64 | 2.02381 | .009466 |
| 4.17 | 64.715 | 1.81101 | .015452 | 4.67 | 106.70 | 2.02816 | .009372 |
| 4.18 | 65.366 | 1.81535 | .015299 | 4.68 | 107.77 | 2.03250 | .009279 |
| 4.19 | 66.023 | 1.81969 | .015146 | 4.69 | 108.85 | 2.03684 | .009187 |
| **4.20** | 66.686 | 1.82404 | 0.014996 | **4.70** | 109.95 | 2.04118 | 0.009095 |
| 4.21 | 67.357 | 1.82838 | .014846 | 4.71 | 111.05 | 2.04553 | .009005 |
| 4.22 | 68.033 | 1.83272 | .014699 | 4.72 | 112.17 | 2.04987 | .008915 |
| 4.23 | 68.717 | 1.83707 | .014552 | 4.73 | 113.30 | 2.05421 | .008826 |
| 4.24 | 69.408 | 1.84141 | .014408 | 4.74 | 114.43 | 2.05856 | .008739 |
| **4.25** | 70.105 | 1.84575 | 0.014264 | **4.75** | 115.58 | 2.06290 | 0.008652 |
| 4.26 | 70.810 | 1.85009 | .014122 | 4.76 | 116.75 | 2.06724 | .008566 |
| 4.27 | 71.522 | 1.85444 | .013982 | 4.77 | 117.92 | 2.07158 | .008480 |
| 4.28 | 72.240 | 1.85878 | .013843 | 4.78 | 119.10 | 2.07593 | .008396 |
| 4.29 | 72.966 | 1.86312 | .013705 | 4.79 | 120.30 | 2.08027 | .008312 |
| **4.30** | 73.700 | 1.86747 | 0.013569 | **4.80** | 121.51 | 2.08461 | 0.008230 |
| 4.31 | 74.440 | 1.87181 | .013434 | 4.81 | 122.73 | 2.08896 | .008148 |
| 4.32 | 75.189 | 1.87615 | .013300 | 4.82 | 123.97 | 2.09330 | .008067 |
| 4.33 | 75.944 | 1.88050 | .013168 | 4.83 | 125.21 | 2.09764 | .007987 |
| 4.34 | 76.708 | 1.88484 | .013037 | 4.84 | 126.47 | 2.10199 | .007907 |
| **4.35** | 77.478 | 1.88918 | 0.012907 | **4.85** | 127.74 | 2.10633 | 0.007828 |
| 4.36 | 78.257 | 1.89352 | .012778 | 4.86 | 129.02 | 2.11067 | .007750 |
| 4.37 | 79.044 | 1.89787 | .012651 | 4.87 | 130.32 | 2.11501 | .007673 |
| 4.38 | 79.838 | 1.90221 | .012525 | 4.88 | 131.63 | 2.11936 | .007597 |
| 4.39 | 80.640 | 1.90655 | .012401 | 4.89 | 132.95 | 2.12370 | .007521 |
| **4.40** | 81.451 | 1.91090 | 0.012277 | **4.90** | 134.29 | 2.12804 | 0.007447 |
| 4.41 | 82.269 | 1.91524 | .012155 | 4.91 | 135.64 | 2.13239 | .007372 |
| 4.42 | 83.096 | 1.91958 | .012034 | 4.92 | 137.00 | 2.13673 | .007299 |
| 4.43 | 83.931 | 1.92392 | .011914 | 4.93 | 138.38 | 2.14107 | .007227 |
| 4.44 | 84.775 | 1.92827 | .011796 | 4.94 | 139.77 | 2.14541 | .007155 |
| **4.45** | 85.627 | 1.93261 | 0.011679 | **4.95** | 141.17 | 2.14976 | 0.007083 |
| 4.46 | 86.488 | 1.93695 | .011562 | 4.96 | 142.59 | 2.15410 | .007013 |
| 4.47 | 87.357 | 1.94130 | .011447 | 4.97 | 144.03 | 2.15844 | .006943 |
| 4.48 | 88.235 | 1.94564 | .011333 | 4.98 | 145.47 | 2.16279 | .006874 |
| 4.49 | 89.121 | 1.94998 | .011221 | 4.99 | 146.94 | 2.16713 | .006806 |
| **4.50** | 90.017 | 1.95433 | 0.011109 | **5.00** | 148.41 | 2.17147 | 0.006738 |

# EXPONENTIAL FUNCTIONS (Continued)

| $x$ | $e^x$ | $Log_{10}(e^x)$ | $e^{-x}$ | $x$ | $e^x$ | $Log_{10}(e^x)$ | $e^{-x}$ |
|---|---|---|---|---|---|---|---|
| **5.00** | 148.41 | 2.17147 | 0.006738 | **5.50** | 244.69 | 2.38862 | 0.0040868 |
| 5.01 | 149.90 | 2.17582 | .006671 | 5.55 | 257.24 | 2.41033 | .0038875 |
| 5.02 | 151.41 | 2.18016 | .006605 | 5.60 | 270.43 | 2.43205 | .0036979 |
| 5.03 | 152.93 | 2.18450 | .006539 | 5.65 | 284.29 | 2.45376 | .0035175 |
| 5.04 | 154.47 | 2.18884 | .006474 | 5.70 | 298.87 | 2.47548 | .0033460 |
| **5.05** | 156.02 | 2.19319 | 0.006409 | **5.75** | 314.19 | 2.49719 | 0.0031828 |
| 5.06 | 157.59 | 2.19753 | .006346 | 5.80 | 330.30 | 2.51891 | .0030276 |
| 5.07 | 159.17 | 2.20187 | .006282 | 5.85 | 347.23 | 2.54062 | .0028799 |
| 5.08 | 160.77 | 2.20622 | .006220 | 5.90 | 365.04 | 2.56234 | .0027394 |
| 5.09 | 162.39 | 2.21056 | .006158 | 5.95 | 383.75 | 2.58405 | .0026058 |
| **5.10** | 164.02 | 2.21490 | 0.006097 | **6.00** | 403.43 | 2.60577 | 0.0024788 |
| 5.11 | 165.67 | 2.21924 | .006036 | 6.05 | 424.11 | 2.62748 | .0023579 |
| 5.12 | 167.34 | 2.22359 | .005976 | 6.10 | 445.86 | 2.64920 | .0022429 |
| 5.13 | 169.02 | 2.22793 | .005917 | 6.15 | 468.72 | 2.67091 | .0021335 |
| 5.14 | 170.72 | 2.23227 | .005858 | 6.20 | 492.75 | 2.69263 | .0020294 |
| **5.15** | 172.43 | 2.23662 | 0.005799 | **6.25** | 518.01 | 2.71434 | 0.0019305 |
| 5.16 | 174.16 | 2.24096 | .005742 | 6.30 | 544.57 | 2.73606 | .0018363 |
| 5.17 | 175.91 | 2.24530 | .005685 | 6.35 | 572.49 | 2.75777 | .0017467 |
| 5.18 | 177.68 | 2.24965 | .005628 | 6.40 | 601.85 | 2.77948 | .0016616 |
| 5.19 | 179.47 | 2.25399 | .005572 | 6.45 | 632.70 | 2.80120 | .0015805 |
| **5.20** | 181.27 | 2.25833 | 0.005517 | **6.50** | 665.14 | 2.82291 | 0.0015034 |
| 5.21 | 183.09 | 2.26267 | .005462 | 6.55 | 699.24 | 2.84463 | .0014301 |
| 5.22 | 184.93 | 2.26702 | .005407 | 6.60 | 735.10 | 2.86634 | .0013604 |
| 5.23 | 186.79 | 2.27136 | .005354 | 6.65 | 772.78 | 2.88806 | .0012940 |
| 5.24 | 188.67 | 2.27570 | .005300 | 6.70 | 812.41 | 2.90977 | .0012309 |
| **5.25** | 190.57 | 2.28005 | 0.005248 | **6.75** | 854.06 | 2.93149 | 0.0011709 |
| 5.26 | 192.48 | 2.28439 | .005195 | 6.80 | 897.85 | 2.95320 | .0011138 |
| 5.27 | 194.42 | 2.28873 | .005144 | 6.85 | 943.88 | 2.97492 | .0010595 |
| 5.28 | 196.37 | 2.29307 | .005092 | 6.90 | 992.27 | 2.99663 | .0010078 |
| 5.29 | 198.34 | 2.29742 | .005042 | 6.95 | 1043.1 | 3.01835 | .0009586 |
| **5.30** | 200.34 | 2.30176 | 0.004992 | **7.00** | 1096.6 | 3.04006 | 0.0009119 |
| 5.31 | 202.35 | 2.30610 | .004942 | 7.05 | 1152.9 | 3.06178 | .0008674 |
| 5.32 | 204.38 | 2.31045 | .004893 | 7.10 | 1212.0 | 3.08349 | .0008251 |
| 5.33 | 206.44 | 2.31479 | .004844 | 7.15 | 1274.1 | 3.10521 | .0007849 |
| 5.34 | 208.51 | 2.31913 | .004796 | 7.20 | 1339.4 | 3.12692 | .0007466 |
| **5.35** | 210.61 | 2.32348 | 0.004748 | **7.25** | 1408.1 | 3.14863 | 0.0007102 |
| 5.36 | 212.72 | 2.32782 | .004701 | 7.30 | 1480.3 | 3.17035 | .0006755 |
| 5.37 | 214.86 | 2.33216 | .004654 | 7.35 | 1556.2 | 3.19206 | .0006426 |
| 5.38 | 217.02 | 2.33650 | .004608 | 7.40 | 1636.0 | 3.21378 | .0006113 |
| 5.39 | 219.20 | 2.34085 | .004562 | 7.45 | 1719.9 | 3.23549 | .0005814 |
| **5.40** | 221.41 | 2.34519 | 0.004517 | **7.50** | 1808.0 | 3.25721 | 0.0005531 |
| 5.41 | 223.63 | 2.34953 | .004472 | 7.55 | 1900.7 | 3.27892 | .0005261 |
| 5.42 | 225.88 | 2.35388 | .004427 | 7.60 | 1998.2 | 3.30064 | .0005005 |
| 5.43 | 228.15 | 2.35822 | .004383 | 7.65 | 2100.6 | 3.32235 | .0004760 |
| 5.44 | 230.44 | 2.36256 | .004339 | 7.70 | 2208.3 | 3.34407 | .0004528 |
| **5.45** | 232.76 | 2.36690 | 0.004296 | **7.75** | 2321.6 | 3.36578 | 0.0004307 |
| 5.46 | 235.10 | 2.37125 | .004254 | 7.80 | 2440.6 | 3.38750 | .0004097 |
| 5.47 | 237.46 | 2.37559 | .004211 | 7.85 | 2565.7 | 3.40921 | .0003898 |
| 5.48 | 239.85 | 2.37993 | .004169 | 7.90 | 2697.3 | 3.43093 | .0003707 |
| 5.49 | 242.26 | 2.38428 | .004128 | 7.95 | 2835.6 | 3.45264 | .0003527 |
| **5.50** | 244.69 | 2.38862 | 0.004087 | **8.00** | 2981.0 | 3.47436 | 0.0003355 |

# HYPERBOLIC FUNCTIONS

The logarithms given below show the mantissa only. The proper characteristic must be added.

| x | Sinh x Value | log₁₀ | Cosh x Value | log₁₀ | Tanh x Value | log₁₀ | Coth x Value | log₁₀ |
|---|---|---|---|---|---|---|---|---|
| **0.00** | 0.00000 | − ∞ | 1.00000 | .00000 | 0.00000 | − ∞ | ∞ | ∞ |
| 0.01 | .01000 | .00001 | 1.00005 | .00002 | .01000 | .99999 | 100.003 | .00001 |
| 0.02 | .02000 | .30106 | 1.00020 | .00009 | .02000 | .30097 | 50.007 | .69903 |
| 0.03 | .03000 | .47719 | 1.00045 | .00020 | .02999 | .47699 | 33.343 | .52301 |
| 0.04 | .04001 | .60218 | 1.00080 | .00035 | .03998 | .60183 | 25.013 | .39817 |
| **0.05** | 0.05002 | .69915 | 1.00125 | .00054 | 0.04996 | .69861 | 20.017 | .30139 |
| 0.06 | .06004 | .77841 | 1.00180 | .00078 | .05993 | .77763 | 16.687 | .22237 |
| 0.07 | .07006 | .84545 | 1.00245 | .00106 | .06989 | .84439 | 14.309 | .15561 |
| 0.08 | .08009 | .90355 | 1.00320 | .00139 | .07983 | .90216 | 12.527 | .09784 |
| 0.09 | .09012 | .95483 | 1.00405 | .00176 | .08976 | .95307 | 11.141 | .04693 |
| **0.10** | 0.10017 | .00072 | 1.00500 | .00217 | 0.09967 | .99856 | 10.0333 | .00144 |
| 0.11 | .11022 | .04227 | 1.00606 | .00262 | .10956 | .03965 | 9.1275 | .96035 |
| 0.12 | .12029 | .08022 | 1.00721 | .00312 | .11943 | .07710 | 8.3733 | .92290 |
| 0.13 | .13037 | .11517 | 1.00846 | .00366 | .12927 | .11151 | 7.7356 | .88849 |
| 0.14 | .14046 | .14755 | 1.00982 | .00424 | .13909 | .14330 | 7.1895 | .85670 |
| **0.15** | 0.15056 | .17772 | 1.01127 | .00487 | 0.14889 | .17285 | 6.7166 | .82715 |
| 0.16 | .16068 | .20597 | 1.01283 | .00554 | .15865 | .20044 | 6.3032 | .79956 |
| 0.17 | .17082 | .23254 | 1.01448 | .00625 | .16838 | .22629 | 5.9389 | .77371 |
| 0.18 | .18097 | .25762 | 1.01624 | .00700 | .17808 | .25062 | 5.6154 | .74938 |
| 0.19 | .19115 | .28136 | 1.01810 | .00779 | .18775 | .27357 | 5.3263 | .72643 |
| **0.20** | 0.20134 | .30392 | 1.02007 | .00863 | 0.19738 | .29529 | 5.0665 | .70471 |
| 0.21 | .21155 | .32541 | 1.02213 | .00951 | .20697 | .31590 | 4.8317 | .68410 |
| 0.22 | .22178 | .34592 | 1.02430 | .01043 | .21652 | .33549 | 4.6186 | .66451 |
| 0.23 | .23203 | .36555 | 1.02657 | .01139 | .22603 | .35416 | 4.4242 | .64584 |
| 0.24 | .24231 | .38437 | 1.02894 | .01239 | .23550 | .37198 | 4.2464 | .62802 |
| **0.25** | 0.25261 | .40245 | 1.03141 | .01343 | 0.24492 | .38902 | 4.0830 | .61098 |
| 0.26 | .26294 | .41986 | 1.03399 | .01452 | .25430 | .40534 | 3.9324 | .59466 |
| 0.27 | .27329 | .43663 | 1.03667 | .01564 | .26362 | .42099 | 3.7933 | .57901 |
| 0.28 | .28367 | .45282 | 1.03946 | .01681 | .27291 | .43601 | 3.6643 | .56399 |
| 0.29 | .29408 | .46847 | 1.04235 | .01801 | .28213 | .45046 | 3.5444 | .54954 |
| **0.30** | 0.30452 | .48362 | 1.04534 | .01926 | 0.29131 | .46436 | 3.4327 | .53564 |
| 0.31 | .31499 | .49830 | 1.04844 | .02054 | .30044 | .47775 | 3.3285 | .52225 |
| 0.32 | .32549 | .51254 | 1.05164 | .02187 | .30951 | .49067 | 3.2309 | .50933 |
| 0.33 | .33602 | .52637 | 1.05495 | .02323 | .31852 | .50314 | 3.1395 | .49686 |
| 0.34 | .34659 | .53981 | 1.05836 | .02463 | .32748 | .51518 | 3.0536 | .48482 |
| **0.35** | 0.35719 | .55290 | 1.06188 | .02607 | 0.33638 | .52682 | 2.9729 | .47318 |
| 0.36 | .36783 | .56564 | 1.06550 | .02755 | .34521 | .53809 | 2.8968 | .46191 |
| 0.37 | .37850 | .57807 | 1.06923 | .02907 | .35399 | .54899 | 2.8249 | .45101 |
| 0.38 | .38921 | .59019 | 1.07307 | .03063 | .36271 | .55956 | 2.7570 | .44044 |
| 0.39 | .39996 | .60202 | 1.07702 | .03222 | .37136 | .56980 | 2.6928 | .43020 |
| **0.40** | 0.41075 | .61358 | 1.08107 | .03385 | 0.37995 | .57973 | 2.6319 | .42027 |
| 0.41 | .42158 | .62488 | 1.08523 | .03552 | .38847 | .58936 | 2.5742 | .41064 |
| 0.42 | .43246 | .63594 | 1.08950 | .03722 | .39693 | .59871 | 2.5193 | .40129 |
| 0.43 | .44337 | .64677 | 1.09388 | .03897 | .40532 | .60780 | 2.4672 | .39220 |
| 0.44 | .45434 | .65738 | 1.09837 | .04075 | .41364 | .61663 | 2.4175 | .38337 |
| **0.45** | 0.46534 | .66777 | 1.10297 | .04256 | 0.42190 | .62521 | 2.3702 | .37479 |
| 0.46 | .47640 | .67797 | 1.10768 | .04441 | .43008 | .63355 | 2.3251 | .36645 |
| 0.47 | .48750 | .68797 | 1.11250 | .04630 | .43820 | .64167 | 2.2821 | .35833 |
| 0.48 | .49865 | .69779 | 1.11743 | .04822 | .44624 | .64957 | 2.2409 | .35043 |
| 0.49 | .50984 | .70744 | 1.12247 | .05018 | .45422 | .65726 | 2.2016 | .34274 |

# HYPERBOLIC FUNCTIONS (Continued)

The logarithms given below show the mantissa only. The proper char=
acteristic must be added.

| $x$ | Sinh $x$ Value | Sinh $x$ log₁₀ | Cosh $x$ Value | Cosh $x$ log₁₀ | Tanh $x$ Value | Tanh $x$ log₁₀ | Coth $x$ Value | Coth $x$ log₁₀ |
|---|---|---|---|---|---|---|---|---|
| **0.50** | 0.52110 | .71692 | 1.12763 | .05217 | 0.46212 | .66475 | 2.1640 | .33525 |
| 0.51 | .53240 | .72624 | 1.13289 | .05419 | .46995 | .67205 | 2.1279 | .32795 |
| 0.52 | .54375 | .73540 | 1.13827 | .05625 | .47770 | .67916 | 2.0934 | .32084 |
| 0.53 | .55516 | .74442 | 1.14377 | .05834 | .48538 | .68608 | 2.0602 | .31392 |
| 0.54 | .56663 | .75330 | 1.14938 | .06046 | .49299 | .69284 | 2.0284 | .30716 |
| **0.55** | 0.57815 | .76204 | 1.15510 | .06262 | 0.50052 | .69942 | 1.9979 | .30058 |
| 0 56 | .58973 | .77065 | 1.16094 | .06481 | .50798 | .70584 | 1.9686 | .29416 |
| 0 57 | .60137 | .77914 | 1.16690 | .06703 | .51536 | .71211 | 1.9404 | .28789 |
| 0.58 | .61307 | .78751 | 1.17297 | .06929 | .52267 | .71822 | 1.9133 | .28178 |
| 0 59 | .62483 | .79576 | 1.17916 | .07157 | .52990 | .72419 | 1.8872 | .27581 |
| **0.60** | 0.63665 | .80390 | 1.18547 | .07389 | 0.53705 | .73001 | 1.8620 | .26999 |
| 0.61 | .64854 | .81194 | 1.19189 | .07624 | .54413 | .73570 | 1.8378 | .26430 |
| 0.62 | .66049 | .81987 | 1.19844 | .07861 | .55113 | .74125 | 1.8145 | .25875 |
| 0.63 | .67251 | .82770 | 1.20510 | .08102 | .55805 | .74667 | 1.7919 | .25333 |
| 0 64 | .68459 | .83543 | 1.21189 | .08346 | .56490 | .75197 | 1.7702 | .24803 |
| **0.65** | 0.69675 | .84308 | 1.21879 | .08593 | 0.57167 | .75715 | 1.7493 | .24285 |
| 0.66 | .70897 | .85063 | 1.22582 | .08843 | .57836 | .76220 | 1.7290 | .23780 |
| 0.67 | .72126 | .85809 | 1.23297 | .09095 | .58498 | .76714 | 1.7095 | .23286 |
| 0.68 | .73363 | .86548 | 1.24025 | .09351 | .59152 | .77197 | 1.6906 | .22803 |
| 0.69 | .74607 | .87278 | 1.24765 | .09609 | .59798 | .77669 | 1.6723 | .22331 |
| **0.70** | 0.75858 | .88000 | 1.25517 | .09870 | 0.60437 | .78130 | 1.6546 | .21870 |
| 0.71 | .77117 | .88715 | 1.26282 | .10134 | .61068 | .78581 | 1.6375 | .21419 |
| 0.72 | .78384 | .89423 | 1.27059 | .10401 | .61691 | .79022 | 1.6210 | .20978 |
| 0.73 | .79659 | .90123 | 1.27849 | .10670 | .62307 | .79453 | 1.6050 | .20547 |
| 0.74 | .80941 | .90817 | 1.28652 | .10942 | .62915 | .79875 | 1.5895 | .20125 |
| **0.75** | 0.82232 | .91504 | 1.29468 | .11216 | 0.63515 | .80288 | 1.5744 | .19712 |
| 0.76 | .83530 | .92185 | 1.30297 | .11493 | .64108 | .80691 | 1.5599 | .19309 |
| 0.77 | .84838 | .92859 | 1.31139 | .11773 | .64693 | .81086 | 1.5458 | .18914 |
| 0.78 | .86153 | .93527 | 1.31994 | .12055 | .65271 | .81472 | 1.5321 | .18528 |
| 0.79 | .87478 | .94190 | 1.32862 | .12340 | .65841 | .81850 | 1.5188 | .18150 |
| **0.80** | 0.88811 | .94846 | 1.33743 | .12627 | 0.66404 | .82219 | 1.5059 | .17781 |
| 0.81 | .90152 | .95498 | 1.34638 | .12917 | .66959 | .82581 | 1.4935 | .17419 |
| 0.82 | .91503 | .96144 | 1.35547 | .13209 | .67507 | .82935 | 1.4813 | .17065 |
| 0.83 | .92863 | .96784 | 1.36468 | .13503 | .68048 | .83281 | 1.4696 | .16719 |
| 0.84 | .94233 | .97420 | 1.37404 | .13800 | .68581 | .83620 | 1.4581 | .16380 |
| **0.85** | 0.95612 | .98051 | 1.38353 | .14099 | 0.69107 | .83952 | 1.4470 | .16048 |
| 0 86 | .97000 | .98677 | 1.39316 | .14400 | .69626 | .84277 | 1.4362 | .15723 |
| 0.87 | .98398 | .99299 | 1.40293 | .14704 | .70137 | .84595 | 1.4258 | .15405 |
| 0.88 | .99806 | .99916 | 1.41284 | .15009 | .70642 | .84906 | 1.4156 | .15094 |
| 0.89 | 1.01224 | .00528 | 1.42289 | .15317 | .71139 | .85211 | 1.4057 | .14789 |
| **0.90** | 1.02652 | .01137 | 1.43309 | .15627 | 0.71630 | .85509 | 1.3961 | .14491 |
| 0.91 | 1.04090 | .01741 | 1.44342 | .15939 | .72113 | .85801 | 1.3867 | .14199 |
| 0.92 | 1.05539 | .02341 | 1.45390 | .16254 | .72590 | .86088 | 1.3776 | .13912 |
| 0.93 | 1.06998 | .02937 | 1.46453 | .16570 | .73059 | .86368 | 1.3687 | .13632 |
| 0.94 | 1.08468 | .03530 | 1.47530 | .16888 | .73522 | .86642 | 1.3601 | .13358 |
| **0.95** | 1.09948 | .04119 | 1.48623 | .17208 | 0.73978 | .86910 | 1.3517 | .13090 |
| 0.96 | 1.11440 | .04704 | 1.49729 | .17531 | .74428 | .87173 | 1.3436 | .12827 |
| 0.97 | 1.12943 | .05286 | 1.50851 | .17855 | .74870 | .87431 | 1.3356 | .12569 |
| 0.98 | 1.14457 | .05864 | 1.51988 | .18181 | .75307 | .87683 | 1.3279 | .12317 |
| 0.99 | 1.15983 | .06439 | 1.53141 | .18509 | .75736 | .87930 | 1.3204 | .12070 |

The logarithms given below show the mantissa only. The proper characteristic must be added.

| $x$ | Sinh $x$ Value | Sinh $x$ log₁₀ | Cosh $x$ Value | Cosh $x$ log₁₀ | Tanh $x$ Value | Tanh $x$ log₁₀ | Coth $x$ Value | Coth $x$ log₁₀ |
|---|---|---|---|---|---|---|---|---|
| **1.00** | 1.17520 | .07011 | 1.54308 | .18839 | 0 76159 | 88172 | 1.3130 | .11828 |
| 1.01 | 1.19069 | .07580 | 1.55491 | .19171 | .76576 | .88409 | 1.3059 | .11591 |
| 1.02 | 1.20630 | .08146 | 1.56689 | .19504 | .76987 | .88642 | 1.2989 | .11358 |
| 1.03 | 1.22203 | .08708 | 1.57904 | .19839 | .77391 | .88869 | 1.2921 | .11131 |
| 1.04 | 1.23788 | .09268 | 1.59134 | .20176 | .77789 | .89092 | 1.2855 | .10908 |
| **1.05** | 1.25386 | .09825 | 1.60379 | .20515 | 0.78181 | .89310 | 1.2791 | .10690 |
| 1.06 | 1.26996 | .10379 | 1.61641 | .20855 | .78566 | .89524 | 1.2728 | .10476 |
| 1.07 | 1.28619 | .10930 | 1.62919 | .21197 | .78946 | .89733 | 1.2667 | .10267 |
| 1.08 | 1.30254 | .11479 | 1.64214 | .21541 | .79320 | .89938 | 1.2607 | .10062 |
| 1.09 | 1.31903 | .12025 | 1.65525 | .21886 | .79688 | .90139 | 1.2549 | .09861 |
| **1.10** | 1.33565 | .12569 | 1.66852 | .22233 | 0.80050 | .90336 | 1.2492 | .09664 |
| 1.11 | 1.35240 | .13111 | 1.68196 | .22582 | .80406 | .90529 | 1.2437 | .09471 |
| 1.12 | 1.36929 | .13649 | 1.69557 | .22931 | .80757 | .90718 | 1.2383 | .09282 |
| 1.13 | 1.38631 | .14186 | 1.70934 | .23283 | .81102 | .90903 | 1.2330 | .09097 |
| 1.14 | 1.40347 | .14720 | 1.72329 | .23636 | .81441 | .91085 | 1.2279 | .08915 |
| **1.15** | 1.42078 | .15253 | 1.73741 | .23990 | 0.81775 | .91262 | 1.2229 | .08738 |
| 1.16 | 1.43822 | .15783 | 1.75171 | .24346 | .82104 | .91436 | 1.2180 | .08564 |
| 1.17 | 1.45581 | .16311 | 1.76618 | .24703 | .82427 | .91607 | 1.2132 | .08393 |
| 1.18 | 1.47355 | .16836 | 1.78083 | .25062 | .82745 | .91774 | 1.2085 | .08226 |
| 1.19 | 1.49143 | .17360 | 1.79565 | .25422 | .83058 | .91938 | 1.2040 | .08062 |
| **1.20** | 1.50946 | .17882 | 1.81066 | .25784 | 0.83365 | .92099 | 1.1995 | .07901 |
| 1.21 | 1.52764 | .18402 | 1.82584 | .26146 | .83668 | .92256 | 1.1952 | .07744 |
| 1.22 | 1.54598 | .18920 | 1.84121 | .26510 | .83965 | .92410 | 1.1910 | .07590 |
| 1.23 | 1.56447 | .19437 | 1.85676 | .26876 | .84258 | .92561 | 1.1868 | .07439 |
| 1.24 | 1.58311 | .19951 | 1.87250 | .27242 | .84546 | .92709 | 1.1828 | .07291 |
| **1.25** | 1.60192 | .20464 | 1.88842 | .27610 | 0.84828 | .92854 | 1.1789 | .07146 |
| 1.26 | 1.62088 | .20975 | 1.90454 | .27979 | .85106 | .92996 | 1.1750 | .07004 |
| 1.27 | 1.64001 | .21485 | 1.92084 | .28349 | .85380 | .93135 | 1.1712 | .06865 |
| 1.28 | 1.65930 | .21993 | 1.93734 | .28721 | .85648 | .93272 | 1.1676 | .06728 |
| 1.29 | 1.67876 | .22499 | 1.95403 | .29093 | .85913 | .93406 | 1.1640 | .06594 |
| **1.30** | 1.69838 | .23004 | 1.97091 | .29467 | 0.86172 | .93537 | 1.1605 | .06463 |
| 1.31 | 1.71818 | .23507 | 1.98800 | .29842 | .86428 | .93665 | 1.1570 | .06335 |
| 1.32 | 1.73814 | .24009 | 2.00528 | .30217 | .86678 | .93791 | 1.1537 | .06209 |
| 1.33 | 1.75828 | .24509 | 2.02276 | .30594 | .86925 | .93914 | 1.1504 | .06086 |
| 1.34 | 1.77860 | .25008 | 2.04044 | .30972 | .87167 | .94035 | 1.1472 | .05965 |
| **1.35** | 1.79909 | .25505 | 2.05833 | .31352 | 0.87405 | .94154 | 1.1441 | .05846 |
| 1.36 | 1.81977 | .26002 | 2.07643 | .31732 | .87639 | .94270 | 1 410 | .05730 |
| 1.37 | 1.84062 | .26496 | 2.09473 | .32113 | .87869 | .94384 | 1.1381 | .05616 |
| 1.38 | 1.86166 | .26990 | 2.11324 | .32495 | .88095 | .94495 | 1.1351 | .05505 |
| 1.39 | 1.88289 | .27482 | 2.13196 | .32878 | .88317 | .94604 | 1.1323 | .05396 |
| **1.40** | 1.90430 | .27974 | 2.15090 | .33262 | 0.88535 | .94712 | 1.1295 | .05288 |
| 1.41 | 1.92591 | .28464 | 2.17005 | .33647 | .88749 | .94817 | 1.1268 | .05183 |
| 1.42 | 1.94770 | .28952 | 2.18942 | .34033 | .88960 | .94919 | 1.1241 | .05081 |
| 1.43 | 1.96970 | .29440 | 2.20900 | .34420 | .89167 | .95020 | 1.1215 | .04980 |
| 1.44 | 1.99188 | .29926 | 2.22881 | .34807 | .89370 | .95119 | 1.1189 | .04881 |
| **1.45** | 2.01427 | .30412 | 2.24884 | .35196 | 0.89569 | .95216 | 1.1165 | .04784 |
| 1.46 | 2 03686 | .30896 | 2.26910 | .35585 | .89765 | .95311 | 1.1140 | .04689 |
| 1.47 | 2.05965 | .31379 | 2.28958 | .35976 | .89958 | .95404 | 1.1116 | .04596 |
| 1.48 | 2.08265 | .31862 | 2.31029 | .36367 | .90147 | .95495 | 1.1093 | .04505 |
| 1.49 | 2.10586 | .32343 | 2.33123 | .36759 | .90332 | .95584 | 1.1070 | .04416 |

# HYPERBOLIC FUNCTIONS (Continued)

The logarithms given below show the mantissa only. The proper characteristic must be added

| x | Sinh x | | Cosh x | | Tanh x | | Coth x | |
|---|--------|-------|--------|-------|--------|-------|--------|-------|
| | Value | log₁₀ | Value | log₁₀ | Value | log₁₀ | Value | log₁₀ |
| **1.50** | 2.12928 | .32823 | 2 35241 | .37151 | 0.90515 | .95672 | **1.**1048 | .04328 |
| 1.51 | 2.15291 | .33303 | 2.37382 | .37545 | .90694 | .95758 | **1.**1026 | .04242 |
| 1.52 | 2.17676 | .33781 | 2.39547 | .37939 | .90870 | .95842 | **1.**1005 | .04158 |
| 1.53 | 2.20082 | .34258 | 2.41736 | .38334 | .91042 | .95924 | 1.0984 | .04076 |
| 1.54 | 2.22510 | .34735 | 2.43949 | .38730 | .91212 | .96005 | 1.0963 | .03995 |
| **1.55** | 2.24961 | .35211 | 2.46186 | .39126 | 0.91379 | .96084 | **1.**0943 | .03916 |
| 1.56 | 2.27434 | .35686 | 2.48448 | .39524 | .91542 | .96162 | 1.0924 | .03838 |
| 1.57 | 2.29930 | .36160 | 2.50735 | .39921 | .91703 | .96238 | 1.0905 | .03762 |
| 1.58 | 2.32449 | .36633 | 2.53047 | .40320 | .91860 | .96313 | 1.0886 | .03687 |
| 1.59 | 2.34991 | .37105 | 2.55384 | .40719 | .92015 | .96386 | 1.0868 | .03614 |
| **1.60** | 2.37557 | .37577 | 2.57746 | .41119 | 0.92167 | .96457 | 1.0850 | .03543 |
| 1.61 | 2.40146 | .38048 | 2.60135 | .41520 | .92316 | .96528 | 1.0832 | .03472 |
| 1.62 | 2.42760 | .38518 | 2.62549 | .41921 | .92462 | .96597 | 1.0815 | .03403 |
| 1.63 | 2.45397 | .38987 | 2.64990 | .42323 | .92606 | .96664 | 1.0798 | .03336 |
| 1.64 | 2.48059 | .39456 | 2.67457 | .42725 | .92747 | .96730 | 1.0782 | .03270 |
| **1.65** | 2.50746 | .39923 | 2.69951 | .43129 | 0.92886 | .96795 | 1.0766 | .03205 |
| 1.66 | 2.53459 | .40391 | 2.72472 | .43532 | .93022 | .96858 | 1.0750 | .03142 |
| 1.67 | 2.56196 | .40857 | 2.75021 | .43937 | .93155 | .96921 | 1.0735 | .03079 |
| 1.68 | 2.58959 | .41323 | 2.77596 | .44341 | .93286 | .96982 | 1.0720 | .03018 |
| 1.69 | 2.61748 | .41788 | 2.80200 | .44747 | .93415 | .97042 | 1.0705 | .02958 |
| **1.70** | 2.64563 | .42253 | 2.82832 | .45153 | .93541 | .97100 | 1.0691 | .02900 |
| 1.71 | 2.67405 | .42717 | 2.85491 | .45559 | .93665 | .97158 | 1.0676 | .02842 |
| 1.72 | 2.70273 | .43180 | 2.88180 | .45966 | .93786 | .97214 | 1.0663 | .02786 |
| 1.73 | 2.73168 | .43643 | 2.90897 | .46374 | .93906 | .97269 | 1.0649 | .02731 |
| 1.74 | 2.76091 | .44105 | 2.93643 | .46782 | .94023 | .97323 | 1.0636 | .02677 |
| **1.75** | 2.79041 | .44567 | 2.96419 | .47191 | 0.94138 | .97376 | 1.0623 | .02624 |
| 1.76 | 2.82020 | .45028 | 2.99224 | .47600 | .94250 | .97428 | 1.0610 | .02572 |
| 1.77 | 2.85026 | .45488 | 3.02059 | .48009 | .94361 | .97479 | 1.0598 | .02521 |
| 1.78 | 2.88061 | .45948 | 3.04925 | .48419 | .94470 | .97529 | 1.0585 | .02471 |
| 1.79 | 2.91125 | .46408 | 3.07821 | .48830 | .94576 | .97578 | 1.0574 | .02422 |
| **1.80** | 2.94217 | .46867 | 3.10747 | .49241 | 0.94681 | .97626 | 1.0562 | .02374 |
| 1.81 | 2.97340 | .47325 | 3 13705 | .49652 | .94783 | .97673 | 1.0550 | .02327 |
| 1 82 | 3.00492 | .47783 | 3.16694 | .50064 | .94884 | .97719 | 1.0539 | .02281 |
| 1.83 | 3.03674 | .48241 | 3 19715 | .50476 | .94983 | .97764 | 1.0528 | .02236 |
| 1.84 | 3.06886 | .48698 | 3.22768 | .50889 | .95080 | .97809 | 1.0518 | .02191 |
| **1.85** | 3.10129 | .49154 | 3.25853 | .51302 | 0.95175 | .97852 | 1.0507 | .02148 |
| 1.86 | 3.13403 | .49610 | 3.28970 | .51716 | .95268 | .97895 | 1.0497 | .02105 |
| 1.87 | 3.16709 | .50066 | 3.32121 | .52130 | .95359 | .97936 | 1.0487 | .02064 |
| 1.88 | 3.20046 | .50521 | 3.35305 | .52544 | .95449 | .97977 | 1.0477 | .02023 |
| 1.89 | 3.23415 | .50976 | 3.38522 | .52959 | .95537 | .98017 | 1.0467 | .01983 |
| **1.90** | 3.26816 | .51430 | 3.41773 | .53374 | 0.95624 | .98057 | 1.0458 | .01943 |
| 1.91 | 3.30250 | .51884 | 3 45058 | .53789 | .95709 | .98095 | 1.0448 | .01905 |
| 1.92 | 3.33718 | 52338 | 3.48378 | .54205 | .95792 | .98133 | 1.0439 | .01867 |
| 1.93 | 3.37218 | .52791 | 3.51733 | .54621 | .95873 | .98170 | 1.0430 | .01830 |
| 1.94 | 3.40752 | .53244 | 3.55123 | .55038 | .95953 | .98206 | 1.0422 | .01794 |
| **1.95** | 3.44321 | .53696 | 3.58548 | .55455 | 0.96032 | .98242 | 1.0413 | .01758 |
| 1.96 | 3.47923 | .54148 | 3.62009 | .55872 | .96109 | .98276 | 1.0405 | .01724 |
| 1.97 | 3.51561 | .54600 | 3.65507 | .56290 | .96185 | .98311 | 1.0397 | .01689 |
| 1.98 | 3.55234 | 55051 | 3.69041 | .56707 | .96259 | .98344 | 1.0389 | .01656 |
| 1.99 | 3.58942 | .55502 | 3.72611 | .57126 | .96331 | .98377 | 1.0381 | .01623 |

# HYPERBOLIC FUNCTIONS (Continued)

The logarithms given below show the mantissa only. The proper characteristic must be added.

| $x$ | Sinh $x$ Value | Sinh $x$ log$_{10}$ | Cosh $x$ Value | Cosh $x$ log$_{10}$ | Tanh $x$ Value | Tanh $x$ log$_{10}$ | Coth $x$ Value | Coth $x$ log$_{10}$ |
|---|---|---|---|---|---|---|---|---|
| **2.00** | 3.62686 | .55953 | 3.76220 | .57544 | 0.96403 | .98409 | 1.0373 | .01591 |
| 2.01 | 3.66466 | .56403 | 3.79865 | .57963 | .96473 | .98440 | 1.0366 | .01560 |
| 2.02 | 3.70283 | .56853 | 3.83549 | .58382 | .96541 | .98471 | 1.0358 | .01529 |
| 2.03 | 3.74138 | .57303 | 3.87271 | .58802 | .96609 | .98502 | 1.0351 | .01498 |
| 2.04 | 3.78029 | .57753 | 3.91032 | .59221 | .96675 | .98531 | 1.0344 | .01469 |
| **2.05** | 3.81958 | .58202 | 3.94832 | .59641 | 0.96740 | .98560 | 1.0337 | .01440 |
| 2.06 | 3.85926 | .58650 | 3.98671 | .60061 | .96803 | .98589 | 1.0330 | .01411 |
| 2.07 | 3.89932 | .59099 | 4.02550 | .60482 | .96865 | .98617 | 1.0324 | .01383 |
| 2.08 | 3.93977 | .59547 | 4.06470 | .60903 | .96926 | .98644 | 1.0317 | .01356 |
| 2.09 | 3.98061 | .59995 | 4.10430 | .61324 | .96986 | .98671 | 1.0311 | .01329 |
| **2.10** | 4.02186 | .60443 | 4.14431 | .61745 | 0.97045 | .98697 | 1.0304 | .01303 |
| 2.11 | 4.06350 | .60890 | 4.18474 | .62167 | .97103 | .98723 | 1.0298 | .01277 |
| 2.12 | 4.10555 | .61337 | 4.22558 | .62589 | .97159 | .98748 | 1.0292 | .01252 |
| 2.13 | 4.14801 | .61784 | 4.26685 | .63011 | .97215 | .98773 | 1.0286 | .01227 |
| 2.14 | 4.19089 | .62231 | 4.30855 | .63433 | .97269 | .98798 | 1.0281 | .01202 |
| **2.15** | 4.23419 | .62677 | 4.35067 | .63856 | 0.97323 | .98821 | 1.0275 | .01179 |
| 2.16 | 4.27791 | .63123 | 4.39323 | .64278 | .97375 | .98845 | 1.0270 | .01155 |
| 2.17 | 4.32205 | .63569 | 4.43623 | .64701 | .97426 | .98868 | 1.0264 | .01132 |
| 2.18 | 4.36663 | .64015 | 4.47967 | .65125 | .97477 | .98890 | 1.0259 | .01110 |
| 2.19 | 4.41165 | .64460 | 4.52356 | .65548 | .97526 | .98912 | 1.0254 | .01088 |
| **2.20** | 4.45711 | .64905 | 4.56791 | .65972 | 0.97574 | .98934 | 1.0249 | .01066 |
| 2.21 | 4.50301 | .65350 | 4.61271 | .66396 | .97622 | .98955 | 1.0244 | .01045 |
| 2.22 | 4.54936 | .65795 | 4.65797 | .66820 | .97668 | .98975 | 1.0239 | .01025 |
| 2.23 | 4.59617 | .66240 | 4.70370 | .67244 | .97714 | .98996 | 1.0234 | .01004 |
| 2.24 | 4.64344 | .66684 | 4.74989 | .67668 | .97759 | .99016 | 1.0229 | .00984 |
| **2.25** | 4.69117 | .67128 | 4.79657 | .68093 | 0.97803 | .99035 | 1.0225 | .00965 |
| 2.26 | 4.73937 | .67572 | 4.84372 | .68518 | .97846 | .99054 | 1.0220 | .00946 |
| 2.27 | 4.78804 | .68016 | 4.89136 | .68943 | .97888 | .99073 | 1.0216 | .00927 |
| 2.28 | 4.83720 | .68459 | 4.93948 | .69368 | .97929 | .99091 | 1.0211 | .00909 |
| 2.29 | 4.88684 | .68903 | 4.98810 | .69794 | .97970 | .99109 | 1.0207 | .00891 |
| **2.30** | 4.93696 | .69346 | 5.03722 | .70219 | 0.98010 | .99127 | 1.0203 | .00873 |
| 2.31 | 4.98758 | .69789 | 5.08684 | .70645 | .98049 | .99144 | 1.0199 | .00856 |
| 2.32 | 5.03870 | .70232 | 5.13697 | .71071 | .98087 | .99161 | 1.0195 | .00839 |
| 2.33 | 5.09032 | .70675 | 5.18762 | .71497 | .98124 | .99178 | 1.0191 | .00822 |
| 2.34 | 5.14245 | .71117 | 5.23878 | .71923 | .98161 | .99194 | 1.0187 | .00806 |
| **2.35** | 5.19510 | .71559 | 5.29047 | .72349 | 0.98197 | .99210 | 1.0184 | .00790 |
| 2.36 | 5.24827 | .72002 | 5.34269 | .72776 | .98233 | .99226 | 1.0180 | .00774 |
| 2.37 | 5.30196 | .72444 | 5.39544 | .73203 | .98267 | .99241 | 1.0176 | .00759 |
| 2.38 | 5.35618 | .72885 | 5.44873 | .73630 | .98301 | .99256 | 1.0173 | .00744 |
| 2.39 | 5.41093 | .73327 | 5.50256 | .74056 | .98335 | .99271 | 1.0169 | .00729 |
| **2.40** | 5.46623 | .73769 | 5.55695 | .74484 | 0.98367 | .99285 | 1.0166 | .00715 |
| 2.41 | 5.52207 | .74210 | 5.61189 | .74911 | .98400 | .99299 | 1.0163 | .00701 |
| 2.42 | 5.57847 | .74652 | 5.66739 | .75338 | .98431 | .99313 | 1.0159 | .00687 |
| 2.43 | 5.63542 | .75093 | 5.72346 | .75766 | .98462 | .99327 | 1.0156 | .00673 |
| 2.44 | 5.69294 | .75534 | 5.78010 | .76194 | .98492 | .99340 | 1.0153 | .00660 |
| **2.45** | 5.75103 | .75975 | 5.83732 | .76621 | 0.98522 | .99353 | 1.0150 | .00647 |
| 2.46 | 5.80969 | .76415 | 5.89512 | .77049 | .98551 | .99366 | 1.0147 | .00634 |
| 2.47 | 5.86893 | .76856 | 5.95352 | .77477 | .98579 | .99379 | 1.0144 | .00621 |
| 2.48 | 5.92876 | .77296 | 6.01250 | .77906 | .98607 | .99391 | 1.0141 | .00609 |
| 2.49 | 5.98918 | .77737 | 6.07209 | .78334 | .98635 | .99403 | 1.0138 | .00597 |

The logarithms given below show the mantissa only. The proper characteristic must be added.

| $x$ | Sinh $x$ Value | Sinh $x$ log₁₀ | Cosh $x$ Value | Cosh $x$ log₁₀ | Tanh $x$ Value | Tanh $x$ log₁₀ | Coth $x$ Value | Coth $x$ log₁₀ |
|---|---|---|---|---|---|---|---|---|
| **2.50** | 6.05020 | .78177 | 6.13229 | .78762 | 0.98661 | .99415 | 1.0136 | .00585 |
| 2.51 | 6.11183 | .78617 | 6.19310 | .79191 | .98688 | .99426 | 1.0133 | .00574 |
| 2.52 | 6.17407 | .79057 | 6.25453 | .79619 | .98714 | .99438 | 1.0130 | .00562 |
| 2.53 | 6.23692 | .79497 | 6.31658 | .80048 | .98739 | .99449 | 1.0128 | .00551 |
| 2.54 | 6.30040 | .79937 | 6.37927 | .80477 | .98764 | .99460 | 1.0125 | .00540 |
| **2.55** | 6.36451 | .80377 | 6.44259 | .80906 | 0.98788 | .99470 | 1.0123 | .00530 |
| 2.56 | 6.42926 | .80816 | 6.50656 | .81335 | .98812 | .99481 | 1.0120 | .00519 |
| 2.57 | 6.49464 | .81256 | 6.57118 | .81764 | .98835 | .99491 | 1.0118 | .00509 |
| 2.58 | 6.56068 | .81695 | 6.63646 | .82194 | .98858 | .99501 | 1.0115 | .00499 |
| 2.59 | 6.62738 | .82134 | 6.70240 | .82623 | .98881 | .99511 | 1.0113 | .00489 |
| **2.60** | 6.69473 | .82573 | 6.76901 | .83052 | 0.98903 | .99521 | 1.0111 | .00479 |
| 2.61 | 6.76276 | .83012 | 6.83629 | .83482 | .98924 | .99530 | 1.0109 | .00470 |
| 2.62 | 6.83146 | .83451 | 6.90426 | .83912 | .98946 | .99540 | 1.0107 | .00460 |
| 2.63 | 6.90085 | .83890 | 6.97292 | .84341 | .98966 | .99549 | 1.0104 | .00451 |
| 2.64 | 6.97092 | .84329 | 7.04228 | .84771 | .98987 | .99558 | 1.0102 | .00442 |
| **2.65** | 7.04169 | .84768 | 7.11234 | .85201 | 0.99007 | .99566 | 1.0100 | .00434 |
| 2.66 | 7.11317 | .85206 | 7.18312 | .85631 | .99026 | .99575 | 1.0098 | .00425 |
| 2.67 | 7.18536 | .85645 | 7.25461 | .86061 | .99045 | .99583 | 1.0096 | .00417 |
| 2.68 | 7.25827 | .86083 | 7.32683 | .86492 | .99064 | .99592 | 1.0094 | .00408 |
| 2.69 | 7.33190 | .86522 | 7.39978 | .86922 | .99083 | .99600 | 1.0093 | .00400 |
| **2.70** | 7.40626 | .86960 | 7.47347 | .87352 | 0.99101 | .99608 | 1.0091 | .00392 |
| 2.71 | 7.48137 | .87398 | 7.54791 | .87783 | .99118 | .99615 | 1.0089 | .00385 |
| 2.72 | 7.55722 | .87836 | 7.62310 | .88213 | .99136 | .99623 | 1 0087 | .00377 |
| 2.73 | 7.63383 | .88274 | 7.69905 | .88644 | .99153 | .99631 | 1.0085 | .00369 |
| 2.74 | 7.71121 | .88712 | 7.77578 | .89074 | .99170 | .99638 | 1.0084 | .00362 |
| **2.75** | 7.78935 | .89150 | 7.85328 | .89505 | 0.99186 | .99645 | 1.0082 | .00355 |
| 2.76 | 7.86828 | .89588 | 7.93157 | .89936 | .99202 | .99652 | 1.0080 | .00348 |
| 2.77 | 7.94799 | .90026 | 8.01065 | .90367 | .99218 | .99659 | 1.0079 | .00341 |
| 2.78 | 8.02849 | .90463 | 8.09053 | .90798 | .99233 | .99666 | 1.0077 | .00334 |
| 2.79 | 8.10980 | .90901 | 8.17122 | .91229 | .99248 | .99672 | 1.0076 | .00328 |
| **2.80** | 8.19192 | .91339 | 8.25273 | .91660 | 0.99263 | .99679 | 1.0074 | .00321 |
| 2.81 | 8.27486 | .91776 | 8.33506 | .92091 | .99278 | .99685 | 1.0073 | .00315 |
| 2.82 | 8.35862 | .92213 | 8.41823 | .92522 | .99292 | .99691 | 1.0071 | .00309 |
| 2.83 | 8.44322 | .92651 | 8.50224 | .92953 | .99306 | .99698 | 1.0070 | .00302 |
| 2.84 | 8.52867 | .93088 | 8.58710 | .93385 | .99320 | .99704 | 1.0069 | .00296 |
| **2.85** | 8.61497 | .93525 | 8.67281 | .93816 | 0.99333 | .99709 | 1.0067 | .00291 |
| 2.86 | 8.70213 | 93963 | 8.75940 | .94247 | .99346 | .99715 | 1.0066 | .00285 |
| 2.87 | 8 79016 | .94400 | 8.84686 | .94679 | .99359 | .99721 | 1.0065 | .00279 |
| 2.88 | 8 87907 | .94837 | 8.93520 | .95110 | .99372 | .99726 | 1.0063 | .00274 |
| 2.89 | 8.96887 | .95274 | 9.02444 | .95542 | .99384 | .99732 | 1.0062 | .00268 |
| **2.90** | 9.05956 | 95711 | 9.11458 | .95974 | 0.99396 | .99737 | 1 0061 | .00263 |
| 2.91 | 9 15116 | .96148 | 9.20564 | .96405 | .99408 | .99742 | 1.0060 | .00258 |
| 2.92 | 9.24368 | .96584 | 9.29761 | .96837 | .99420 | .99747 | 1.0058 | .00253 |
| 2.93 | 9.33712 | .97021 | 9.39051 | .97269 | .99431 | .99752 | 1.0057 | .00248 |
| 2.94 | 9.43149 | .97458 | 9.48436 | .97701 | .99443 | .99757 | 1.0056 | .00243 |
| **2.95** | 9.52681 | .97895 | 9.57915 | .98133 | 0.99454 | .99762 | 1.0055 | .00238 |
| 2.96 | 9.62308 | 98331 | 9.67490 | .98565 | .99464 | .99767 | 1.0054 | .00233 |
| 2.97 | 9 72031 | .98768 | 9.77161 | .98997 | .99475 | .99771 | 1.0053 | .00229 |
| 2.98 | 9 81851 | .99205 | 9.86930 | .99429 | .99485 | .99776 | 1.0052 | .00224 |
| 2.99 | 9.91770 | .99641 | 9.96798 | .99861 | .99496 | .99780 | 1.0051 | .00220 |
| **3.00** | 10.01787 | 00078 | 10.06766 | .00293 | 0.99505 | .99785 | 1.0050 | .00215 |

# HYPERBOLIC FUNCTIONS (Continued)

The logarithms given below show the mantissa only. The proper characteristic must be added.

| $x$ | Sinh $x$ Value | log₁₀ | Cosh $x$ Value | log₁₀ | Tanh $x$ Value | log₁₀ | Coth $x$ Value | log₁₀ |
|---|---|---|---|---|---|---|---|---|
| 3.0 | 10.0179 | .00078 | 10.0677 | .00293 | 0.99505 | .99785 | 1.0050 | .00215 |
| 3.1 | 11.0765 | .04440 | 11.1215 | .04616 | .99595 | .99824 | 1.0041 | .00176 |
| 3.2 | 12.2459 | .08799 | 12.2866 | .08943 | .99668 | .99856 | 1.0033 | .00144 |
| 3.3 | 13.5379 | .13155 | 13.5748 | .13273 | .99728 | .99882 | 1.0027 | .00118 |
| 3.4 | 14.9654 | .17509 | 14.9987 | .17605 | .99777 | .99903 | 1.0022 | .00097 |
| 3.5 | 16.5426 | .21860 | 16.5728 | .21940 | 0.99818 | .99921 | 1.0018 | .00079 |
| 3.6 | 18.2855 | .26211 | 18.3128 | .26275 | .99851 | .99935 | 1.0015 | .00065 |
| 3.7 | 20.2113 | .30559 | 20.2360 | .30612 | .99878 | .99947 | 1.0012 | .00053 |
| 3.8 | 22.3394 | .34907 | 22.3618 | .34951 | .99900 | .99957 | 1.0010 | .00043 |
| 3.9 | 24.6911 | .39254 | 24.7113 | .39290 | .99918 | .99964 | 1.0008 | .00036 |
| 4.0 | 27.2899 | .43600 | 27.3082 | .43629 | 0.99933 | .99971 | 1.0007 | .00029 |
| 4.1 | 30.1619 | .47946 | 30.1784 | .47970 | .99945 | .99976 | 1.0005 | .00024 |
| 4.2 | 33.3357 | .52291 | 33.3507 | .52310 | .99955 | .99980 | 1.0004 | .00020 |
| 4.3 | 36.8431 | .56636 | 36.8567 | .56652 | .99963 | .99984 | 1.0004 | .00016 |
| 4.4 | 40.7193 | .60980 | 40.7316 | .60993 | .99970 | .99987 | 1.0003 | .00013 |
| 4.5 | 45.0030 | .65324 | 45.0141 | .65335 | 0.99975 | .99989 | 1.0002 | .00011 |
| 4.6 | 49.7371 | .69668 | 49.7472 | .69677 | .99980 | .99991 | 1.0002 | .00009 |
| 4.7 | 54.9690 | .74012 | 54.9781 | .74019 | .99983 | .99993 | 1.0002 | .00007 |
| 4.8 | 60.7511 | .78355 | 60.7593 | .78361 | .99986 | .99994 | 1.0001 | .00006 |
| 4.9 | 67.1412 | .82699 | 67.1486 | .82704 | .99989 | .99995 | 1.0001 | .00005 |
| 5.0 | 74.2032 | .87042 | 74.2099 | .87046 | 0.99991 | .99996 | 1.0001 | .00004 |
| 5.1 | 82.008 | .91386 | 82.014 | .91389 | .99993 | .99997 | 1.0001 | .00003 |
| 5.2 | 90.633 | .95729 | 90.639 | .95731 | .99994 | .99997 | 1.0001 | .00003 |
| 5.3 | 100.17 | .00072 | 100.17 | .00074 | .99995 | .99998 | 1.0000 | .00002 |
| 5.4 | 110.70 | .04415 | 110.71 | .04417 | .99996 | .99998 | 1.0000 | .00002 |
| 5.5 | 122.34 | .08758 | 122.35 | .08760 | 0.99997 | .99999 | 1.0000 | .00001 |
| 5.6 | 135.21 | .13101 | 135.22 | .13103 | .99997 | .99999 | 1.0000 | .00001 |
| 5.7 | 149.43 | .17444 | 149.44 | .17445 | .99998 | .99999 | 1.0000 | .00001 |
| 5.8 | 165.15 | .21787 | 165.15 | .21788 | .99998 | .99999 | 1.0000 | .00001 |
| 5.9 | 182.52 | .26130 | 182.52 | .26131 | .99998 | .99999 | 1.0000 | .00001 |
| 6.0 | 201.71 | .30473 | 201.72 | .30474 | 0.99999 | .00000 | 1.0000 | .00000 |
| 6.1 | 222.93 | .34817 | 222.93 | .34817 | .99999 | .00000 | 1.0000 | .00000 |
| 6.2 | 246.37 | .39159 | 246.38 | .39161 | .99999 | .00000 | 1.0000 | .00000 |
| 6.3 | 272.29 | .43503 | 272.29 | .43503 | .99999 | .00000 | 1.0000 | .00000 |
| 6.4 | 300.92 | .47845 | 300.92 | .47845 | .99999 | .00000 | 1.0000 | .00000 |
| 6.5 | 332.57 | .52188 | 332.57 | .52188 | 1.0000 | .00000 | 1.0000 | .00000 |
| 6.6 | 367.55 | .56532 | 367.55 | .56532 | 1.0000 | .00000 | 1.0000 | .00000 |
| 6.7 | 406.20 | .60874 | 406.20 | .60874 | 1.0000 | .00000 | 1.0000 | .00000 |
| 6.8 | 448.92 | .65217 | 448.92 | .65217 | 1.0000 | .00000 | 1.0000 | .00000 |
| 6.9 | 496.14 | .69560 | 496.14 | .69560 | 1.0000 | .00000 | 1.0000 | .00000 |
| 7.0 | 548.32 | .73903 | 548.32 | .73903 | 1.0000 | .00000 | 1.0000 | .00000 |
| 7.1 | 605.98 | .78246 | 605.98 | .78246 | 1.0000 | .00000 | 1.0000 | .00000 |
| 7.2 | 669.72 | .82589 | 669.72 | .82589 | 1.0000 | .00000 | 1.0000 | .00000 |
| 7.3 | 740.15 | .86932 | 740.15 | .86932 | 1.0000 | .00000 | 1.0000 | .00000 |
| 7.4 | 817.99 | .91275 | 817.99 | .91275 | 1.0000 | .00000 | 1.0000 | .00000 |
| 7.5 | 904.02 | .95618 | 904.02 | .95618 | 1.0000 | .00000 | 1.0000 | .00000 |
| 7.6 | 999.10 | .99961 | 999.10 | .99961 | 1.0000 | .00000 | 1.0000 | .00000 |
| 7.7 | 1104.2 | .04305 | 1104.2 | .04305 | 1.0000 | .00000 | 1.0000 | .00000 |
| 7.8 | 1220.3 | .08647 | 1220.3 | .08647 | 1.0000 | .00000 | 1.0000 | .00000 |
| 7.9 | 1348.6 | .12988 | 1348.6 | .12988 | 1.0000 | .00000 | 1.0000 | .00000 |
| 8.0 | 1490.5 | .17333 | 1490.5 | .17333 | 1.0000 | .00000 | 1.0000 | .00000 |

# HYPERBOLIC FUNCTIONS (Continued)

The logarithms given below show the mantissa only. The proper characteristic must be added.

| x | Sinh x Value | log₁₀ | Cosh x Value | log₁₀ | Tanh x Value | log₁₀ | Coth x Value | log₁₀ |
|---|---|---|---|---|---|---|---|---|
| **8.0** | 1490.5 | .17333 | 1490.5 | .17333 | 1.0000 | .00000 | 1.0000 | .00000 |
| 8.1 | 1647.2 | .21675 | 1647.2 | .21675 | 1.0000 | .00000 | 1.0000 | .00000 |
| 8.2 | 1820.5 | .26019 | 1820.5 | .26019 | 1.0000 | .00000 | 1.0000 | .00000 |
| 8.3 | 2011.9 | .30360 | 2011.9 | .30360 | 1.0000 | .00000 | 1.0000 | .00000 |
| 8.4 | 2223.5 | .34704 | 2223.5 | .34704 | 1.0000 | .00000 | 1.0000 | .00000 |
| **8.5** | 2457.4 | .39048 | 2457.4 | .39048 | 1.0000 | .00000 | 1.0000 | .00000 |
| 8.6 | 2715.8 | .43390 | 2715.8 | .43390 | 1.0000 | .00000 | 1.0000 | .00000 |
| 8.7 | 3001.5 | .47734 | 3001.5 | .47734 | 1.0000 | .00000 | 1.0000 | .00000 |
| 8.8 | 3317.1 | .52076 | 3317.1 | .52076 | 1.0000 | .00000 | 1.0000 | .00000 |
| 8.9 | 3666.0 | .56419 | 3666.0 | .56419 | 1.0000 | .00000 | 1.0000 | .00000 |
| **9.0** | 4051.5 | .60762 | 4051.5 | .60762 | 1.0000 | .00000 | 1.0000 | .00000 |
| 9.1 | 4477.6 | .65105 | 4477.6 | .65105 | 1.0000 | .00000 | 1.0000 | .00000 |
| 9.2 | 4948.6 | .69448 | 4948.6 | .69448 | 1.0000 | .00000 | 1.0000 | .00000 |
| 9.3 | 5469.0 | .73791 | 5469.0 | .73791 | 1.0000 | .00000 | 1.0000 | .00000 |
| 9.4 | 6044.2 | .78134 | 6044.2 | .78134 | 1.0000 | .00000 | 1.0000 | .00000 |
| **9.5** | 6679.9 | .82477 | 6679.9 | .82477 | 1.0000 | .00000 | 1.0000 | .00000 |
| 9.6 | 7382.4 | .86820 | 7382.4 | .86820 | 1.0000 | .00000 | 1.0000 | .00000 |
| 9.7 | 8158.8 | .91163 | 8158.8 | .91163 | 1.0000 | .00000 | 1.0000 | .00000 |
| 9.8 | 9016.9 | .95506 | 9016.9 | .95506 | 1.0000 | .00000 | 1.0000 | .00000 |
| 9.9 | 9965.2 | .99849 | 9965.2 | .99849 | 1.0000 | .00000 | 1.0000 | .00000 |
| **10.0** | 11013.2 | .04191 | 11013.2 | .04191 | 1.0000 | .0000 | 1.0000 | .00000 |

## FACTORIALS, EXACT VALUES AND RECIPROCALS

| n | n! | n | n! | n | 1/n! | n | 1/n! |
|---|---|---|---|---|---|---|---|
| 1 | 1 | 11 | 39916800 | 1 | 1. | 11 | .25052 × 10⁻⁷ |
| 2 | 2 | 12 | 479001600 | 2 | 0.5 | 12 | .20877 × 10⁻⁸ |
| 3 | 6 | 13 | 6227020800 | 3 | .16667 | 13 | .16059 × 10⁻⁹ |
| 4 | 24 | 14 | 87178291200 | 4 | .41667 × 10⁻¹ | 14 | .11471 × 10⁻¹⁰ |
| 5 | 120 | 15 | 1307674368000 | 5 | .83333 × 10⁻² | 15 | .76472 × 10⁻¹² |
| 6 | 720 | 16 | 20922789888000 | 6 | .13889 × 10⁻² | 16 | .47795 × 10⁻¹³ |
| 7 | 5040 | 17 | 355687428096000 | 7 | .19841 × 10⁻³ | 17 | .28115 × 10⁻¹⁴ |
| 8 | 40320 | 18 | 6402373705728000 | 8 | .24802 × 10⁻⁴ | 18 | .15619 × 10⁻¹⁵ |
| 9 | 362880 | 19 | 121645100408832000 | 9 | .27557 × 10⁻⁵ | 19 | .82206 × 10⁻¹⁷ |
| 10 | 3628800 | 20 | 2432902008176640000 | 10 | .27557 × 10⁻⁶ | 20 | .41103 × 10⁻¹⁸ |

## MILS—RADIANS—DEGREES

1 mil = 0.00098175 radians = 0.05625° = 3.375' = 202.5''
1000 mils = 0.98175 radians = 56.25°
6400 mils = 360° = 2π radians
1 radian = 1018.6 mils
1° = 17.777778 mils
1' = 0.296296 mils
1'' = 0.0049382 mils

## DEGREES—RADIANS

1 radian = 57° 17' 44'' .80625

|  | log |
|---|---|
| 1 radian = 57.29577 95131 degrees | 1.75812 26324 |
| 1 radian = 3437.74677 07849 minutes | 3.53627 38828 |
| 1 radian = 206264.80625 seconds | 5.31442 51332 |
| 1 degree = 0.01745 32925 19943 radians | 8.24187 73676−10 |
| 1 minute = 0.00029 08882 08666 radians | 6.46372 61172−10 |
| 1 second = 0.00000 48481 36811 radians | 4.68557 48668−10 |

# DEGREES—RADIANS

The table gives in radians the angle which is expressed in degrees and minutes at the side and top. Angles expressed to the nearest minute and second can readily be converted to radians by adding to the equivalent of the whole number of degrees the equivalents of the minutes and seconds found on the third page of this table.

| °  | 00′     | 10      | 20      | 30      | 40      | 50      |
|----|---------|---------|---------|---------|---------|---------|
| 0  | 0.00000 | 0.00291 | 0.00582 | 0.00873 | 0.01164 | 0.01454 |
| 1  | 0.01745 | 0.02036 | 0.02327 | 0.02618 | 0.02909 | 0.03200 |
| 2  | 0.03491 | 0.03782 | 0.04072 | 0.04363 | 0.04654 | 0.04945 |
| 3  | 0.05236 | 0.05527 | 0.05818 | 0.06109 | 0.06400 | 0.06690 |
| 4  | 0.06981 | 0.07272 | 0.07563 | 0.07854 | 0.08145 | 0.08436 |
| 5  | 0.08727 | 0.09018 | 0.09308 | 0.09599 | 0.09890 | 0.10181 |
| 6  | 0.10472 | 0.10763 | 0.11054 | 0.11345 | 0.11636 | 0.11926 |
| 7  | 0.12217 | 0.12508 | 0.12799 | 0.13090 | 0.13381 | 0.13672 |
| 8  | 0.13963 | 0.14254 | 0.14544 | 0.14835 | 0.15126 | 0.15417 |
| 9  | 0.15708 | 0.15999 | 0.16290 | 0.16581 | 0.16872 | 0.17162 |
| 10 | 0.17453 | 0.17744 | 0.18035 | 0.18326 | 0.18617 | 0.18908 |
| 11 | 0.19199 | 0.19490 | 0.19780 | 0.20071 | 0.20362 | 0.20653 |
| 12 | 0.20944 | 0.21235 | 0.21526 | 0.21817 | 0.22108 | 0.22398 |
| 13 | 0.22689 | 0.22980 | 0.23271 | 0.23562 | 0.23853 | 0.24144 |
| 14 | 0.24435 | 0.24725 | 0.25016 | 0.25307 | 0.25598 | 0.25889 |
| 15 | 0.26180 | 0.26471 | 0.26762 | 0.27053 | 0.27343 | 0.27634 |
| 16 | 0.27925 | 0.28216 | 0.28507 | 0.28798 | 0.29089 | 0.29380 |
| 17 | 0.29671 | 0.29961 | 0.30252 | 0.30543 | 0.30834 | 0.31125 |
| 18 | 0.31416 | 0.31707 | 0.31998 | 0.32289 | 0.32579 | 0.32870 |
| 19 | 0.33161 | 0.33452 | 0.33743 | 0.34034 | 0.34325 | 0.34616 |
| 20 | 0.34907 | 0.35197 | 0.35488 | 0.35779 | 0.36070 | 0.36361 |
| 21 | 0.36652 | 0.36943 | 0.37234 | 0.37525 | 0.37815 | 0.38106 |
| 22 | 0.38397 | 0.38688 | 0.38979 | 0.39270 | 0.39561 | 0.39852 |
| 23 | 0.40143 | 0.40433 | 0.40724 | 0.41015 | 0.41306 | 0.41597 |
| 24 | 0.41888 | 0.42179 | 0.42470 | 0.42761 | 0.43051 | 0.43342 |
| 25 | 0.43633 | 0.43924 | 0.44215 | 0.44506 | 0.44797 | 0.45088 |
| 26 | 0.45379 | 0.45669 | 0.45960 | 0.46251 | 0.46542 | 0.46833 |
| 27 | 0.47124 | 0.47415 | 0.47706 | 0.47997 | 0.48287 | 0.48578 |
| 28 | 0.48869 | 0.49160 | 0.49451 | 0.49742 | 0.50033 | 0.50324 |
| 29 | 0.50615 | 0.50905 | 0.51196 | 0.51487 | 0.51778 | 0.52069 |
| 30 | 0.52360 | 0.52651 | 0.52942 | 0.53233 | 0.53523 | 0.53814 |
| 31 | 0.54105 | 0.54396 | 0.54687 | 0.54978 | 0.55269 | 0.55560 |
| 32 | 0.55851 | 0.56141 | 0.56432 | 0.56723 | 0.57014 | 0.57305 |
| 33 | 0.57596 | 0.57887 | 0.58178 | 0.58469 | 0.58759 | 0.59050 |
| 34 | 0.59341 | 0.59632 | 0.59923 | 0.60214 | 0.60505 | 0.60796 |
| 35 | 0.61087 | 0.61377 | 0.61668 | 0.61959 | 0.62250 | 0.62541 |
| 36 | 0.62832 | 0.63123 | 0.63414 | 0.63705 | 0.63995 | 0.64286 |
| 37 | 0.64577 | 0.64868 | 0.65159 | 0.65450 | 0.65741 | 0.66032 |
| 38 | 0.66323 | 0.66613 | 0.66904 | 0.67195 | 0.67486 | 0.67777 |
| 39 | 0.68068 | 0.68359 | 0.68650 | 0.68941 | 0.69231 | 0.69522 |
| 40 | 0.69813 | 0.70104 | 0.70395 | 0.70686 | 0.70977 | 0.71268 |
| 41 | 0.71558 | 0.71849 | 0.72140 | 0.72431 | 0.72722 | 0.73013 |
| 42 | 0.73304 | 0.73595 | 0.73886 | 0.74176 | 0.74467 | 0.74758 |
| 43 | 0.75049 | 0.75340 | 0.75631 | 0.75922 | 0.76213 | 0.76504 |
| 44 | 0.76794 | 0.77085 | 0.77376 | 0.77667 | 0.77958 | 0.78249 |
| 45 | 0.78540 | 0.78831 | 0.79122 | 0.79412 | 0.79703 | 0.79994 |
| 46 | 0.80285 | 0.80576 | 0.80867 | 0.81158 | 0.81449 | 0.81740 |
| 47 | 0.82030 | 0.82321 | 0.82612 | 0.82903 | 0.83194 | 0.83485 |
| 48 | 0.83776 | 0.84067 | 0.84358 | 0.84648 | 0.84939 | 0.85230 |
| 49 | 0.85521 | 0.85812 | 0.86103 | 0.86394 | 0.86685 | 0.86976 |
| 50 | 0.87266 | 0.87557 | 0.87848 | 0.88139 | 0.88430 | 0.88721 |

| °   | 00′ | 10 | 20 | 30 | 40 | 50 |
|-----|---------|---------|---------|---------|---------|---------|
| **50** | 0.87266 | 0.87557 | 0.87848 | 0.88139 | 0.88430 | 0.88721 |
| 51  | 0.89012 | 0.89303 | 0.89594 | 0.89884 | 0.90175 | 0.90466 |
| 52  | 0.90757 | 0.91048 | 0.91339 | 0.91630 | 0.91921 | 0.92212 |
| 53  | 0.92502 | 0.92793 | 0.93084 | 0.93375 | 0.93666 | 0.93957 |
| 54  | 0.94248 | 0.94539 | 0.94830 | 0.95120 | 0.95411 | 0.95702 |
| **55** | 0.95993 | 0.96284 | 0.96575 | 0.96866 | 0.97157 | 0.97448 |
| 56  | 0.97738 | 0.98029 | 0.98320 | 0.98611 | 0.98902 | 0.99193 |
| 57  | 0.99484 | 0.99775 | 1.00066 | 1.00356 | 1.00647 | 1.00938 |
| 58  | 1.01229 | 1.01520 | 1.01811 | 1.02102 | 1.02393 | 1.02684 |
| 59  | 1.02974 | 1.03265 | 1.03556 | 1.03847 | 1.04138 | 1.04429 |
| **60** | 1.04720 | 1.05011 | 1.05302 | 1.05592 | 1.05883 | 1.06174 |
| 61  | 1.06465 | 1.06756 | 1.07047 | 1.07338 | 1.07629 | 1.07920 |
| 62  | 1.08210 | 1.08501 | 1.08792 | 1.09083 | 1.09374 | 1.09665 |
| 63  | 1.09956 | 1.10247 | 1.10538 | 1.10828 | 1.11119 | 1.11410 |
| 64  | 1.11701 | 1.11992 | 1.12283 | 1.12574 | 1.12865 | 1.13156 |
| **65** | 1.13446 | 1.13737 | 1.14028 | 1.14319 | 1.14610 | 1.14901 |
| 66  | 1.15192 | 1.15483 | 1.15774 | 1.16064 | 1.16355 | 1.16646 |
| 67  | 1.16937 | 1.17228 | 1.17519 | 1.17810 | 1.18101 | 1.18392 |
| 68  | 1.18682 | 1.18973 | 1.19264 | 1.19555 | 1.19846 | 1.20137 |
| 69  | 1.20428 | 1.20719 | 1.21009 | 1.21300 | 1.21591 | 1.21882 |
| **70** | 1.22173 | 1.22464 | 1.22755 | 1.23046 | 1.23337 | 1.23627 |
| 71  | 1.23918 | 1.24209 | 1.24500 | 1.24791 | 1.25082 | 1.25373 |
| 72  | 1.25664 | 1.25955 | 1.26245 | 1.26536 | 1.26827 | 1.27118 |
| 73  | 1.27409 | 1.27700 | 1.27991 | 1.28282 | 1.28573 | 1.28863 |
| 74  | 1.29154 | 1.29445 | 1.29736 | 1.30027 | 1.30318 | 1.30609 |
| **75** | 1.30900 | 1.31191 | 1.31481 | 1.31772 | 1.32063 | 1.32354 |
| 76  | 1.32645 | 1.32936 | 1.33227 | 1.33518 | 1.33809 | 1.34099 |
| 77  | 1.34390 | 1.34681 | 1.34972 | 1.35263 | 1.35554 | 1.35845 |
| 78  | 1.36136 | 1.36427 | 1.36717 | 1.37008 | 1.37299 | 1.37590 |
| 79  | 1.37881 | 1.38172 | 1.38463 | 1.38754 | 1.39045 | 1.39335 |
| **80** | 1.39626 | 1.39917 | 1.40208 | 1.40499 | 1.40790 | 1.41081 |
| 81  | 1.41372 | 1.41663 | 1.41953 | 1.42244 | 1.42535 | 1.42826 |
| 82  | 1.43117 | 1.43408 | 1.43699 | 1.43990 | 1.44281 | 1.44571 |
| 83  | 1.44862 | 1.45153 | 1.45444 | 1.45735 | 1.46026 | 1.46317 |
| 84  | 1.46608 | 1.46899 | 1.47189 | 1.47480 | 1.47771 | 1.48062 |
| **85** | 1.48353 | 1.48644 | 1.48935 | 1.49226 | 1.49517 | 1.49807 |
| 86  | 1.50098 | 1.50389 | 1.50680 | 1.50971 | 1.51262 | 1.51553 |
| 87  | 1.51844 | 1.52135 | 1.52425 | 1.52716 | 1.53007 | 1.53298 |
| 88  | 1.53589 | 1.53880 | 1.54171 | 1.54462 | 1.54753 | 1.55043 |
| 89  | 1.55334 | 1.55625 | 1.55916 | 1.56207 | 1.56498 | 1.56789 |
| **90** | 1.57080 | 1.57371 | 1.57661 | 1.57952 | 1.58243 | 1.58534 |
| 91  | 1.58825 | 1.59116 | 1.59407 | 1.59698 | 1.59989 | 1.60279 |
| 92  | 1.60570 | 1.60861 | 1.61152 | 1.61443 | 1.61734 | 1.62025 |
| 93  | 1.62316 | 1.62607 | 1.62897 | 1.63188 | 1.63479 | 1.63770 |
| 94  | 1.64061 | 1.64352 | 1.64643 | 1.64934 | 1.65225 | 1.65515 |
| **95** | 1.65806 | 1.66097 | 1.66388 | 1.66679 | 1.66970 | 1.67261 |
| 96  | 1.67552 | 1.67842 | 1.68133 | 1.68424 | 1.68715 | 1.69006 |
| 97  | 1.69297 | 1.69588 | 1.69879 | 1.70170 | 1.70460 | 1.70751 |
| 98  | 1.71042 | 1.71333 | 1.71624 | 1.71915 | 1.72206 | 1.72497 |
| 99  | 1.72788 | 1.73078 | 1.73369 | 1.73660 | 1.73951 | 1.74242 |
| **100** | 1.74533 | 1.74824 | 1.75115 | 1.75406 | 1.75696 | 1.75987 |
| 101 | 1.76278 | 1.76569 | 1.76860 | 1.77151 | 1.77442 | 1.77733 |
| 102 | 1.78024 | 1.78314 | 1.78605 | 1.78896 | 1.79187 | 1.79478 |
| 103 | 1.79769 | 1.80060 | 1.80351 | 1.80642 | 1.80932 | 1.81223 |
| 104 | 1.81514 | 1.81805 | 1.82096 | 1.82387 | 1.82678 | 1.82969 |
| **105** | 1.83260 | 1.83550 | 1.83841 | 1.84132 | 1.84423 | 1.84714 |
| 106 | 1.85004 | 1.85296 | 1.85587 | 1.85878 | 1.86168 | 1.86459 |
| 107 | 1.86750 | 1.87041 | 1.87332 | 1.87623 | 1.87914 | 1.88205 |
| 108 | 1.88496 | 1.88786 | 1.89077 | 1.89368 | 1.89659 | 1.89950 |
| 109 | 1.90241 | 1.90532 | 1.90823 | 1.91114 | 1.91404 | 1.91695 |
| **110** | 1.91986 | 1.92277 | 1.92568 | 1.92859 | 1.93150 | 1.93441 |

# DEGREES—RADIANS (Concluded)

| Deg. | Radians | Deg. | Radians | Min. | Radians | Sec. | Radians |
|------|---------|------|---------|------|---------|------|---------|
| **90** | 1.57080 | **150** | 2.61799 | **0** | 0.00000 | **0** | 0.00000 |
| 91 | 1.58825 | 151 | 2.63545 | 1 | 0.00029 | 1 | 0.00000 |
| 92 | 1.60570 | 152 | 2.65290 | 2 | 0.00058 | 2 | 0.00001 |
| 93 | 1.62316 | 153 | 2.67035 | 3 | 0.00087 | 3 | 0.00001 |
| 94 | 1.64061 | 154 | 2.68781 | 4 | 0.00116 | 4 | 0.00002 |
| **95** | 1.65806 | **155** | 2.70526 | **5** | 0.00145 | **5** | 0.00002 |
| 96 | 1.67552 | 156 | 2.72271 | 6 | 0.00175 | 6 | 0.00003 |
| 97 | 1.69297 | 157 | 2.74017 | 7 | 0.00204 | 7 | 0.00003 |
| 98 | 1.71042 | 158 | 2.75762 | 8 | 0.00233 | 8 | 0.00004 |
| 99 | 1.72788 | 159 | 2.77507 | 9 | 0.00262 | 9 | 0.00004 |
| **100** | 1.74533 | **160** | 2.79253 | **10** | 0.00291 | **10** | 0.00005 |
| 101 | 1.76278 | 161 | 2.80998 | 11 | 0.00320 | 11 | 0.00005 |
| 102 | 1.78024 | 162 | 2.82743 | 12 | 0.00349 | 12 | 0.00006 |
| 103 | 1.79769 | 163 | 2.84489 | 13 | 0.00378 | 13 | 0.00006 |
| 104 | 1.81514 | 164 | 2.86234 | 14 | 0.00407 | 14 | 0.00007 |
| **105** | 1.83260 | **165** | 2.87979 | **15** | 0.00436 | **15** | 0.00007 |
| 106 | 1.85005 | 166 | 2.89725 | 16 | 0.00465 | 16 | 0.00008 |
| 107 | 1.86750 | 167 | 2.91470 | 17 | 0.00495 | 17 | 0.00008 |
| 108 | 1.88496 | 168 | 2.93215 | 18 | 0.00524 | 18 | 0.00009 |
| 109 | 1.90241 | 169 | 2.94961 | 19 | 0.00553 | 19 | 0.00009 |
| **110** | 1.91986 | **170** | 2.96706 | **20** | 0.00582 | **20** | 0.00010 |
| 111 | 1.93732 | 171 | 2.98451 | 21 | 0.00611 | 21 | 0.00010 |
| 112 | 1.95477 | 172 | 3.00197 | 22 | 0.00640 | 22 | 0.00011 |
| 113 | 1.97222 | 173 | 3.01942 | 23 | 0.00669 | 23 | 0.00011 |
| 114 | 1.98968 | 174 | 3.03687 | 24 | 0.00698 | 24 | 0.00012 |
| **115** | 2.00713 | **175** | 3.05433 | **25** | 0.00727 | **25** | 0.00012 |
| 116 | 2.02458 | 176 | 3.07178 | 26 | 0.00756 | 26 | 0.00013 |
| 117 | 2.04204 | 177 | 3.08923 | 27 | 0.00785 | 27 | 0.00013 |
| 118 | 2.05949 | 178 | 3.10669 | 28 | 0.00814 | 28 | 0.00014 |
| 119 | 2.07694 | 179 | 3.12414 | 29 | 0.00844 | 29 | 0.00014 |
| **120** | 2.09440 | **180** | 3.14159 | **30** | 0.00873 | **30** | 0.00015 |
| 121 | 2.11185 | 190 | 3.31613 | 31 | 0.00902 | 31 | 0.00015 |
| 122 | 2.12930 | 200 | 3.49066 | 32 | 0.00931 | 32 | 0.00016 |
| 123 | 2.14676 | 210 | 3.66519 | 33 | 0.00960 | 33 | 0.00016 |
| 124 | 2.16421 | 220 | 3.83972 | 34 | 0.00989 | 34 | 0.00016 |
| **125** | 2.18166 | **230** | 4.01426 | **35** | 0.01018 | **35** | 0.00017 |
| 126 | 2.19911 | 240 | 4.18879 | 36 | 0.01047 | 36 | 0.00017 |
| 127 | 2.21657 | 250 | 4.36332 | 37 | 0.01076 | 37 | 0.00018 |
| 128 | 2.23402 | 260 | 4.53786 | 38 | 0.01105 | 38 | 0.00018 |
| 129 | 2.25147 | 270 | 4.71239 | 39 | 0.01134 | 39 | 0.00019 |
| **130** | 2.26893 | **280** | 4.88692 | **40** | 0.01164 | **40** | 0.00019 |
| 131 | 2.28638 | 290 | 5.06145 | 41 | 0.01193 | 41 | 0.00020 |
| 132 | 2.30383 | 300 | 5.23599 | 42 | 0.01222 | 42 | 0.00020 |
| 133 | 2.32129 | 310 | 5.41052 | 43 | 0.01251 | 43 | 0.00021 |
| 134 | 2.33874 | 320 | 5.58505 | 44 | 0.01280 | 44 | 0.00021 |
| **135** | 2.35619 | **330** | 5.75959 | **45** | 0.01309 | **45** | 0.00022 |
| 136 | 2.37365 | 340 | 5.93412 | 46 | 0.01338 | 46 | 0.00022 |
| 137 | 2.39110 | 350 | 6.10865 | 47 | 0.01367 | 47 | 0.00023 |
| 138 | 2.40855 | 360 | 6.28319 | 48 | 0.01396 | 48 | 0.00023 |
| 139 | 2.42601 | 370 | 6.45772 | 49 | 0.01425 | 49 | 0.00024 |
| **140** | 2.44346 | **380** | 6.63225 | **50** | 0.01454 | **50** | 0.00024 |
| 141 | 2.46091 | 390 | 6.80678 | 51 | 0.01484 | 51 | 0.00025 |
| 142 | 2.47837 | 400 | 6.98132 | 52 | 0.01513 | 52 | 0.00025 |
| 143 | 2.49582 | 410 | 7.15585 | 53 | 0.01542 | 53 | 0.00026 |
| 144 | 2.51327 | 420 | 7.33038 | 54 | 0.01571 | 54 | 0.00026 |
| **145** | 2.53073 | **430** | 7.50492 | **55** | 0.01600 | **55** | 0.00027 |
| 146 | 2.54818 | 440 | 7.67945 | 56 | 0.01629 | 56 | 0.00027 |
| 147 | 2.56563 | 450 | 7.85398 | 57 | 0.01658 | 57 | 0.00028 |
| 148 | 2.58309 | 460 | 8.02851 | 58 | 0.01687 | 58 | 0.00028 |
| 149 | 2.60054 | 470 | 8.20305 | 59 | 0.01716 | 59 | 0.00029 |
| **150** | 2.61799 | **480** | 8.37758 | **60** | 0.01745 | **60** | 0.00029 |

# DEGREES, MINUTES, AND SECONDS TO RADIANS

| Units in degrees, minutes *or* seconds | Degrees to Radians | Minutes to Radians | Seconds to Radians |
|---|---|---|---|
| 10 | 0.174 5329 | 0.002 9089 | 0.000 0485 |
| 20 | 0.349 0659 | 0.005 8178 | 0.000 0970 |
| 30 | 0.523 5988 | 0.008 7266 | 0.000 1454 |
| 40 | 0.698 1317 | 0.011 6355 | 0.000 1939 |
| 50 | 0.872 6646 | 0.014 5444 | 0.000 2424 |
| 60 | 1.047 1976 | 0.017 4533 | 0.000 2909 |
| 70 | 1.221 7305 | (0.020 3622) | (0.000 3394) |
| 80 | 1.396 2634 | (0.023 2711) | (0.000 3879) |
| 90 | 1.570 7963 | (0.026 1800) | (0.000 4364) |
| 100 | 1.745 3293 | ............ | ............ |
| 200 | 3.490 6585 | ............ | ............ |
| 300 | 5.235 9878 | ............ | ............ |

where n = 1, 2, 3, 4, etc.  n(100°) = n(1.745 3293)

# *RADIANS TO DEGREES, MINUTES, AND SECONDS

| Radians | 1.0 | 0.1 | 0.01 | 0.001 | 0.0001 |
|---|---|---|---|---|---|
| 1 | 57° 17′ 44.8″ | 5° 43′ 46.5″ | 0° 34′ 22.6″ | 0° 03′ 26.3″ | 0° 00′ 20.6″ |
| 2 | 114° 35′ 29.6″ | 11° 27′ 33.0″ | 1° 08′ 45.3″ | 0° 06′ 52.5″ | 0° 00′ 41.3″ |
| 3 | 171° 53′ 14.4″ | 17° 11′ 19.4″ | 1° 43′ 07.9″ | 0° 10′ 18.8″ | 0° 01′ 01.9″ |
| 4 | 229° 10′ 59.2″ | 22° 55′ 05.9″ | 2° 17′ 30.6″ | 0° 13′ 45.1″ | 0° 01′ 22.5″ |
| 5 | 286° 28′ 44.0″ | 28° 38′ 52.4″ | 2° 51′ 53.2″ | 0° 17′ 11.3″ | 0° 01′ 43.1″ |
| 6 | 343° 46′ 28.8″ | 34° 22′ 38.9″ | 3° 26′ 15.9″ | 0° 20′ 37.6″ | 0° 02′ 03.8″ |
| 7 | 401° 04′ 13.6″ | 40° 06′ 25.4″ | 4° 00′ 38.5″ | 0° 24′ 03.9″ | 0° 02′ 24.4″ |
| 8 | 458° 21′ 58.4″ | 45° 50′ 11.8″ | 4° 35′ 01.2″ | 0° 27′ 30.1″ | 0° 02′ 45.0″ |
| 9 | 515° 39′ 43.3″ | 51° 33′ 58.3″ | 5° 09′ 23.8″ | 0° 30′ 56.4″ | 0° 03′ 05.6″ |

* If 3.214 is desired in degrees, minutes and seconds it is obtained as follows:

$$
\begin{array}{rl}
3 = & 171° \ 53′ \ 14.4″ \\
.2 = & 11° \ 27′ \ 33.0″ \\
.01 = & 0° \ 34′ \ 22.6″ \\
.004 = & 0° \ 13′ \ 45.1″ \\
\hline
3.214 = & 184° \ \ 8′ \ 55.1″
\end{array}
$$

# DEGREES AND DECIMAL FRACTIONS TO RADIANS

The table below facilitates conversion of an angle expressed in degrees and decimal fractions into radians. To convert 25.78 into radians, find the equivalents, successively, of 20°, 5°, 0°.7, 0°.08 and add.

| Deg. | Radians | Deg. | Radians | Deg. | Radians | Deg. | Radians | Deg. | Radians |
|---|---|---|---|---|---|---|---|---|---|
| 10 | 0.174533 | 1 | 0.017453 | 0.1 | 0.001745 | 0.01 | 0.000175 | 0.001 | 0.000017 |
| 20 | 0.349066 | 2 | .034907 | .2 | .003491 | .02 | .000349 | .002 | .000035 |
| 30 | 0.523599 | 3 | .052360 | .3 | .005236 | .03 | .000524 | .003 | .000052 |
| 40 | 0.698132 | 4 | .069813 | .4 | .006981 | .04 | .000698 | .004 | .000070 |
| 50 | 0.872665 | 5 | .087266 | .5 | .008727 | .05 | .000873 | .005 | .000087 |
| 60 | 1.047198 | 6 | .104720 | .6 | .010472 | .06 | .001047 | .006 | .000105 |
| 70 | 1.221730 | 7 | .122173 | .7 | .012217 | .07 | .001222 | .007 | .000122 |
| 80 | 1.396263 | 8 | .139626 | .8 | .013963 | .08 | .001396 | .008 | .000140 |
| 90 | 1.570796 | 9 | .157080 | .9 | .015708 | .09 | .001571 | .009 | .000157 |

## RADIANS TO DEGREES AND DECIMALS

| Radians | Degrees | Radians | Degrees | Radians | Degrees | Radians | Degrees |
|---|---|---|---|---|---|---|---|
| 1 | 57.2958 | 0.1 | 5.7296 | 0.01 | 0.5730 | 0.001 | 0.0573 |
| 2 | 114.5916 | .2 | 11.4592 | .02 | 1.1459 | .002 | .1146 |
| 3 | 171.8873 | .3 | 17.1887 | .03 | 1.7189 | .003 | .1719 |
| 4 | 229.1831 | .4 | 22.9183 | .04 | 2.2918 | .004 | .2292 |
| 5 | 286.4789 | .5 | 28.6479 | .05 | 2.8648 | .005 | .2865 |
| 6 | 343.7747 | .6 | 34.3775 | .06 | 3.4377 | .006 | .3438 |
| 7 | 401.0705 | .7 | 40.1070 | .07 | 4.0107 | .007 | .4011 |
| 8 | 458.3662 | .8 | 45.8366 | .08 | 4.5837 | .008 | .4584 |
| 9 | 515.6620 | .9 | 51.5662 | .09 | 5.1566 | .009 | .5157 |
| 10 | 572.9578 | 1.0 | 57.2958 | .10 | 5.7296 | .010 | .5730 |

## RADIANS—DEGREES

Multiples and Fractions of $\pi$ Radians in Degrees

| Radians | Radians | Deg. | Radians | Radians | Deg. | Radians | Radians | Deg. |
|---|---|---|---|---|---|---|---|---|
| $\pi$ | 3.1416 | 180 | $\pi/2$ | 1.5708 | 90 | $2\pi/3$ | 2.0944 | 120 |
| $2\pi$ | 6.2832 | 360 | $\pi/3$ | 1.0472 | 60 | $3\pi/4$ | 2.3562 | 135 |
| $3\pi$ | 9.4248 | 540 | $\pi/4$ | 0.7854 | 45 | $5\pi/6$ | 2.6180 | 150 |
| $4\pi$ | 12.5664 | 720 | $\pi/5$ | 0.6283 | 36 | $7\pi/6$ | 3.6652 | 210 |
| $5\pi$ | 15.7080 | 900 | $\pi/6$ | 0.5236 | 30 | $5\pi/4$ | 3.9270 | 225 |
| $6\pi$ | 18.8496 | 1080 | $\pi/7$ | 0.4488 | 25.714 | $4\pi/3$ | 4.1888 | 240 |
| $7\pi$ | 21.9911 | 1260 | $\pi/8$ | 0.3927 | 22.5 | $3\pi/2$ | 4.7124 | 270 |
| $8\pi$ | 25.1327 | 1440 | $\pi/9$ | 0.3491 | 20 | $5\pi/3$ | 5.2360 | 300 |
| $9\pi$ | 28.2743 | 1620 | $\pi/10$ | 0.3142 | 18 | $7\pi/4$ | 5.4978 | 315 |
| $10\pi$ | 31.4159 | 1800 | $\pi/12$ | 0.2618 | 15 | $11\pi/6$ | 5.7596 | 330 |

## CONVERSION OF ANGLES FROM ARC TO TIME

| Arc | Time | Arc | Time | Arc | Time | Arc | Time |
|---|---|---|---|---|---|---|---|
| ° | h m | ° | h m | " | s | " | s |
| ' | m s | ' | m s | | | | |
| 0 | 0 00 | 20 | 1 20 | 0 | 0.00 | 8 | 0.53 |
| 1 | 0 04 | 30 | 2 00 | 1 | 0.07 | 9 | 0.60 |
| 2 | 0 08 | 40 | 2 40 | 2 | 0.13 | 10 | 0.67 |
| 3 | 0 12 | 50 | 3 20 | 3 | 0.20 | 20 | 1.33 |
| 4 | 0 16 | 60 | 4 00 | 4 | 0.27 | 30 | 2.00 |
| 5 | 0 20 | 70 | 4 40 | 5 | 0.33 | 40 | 2.67 |
| 6 | 0 24 | 80 | 5 20 | 6 | 0.40 | 50 | 3.33 |
| 7 | 0 28 | 90 | 6 00 | 7 | 0.47 | 60 | 4.00 |
| 8 | 0 32 | 100 | 6 40 | | | | |
| 9 | 0 36 | 200 | 13 20 | | | | |
| 10 | 0 40 | 300 | 20 00 | | | | |

# MINUTES AND SECONDS TO DECIMAL PARTS OF A DEGREE

| MINUTES AND SECONDS TO DECIMAL PARTS OF A DEG. | | | | DECIMAL PARTS OF A DEGREE TO MINUTES AND SECONDS | | | | | |
|---|---|---|---|---|---|---|---|---|---|
| Min. | Degrees | Sec. | Degrees | Deg. | ' | " | Deg. | ' | " |
| 0 | 0.00000 | 0 | 0.00000 | 0.00 | 0 | 00 | 0.60 | 36 | |
| 1 | .01667 | 1 | .00028 | .01 | 0 | 36 | .61 | 36 | 36 |
| 2 | .03333 | 2 | .00056 | .02 | 1 | 12 | .62 | 37 | 12 |
| 3 | .05 | 3 | .00083 | .03 | 1 | 48 | .63 | 37 | 48 |
| 4 | .06667 | 4 | .00111 | .04 | 2 | 24 | .64 | 38 | 24 |
| 5 | .08333 | 5 | .00139 | .05 | 3 | | .65 | 39 | |
| 6 | .10 | 6 | .00167 | .06 | 3 | 36 | .66 | 39 | 36 |
| 7 | .11667 | 7 | .00194 | .07 | 4 | 12 | .67 | 40 | 12 |
| 8 | .13333 | 8 | .00222 | .08 | 4 | 48 | .68 | 40 | 48 |
| 9 | .15 | 9 | .0025 | .09 | 5 | 24 | .69 | 41 | 24 |
| 10 | 0.16667 | 10 | 0.00278 | 0.10 | 6 | | 0.70 | 42 | |
| 11 | .18333 | 11 | .00306 | .11 | 6 | 36 | .71 | 42 | 36 |
| 12 | .20 | 12 | .00333 | .12 | 7 | 12 | .72 | 43 | 12 |
| 13 | .21667 | 13 | .00361 | .13 | 7 | 48 | .73 | 43 | 48 |
| 14 | .23333 | 14 | .00389 | .14 | 8 | 24 | .74 | 44 | 24 |
| 15 | .25 | 15 | .00417 | .15 | 9 | | .75 | 45 | |
| 16 | .26667 | 16 | .00444 | .16 | 9 | 36 | .76 | 45 | 36 |
| 17 | .28333 | 17 | .00472 | .17 | 10 | 12 | .77 | 46 | 12 |
| 18 | .30 | 18 | .005 | .18 | 10 | 48 | .78 | 46 | 48 |
| 19 | .31667 | 19 | .00528 | .19 | 11 | 24 | .79 | 47 | 24 |
| 20 | 0.33333 | 20 | 0.00556 | 0.20 | 12 | | 0.80 | 48 | |
| 21 | .35 | 21 | .00583 | .21 | 12 | 36 | .81 | 48 | 36 |
| 22 | .36667 | 22 | .00611 | .22 | 13 | 12 | .82 | 49 | 12 |
| 23 | .38333 | 23 | .00639 | .23 | 13 | 48 | .83 | 49 | 48 |
| 24 | .40 | 24 | .00667 | .24 | 14 | 24 | .84 | 50 | 24 |
| 25 | .41667 | 25 | .00694 | .25 | 15 | | .85 | 51 | |
| 26 | .43333 | 26 | .00722 | .26 | 15 | 36 | .86 | 51 | 36 |
| 27 | .45 | 27 | .0075 | .27 | 16 | 12 | .87 | 52 | 12 |
| 28 | .46667 | 28 | .00778 | .28 | 16 | 48 | .88 | 52 | 48 |
| 29 | .48333 | 29 | .00806 | .29 | 17 | 24 | .89 | 53 | 24 |
| 30 | 0.50 | 30 | 0.00833 | 0.30 | 18 | | 0.90 | 54 | |
| 31 | .51667 | 31 | .00861 | .31 | 18 | 36 | .91 | 54 | 36 |
| 32 | .53333 | 32 | .00889 | .32 | 19 | 12 | .92 | 55 | 12 |
| 33 | .55 | 33 | .00917 | .33 | 19 | 48 | .93 | 55 | 48 |
| 34 | .56667 | 34 | .00944 | .34 | 20 | 24 | .94 | 56 | 24 |
| 35 | .58333 | 35 | .00972 | .35 | 21 | | .95 | 57 | |
| 36 | .60 | 36 | .01 | .36 | 21 | 36 | .96 | 57 | 36 |
| 37 | .61667 | 37 | .01028 | .37 | 22 | 12 | .97 | 58 | 12 |
| 38 | .63333 | 38 | .01056 | .38 | 22 | 48 | .98 | 58 | 48 |
| 39 | .65 | 39 | .01083 | .39 | 23 | 24 | .99 | 59 | 24 |
| 40 | 0.66667 | 40 | 0.01111 | 0.40 | 24 | | 1.00 | 60 | |
| 41 | .68333 | 41 | .01139 | .41 | 24 | 36 | | | |
| 42 | .70 | 42 | .01167 | .42 | 25 | 12 | | | |
| 43 | .71667 | 43 | .01194 | .43 | 25 | 48 | | | |
| 44 | .73333 | 44 | .01222 | .44 | 26 | 24 | | | |
| 45 | .75 | 45 | .0125 | .45 | 27 | | | | |
| 46 | .76667 | 46 | .01278 | .46 | 27 | 36 | | | |
| 47 | .78333 | 47 | .01306 | .47 | 28 | 12 | | | |
| 48 | .80 | 48 | .01333 | .48 | 28 | 48 | | | |
| 49 | .81667 | 49 | .01361 | .49 | 29 | 24 | | | |
| 50 | 0.83333 | 50 | 0.01389 | 0.50 | 30 | | | | |
| 51 | .85 | 51 | .01417 | .51 | 30 | 36 | | | |
| 52 | .86667 | 52 | .01444 | .52 | 31 | 12 | | | |
| 53 | .88333 | 53 | .01472 | .53 | 31 | 48 | | | |
| 54 | .90 | 54 | .015 | .54 | 32 | 24 | | | |
| 55 | .91667 | 55 | .01528 | .55 | 33 | | | | |
| 56 | .93333 | 56 | .01556 | .56 | 33 | 36 | | | |
| 57 | .95 | 57 | .01583 | .57 | 34 | 12 | | | |
| 58 | .96667 | 58 | .01611 | .58 | 34 | 48 | | | |
| 59 | .98333 | 59 | .01639 | .59 | 35 | 24 | | | |
| 60 | 1.00 | 60 | 0.01667 | 0.60 | 36 | | | | |

| Deg. | Sec. |
|---|---|
| 0.000 | 0.0 |
| .001 | 3.6 |
| .002 | 7.2 |
| .003 | 10.8 |
| .004 | 14.4 |
| .005 | 18. |
| .006 | 21.6 |
| .007 | 25.2 |
| .008 | 28.8 |
| .009 | 32.4 |
| 0.010 | 36. |

# NUMERICAL TABLES
## Reciprocals, Circumference and Area of Circles

**As a** matter of convenience, the values of $1000 \times (1/n)$ are given in the table. To obtain the actual value of the reciprocal, shift the decimal point three places to the left.

Circumferences and areas of circles are given for the values of $n$ as the diameter.

| $n$ | $1000-\dfrac{1}{n}$ | Circumference $\pi n$ | Area $\dfrac{\pi n^2}{4}$ | $n$ | $1000-\dfrac{1}{n}$ | Circumference $\pi n$ | Area $\dfrac{\pi n^2}{4}$ |
|---|---|---|---|---|---|---|---|
| 0 | ∞ | 0.000000 | .0000000 | 50 | 20.00000 | 157.0796 | 1963.495 |
| 1 | 1000.000 | 3.141593 | .7853982 | 51 | 19.60784 | 160.2212 | 2042.821 |
| 2 | 500.0000 | 6.283185 | 3.141593 | 52 | 19.23077 | 163.3628 | 2123.717 |
| 3 | 333.3333 | 9.424778 | 7.068583 | 53 | 18.86792 | 166.5044 | 2206.183 |
| 4 | 250.0000 | 12.56637 | 12.56637 | 54 | 18.51852 | 169.6460 | 2290.221 |
| 5 | 200.0000 | 15.70796 | 19.63495 | 55 | 18.18182 | 172.7876 | 2375.829 |
| 6 | 166.6667 | 18.84956 | 28.27433 | 56 | 17.85714 | 175.9292 | 2463.009 |
| 7 | 142.8571 | 21.99115 | 38.48451 | 57 | 17.54386 | 179.0708 | 2551.759 |
| 8 | 125.0000 | 25.13274 | 50.26548 | 58 | 17.24138 | 182.2124 | 2642.079 |
| 9 | 111.1111 | 28.27433 | 63.61725 | 59 | 16.94915 | 185.3540 | 2733.971 |
| 10 | 100.0000 | 31.41593 | 78.53982 | 60 | 16.66667 | 188.4956 | 2827.433 |
| 11 | 90.90909 | 34.55752 | 95.03318 | 61 | 16.39344 | 191.6372 | 2922.467 |
| 12 | 83.33333 | 37.69911 | 113.0973 | 62 | 16.12903 | 194.7787 | 3019.071 |
| 13 | 76.92308 | 40.84070 | 132.7323 | 63 | 15.87302 | 197.9203 | 3117.245 |
| 14 | 71.42857 | 43.98230 | 153.9380 | 64 | 15.62500 | 201.0619 | 3216.991 |
| 15 | 66.66667 | 47.12389 | 176.7146 | 65 | 15.38462 | 204.2035 | 3318.307 |
| 16 | 62.50000 | 50.26548 | 201.0619 | 66 | 15.15152 | 207.3451 | 3421.194 |
| 17 | 58.82353 | 53.40708 | 226.9801 | 67 | 14.92537 | 210.4867 | 3525.652 |
| 18 | 55.55556 | 56.54867 | 254.4690 | 68 | 14.70588 | 213.6283 | 3631.681 |
| 19 | 52.63158 | 59.69026 | 283.5287 | 69 | 14.49275 | 216.7699 | 3739.281 |
| 20 | 50.00000 | 62.83185 | 314.1593 | 70 | 14.28571 | 219.9115 | 3848.451 |
| 21 | 47.61905 | 65.97345 | 346.3606 | 71 | 14.08451 | 223.0531 | 3959.192 |
| 22 | 45.45455 | 69.11504 | 380.1327 | 72 | 13.88889 | 226.1947 | 4071.504 |
| 23 | 43.47826 | 72.25663 | 415.4756 | 73 | 13.69863 | 229.3363 | 4185.387 |
| 24 | 41.66667 | 75.39822 | 452.3893 | 74 | 13.51351 | 232.4779 | 4300.840 |
| 25 | 40.00000 | 78.53982 | 490.8739 | 75 | 13.33333 | 235.6194 | 4417.865 |
| 26 | 38.46154 | 81.68141 | 530.9292 | 76 | 13.15789 | 238.7610 | 4536.460 |
| 27 | 37.03704 | 84.82300 | 572.5553 | 77 | 12.98701 | 241.9026 | 4656.626 |
| 28 | 35.71429 | 87.96459 | 615.7522 | 78 | 12.82051 | 245.0442 | 4778.362 |
| 29 | 34.48276 | 91.10619 | 660.5199 | 79 | 12.65823 | 248.1858 | 4901.670 |
| 30 | 33.33333 | 94.24778 | 706.8583 | 80 | 12.50000 | 251.3274 | 5026.548 |
| 31 | 32.25806 | 97.38937 | 754.7676 | 81 | 12.34568 | 254.4690 | 5152.997 |
| 32 | 31.25000 | 100.5310 | 804.2477 | 82 | 12.19512 | 257.6106 | 5281.017 |
| 33 | 30.30303 | 103.6726 | 855.2986 | 83 | 12.04819 | 260.7522 | 5410.608 |
| 34 | 29.41176 | 106.8142 | 907.9203 | 84 | 11.90476 | 263.8938 | 5541.769 |
| 35 | 28.57143 | 109.9557 | 962.1128 | 85 | 11.76471 | 267.0354 | 5674.502 |
| 36 | 27.77778 | 113.0973 | 1017.876 | 86 | 11.62791 | 270.1770 | 5808.805 |
| 37 | 27.02703 | 116.2389 | 1075.210 | 87 | 11.49425 | 273.3186 | 5944.679 |
| 38 | 26.31579 | 119.3805 | 1134.115 | 88 | 11.36364 | 276.4602 | 6082.123 |
| 39 | 25.64103 | 122.5221 | 1194.591 | 89 | 11.23596 | 279.6017 | 6221.139 |
| 40 | 25.00000 | 125.6637 | 1256.637 | 90 | 11.11111 | 282.7433 | 6361.725 |
| 41 | 24.39024 | 128.8053 | 1320.254 | 91 | 10.98901 | 285.8849 | 6503.882 |
| 42 | 23.80952 | 131.9469 | 1385.442 | 92 | 10.86957 | 289.0265 | 6647.610 |
| 43 | 23.25581 | 135.0885 | 1452.201 | 93 | 10.75269 | 292.1681 | 6792.909 |
| 44 | 22.72727 | 138.2301 | 1520.531 | 94 | 10.63830 | 295.3097 | 6939.778 |
| 45 | 22.22222 | 141.3717 | 1590.431 | 95 | 10.52632 | 298.4513 | 7088.218 |
| 46 | 21.73913 | 144.5133 | 1661.903 | 96 | 10.41667 | 301.5929 | 7238.229 |
| 47 | 21.27660 | 147.6549 | 1734.945 | 97 | 10.30928 | 304.7345 | 7389.811 |
| 48 | 20.83333 | 150.7964 | 1809.557 | 98 | 10.20408 | 307.8761 | 7542.964 |
| 49 | 20.40816 | 153.9380 | 1885.741 | 99 | 10.10101 | 311.0177 | 7697.687 |
| 50 | 20.00000 | 157.0796 | 1963.495 | 100 | 10.00000 | 314.1593 | 7853.982 |

175

| $n$ | $1000\dfrac{1}{n}$ | Circum-ference $\pi n$ | Area $\dfrac{\pi n^2}{4}$ | $n$ | $1000\dfrac{1}{n}$ | Circum-ference $\pi n$ | Area $\dfrac{\pi n^2}{4}$ |
|---|---|---|---|---|---|---|---|
| **100** | 10.00000 | 314.1593 | 7853.982 | **150** | 6.666 667 | 471.2389 | 17671.46 |
| 101 | 9.900 990 | 317.3009 | 8011.847 | 151 | 6.622 517 | 474.3805 | 17907.86 |
| 102 | 9.803 922 | 320.4425 | 8171.282 | 152 | 6.578 947 | 477.5221 | 18145.84 |
| 103 | 9.708 738 | 323.5840 | 8332.289 | 153 | 6.535 948 | 480.6637 | 18385.39 |
| 104 | 9.615 385 | 326.7256 | 8494.867 | 154 | 6.493 506 | 483.8053 | 18626.50 |
| 105 | 9.523 810 | 329.8672 | 8659.015 | 155 | 6.451 613 | 486.9469 | 18869.19 |
| 106 | 9.433 962 | 333.0088 | 8824.734 | 156 | 6.410 256 | 490.0885 | 19113.45 |
| 107 | 9.345 794 | 336.1504 | 8992.024 | 157 | 6.369 427 | 493.2300 | 19359.28 |
| 108 | 9.259 259 | 339.2920 | 9160.884 | 158 | 6.329 114 | 496.3716 | 19606.68 |
| 109 | 9.174 312 | 342.4336 | 9331.316 | 159 | 6.289 308 | 499.5132 | 19855.65 |
| **110** | 9.090 909 | 345.5752 | 9503.318 | **160** | 6.250 000 | 502.6548 | 20106.19 |
| 111 | 9.009 009 | 348.7168 | 9676.891 | 161 | 6.211 180 | 505.7964 | 20358.31 |
| 112 | 8.928 571 | 351.8584 | 9852.035 | 162 | 6.172 840 | 508.9380 | 20611.99 |
| 113 | 8.849 558 | 355.0000 | 10028.75 | 163 | 6.134 969 | 512.0796 | 20867.24 |
| 114 | 8.771 930 | 358.1416 | 10207.03 | 164 | 6.097 561 | 515.2212 | 21124.07 |
| 115 | 8.695 652 | 361.2832 | 10386.89 | 165 | 6.060 606 | 518.3628 | 21382.46 |
| 116 | 8.620 690 | 364.4247 | 10568.32 | 166 | 6.024 096 | 521.5044 | 21642.43 |
| 117 | 8.547 009 | 367.5663 | 10751.32 | 167 | 5.988 024 | 524.6460 | 21903.97 |
| 118 | 8.474 576 | 370.7079 | 10935.88 | 168 | 5.952 381 | 527.7876 | 22167.08 |
| 119 | 8.403 361 | 373.8495 | 11122.02 | 169 | 5.917 160 | 530.9292 | 22431.76 |
| **120** | 8.333 333 | 376.9911 | 11309.73 | **170** | 5.882 353 | 534.0708 | 22698.01 |
| 121 | 8.264 463 | 380.1327 | 11499.01 | 171 | 5.847 953 | 537.2123 | 22965.83 |
| 122 | 8.196 721 | 383.2743 | 11689.87 | 172 | 5.813 953 | 540 3539 | 23235.22 |
| 123 | 8.130 081 | 386.4159 | 11882.29 | 173 | 5.780 347 | 543.4955 | 23506.18 |
| 124 | 8.064 516 | 389.5575 | 12076.28 | 174 | 5.747 126 | 546.6371 | 23778.71 |
| 125 | 8.000 000 | 392.6991 | 12271.85 | 175 | 5.714 286 | 549.7787 | 24052.82 |
| 126 | 7.936 508 | 395.8407 | 12468.98 | 176 | 5.681 818 | 552.9203 | 24328 49 |
| 127 | 7.874 016 | 398.9823 | 12667.69 | 177 | 5.649 718 | 556.0619 | 24605.74 |
| 128 | 7.812 500 | 402.1239 | 12867.96 | 178 | 5 617 978 | 559.2035 | 24884.56 |
| 129 | 7.751 938 | 405.2655 | 13069.81 | 179 | 5.586 592 | 562.3451 | 25164.94 |
| **130** | 7.692 308 | 408.4070 | 13273.23 | **180** | 5.555 556 | 565.4867 | 25446.90 |
| 131 | 7.633 588 | 411.5486 | 13478.22 | 181 | 5.524 862 | 568.6283 | 25730.43 |
| 132 | 7.575 758 | 414.6902 | 13684.78 | 182 | 5.494 505 | 571.7699 | 26015.53 |
| 133 | 7.518 797 | 417.8318 | 13892.91 | 183 | 5.464 481 | 574.9115 | 26302.20 |
| 134 | 7.462 687 | 420.9734 | 14102.61 | 184 | 5.434 783 | 578.0530 | 26590.44 |
| 135 | 7.407 407 | 424 1150 | 14313.88 | 185 | 5.405 405 | 581.1946 | 26880.25 |
| 136 | 7.352 941 | 427.2566 | 14526.72 | 186 | 5.376 344 | 584.3362 | 27171.63 |
| 137 | 7.299 270 | 430.3982 | 14741.14 | 187 | 5.347 594 | 587.4778 | 27464.59 |
| 138 | 7.246 377 | 433.5398 | 14957.12 | 188 | 5.319 149 | 590.6194 | 27759.11 |
| 139 | 7.194 245 | 436.6814 | 15174.68 | 189 | 5.291 005 | 593.7610 | 28055.21 |
| **140** | 7.142 857 | 439.8230 | 15393.80 | **190** | 5.263 158 | 596.9026 | 28352.87 |
| 141 | 7.092 199 | 442.9646 | 15614.50 | 191 | 5.235 602 | 600.0442 | 28652.11 |
| 142 | 7.042 254 | 446.1062 | 15836.77 | 192 | 5.208 333 | 603.1858 | 28952.92 |
| 143 | 6.993 007 | 449.2477 | 16060.61 | 193 | 5.181 347 | 606.3274 | 29255.30 |
| 144 | 6.944 444 | 452.3893 | 16286.02 | 194 | 5.154 639 | 609.4690 | 29559.25 |
| 145 | 6.896 552 | 455.5309 | 16513.00 | 195 | 5.128 205 | 612.6106 | 29864.77 |
| 146 | 6.849 315 | 458.6725 | 16741.55 | 196 | 5.102 041 | 615.7522 | 30171.86 |
| 147 | 6.802 721 | 461.8141 | 16971.67 | 197 | 5.076 142 | 618.8938 | 30480.52 |
| 148 | 6.756 757 | 464.9557 | 17203.36 | 198 | 5.050 505 | 622.0353 | 30790.75 |
| 149 | 6.711 409 | 468.0973 | 17436.62 | 199 | 5.025 126 | 625.1769 | 31102.55 |
| **150** | 6.666 667 | 471.2389 | 17671.46 | **200** | 5.000 000 | 628.3185 | 31415.93 |

| $n$ | $1000-\dfrac{1}{n}$ | Circumference $\pi n$ | Area $\dfrac{\pi n^2}{4}$ | $n$ | $1000-\dfrac{1}{n}$ | Circumference $\pi n$ | Area $\dfrac{\pi n^2}{4}$ |
|---|---|---|---|---|---|---|---|
| **200** | 5.000 000 | 628.3185 | 31415.93 | **250** | 4.000 000 | 785.3982 | 49087.39 |
| 201 | 4.975 124 | 631.4601 | 31730.87 | 251 | 3.984 064 | 788.5398 | 49480.87 |
| 202 | 4.950 495 | 634.6017 | 32047.39 | 252 | 3.968 254 | 791.6813 | 49875.92 |
| 203 | 4.926 108 | 637.7433 | 32365.47 | 253 | 3.952 569 | 794.8229 | 50272.55 |
| 204 | 4.901 961 | 640.8849 | 32685.13 | 254 | 3.937 008 | 797.9645 | 50670.75 |
| 205 | 4.878 049 | 644.0265 | 33006.36 | 255 | 3.921 569 | 801.1061 | 51070.52 |
| 206 | 4.854 369 | 647.1681 | 33329.16 | 256 | 3.906 250 | 804.2477 | 51471.85 |
| 207 | 4.830 918 | 650.3097 | 33653.53 | 257 | 3.891 051 | 807.3893 | 51874.76 |
| 208 | 4.807 692 | 653.4513 | 33979.47 | 258 | 3.875 969 | 810.5309 | 52279.24 |
| 209 | 4.784 689 | 656.5929 | 34306.98 | 259 | 3.861 004 | 813.6725 | 52685.29 |
| **210** | 4.761 905 | 659.7345 | 34636.06 | **260** | 3.846 154 | 816.8141 | 53092.92 |
| 211 | 4.739 336 | 662.8760 | 34966.71 | 261 | 3.831 418 | 819.9557 | 53502.11 |
| 212 | 4.716 981 | 666.0176 | 35298.94 | 262 | 3.816 794 | 823.0973 | 53912.87 |
| 213 | 4.694 836 | 669.1592 | 35632.73 | 263 | 3.802 281 | 826.2389 | 54325.21 |
| 214 | 4.672 897 | 672.3008 | 35968.09 | 264 | 3.787 879 | 829.3805 | 54739.11 |
| 215 | 4.651 163 | 675.4424 | 36305.03 | 265 | 3.773 585 | 832.5221 | 55154.59 |
| 216 | 4.629 630 | 678.5840 | 36643.54 | 266 | 3.759 398 | 835.6636 | 55571.63 |
| 217 | 4.608 295 | 681.7256 | 36983.61 | 267 | 3.745 318 | 838.8052 | 55990.25 |
| 218 | 4.587 156 | 684.8672 | 37325.26 | 268 | 3.731 343 | 841.9468 | 56410.44 |
| 219 | 4.566 210 | 688.0088 | 37668.48 | 269 | 3.717 472 | 845.0884 | 56832.20 |
| **220** | 4.545 455 | 691.1504 | 38013.27 | **270** | 3.703 704 | 848.2300 | 57255.53 |
| 221 | 4.524 887 | 694.2920 | 38359.63 | 271 | 3.690 037 | 851.3716 | 57680.43 |
| 222 | 4.504 505 | 697.4336 | 38707.56 | 272 | 3.676 471 | 854.5132 | 58106.90 |
| 223 | 4.484 305 | 700.5752 | 39057.07 | 273 | 3.663 004 | 857.6548 | 58534.94 |
| 224 | 4.464 286 | 703.7168 | 39408.14 | 274 | 3.649 635 | 860.7964 | 58964.55 |
| 225 | 4.444 444 | 706.8583 | 39760.78 | 275 | 3.636 364 | 863.9380 | 59395.74 |
| 226 | 4.424 779 | 709.9999 | 40115.00 | 276 | 3.623 188 | 867.0796 | 59828.49 |
| 227 | 4.405 286 | 713.1415 | 40470.78 | 277 | 3.610 108 | 870.2212 | 60262.82 |
| 228 | 4.385 965 | 716.2831 | 40828.14 | 278 | 3.597 122 | 873.3628 | 60698.71 |
| 229 | 4.366 812 | 719.4247 | 41187.07 | 279 | 3.584 229 | 876.5044 | 61136.18 |
| **230** | 4.347 826 | 722.5663 | 41547.56 | **280** | 3.571 429 | 879.6459 | 61575.22 |
| 231 | 4.329 004 | 725.7079 | 41909.63 | 281 | 3.558 719 | 882.7875 | 62015.82 |
| 232 | 4.310 345 | 728.8495 | 42273.27 | 282 | 3.546 099 | 885.9291 | 62458.00 |
| 233 | 4.291 845 | 731.9911 | 42638.48 | 283 | 3.533 569 | 889.0707 | 62901.75 |
| 234 | 4.273 504 | 735.1327 | 43005.26 | 284 | 3.521 127 | 892.2123 | 63347.07 |
| 235 | 4.255 319 | 738.2743 | 43373.61 | 285 | 3.508 772 | 895.3539 | 63793.97 |
| 236 | 4.237 288 | 741.4159 | 43743.54 | 286 | 3.496 503 | 898.4955 | 64242.43 |
| 237 | 4.219 409 | 744.5575 | 44115.03 | 287 | 3.484 321 | 901.6371 | 64692.46 |
| 238 | 4.201 681 | 747.6991 | 44488.09 | 288 | 3.472 222 | 904.7787 | 65144.07 |
| 239 | 4.184 100 | 750.8406 | 44862.73 | 289 | 3.460 208 | 907.9203 | 65597.24 |
| **240** | 4.166 667 | 753.9822 | 45238.93 | **290** | 3.448 276 | 911.0619 | 66051.99 |
| 241 | 4.149 378 | 757.1238 | 45616.71 | 291 | 3.436 426 | 914.2035 | 66508.30 |
| 242 | 4.132 231 | 760.2654 | 45996.06 | 292 | 3.424 658 | 917.3451 | 66966.19 |
| 243 | 4.115 226 | 763.4070 | 46376.98 | 293 | 3.412 969 | 920.4866 | 67425.65 |
| 244 | 4.098 361 | 766.5486 | 46759.47 | 294 | 3.401 361 | 923.6282 | 67886.68 |
| 245 | 4.081 633 | 769.6902 | 47143.52 | 295 | 3.389 831 | 926.7698 | 68349.28 |
| 246 | 4.065 041 | 772.8318 | 47529.16 | 296 | 3.378 378 | 929.9114 | 68813.45 |
| 247 | 4.048 583 | 775.9734 | 47916.36 | 297 | 3.367 003 | 933.0530 | 69279.19 |
| 248 | 4.032 258 | 779.1150 | 48305.13 | 298 | 3.355 705 | 936.1946 | 69746.50 |
| 249 | 4.016 064 | 782.2566 | 48695.47 | 299 | 3.344 482 | 939.3362 | 70215.38 |
| **250** | 4.000 000 | 785.3982 | 49087.39 | **300** | 3.333 333 | 942.4778 | 70685.83 |

# RECIPROCALS, CIRCUMFERENCE AND AREA OF CIRCLES
## (Continued)

| $n$ | $1000\dfrac{1}{n}$ | Circumference $\pi n$ | Area $\dfrac{\pi n^2}{4}$ | $n$ | $1000\dfrac{1}{n}$ | Circumference $\pi n$ | Area $\dfrac{\pi n^2}{4}$ |
|---|---|---|---|---|---|---|---|
| **300** | 3.333 333 | 942.4778 | 70685.83 | **350** | 2.857 143 | 1099.557 | 96211.28 |
| 301 | 3.322 259 | 945.6194 | 71157.86 | 351 | 2.849 003 | 1102.699 | 96761.84 |
| 302 | 3.311 258 | 948.7610 | 71631.45 | 352 | 2.840 909 | 1105.841 | 97313.97 |
| 303 | 3.300 330 | 951.9026 | 72106.62 | 353 | 2.832 861 | 1108.982 | 97867.68 |
| 304 | 3.289 474 | 955.0442 | 72583.36 | 354 | 2.824 859 | 1112.124 | 98422.96 |
| 305 | 3.278 689 | 958.1858 | 73061.66 | 355 | 2.816 901 | 1115.265 | 98979.80 |
| 306 | 3.267 974 | 961.3274 | 73541.54 | 356 | 2.808 989 | 1118.407 | 99538.22 |
| 307 | 3.257 329 | 964.4689 | 74022.99 | 357 | 2.801 120 | 1121.549 | 100 098.2 |
| 308 | 3 246 753 | 967.6105 | 74506.01 | 358 | 2.793 296 | 1124.690 | 100 659.8 |
| 309 | 3.236 246 | 970.7521 | 74990.60 | 359 | 2.785 515 | 1127.832 | 101 222.9 |
| **310** | 3.225 806 | 973.8937 | 75476.76 | **360** | 2.777 778 | 1130.973 | 101 787.6 |
| 311 | 3.215 434 | 977.0353 | 75964.50 | 361 | 2.770 083 | 1134.115 | 102 353.9 |
| 312 | 3.205 128 | 980.1769 | 76453.80 | 362 | 2.762 431 | 1137.257 | 102 921.7 |
| 313 | 3.194 888 | 983.3185 | 76944.67 | 363 | 2.754 821 | 1140.398 | 103 491.1 |
| 314 | 3.184 713 | 986.4601 | 77437.12 | 364 | 2.747 253 | 1143.540 | 104 062.1 |
| 315 | 3.174 603 | 989.6017 | 77931.13 | 365 | 2.739 726 | 1146.681 | 104 634.7 |
| 316 | 3.164 557 | 992.7433 | 78426.72 | 366 | 2.732 240 | 1149.823 | 105 208.8 |
| 317 | 3.154 574 | 995.8849 | 78923.88 | 367 | 2.724 796 | 1152.965 | 105 784.5 |
| 318 | 3.144 654 | 999.0265 | 79422.60 | 368 | 2.717 391 | 1156.106 | 106 361.8 |
| 319 | 3.134 796 | 1002.168 | 79922.90 | 369 | 2.710 027 | 1159.248 | 106 940.6 |
| **320** | 3.125 000 | 1005.310 | 80424.77 | **370** | 2.702 703 | 1162.389 | 107 521.0 |
| 321 | 3.115 265 | 1008.451 | 80928.21 | 371 | 2.695 418 | 1165.531 | 108 103.0 |
| 322 | 3.105 590 | 1011.593 | 81433.22 | 372 | 2.688 172 | 1168.672 | 108 686.5 |
| 323 | 3.095 975 | 1014.734 | 81939.80 | 373 | 2.680 965 | 1171.814 | 109 271.7 |
| 324 | 3.086 420 | 1017.876 | 82447.96 | 374 | 2.673 797 | 1174.956 | 109 858.4 |
| 325 | 3.076 923 | 1021.018 | 82957.68 | 375 | 2.666 667 | 1178.097 | 110 446.6 |
| 326 | 3.067 485 | 1024.159 | 83468.98 | 376 | 2.659 574 | 1181.239 | 111 036.5 |
| 327 | 3.058 104 | 1027.301 | 83981.84 | 377 | 2.652 520 | 1184.380 | 111 627.9 |
| 328 | 3.048 780 | 1030.442 | 84496.28 | 378 | 2.645 503 | 1187.522 | 112 220.8 |
| 329 | 3.039 514 | 1033.584 | 85012.28 | 379 | 2.638 522 | 1190.664 | 112 815.4 |
| **330** | 3.030 303 | 1036.726 | 85529.86 | **380** | 2.631 579 | 1193.805 | 113 411.5 |
| 331 | 3.021 148 | 1039.867 | 86049.01 | 381 | 2.624 672 | 1196.947 | 114 009.2 |
| 332 | 3.012 048 | 1043.009 | 86569.73 | 382 | 2.617 801 | 1200.088 | 114 608.4 |
| 333 | 3.003 003 | 1046.150 | 87092.02 | 383 | 2.610 966 | 1203.230 | 115 209.3 |
| 334 | 2.994 012 | 1049.292 | 87615.88 | 384 | 2.604 167 | 1206.372 | 115 811.7 |
| 335 | 2.985 075 | 1052.434 | 88141.31 | 385 | 2.597 403 | 1209.513 | 116 415.6 |
| 336 | 2.976 190 | 1055.575 | 88668.31 | 386 | 2.590 674 | 1212 655 | 117 021.2 |
| 337 | 2.967 359 | 1058.717 | 89196.88 | 387 | 2.583 979 | 1215.796 | 117 628.3 |
| 338 | 2.958 580 | 1061.858 | 89727.03 | 388 | 2.577 320 | 1218.938 | 118 237.0 |
| 339 | 2.949 853 | 1065.000 | 90258.74 | 389 | 2.570 694 | 1222.080 | 118 847.2 |
| **340** | 2.941 176 | 1068.142 | 90792.03 | **390** | 2.564 103 | 1225.221 | 119 459.1 |
| 341 | 2.932 551 | 1071.283 | 91326.88 | 391 | 2.557 545 | 1228.363 | 120 072.5 |
| 342 | 2.923 977 | 1074.425 | 91863.31 | 392 | 2.551 020 | 1231.504 | 120 687.4 |
| 343 | 2.915 452 | 1077.566 | 92401.31 | 393 | 2.544 529 | 1234.646 | 121 304.0 |
| 344 | 2.906 977 | 1080.708 | 92940.88 | 394 | 2.538 071 | 1237.788 | 121 922.1 |
| 345 | 2.898 551 | 1083.849 | 93482.02 | 395 | 2.531 646 | 1240.929 | 122 541.7 |
| 346 | 2.890 173 | 1086.991 | 94024.73 | 396 | 2.525 253 | 1244.071 | 123 163.0 |
| 347 | 2.881 844 | 1090.133 | 94569.01 | 397 | 2.518 892 | 1247.212 | 123 785.8 |
| 348 | 2.873 563 | 1093.274 | 95114.86 | 398 | 2.512 563 | 1250.354 | 124 410.2 |
| 349 | 2.865 330 | 1096.416 | 95662.28 | 399 | 2.506 266 | 1253.495 | 125 036.2 |
| **350** | 2.857 143 | 1099.557 | 96211.28 | **400** | 2.500 000 | 1256.637 | 125 663.7 |

| $n$ | $\dfrac{1}{1000-n}$ | Circumference $\pi n$ | Area $\dfrac{\pi n^2}{4}$ | $n$ | $\dfrac{1}{1000-n}$ | Circumference $\pi n$ | Area $\dfrac{\pi n^2}{4}$ |
|---|---|---|---|---|---|---|---|
| 400 | 2.500 000 | 1256.637 | 125 663.7 | 450 | 2.222 222 | 1413.717 | 159 043.1 |
| 401 | 2.493 766 | 1259.779 | 126 292.8 | 451 | 2.217 295 | 1416.858 | 159 750.8 |
| 402 | 2.487 562 | 1262.920 | 126 923.5 | 452 | 2.212 389 | 1420.000 | 160 460.0 |
| 403 | 2.481 390 | 1266.062 | 127 555.7 | 453 | 2.207 506 | 1423.141 | 161 170.9 |
| 404 | 2.475 248 | 1269.203 | 128 189.5 | 454 | 2.202 643 | 1426.283 | 161 883.1 |
| 405 | 2.469 136 | 1272.345 | 128 824.9 | 455 | 2.197 802 | 1429.425 | 162 597.1 |
| 406 | 2.463 054 | 1275.487 | 129 461.9 | 456 | 2.192 982 | 1432.566 | 163 312.6 |
| 407 | 2.457 002 | 1278.628 | 130 100.4 | 457 | 2.188 184 | 1435.708 | 164 029.6 |
| 408 | 2.450 980 | 1281.770 | 130 740.5 | 458 | 2.183 406 | 1438.849 | 164 748.3 |
| 409 | 2.444 988 | 1284.911 | 131 382.2 | 459 | 2.178 649 | 1441.991 | 165 468.5 |
| 410 | 2.439 024 | 1288.053 | 132 025.4 | 460 | 2.173 913 | 1445.133 | 166 190.3 |
| 411 | 2.433 090 | 1291.195 | 132 670.2 | 461 | 2.169 197 | 1448.274 | 166 913.6 |
| 412 | 2.427 184 | 1294.336 | 133 316.6 | 462 | 2.164 502 | 1451.416 | 167 638.5 |
| 413 | 2.421 308 | 1297.478 | 133 964.6 | 463 | 2.159 827 | 1454.557 | 168 365.0 |
| 414 | 2.415 459 | 1300.619 | 134 614.1 | 464 | 2.155 172 | 1457.699 | 169 093.1 |
| 415 | 2.409 639 | 1303.761 | 135 265.2 | 465 | 2.150 538 | 1460.841 | 169 822.7 |
| 416 | 2.403 846 | 1306.903 | 135 917.9 | 466 | 2.145 923 | 1463.982 | 170 553.9 |
| 417 | 2.398 082 | 1310.044 | 136 572.1 | 467 | 2.141 328 | 1467.124 | 171 286.7 |
| 418 | 2.392 344 | 1313.186 | 137 227.9 | 468 | 2.136 752 | 1470.265 | 172 021.0 |
| 419 | 2.386 635 | 1316.327 | 137 885.3 | 469 | 2.132 196 | 1473.407 | 172 757.0 |
| 420 | 2.380 952 | 1319.469 | 138 544.2 | 470 | 2.127 660 | 1476.549 | 173 494.5 |
| 421 | 2.375 297 | 1322.611 | 139 204.8 | 471 | 2.123 142 | 1479.690 | 174 233.5 |
| 422 | 2.369 668 | 1325.752 | 139 866.8 | 472 | 2.118 644 | 1482.832 | 174 974.1 |
| 423 | 2.364 066 | 1328.894 | 140 530.5 | 473 | 2.114 165 | 1485.973 | 175 716.3 |
| 424 | 2.358 491 | 1332.035 | 141 195.7 | 474 | 2.109 705 | 1489.115 | 176 460.1 |
| 425 | 2.352 941 | 1335.177 | 141 862.5 | 475 | 2.105 263 | 1492.257 | 177 205.5 |
| 426 | 2.347 418 | 1338.318 | 142 530.9 | 476 | 2.100 840 | 1495.398 | 177 952.4 |
| 427 | 2.341 920 | 1341.460 | 143 200.9 | 477 | 2.096 436 | 1498.540 | 178 700.9 |
| 428 | 2.336 449 | 1344.602 | 143 872.4 | 478 | 2.092 050 | 1501.681 | 179 450.9 |
| 429 | 2.331 002 | 1347.743 | 144 545.5 | 479 | 2.087 683 | 1504.823 | 180 202.5 |
| 430 | 2.325 581 | 1350.885 | 145 220.1 | 480 | 2.083 333 | 1507.964 | 180 955.7 |
| 431 | 2.320 186 | 1354.026 | 145 896.3 | 481 | 2.079 002 | 1511.106 | 181 710.5 |
| 432 | 2.314 815 | 1357.168 | 146 574.1 | 482 | 2.074 689 | 1514.248 | 182 466.8 |
| 433 | 2.309 469 | 1360.310 | 147 253.5 | 483 | 2.070 393 | 1517.389 | 183 224.8 |
| 434 | 2.304 147 | 1363.451 | 147 934.5 | 484 | 2.066 116 | 1520.531 | 183 984.2 |
| 435 | 2.298 851 | 1366.593 | 148 617.0 | 485 | 2.061 856 | 1523.672 | 184 745.3 |
| 436 | 2.293 578 | 1369.734 | 149 301.0 | 486 | 2.057 613 | 1526.814 | 185 507.9 |
| 437 | 2.288 330 | 1372.876 | 149 986.7 | 487 | 2.053 388 | 1529.956 | 186 272.1 |
| 438 | 2.283 105 | 1376.018 | 150 673.9 | 488 | 2.049 180 | 1533.097 | 187 037.9 |
| 439 | 2.277 904 | 1379.159 | 151 362.7 | 489 | 2.044 990 | 1536.239 | 187 805.2 |
| 440 | 2.272 727 | 1382.301 | 152 053.1 | 490 | 2.040 816 | 1539.380 | 188 574.1 |
| 441 | 2.267 574 | 1385.442 | 152 745.0 | 491 | 2.036 660 | 1542.522 | 189 344.6 |
| 442 | 2.262 443 | 1388.584 | 153 438.5 | 492 | 2.032 520 | 1545.664 | 190 116.6 |
| 443 | 2.257 336 | 1391.726 | 154 133.6 | 493 | 2.028 398 | 1548.805 | 190 890.2 |
| 444 | 2.252 252 | 1394.867 | 154 830.3 | 494 | 2.024 291 | 1551.947 | 191 665.4 |
| 445 | 2.247 191 | 1398.009 | 155 528.5 | 495 | 2.020 202 | 1555.088 | 192 442.2 |
| 446 | 2.242 152 | 1401.150 | 156 228.3 | 496 | 2.016 129 | 1558.230 | 193 220.5 |
| 447 | 2.237 136 | 1404.292 | 156 929.6 | 497 | 2.012 072 | 1561.372 | 194 000.4 |
| 448 | 2.232 143 | 1407.434 | 157 632.6 | 498 | 2.008 032 | 1564.513 | 194 781.9 |
| 449 | 2.227 171 | 1410.575 | 158 337.1 | 499 | 2.004 008 | 1567.655 | 195 564.9 |
| 450 | 2.222 222 | 1413.717 | 159 043.1 | 500 | 2.000 000 | 1570.796 | 196 349.5 |

| $n$ | $1000-\dfrac{1}{n}$ | Circumference $\pi n$ | Area $\dfrac{\pi n^2}{4}$ | $n$ | $1000-\dfrac{1}{n}$ | Circumference $\pi n$ | Area $\dfrac{\pi n^2}{4}$ |
|---|---|---|---|---|---|---|---|
| **500** | 2.000 000 | 1570.796 | 196 349.5 | **550** | 1.818 182 | 1727.876 | 237 582.9 |
| 501 | 1.996 008 | 1573.938 | 197 135.7 | 551 | 1.814 882 | 1731.018 | 238 447.7 |
| 502 | 1.992 032 | 1577.080 | 197 923.5 | 552 | 1.811 594 | 1734.159 | 239 314.0 |
| 503 | 1.988 072 | 1580.221 | 198 712.8 | 553 | 1.808 318 | 1737.301 | 240 181.8 |
| 504 | 1.984 127 | 1583.363 | 199 503.7 | 554 | 1.805 054 | 1740.442 | 241 051.3 |
| 505 | 1.980 198 | 1586.504 | 200 296.2 | 555 | 1.801 802 | 1743.584 | 241 922.3 |
| 506 | 1.976 285 | 1589.646 | 201 090.2 | 556 | 1.798 561 | 1746.726 | 242 794.8 |
| 507 | 1.972 387 | 1592.787 | 201 885.8 | 557 | 1.795 332 | 1749.867 | 243 669.0 |
| 508 | 1.968 504 | 1595.929 | 202 683.0 | 558 | 1.792 115 | 1753.009 | 244 544.7 |
| 509 | 1.964 637 | 1599.071 | 203 481.7 | 559 | 1.788 909 | 1756.150 | 245 422.0 |
| **510** | 1.960 784 | 1602.212 | 204 282.1 | **560** | 1.785 714 | 1759.292 | 246 300.9 |
| 511 | 1.956 947 | 1605.354 | 205 084.0 | 561 | 1.782 531 | 1762.433 | 247 181.3 |
| 512 | 1.953 125 | 1608.495 | 205 887.4 | 562 | 1.779 359 | 1765.575 | 248 063.3 |
| 513 | 1.949 318 | 1611.637 | 206 692.4 | 563 | 1.776 199 | 1768.717 | 248 946.9 |
| 514 | 1.945 525 | 1614.779 | 207 499.1 | 564 | 1.773 050 | 1771.858 | 249 832.0 |
| 515 | 1.941 748 | 1617.920 | 208 307.2 | 565 | 1.769 912 | 1775.000 | 250 718.7 |
| 516 | 1.937 984 | 1621.062 | 209 117.0 | 566 | 1.766 784 | 1778.141 | 251 607.0 |
| 517 | 1.934 236 | 1624.203 | 209 928.3 | 567 | 1.763 668 | 1781.283 | 252 496.9 |
| 518 | 1.930 502 | 1627.345 | 210 741.2 | 568 | 1.760 563 | 1784.425 | 253 388.3 |
| 519 | 1.926 782 | 1630.487 | 211 555.6 | 569 | 1.757 469 | 1787.566 | 254 281.3 |
| **520** | 1.923 077 | 1633.628 | 212 371.7 | **570** | 1.754 386 | 1790.708 | 255 175.9 |
| 521 | 1.919 386 | 1636.770 | 213 189.3 | 571 | 1.751 313 | 1793.849 | 256 072.0 |
| 522 | 1.915 709 | 1639.911 | 214 008.4 | 572 | 1.748 252 | 1796.991 | 256 969.7 |
| 523 | 1.912 046 | 1643.053 | 214 829.2 | 573 | 1.745 201 | 1800.133 | 257 869.0 |
| 524 | 1.908 397 | 1646.195 | 215 651.5 | 574 | 1.742 160 | 1803.274 | 258 769.8 |
| 525 | 1.904 762 | 1649.336 | 216 475.4 | 575 | 1.739 130 | 1806.416 | 259 672.3 |
| 526 | 1.901 141 | 1652.478 | 217 300.8 | 576 | 1.736 111 | 1809.557 | 260 576.3 |
| 527 | 1.897 533 | 1655.619 | 218 127.8 | 577 | 1.733 102 | 1812.699 | 261 481.8 |
| 528 | 1.893 939 | 1658.761 | 218 956.4 | 578 | 1.730 104 | 1815.841 | 262 389.0 |
| 529 | 1.890 359 | 1661.903 | 219 786.6 | 579 | 1.727 116 | 1818.982 | 263 297.7 |
| **530** | 1.886 792 | 1665.044 | 220 618.3 | **580** | 1.724 138 | 1822.124 | 264 207.9 |
| 531 | 1.883 239 | 1668.186 | 221 451.7 | 581 | 1.721 170 | 1825.265 | 265 119.8 |
| 532 | 1.879 699 | 1671.327 | 222 286.5 | 582 | 1.718 213 | 1828.407 | 266 033.2 |
| 533 | 1.876 173 | 1674.469 | 223 123.0 | 583 | 1.715 266 | 1831.549 | 266 948.2 |
| 534 | 1.872 659 | 1677.610 | 223 961.0 | 584 | 1.712 329 | 1834.690 | 267 864.8 |
| 535 | 1.869 159 | 1680.752 | 224 800.6 | 585 | 1.709 402 | 1837.832 | 268 782.9 |
| 536 | 1.865 672 | 1683.894 | 225 641.8 | 586 | 1.706 485 | 1840.973 | 269 702.6 |
| 537 | 1.862 197 | 1687.035 | 226 484.5 | 587 | 1.703 578 | 1844.115 | 270 623.9 |
| 538 | 1.858 736 | 1690.177 | 227 328.8 | 588 | 1.700 680 | 1847.256 | 271 546.7 |
| 539 | 1.855 288 | 1693.318 | 228 174.7 | 589 | 1.697 793 | 1850.398 | 272 471.1 |
| **540** | 1.851 852 | 1696.460 | 229 022.1 | **590** | 1.694 915 | 1853.540 | 273 397.1 |
| 541 | 1.848 429 | 1699.602 | 229 871.1 | 591 | 1.692 047 | 1856.681 | 274 324.7 |
| 542 | 1.845 018 | 1702.743 | 230 721.7 | 592 | 1.689 189 | 1859.823 | 275 253.8 |
| 543 | 1.841 621 | 1705.885 | 231 573.9 | 593 | 1.686 341 | 1862.964 | 276 184.5 |
| 544 | 1.838 235 | 1709.026 | 232 427.6 | 594 | 1.683 502 | 1866.106 | 277 116.7 |
| 545 | 1.834 862 | 1712.168 | 233 282.9 | 595 | 1.680 672 | 1869.248 | 278 050.6 |
| 546 | 1.831 502 | 1715.310 | 234 139.8 | 596 | 1.677 852 | 1872.389 | 278 986.0 |
| 547 | 1.828 154 | 1718.451 | 234 998.2 | 597 | 1.675 042 | 1875.531 | 279 923.0 |
| 548 | 1.824 818 | 1721.593 | 235.858.2 | 598 | 1.672 241 | 1878.672 | 280 861.5 |
| 549 | 1.821 494 | 1724.734 | 236 719.8 | 599 | 1.669 449 | 1881.814 | 281 801.6 |
| **550** | 1.818 182 | 1727.876 | 237.582.9 | **600** | 1.666 667 | 1884.956 | 282 743.3 |

| $n$ | $1000\frac{1}{n}$ | Circumference $\pi n$ | Area $\frac{\pi n^2}{4}$ | $n$ | $1000\frac{1}{n}$ | Circumference $\pi n$ | Area $\frac{\pi n^2}{4}$ |
|---|---|---|---|---|---|---|---|
| 600 | 1.666 667 | 1884.956 | 282 743.3 | 650 | 1.538 462 | 2042.035 | 331 830.7 |
| 601 | 1.663 894 | 1888.097 | 283 686.6 | 651 | 1.536 098 | 2045.177 | 332 852.5 |
| 602 | 1.661 130 | 1891.239 | 284 631.4 | 652 | 1.533 742 | 2048.318 | 333 875.9 |
| 603 | 1.658 375 | 1894.380 | 285 577.8 | 653 | 1.531 394 | 2051.460 | 334 900.8 |
| 604 | 1.655 629 | 1897.522 | 286 525.8 | 654 | 1.529 052 | 2054.602 | 335 927.4 |
| 605 | 1.652 893 | 1900.664 | 287 475.4 | 655 | 1.526 718 | 2057.743 | 336 955.4 |
| 606 | 1.650 165 | 1903.805 | 288 426.5 | 656 | 1.524 390 | 2060.885 | 337 985.1 |
| 607 | 1.647 446 | 1906.947 | 289 379.2 | 657 | 1.522 070 | 2064.026 | 339 016.3 |
| 608 | 1.644 737 | 1910.088 | 290 333.4 | 658 | 1.519 757 | 2067.168 | 340 049.1 |
| 609 | 1.642 036 | 1913.230 | 291 289.3 | 659 | 1.517 451 | 2070.310 | 341 083.5 |
| 610 | 1.639 344 | 1916.372 | 292 246.7 | 660 | 1.515 152 | 2073.451 | 342 119.4 |
| 611 | 1.636 661 | 1919.513 | 293 205.6 | 661 | 1.512 859 | 2076.593 | 343 157.0 |
| 612 | 1.633 987 | 1922.655 | 294 166.2 | 662 | 1.510 574 | 2079.734 | 344 196.0 |
| 613 | 1.631 321 | 1925.796 | 295 128.3 | 663 | 1.508 296 | 2082.876 | 345 236.7 |
| 614 | 1.628 664 | 1928.938 | 296 092.0 | 664 | 1.506 024 | 2086.018 | 346 278.9 |
| 615 | 1.626 016 | 1932.079 | 297 057.2 | 665 | 1.503 759 | 2089.159 | 347 322.7 |
| 616 | 1.623 377 | 1935.221 | 298 024.0 | 666 | 1.501 502 | 2092.301 | 348 368.1 |
| 617 | 1.620 746 | 1938.363 | 298 992.4 | 667 | 1.499 250 | 2095.442 | 349 415.0 |
| 618 | 1.618 123 | 1941.504 | 299 962.4 | 668 | 1.497 006 | 2098.584 | 350 463.5 |
| 619 | 1.615 509 | 1944.646 | 300 933.9 | 669 | 1.494 768 | 2101.725 | 351 513.6 |
| 620 | 1.612 903 | 1947.787 | 301 907.1 | 670 | 1.492 537 | 2104.867 | 352 565.2 |
| 621 | 1.610 306 | 1950.929 | 302 881.7 | 671 | 1.490 313 | 2108.009 | 353 618.5 |
| 622 | 1.607 717 | 1954.071 | 303 858.0 | 672 | 1.488 095 | 2111.150 | 354 673.2 |
| 623 | 1.605 136 | 1957.212 | 304 835.8 | 673 | 1.485 884 | 2114.292 | 355 729.6 |
| 624 | 1.602 564 | 1960.354 | 305 815.2 | 674 | 1.483 680 | 2117.433 | 356 787.5 |
| 625 | 1.600 000 | 1963.495 | 306 796.2 | 675 | 1.481 481 | 2120.575 | 357 847.0 |
| 626 | 1.597 444 | 1966.637 | 307 778.7 | 676 | 1.479 290 | 2123.717 | 358 908.1 |
| 627 | 1.594 896 | 1969.779 | 308 762.8 | 677 | 1.477 105 | 2126.858 | 359 970.8 |
| 628 | 1.592 357 | 1972.920 | 309 748.5 | 678 | 1.474 926 | 2130.000 | 361 035.0 |
| 629 | 1.589 825 | 1976.062 | 310 735.7 | 679 | 1.472 754 | 2133.141 | 362 100.8 |
| 630 | 1.587 302 | 1979.203 | 311 724.5 | 680 | 1.470 588 | 2136.283 | 363 168.1 |
| 631 | 1.584 786 | 1982.345 | 312 714.9 | 681 | 1.468 429 | 2139.425 | 364 237.0 |
| 632 | 1.582 278 | 1985.437 | 313 706.9 | 682 | 1.466 276 | 2142.566 | 365 307.5 |
| 633 | 1.579 779 | 1988.628 | 314 700.4 | 683 | 1.464 129 | 2145.708 | 366 379.6 |
| 634 | 1.577 287 | 1991.770 | 315 695.5 | 684 | 1.461 988 | 2148.849 | 367 453.2 |
| 635 | 1.574 803 | 1994.911 | 316 692.2 | 685 | 1.459 854 | 2151.991 | 368 528.5 |
| 636 | 1.572 327 | 1998.053 | 317 690.4 | 686 | 1.457 726 | 2155.133 | 369 605.2 |
| 637 | 1.569 859 | 2001.195 | 318 690.2 | 687 | 1.455 604 | 2158.274 | 370 683.6 |
| 638 | 1.567 398 | 2004.336 | 319 691.6 | 688 | 1.453 488 | 2161.416 | 371 763.5 |
| 639 | 1.564 945 | 2007.478 | 320 694.6 | 689 | 1.451 379 | 2164.557 | 372 845.0 |
| 640 | 1.562 500 | 2010.619 | 321 699.1 | 690 | 1.449 275 | 2167.699 | 373 928.1 |
| 641 | 1.560 062 | 2013.761 | 322 705.2 | 691 | 1.447 178 | 2170.841 | 375 012.7 |
| 642 | 1.557 632 | 2016.902 | 323 712.8 | 692 | 1.445 087 | 2173.982 | 376 098.9 |
| 643 | 1.555 210 | 2020.044 | 324 722.1 | 693 | 1.443 001 | 2177.124 | 377 186.7 |
| 644 | 1.552 795 | 2023.186 | 325 732.9 | 694 | 1.440 922 | 2180.265 | 378 276.0 |
| 645 | 1.550 388 | 2026.327 | 326 745.3 | 695 | 1.438 849 | 2183.407 | 379 366.9 |
| 646 | 1.547 988 | 2029.469 | 327 759.2 | 696 | 1.436 782 | 2186.548 | 380 459.4 |
| 647 | 1.545 595 | 2032.610 | 328 774.7 | 697 | 1.434 720 | 2189.690 | 381 553.5 |
| 648 | 1.543 210 | 2035.752 | 329 791.8 | 698 | 1.432 665 | 2192.832 | 382 649.1 |
| 649 | 1.540 832 | 2038.894 | 330 810.5 | 699 | 1.430 615 | 2195.973 | 383 746.3 |
| 650 | 1.538 462 | 2042.035 | 331 830.7 | 700 | 1.428 571 | 2199.115 | 384 845.1 |

# RECIPROCALS, CIRCUMFERENCE AND AREA OF CIRCLES
## (Continued)

| $n$ | $\dfrac{1}{1000-n}$ | Circumference $\pi n$ | Area $\dfrac{\pi n^2}{4}$ | $n$ | $\dfrac{1}{1000-n}$ | Circumference $\pi n$ | Area $\dfrac{\pi n^2}{4}$ |
|---|---|---|---|---|---|---|---|
| 700 | 1.428 571 | 2199.115 | 384 845.1 | 750 | 1.333 333 | 2356.194 | 441 786.5 |
| 701 | 1.426 534 | 2202.256 | 385 945.4 | 751 | 1.331 558 | 2359.336 | 442 965.3 |
| 702 | 1.424 501 | 2205.398 | 387 047.4 | 752 | 1.329 787 | 2362.478 | 444 145.8 |
| 703 | 1.422 475 | 2208.540 | 388 150.8 | 753 | 1.328 021 | 2365.619 | 445 327.8 |
| 704 | 1.420 455 | 2211.681 | 389 255.9 | 754 | 1.326 260 | 2368.761 | 446 511.4 |
| 705 | 1.418 440 | 2214.823 | 390 362.5 | 755 | 1.324 503 | 2371.902 | 447 696.6 |
| 706 | 1.416 431 | 2217.964 | 391 470.7 | 756 | 1.322 751 | 2375.044 | 448 883.3 |
| 707 | 1.414 427 | 2221.106 | 392 580.5 | 757 | 1.321 004 | 2378.186 | 450 071.6 |
| 708 | 1.412 429 | 2224.248 | 393 691.8 | 758 | 1.319 261 | 2381.327 | 451 261.5 |
| 709 | 1.410 437 | 2227.389 | 394 804.7 | 759 | 1.317 523 | 2384.469 | 452 453.0 |
| 710 | 1.408 451 | 2230.531 | 395 919.2 | 760 | 1.315 789 | 2387.610 | 453 646.0 |
| 711 | 1.406 470 | 2233.672 | 397 035.3 | 761 | 1.314 060 | 2390.752 | 454 840.6 |
| 712 | 1.404 494 | 2236.814 | 398 152.9 | 762 | 1.312 336 | 2393.894 | 456 036.7 |
| 713 | 1.402 525 | 2239.956 | 399 272.1 | 763 | 1.310 616 | 2397.035 | 457 234.5 |
| 714 | 1.400 560 | 2243.097 | 400 392.8 | 764 | 1.308 901 | 2400.177 | 458 433.8 |
| 715 | 1.398 601 | 2246.239 | 401 515.2 | 765 | 1.307 190 | 2403.318 | 459 634.6 |
| 716 | 1.396 648 | 2249.380 | 402 639.1 | 766 | 1.305 483 | 2406.460 | 460 837.1 |
| 717 | 1.394 700 | 2252.522 | 403 764.6 | 767 | 1.303 781 | 2409.602 | 462 041.1 |
| 718 | 1.392 758 | 2255.664 | 404 891.6 | 768 | 1.302 083 | 2412.743 | 463 246.7 |
| 719 | 1.390 821 | 2258.805 | 406 020.2 | 769 | 1.300 390 | 2415.885 | 464 453.8 |
| 720 | 1.388 889 | 2261.947 | 407 150.4 | 770 | 1.298 701 | 2419.026 | 465 662.6 |
| 721 | 1.386 963 | 2265.088 | 408 282.2 | 771 | 1.297 017 | 2422.168 | 466 872.9 |
| 722 | 1.385 042 | 2268.230 | 409 415.5 | 772 | 1.295 337 | 2425.310 | 468 084.7 |
| 723 | 1.383 126 | 2271.371 | 410 550.4 | 773 | 1.293 661 | 2428.451 | 469 298.2 |
| 724 | 1.381 215 | 2274.513 | 411 686.9 | 774 | 1.291 990 | 2431.593 | 470 513.2 |
| 725 | 1.379 310 | 2277.655 | 412 824.9 | 775 | 1.290 323 | 2434.734 | 471 729.8 |
| 726 | 1.377 410 | 2280.796 | 413 964.5 | 776 | 1.288 660 | 2437.876 | 472 947.9 |
| 727 | 1.375 516 | 2283.938 | 415 105.7 | 777 | 1.287 001 | 2441.017 | 474 167.6 |
| 728 | 1.373 626 | 2287.079 | 416 248.5 | 778 | 1.285 347 | 2444.159 | 475 388.9 |
| 729 | 1.371 742 | 2290.221 | 417 392.8 | 779 | 1.283 697 | 2447.301 | 476 611.8 |
| 730 | 1.369 863 | 2293.363 | 418 538.7 | 780 | 1.282 051 | 2450.442 | 477 836.2 |
| 731 | 1.367 989 | 2296.504 | 419 686.1 | 781 | 1.280 410 | 2453.584 | 479 062.2 |
| 732 | 1.366 120 | 2299.646 | 420 835.2 | 782 | 1.278 772 | 2456.725 | 480 289.8 |
| 733 | 1.364 256 | 2302.787 | 421 985.8 | 783 | 1.277 139 | 2459.867 | 481 519.0 |
| 734 | 1.362 398 | 2305.929 | 423 138.0 | 784 | 1.275 510 | 2463.009 | 482 749.7 |
| 735 | 1.360 544 | 2309.071 | 424 291.7 | 785 | 1.273 885 | 2466.150 | 483 982.0 |
| 736 | 1.358 696 | 2312.212 | 425 447.0 | 786 | 1.272 265 | 2469.292 | 485 215.8 |
| 737 | 1.356 852 | 2315.354 | 426 603.9 | 787 | 1.270 648 | 2472.433 | 486 451.3 |
| 738 | 1.355 014 | 2318.495 | 427 762.4 | 788 | 1.269 036 | 2475.575 | 487 688.3 |
| 739 | 1.353 180 | 2321.637 | 428 922.4 | 789 | 1.267 427 | 2478.717 | 488 926.9 |
| 740 | 1.351 351 | 2324.779 | 430 084.0 | 790 | 1.265 823 | 2481.858 | 490 167.0 |
| 741 | 1.349 528 | 2327.920 | 431 247.2 | 791 | 1.264 223 | 2485.000 | 491 408.7 |
| 742 | 1.347 709 | 2331.062 | 432 412.0 | 792 | 1.262 626 | 2488.141 | 492 652.0 |
| 743 | 1.345 895 | 2334.203 | 433 578.3 | 793 | 1.261 034 | 2491.283 | 493 896.8 |
| 744 | 1.344 086 | 2337.345 | 434 746.2 | 794 | 1.259 446 | 2494.425 | 495 143.3 |
| 745 | 1.342 282 | 2340.487 | 435 915.6 | 795 | 1.257 862 | 2497.566 | 496 391.3 |
| 746 | 1.340 483 | 2343.628 | 437 086.6 | 796 | 1.256 281 | 2500.708 | 497 640.8 |
| 747 | 1.338 688 | 2346.770 | 438 259.2 | 797 | 1.254 705 | 2503.849 | 498 892.0 |
| 748 | 1.336 898 | 2349.911 | 439 433.4 | 798 | 1.253 133 | 2506.991 | 500 144.7 |
| 749 | 1.335 113 | 2353.053 | 440 609.2 | 799 | 1.251 564 | 2510.133 | 501 399.0 |
| 750 | 1.333 333 | 2356.194 | 441 786.5 | 800 | 1.250 000 | 2513.274 | 502 654.8 |

# RECIPROCALS, CIRCUMFERENCE AND AREA OF CIRCLES
## (Continued)

| $n$ | $1000\frac{1}{n}$ | Circum-ference $\pi n$ | Area $\frac{\pi n^2}{4}$ | $n$ | $1000\frac{1}{n}$ | Circum-ference $\pi n$ | Area $\frac{\pi n^2}{4}$ |
|---|---|---|---|---|---|---|---|
| 800 | 1.250 000 | 2513.274 | 502 654.8 | 850 | 1.176 471 | 2670.354 | 567 450.2 |
| 801 | 1.248 439 | 2516.416 | 503 912.2 | 851 | 1.175 088 | 2673.495 | 568 786.1 |
| 802 | 1.246 883 | 2519.557 | 505 171.2 | 852 | 1.173 709 | 2676.637 | 570 123.7 |
| 803 | 1.245 330 | 2522.699 | 506 431.8 | 853 | 1.172 333 | 2679.779 | 571 462.8 |
| 804 | 1.243 781 | 2525.840 | 507 693.9 | 854 | 1.170 960 | 2682.920 | 572 803.4 |
| 805 | 1.242 236 | 2528.982 | 508 957.6 | 855 | 1.169 591 | 2686.062 | 574 145.7 |
| 806 | 1.240 695 | 2532.124 | 510 222.9 | 856 | 1.168 224 | 2689.203 | 575 489.5 |
| 807 | 1.239 157 | 2535.265 | 511 489.8 | 857 | 1.166 861 | 2692.345 | 576 834.8 |
| 808 | 1.237 624 | 2538.407 | 512 758.2 | 858 | 1.165 501 | 2695.486 | 578 181.9 |
| 809 | 1.236 094 | 2541.548 | 514 028.2 | 859 | 1.164 144 | 2698.628 | 579 530.4 |
| 810 | 1.234 568 | 2544.690 | 515 299.7 | 860 | 1.162 791 | 2701.770 | 580 880.5 |
| 811 | 1.233 046 | 2547.832 | 516 572.9 | 861 | 1.161 440 | 2704.911 | 582 232.2 |
| 812 | 1.231 527 | 2550.973 | 517 847.6 | 862 | 1.160 093 | 2708.053 | 583 585.4 |
| 813 | 1.230 012 | 2554.115 | 519 123.8 | 863 | 1.158 749 | 2711.194 | 584 940.2 |
| 814 | 1.228 501 | 2557.256 | 520 401.7 | 864 | 1.157 407 | 2714.336 | 586 296.6 |
| 815 | 1.226 994 | 2560.398 | 521 681.1 | 865 | 1.156 069 | 2717.478 | 587 654.5 |
| 816 | 1.225 490 | 2563.540 | 522 962.1 | 866 | 1.154 734 | 2720.619 | 589 014.1 |
| 817 | 1.223 990 | 2566.681 | 524 244.6 | 867 | 1.153 403 | 2723.761 | 590 375.2 |
| 818 | 1.222 494 | 2569.823 | 525 528.8 | 868 | 1.152 074 | 2726.902 | 591 737.8 |
| 819 | 1.221 001 | 2572.964 | 526 814.5 | 869 | 1.150 748 | 2730.044 | 593 102.1 |
| 820 | 1.219 512 | 2576.106 | 528 101.7 | 870 | 1.149 425 | 2733.186 | 594 467.9 |
| 821 | 1.218 027 | 2579.248 | 529 390.6 | 871 | 1.148 106 | 2736.327 | 595 835.2 |
| 822 | 1.216 545 | 2582.389 | 530 681.0 | 872 | 1.146 789 | 2739.469 | 597 204.2 |
| 823 | 1.215 067 | 2585.531 | 531 973.0 | 873 | 1.145 475 | 2742.610 | 598 574.7 |
| 824 | 1.213 592 | 2588.672 | 533 266.5 | 874 | 1.144 165 | 2745.752 | 599 946.9 |
| 825 | 1.212 121 | 2591.814 | 534 561.6 | 875 | 1.142 857 | 2748.894 | 601 320.8 |
| 826 | 1.210 654 | 2594.956 | 535 858.3 | 876 | 1.141 553 | 2752.035 | 602 695.7 |
| 827 | 1.209 190 | 2598.097 | 537 156.6 | 877 | 1.140 251 | 2755.177 | 604 072.5 |
| 828 | 1.207 729 | 2601.239 | 538 456.4 | 878 | 1.138 952 | 2758.318 | 605 450.9 |
| 829 | 1.206 273 | 2604.380 | 539 757.8 | 879 | 1.137 656 | 2761.460 | 606 830.8 |
| 830 | 1.204 819 | 2607.522 | 541 060.8 | 880 | 1.136 364 | 2764.602 | 608 212.8 |
| 831 | 1.203 369 | 2610.663 | 542 365.3 | 881 | 1.135 074 | 2767.743 | 609 595.6 |
| 832 | 1.201 923 | 2613.805 | 543 671.5 | 882 | 1.133 787 | 2770.885 | 610 980.1 |
| 833 | 1.200 480 | 2616.947 | 544 979.1 | 883 | 1.132 503 | 2774.026 | 612 366.2 |
| 834 | 1.199 041 | 2620.088 | 546 288.4 | 884 | 1.131 222 | 2777.168 | 613 754.1 |
| 835 | 1.197 605 | 2623.230 | 547 599.2 | 885 | 1.129 944 | 2780.309 | 615 143.5 |
| 836 | 1.196 172 | 2626.371 | 548 911.6 | 886 | 1.128 668 | 2783.451 | 616 534.4 |
| 837 | 1.194 743 | 2629.513 | 550 225.6 | 887 | 1.127 396 | 2786.593 | 617 926.8 |
| 838 | 1.193 317 | 2632.655 | 551 541.1 | 888 | 1.126 126 | 2789.734 | 619 321.0 |
| 839 | 1.191 895 | 2635.796 | 552 858.3 | 889 | 1.124 859 | 2792.876 | 620 716.7 |
| 840 | 1.190 476 | 2638.938 | 554 176.9 | 890 | 1.123 596 | 2796.017 | 622 113.9 |
| 841 | 1.189 061 | 2642.079 | 555 497.2 | 891 | 1.122 334 | 2799.159 | 623 512.7 |
| 842 | 1.187 648 | 2645.221 | 556 819.0 | 892 | 1.121 076 | 2802.301 | 624 913.0 |
| 843 | 1.186 240 | 2648.363 | 558 142.4 | 893 | 1.119 821 | 2805.442 | 626 315.0 |
| 844 | 1.184 834 | 2651.504 | 559 467.4 | 894 | 1.118 568 | 2808.584 | 627 718.5 |
| 845 | 1.183 432 | 2654.646 | 560 793.9 | 895 | 1.117 318 | 2811.725 | 629 123.6 |
| 846 | 1.182 033 | 2657.787 | 562 122.0 | 896 | 1.116 071 | 2814.867 | 630 530.2 |
| 847 | 1.180 638 | 2660.929 | 563 451.7 | 897 | 1.114 827 | 2818.009 | 631 938.4 |
| 848 | 1.179 245 | 2664.071 | 564 783.0 | 898 | 1.113 586 | 2821.150 | 633 348.2 |
| 849 | 1.177 856 | 2667.212 | 566 115.8 | 899 | 1.112 347 | 2824.292 | 634 759.6 |
| **850** | **1.176 471** | **2670.354** | **567 450.2** | **900** | 1.111 111 | 2827.433 | 636 172.5 |

183

| $n$ | $1000-\dfrac{1}{n}$ | Circumference $\pi n$ | Area $\dfrac{\pi n^2}{4}$ | $n$ | $1000-\dfrac{1}{n}$ | Circumference $\pi n$ | Area $\dfrac{\pi n^2}{4}$ |
|---|---|---|---|---|---|---|---|
| 900 | 1.111 111 | 2827.433 | 636 172.5 | 950 | 1.052 632 | 2984.513 | 708 821.8 |
| 901 | 1.109 878 | 2830.575 | 637 587.0 | 951 | 1.051 525 | 2987.655 | 710 314.9 |
| 902 | 1.108 647 | 2833.717 | 639 003.1 | 952 | 1.050 420 | 2990.796 | 711 809.5 |
| 903 | 1.107 420 | 2836.858 | 640 420.7 | 953 | 1.049 318 | 2993.938 | 713 305.7 |
| 904 | 1.106 195 | 2840.000 | 641 839.9 | 954 | 1.048 218 | 2997.079 | 714 803.4 |
| 905 | 1.104 972 | 2843.141 | 643 260.7 | 955 | 1.047 120 | 3000.221 | 716 302.8 |
| 906 | 1.103 753 | 2846.283 | 644 683.1 | 956 | 1.046 025 | 3003.363 | 717 803.7 |
| 907 | 1.102 536 | 2849.425 | 646 107.0 | 957 | 1.044 932 | 3006.504 | 719 306.1 |
| 908 | 1.101 322 | 2852.566 | 647 532.5 | 958 | 1.043 841 | 3009.646 | 720 810.2 |
| 909 | 1.100 110 | 2855.708 | 648 959.6 | 959 | 1.042 753 | 3012.787 | 722 315.8 |
| 910 | 1.098 901 | 2858.849 | 650 388.2 | 960 | 1.041 667 | 3015.929 | 723 822.9 |
| 911 | 1.097 695 | 2861.991 | 651 818.4 | 961 | 1.040 583 | 3019.071 | 725 331.7 |
| 912 | 1.096 491 | 2865.133 | 653 250.2 | 962 | 1.039 501 | 3022.212 | 726 842.0 |
| 913 | 1.095 290 | 2868.274 | 654 683.6 | 963 | 1.038 422 | 3025.354 | 728 353.9 |
| 914 | 1.094 092 | 2871.416 | 656 118.5 | 964 | 1.037 344 | 3028.495 | 729 867.4 |
| 915 | 1.092 896 | 2874.557 | 657 555.0 | 965 | 1.036 269 | 3031.637 | 731 382.4 |
| 916 | 1.091 703 | 2877.699 | 658 993.0 | 966 | 1.035 197 | 3034.779 | 732 899.0 |
| 917 | 1.090 513 | 2880.840 | 660 432.7 | 967 | 1.034 126 | 3037.920 | 734 417.3 |
| 918 | 1.089 325 | 2883.982 | 661 873.9 | 968 | 1.033 058 | 3041.062 | 735 936.9 |
| 919 | 1.088 139 | 2887.124 | 663 316.7 | 969 | 1.031 992 | 3044.203 | 737 458.2 |
| 920 | 1.086 957 | 2890.265 | 664 761.0 | 970 | 1.030 928 | 3047.345 | 738 981.1 |
| 921 | 1.085 776 | 2893.407 | 666 206.9 | 971 | 1.029 866 | 3050.486 | 740 505.6 |
| 922 | 1.084 599 | 2896.548 | 667 654.4 | 972 | 1.028 807 | 3053.628 | 742 031.6 |
| 923 | 1.083 424 | 2899.690 | 669 103.5 | 973 | 1.027 749 | 3056.770 | 743 559.2 |
| 924 | 1.082 251 | 2902.832 | 670 554.1 | 974 | 1.026 694 | 3059.911 | 745 088.4 |
| 925 | 1.081 081 | 2905.973 | 672 006.3 | 975 | 1.025 641 | 3063.053 | 746 619.1 |
| 926 | 1.079 914 | 2909.115 | 673 460.1 | 976 | 1.024 590 | 3066.194 | 748 151.4 |
| 927 | 1.078 749 | 2912.256 | 674 915.4 | 977 | 1.023 541 | 3069.336 | 749 685.3 |
| 928 | 1.077 586 | 2915.398 | 676 372.3 | 978 | 1.022 495 | 3072.478 | 751 220.8 |
| 929 | 1.076 426 | 2918.540 | 677 830.8 | 979 | 1.021 450 | 3075.619 | 752 757.8 |
| 930 | 1.075 269 | 2921.681 | 679 290.9 | 980 | 1.020 408 | 3078.761 | 754 296.4 |
| 931 | 1.074 114 | 2924.823 | 680 752.5 | 981 | 1.019 368 | 3081.902 | 755 836.6 |
| 932 | 1.072 961 | 2927.964 | 682 215.7 | 982 | 1.018 330 | 3085.044 | 757 378.3 |
| 933 | 1.071 811 | 2931.106 | 683 680.5 | 983 | 1.017 294 | 3088.186 | 758 921.6 |
| 934 | 1.070 664 | 2934.248 | 685 146.8 | 984 | 1.016 260 | 3091.327 | 760 466.5 |
| 935 | 1.069 519 | 2937.389 | 686 614.7 | 985 | 1.015 228 | 3094.469 | 762 012.9 |
| 936 | 1.068 376 | 2940.531 | 688 084.2 | 986 | 1.014 199 | 3097.610 | 763 561.0 |
| 937 | 1.067 236 | 2943.672 | 689 555.2 | 987 | 1.013 171 | 3100.752 | 765 110.5 |
| 938 | 1.066 098 | 2946.814 | 691 027.9 | 988 | 1.012 146 | 3103.894 | 766 661.7 |
| 939 | 1.064 963 | 2949.956 | 692 502.1 | 989 | 1.011 122 | 3107.035 | 768 214.4 |
| 940 | 1.063 830 | 2953.097 | 693 977.8 | 990 | 1.010 101 | 3110.177 | 769 768.7 |
| 941 | 1.062 699 | 2956.239 | 695 455.2 | 991 | 1.009 082 | 3113.318 | 771 324.6 |
| 942 | 1.061 571 | 2959.380 | 696 934.1 | 992 | 1.008 065 | 3116.460 | 772 882.1 |
| 943 | 1.060 445 | 2962.522 | 698 414.5 | 993 | 1.007 049 | 3119.602 | 774 441.1 |
| 944 | 1.059 322 | 2965.663 | 699 896.6 | 994 | 1.006 036 | 3122.743 | 776 001.7 |
| 945 | 1.058 201 | 2968.805 | 701 380.2 | 995 | 1.005 025 | 3125.885 | 777 563.8 |
| 946 | 1.057 082 | 2971.947 | 702 865.4 | 996 | 1.004 016 | 3129.026 | 779 127.5 |
| 947 | 1.055 966 | 2975.088 | 704 352.1 | 997 | 1.003 009 | 3132.168 | 780 692.8 |
| 948 | 1.054 852 | 2978.230 | 705 840.5 | 998 | 1.002 004 | 3135.309 | 782 259.7 |
| 949 | 1.053 741 | 2981.371 | 707 330.4 | 999 | 1.001 001 | 3138.451 | 783 828.3 |
| 950 | 1.052 632 | 2984.513 | 708 821.8 | 1000 | 1.000 000 | 3141.593 | 785 398.2 |

## Squares, Cubes and Roots

Roots of numbers other than those given directly may be found by the following relations:

$$\sqrt{100n} = 10\sqrt{n}; \quad \sqrt{1000n} = 10\sqrt{10n}; \quad \sqrt{\frac{1}{10}n} = \frac{1}{10}\sqrt{10n}; \quad \sqrt{\frac{1}{100}n} = \frac{1}{10}\sqrt{n},$$

$$\sqrt{\frac{1}{1000}n} = \frac{1}{100}\sqrt{10n}; \quad \sqrt[3]{1000n} = 10\sqrt[3]{n}; \quad \sqrt[3]{10,000n} = 10\sqrt[3]{10n}; \quad \sqrt[3]{100,000n} =$$

$$10\sqrt[3]{100n}; \quad \sqrt[3]{\frac{1}{10}n} = \frac{1}{10}\sqrt[3]{100n}; \quad \sqrt[3]{\frac{1}{100}n} = \frac{1}{10}\sqrt[3]{10n}; \quad \sqrt[3]{\frac{1}{1000}n} = \frac{1}{10}\sqrt[3]{n}.$$

| $n$ | $n^2$ | $\sqrt{n}$ | $\sqrt{10n}$ | $n^3$ | $\sqrt[3]{n}$ | $\sqrt[3]{10n}$ | $\sqrt[3]{100n}$ |
|---|---|---|---|---|---|---|---|
| 1 | 1 | 1.000 000 | 3.162 278 | 1 | 1.000 000 | 2.154 435 | 4.641 589 |
| 2 | 4 | 1.414 214 | 4.472 136 | 8 | 1.259 921 | 2.714 418 | 5.848 035 |
| 3 | 9 | 1.732 051 | 5.477 226 | 27 | 1.442 250 | 3.107 233 | 6.694 330 |
| 4 | 16 | 2.000 000 | 6.324 555 | 64 | 1.587 401 | 3.419 952 | 7.368 063 |
| 5 | 25 | 2.236 068 | 7.071 068 | 125 | 1.709 976 | 3.684 031 | 7.937 005 |
| 6 | 36 | 2.449 490 | 7.745 967 | 216 | 1.817 121 | 3.914 868 | 8.434 327 |
| 7 | 49 | 2.645 751 | 8.366 600 | 343 | 1.912 931 | 4.121 285 | 8.879 040 |
| 8 | 64 | 2.828 427 | 8.944 272 | 512 | 2.000 000 | 4.308 869 | 9.283 178 |
| 9 | 81 | 3.000 000 | 9.486 833 | 729 | 2.080 084 | 4.481 405 | 9.654 894 |
| 10 | 100 | 3.162 278 | 10.00000 | 1 000 | 2.154 435 | 4.641 589 | 10.00000 |
| 11 | 121 | 3.316 625 | 10.48809 | 1 331 | 2.223 980 | 4.791 420 | 10.32280 |
| 12 | 144 | 3.464 102 | 10.95445 | 1 728 | 2.289 428 | 4.932 424 | 10.62659 |
| 13 | 169 | 3.605 551 | 11.40175 | 2 197 | 2.351 335 | 5.065 797 | 10.91393 |
| 14 | 196 | 3.741 657 | 11.83216 | 2 744 | 2.410 142 | 5.192 494 | 11.18689 |
| 15 | 225 | 3.872 983 | 12.24745 | 3 375 | 2.466 212 | 5.313 293 | 11.44714 |
| 16 | 256 | 4.000 000 | 12.64911 | 4 096 | 2.519 842 | 5.428 835 | 11.69607 |
| 17 | 289 | 4.123 106 | 13.03840 | 4 913 | 2.571 282 | 5.539 658 | 11.93483 |
| 18 | 324 | 4.242 641 | 13.41641 | 5 832 | 2.620 741 | 5.646 216 | 12.16440 |
| 19 | 361 | 4.358 899 | 13.78405 | 6 859 | 2.668 402 | 5.748 897 | 12.38562 |
| 20 | 400 | 4.472 136 | 14.14214 | 8 000 | 2.714 418 | 5.848 035 | 12.59921 |
| 21 | 441 | 4.582 576 | 14.49138 | 9 261 | 2.758 924 | 5.943 922 | 12.80579 |
| 22 | 484 | 4.690 416 | 14.83240 | 10 648 | 2.802 039 | 6.036 811 | 13.00591 |
| 23 | 529 | 4.795 832 | 15.16575 | 12 167 | 2.843 867 | 6.126 926 | 13.20006 |
| 24 | 576 | 4.898 979 | 15.49193 | 13 824 | 2.884 499 | 6.214 465 | 13.38866 |
| 25 | 625 | 5.000 000 | 15.81139 | 15 625 | 2.924 018 | 6.299 605 | 13.57209 |
| 26 | 676 | 5.099 020 | 16.12452 | 17 576 | 2.962 496 | 6.382 504 | 13.75069 |
| 27 | 729 | 5.196 152 | 16.43168 | 19 683 | 3.000 000 | 6.463 304 | 13.92477 |
| 28 | 784 | 5.291 503 | 16.73320 | 21 952 | 3.036 589 | 6.542 133 | 14.09460 |
| 29 | 841 | 5.385 165 | 17.02939 | 24 389 | 3.072 317 | 6.619 106 | 14.26043 |
| 30 | 900 | 5.477 226 | 17.32051 | 27 000 | 3.107 233 | 6.694 330 | 14.42250 |
| 31 | 961 | 5.567 764 | 17.60682 | 29 791 | 3.141 381 | 6.767 899 | 14.58100 |
| 32 | 1 024 | 5.656 854 | 17.88854 | 32 768 | 3.174 802 | 6.839 904 | 14.73613 |
| 33 | 1 089 | 5.744 563 | 18.16590 | 35 937 | 3.207 534 | 6.910 423 | 14.88806 |
| 34 | 1 156 | 5.830 952 | 18.43909 | 39 304 | 3.239 612 | 6.979 532 | 15.03695 |
| 35 | 1 225 | 5.916 080 | 18.70829 | 42 875 | 3.271 066 | 7.047 299 | 15.18294 |
| 36 | 1 296 | 6.000 000 | 18.97367 | 46 656 | 3.301 927 | 7.113 787 | 15.32619 |
| 37 | 1 369 | 6.082 763 | 19.23538 | 50 653 | 3.332 222 | 7.179 054 | 15.46680 |
| 38 | 1 444 | 6.164 414 | 19.49359 | 54 872 | 3.361 975 | 7.243 156 | 15.60491 |
| 39 | 1 521 | 6.244 998 | 19.74842 | 59 319 | 3.391 211 | 7.306 144 | 15.74061 |
| 40 | 1 600 | 6.324 555 | 20.00000 | 64 000 | 3.419 952 | 7.368 063 | 15.87401 |
| 41 | 1 681 | 6.403 124 | 20.24846 | 68 921 | 3.448 217 | 7.428 959 | 16.00521 |
| 42 | 1 764 | 6.480 741 | 20.49390 | 74 088 | 3.476 027 | 7.488 872 | 16.13429 |
| 43 | 1 849 | 6.557 439 | 20.73644 | 79 507 | 3.503 398 | 7.547 842 | 16.26133 |
| 44 | 1 936 | 6.633 250 | 20.97618 | 85 184 | 3.530 348 | 7.605 905 | 16.38643 |
| 45 | 2 025 | 6.708 204 | 21.21320 | 91 125 | 3.556 893 | 7.663 094 | 16.50964 |
| 46 | 2 116 | 6.782 330 | 21.44761 | 97 336 | 3.583 048 | 7.719 443 | 16.63103 |
| 47 | 2 209 | 6.855 655 | 21.67948 | 103 823 | 3.608 826 | 7.774 980 | 16.75069 |
| 48 | 2 304 | 6.928 203 | 21.90890 | 110 592 | 3.634 241 | 7.829 735 | 16.86865 |
| 49 | 2 401 | 7.000 000 | 22.13594 | 117 649 | 3.659 306 | 7.883 735 | 16.98499 |
| 50 | 2 500 | 7.071 068 | 22.36068 | 125 000 | 3.684 031 | 7.937 005 | 17.09976 |

185

| $n$ | $n^2$ | $\sqrt{n}$ | $\sqrt{10n}$ | $n^3$ | $\sqrt[3]{n}$ | $\sqrt[3]{10n}$ | $\sqrt[3]{100n}$ |
|---|---|---|---|---|---|---|---|
| 50 | 2 500 | 7.071 068 | 22.36068 | 125 000 | 3.684 031 | 7.937 005 | 17.09976 |
| 51 | 2 601 | 7.141 428 | 22.58318 | 132 651 | 3.708 430 | 7.989 570 | 17.21301 |
| 52 | 2 704 | 7.211 103 | 22.80351 | 140 608 | 3.732 511 | 8.041 452 | 17.32478 |
| 53 | 2 809 | 7.280 110 | 23.02173 | 148 877 | 3.756 286 | 8.092 672 | 17.43513 |
| 54 | 2 916 | 7.348 469 | 23.23790 | 157 464 | 3.779 763 | 8.143 253 | 17.54411 |
| 55 | 3 025 | 7.416 198 | 23.45208 | 166 375 | 3.802 952 | 8.193 213 | 17.65174 |
| 56 | 3 136 | 7.483 315 | 23.66432 | 175 616 | 3.825 862 | 8.242 571 | 17.75808 |
| 57 | 3 249 | 7.549 834 | 23.87467 | 185 193 | 3.848 501 | 8.291 344 | 17.86316 |
| 58 | 3 364 | 7.615 773 | 24.08319 | 195 112 | 3.870 877 | 8.339 551 | 17.96702 |
| 59 | 3 481 | 7.681 146 | 24.28992 | 205 379 | 3.892 996 | 8.387 207 | 18.06969 |
| 60 | 3 600 | 7.745 967 | 24.49490 | 216 000 | 3.914 868 | 8.434 327 | 18.17121 |
| 61 | 3 721 | 7.810 250 | 24.69818 | 226 981 | 3.936 497 | 8.480 926 | 18.27160 |
| 62 | 3 844 | 7.874 008 | 24.89980 | 238 328 | 3.957 892 | 8.527 019 | 18.37091 |
| 63 | 3 969 | 7.937 254 | 25.09980 | 250 047 | 3.979 057 | 8.572 619 | 18.46915 |
| 64 | 4 096 | 8.000 000 | 25.29822 | 262 144 | 4.000 000 | 8.617 739 | 18.56636 |
| 65 | 4 225 | 8.062 258 | 25.49510 | 274 625 | 4.020 726 | 8.662 391 | 18.66256 |
| 66 | 4 356 | 8.124 038 | 25.69047 | 287 496 | 4.041 240 | 8.706 588 | 18.75777 |
| 67 | 4 489 | 8.185 353 | 25.88436 | 300 763 | 4.061 548 | 8.750 340 | 18.85204 |
| 68 | 4 624 | 8.246 211 | 26.07681 | 314 432 | 4.081 655 | 8.793 659 | 18.94536 |
| 69 | 4 761 | 8.306 624 | 26.26785 | 328 509 | 4.101 566 | 8.836 556 | 19.03778 |
| 70 | 4 900 | 8.366 600 | 26.45751 | 343 000 | 4.121 285 | 8.879 040 | 19.12931 |
| 71 | 5 041 | 8.426 150 | 26.64583 | 357 911 | 4.140 818 | 8.921 121 | 19.21997 |
| 72 | 5 184 | 8.485 281 | 26.83282 | 373 248 | 4.160 168 | 8.962 809 | 19.30979 |
| 73 | 5 329 | 8.544 004 | 27.01851 | 389 017 | 4.179 339 | 9.004 113 | 19.39877 |
| 74 | 5 476 | 8.602 325 | 27.20294 | 405 224 | 4.198 336 | 9.045 042 | 19.48695 |
| 75 | 5 625 | 8.660 254 | 27.38613 | 421 875 | 4.217 163 | 9.085 603 | 19.57434 |
| 76 | 5 776 | 8.717 798 | 27.56810 | 438 976 | 4.235 824 | 9.125 805 | 19.66095 |
| 77 | 5 929 | 8.774 964 | 27.74887 | 456 533 | 4.254 321 | 9.165 656 | 19.74681 |
| 78 | 6 084 | 8.831 761 | 27.92848 | 474 552 | 4.272 659 | 9.205 164 | 19.83192 |
| 79 | 6 241 | 8.888 194 | 28.10694 | 493 039 | 4.290 840 | 9.244 335 | 19.91632 |
| 80 | 6 400 | 8.944 272 | 28.28427 | 512 000 | 4.308 869 | 9.283 178 | 20.00000 |
| 81 | 6 561 | 9 000 000 | 28.46050 | 531 441 | 4.326 749 | 9.321 698 | 20.08299 |
| 82 | 6 724 | 9.055 385 | 28.63564 | 551 368 | 4.344 481 | 9.359 902 | 20.16530 |
| 83 | 6 889 | 9.110 434 | 28.80972 | 571 787 | 4.362 071 | 9.397 796 | 20.24694 |
| 84 | 7 056 | 9.165 151 | 28.98275 | 592 704 | 4.379 519 | 9.435 388 | 20.32793 |
| 85 | 7 225 | 9.219 544 | 29.15476 | 614 125 | 4.396 830 | 9.472 682 | 20.40828 |
| 86 | 7 396 | 9.273 618 | 29.32576 | 636 056 | 4.414 005 | 9.509 685 | 20.48800 |
| 87 | 7 569 | 9.327 379 | 29.49576 | 658 503 | 4.431 048 | 9.546 403 | 20.56710 |
| 88 | 7 744 | 9.380 832 | 29.66479 | 681 472 | 4.447 960 | 9.582 840 | 20.64560 |
| 89 | 7 921 | 9.433 981 | 29.83287 | 704 969 | 4.464 745 | 9.619 002 | 20.72351 |
| 90 | 8 100 | 9.486 833 | 30.00000 | 729 000 | 4.481 405 | 9.654 894 | 20.80084 |
| 91 | 8 281 | 9.539 392 | 30.16621 | 753 571 | 4.497 941 | 9.690 521 | 20.87759 |
| 92 | 8 464 | 9.591 663 | 30.33150 | 778 688 | 4.514 357 | 9.725 888 | 20.95379 |
| 93 | 8 649 | 9.643 651 | 30.49590 | 804 357 | 4.530 655 | 9.761 000 | 21.02944 |
| 94 | 8 836 | 9.695 360 | 30.65942 | 830 584 | 4.546 836 | 9.795 861 | 21.10454 |
| 95 | 9 025 | 9.746 794 | 30.82207 | 857 375 | 4.562 903 | 9.830 476 | 21.17912 |
| 96 | 9 216 | 9.797 959 | 30.98387 | 884 736 | 4.578 857 | 9.864 848 | 21.25317 |
| 97 | 9 409 | 9.848 858 | 31.14482 | 912 673 | 4.594 701 | 9.898 983 | 21.32671 |
| 98 | 9 604 | 9.899 495 | 31.30495 | 941 192 | 4.610 436 | 9.932 884 | 21.39975 |
| 99 | 9 801 | 9.949 874 | 31.46427 | 970 299 | 4.626 065 | 9.966 555 | 21.47229 |
| 100 | 10 000 | 10.00000 | 31.62278 | 1 000 000 | 4.641 589 | 10.00000 | 21.54435 |

| $n$ | $n^2$ | $\sqrt{n}$ | $\sqrt{10n}$ | $n^3$ | $\sqrt[3]{n}$ | $\sqrt[3]{10n}$ | $\sqrt[3]{100n}$ |
|---|---|---|---|---|---|---|---|
| 100 | 10 000 | 10.00000 | 31.62278 | 1 000 000 | 4.641 589 | 10.00000 | 21.54435 |
| 101 | 10 201 | 10.04988 | 31.78050 | 1 030 301 | 4.657 010 | 10.03322 | 21.61592 |
| 102 | 10 404 | 10.09950 | 31.93744 | 1 061 208 | 4.672 329 | 10.06623 | 21.68703 |
| 103 | 10 609 | 10.14889 | 32.09361 | 1 092 727 | 4.687 548 | 10.09902 | 21.75767 |
| 104 | 10 816 | 10.19804 | 32.24903 | 1 124 864 | 4.702 669 | 10.13159 | 21.82786 |
| 105 | 11 025 | 10.24695 | 32.40370 | 1 157 625 | 4.717 694 | 10.16396 | 21.89760 |
| 106 | 11 236 | 10.29563 | 32.55764 | 1 191 016 | 4.732 623 | 10.19613 | 21.96689 |
| 107 | 11 449 | 10.34408 | 32.71085 | 1 225 043 | 4.747 459 | 10.22809 | 22.03575 |
| 108 | 11 664 | 10.39230 | 32.86335 | 1 259 712 | 4.762 203 | 10.25986 | 22.10419 |
| 109 | 11 881 | 10.44031 | 33.01515 | 1 295 029 | 4.776 856 | 10.29142 | 22.17220 |
| 110 | 12 100 | 10.48809 | 33.16625 | 1 331 000 | 4.791 420 | 10.32280 | 22.23980 |
| 111 | 12 321 | 10.55565 | 33.31666 | 1 367 631 | 4.805 896 | 10.35399 | 22.30699 |
| 112 | 12 544 | 10.58301 | 33.46640 | 1 404 928 | 4.820 285 | 10.38499 | 22.37378 |
| 113 | 12 769 | 10.63015 | 33.61547 | 1 442 897 | 4.834 588 | 10.41580 | 22.44017 |
| 114 | 12 996 | 10.67708 | 33.76389 | 1 481 544 | 4.848 808 | 10.44644 | 22.50617 |
| 115 | 13 225 | 10.72381 | 33.91165 | 1 520 875 | 4.862 944 | 10.47690 | 22.57179 |
| 116 | 13 456 | 10.77033 | 34.05877 | 1 560 896 | 4.876 999 | 10.50718 | 22.63702 |
| 117 | 13 689 | 10.81665 | 34.20526 | 1 601 613 | 4.890 973 | 10.53728 | 22.70189 |
| 118 | 13 924 | 10.86278 | 34.35113 | 1 643 032 | 4.904 868 | 10.56722 | 22.76638 |
| 119 | 14 161 | 10.90871 | 34.49638 | 1 685 159 | 4.918 685 | 10.59699 | 22.83051 |
| 120 | 14 400 | 10.95445 | 34.64102 | 1 728 000 | 4.932 424 | 10.62659 | 22.89428 |
| 121 | 14 641 | 11.00000 | 34.78505 | 1 771 561 | 4.946 087 | 10.65602 | 22.95770 |
| 122 | 14 884 | 11.04536 | 34.92850 | 1 815 848 | 4.959 676 | 10.68530 | 23.02078 |
| 123 | 15 129 | 11.09054 | 35.07136 | 1 860 867 | 4.973 190 | 10.71441 | 23.08350 |
| 124 | 15 376 | 11.13553 | 35.21363 | 1 906 624 | 4.986 631 | 10.74337 | 23.14589 |
| 125 | 15 625 | 11.18034 | 35.35534 | 1 953 125 | 5.000 000 | 10.77217 | 23.20794 |
| 126 | 15 876 | 11.22497 | 35.49648 | 2 000 376 | 5.013 298 | 10.80082 | 23.26967 |
| 127 | 16 129 | 11.26943 | 35.63706 | 2 048 383 | 5.026 526 | 10.82932 | 23.33107 |
| 128 | 16 384 | 11.31371 | 35.77709 | 2 097 152 | 5.039 684 | 10.85767 | 23.39214 |
| 129 | 16 641 | 11.35782 | 35.91657 | 2 146 689 | 5.052 774 | 10.88587 | 23.45290 |
| 130 | 16 900 | 11.40175 | 36.05551 | 2 197 000 | 5.065 797 | 10.91393 | 23.51335 |
| 131 | 17 161 | 11.44552 | 36.19392 | 2 248 091 | 5.078 753 | 10.94184 | 23.57348 |
| 132 | 17 424 | 11.48913 | 36.33180 | 2 299 968 | 5.091 643 | 10.96961 | 23.63332 |
| 133 | 17 689 | 11.53256 | 36.46917 | 2 352 637 | 5.104 469 | 10.99724 | 23.69285 |
| 134 | 17 956 | 11.57584 | 36.60601 | 2 406 104 | 5.117 230 | 11.02474 | 23.75208 |
| 135 | 18 225 | 11.61895 | 36.74235 | 2 460 375 | 5.129 928 | 11.05209 | 23.81102 |
| 136 | 18 496 | 11.66190 | 36.87818 | 2 515 456 | 5.142 563 | 11.07932 | 23.86966 |
| 137 | 18 769 | 11.70470 | 37.01351 | 2 571 353 | 5.155 137 | 11.10641 | 23.92803 |
| 138 | 19 044 | 11.74734 | 37.14835 | 2 628 072 | 5.167 649 | 11.13336 | 23.98610 |
| 139 | 19 321 | 11.78983 | 37.28270 | 2 685 619 | 5.180 101 | 11.16019 | 24.04390 |
| 140 | 19 600 | 11.83216 | 37.41657 | 2 744 000 | 5.192 494 | 11.18689 | 24.10142 |
| 141 | 19 881 | 11.87434 | 37.54997 | 2 803 221 | 5.204 828 | 11.21346 | 24.15867 |
| 142 | 20 164 | 11.91638 | 37.68289 | 2 863 288 | 5.217 103 | 11.23991 | 24.21565 |
| 143 | 20 449 | 11.95826 | 37.81534 | 2 924 207 | 5.229 322 | 11.26623 | 24.27236 |
| 144 | 20 736 | 12.00000 | 37.94733 | 2 985 984 | 5.241 483 | 11.29243 | 24.32881 |
| 145 | 21 025 | 12.04159 | 38.07887 | 3 048 625 | 5.253 588 | 11.31851 | 24.38499 |
| 146 | 21 316 | 12.08305 | 38.20995 | 3 112 136 | 5.265 637 | 11.34447 | 24.44092 |
| 147 | 21 609 | 12.12436 | 38.34058 | 3 176 523 | 5.277 632 | 11.37031 | 24.49660 |
| 148 | 21 904 | 12.16553 | 38.47077 | 3 241 792 | 5.289 572 | 11.39604 | 24.55202 |
| 149 | 22 201 | 12.20656 | 38.60052 | 3 307 949 | 5.301 459 | 11.42165 | 24.60719 |
| 150 | 22 500 | 12.24745 | 38.72983 | 3 375 000 | 5.313 293 | 11.44714 | 24.66212 |

| $n$ | $n^2$ | $\sqrt{n}$ | $\sqrt{10n}$ | $n^3$ | $\sqrt[3]{n}$ | $\sqrt[3]{10n}$ | $\sqrt[3]{100n}$ |
|---|---|---|---|---|---|---|---|
| **150** | 22 500 | 12.24745 | 38.72983 | 3 375 000 | 5.313 293 | 11.44714 | 24.66212 |
| 151 | 22 801 | 12.28821 | 38.85872 | 3 442 951 | 5.325 074 | 11.47252 | 24.71680 |
| 152 | 23 104 | 12.32883 | 38.98718 | 3 511 808 | 5.336 803 | 11.49779 | 24.77125 |
| 153 | 23 409 | 12.36932 | 39.11521 | 3 581 577 | 5.348 481 | 11.52295 | 24.82545 |
| 154 | 23 716 | 12.40967 | 39.24283 | 3 652 264 | 5.360 108 | 11.54800 | 24.87942 |
| **155** | 24 025 | 12.44990 | 39.37004 | 3 723 875 | 5.371 685 | 11 57295 | 24.93315 |
| 156 | 24 336 | 12.49000 | 39.49684 | 3 796 416 | 5.383 213 | 11.59778 | 24.98666 |
| 157 | 24 649 | 12.52996 | 39.62323 | 3 869 893 | 5.394 691 | 11.62251 | 25.03994 |
| 158 | 24 964 | 12.56981 | 39.74921 | 3 944 312 | 5.406 120 | 11.64713 | 25.09299 |
| 159 | 25 281 | 12.60952 | 39.87480 | 4 019 679 | 5.417 502 | 11.67165 | 25.14581 |
| **160** | 25 600 | 12.64911 | 40.00000 | 4 096 000 | 5.428 835 | 11.69607 | 25.19842 |
| 161 | 25 921 | 12.68858 | 40.12481 | 4 173 281 | 5.440 122 | 11.72039 | 25.25081 |
| 162 | 26 244 | 12.72792 | 40.24922 | 4 251 528 | 5.451 362 | 11.74460 | 25.30298 |
| 163 | 26 569 | 12.76715 | 40.37326 | 4 330 747 | 5.462 556 | 11.76872 | 25.35494 |
| 164 | 26 896 | 12.80625 | 40.49691 | 4 410 944 | 5.473 704 | 11.79274 | 25.40668 |
| **165** | 27 225 | 12.84523 | 40.62019 | 4 492 125 | 5.484 807 | 11.81666 | 25.45822 |
| 166 | 27 556 | 12.88410 | 40.74310 | 4 574 296 | 5.495 865 | 11.84048 | 25.50954 |
| 167 | 27 889 | 12.92285 | 40.86563 | 4 657 463 | 5.506 878 | 11.86421 | 25.56067 |
| 168 | 28 224 | 12.96148 | 40.98780 | 4 741 632 | 5.517 848 | 11.88784 | 25.61158 |
| 169 | 28 561 | 13.00000 | 41.10961 | 4 826 809 | 5.528 775 | 11.91138 | 25.66230 |
| **170** | 28 900 | 13.03840 | 41.23106 | 4 913 000 | 5.539 658 | 11.93483 | 25.71282 |
| 171 | 29 241 | 13.07670 | 41.35215 | 5 000 211 | 5.550 499 | 11.95819 | 25.76313 |
| 172 | 29 584 | 13.11488 | 41.47288 | 5 088 448 | 5.561 298 | 11.98145 | 25.81326 |
| 173 | 29 929 | 13.15295 | 41.59327 | 5 177 717 | 5.572 055 | 12.00463 | 25.86319 |
| 174 | 30 276 | 13.19091 | 41.71331 | 5 268 024 | 5.582 770 | 12.02771 | 25.91292 |
| **175** | 30 625 | 13.22876 | 41.83300 | 5 359 375 | 5.593 445 | 12.05071 | 25.96247 |
| 176 | 30 976 | 13.26650 | 41.95235 | 5 451 776 | 5.604 079 | 12.07362 | 26.01183 |
| 177 | 31 329 | 13.30413 | 42.07137 | 5 545 233 | 5.614 672 | 12.09645 | 26.06100 |
| 178 | 31 684 | 13.34166 | 42.19005 | 5 639 752 | 5.625 226 | 12.11918 | 26.10999 |
| 179 | 32 041 | 13.37909 | 42.30839 | 5 735 339 | 5.635 741 | 12.14184 | 26.15879 |
| **180** | 32 400 | 13.41641 | 42.42641 | 5 832 000 | 5.646 216 | 12.16440 | 26.20741 |
| 181 | 32 761 | 13.45362 | 42.54409 | 5 929 741 | 5.656 653 | 12.18689 | 26.25586 |
| 182 | 33 124 | 13.49074 | 42.66146 | 6 028 568 | 5.667 051 | 12.20929 | 26.30412 |
| 183 | 33 489 | 13.52775 | 42.77850 | 6 128 487 | 5.677 411 | 12.23161 | 26.35221 |
| 184 | 33 856 | 13.56466 | 42.89522 | 6 229 504 | 5.687 734 | 12.25385 | 26.40012 |
| **185** | 34 225 | 13.60147 | 43.01163 | 6 331 625 | 5.698 019 | 12.27601 | 26.44786 |
| 186 | 34 596 | 13.63818 | 43.12772 | 6 434 856 | 5.708 267 | 12.29809 | 26.49543 |
| 187 | 34 969 | 13.67479 | 43.24350 | 6 539 203 | 5.718 479 | 12.32009 | 26.54283 |
| 188 | 35 344 | 13.71131 | 43.35897 | 6 644 672 | 5.728 654 | 12.34201 | 26.59006 |
| 189 | 35 721 | 13.74773 | 43.47413 | 6 751 269 | 5.738 794 | 12.36386 | 26.63712 |
| **190** | 36 100 | 13.78405 | 43.58899 | 6 859 000 | 5.748 897 | 12.38562 | 26.68402 |
| 191 | 36 481 | 13.82027 | 43.70355 | 6 967 871 | 5.758 965 | 12.40731 | 26.73075 |
| 192 | 36 864 | 13.85641 | 43.81780 | 7 077 888 | 5.768 998 | 12.42893 | 26.77732 |
| 193 | 37 249 | 13.89244 | 43.93177 | 7 189 057 | 5.778 997 | 12.45047 | 26.82373 |
| 194 | 37 636 | 13.92839 | 44.04543 | 7 301 384 | 5.788 960 | 12.47194 | 26.86997 |
| **195** | 38 025 | 13.96424 | 44.15880 | 7 414 875 | 5.798 890 | 12.49333 | 26.91606 |
| 196 | 38 416 | 14.00000 | 44.27189 | 7 529 536 | 5.808 786 | 12.51465 | 26.96199 |
| 197 | 38 809 | 14.03567 | 44.38468 | 7 645 373 | 5.818 648 | 12.53590 | 27.00777 |
| 198 | 39 204 | 14.07125 | 44.49719 | 7 762 392 | 5.828 477 | 12.55707 | 27.05339 |
| 199 | 39 601 | 14.10674 | 44.60942 | 7 880 599 | 5.838 272 | 12.57818 | 27.09886 |
| **200** | 40 000 | 14.14214 | 44.72136 | 8 000 000 | 5.848 035 | 12.59921 | 27.14418 |

# SQUARES, CUBES AND ROOTS (Continued)

| $n$ | $n^2$ | $\sqrt{n}$ | $\sqrt{10n}$ | $n^3$ | $\sqrt[3]{n}$ | $\sqrt[3]{10n}$ | $\sqrt[3]{100n}$ |
|---|---|---|---|---|---|---|---|
| **200** | 40 000 | 14.14214 | 44.72136 | 8 000 000 | 5.848 035 | 12.59921 | 27.14418 |
| 201 | 40 401 | 14.17745 | 44.83302 | 8 120 601 | 5.857 766 | 12.62017 | 27.18934 |
| 202 | 40 804 | 14.21267 | 44.94441 | 8 242 408 | 5.867 464 | 12.64107 | 27.23436 |
| 203 | 41 209 | 14.24781 | 45.05552 | 8 365 427 | 5.877 131 | 12.66189 | 27.27922 |
| 204 | 41 616 | 14.28286 | 45.16636 | 8 489 664 | 5.886 765 | 12.68265 | 27.32394 |
| 205 | 42 025 | 14.31782 | 45.27693 | 8 615 125 | 5.896 369 | 12.70334 | 27.36852 |
| 206 | 42 436 | 14.35270 | 45.38722 | 8 741 816 | 5.905 941 | 12.72396 | 27.41295 |
| 207 | 42 849 | 14.38749 | 45.49725 | 8 869 743 | 5.915 482 | 12.74452 | 27.45723 |
| 208 | 43 264 | 14.42221 | 45.60702 | 8 998 912 | 5.924 992 | 12.76501 | 27.50138 |
| 209 | 43 681 | 14.45683 | 45.71652 | 9 129 329 | 5.934 472 | 12.78543 | 27.54538 |
| **210** | 44 100 | 14.49138 | 45.82576 | 9 261 000 | 5.943 922 | 12.80579 | 27.58924 |
| 211 | 44 521 | 14.52584 | 45.93474 | 9 393 931 | 5.953 342 | 12.82609 | 27.63296 |
| 212 | 44 944 | 14.56022 | 46.04346 | 9 528 128 | 5.962 732 | 12.84632 | 27.67655 |
| 213 | 45 369 | 14.59452 | 46.15192 | 9 663 597 | 5.972 093 | 12.86648 | 27.72000 |
| 214 | 45 796 | 14.62874 | 46.26013 | 9 800 344 | 5.981 424 | 12.88659 | 27.76331 |
| 215 | 46 225 | 14.66288 | 46.36809 | 9 938 375 | 5.990 726 | 12.90663 | 27.80649 |
| 216 | 46 656 | 14.69694 | 46.47580 | 10 077 696 | 6.000 000 | 12.92661 | 27.84953 |
| 217 | 47 089 | 14.73092 | 46.58326 | 10 218 313 | 6.009 245 | 12.94653 | 27.89244 |
| 218 | 47 524 | 14.76482 | 46.69047 | 10 360 232 | 6.018 462 | 12.96638 | 27.93522 |
| 219 | 47 961 | 14.79865 | 46.79744 | 10 503 459 | 6.027 650 | 12.98618 | 27.97787 |
| **220** | 48 400 | 14.83240 | 46.90416 | 10 648 000 | 6.036 811 | 13.00591 | 28.02039 |
| 221 | 48 841 | 14.86607 | 47.01064 | 10 793 861 | 6.045 944 | 13.02559 | 28.06278 |
| 222 | 49 284 | 14.89966 | 47.11688 | 10 941 048 | 6.055 049 | 13.04521 | 28.10505 |
| 223 | 49 729 | 14.93318 | 47.22288 | 11 089 567 | 6.064 127 | 13.06477 | 28.14718 |
| 224 | 50 176 | 14.96663 | 47.32864 | 11 239 424 | 6.073 178 | 13.08427 | 28.18919 |
| 225 | 50 625 | 15.00000 | 47.43416 | 11 390 625 | 6.082 202 | 13.10371 | 28.23108 |
| 226 | 51 076 | 15.03330 | 47.53946 | 11 543 176 | 6.091 199 | 13.12309 | 28.27284 |
| 227 | 51 529 | 15.06652 | 47.64452 | 11 697 083 | 6.100 170 | 13.14242 | 28.31448 |
| 228 | 51 984 | 15.09967 | 47.74935 | 11 852 352 | 6.109 115 | 13.16169 | 28.35600 |
| 229 | 52 441 | 15.13275 | 47.85394 | 12 008 989 | 6.118 033 | 13.18090 | 28.39739 |
| **230** | 52 900 | 15.16575 | 47.95832 | 12 167 000 | 6.126 926 | 13.20006 | 28.43867 |
| 231 | 53 361 | 15.19868 | 48.06246 | 12 326 391 | 6.135 792 | 13.21916 | 28.47983 |
| 232 | 53 824 | 15.23155 | 48.16638 | 12 487 168 | 6.144 634 | 13.23821 | 28.52086 |
| 233 | 54 289 | 15.26434 | 48.27007 | 12 649 337 | 6.153 449 | 13.25721 | 28.56178 |
| 234 | 54 756 | 15.29706 | 48.37355 | 12 812 904 | 6.162 240 | 13.27614 | 28.60259 |
| 235 | 55 225 | 15.32971 | 48.47680 | 12 977 875 | 6.171 006 | 13.29503 | 28.64327 |
| 236 | 55 696 | 15.36229 | 48.57983 | 13 144 256 | 6.179 747 | 13.31386 | 28.68384 |
| 237 | 56 169 | 15.39480 | 48.68265 | 13 312 053 | 6.188 463 | 13.33264 | 28.72430 |
| 238 | 56 644 | 15.42725 | 48.78524 | 13 481 272 | 6.197 154 | 13.35136 | 28.76464 |
| 239 | 57 121 | 15.45962 | 48.88763 | 13 651 919 | 6.205 822 | 13.37004 | 28.80487 |
| **240** | 57 600 | 15.49193 | 48.98979 | 13 824 000 | 6.214 465 | 13.38866 | 28.84499 |
| 241 | 58 081 | 15.52417 | 49.09175 | 13 997 521 | 6.223 084 | 13.40723 | 28.88500 |
| 242 | 58 564 | 15.55635 | 49.19350 | 14 172 488 | 6.231 680 | 13.42575 | 28.92489 |
| 243 | 59 049 | 15.58846 | 49.29503 | 14 348 907 | 6.240 251 | 13.44421 | 28.96468 |
| 244 | 59 536 | 15.62050 | 49.39636 | 14 526 784 | 6.248 800 | 13.46263 | 29.00436 |
| 245 | 60 025 | 15.65248 | 49.49747 | 14 706 125 | 6.257 325 | 13.48100 | 29.04393 |
| 246 | 60 516 | 15.68439 | 49.59839 | 14 886 936 | 6.265 827 | 13.49931 | 29.08339 |
| 247 | 61 009 | 15.71623 | 49.69909 | 15 069 223 | 6.274 305 | 13.51758 | 29.12275 |
| 248 | 61 504 | 15.74802 | 49.79960 | 15 252 992 | 6.282 761 | 13.53580 | 29.16199 |
| 249 | 62 001 | 15.77973 | 49.89990 | 15 438 249 | 6.291 195 | 13.55397 | 29.20114 |
| **250** | 62 500 | 15.81139 | 50.00000 | 15 625 000 | 6.299 605 | 13.57209 | 29.24018 |

| $n$ | $n^2$ | $\sqrt{n}$ | $\sqrt{10n}$ | $n^3$ | $\sqrt[3]{n}$ | $\sqrt[3]{10n}$ | $\sqrt[3]{100n}$ |
|---|---|---|---|---|---|---|---|
| **250** | 62 500 | 15.81139 | 50.00000 | 15 625 000 | 6.299 605 | 13.57209 | 29.24018 |
| 251 | 63 001 | 15.84298 | 50.09990 | 15 813 251 | 6.307 994 | 13.59016 | 29.27911 |
| 252 | 63 504 | 15.87451 | 50.19960 | 16 003 008 | 6.316 360 | 13.60818 | 29.31794 |
| 253 | 64 009 | 15.90597 | 50.29911 | 16 194 277 | 6.324 704 | 13.62616 | 29.35667 |
| 254 | 64 516 | 15.93738 | 50.39841 | 16 387 064 | 6.333 026 | 13.64409 | 29.39530 |
| 255 | 65 025 | 15.96872 | 50.49752 | 16 581 375 | 6.341 326 | 13.66197 | 29.43383 |
| 256 | 65 536 | 16.00000 | 50.59644 | 16 777 216 | 6.349 604 | 13.67981 | 29.47225 |
| 257 | 66 049 | 16.03122 | 50.69517 | 16 974 593 | 6.357 861 | 13.69760 | 29.51058 |
| 258 | 66 564 | 16.06238 | 50.79370 | 17 173 512 | 6.366 097 | 13.71534 | 29.54880 |
| 259 | 67 081 | 16.09348 | 50.89204 | 17 373 979 | 6.374 311 | 13.73304 | 29.58693 |
| **260** | 67 600 | 16.12452 | 50.99020 | 17 576 000 | 6.382 504 | 13.75069 | 29.62496 |
| 261 | 68 121 | 16.15549 | 51.08816 | 17 779 581 | 6.390 677 | 13.76830 | 29.66289 |
| 262 | 68 644 | 16.18641 | 51.18594 | 17 984 728 | 6.398 828 | 13.78586 | 29.70073 |
| 263 | 69 169 | 16.21727 | 51.28353 | 18 191 447 | 6.406 959 | 13.80337 | 29.73847 |
| 264 | 69 696 | 16.24808 | 51.38093 | 18 399 744 | 6.415 069 | 13.82085 | 29.77611 |
| 265 | 70 225 | 16.27882 | 51.47815 | 18 609 625 | 6.423 158 | 13.83828 | 29.81366 |
| 266 | 70 756 | 16.30951 | 51.57519 | 18 821 096 | 6.431 228 | 13.85566 | 29.85111 |
| 267 | 71 289 | 16 34013 | 51.67204 | 19 034 163 | 6.439 277 | 13.87300 | 29.88847 |
| 268 | 71 824 | 16.37071 | 51.76872 | 19 248 832 | 6.447 306 | 13.89030 | 29.92574 |
| 269 | 72 361 | 16.40122 | 51.86521 | 19 465 109 | 6.455 315 | 13.90755 | 29.96292 |
| **270** | 72 900 | 16.43168 | 51.96152 | 19 683 000 | 6.463 304 | 13.92477 | 30.00000 |
| 271 | 73 441 | 16.46208 | 52.05766 | 19 902 511 | 6.471 274 | 13.94194 | 30.03699 |
| 272 | 73 984 | 16.49242 | 52.15362 | 20 123 648 | 6.479 224 | 13.95906 | 30.07389 |
| 273 | 74 529 | 16.52271 | 52.24940 | 20 346 417 | 6.487 154 | 13.97615 | 30.11070 |
| 274 | 75 076 | 16.55295 | 52.34501 | 20 570 824 | 6.495 065 | 13.99319 | 30.14742 |
| 275 | 75 625 | 16.58312 | 52.44044 | 20 796 875 | 6.502 957 | 14.01020 | 30.18405 |
| 276 | 76 176 | 16.61325 | 52.53570 | 21 024 576 | 6.510 830 | 14.02716 | 30.22060 |
| 277 | 76 729 | 16.64332 | 52.63079 | 21 253 933 | 6.518 684 | 14.04408 | 30.25705 |
| 278 | 77 284 | 16.67333 | 52.72571 | 21 484 952 | 6.526 519 | 14.06096 | 30.29342 |
| 279 | 77 841 | 16.70329 | 52.82045 | 21 717 639 | 6.534 335 | 14.07780 | 30.32970 |
| **280** | 78 400 | 16.73320 | 52.91503 | 21 952 000 | 6.542 133 | 14.09460 | 30.36589 |
| 281 | 78 961 | 16.76305 | 53.00943 | 22 188 041 | 6.549 912 | 14.11136 | 30.40200 |
| 282 | 79 524 | 16.79286 | 53.10367 | 22 425 768 | 6.557 672 | 14.12808 | 30.43802 |
| 283 | 80 089 | 16.82260 | 53.19774 | 22 665 187 | 6.565 414 | 14.14476 | 30.47395 |
| 284 | 80 656 | 16.85230 | 53.29165 | 22 906 304 | 6.573 138 | 14.16140 | 30.50981 |
| 285 | 81 225 | 16.88194 | 53.38539 | 23 149 125 | 6.580 844 | 14.17800 | 30.54557 |
| 286 | 81 796 | 16.91153 | 53.47897 | 23 393 656 | 6.588 532 | 14.19456 | 30.58126 |
| 287 | 82 369 | 16.94107 | 53.57238 | 23 639 903 | 6.596 202 | 14.21109 | 30.61686 |
| 288 | 82 944 | 16.97056 | 53.66563 | 23 887 872 | 6.603 854 | 14.22757 | 30.65238 |
| 289 | 83 521 | 17.00000 | 53.75872 | 24 137 569 | 6.611 489 | 14.24402 | 30.68781 |
| **290** | 84 100 | 17 02939 | 53.85165 | 24 389 000 | 6.619 106 | 14.26043 | 30.72317 |
| 291 | 84 681 | 17.05872 | 53.94442 | 24 642 171 | 6.626 705 | 14.27680 | 30.75844 |
| 292 | 85 264 | 17.08801 | 54.03702 | 24 897 088 | 6.634 287 | 14.29314 | 30.79363 |
| 293 | 85 849 | 17.11724 | 54.12947 | 25 153 757 | 6.641 852 | 14.30944 | 30.82875 |
| 294 | 86 436 | 17.14643 | 54.22177 | 25 412 184 | 6.649 400 | 14.32570 | 30.86378 |
| 295 | 87 025 | 17.17556 | 54.31390 | 25 672 375 | 6.656 930 | 14.34192 | 30.89873 |
| 296 | 87 616 | 17.20465 | 54.40588 | 25 934 336 | 6.664 444 | 14.35811 | 30.93361 |
| 297 | 88 209 | 17.23369 | 54.49771 | 26 198 073 | 6.671 940 | 14.37426 | 30.96840 |
| 298 | 88 804 | 17.26268 | 54.58938 | 26 463 592 | 6.679 420 | 14.39037 | 31.00312 |
| 299 | 89 401 | 17.29162 | 54.68089 | 26 730 899 | 6.686 883 | 14.40645 | 31.03776 |
| **300** | 90 000 | 17.32051 | 54.77226 | 27 000 000 | 6.694 330 | 14.42250 | 31.07233 |

# SQUARES, CUBES AND ROOTS (Continued)

| $n$ | $n^2$ | $\sqrt{n}$ | $\sqrt{10n}$ | $n^3$ | $\sqrt[3]{n}$ | $\sqrt[3]{10n}$ | $\sqrt[3]{100n}$ |
|---|---|---|---|---|---|---|---|
| **300** | 90 000 | 17.32051 | 54.77226 | 27 000 000 | 6.694 330 | 14.42250 | 31.07233 |
| 301 | 90 601 | 17.34935 | 54.86347 | 27 270 901 | 6.701 759 | 14.43850 | 31.10681 |
| 302 | 91 204 | 17.37815 | 54.95453 | 27 543 608 | 6.709 173 | 14.45447 | 31.14122 |
| 303 | 91 809 | 17.40690 | 55.04544 | 27 818 127 | 6.716 570 | 14.47041 | 31.17556 |
| 304 | 92 416 | 17.43560 | 55.13620 | 28 094 464 | 6.723 951 | 14.48631 | 31.20982 |
| 305 | 93 025 | 17.46425 | 55.22681 | 28 372 625 | 6.731 315 | 14.50218 | 31.24400 |
| 306 | 93 636 | 17.49286 | 55.31727 | 28 652 616 | 6.738 664 | 14.51801 | 31.27811 |
| 307 | 94 249 | 17.52142 | 55.40758 | 28 934 443 | 6.745 997 | 14.53381 | 31.31214 |
| 308 | 94 864 | 17.54993 | 55.49775 | 29 218 112 | 6.753 313 | 14.54957 | 31.34610 |
| 309 | 95 481 | 17.57840 | 55.58777 | 29 503 629 | 6.760 614 | 14.56530 | 31.37999 |
| **310** | 96 100 | 17.60682 | 55.67764 | 29 791 000 | 6.767 899 | 14.58100 | 31.41381 |
| 311 | 96 721 | 17.63519 | 55.76737 | 30 080 231 | 6.775 169 | 14.59666 | 31.44755 |
| 312 | 97 344 | 17.66352 | 55.85696 | 30 371 328 | 6.782 423 | 14.61229 | 31.48122 |
| 313 | 97 969 | 17.69181 | 55.94640 | 30 664 297 | 6.789 661 | 14.62788 | 31.51482 |
| 314 | 98 596 | 17.72005 | 56.03570 | 30 959 144 | 6.796 884 | 14.64344 | 31.54834 |
| 315 | 99 225 | 17.74824 | 56.12486 | 31 255 875 | 6.804 092 | 14.65897 | 31.58180 |
| 316 | 99 856 | 17.77639 | 56.21388 | 31 554 496 | 6.811 285 | 14.67447 | 31.61518 |
| 317 | 100 489 | 17.80449 | 56.30275 | 31 855 013 | 6.818 462 | 14.68993 | 31.64850 |
| 318 | 101 124 | 17.83255 | 56.39149 | 32 157 432 | 6.825 624 | 14.70536 | 31.68174 |
| 319 | 101 761 | 17.86057 | 56.48008 | 32 461 759 | 6.832 771 | 14.72076 | 31.71492 |
| **320** | 102 400 | 17.88854 | 56.56854 | 32 768 000 | 6.839 904 | 14.73613 | 31.74802 |
| 321 | 103 041 | 17.91647 | 56.65686 | 33 076 161 | 6.847 021 | 14.75146 | 31.78106 |
| 322 | 103 684 | 17.94436 | 56.74504 | 33 386 248 | 6.854 124 | 14.76676 | 31.81403 |
| 323 | 104 329 | 17.97220 | 56.83309 | 33 698 267 | 6.861 212 | 14.78203 | 31.84693 |
| 324 | 104 976 | 18.00000 | 56.92100 | 34 012 224 | 6.868 285 | 14.79727 | 31.87976 |
| 325 | 105 625 | 18.02776 | 57.00877 | 34 328 125 | 6.875 344 | 14.81248 | 31.91252 |
| 326 | 106 276 | 18.05547 | 57.09641 | 34 645 976 | 6.882 389 | 14.82766 | 31.94522 |
| 327 | 106 929 | 18.08314 | 57.18391 | 34 965 783 | 6.889 419 | 14.84280 | 31.97785 |
| 328 | 107 584 | 18.11077 | 57.27128 | 35 287 552 | 6.896 434 | 14.85792 | 32.01041 |
| 329 | 108 241 | 18.13836 | 57.35852 | 35 611 289 | 6.903 436 | 14.87300 | 32.04291 |
| **330** | 108 900 | 18.16590 | 57.44563 | 35 937 000 | 6.910 423 | 14.88806 | 32.07534 |
| 331 | 109 561 | 18.19341 | 57.53260 | 36 264 691 | 6.917 396 | 14.90308 | 32.10771 |
| 332 | 110 224 | 18.22087 | 57.61944 | 36 594 368 | 6.924 356 | 14.91807 | 32.14001 |
| 333 | 110 889 | 18.24829 | 57.70615 | 36 926 037 | 6.931 301 | 14.93303 | 32.17225 |
| 334 | 111 556 | 18.27567 | 57.79273 | 37 259 704 | 6.938 232 | 14.94797 | 32.20442 |
| 335 | 112 225 | 18.30301 | 57.87918 | 37 595 375 | 6.945 150 | 14.96287 | 32.23653 |
| 336 | 112 896 | 18.33030 | 57.96551 | 37 933 056 | 6.952 053 | 14.97774 | 32.26857 |
| 337 | 113 569 | 18.35756 | 58.05170 | 38 272 753 | 6.958 943 | 14.99259 | 32.30055 |
| 338 | 114 244 | 18.38478 | 58.13777 | 38 614 472 | 6.965 820 | 15.00740 | 32.33247 |
| 339 | 114 921 | 18.41195 | 58.22371 | 38 958 219 | 6.972 683 | 15.02219 | 32.36433 |
| **340** | 115 600 | 18.43909 | 58.30952 | 39 304 000 | 6.979 532 | 15.03695 | 32.39612 |
| 341 | 116 281 | 18.46619 | 58.39521 | 39 651 821 | 6.986 368 | 15.05167 | 32.42785 |
| 342 | 116 964 | 18.49324 | 58.48077 | 40 001 688 | 6.993 191 | 15.06637 | 32.45952 |
| 343 | 117 649 | 18.52026 | 58.56620 | 40 353 607 | 7.000 000 | 15.08104 | 32.49112 |
| 344 | 118 336 | 18.54724 | 58.65151 | 40 707 584 | 7.006 796 | 15.09568 | 32.52267 |
| 345 | 119 025 | 18.57418 | 58.73670 | 41 063 625 | 7.013 579 | 15.11030 | 32.55415 |
| 346 | 119 716 | 18.60108 | 58.82176 | 41 421 736 | 7.020 349 | 15.12488 | 32.58557 |
| 347 | 120 409 | 18.62794 | 58.90671 | 41 781 923 | 7.027 106 | 15.13944 | 32.61694 |
| 348 | 121 104 | 18.65476 | 58.99152 | 42 144 192 | 7.033 850 | 15.15397 | 32.64824 |
| **349** | 121 801 | 18.68154 | 59.07622 | 42 508 549 | 7.040 581 | 15.16847 | 32.67948 |
| **350** | 122 500 | 18.70829 | 59.16080 | 42 875 000 | 7.047 299 | 15.18294 | 32.71066 |

# SQUARES, CUBES AND ROOTS (Continued)

| $n$ | $n^2$ | $\sqrt{n}$ | $\sqrt{10n}$ | $n^3$ | $\sqrt[3]{n}$ | $\sqrt[3]{10n}$ | $\sqrt[3]{100n}$ |
|---|---|---|---|---|---|---|---|
| **350** | 122 500 | 18.70829 | 59.16080 | 42 875 000 | 7.047 299 | 15.18294 | 32.71066 |
| 351 | 123 201 | 18.73499 | 59.24525 | 43 243 551 | 7.054 004 | 15.19739 | 32.74179 |
| 352 | 123 904 | 18.76166 | 59.32959 | 43 614 208 | 7.060 697 | 15.21181 | 32.77285 |
| 353 | 124 609 | 18.78829 | 59.41380 | 43 986 977 | 7.067 377 | 15.22620 | 32.80386 |
| 354 | 125 316 | 18.81489 | 59.49790 | 44 361 864 | 7.074 044 | 15.24057 | 32.83480 |
| **355** | 126 025 | 18.84144 | 59.58188 | 44 738 875 | 7.080 699 | 15.25490 | 32.86569 |
| 356 | 126 736 | 18.86796 | 59.66574 | 45 118 016 | 7.087 341 | 15.26921 | 32.89652 |
| 357 | 127 449 | 18.89444 | 59.74948 | 45 499 293 | 7.093 971 | 15.28350 | 32.92730 |
| 358 | 128 164 | 18.92089 | 59.83310 | 45 882 712 | 7.100 588 | 15.29775 | 32.95801 |
| 359 | 128 881 | 18.94730 | 59.91661 | 46 268 279 | 7.107 194 | 15.31198 | 32.98867 |
| **360** | 129 600 | 18.97367 | 60.00000 | 46 656 000 | 7.113 787 | 15.32619 | 33.01927 |
| 361 | 130 321 | 19.00000 | 60.08328 | 47 045 881 | 7.120 367 | 15.34037 | 33.04982 |
| 362 | 131 044 | 19.02630 | 60.16644 | 47 437 928 | 7.126 936 | 15.35452 | 33.08031 |
| 363 | 131 769 | 19.05256 | 60.24948 | 47 832 147 | 7.133 492 | 15.36864 | 33.11074 |
| 364 | 132 496 | 19.07878 | 60.33241 | 48 228 544 | 7.140 037 | 15.38274 | 33.14112 |
| **365** | 133 225 | 19.10497 | 60.41523 | 48 627 125 | 7.146 569 | 15.39682 | 33.17144 |
| 366 | 133 956 | 19.13113 | 60.49793 | 49 027 896 | 7.153 090 | 15.41087 | 33.20170 |
| 367 | 134 689 | 19.15724 | 60.58052 | 49 430 863 | 7.159 599 | 15.42489 | 33.23191 |
| 368 | 135 424 | 19.18333 | 60.66300 | 49 836 032 | 7.166 096 | 15.43889 | 33.26207 |
| 369 | 136 161 | 19.20937 | 60.74537 | 50 243 409 | 7.172 581 | 15.45286 | 33.29217 |
| **370** | 136 900 | 19.23538 | 60.82763 | 50 653 000 | 7.179 054 | 15.46680 | 33.32222 |
| 371 | 137 641 | 19.26136 | 60.90977 | 51 064 811 | 7.185 516 | 15.48073 | 33.35221 |
| 372 | 138 384 | 19.28730 | 60.99180 | 51 478 848 | 7.191 966 | 15.49462 | 33.38215 |
| 373 | 139 129 | 19.31321 | 61.07373 | 51 895 117 | 7.198 405 | 15.50849 | 33.41204 |
| 374 | 139 876 | 19.33908 | 61.15554 | 52 313 624 | 7.204 832 | 15.52234 | 33.44187 |
| **375** | 140 625 | 19.36492 | 61.23724 | 52 734 375 | 7.211 248 | 15.53616 | 33.47165 |
| 376 | 141 376 | 19.39072 | 61.31884 | 53 157 376 | 7.217 652 | 15.54996 | 33.50137 |
| 377 | 142 129 | 19.41649 | 61.40033 | 53 582 633 | 7.224 045 | 15.56373 | 33.53105 |
| 378 | 142 884 | 19.44222 | 61.48170 | 54 010 152 | 7.230 427 | 15.57748 | 33.56067 |
| 379 | 143 641 | 19.46792 | 61.56298 | 54 439 939 | 7.236 797 | 15.59121 | 33.59024 |
| **380** | 144 400 | 19.49359 | 61.64414 | 54 872 000 | 7.243 156 | 15.60491 | 33.61975 |
| 381 | 145 161 | 19.51922 | 61.72520 | 55 306 341 | 7.249 505 | 15.61858 | 33.64922 |
| 382 | 145 924 | 19.54482 | 61.80615 | 55 742 968 | 7.255 842 | 15.63224 | 33.67863 |
| 383 | 146 689 | 19.57039 | 61.88699 | 56 181 887 | 7.262 167 | 15.64587 | 33.70800 |
| 384 | 147 456 | 19.59592 | 61.96773 | 56 623 104 | 7.268 482 | 15.65947 | 33.73731 |
| **385** | 148 225 | 19.62142 | 62.04837 | 57 066 625 | 7.274 786 | 15.67305 | 33.76657 |
| 386 | 148 996 | 19.64688 | 62.12890 | 57 512 456 | 7.281 079 | 15.68661 | 33.79578 |
| 387 | 149 769 | 19.67232 | 62.20932 | 57 960 603 | 7.287 362 | 15.70014 | 33.82494 |
| 388 | 150 544 | 19.69772 | 62.28965 | 58 411 072 | 7.293 633 | 15.71366 | 33.85405 |
| 389 | 151 321 | 19.72308 | 62.36986 | 58 863 869 | 7.299 894 | 15.72714 | 33.88310 |
| **390** | 152 100 | 19.74842 | 62.44998 | 59 319 000 | 7.306 144 | 15.74061 | 33.91211 |
| 391 | 152 881 | 19.77372 | 62.52999 | 59 776 471 | 7.312 383 | 15.75405 | 33.94107 |
| 392 | 153 664 | 19.79899 | 62.60990 | 60 236 288 | 7.318 611 | 15.76747 | 33.96999 |
| 393 | 154 449 | 19.82423 | 62.68971 | 60 698 457 | 7.324 829 | 15.78087 | 33.99885 |
| 394 | 155 236 | 19.84943 | 62.76942 | 61 162 984 | 7.331 037 | 15.79424 | 34.02766 |
| **395** | 156 025 | 19.87461 | 62.84903 | 61 629 875 | 7.337 234 | 15.80759 | 34.05642 |
| 396 | 156 816 | 19.89975 | 62.92853 | 62 099 136 | 7.343 420 | 15.82092 | 34.08514 |
| 397 | 157 609 | 19.92486 | 63.00794 | 62 570 773 | 7.349 597 | 15.83423 | 34.11381 |
| 398 | 158 404 | 19.94994 | 63.08724 | 63 044 792 | 7.355 762 | 15.84751 | 34.14242 |
| **399** | 159 201 | 19.97498 | 63.16645 | 63 521 199 | 7.361 918 | 15.86077 | 34.17100 |
| **400** | 160 000 | 20.00000 | 63.24555 | 64 000 000 | 7.368 063 | 15.87401 | 34.19952 |

| $n$ | $n^2$ | $\sqrt{n}$ | $\sqrt{10n}$ | $n^3$ | $\sqrt[3]{n}$ | $\sqrt[3]{10n}$ | $\sqrt[3]{100n}$ |
|---|---|---|---|---|---|---|---|
| **400** | 160 000 | 20.00000 | 63.24555 | 64 000 000 | 7.368 063 | 15.87401 | 34.19952 |
| 401 | 160 801 | 20.02498 | 63.32456 | 64 481 201 | 7.374 198 | 15.88723 | 34.22799 |
| 402 | 161 604 | 20.04994 | 63.40347 | 64 964 808 | 7.380 323 | 15.90042 | 34.25642 |
| 403 | 162 409 | 20.07486 | 63.48228 | 65 450 827 | 7.386 437 | 15.91360 | 34.28480 |
| 404 | 163 216 | 20.09975 | 63.56099 | 65 939 264 | 7.392 542 | 15.92675 | 34.31314 |
| 405 | 164 025 | 20.12461 | 63.63961 | 66 430 125 | 7.398 636 | 15.93988 | 34.34143 |
| 406 | 164 836 | 20.14944 | 63.71813 | 66 923 416 | 7.404 721 | 15.95299 | 34.36967 |
| 407 | 165 649 | 20.17424 | 63.79655 | 67 419 143 | 7.410 795 | 15.96607 | 34.39786 |
| 408 | 166 464 | 20.19901 | 63.87488 | 67 917 312 | 7.416 860 | 15.97914 | 34.42601 |
| 409 | 167 281 | 20.22375 | 63.95311 | 68 417 929 | 7.422 914 | 15.99218 | 34.45412 |
| **410** | 168 100 | 20.24846 | 64.03124 | 68 921 000 | 7.428 959 | 16.00521 | 34.48217 |
| 411 | 168 921 | 20.27313 | 64.10928 | 69 426 531 | 7.434 994 | 16.01821 | 34.51018 |
| 412 | 169 744 | 20.29778 | 64.18723 | 69 934 528 | 7.441 019 | 16.03119 | 34.53815 |
| 413 | 170 569 | 20.32240 | 64.26508 | 70 444 997 | 7.447 034 | 16.04415 | 34.56607 |
| 414 | 171 396 | 20.34699 | 64.34283 | 70 957 944 | 7.453 040 | 16.05709 | 34.59395 |
| 415 | 172 225 | 20.37155 | 64.42049 | 71 473 375 | 7.459 036 | 16.07001 | 34.62178 |
| 416 | 173 056 | 20.39608 | 64.49806 | 71 991 296 | 7.465 022 | 16.08290 | 34.64956 |
| 417 | 173 889 | 20.42058 | 64.57554 | 72 511 713 | 7.470 999 | 16.09578 | 34.67731 |
| 418 | 174 724 | 20.44505 | 64.65292 | 73 034 632 | 7.476 966 | 16.10864 | 34.70500 |
| 419 | 175 561 | 20.46949 | 64.73021 | 73 560 059 | 7.482 924 | 16.12147 | 34.73266 |
| **420** | 176 400 | 20.49390 | 64.80741 | 74 088 000 | 7.488 872 | 16.13429 | 34.76027 |
| 421 | 177 241 | 20.51828 | 64.88451 | 74 618 461 | 7.494 811 | 16.14708 | 34.78783 |
| 422 | 178 084 | 20.54264 | 64.96153 | 75 151 448 | 7.500 741 | 16.15986 | 34.81535 |
| 423 | 178 929 | 20.56696 | 65.03845 | 75 686 967 | 7.506 661 | 16.17261 | 34.84283 |
| 424 | 179 776 | 20.59126 | 65.11528 | 76 225 024 | 7.512 572 | 16.18534 | 34.87027 |
| 425 | 180 625 | 20.61553 | 65.19202 | 76 765 625 | 7.518 473 | 16.19806 | 34.89766 |
| 426 | 181 476 | 20.63977 | 65.26868 | 77 308 776 | 7.524 365 | 16.21075 | 34.92501 |
| 427 | 182 329 | 20.66398 | 65.34524 | 77 854 483 | 7.530 248 | 16.22343 | 34.95232 |
| 428 | 183 184 | 20.68816 | 65.42171 | 78 402 752 | 7.536 122 | 16.23608 | 34.97958 |
| 429 | 184 041 | 20.71232 | 65.49809 | 78 953 589 | 7.541 987 | 16.24872 | 35.00680 |
| **430** | 184 900 | 20.73644 | 65.57439 | 79 507 000 | 7.547 842 | 16.26133 | 35.03398 |
| 431 | 185 761 | 20.76054 | 65.65059 | 80 062 991 | 7.553 689 | 16.27393 | 35.06112 |
| 432 | 186 624 | 20.78461 | 65.72671 | 80 621 568 | 7.559 526 | 16.28651 | 35.08821 |
| 433 | 187 489 | 20.80865 | 65.80274 | 81 182 737 | 7.565 355 | 16.29906 | 35.11527 |
| 434 | 188 356 | 20.83267 | 65.87868 | 81 746 504 | 7.571 174 | 16.31160 | 35.14228 |
| 435 | 189 225 | 20.85665 | 65.95453 | 82 312 875 | 7.576 985 | 16.32412 | 35.16925 |
| 436 | 190 096 | 20.88061 | 66.03030 | 82 881 856 | 7.582 787 | 16.33662 | 35.19618 |
| 437 | 190 969 | 20.90454 | 66.10598 | 83 453 453 | 7.588 579 | 16.34910 | 35.22307 |
| 438 | 191 844 | 20.92845 | 66.18157 | 84 027 672 | 7.594 363 | 16.36156 | 35.24991 |
| 439 | 192 721 | 20.95233 | 66.25708 | 84 604 519 | 7.600 139 | 16.37400 | 35.27672 |
| **440** | 193 600 | 20.97618 | 66.33250 | 85 184 000 | 7.605 905 | 16.38643 | 35.30348 |
| 441 | 194 481 | 21.00000 | 66.40783 | 85 766 121 | 7.611 663 | 16.39883 | 35.33021 |
| 442 | 195 364 | 21.02380 | 66.48308 | 86 350 888 | 7.617 412 | 16.41122 | 35.35689 |
| 443 | 196 249 | 21.04757 | 66.55825 | 86 938 307 | 7.623 152 | 16.42358 | 35.38354 |
| 444 | 197 136 | 21.07131 | 66.63332 | 87 528 384 | 7.628 884 | 16.43593 | 35.41014 |
| 445 | 198 025 | 21.09502 | 66.70832 | 88 121 125 | 7.634 607 | 16.44826 | 35.43671 |
| 446 | 198 916 | 21.11871 | 66.78323 | 88 716 536 | 7.640 321 | 16.46057 | 35.46323 |
| 447 | 199 809 | 21.14237 | 66.85806 | 89 314 623 | 7.646 027 | 16.47287 | 35.48971 |
| 448 | 200 704 | 21.16601 | 66.93280 | 89 915 392 | 7.651 725 | 16.48514 | 35.51616 |
| 449 | 201 601 | 21.18962 | 67.00746 | 90 518 849 | 7.657 414 | 16.49740 | 35.54257 |
| **450** | 202 500 | 21.21320 | 67.08204 | 91 125 000 | 7.663 094 | 16.50964 | 35.56893 |

# SQUARES, CUBES AND ROOTS (Continued)

| $n$ | $n^2$ | $\sqrt{n}$ | $\sqrt{10n}$ | $n^3$ | $\sqrt[3]{n}$ | $\sqrt[3]{10n}$ | $\sqrt[3]{100n}$ |
|---|---|---|---|---|---|---|---|
| **450** | 202 500 | 21.21320 | 67.08204 | 91 125 000 | 7.663 094 | 16.50964 | 35.56893 |
| 451 | 203 401 | 21.23676 | 67.15653 | 91 733 851 | 7.668 766 | 16.52186 | 35.59526 |
| 452 | 204 304 | 21.26029 | 67.23095 | 92 345 408 | 7.674 430 | 16.53406 | 35.62155 |
| 453 | 205 209 | 21.28380 | 67.30527 | 92 959 677 | 7.680 086 | 16.54624 | 35.64780 |
| 454 | 206 116 | 21.30728 | 67.37952 | 93 576 664 | 7.685 733 | 16.55841 | 35.67401 |
| **455** | 207 025 | 21.33073 | 67.45369 | 94 196 375 | 7.691 372 | 16.57056 | 35.70018 |
| 456 | 207 936 | 21.35416 | 67.52777 | 94 818 816 | 7.697 002 | 16.58269 | 35.72632 |
| 457 | 208 849 | 21.37756 | 67.60178 | 95 443 993 | 7.702 625 | 16.59480 | 35.75242 |
| 458 | 209 764 | 21.40093 | 67.67570 | 96 071 912 | 7.708 239 | 16.60690 | 35.77848 |
| 459 | 210 681 | 21.42429 | 67.74954 | 96 702 579 | 7.713 845 | 16.61897 | 35.80450 |
| **460** | 211 600 | 21.44761 | 67.82330 | 97 336 000 | 7.719 443 | 16.63103 | 35.83048 |
| 461 | 212 521 | 21.47091 | 67.89698 | 97 972 181 | 7.725 032 | 16.64308 | 35.85642 |
| 462 | 213 444 | 21.49419 | 67.97058 | 98 611 128 | 7.730 614 | 16.65510 | 35.88233 |
| 463 | 214 369 | 21.51743 | 68.04410 | 99 252 847 | 7.736 188 | 16.66711 | 35.90820 |
| 464 | 215 296 | 21.54066 | 68.11755 | 99 897 344 | 7.741 753 | 16.67910 | 35.93404 |
| **465** | 216 225 | 21 56386 | 68.19091 | 100 544 625 | 7.747 311 | 16.69108 | 35.95983 |
| 466 | 217 156 | 21.58703 | 68.26419 | 101 194 696 | 7.752 861 | 16.70303 | 35.98559 |
| 467 | 218 089 | 21.61018 | 68.33740 | 101 847 563 | 7.758 402 | 16.71497 | 36.01131 |
| 468 | 219 024 | 21.63331 | 68.41053 | 102 503 232 | 7.763 936 | 16.72689 | 36.03700 |
| 469 | 219 961 | 21.65641 | 68.48357 | 103 161 709 | 7.769 462 | 16.73880 | 36.06265 |
| **470** | 220 900 | 21.67948 | 68.55655 | 103 823 000 | 7.774 980 | 16.75069 | 36.08826 |
| 471 | 221 841 | 21.70253 | 68.62944 | 104 487 111 | 7.780 490 | 16.76256 | 36.11384 |
| 472 | 222 784 | 21.72556 | 68.70226 | 105 154 048 | 7.785 993 | 16.77441 | 36.13938 |
| 473 | 223 729 | 21.74856 | 68.77500 | 105 823 817 | 7.791 488 | 16.78625 | 36.16488 |
| 474 | 224 676 | 21.77154 | 68.84766 | 106 496 424 | 7.796 975 | 16.79807 | 36.19035 |
| **475** | 225 625 | 21.79449 | 68.92024 | 107 171 875 | 7.802 454 | 16.80988 | 36.21578 |
| 476 | 226 576 | 21.81742 | 68.99275 | 107 850 176 | 7.807 925 | 16.82167 | 36.24118 |
| 477 | 227 529 | 21.84033 | 69.06519 | 108 531 333 | 7.813 389 | 16.83344 | 36.26654 |
| 478 | 228 484 | 21.86321 | 69.13754 | 109 215 352 | 7.818 846 | 16.84519 | 36.29187 |
| 479 | 229 441 | 21.88607 | 69.20983 | 109 902 239 | 7.824 294 | 16.85693 | 36.31716 |
| **480** | 230 400 | 21.90890 | 69.28203 | 110 592 000 | 7.829 735 | 16.86865 | 36.34241 |
| 481 | 231 361 | 21.93171 | 69.35416 | 111 284 641 | 7.835 169 | 16.88036 | 36.36763 |
| 482 | 232 324 | 21.95450 | 69.42622 | 111 980 168 | 7.840 595 | 16.89205 | 36.39282 |
| 483 | 233 289 | 21.97726 | 69.49820 | 112 678 587 | 7.846 013 | 16.90372 | 36.41797 |
| 484 | 234 256 | 22.00000 | 69.57011 | 113 379 904 | 7.851 424 | 16.91538 | 36.44308 |
| **485** | 235 225 | 22.02272 | 69.64194 | 114.084 125 | 7.856 828 | 16.92702 | 36.46817 |
| 486 | 236 196 | 22.04541 | 69.71370 | 114 791 256 | 7.862 224 | 16.93865 | 36.49321 |
| 487 | 237 169 | 22.06808 | 69.78539 | 115 501 303 | 7.867 613 | 16.95026 | 36.51822 |
| 488 | 238 144 | 22.09072 | 69.85700 | 116 214 272 | 7.872 994 | 16.96185 | 36.54320 |
| 489 | 239 121 | 22.11334 | 69.92853 | 116 930 169 | 7.878 368 | 16.97343 | 36.56815 |
| **490** | 240 100 | 22.13594 | 70.00000 | 117 649 000 | 7.883 735 | 16.98499 | 36.59306 |
| 491 | 241 081 | 22.15852 | 70.07139 | 118 370 771 | 7.889 095 | 16.99654 | 36.61793 |
| 492 | 242 064 | 22.18107 | 70.14271 | 119 095 488 | 7.894 447 | 17.00807 | 36.64278 |
| 493 | 243 049 | 22.20360 | 70.21396 | 119 823 157 | 7.899 792 | 17.01959 | 36.66758 |
| 494 | 244 036 | 22.22611 | 70.28513 | 120 553 784 | 7.905 129 | 17.03108 | 36.69236 |
| **495** | 245 025 | 22.24860 | 70.35624 | 121 287 375 | 7.910 460 | 17.04257 | 36.71710 |
| 496 | 246 016 | 22.27106 | 70.42727 | 122 023 936 | 7.915 783 | 17.05404 | 36.74181 |
| 497 | 247 009 | 22.29350 | 70.49823 | 122 763 473 | 7.921 099 | 17.06549 | 36.76649 |
| 498 | 248 004 | 22.31591 | 70.56912 | 123 505 992 | 7.926 408 | 17.07693 | 36.79113 |
| 499 | 249 001 | 22.33831 | 70.63993 | 124 251 499 | 7.931 710 | 17.08835 | 36.81574 |
| **500** | 250 000 | 22.36068 | 70.71068 | 125 000 000 | 7.937 005 | 17.09976 | 36.84031 |

# SQUARES, CUBES AND ROOTS (Continued)

| $n$ | $n^2$ | $\sqrt{n}$ | $\sqrt{10n}$ | $n^3$ | $\sqrt[3]{n}$ | $\sqrt[3]{10n}$ | $\sqrt[3]{100n}$ |
|---|---|---|---|---|---|---|---|
| **500** | 250 000 | 22.36068 | 70.71068 | 125 000 000 | 7.937 005 | 17.09976 | 36.84031 |
| 501 | 251 001 | 22.38303 | 70.78135 | 125 751 501 | 7.942 293 | 17.11115 | 36.86486 |
| 502 | 252 004 | 22.40536 | 70.85196 | 126 506 008 | 7.947 574 | 17.12253 | 36.88937 |
| 503 | 253 009 | 22.42766 | 70.92249 | 127 263 527 | 7.952 848 | 17.13389 | 36.91385 |
| 504 | 254 016 | 22.44994 | 70.99296 | 128 024 064 | 7.958 114 | 17.14524 | 36.93830 |
| **505** | 255 025 | 22.47221 | 71.06335 | 128 787 625 | 7.963 374 | 17.15657 | 36.96271 |
| 506 | 256 036 | 22.49444 | 71.13368 | 129 554 216 | 7.968 627 | 17.16789 | 36.98709 |
| 507 | 257 049 | 22.51666 | 71.20393 | 130 323 843 | 7.973 873 | 17.17919 | 37.01144 |
| 508 | 258 064 | 22.53886 | 71.27412 | 131 096 512 | 7.979 112 | 17.19048 | 37.03576 |
| 509 | 259 081 | 22.56103 | 71.34424 | 131 872 229 | 7.984 344 | 17.20175 | 37.06004 |
| **510** | 260 100 | 22.58318 | 71.41428 | 132 651 000 | 7.989 570 | 17.21301 | 37.08430 |
| 511 | 261 121 | 22.60531 | 71.48426 | 133 432 831 | 7.994 788 | 17.22425 | 37.10852 |
| 512 | 262 144 | 22.62742 | 71.55418 | 134 217 728 | 8.000 000 | 17.23548 | 37.13271 |
| 513 | 263 169 | 22.64950 | 71.62402 | 135 005 697 | 8.005 205 | 17.24669 | 37.15687 |
| 514 | 264 196 | 22.67157 | 71.69379 | 135 796 744 | 8.010 403 | 17.25789 | 37.18100 |
| **515** | 265 225 | 22.69361 | 71.76350 | 136 590 875 | 8.015 595 | 17.26908 | 37.20509 |
| 516 | 266 256 | 22.71563 | 71.83314 | 137 388 096 | 8.020 779 | 17.28025 | 37.22916 |
| 517 | 267 289 | 22.73763 | 71.90271 | 138 188 413 | 8.025 957 | 17.29140 | 37.25319 |
| 518 | 268 324 | 22.75961 | 71.97222 | 138 991 832 | 8.031 129 | 17.30254 | 37.27720 |
| 519 | 269 361 | 22.78157 | 72.04165 | 139 798 359 | 8.036 293 | 17.31367 | 37.30117 |
| **520** | 270 400 | 22.80351 | 72.11103 | 140 608 000 | 8.041 452 | 17.32478 | 37.32511 |
| 521 | 271 441 | 22.82542 | 72.18033 | 141 420 761 | 8.046 603 | 17.33588 | 37.34902 |
| 522 | 272 484 | 22.84732 | 72.24957 | 142 236 648 | 8.051 748 | 17.34696 | 37.37290 |
| 523 | 273 529 | 22.86919 | 72.31874 | 143 055 667 | 8.056 886 | 17.35804 | 37.39675 |
| 524 | 274 576 | 22.89105 | 72.38784 | 143 877 824 | 8.062 018 | 17.36909 | 37.42057 |
| **525** | 275 625 | 22.91288 | 72.45688 | 144 703 125 | 8.067 143 | 17.38013 | 37.44436 |
| 526 | 276 676 | 22.93469 | 72.52586 | 145 531 576 | 8.072 262 | 17.39116 | 37.46812 |
| 527 | 277 729 | 22.95648 | 72.59477 | 146 363 183 | 8.077 374 | 17.40218 | 37.49185 |
| 528 | 278 784 | 22.97825 | 72.66361 | 147 197 952 | 8.082 480 | 17.41318 | 37.51555 |
| 529 | 279 841 | 23.00000 | 72.73239 | 148 035 889 | 8.087 579 | 17.42416 | 37.53922 |
| **530** | 280 900 | 23.02173 | 72.80110 | 148 877 000 | 8.092 672 | 17.43513 | 37.56286 |
| 531 | 281 961 | 23.04344 | 72.86975 | 149 721 291 | 8.097 759 | 17.44609 | 37.58647 |
| 532 | 283 024 | 23.06513 | 72.93833 | 150 568 768 | 8.102 839 | 17.45704 | 37.61005 |
| 533 | 284 089 | 23.08679 | 73.00685 | 151 419 437 | 8.107 913 | 17.46797 | 37.63360 |
| 534 | 285 156 | 23.10844 | 73.07530 | 152 273 304 | 8.112 980 | 17.47889 | 37.65712 |
| **535** | 286 225 | 23.13007 | 73.14369 | 153 130 375 | 8.118 041 | 17.48979 | 37.68061 |
| 536 | 287 296 | 23.15167 | 73.21202 | 153 990 656 | 8.123 096 | 17.50068 | 37.70407 |
| 537 | 288 369 | 23.17326 | 73.28028 | 154 854 153 | 8.128 145 | 17.51156 | 37.72751 |
| 538 | 289 444 | 23.19483 | 73.34848 | 155 720 872 | 8.133 187 | 17.52242 | 37.75091 |
| 539 | 290 521 | 23.21637 | 73.41662 | 156 590 819 | 8.138 223 | 17.53327 | 37.77429 |
| **540** | 291 600 | 23.23790 | 73.48469 | 157 464 000 | 8.143 253 | 17.54411 | 37.79763 |
| 541 | 292 681 | 23.25941 | 73.55270 | 158 340 421 | 8.148 276 | 17.55493 | 37.82095 |
| 542 | 293 764 | 23.28089 | 73.62065 | 159 220 088 | 8.153 294 | 17.56574 | 37.84424 |
| 543 | 294 849 | 23.30236 | 73.68853 | 160 103 007 | 8.158 305 | 17.57654 | 37.86750 |
| 544 | 295 936 | 23.32381 | 73.75636 | 160 989 184 | 8.163 310 | 17.58732 | 37.89073 |
| **545** | 297 025 | 23.34524 | 73.82412 | 161 878 625 | 8.168 309 | 17.59809 | 37.91393 |
| 546 | 298 116 | 23.36664 | 73.89181 | 162 771 336 | 8.173 302 | 17.60885 | 37.93711 |
| 547 | 299 209 | 23.38803 | 73.95945 | 163 667 323 | 8.178 289 | 17.61959 | 37.96025 |
| 548 | 300 304 | 23.40940 | 74.02702 | 164 566 592 | 8.183 269 | 17.63032 | 37.98337 |
| 549 | 301 401 | 23.43075 | 74.09453 | 165 469 149 | 8.188 244 | 17.64104 | 38.00646 |
| **550** | 302 500 | 23.45208 | 74.16198 | 166 375 000 | 8.193 213 | 17.65174 | 38.02952 |

195

| $n$ | $n^2$ | $\sqrt{n}$ | $\sqrt{10n}$ | $n^3$ | $\sqrt[3]{n}$ | $\sqrt[3]{10n}$ | $\sqrt[3]{100n}$ |
|---|---|---|---|---|---|---|---|
| 550 | 302 500 | 23.45208 | 74.16198 | 166 375 000 | 8.193 213 | 17.65174 | 38.02952 |
| 551 | 303 601 | 23.47339 | 74.22937 | 167 284 151 | 8.198 175 | 17.66243 | 38.05256 |
| 552 | 304 704 | 23.49468 | 74.29670 | 168 196 608 | 8.203 132 | 17.67311 | 38.07557 |
| 553 | 305 809 | 23.51595 | 74.36397 | 169 112 377 | 8.208 082 | 17.68378 | 38.09854 |
| 554 | 306 916 | 23.53720 | 74.43118 | 170 031 464 | 8.213 027 | 17.69443 | 38.12149 |
| 555 | 308 025 | 23.55844 | 74.49832 | 170 953 875 | 8.217 966 | 17.70507 | 38.14442 |
| 556 | 309 136 | 23.57965 | 74.56541 | 171 879 616 | 8.222 899 | 17.71570 | 38.16731 |
| 557 | 310 249 | 23.60085 | 74.63243 | 172 808 693 | 8.227 825 | 17.72631 | 38.19018 |
| 558 | 311 364 | 23.62202 | 74.69940 | 173 741 112 | 8.232 746 | 17.73691 | 38.21302 |
| 559 | 312 481 | 23.64318 | 74.76630 | 174 676 879 | 8.237 661 | 17.74750 | 38.23584 |
| 560 | 313 600 | 23.66432 | 74.83315 | 175 616 000 | 8.242 571 | 17.75808 | 38.25862 |
| 561 | 314 721 | 23.68544 | 74.89993 | 176 558 481 | 8.247 474 | 17.76864 | 38.28138 |
| 562 | 315 844 | 23.70654 | 74.96666 | 177 504 328 | 8.252 372 | 17.77920 | 38.30412 |
| 563 | 316 969 | 23.72762 | 75.03333 | 178 453 547 | 8.257 263 | 17.78973 | 38.32682 |
| 564 | 318 096 | 23.74868 | 75.09993 | 179 406 144 | 8.262 149 | 17.80026 | 38.34950 |
| 565 | 319 225 | 23.76973 | 75.16648 | 180 362 125 | 8.267 029 | 17.81077 | 38.37215 |
| 566 | 320 356 | 23.79075 | 75.23297 | 181 321 496 | 8.271 904 | 17.82128 | 38.39478 |
| 567 | 321 489 | 23.81176 | 75.29940 | 182 284 263 | 8.276 773 | 17.83177 | 38.41737 |
| 568 | 322 624 | 23.83275 | 75.36577 | 183 250 432 | 8.281 635 | 17.84224 | 38.43995 |
| 569 | 323 761 | 23.85372 | 75.43209 | 184 220 009 | 8.286 493 | 17.85271 | 38.46249 |
| 570 | 324 900 | 23.87467 | 75.49834 | 185 193 000 | 8.291 344 | 17.86316 | 38.48501 |
| 571 | 326 041 | 23.89561 | 75.56454 | 186 169 411 | 8.296 190 | 17.87360 | 38.50750 |
| 572 | 327 184 | 23.91652 | 75.63068 | 187 149 248 | 8.301 031 | 17.88403 | 38.52997 |
| 573 | 328 329 | 23.93742 | 75.69676 | 188 132 517 | 8.305 865 | 17.89444 | 38.55241 |
| 574 | 329 476 | 23.95830 | 75.76279 | 189 119 224 | 8.310 694 | 17.90485 | 38.57482 |
| 575 | 330 625 | 23.97916 | 75.82875 | 190 109 375 | 8.315 517 | 17.91524 | 38.59721 |
| 576 | 331 776 | 24.00000 | 75.89466 | 191 102 976 | 8.320 335 | 17.92562 | 38.61958 |
| 577 | 332 929 | 24.02082 | 75.96052 | 192 100 033 | 8.325 148 | 17.93599 | 38.64191 |
| 578 | 334 084 | 24.04163 | 76.02631 | 193 100 552 | 8.329 954 | 17.94634 | 38.66422 |
| 579 | 335 241 | 24.06242 | 76.09205 | 194 104 539 | 8.334 755 | 17.95669 | 38.68651 |
| 580 | 336 400 | 24.08319 | 76.15773 | 195 112 000 | 8.339 551 | 17.96702 | 38.70877 |
| 581 | 337 561 | 24.10394 | 76.22336 | 196 122 941 | 8.344 341 | 17.97734 | 38.73100 |
| 582 | 338 724 | 24.12468 | 76.28892 | 197 137 368 | 8.349 126 | 17.98765 | 38.75321 |
| 583 | 339 889 | 24.14539 | 76.35444 | 198 155 287 | 8.353 905 | 17.99794 | 38.77539 |
| 584 | 341 056 | 24.16609 | 76.41989 | 199 176 704 | 8.358 678 | 18.00823 | 38.79755 |
| 585 | 342 225 | 24.18677 | 76.48529 | 200 201 625 | 8.363 447 | 18.01850 | 38.81968 |
| 586 | 343 396 | 24.20744 | 76.55064 | 201 230 056 | 8.368 209 | 18.02876 | 38.84179 |
| 587 | 344 569 | 24.22808 | 76.61593 | 202 262 003 | 8.372 967 | 18.03901 | 38.86387 |
| 588 | 345 744 | 24.24871 | 76.68116 | 203 297 472 | 8.377 719 | 18.04925 | 38.88593 |
| 589 | 346 921 | 24.26932 | 76.74634 | 204 336 469 | 8.382 465 | 18.05947 | 38.90796 |
| 590 | 348 100 | 24.28992 | 76.81146 | 205 379 000 | 8.387 207 | 18.06969 | 38.92996 |
| 591 | 349 281 | 24.31049 | 76.87652 | 206 425 071 | 8.391 942 | 18.07989 | 38.95195 |
| 592 | 350 464 | 24.33105 | 76.94154 | 207 474 688 | 8.396 673 | 18.09008 | 38.97390 |
| 593 | 351 649 | 24.35159 | 77.00649 | 208 527 857 | 8.401 398 | 18.10026 | 38.99584 |
| 594 | 352 836 | 24.37212 | 77.07140 | 209 584 584 | 8.406 118 | 18.11043 | 39.01774 |
| 595 | 354 025 | 24.39262 | 77.13624 | 210 644 875 | 8.410 833 | 18.12059 | 39.03963 |
| 596 | 355 216 | 24.41311 | 77.20104 | 211 708 736 | 8.415 542 | 18.13074 | 39.06149 |
| 597 | 356 409 | 24.43358 | 77.26578 | 212 776 173 | 8.420 246 | 18.14087 | 39.08332 |
| 598 | 357 604 | 24.45404 | 77.33046 | 213 847 192 | 8.424 945 | 18.15099 | 39.10513 |
| 599 | 358 801 | 24.47448 | 77.39509 | 214 921 799 | 8.429 638 | 18.16111 | 39.12692 |
| 600 | 360 000 | 24.49490 | 77.45967 | 216 000 000 | 8.434 327 | 18.17121 | 39.14868 |

| $n$ | $n^2$ | $\sqrt{n}$ | $\sqrt{10n}$ | $n^3$ | $\sqrt[3]{n}$ | $\sqrt[3]{10n}$ | $\sqrt[3]{100n}$ |
|---|---|---|---|---|---|---|---|
| **600** | 360 000 | 24.49490 | 77.45967 | 216 000 000 | 8.434 327 | 18.17121 | 39.14868 |
| 601 | 361 201 | 24.51530 | 77.52419 | 217 081 801 | 8.439 010 | 18.18130 | 39.17041 |
| 602 | 362 404 | 24.53569 | 77.58866 | 218 167 208 | 8.443 688 | 18.19137 | 39.19213 |
| 603 | 363 609 | 24.55606 | 77.65307 | 219 256 227 | 8.448 361 | 18.20144 | 39.21382 |
| 604 | 364 816 | 24.57641 | 77.71744 | 220 348 864 | 8.453 028 | 18.21150 | 39.23548 |
| **605** | 366 025 | 24.59675 | 77.78175 | 221 445 125 | 8.457 691 | 18.22154 | 39.25712 |
| 606 | 367 236 | 24.61707 | 77.84600 | 222 545 016 | 8.462 348 | 18.23158 | 39.27874 |
| 607 | 368 449 | 24.63737 | 77.91020 | 223 648 543 | 8.467 000 | 18.24160 | 39.30033 |
| 608 | 369 664 | 24.65766 | 77.97435 | 224 755 712 | 8.471 647 | 18.25161 | 39.32190 |
| 609 | 370 881 | 24.67793 | 78.03845 | 225 866 529 | 8.476 289 | 18.26161 | 39.34345 |
| **610** | 372 100 | 24.69818 | 78.10250 | 226 981 000 | 8.480 926 | 18.27160 | 39.36497 |
| 611 | 373 321 | 24.71841 | 78.16649 | 228 099 131 | 8.485 558 | 18.28158 | 39.38647 |
| 612 | 374 544 | 24.73863 | 78.23043 | 229 220 928 | 8.490 185 | 18.29155 | 39.40795 |
| 613 | 375 769 | 24.75884 | 78.29432 | 230 346 397 | 8.494 807 | 18.30151 | 39.42940 |
| 614 | 376 996 | 24.77902 | 78.35815 | 231 475 544 | 8.499 423 | 18.31145 | 39.45083 |
| **615** | 378 225 | 24.79919 | 78.42194 | 232 608 375 | 8.504 035 | 18.32139 | 39.47223 |
| 616 | 379 456 | 24.81935 | 78.48567 | 233 744 896 | 8.508 642 | 18.33131 | 39.49362 |
| 617 | 380 689 | 24.83948 | 78.54935 | 234 885 113 | 8.513 243 | 18.34123 | 39.51498 |
| 618 | 381 924 | 24.85961 | 78.61298 | 236 029 032 | 8.517 840 | 18.35113 | 39.53631 |
| 619 | 383 161 | 24.87971 | 78.67655 | 237 176 659 | 8.522 432 | 18.36102 | 39.55763 |
| **620** | 384 400 | 24.89980 | 78.74008 | 238 328 000 | 8.527 019 | 18.37091 | 39.57892 |
| 621 | 385 641 | 24.91987 | 78.80355 | 239 483 061 | 8.531 601 | 18.38078 | 39.60018 |
| 622 | 386 884 | 24.93993 | 78.86698 | 240 641 848 | 8.536 178 | 18.39064 | 39.62143 |
| 623 | 388 129 | 24.95997 | 78.93035 | 241 804 367 | 8.540 750 | 18.40049 | 39.64265 |
| 624 | 389 376 | 24.97999 | 78.99367 | 242 970 624 | 8.545 317 | 18.41033 | 39.66385 |
| **625** | 390 625 | 25.00000 | 79.05694 | 244 140 625 | 8.549 880 | 18.42016 | 39.68503 |
| 626 | 391 876 | 25.01999 | 79.12016 | 245 314 376 | 8.554 437 | 18.42998 | 39.70618 |
| 627 | 393 129 | 25.03997 | 79.18333 | 246 491 883 | 8.558 990 | 18.43978 | 39.72731 |
| 628 | 394 384 | 25.05993 | 79.24645 | 247 673 152 | 8.563 538 | 18.44958 | 39.74842 |
| 629 | 395 641 | 25.07987 | 79.30952 | 248 858 189 | 8.568 081 | 18.45937 | 39.76951 |
| **630** | 396 900 | 25.09980 | 79.37254 | 250 047 000 | 8.572 619 | 18.46915 | 39.79057 |
| 631 | 398 161 | 25.11971 | 79.43551 | 251 239 591 | 8.577 152 | 18.47891 | 39.81161 |
| 632 | 399 424 | 25.13961 | 79.49843 | 252 435 968 | 8.581 681 | 18.48867 | 39.83263 |
| 633 | 400 689 | 25.15949 | 79.56130 | 253 636 137 | 8.586 205 | 18.49842 | 39.85363 |
| 634 | 401 956 | 25.17936 | 79.62412 | 254 840 104 | 8.590 724 | 18.50815 | 39.87461 |
| **635** | 403 225 | 25.19921 | 79.68689 | 256 047 875 | 8.595 238 | 18.51788 | 39.89556 |
| 636 | 404 496 | 25.21904 | 79.74961 | 257 259 456 | 8.599 748 | 18.52759 | 39.91649 |
| 637 | 405 769 | 25.23886 | 79.81228 | 258 474 853 | 8.604 252 | 18.53730 | 39.93740 |
| 638 | 407 044 | 25.25866 | 79.87490 | 259 694 072 | 8.608 753 | 18.54700 | 39.95829 |
| 639 | 408 321 | 25.27845 | 79.93748 | 260 917 119 | 8.613 248 | 18.55668 | 39.97916 |
| **640** | 409 600 | 25.29822 | 80.00000 | 262 144 000 | 8.617 739 | 18.56636 | 40.00000 |
| 641 | 410 881 | 25.31798 | 80.06248 | 263 374 721 | 8.622 225 | 18.57602 | 40.02082 |
| 642 | 412 164 | 25.33772 | 80.12490 | 264 609 288 | 8.626 706 | 18.58568 | 40.04162 |
| 643 | 413 449 | 25.35744 | 80.18728 | 265 847 707 | 8.631 183 | 18.59532 | 40.06240 |
| 644 | 414 736 | 25.37716 | 80.24961 | 267 089 984 | 8.635 655 | 18.60495 | 40.08316 |
| **645** | 416 025 | 25.39685 | 80.31189 | 268 336 125 | 8.640 123 | 18.61458 | 40.10390 |
| 646 | 417 316 | 25.41653 | 80.37413 | 269 586 136 | 8.644 585 | 18.62419 | 40.12461 |
| 647 | 418 609 | 25.43619 | 80.43631 | 270 840 023 | 8.649 044 | 18.63380 | 40.14530 |
| 648 | 419 904 | 25.45584 | 80.49845 | 272 097 792 | 8.653 497 | 18.64340 | 40.16598 |
| 649 | 421 201 | 25.47548 | 80.56054 | 273 359 449 | 8.657 947 | 18.65298 | 40.18663 |
| **650** | 422 500 | 25.49510 | 80.62258 | 274 625 000 | 8.662 391 | 18.66256 | 40.20726 |

| $n$ | $n^2$ | $\sqrt{n}$ | $\sqrt{10n}$ | $n^3$ | $\sqrt[3]{n}$ | $\sqrt[3]{10n}$ | $\sqrt[3]{100n}$ |
|---|---|---|---|---|---|---|---|
| **650** | 422 500 | 25.49510 | 80.62258 | 274 625 000 | 8.662 391 | 18.66256 | 40.20726 |
| 651 | 423 801 | 25.51470 | 80.68457 | 275 894 451 | 8.666 831 | 18.67212 | 40.22787 |
| 652 | 425 104 | 25.53429 | 80.74652 | 277 167 808 | 8.671 266 | 18.68168 | 40.24845 |
| 653 | 426 409 | 25.55386 | 80.80842 | 278 445 077 | 8.675 697 | 18.69122 | 40.26902 |
| 654 | 427 716 | 25.57342 | 80.87027 | 279 726 264 | 8.680 124 | 18.70076 | 40.28957 |
| **655** | 429 025 | 25.59297 | 80.93207 | 281 011 375 | 8.684 546 | 18.71029 | 40.31009 |
| 656 | 430 336 | 25.61250 | 80.99383 | 282 300 416 | 8.688 963 | 18.71980 | 40.33059 |
| 657 | 431 649 | 25.63201 | 81.05554 | 283 593 393 | 8.693 376 | 18.72931 | 40.35108 |
| 658 | 432 964 | 25.65151 | 81.11720 | 284 890 312 | 8.697 784 | 18.73881 | 40.37154 |
| 659 | 434 281 | 25.67100 | 81.17881 | 286 191 179 | 8.702 188 | 18.74830 | 40.39198 |
| **660** | 435 600 | 25.69047 | 81.24038 | 287 496 000 | 8.706 588 | 18.75777 | 40.41240 |
| 661 | 436 921 | 25.70992 | 81.30191 | 288 804 781 | 8.710 983 | 18.76724 | 40.43280 |
| 662 | 438 244 | 25.72936 | 81.36338 | 290 117 528 | 8.715 373 | 18.77670 | 40.45318 |
| 663 | 439 569 | 25.74879 | 81.42481 | 291 434 247 | 8.719 760 | 18.78615 | 40.47354 |
| 664 | 440 896 | 25.76820 | 81.48620 | 292 754 944 | 8.724 141 | 18.79559 | 40.49388 |
| **665** | 442 225 | 25.78759 | 81.54753 | 294 079 625 | 8.728 519 | 18.80502 | 40.51420 |
| 666 | 443 556 | 25.80698 | 81.60882 | 295 408 296 | 8.732 892 | 18.81444 | 40.53449 |
| 667 | 444 889 | 25.82634 | 81.67007 | 296 740 963 | 8.737 260 | 18.82386 | 40.55477 |
| 668 | 446 224 | 25.84570 | 81.73127 | 298 077 632 | 8.741 625 | 18.83326 | 40.57503 |
| 669 | 447 561 | 25.86503 | 81.79242 | 299 418 309 | 8.745 985 | 18.84265 | 40.59526 |
| **670** | 448 900 | 25.88436 | 81.85353 | 300 763 000 | 8.750 340 | 18.85204 | 40.61548 |
| 671 | 450 241 | 25.90367 | 81.91459 | 302 111 711 | 8.754 691 | 18.86141 | 40.63568 |
| 672 | 451 584 | 25.92296 | 81.97561 | 303 464 448 | 8.759 038 | 18.87078 | 40.65585 |
| 673 | 452 929 | 25.94224 | 82.03658 | 304 821 217 | 8.763 381 | 18.88013 | 40.67601 |
| 674 | 454 276 | 25.96151 | 82.09750 | 306 182 024 | 8.767 719 | 18.88948 | 40.69615 |
| **675** | 455 625 | 25.98076 | 82.15838 | 307 546 875 | 8.772 053 | 18.89882 | 40.71626 |
| 676 | 456 976 | 26.00000 | 82.21922 | 308 915 776 | 8.776 383 | 18.90814 | 40.73636 |
| 677 | 458 329 | 26.01922 | 82.28001 | 310 288 733 | 8.780 708 | 18.91746 | 40.75644 |
| 678 | 459 684 | 26.03843 | 82.34076 | 311 665 752 | 8.785 030 | 18.92677 | 40.77650 |
| 679 | 461 041 | 26.05763 | 82.40146 | 313 046 839 | 8.789 347 | 18.93607 | 40.79653 |
| **680** | 462 400 | 26.07681 | 82.46211 | 314 432 000 | 8.793 659 | 18.94536 | 40.81655 |
| 681 | 463 761 | 26.09598 | 82.52272 | 315 821 241 | 8.797 968 | 18.95465 | 40.83655 |
| 682 | 465 124 | 26.11513 | 82.58329 | 317 214 568 | 8.802 272 | 18.96392 | 40.85653 |
| 683 | 466 489 | 26.13427 | 82.64381 | 318 611 987 | 8.806 572 | 18.97318 | 40.87649 |
| 684 | 467 856 | 26.15339 | 82.70429 | 320 013 504 | 8.810 868 | 18.98244 | 40.89643 |
| **685** | 469 225 | 26.17250 | 82.76473 | 321 419 125 | 8.815 160 | 18.99169 | 40.91635 |
| 686 | 470 596 | 26.19160 | 82.82512 | 322 828 856 | 8.819 447 | 19.00092 | 40.93625 |
| 687 | 471 969 | 26.21068 | 82.88546 | 324 242 703 | 8.823 731 | 19.01015 | 40.95613 |
| 688 | 473 344 | 26.22975 | 82.94577 | 325 660 672 | 8.828 010 | 19.01937 | 40.97599 |
| 689 | 474 721 | 26.24881 | 83.00602 | 327 082 769 | 8.832 285 | 19.02858 | 40.99584 |
| **690** | 476 100 | 26.26785 | 83.06624 | 328 509 000 | 8.836 556 | 19.03778 | 41.01566 |
| 691 | 477 481 | 26.28688 | 83.12641 | 329 939 371 | 8.840 823 | 19.04698 | 41.03546 |
| 692 | 478 864 | 26.30589 | 83.18654 | 331 373 888 | 8.845 085 | 19.05616 | 41.05525 |
| 693 | 480 249 | 26.32489 | 83.24662 | 332 812 557 | 8.849 344 | 19.06533 | 41.07502 |
| 694 | 481 636 | 26.34388 | 83.30666 | 334 255 384 | 8.853 599 | 19.07450 | 41.09476 |
| **695** | 483 025 | 26.36285 | 83.36666 | 335 702 375 | 8.857 849 | 19.08366 | 41.11449 |
| 696 | 484 416 | 26.38181 | 83.42661 | 337 153 536 | 8.862 095 | 19.09281 | 41.13420 |
| 697 | 485 809 | 26.40076 | 83.48653 | 338 608 873 | 8.866 338 | 19.10195 | 41.15389 |
| 698 | 487 204 | 26.41969 | 83.54639 | 340 068 392 | 8.870 576 | 19.11108 | 41.17357 |
| 699 | 488 601 | 26.43861 | 83.60622 | 341 532 099 | 8.874 810 | 19.12020 | 41.19322 |
| **700** | 490 000 | 26.45751 | 83.66600 | 343 000 000 | 8.879 040 | 19.12931 | 41.21285 |

| $n$ | $n^2$ | $\sqrt{n}$ | $\sqrt{10n}$ | $n^3$ | $\sqrt[3]{n}$ | $\sqrt[3]{10n}$ | $\sqrt[3]{100n}$ |
|---|---|---|---|---|---|---|---|
| **700** | 490 000 | 26.45751 | 83.66600 | 343 000 000 | 8.879 040 | 19.12931 | 41 21285 |
| 701 | 491 401 | 26.47640 | 83.72574 | 344 472 101 | 8.883 266 | 19.13842 | 41.23247 |
| 702 | 492 804 | 26.49528 | 83.78544 | 345 948 408 | 8.887 488 | 19.14751 | 41.25207 |
| 703 | 494 209 | 26.51415 | 83.84510 | 347 428 927 | 8.891 706 | 19.15660 | 41.27164 |
| 704 | 495 616 | 26.53300 | 83.90471 | 348 913 664 | 8.895 920 | 19.16568 | 41.29120 |
| 705 | 497 025 | 26.55184 | 83.96428 | 350 402 625 | 8.900 130 | 19.17475 | 41.31075 |
| 706 | 498 436 | 26.57066 | 84.02381 | 351 895 816 | 8.904 337 | 19.18381 | 41.33027 |
| 707 | 499 849 | 26.58947 | 84.08329 | 353 393 243 | 8.908 539 | 19.19286 | 41.34977 |
| 708 | 501 264 | 26.60827 | 84.14274 | 354 894 912 | 8.912 737 | 19.20191 | 41.36926 |
| 709 | 502 681 | 26.62705 | 84.20214 | 356 400 829 | 8.916 931 | 19.21095 | 41.38873 |
| **710** | 504 100 | 26.64583 | 84.26150 | 357 911 000 | 8.921 121 | 19.21997 | 41.40818 |
| 711 | 505 521 | 26.66458 | 84.32082 | 359 425 431 | 8.925 308 | 19.22899 | 41.42761 |
| 712 | 506 944 | 26.68333 | 84.38009 | 360 944 128 | 8.929 490 | 19.23800 | 41.44702 |
| 713 | 508 369 | 26.70206 | 84.43933 | 362 467 097 | 8.933 669 | 19.24701 | 41.46642 |
| 714 | 509 796 | 26.72078 | 84.49852 | 363 994 344 | 8.937 843 | 19.25600 | 41.48579 |
| 715 | 511 225 | 26.73948 | 84.55767 | 365 525 875 | 8.942 014 | 19.26499 | 41.50515 |
| 716 | 512 656 | 26.75818 | 84.61678 | 367 061 696 | 8.946 181 | 19.27396 | 41.52449 |
| 717 | 514 089 | 26.77686 | 84.67585 | 368 601 813 | 8.950 344 | 19.28293 | 41.54382 |
| 718 | 515 524 | 26.79552 | 84.73488 | 370 146 232 | 8.954 503 | 19.29189 | 41.56312 |
| 719 | 516 961 | 26.81418 | 84.79387 | 371 694 959 | 8.958 658 | 19.30084 | 41.58241 |
| **720** | 518 400 | 26.83282 | 84.85281 | 373 248 000 | 8.962 809 | 19.30979 | 41.60168 |
| 721 | 519 841 | 26.85144 | 84.91172 | 374 805 361 | 8.966 957 | 19.31872 | 41.62093 |
| 722 | 521 284 | 26.87006 | 84.97058 | 376 367 048 | 8.971 101 | 19.32765 | 41.64016 |
| 723 | 522 729 | 26.88866 | 85.02941 | 377 933 067 | 8.975 241 | 19.33657 | 41.65938 |
| 724 | 524 176 | 26.90725 | 85.08819 | 379 503 424 | 8.979 377 | 19.34548 | 41.67857 |
| 725 | 525 625 | 26.92582 | 85.14693 | 381 078 125 | 8.983 509 | 19.35438 | 41.69775 |
| 726 | 527 076 | 26.94439 | 85.20563 | 382 657 176 | 8.987 637 | 19.36328 | 41.71692 |
| 727 | 528 529 | 26.96294 | 85.26429 | 384 240 583 | 8.991 762 | 19.37216 | 41.73606 |
| 728 | 529 984 | 26.98148 | 85.32292 | 385 828 352 | 8.995 883 | 19.38104 | 41.75519 |
| 729 | 531 441 | 27.00000 | 85.38150 | 387 420 489 | 9.000 000 | 19.38991 | 41.77430 |
| **730** | 532 900 | 27.01851 | 85.44004 | 389 017 000 | 9.004 113 | 19.39877 | 41.79339 |
| 731 | 534 361 | 27.03701 | 85.49854 | 390 617 891 | 9.008 223 | 19.40763 | 41.81247 |
| 732 | 535 824 | 27.05550 | 85.55700 | 392 223 168 | 9.012 329 | 19.41647 | 41.83152 |
| 733 | 537 289 | 27.07397 | 85.61542 | 393 832 837 | 9.016 431 | 19.42531 | 41.85056 |
| 734 | 538 756 | 27.09243 | 85.67380 | 395 446 904 | 9.020 529 | 19.43414 | 41.86959 |
| 735 | 540 225 | 27.11088 | 85.73214 | 397 065 375 | 9.024 624 | 19.44296 | 41.88859 |
| 736 | 541 696 | 27.12932 | 85.79044 | 398 688 256 | 9.028 715 | 19.45178 | 41.90758 |
| 737 | 543 169 | 27.14774 | 85.84870 | 400 315 553 | 9.032 802 | 19.46058 | 41.92655 |
| 738 | 544 644 | 27.16616 | 85.90693 | 401 947 272 | 9.036 886 | 19.46938 | 41.94551 |
| 739 | 546 121 | 27.18455 | 85.96511 | 403 583 419 | 9.040 966 | 19.47817 | 41.96444 |
| **740** | 547 600 | 27.20294 | 86.02325 | 405 224 000 | 9.045 042 | 19.48695 | 41.98336 |
| 741 | 549 081 | 27.22132 | 86.08136 | 406 869 021 | 9.049 114 | 19.49573 | 42.00227 |
| 742 | 550 564 | 27.23968 | 86.13942 | 408 518 488 | 9.053 183 | 19.50449 | 42.02115 |
| 743 | 552 049 | 27.25803 | 86.19745 | 410 172 407 | 9.057 248 | 19.51325 | 42.04002 |
| 744 | 553 536 | 27.27636 | 86.25543 | 411 830 784 | 9.061 310 | 19.52200 | 42.05887 |
| 745 | 555 025 | 27.29469 | 86.31338 | 413 493 625 | 9.065 368 | 19.53074 | 42.07771 |
| 746 | 556 516 | 27.31300 | 86.37129 | 415 160 936 | 9.069 422 | 19.53948 | 42.09653 |
| 747 | 558 009 | 27.33130 | 86.42916 | 416 832 723 | 9.073 473 | 19.54820 | 42.11533 |
| 748 | 559 504 | 27.34959 | 86.48699 | 418 508 992 | 9.077 520 | 19.55692 | 42.13411 |
| 749 | 561 001 | 27.36786 | 86.54479 | 420 189 749 | 9.081 563 | 19.56563 | 42.15288 |
| **750** | 562 500 | 27.38613 | 86.60254 | 421 875 000 | 9.085 603 | 19.57434 | 42.17163 |

| $n$ | $n^2$ | $\sqrt{n}$ | $\sqrt{10n}$ | $n^3$ | $\sqrt[3]{n}$ | $\sqrt[3]{10n}$ | $\sqrt[3]{100n}$ |
|---|---|---|---|---|---|---|---|
| **750** | 562 500 | 27.38613 | 86.60254 | 421 875 000 | 9.085 603 | 19.57434 | 42.17163 |
| 751 | 564 001 | 27.40438 | 86.66026 | 423 564 751 | 9.089 639 | 19.58303 | 42.19037 |
| 752 | 565 504 | 27.42262 | 86.71793 | 425 259 008 | 9.093 672 | 19.59172 | 42.20909 |
| 753 | 567 009 | 27.44085 | 86.77557 | 426 957 777 | 9.097 701 | 19.60040 | 42.22779 |
| 754 | 568 516 | 27.45906 | 86.83317 | 428 661 064 | 9.101 727 | 19.60908 | 42.24647 |
| **755** | 570 025 | 27.47726 | 86.89074 | 430 368 875 | 9.105 748 | 19.61774 | 42.26514 |
| 756 | 571 536 | 27.49545 | 86.94826 | 432 081 216 | 9.109 767 | 19.62640 | 42.28379 |
| 757 | 573 049 | 27.51363 | 87.00575 | 433 798 093 | 9.113 782 | 19.63505 | 42.30243 |
| 758 | 574 564 | 27.53180 | 87.06320 | 435 519 512 | 9.117 793 | 19.64369 | 42.32105 |
| 759 | 576 081 | 27.54995 | 87.12061 | 437 245 479 | 9.121 801 | 19.65232 | 42.33965 |
| **760** | 577 600 | 27.56810 | 87.17798 | 438 976 000 | 9.125 805 | 19.66095 | 42.35824 |
| 761 | 579 121 | 27.58623 | 87.23531 | 440 711 081 | 9.129 806 | 19.66957 | 42.37681 |
| 762 | 580 644 | 27.60435 | 87.29261 | 442 450 728 | 9.133 803 | 19.67818 | 42.39536 |
| 763 | 582 169 | 27.62245 | 87.34987 | 444 194 947 | 9.137 797 | 19.68679 | 42.41390 |
| 764 | 583 696 | 27.64055 | 87.40709 | 445 943 744 | 9.141 787 | 19.69538 | 42.43242 |
| **765** | 585 225 | 27.65863 | 87.46428 | 447 697 125 | 9.145 774 | 19.70397 | 42.45092 |
| 766 | 586 756 | 27.67671 | 87.52143 | 449 455 096 | 9.149 758 | 19.71256 | 42.46941 |
| 767 | 588 289 | 27.69476 | 87.57854 | 451 217 663 | 9.153 738 | 19.72113 | 42.48789 |
| 768 | 589 824 | 27.71281 | 87.63561 | 452 984 832 | 9.157 714 | 19.72970 | 42.50634 |
| 769 | 591 361 | 27.73085 | 87.69265 | 454 756 609 | 9.161 687 | 19.73826 | 42.52478 |
| **770** | 592 900 | 27.74887 | 87.74964 | 456 533 000 | 9.165 656 | 19.74681 | 42.54321 |
| 771 | 594 441 | 27.76689 | 87.80661 | 458 314 011 | 9.169 623 | 19.75535 | 42.56162 |
| 772 | 595 984 | 27.78489 | 87.86353 | 460 099 648 | 9.173 585 | 19.76389 | 42.58001 |
| 773 | 597 529 | 27.80288 | 87.92042 | 461 889 917 | 9.177 544 | 19.77242 | 42.59839 |
| 774 | 599 076 | 27.82086 | 87.97727 | 463 684 824 | 9.181 500 | 19.78094 | 42.61675 |
| **775** | 600 625 | 27.83882 | 88.03408 | 465 484 375 | 9.185 453 | 19.78946 | 42.63509 |
| 776 | 602 176 | 27.85678 | 88.09086 | 467 288 576 | 9.189 402 | 19.79797 | 42.65342 |
| 777 | 603 729 | 27.87472 | 88.14760 | 469 097 433 | 9.193 347 | 19.80647 | 42.67174 |
| 778 | 605 284 | 27.89265 | 88.20431 | 470 910 952 | 9.197 290 | 19.81496 | 42.69004 |
| 779 | 606 841 | 27.91057 | 88.26098 | 472 729 139 | 9.201 229 | 19.82345 | 42.70832 |
| **780** | 608 400 | 27.92848 | 88.31761 | 474 552 000 | 9.205 164 | 19.83192 | 42.72659 |
| 781 | 609 961 | 27.94638 | 88.37420 | 476 379 541 | 9.209 096 | 19.84040 | 42.74484 |
| 782 | 611 524 | 27.96426 | 88.43076 | 478 211 768 | 9.213 025 | 19.84886 | 42.76307 |
| 783 | 613 089 | 27.98214 | 88.48729 | 480 048 687 | 9.216 950 | 19.85732 | 42.78129 |
| 784 | 614 656 | 28.00000 | 88.54377 | 481 890 304 | 9.220 873 | 19.86577 | 42.79950 |
| **785** | 616 225 | 28.01785 | 88.60023 | 483 736 625 | 9.224 791 | 19.87421 | 42.81769 |
| 786 | 617 796 | 28.03569 | 88.65664 | 485 587 656 | 9.228 707 | 19.88265 | 42.83586 |
| 787 | 619 369 | 28.05352 | 88.71302 | 487 443 403 | 9.232 619 | 19.89107 | 42.85402 |
| 788 | 620 944 | 28.07134 | 88.76936 | 489 303 872 | 9.236 528 | 19.89950 | 42.87216 |
| 789 | 622 521 | 28.08914 | 88.82567 | 491 169 069 | 9.240 433 | 19.90791 | 42.89029 |
| **790** | 624 100 | 28.10694 | 88.88194 | 493 039 000 | 9.244 335 | 19.91632 | 42.90840 |
| 791 | 625 681 | 28.12472 | 88.93818 | 494 913 671 | 9.248 234 | 19.92472 | 42.92650 |
| 792 | 627 264 | 28.14249 | 88.99438 | 496 793 088 | 9.252 130 | 19.93311 | 42.94458 |
| 793 | 628 849 | 28.16026 | 89.05055 | 498 677 257 | 9.256 022 | 19.94150 | 42.96265 |
| 794 | 630 436 | 28.17801 | 89.10668 | 500 566 184 | 9.259 911 | 19.94987 | 42.98070 |
| **795** | 632 025 | 28.19574 | 89.16277 | 502 459 875 | 9.263 797 | 19.95825 | 42.99874 |
| 796 | 633 616 | 28.21347 | 89.21883 | 504 358 336 | 9.267 680 | 19.96661 | 43.01676 |
| 797 | 635 209 | 28.23119 | 89.27486 | 506 261 573 | 9.271 559 | 19.97497 | 43.03477 |
| 798 | 636 804 | 28.24889 | 89.33085 | 508 169 592 | 9.275 435 | 19.98332 | 43.05276 |
| 799 | 638 401 | 28.26659 | 89.38680 | 510 082 399 | 9.279 308 | 19.99166 | 43.07073 |
| **800** | 640 000 | 28.28427 | 89.44272 | 512 000 000 | 9.283 178 | 20.00000 | 43.08869 |

| $n$ | $n^2$ | $\sqrt{n}$ | $\sqrt{10n}$ | $n^3$ | $\sqrt[3]{n}$ | $\sqrt[3]{10n}$ | $\sqrt[3]{100n}$ |
|---|---|---|---|---|---|---|---|
| 800 | 640 000 | 28.28427 | 89.44272 | 512 000 000 | 9.283 178 | 20.00000 | 43.08869 |
| 801 | 641 601 | 28.30194 | 89.49860 | 513 922 401 | 9.287 044 | 20.00833 | 43.10664 |
| 802 | 643 204 | 28.31960 | 89.55445 | 515 849 608 | 9.290 907 | 20.01665 | 43.12457 |
| 803 | 644 809 | 28.33725 | 89.61027 | 517 781 627 | 9.294 767 | 20.02497 | 43.14249 |
| 804 | 646 416 | 28.35489 | 89.66605 | 519 718 464 | 9.298 624 | 20.03328 | 43.16039 |
| 805 | 648 025 | 28.37252 | 89.72179 | 521 660 125 | 9.302 477 | 20.04158 | 43.17828 |
| 806 | 649 636 | 28.39014 | 89.77750 | 523 606 616 | 9.306 328 | 20.04988 | 43.19615 |
| 807 | 651 249 | 28.40775 | 89.83318 | 525 557 943 | 9.310 175 | 20.05816 | 43.21400 |
| 808 | 652 864 | 28.42534 | 89.88882 | 527 514 112 | 9.314 019 | 20.06645 | 43.23185 |
| 809 | 654 481 | 28.44293 | 89.94443 | 529 475 129 | 9.317 860 | 20.07472 | 43.24967 |
| 810 | 656 100 | 28.46050 | 90.00000 | 531 441 000 | 9.321 698 | 20.08299 | 43.26749 |
| 811 | 657 721 | 28.47806 | 90.05554 | 533 411 731 | 9.325 532 | 20.09125 | 43.28529 |
| 812 | 659 344 | 28.49561 | 90.11104 | 535 387 328 | 9.329 363 | 20.09950 | 43.30307 |
| 813 | 660 969 | 28.51315 | 90.16651 | 537 367 797 | 9.333 192 | 20.10775 | 43.32084 |
| 814 | 662 596 | 28.53069 | 90.22195 | 539 353 144 | 9.337 017 | 20.11599 | 43.33859 |
| 815 | 664 225 | 28.54820 | 90.27735 | 541 343 375 | 9.340 839 | 20.12423 | 43.35633 |
| 816 | 665 856 | 28.56571 | 90.33272 | 543 338 496 | 9.344 657 | 20.13245 | 43.37406 |
| 817 | 667 489 | 28.58321 | 90.38805 | 545 338 513 | 9.348 473 | 20.14067 | 43.39177 |
| 818 | 669 124 | 28.60070 | 90.44335 | 547 343 432 | 9.352 286 | 20.14889 | 43.40947 |
| 819 | 670 761 | 28.61818 | 90.49862 | 549 353 259 | 9.356 095 | 20.15710 | 43.42715 |
| 820 | 672 400 | 28.63564 | 90.55385 | 551 368 000 | 9.359 902 | 20.16530 | 43.44481 |
| 821 | 674 041 | 28.65310 | 90.60905 | 553 387 661 | 9.363 705 | 20.17349 | 43.46247 |
| 822 | 675 684 | 28.67054 | 90.66422 | 555 412 248 | 9.367 505 | 20.18168 | 43.48011 |
| 823 | 677 329 | 28.68798 | 90.71935 | 557 441 767 | 9.371 302 | 20.18986 | 43.49773 |
| 824 | 678 976 | 28.70540 | 90.77445 | 559 476 224 | 9.375 096 | 20.19803 | 43.51534 |
| 825 | 680 625 | 28.72281 | 90.82951 | 561 515 625 | 9.378 887 | 20.20620 | 43.53294 |
| 826 | 682 276 | 28.74022 | 90.88454 | 563 559 976 | 9.382 675 | 20.21436 | 43.55052 |
| 827 | 683 929 | 28.75761 | 90.93954 | 565 609 283 | 9.386 460 | 20.22252 | 43.56809 |
| 828 | 685 584 | 28.77499 | 90.99451 | 567 663 552 | 9.390 242 | 20.23066 | 43.58564 |
| 829 | 687 241 | 28.79236 | 91.04944 | 569 722 789 | 9.394 021 | 20.23880 | 43.60318 |
| 830 | 688 900 | 28.80972 | 91.10434 | 571 787 000 | 9.397 796 | 20.24694 | 43.62071 |
| 831 | 690 561 | 28.82707 | 91.15920 | 573 856 191 | 9.401 569 | 20.25507 | 43.63822 |
| 832 | 692 224 | 28.84441 | 91.21403 | 575 930 368 | 9.405 339 | 20.26319 | 43.65572 |
| 833 | 693 889 | 28.86174 | 91.26883 | 578 009 537 | 9.409 105 | 20.27130 | 43.67320 |
| 834 | 695 556 | 28.87906 | 91.32360 | 580 093 704 | 9.412 869 | 20.27941 | 43.69067 |
| 835 | 697 225 | 28.89637 | 91.37833 | 582 182 875 | 9.416 630 | 20.28751 | 43.70812 |
| 836 | 698 896 | 28.91366 | 91.43304 | 584 277 056 | 9.420 387 | 20.29561 | 43.72556 |
| 837 | 700 569 | 28.93095 | 91.48770 | 586 376 253 | 9.424 142 | 20.30370 | 43.74299 |
| 838 | 702 244 | 28.94823 | 91.54234 | 588 480 472 | 9.427 894 | 20.31178 | 43.76041 |
| 839 | 703 921 | 28.96550 | 91.59694 | 590 589 719 | 9.431 642 | 20.31986 | 43.77781 |
| 840 | 705 600 | 28.98275 | 91.65151 | 592 704 000 | 9.435 388 | 20.32793 | 43.79519 |
| 841 | 707 281 | 29.00000 | 91.70605 | 594 823 321 | 9.439 131 | 20.33599 | 43.81256 |
| 842 | 708 964 | 29.01724 | 91.76056 | 596 947 688 | 9.442 870 | 20.34405 | 43.82992 |
| 843 | 710 649 | 29.03446 | 91.81503 | 599 077 107 | 9.446 607 | 20.35210 | 43.84727 |
| 844 | 712 336 | 29.05168 | 91.86947 | 601 211 584 | 9.450 341 | 20.36014 | 43.86460 |
| 845 | 714 025 | 29.06888 | 91.92388 | 603 351 125 | 9.454 072 | 20.36818 | 43.88191 |
| 846 | 715 716 | 29.08608 | 91.97826 | 605 495 736 | 9.457 800 | 20.37621 | 43.89922 |
| 847 | 717 409 | 29.10326 | 92.03260 | 607 645 423 | 9.461 525 | 20.38424 | 43.91651 |
| 848 | 719 104 | 29.12044 | 92.08692 | 609 800 192 | 9.465 247 | 20.39226 | 43.93378 |
| 849 | 720 801 | 29.13760 | 92.14120 | 611 960 049 | 9.468 966 | 20.40027 | 43.95105 |
| 850 | 722 500 | 29.15476 | 92.19544 | 614 125 000 | 9.472 682 | 20.40828 | 43.96830 |

| $n$ | $n^2$ | $\sqrt{n}$ | $\sqrt{10n}$ | $n^3$ | $\sqrt[3]{n}$ | $\sqrt[3]{10n}$ | $\sqrt[3]{100n}$ |
|---|---|---|---|---|---|---|---|
| **850** | 722 500 | 29.15476 | 92.19544 | 614 125 000 | 9.472 682 | 20.40828 | 43.96830 |
| 851 | 724 201 | 29.17190 | 92.24966 | 616 295 051 | 9.476 396 | 20.41628 | 43.98553 |
| 852 | 725 904 | 29.18904 | 92.30385 | 618 470 208 | 9.480 106 | 20.42427 | 44.00275 |
| 853 | 727 609 | 29.20616 | 92.35800 | 620 650 477 | 9.483 814 | 20.43226 | 44.01996 |
| 854 | 729 316 | 29.22328 | 92.41212 | 622 835 864 | 9.487 518 | 20.44024 | 44.03716 |
| **855** | 731 025 | 29.24038 | 92.46621 | 625 026 375 | 9.491 220 | 20.44821 | 44.05434 |
| 856 | 732 736 | 29.25748 | 92.52027 | 627 222 016 | 9.494 919 | 20.45618 | 44.07151 |
| 857 | 734 449 | 29.27456 | 92.57429 | 629 422 793 | 9.498 615 | 20.46415 | 44.08866 |
| 858 | 736 164 | 29.29164 | 92.62829 | 631 628 712 | 9.502 308 | 20.47210 | 44.10581 |
| 859 | 737 881 | 29.30870 | 92.68225 | 633 839 779 | 9.505 998 | 20.48005 | 44.12293 |
| **860** | 739 600 | 29.32576 | 92.73618 | 636 056 000 | 9.509 685 | 20.48800 | 44.14005 |
| 861 | 741 321 | 29.34280 | 92.79009 | 638 277 381 | 9.513 370 | 20.49593 | 44.15715 |
| 862 | 743 044 | 29.35984 | 92.84396 | 640 503 928 | 9.517 052 | 20.50387 | 44.17424 |
| 863 | 744 769 | 29.37686 | 92.89779 | 642 735 647 | 9.520 730 | 20.51179 | 44.19132 |
| 864 | 746 496 | 29.39388 | 92.95160 | 644 972 544 | 9.524 406 | 20.51971 | 44.20838 |
| **865** | 748 225 | 29.41088 | 93.00538 | 647 214 625 | 9.528 079 | 20.52762 | 44.22543 |
| 866 | 749 956 | 29.42788 | 93.05912 | 649 461 896 | 9.531 750 | 20.53553 | 44.24246 |
| 867 | 751 689 | 29.44486 | 93.11283 | 651 714 363 | 9.535 417 | 20.54343 | 44.25949 |
| 868 | 753 424 | 29.46184 | 93.16652 | 653 972 032 | 9.539 082 | 20.55133 | 44.27650 |
| 869 | 755 161 | 29.47881 | 93.22017 | 656 234 909 | 9.542 744 | 20.55922 | 44.29349 |
| **870** | 756 900 | 29.49576 | 93.27379 | 658 503 000 | 9.546 403 | 20.56710 | 44.31048 |
| 871 | 758 641 | 29.51271 | 93.32738 | 660 776 311 | 9.550 059 | 20.57498 | 44.32745 |
| 872 | 760 384 | 29.52965 | 93.38094 | 663 054 848 | 9.553 712 | 20.58285 | 44.34440 |
| 873 | 762 129 | 29.54657 | 93.43447 | 665 338 617 | 9.557 363 | 20.59071 | 44.36135 |
| 874 | 763 876 | 29.56349 | 93.48797 | 667 627 624 | 9.561 011 | 20.59857 | 44.37828 |
| **875** | 765 625 | 29.58040 | 93.54143 | 669 921 875 | 9.564 656 | 20.60643 | 44.39520 |
| 876 | 767 376 | 29.59730 | 93.59487 | 672 221 376 | 9.568 298 | 20.61427 | 44.41211 |
| 877 | 769 129 | 29.61419 | 93.64828 | 674 526 133 | 9.571 938 | 20.62211 | 44.42900 |
| 878 | 770 884 | 29.63106 | 93.70165 | 676 836 152 | 9.575 574 | 20.62995 | 44.44588 |
| 879 | 772 641 | 29.64793 | 93.75500 | 679 151 439 | 9.579 208 | 20.63778 | 44.46275 |
| **880** | 774 400 | 29.66479 | 93.80832 | 681 472 000 | 9.582 840 | 20.64560 | 44.47960 |
| 881 | 776 161 | 29.68164 | 93.86160 | 683 797 841 | 9.586 468 | 20.65342 | 44.49644 |
| 882 | 777 924 | 29.69848 | 93.91486 | 686 128 968 | 9.590 094 | 20.66123 | 44.51327 |
| 883 | 779 689 | 29.71532 | 93.96808 | 688 465 387 | 9.593 717 | 20.66904 | 44.53009 |
| 884 | 781 456 | 29.73214 | 94.02127 | 690 807 104 | 9.597 337 | 20.67684 | 44.54689 |
| **885** | 783 225 | 29.74895 | 94.07444 | 693 154 125 | 9.600 955 | 20.68463 | 44.56368 |
| 886 | 784 996 | 29.76575 | 94.12757 | 695 506 456 | 9.604 570 | 20.69242 | 44.58046 |
| 887 | 786 769 | 29.78255 | 94.18068 | 697 864 103 | 9.608 182 | 20.70020 | 44.59723 |
| 888 | 788 544 | 29.79933 | 94.23375 | 700 227 072 | 9.611 791 | 20.70798 | 44.61398 |
| 889 | 790 321 | 29.81610 | 94.28680 | 702 595 369 | 9.615 398 | 20.71575 | 44.63072 |
| **890** | 792 100 | 29.83287 | 94.33981 | 704 969 000 | 9.619 002 | 20.72351 | 44.64745 |
| 891 | 793 881 | 29.84962 | 94.39280 | 707 347 971 | 9.622 603 | 20.73127 | 44.66417 |
| 892 | 795 664 | 29.86637 | 94.44575 | 709 732 288 | 9.626 202 | 20.73902 | 44.68087 |
| 893 | 797 449 | 29.88311 | 94.49868 | 712 121 957 | 9.629 797 | 20.74677 | 44.69756 |
| 894 | 799 236 | 29.89983 | 94.55157 | 714 516 984 | 9.633 391 | 20.75451 | 44.71424 |
| **895** | 801 025 | 29.91655 | 94.60444 | 716 917 375 | 9.636 981 | 20.76225 | 44.73090 |
| 896 | 802 816 | 29.93326 | 94.65728 | 719 323 136 | 9.640 569 | 20.76998 | 44.74756 |
| 897 | 804 609 | 29.94996 | 94.71008 | 721 734 273 | 9.644 154 | 20.77770 | 44.76420 |
| 898 | 806 404 | 29.96665 | 94.76286 | 724 150 792 | 9.647 737 | 20.78542 | 44.78083 |
| 899 | 808 201 | 29.98333 | 94.81561 | 726 572 699 | 9.651 317 | 20.79313 | 44.79744 |
| **900** | 810 000 | 30.00000 | 94.86833 | 729 000 000 | 9.654 894 | 20.80084 | 44.81405 |

| $n$ | $n^2$ | $\sqrt{n}$ | $\sqrt{10n}$ | $n^3$ | $\sqrt[3]{n}$ | $\sqrt[3]{10n}$ | $\sqrt[3]{100n}$ |
|---|---|---|---|---|---|---|---|
| **900** | 810 000 | 30.00000 | 94.86833 | 729 000 000 | 9.654 894 | 20.80084 | 44.81405 |
| **901** | 811 801 | 30.01666 | 94.92102 | 731 432 701 | 9.658 468 | 20.80854 | 44.83064 |
| **902** | 813 604 | 30.03331 | 94.97368 | 733 870 808 | 9.662 040 | 20.81623 | 44.84722 |
| **903** | 815 409 | 30.04996 | 95.02631 | 736 314 327 | 9.665 610 | 20.82392 | 44.86379 |
| **904** | 817 216 | 30.06659 | 95.07891 | 738 763 264 | 9.669 176 | 20.83161 | 44.88034 |
| **905** | 819 025 | 30.08322 | 95.13149 | 741 217 625 | 9.672 740 | 20.83929 | 44.89688 |
| **906** | 820 836 | 30.09983 | 95.18403 | 743 677 416 | 9.676 302 | 20.84696 | 44.91341 |
| **907** | 822 649 | 30.11644 | 95.23655 | 746 142 643 | 9.679 860 | 20.85463 | 44.92993 |
| **908** | 824 464 | 30.13304 | 95.28903 | 748 613 312 | 9.683 417 | 20.86229 | 44.94644 |
| **909** | 826 281 | 30.14963 | 95.34149 | 751 089 429 | 9.686 970 | 20.86994 | 44.96293 |
| **910** | 828 100 | 30.16621 | 95.39392 | 753 571 000 | 9.690 521 | 20.87759 | 44.97941 |
| **911** | 829 921 | 30.18278 | 95.44632 | 756 058 031 | 9.694 069 | 20.88524 | 44.99588 |
| **912** | 831 744 | 30.19934 | 95.49869 | 758 550 528 | 9.697 615 | 20.89288 | 45.01234 |
| **913** | 833 569 | 30.21589 | 95.55103 | 761 048 497 | 9.701 158 | 20.90051 | 45.02879 |
| **914** | 835 396 | 30.23243 | 95.60335 | 763 551 944 | 9.704 699 | 20.90814 | 45.04522 |
| **915** | 837 225 | 30.24897 | 95.65563 | 766 060 875 | 9.708 237 | 20.91576 | 45.06164 |
| **916** | 839 056 | 30.26549 | 95.70789 | 768 575 296 | 9.711 772 | 20.92338 | 45.07805 |
| **917** | 840 889 | 30.28201 | 95.76012 | 771 095 213 | 9.715 305 | 20.93099 | 45.09445 |
| **918** | 842 724 | 30.29851 | 95.81232 | 773 620 632 | 9.718 835 | 20.93860 | 45.11084 |
| **919** | 844 561 | 30.31501 | 95.86449 | 776 151 559 | 9.722 363 | 20.94620 | 45.12721 |
| **920** | 846 400 | 30.33150 | 95.91663 | 778 688 000 | 9.725 888 | 20.95379 | 45.14357 |
| **921** | 848 241 | 30.34798 | 95.96874 | 781 229 961 | 9.729 411 | 20.96138 | 45.15992 |
| **922** | 850 084 | 30.36445 | 96.02083 | 783 777 448 | 9.732 931 | 20.96896 | 45.17626 |
| **923** | 851 929 | 30.38092 | 96.07289 | 786 330 467 | 9.736 448 | 20.97654 | 45.19259 |
| **924** | 853 776 | 30.39737 | 96.12492 | 788 889 024 | 9.739 963 | 20.98411 | 45.20891 |
| **925** | 855 625 | 30.41381 | 96.17692 | 791 453 125 | 9.743 476 | 20.99168 | 45.22521 |
| **926** | 857 476 | 30.43025 | 96.22889 | 794 022 776 | 9.746 986 | 20.99924 | 45.24150 |
| **927** | 859 329 | 30.44667 | 96.28084 | 796 597 983 | 9.750 493 | 21.00680 | 45.25778 |
| **928** | 861 184 | 30.46309 | 96.33276 | 799 178 752 | 9.753 998 | 21.01435 | 45.27405 |
| **929** | 863 041 | 30.47950 | 96.38465 | 801 765 089 | 9.757 500 | 21.02190 | 45.29030 |
| **930** | 864 900 | 30.49590 | 96.43651 | 804 357 000 | 9.761 000 | 21.02944 | 45.30655 |
| **931** | 866 761 | 30.51229 | 96.48834 | 806 954 491 | 9.764 497 | 21.03697 | 45.32278 |
| **932** | 868 624 | 30.52868 | 96.54015 | 809 557 568 | 9.767 992 | 21.04450 | 45.33900 |
| **933** | 870 489 | 30.54505 | 96.59193 | 812 166 237 | 9.771 485 | 21.05203 | 45.35521 |
| **934** | 872 356 | 30.56141 | 96.64368 | 814 780 504 | 9.774 974 | 21.05954 | 45.37141 |
| **935** | 874 225 | 30.57777 | 96.69540 | 817 400 375 | 9.778 462 | 21.06706 | 45.38760 |
| **936** | 876 096 | 30.59412 | 96.74709 | 820 025 856 | 9.781 946 | 21.07456 | 45.40377 |
| **937** | 877 969 | 30.61046 | 96.79876 | 822 656 953 | 9.785 429 | 21.08207 | 45.41994 |
| **938** | 879 844 | 30.62679 | 96.85040 | 825 293 672 | 9.788 909 | 21.08956 | 45.43609 |
| **939** | 881 721 | 30.64311 | 96.90201 | 827 936 019 | 9.792 386 | 21.09706 | 45.45223 |
| **940** | 883 600 | 30.65942 | 96.95360 | 830 584 000 | 9.795 861 | 21.10454 | 45.46836 |
| **941** | 885 481 | 30.67572 | 97.00515 | 833 237 621 | 9.799 334 | 21.11202 | 45.48448 |
| **942** | 887 364 | 30.69202 | 97.05668 | 835 896 888 | 9.802 804 | 21.11950 | 45.50058 |
| **943** | 889 249 | 30.70831 | 97.10819 | 838 561 807 | 9.806 271 | 21.12697 | 45.51668 |
| **944** | 891 136 | 30.72458 | 97.15966 | 841 232 384 | 9.809 736 | 21.13444 | 45.53276 |
| **945** | 893 025 | 30.74085 | 97.21111 | 843 908 625 | 9.813 199 | 21.14190 | 45.54883 |
| **946** | 894 916 | 30.75711 | 97.26253 | 846 590 536 | 9.816 659 | 21.14935 | 45.56490 |
| **947** | 896 809 | 30.77337 | 97.31393 | 849 278 123 | 9.820 117 | 21.15680 | 45.58095 |
| **948** | 898 704 | 30.78961 | 97.36529 | 851 971 392 | 9.823 572 | 21.16424 | 45.59698 |
| **949** | 900 601 | 30.80584 | 97.41663 | 854 670 349 | 9.827 025 | 21.17168 | 45.61301 |
| **950** | 902 500 | 30.82207 | 97.46794 | 857 375 000 | 9.830 476 | 21.17912 | 45.62903 |

## SQUARES, CUBES AND ROOTS (Continued)

| $n$ | $n^2$ | $\sqrt{n}$ | $\sqrt{10n}$ | $n^3$ | $\sqrt[3]{n}$ | $\sqrt[3]{10n}$ | $\sqrt[3]{100n}$ |
|---|---|---|---|---|---|---|---|
| **950** | 902 500 | 30.82207 | 97.46794 | 857 375 000 | 9.830 476 | 21.17912 | 45.62903 |
| **951** | 904 401 | 30.83829 | 97.51923 | 860 085 351 | 9.833 924 | 21.18655 | 45.64503 |
| **952** | 906 304 | 30.85450 | 97.57049 | 862 801 408 | 9.837 369 | 21.19397 | 45.66102 |
| **953** | 908 209 | 30.87070 | 97.62172 | 865 523 177 | 9.840 813 | 21.20139 | 45.67701 |
| **954** | 910 116 | 30.88689 | 97.67292 | 868 250 664 | 9.844 254 | 21.20880 | 45.69298 |
| **955** | 912 025 | 30.90307 | 97.72410 | 870 983 875 | 9.847 692 | 21.21621 | 45.70894 |
| **956** | 913 936 | 30.91925 | 97.77525 | 873 722 816 | 9.851 128 | 21.22361 | 45.72489 |
| **957** | 915 849 | 30.93542 | 97.82638 | 876 467 493 | 9.854 562 | 21.23101 | 45.74082 |
| **958** | 917 764 | 30.95158 | 97.87747 | 879 217 912 | 9.857 993 | 21.23840 | 45.75675 |
| **959** | 919 681 | 30.96773 | 97.92855 | 881 974 079 | 9.861 422 | 21.24579 | 45.77267 |
| **960** | 921 600 | 30.98387 | 97.97959 | 884 736 000 | 9.864 848 | 21.25317 | 45.78857 |
| **961** | 923 521 | 31.00000 | 98.03061 | 887 503 681 | 9.868 272 | 21.26055 | 45.80446 |
| **962** | 925 444 | 31.01612 | 98.08160 | 890 277 128 | 9.871 694 | 21.26792 | 45.82035 |
| **963** | 927 369 | 31.03224 | 98.13256 | 893 056 347 | 9.875 113 | 21.27529 | 45.83622 |
| **964** | 929 296 | 31.04835 | 98.18350 | 895 841 344 | 9.878 530 | 21.28265 | 45.85208 |
| **965** | 931 225 | 31.06445 | 98.23441 | 898 632 125 | 9.881 945 | 21.29001 | 45.86793 |
| **966** | 933 156 | 31.08054 | 98.28530 | 901 428 696 | 9.885 357 | 21.29736 | 45.88376 |
| **967** | 935 089 | 31.09662 | 98.33616 | 904 231 063 | 9.888 767 | 21.30470 | 45.89959 |
| **968** | 937 024 | 31.11270 | 98.38699 | 907 039 232 | 9.892 175 | 21.31204 | 45.91541 |
| **969** | 938 961 | 31.12876 | 98.43780 | 909 853 209 | 9.895 580 | 21.31938 | 45.93121 |
| **970** | 940 900 | 31.14482 | 98.48858 | 912 673 000 | 9.898 983 | 21.32671 | 45.94701 |
| **971** | 942 841 | 31.16087 | 98.53933 | 915 498 611 | 9.902 384 | 21.33404 | 45.96279 |
| **972** | 944 784 | 31.17691 | 98.59006 | 918 330 048 | 9.905 782 | 21.34136 | 45.97857 |
| **973** | 946 729 | 31.19295 | 98.64076 | 921 167 317 | 9.909 178 | 21.34868 | 45.99433 |
| **974** | 948 676 | 31.20897 | 98.69144 | 924 010 424 | 9.912 571 | 21.35599 | 46.01008 |
| **975** | 950 625 | 31.22499 | 98.74209 | 926 859 375 | 9.915 962 | 21.36329 | 46.02582 |
| **976** | 952 576 | 31.24100 | 98.79271 | 929 714 176 | 9.919 351 | 21.37059 | 46.04155 |
| **977** | 954 529 | 31.25700 | 98.84331 | 932 574 833 | 9.922 738 | 21.37789 | 46.05727 |
| **978** | 956 484 | 31.27299 | 98.89388 | 935 441 352 | 9.926 122 | 21.38518 | 46.07298 |
| **979** | 958 441 | 31.28898 | 98.94443 | 938 313 739 | 9.929 504 | 21.39247 | 46.08868 |
| **980** | 960 400 | 31.30495 | 98.99495 | 941 192 000 | 9.932 884 | 21.39975 | 46.10436 |
| **981** | 962 361 | 31.32092 | 99.04544 | 944 076 141 | 9.936 261 | 21.40703 | 46.12004 |
| **982** | 964 324 | 31.33688 | 99.09591 | 946 966 168 | 9.939 636 | 21.41430 | 46.13571 |
| **983** | 966 289 | 31.35283 | 99.14636 | 949 862 087 | 9.943 009 | 21.42156 | 46.15136 |
| **984** | 968 256 | 31.36877 | 99.19677 | 952 763 904 | 9.946 380 | 21.42883 | 46.16700 |
| **985** | 970 225 | 31.38471 | 99.24717 | 955 671 625 | 9.949 748 | 21.43608 | 46.18264 |
| **986** | 972 196 | 31.40064 | 99.29753 | 958 585 256 | 9.953 114 | 21.44333 | 46.19826 |
| **987** | 974 169 | 31.41656 | 99.34787 | 961 504 803 | 9.956 478 | 21.45058 | 46.21387 |
| **988** | 976 144 | 31.43247 | 99.39819 | 964 430 272 | 9.959 839 | 21.45782 | 46.22948 |
| **989** | 978 121 | 31.44837 | 99.44848 | 967 361 669 | 9.963 198 | 21.46506 | 46.24507 |
| **990** | 980 100 | 31.46427 | 99.49874 | 970 299 000 | 9.966 555 | 21.47229 | 46.26065 |
| **991** | 982 081 | 31.48015 | 99.54898 | 973 242 271 | 9.969 910 | 21.47952 | 46.27622 |
| **992** | 984 064 | 31.49603 | 99.59920 | 976 191 488 | 9.973 262 | 21.48674 | 46.29178 |
| **993** | 986 049 | 31.51190 | 99.64939 | 979 146 657 | 9.976 612 | 21.49396 | 46.30733 |
| **994** | 988 036 | 31.52777 | 99.69955 | 982 107 784 | 9.979 960 | 21.50117 | 46.32287 |
| **995** | 990 025 | 31.54362 | 99.74969 | 985 074 875 | 9.983 305 | 21.50838 | 46.33840 |
| **996** | 992 016 | 31.55947 | 99.79980 | 988 047 936 | 9.986 649 | 21.51558 | 46.35392 |
| **997** | 994 009 | 31.57531 | 99.84989 | 991 026 973 | 9.989 990 | 21.52278 | 46.36943 |
| **998** | 996 004 | 31.59114 | 99.89995 | 994 011 992 | 9.993 329 | 21.52997 | 46.38492 |
| **999** | 998 001 | 31.60696 | 99.94999 | 997 002 999 | 9.996 666 | 21.53716 | 46.40041 |
| **1000** | 1 000 000 | 31.62278 | 100.00000 | 1 000 000 000 | 10.000 000 | 21.54435 | 46.41589 |

# POWERS OF NUMBERS

| $n$ | $n^4$ | $n^5$ | $n^6$ | $n^7$ | $n^8$ |
|---|---|---|---|---|---|
| 1 | 1 | 1 | 1 | 1 | 1 |
| 2 | 16 | 32 | 64 | 128 | 256 |
| 3 | 81 | 243 | 729 | 2187 | 6561 |
| 4 | 256 | 1024 | 4096 | 16384 | 65536 |
| 5 | 625 | 3125 | 15625 | 78125 | 390625 |
| 6 | 1296 | 7776 | 46656 | 279936 | 1679616 |
| 7 | 2401 | 16807 | 117649 | 823543 | 5764801 |
| 8 | 4096 | 32768 | 262144 | 2097152 | 16777216 |
| 9 | 6561 | 59049 | 531441 | 4782969 | 43046721 |
| | | | | | $\times 10^8$ |
| 10 | 10000 | 100000 | 1000000 | 10000000 | 1.000000 |
| 11 | 14641 | 161051 | 1771561 | 19487171 | 2.143589 |
| 12 | 20736 | 248832 | 2985984 | 35831808 | 4.299817 |
| 13 | 28561 | 371293 | 4826809 | 62748517 | 8.157307 |
| 14 | 38416 | 537824 | 7529536 | 105413504 | 14.757891 |
| 15 | 50625 | 759375 | 11390625 | 170859375 | 25.628906 |
| 16 | 65536 | 1048576 | 16777216 | 268435456 | 42.949673 |
| 17 | 83521 | 1419857 | 24137569 | 410338673 | 69.757574 |
| 18 | 104976 | 1889568 | 34012224 | 612220032 | 110.199606 |
| 19 | 130321 | 2476099 | 47045881 | 893871739 | 169.835630 |
| | | | | $\times 10^9$ | $\times 10^{10}$ |
| 20 | 160000 | 3200000 | 64000000 | 1.280000 | 2.560000 |
| 21 | 194481 | 4084101 | 85766121 | 1.801089 | 3.782286 |
| 22 | 234256 | 5153632 | 113379904 | 2.494358 | 5.487587 |
| 23 | 279841 | 6436343 | 148035889 | 3.404825 | 7.831099 |
| 24 | 331776 | 7962624 | 191102976 | 4.586471 | 11.007531 |
| 25 | 390625 | 9765625 | 244140625 | 6.103516 | 15.258789 |
| 26 | 456976 | 11881376 | 308915776 | 8.031810 | 20.882706 |
| 27 | 531441 | 14348907 | 387420489 | 10.460353 | 28.242954 |
| 28 | 614656 | 17210368 | 481890304 | 13.492929 | 37.780200 |
| 29 | 707281 | 20511149 | 594823321 | 17.249876 | 50.024641 |
| | | | $\times 10^8$ | $\times 10^{10}$ | $\times 10^{11}$ |
| 30 | 810000 | 24300000 | 7.290000 | 2.187000 | 6.561000 |
| 31 | 923521 | 28629151 | 8.875037 | 2.751261 | 8.528910 |
| 32 | 1048576 | 33554432 | 10.737418 | 3.435974 | 10.995116 |
| 33 | 1185921 | 39135393 | 12.914680 | 4.261844 | 14.064086 |
| 34 | 1336336 | 45435424 | 15.448044 | 5.252335 | 17.857939 |
| 35 | 1500625 | 52521875 | 18.382656 | 6.433930 | 22.518754 |
| 36 | 1679616 | 60466176 | 21.767823 | 7.836416 | 28.211099 |
| 37 | 1874161 | 69343957 | 25.657264 | 9.493188 | 35.124795 |
| 38 | 2085136 | 79235168 | 30.109364 | 11.441558 | 43.477921 |
| 39 | 2313441 | 90224199 | 35.187438 | 13.723101 | 53.520093 |
| | | | $\times 10^9$ | $\times 10^{10}$ | $\times 10^{12}$ |
| 40 | 2560000 | 102400000 | 4.096000 | 16.384000 | 6.553600 |
| 41 | 2825761 | 115856201 | 4.750104 | 19.475427 | 7.984925 |
| 42 | 3111696 | 130691232 | 5.489032 | 23.053933 | 9.682652 |
| 43 | 3418801 | 147008443 | 6.321363 | 27.181861 | 11.688200 |
| 44 | 3748096 | 164916224 | 7.256314 | 31.927781 | 14.048224 |
| 45 | 4100625 | 184528125 | 8.303766 | 37.366945 | 16.815125 |
| 46 | 4477456 | 205962976 | 9.474297 | 43.581766 | 20.047612 |
| 47 | 4879681 | 229345007 | 10.779215 | 50.662312 | 23.811287 |
| 48 | 5308416 | 254803968 | 12.230590 | 58.706834 | 28.179280 |
| 49 | 5764801 | 282475249 | 13.841287 | 67.822307 | 33.232931 |
| 50 | 6250000 | 312500000 | 15.625000 | 78.125000 | 39.062500 |

| $n$ | $n^4$ | $n^5$ | $n^6$ | $n^7$ | $n^8$ |
|---|---|---|---|---|---|
| | | | $\times 10^9$ | $\times 10^{11}$ | $\times 10^{13}$ |
| **50** | 6250000 | 312500000 | 15.625000 | 7.812500 | 3.906250 |
| 51 | 6765201 | 345025251 | 17.596288 | 8.974107 | 4.576794 |
| 52 | 7311616 | 380204032 | 19.770610 | 10.280717 | 5.345973 |
| 53 | 7890481 | 418195493 | 22.164361 | 11.747111 | 6.225969 |
| 54 | 8503056 | 459165024 | 24.794911 | 13.389252 | 7.230196 |
| 55 | 9150625 | 503284375 | 27.680641 | 15.224352 | 8.373394 |
| 56 | 9834496 | 550731776 | 30.840979 | 17.270948 | 9.671731 |
| 57 | 10556001 | 601692057 | 34.296447 | 19.548975 | 11.142916 |
| 58 | 11316496 | 656356768 | 38.068693 | 22.079842 | 12.806308 |
| 59 | 12117361 | 714924299 | 42.180534 | 24.886515 | 14.683044 |
| | | $\times 10^8$ | $\times 10^{10}$ | $\times 10^{11}$ | $\times 10^{13}$ |
| **60** | 12960000 | 7.776000 | 4.665600 | 27.993600 | 16.796160 |
| 61 | 13845841 | 8.445963 | 5.152037 | 31.427428 | 19.170731 |
| 62 | 14776336 | 9.161328 | 5.680024 | 35.216146 | 21.834011 |
| 63 | 15752961 | 9.924365 | 6.252350 | 39.389806 | 24.815578 |
| 64 | 16777216 | 10.737418 | 6.871948 | 43.980465 | 28.147498 |
| 65 | 17850625 | 11.602906 | 7.541889 | 49.022279 | 31.864481 |
| 66 | 18974736 | 12.523326 | 8.265395 | 54.551607 | 36.004061 |
| 67 | 20151121 | 13.501251 | 9.045838 | 60.607116 | 40.606768 |
| 68 | 21381376 | 14.539336 | 9.886748 | 67.229888 | 45.716324 |
| 69 | 22667121 | 15.640313 | 10.791816 | 74.463533 | 51.379837 |
| | | $\times 10^8$ | $\times 10^{10}$ | $\times 10^{12}$ | $\times 10^{14}$ |
| **70** | 24010000 | 16.807000 | 11.764900 | 8.235430 | 5.764801 |
| 71 | 25411681 | 18.042294 | 12.810028 | 9.095120 | 6.457535 |
| 72 | 26873856 | 19.349176 | 13.931407 | 10.030613 | 7.222041 |
| 73 | 28398241 | 20.730716 | 15.133423 | 11.047399 | 8.064601 |
| 74 | 29986576 | 22.190066 | 16.420649 | 12.151280 | 8.991947 |
| 75 | 31640625 | 23.730469 | 17.797852 | 13.348389 | 10.011292 |
| 76 | 33362176 | 25.355254 | 19.269993 | 14.645195 | 11.130348 |
| 77 | 35153041 | 27.067842 | 20.842238 | 16.048523 | 12.357363 |
| 78 | 37015056 | 28.871744 | 22.519960 | 17.565569 | 13.701144 |
| 79 | 38950081 | 30.770564 | 24.308746 | 19.203909 | 15.171088 |
| | | $\times 10^8$ | $\times 10^{10}$ | $\times 10^{12}$ | $\times 10^{14}$ |
| **80** | 40960000 | 32.768000 | 26.214400 | 20.971520 | 16.777216 |
| 81 | 43046721 | 34.867844 | 28.242954 | 22.876792 | 18.530202 |
| 82 | 45212176 | 37.073984 | 30.400667 | 24.928547 | 20.441409 |
| 83 | 47458321 | 39.390406 | 32.694037 | 27.136051 | 22.522922 |
| 84 | 49787136 | 41.821194 | 35.129803 | 29.509035 | 24.787589 |
| 85 | 52200625 | 44.370531 | 37.714952 | 32.057709 | 27.249053 |
| 86 | 54700816 | 47.042702 | 40.456724 | 34.792782 | 29.921793 |
| 87 | 57289761 | 49.842092 | 43.362620 | 37.725479 | 32.821167 |
| 88 | 59969536 | 52.773192 | 46.440409 | 40.867560 | 35.963452 |
| 89 | 62742241 | 55.840594 | 49.698129 | 44.231335 | 39.365888 |
| | | $\times 10^9$ | $\times 10^{11}$ | $\times 10^{13}$ | $\times 10^{15}$ |
| **90** | 65610000 | 5.904900 | 5.314410 | 4.782969 | 4.304672 |
| 91 | 68574961 | 6.240321 | 5.678693 | 5.167610 | 4.702525 |
| 92 | 71639296 | 6.590815 | 6.063550 | 5.578466 | 5.132189 |
| 93 | 74805201 | 6.956884 | 6.469902 | 6.017009 | 5.595818 |
| 94 | 78074896 | 7.339040 | 6.898698 | 6.484776 | 6.095689 |
| 95 | 81450625 | 7.737809 | 7.350919 | 6.983373 | 6.634204 |
| 96 | 84934656 | 8.153727 | 7.827578 | 7.514475 | 7.213896 |
| 97 | 88529281 | 8.587340 | 8.329720 | 8.079828 | 7.837434 |
| 98 | 92238816 | 9.039208 | 8.858424 | 8.681255 | 8.507630 |
| 99 | 96059601 | 9.509900 | 9.414801 | 9.320653 | 9.227447 |
| **100** | 100000000 | 10.000000 | 10.000000 | 10.000000 | 10.000000 |

# POWERS OF TWO

| $n$ | $2^n$ | $n$ | $2^n$ |
|---|---|---|---|
| 1 | 2 | 41 | 21990 23255 552 |
| 2 | 4 | 42 | 43980 46511 104 |
| 3 | 8 | 43 | 87960 93022 208 |
| 4 | 16 | 44 | 17592 18604 4416 |
| 5 | 32 | 45 | 35184 37208 8832 |
| 6 | 64 | 46 | 70368 74417 7664 |
| 7 | 128 | 47 | 14073 74883 55328 |
| 8 | 256 | 48 | 28147 49767 10656 |
| 9 | 512 | 49 | 56294 99534 21312 |
| 10 | 1024 | 50 | 11258 99906 84262 4 |
| 11 | 2048 | 51 | 22517 99813 68524 8 |
| 12 | 4096 | 52 | 45035 99627 37049 6 |
| 13 | 8192 | 53 | 90071 99254 74099 2 |
| 14 | 16384 | 54 | 18014 39850 94819 84 |
| 15 | 32768 | 55 | 36028 79701 89639 68 |
| 16 | 65536 | 56 | 72057 59403 79279 36 |
| 17 | 13107 2 | 57 | 14411 51880 75855 872 |
| 18 | 26214 4 | 58 | 28823 03761 51711 744 |
| 19 | 52428 8 | 59 | 57646 07523 03423 488 |
| 20 | 10485 76 | 60 | 11529 21504 60684 6976 |
| 21 | 20971 52 | 61 | 23058 43009 21369 3952 |
| 22 | 41943 04 | 62 | 46116 86018 42738 7904 |
| 23 | 83886 08 | 63 | 92233 72036 85477 5808 |
| 24 | 16777 216 | 64 | 18446 74407 37095 51616 |
| 25 | 33554 432 | 65 | 36893 48814 74191 03232 |
| 26 | 67108 864 | 66 | 73786 97629 48382 06464 |
| 27 | 13421 7728 | 67 | 14757 39525 89676 41292 8 |
| 28 | 26843 5456 | 68 | 29514 79051 79352 82585 6 |
| 29 | 53687 0912 | 69 | 59029 58103 58705 65171 2 |
| 30 | 10737 41824 | 70 | 11805 91620 71741 13034 24 |
| 31 | 21474 83648 | 71 | 23611 83241 43482 26068 48 |
| 32 | 42949 67296 | 72 | 47223 66482 86964 52136 96 |
| 33 | 85899 34592 | 73 | 94447 32965 73929 04273 92 |
| 34 | 17179 86918 4 | 74 | 18889 46593 14785 80854 784 |
| 35 | 34359 73836 8 | 75 | 37778 93186 29571 61709 568 |
| 36 | 68719 47673 6 | 76 | 75557 86372 59143 23419 136 |
| 37 | 13743 89534 72 | 77 | 15111 57274 51828 64683 8272 |
| 38 | 27487 79069 44 | 78 | 30223 14549 03657 29367 6544 |
| 39 | 54975 58138 88 | 79 | 60446 29098 07314 58735 3088 |
| 40 | 10995 11627 776 | 80 | 12089 25819 61462 91747 06176 |

| $n$ | $2^n$ |
|---|---|
| 81 | 24178 51639 22925 83494 12352 |
| 82 | 48357 03278 45851 66988 24704 |
| 83 | 96714 06556 91703 33976 49408 |
| 84 | 19342 81311 38340 66795 29881 6 |
| 85 | 38685 62622 76681 33590 59763 2 |
| 86 | 77371 25245 53362 67181 19526 4 |
| 87 | 15474 25049 10672 53436 23905 28 |
| 88 | 30948 50098 21345 06872 47810 56 |
| 89 | 61897 00196 42690 13744 95621 12 |
| 90 | 12379 40039 28538 02748 99124 224 |
| 91 | 24758 80078 57076 05497 98248 448 |
| 92 | 49517 60157 14152 10995 96496 896 |
| 93 | 99035 20314 28304 21991 92993 792 |
| 94 | 19807 04062 85660 84398 38598 7584 |
| 95 | 39614 08125 71321 68796 77197 5168 |
| 96 | 79228 16251 42643 37593 54395 0336 |
| 97 | 15845 63250 28528 67518 70879 00672 |
| 98 | 31691 26500 57057 35037 41758 01344 |
| 99 | 63382 53001 14114 70074 83516 02688 |
| 100 | 12676 50600 22822 94014 96703 20537 6 |
| 101 | 25353 01200 45645 88029 93406 41075 2 |

207

# FACTORIALS AND THEIR LOGARITHMS

| $n$ | $n!$ | $\log n!$ | $n$ | $n!$ | $\log n!$ |
|---|---|---|---|---|---|
| | | | **50** | $3.0414 \times 10^{64}$ | 64.48307 |
| 1 | 1.0000 | 0.00000 | 51 | $1.5511 \times 10^{66}$ | 66.19065 |
| 2 | 2.0000 | 0.30103 | 52 | $8.0658 \times 10^{67}$ | 67.90665 |
| 3 | 6.0000 | 0.77815 | 53 | $4.2749 \times 10^{69}$ | 69.63092 |
| 4 | $2.4000 \times 10$ | 1.38021 | 54 | $2.3084 \times 10^{71}$ | 71.36332 |
| **5** | $1.2000 \times 10^2$ | 2.07918 | **55** | $1.2696 \times 10^{73}$ | 73.10368 |
| 6 | $7.2000 \times 10^2$ | 2.85733 | 56 | $7.1100 \times 10^{74}$ | 74.85187 |
| 7 | $5.0400 \times 10^3$ | 3.70243 | 57 | $4.0527 \times 10^{76}$ | 76.60774 |
| 8 | $4.0320 \times 10^4$ | 4.60552 | 58 | $2.3506 \times 10^{78}$ | 78.37117 |
| 9 | $3.6288 \times 10^5$ | 5.55976 | 59 | $1.3868 \times 10^{80}$ | 80.14202 |
| **10** | $3.6288 \times 10^6$ | 6.55976 | **60** | $8.3210 \times 10^{81}$ | 81.92017 |
| 11 | $3.9917 \times 10^7$ | 7.60116 | 61 | $5.0758 \times 10^{83}$ | 83.70550 |
| 12 | $4.7900 \times 10^8$ | 8.68034 | 62 | $3.1470 \times 10^{85}$ | 85.49790 |
| 13 | $6.2270 \times 10^9$ | 9.79428 | 63 | $1.9826 \times 10^{87}$ | 87.29724 |
| 14 | $8.7178 \times 10^{10}$ | 10.94041 | 64 | $1.2689 \times 10^{89}$ | 89.10342 |
| **15** | $1.3077 \times 10^{12}$ | 12.11650 | **65** | $8.2477 \times 10^{90}$ | 90.91633 |
| 16 | $2.0923 \times 10^{13}$ | 13.32062 | 66 | $5.4435 \times 10^{92}$ | 92.73587 |
| 17 | $3.5569 \times 10^{14}$ | 14.55107 | 67 | $3.6471 \times 10^{94}$ | 94.56195 |
| 18 | $6.4024 \times 10^{15}$ | 15.80634 | 68 | $2.4800 \times 10^{96}$ | 96.39446 |
| 19 | $1.2165 \times 10^{17}$ | 17.08509 | 69 | $1.7112 \times 10^{98}$ | 98.23331 |
| **20** | $2.4329 \times 10^{18}$ | 18.38612 | **70** | $1.1979 \times 10^{100}$ | 100.07841 |
| 21 | $5.1091 \times 10^{19}$ | 19.70834 | 71 | $8.5048 \times 10^{101}$ | 101.92966 |
| 22 | $1.1240 \times 10^{21}$ | 21.05077 | 72 | $6.1234 \times 10^{103}$ | 103.78700 |
| 23 | $2.5852 \times 10^{22}$ | 22.41249 | 73 | $4.4701 \times 10^{105}$ | 105.65032 |
| 24 | $6.2045 \times 10^{23}$ | 23.79271 | 74 | $3.3079 \times 10^{107}$ | 107.51955 |
| **25** | $1.5511 \times 10^{25}$ | 25.19065 | **75** | $2.4809 \times 10^{109}$ | 109.39461 |
| 26 | $4.0329 \times 10^{26}$ | 26.60562 | 76 | $1.8855 \times 10^{111}$ | 111.27543 |
| 27 | $1.0889 \times 10^{28}$ | 28.03698 | 77 | $1.4518 \times 10^{113}$ | 113.16192 |
| 28 | $3.0489 \times 10^{29}$ | 29.48414 | 78 | $1.1324 \times 10^{115}$ | 115.05401 |
| 29 | $8.8418 \times 10^{30}$ | 30.94654 | 79 | $8.9462 \times 10^{116}$ | 116.95164 |
| **30** | $2.0625 \times 10^{32}$ | 32.42366 | **80** | $7.1569 \times 10^{118}$ | 118.85473 |
| 31 | $8.2228 \times 10^{33}$ | 33.91502 | 81 | $5.7971 \times 10^{120}$ | 120.76321 |
| 32 | $2.6313 \times 10^{35}$ | 35.42017 | 82 | $4.7536 \times 10^{122}$ | 122.67703 |
| 33 | $8.6833 \times 10^{36}$ | 36.93869 | 83 | $3.9455 \times 10^{124}$ | 124.59610 |
| 34 | $2.9523 \times 10^{38}$ | 38.47016 | 84 | $3.3142 \times 10^{126}$ | 126.52038 |
| **35** | $1.0333 \times 10^{40}$ | 40.01423 | **85** | $2.8171 \times 10^{128}$ | 128.44980 |
| 36 | $3.7199 \times 10^{41}$ | 41.57054 | 86 | $2.4227 \times 10^{130}$ | 130.38430 |
| 37 | $1.3764 \times 10^{43}$ | 43.13874 | 87 | $2.1078 \times 10^{132}$ | 132.32382 |
| 38 | $5.2302 \times 10^{44}$ | 44.71852 | 88 | $1.8548 \times 10^{134}$ | 134.26830 |
| 39 | $2.0398 \times 10^{46}$ | 46.30959 | 89 | $1.6508 \times 10^{136}$ | 136.21769 |
| **40** | $8.1592 \times 10^{47}$ | 47.91165 | **90** | $1.4857 \times 10^{138}$ | 138.17194 |
| 41 | $3.3453 \times 10^{49}$ | 49.52443 | 91 | $1.3520 \times 10^{140}$ | 140.13098 |
| 42 | $1.4050 \times 10^{51}$ | 51.14768 | 92 | $1.2438 \times 10^{142}$ | 142.09477 |
| 43 | $6.0415 \times 10^{52}$ | 52.78115 | 93 | $1.1568 \times 10^{144}$ | 144.06325 |
| 44 | $2.6583 \times 10^{54}$ | 54.42460 | 94 | $1.0874 \times 10^{146}$ | 146.03638 |
| **45** | $1.1962 \times 10^{56}$ | 56.07781 | **95** | $1.0330 \times 10^{148}$ | 148.01410 |
| 46 | $5.5026 \times 10^{57}$ | 57.74057 | 96 | $9.9168 \times 10^{149}$ | 149.99637 |
| 47 | $2.5862 \times 10^{59}$ | 59.41267 | 97 | $9.6193 \times 10^{151}$ | 151.98314 |
| 48 | $1.2414 \times 10^{61}$ | 61.09391 | 98 | $9.4269 \times 10^{153}$ | 153.97437 |
| 49 | $6.0828 \times 10^{62}$ | 62.78410 | 99 | $9.3326 \times 10^{155}$ | 155.97000 |
| **50** | $3.0414 \times 10^{64}$ | 64.48307 | **100** | $9.3326 \times 10^{157}$ | 157.97000 |

# FACTORS FOR COMPUTING PROBABLE ERRORS

| $n$ | $\dfrac{1}{\sqrt{n}}$ | $\dfrac{1}{\sqrt{n(n-1)}}$ | $\dfrac{.6745}{\sqrt{n-1}}$ | $\dfrac{.6745}{\sqrt{n(n-1)}}$ | $\dfrac{.8453}{n\sqrt{n-1}}$ | $\dfrac{.8453}{\sqrt{n(n-1)}}$ |
|---|---|---|---|---|---|---|
| 2 | .707107 | .707107 | .6745 | .4769 | .4227 | .5978 |
| 3 | .577350 | .408248 | .4769 | .2754 | .1993 | .3451 |
| 4 | .500000 | .288675 | .3894 | .1947 | .1220 | .2440 |
| 5 | .447214 | .223607 | .3372 | .1508 | .0845 | .1890 |
| 6 | .408248 | .182574 | .3016 | .1231 | .0630 | .1543 |
| 7 | .377964 | .154303 | .2754 | .1041 | .0493 | .1304 |
| 8 | .353553 | .133631 | .2549 | .0901 | .0399 | .1130 |
| 9 | .333333 | .117851 | .2385 | .0795 | .0332 | .0996 |
| 10 | .316228 | .105409 | .2248 | .0711 | .0282 | .0891 |
| 11 | .301511 | .095346 | .2133 | .0643 | .0243 | .0806 |
| 12 | .288675 | .087039 | .2034 | .0587 | .0212 | .0736 |
| 13 | .277350 | .080064 | .1947 | .0540 | .0188 | .0677 |
| 14 | .267261 | .074125 | .1871 | .0500 | .0167 | .0627 |
| 15 | .258199 | .069007 | .1803 | .0465 | .0151 | .0583 |
| 16 | .250000 | .064550 | .1742 | .0435 | .0136 | .0546 |
| 17 | .242536 | .060634 | .1686 | .0409 | .0124 | .0513 |
| 18 | .235702 | .057166 | .1636 | .0386 | .0114 | .0483 |
| 19 | .229416 | .054074 | .1590 | .0365 | .0105 | .0457 |
| 20 | .223607 | .051299 | .1547 | .0346 | .0097 | .0434 |
| 21 | .218218 | .048795 | .1508 | .0329 | .0090 | .0412 |
| 22 | .213201 | .046524 | .1472 | .0314 | .0084 | .0393 |
| 23 | .208514 | .044455 | .1438 | .0300 | .0078 | .0376 |
| 24 | .204124 | .042563 | .1406 | .0287 | .0073 | .0360 |
| 25 | .200000 | .040825 | .1377 | .0275 | .0069 | .0345 |
| 26 | .196116 | .039223 | .1349 | .0265 | .0065 | .0332 |
| 27 | .192450 | .037743 | .1323 | .0255 | .0061 | .0319 |
| 28 | .188982 | .036370 | .1298 | .0245 | .0058 | .0307 |
| 29 | .185695 | .035093 | .1275 | .0237 | .0055 | .0297 |
| 30 | .182574 | .033903 | .1252 | .0229 | .0052 | .0287 |
| 31 | .179605 | .032791 | .1231 | .0221 | .0050 | .0277 |
| 32 | .176777 | .031750 | .1211 | .0214 | .0047 | .0268 |
| 33 | .174078 | .030773 | .1192 | .0208 | .0045 | .0260 |
| 34 | .171499 | .029854 | .1174 | .0201 | .0043 | .0252 |
| 35 | .169031 | .028989 | .1157 | .0196 | .0041 | .0245 |
| 36 | .166667 | .028172 | .1140 | .0190 | .0040 | .0238 |
| 37 | .164399 | .027400 | .1124 | .0185 | .0038 | .0232 |
| 38 | .162221 | .026669 | .1109 | .0180 | .0037 | .0225 |
| 39 | .160128 | .025976 | .1094 | .0175 | .0035 | .0220 |
| 40 | .158114 | .025318 | .1080 | .0171 | .0034 | .0214 |
| 41 | .156174 | .024693 | .1066 | .0167 | .0033 | .0209 |
| 42 | .154303 | .024098 | .1053 | .0163 | .0031 | .0204 |
| 43 | .152499 | .023531 | .1041 | .0159 | .0030 | .0199 |
| 44 | .150756 | .022990 | .1029 | .0155 | .0029 | .0194 |
| 45 | .149071 | .022473 | .1017 | .0152 | .0028 | .0190 |
| 46 | .147442 | .021979 | .1005 | .0148 | .0027 | .0186 |
| 47 | .145865 | .021507 | .0994 | .0145 | .0027 | .0182 |
| 48 | .144338 | .021054 | .0984 | .0142 | .0026 | .0178 |
| 49 | .142857 | .020620 | .0974 | .0139 | .0025 | .0174 |
| 50 | .141421 | .020203 | .0964 | .0136 | .0024 | .0171 |

| $n$ | $\dfrac{1}{\sqrt{n}}$ | $\dfrac{1}{\sqrt{n(n-1)}}$ | $\dfrac{.6745}{\sqrt{n-1}}$ | $\dfrac{.6745}{\sqrt{n(n-1)}}$ | $\dfrac{.8453}{n\sqrt{n-1}}$ | $\dfrac{.8453}{\sqrt{n(n-1)}}$ |
|---|---|---|---|---|---|---|
| 50 | .141421 | .020203 | .0964 | .0136 | .0024 | .0171 |
| 51 | .140028 | .019803 | .0954 | .0134 | .0023 | .0167 |
| 52 | .138675 | .019418 | .0945 | .0131 | .0023 | .0164 |
| 53 | .137361 | .019048 | .0935 | .0129 | .0022 | .0161 |
| 54 | .136083 | .018692 | .0927 | .0126 | .0022 | .0158 |
| 55 | .134840 | .018349 | .0918 | .0124 | .0021 | .0155 |
| 56 | .133631 | .018019 | .0910 | .0122 | .0020 | .0152 |
| 57 | .132453 | .017700 | .0901 | .0119 | .0020 | .0150 |
| 58 | .131306 | .017392 | .0893 | .0117 | .0019 | .0147 |
| 59 | .130189 | .017095 | .0886 | .0115 | .0019 | .0145 |
| 60 | .129099 | .016807 | .0878 | .0113 | .0018 | .0142 |
| 61 | .128037 | .016529 | .0871 | .0112 | .0018 | .0140 |
| 62 | .127000 | .016261 | .0864 | .0110 | .0018 | .0138 |
| 63 | .125988 | .016001 | .0857 | .0108 | .0017 | .0135 |
| 64 | .125000 | .015749 | .0850 | .0106 | .0017 | .0133 |
| 65 | .124035 | .015504 | .0843 | .0105 | .0016 | .0131 |
| 66 | .123091 | .015268 | .0837 | .0103 | .0016 | .0129 |
| 67 | .122169 | .015038 | .0830 | .0101 | .0016 | .0127 |
| 68 | .121268 | .014815 | .0824 | .0100 | .0015 | .0125 |
| 69 | .120386 | .014599 | .0818 | .0099 | .0015 | .0123 |
| 70 | .119523 | .014389 | .0812 | .0097 | .0015 | .0122 |
| 71 | .118678 | .014185 | .0806 | .0096 | .0014 | .0120 |
| 72 | .117851 | .013986 | .0801 | .0094 | .0014 | .0118 |
| 73 | .117041 | .013793 | .0795 | .0093 | .0014 | .0117 |
| 74 | .116248 | .013606 | .0789 | .0092 | .0013 | .0115 |
| 75 | .115470 | .013423 | .0784 | .0091 | .0013 | .0113 |
| 76 | .114708 | .013245 | .0779 | .0089 | .0013 | .0112 |
| 77 | .113961 | .013072 | .0773 | .0088 | .0013 | .0111 |
| 78 | .113228 | .012904 | .0769 | .0087 | .0012 | .0109 |
| 79 | .112509 | .012739 | .0764 | .0086 | .0012 | .0108 |
| 80 | .111803 | .012579 | .0759 | .0085 | .0012 | .0106 |
| 81 | .111111 | .012423 | .0754 | .0084 | .0012 | .0105 |
| 82 | .110432 | .012270 | .0749 | .0083 | .0012 | .0104 |
| 83 | .109764 | .012121 | .0745 | .0082 | .0011 | .0103 |
| 84 | .109109 | .011976 | .0740 | .0081 | .0011 | .0101 |
| 85 | .108465 | .011835 | .0736 | .0080 | .0011 | .0100 |
| 86 | .107833 | .011696 | .0732 | .0079 | .0011 | .0099 |
| 87 | .107211 | .011561 | .0727 | .0078 | .0011 | .0098 |
| 88 | .106600 | .011429 | .0723 | .0077 | .0010 | .0097 |
| 89 | .106000 | .011300 | .0719 | .0076 | .0010 | .0096 |
| 90 | .105409 | .011173 | .0715 | .0075 | .0010 | .0094 |
| 91 | .104828 | .011050 | .0711 | .0075 | .0010 | .0093 |
| 92 | .104257 | .010929 | .0707 | .0074 | .0010 | .0092 |
| 93 | .103695 | .010811 | .0703 | .0073 | .0010 | .0091 |
| 94 | .103142 | .010695 | .0699 | .0072 | .0009 | .0090 |
| 95 | .102598 | .010582 | .0696 | .0071 | .0009 | .0089 |
| 96 | .102062 | .010471 | .0692 | .0071 | .0009 | .0089 |
| 97 | .101535 | .010363 | .0688 | .0070 | .0009 | .0088 |
| 98 | .101015 | .010257 | .0685 | .0069 | .0009 | .0087 |
| 99 | .100504 | .010152 | .0681 | .0069 | .0009 | .0086 |
| 100 | .100000 | .010050 | .0678 | .0068 | .0008 | .0085 |

# PROBABILITY OF OCCURRENCE OF DEVIATIONS

Valid for thirty or more samples.

Probability of occurrence, expressed as per cent, and odds against a deviation as great or greater than that designated is given for various ratios of the deviation to the probable error and to the standard deviation.

(From Pearl, Medical Biometry and Statistics, W. B. Saunders Company, publishers, by permission.)

| Ratio dev. to P.E. | Probable occurrence % | Odds against, to 1 | Ratio dev. to std. dev. | Probable occurrence % | Odds against, to 1 |
|---|---|---|---|---|---|
| 1.0 | 50.00 | 1.00 | 0.67449 | 50.00 | 1.00 |
| 1.1 | 45.81 | 1.18 | 0.7 | 48.39 | 1.07 |
| 1.2 | 41.83 | 1.39 | 0.8 | 42.37 | 1.36 |
| 1.3 | 38.06 | 1.63 | 0.9 | 36.81 | 1.72 |
| 1.4 | 34.50 | 1.90 | 1.0 | 31.73 | 2.15 |
| 1.5 | 31.17 | 2.21 | 1.1 | 27.13 | 2.69 |
| 1.6 | 28.05 | 2.57 | 1.2 | 23.01 | 3.35 |
| 1.7 | 25.15 | 2.98 | 1.3 | 19.36 | 4.17 |
| 1.8 | 22.47 | 3.45 | 1.4 | 16.15 | 5.19 |
| 1.9 | 20.00 | 4.00 | 1.5 | 13.36 | 6.48 |
| 2.0 | 17.73 | 4.64 | 1.6 | 10.96 | 8.12 |
| 2.1 | 15.67 | 5.38 | 1.7 | 8.91 | 10.22 |
| 2.2 | 13.78 | 6.25 | 1.8 | 7.19 | 12.92 |
| 2.3 | 12.08 | 7.28 | 1.9 | 5.74 | 16.41 |
| 2.4 | 10.55 | 8.48 | 2.0 | 4.55 | 20.98 |
| 2.5 | 9.18 | 9.90 | 2.1 | 3.57 | 26.99 |
| 2.6 | 7.95 | 11.58 | 2.2 | 2.78 | 34.96 |
| 2.7 | 6.86 | 13.58 | 2.3 | 2.14 | 45.62 |
| 2.8 | 5.89 | 15.96 | 2.4 | 1.64 | 59.99 |
| 2.9 | 5.05 | 18.82 | 2.5 | 1.24 | 79.52 |
| 3.0 | 4.30 | 22.24 | 2.6 | .932 | 106.3 |
| 3.1 | 3.65 | 26.37 | 2.7 | .693 | 143.2 |
| 3.2 | 3.09 | 31.36 | 2.8 | .511 | 194.7 |
| 3.3 | 2.60 | 37.42 | 2.9 | .373 | 267.0 |
| 3.4 | 2.18 | 44.80 | 3.0 | .270 | 369.4 |
| 3.5 | 1.82 | 53.82 | 3.1 | .194 | 515.7 |
| 3.6 | 1.52 | 64.89 | 3.2 | .137 | 726.7 |
| 3.7 | 1.26 | 78.53 | 3.3 | .0967 | 1,033. |
| 3.8 | 1.04 | 95.38 | 3.4 | .0674 | 1,483. |
| 3.9 | .853 | 116.3 | 3.5 | .0465 | 2,149. |
| 4.0 | .698 | 142.3 | 3.6 | .0318 | 3,142. |
| 4.1 | .569 | 174.9 | 3.7 | .0216 | 4,637. |
| 4.2 | .461 | 215.8 | 3.8 | .0145 | 6,915. |
| 4.3 | .373 | 267.2 | 3.9 | .00962 | 10,394. |
| 4.4 | .300 | 332.4 | 4.0 | .00634 | 15,772. |
| 4.5 | .240 | 415.0 | 5.0 | $5.73 \times 10^{-5}$ | $1.744 \times 10^6$ |
| 4.6 | .192 | 520.4 | 6.0 | $2.0 \times 10^{-7}$ | $5.0 \times 10^8$ |
| 4.7 | .152 | 655.3 | 7.0 | $2.6 \times 10^{-10}$ | $3.9 \times 10^{11}$ |
| 4.8 | .121 | 828.3 | | | |
| 4.9 | .0950 | 1,052. | | | |
| 5.0 | .0745 | 1,341. | | | |
| 6.0 | .0052 | 19,300. | | | |
| 7.0 | .00023 | $4.27 \times 10^5$ | | | |
| 8.0 | $6.8 \times 10^{-6}$ | $1.47 \times 10^7$ | | | |
| 9.0 | $1.3 \times 10^{-7}$ | $7.30 \times 10^8$ | | | |
| 10.0 | $1.5 \times 10^{-9}$ | $6.5 \times 10^{10}$ | | | |

## NORMAL CURVE OF ERROR

If $x$ is measured in "$\sigma$-units" from the mean* the following tables give the values for the area integral

$$\int_0^t \phi(x)dx, \ \phi(x), \ \phi''(x) = (x^2 - 1)\phi(x), \ \phi'''(x)$$
$$= (3x - x^3)\phi(x), \text{ and } \phi^{iv}(x) = (x^4 - 6x^2 + 3)\phi(x)$$

for value $x = t$.

It should be noted that other probability integrals can be calculated from these tables. For example:

$$\int_0^t \phi(x)dx = \frac{1}{2} \text{ erf } \left(\frac{t}{\sqrt{2}}\right), \text{ where erf } \left(\frac{t}{\sqrt{2}}\right),$$

represents the error function associated with the normal curve.

To evaluate erf (2.3) proceed as follows:

Since $\dfrac{t}{\sqrt{2}} = 2.3$, one finds $t = (2.3) \ \sqrt{2} = (2.3)(1.414) = 3.25$.

In entry for area opposite $t = 3.25$, the value 0.4994 is given. Thus erf (2.3) = 2 (0.4994) = 0.9988.

* See index for Probability, formulae.

# NORMAL CURVE OF ERROR

## Normal Curve $\phi(x) = \dfrac{1}{\sqrt{2\pi}}\, e^{-\frac{x^2}{2}}$

| $t$ | Area | Ordinate $\phi(x)$ | Second derivative $\phi''(x)$ | Third derivative $\phi'''(x)$ | Fourth derivative $\phi^{\mathrm{iv}}(x)$ | $t$ | Area | Ordinate $\phi(x)$ | Second derivative $\phi''(x)$ | Third derivative $\phi'''(x)$ | Fourth derivative $\phi^{\mathrm{iv}}(x)$ |
|---|---|---|---|---|---|---|---|---|---|---|---|
| .00 | .0000 | .3989 | − .3989 | .0000 | 1.1968 | .50 | .1915 | .3521 | − .2641 | .4841 | .5501 |
| .01 | .0040 | .3989 | − .3989 | .0120 | 1.1965 | .51 | .1950 | .3503 | − .2592 | .4895 | .5279 |
| .02 | .0080 | .3989 | − .3987 | .0239 | 1.1956 | .52 | .1985 | .3485 | − .2543 | .4947 | .5056 |
| .03 | .0120 | .3988 | − .3984 | .0359 | 1.1941 | .53 | .2019 | .3467 | − .2493 | .4996 | .4831 |
| .04 | .0160 | .3986 | − .3980 | .0478 | 1.1920 | .54 | .2054 | .3448 | − .2443 | .5043 | .4605 |
| .05 | .0199 | .3984 | − .3975 | .0597 | 1.1894 | .55 | .2088 | .3429 | − .2392 | .5088 | .4378 |
| .06 | .0239 | .3982 | − .3968 | .0716 | 1.1861 | .56 | .2123 | .3411 | − .2341 | .5131 | .4150 |
| .07 | .0279 | .3980 | − .3960 | .0834 | 1.1822 | .57 | .2157 | .3391 | − .2289 | .5171 | .3921 |
| .08 | .0319 | .3977 | − .3951 | .0952 | 1.1778 | .58 | .2190 | .3372 | − .2238 | .5209 | .3691 |
| .09 | .0359 | .3973 | − .3941 | .1070 | 1.1727 | .59 | .2224 | .3352 | − .2185 | .5245 | .3461 |
| .10 | .0398 | .3970 | − .3930 | .1187 | 1.1671 | .60 | .2258 | .3332 | − .2133 | .5278 | .3231 |
| .11 | .0438 | .3965 | − .3917 | .1303 | 1.1609 | .61 | .2291 | .3312 | − .2080 | .5309 | .3000 |
| .12 | .0478 | .3961 | − .3904 | .1419 | 1.1541 | .62 | .2324 | .3292 | − .2027 | .5338 | .2770 |
| .13 | .0517 | .3956 | − .3889 | .1534 | 1.1468 | .63 | .2357 | .3271 | − .1973 | .5365 | .2539 |
| .14 | .0557 | .3951 | − .3873 | .1648 | 1.1389 | .64 | .2389 | .3251 | − .1919 | .5389 | .2309 |
| .15 | .0596 | .3945 | − .3856 | .1762 | 1.1304 | .65 | .2422 | .3230 | − .1865 | .5411 | .2078 |
| .16 | .0636 | .3939 | − .3838 | .1874 | 1.1214 | .66 | .2454 | .3209 | − .1811 | .5431 | .1849 |
| .17 | .0675 | .3932 | − .3819 | .1986 | 1.1118 | .67 | .2486 | .3187 | − .1757 | .5448 | .1620 |
| .18 | .0714 | .3925 | − .3798 | .2097 | 1.1017 | .68 | .2518 | .3166 | − .1702 | .5463 | .1391 |
| .19 | .0754 | .3918 | − .3777 | .2206 | 1.0911 | .69 | .2549 | .3144 | − .1647 | .5476 | .1164 |
| .20 | .0793 | .3910 | − .3754 | .2315 | 1.0799 | .70 | .2580 | .3123 | − .1593 | .5486 | .0937 |
| .21 | .0832 | .3902 | − .3730 | .2422 | 1.0682 | .71 | .2612 | .3101 | − .1538 | .5495 | .0712 |
| .22 | .0871 | .3894 | − .3706 | .2529 | 1.0560 | .72 | .2642 | .3079 | − .1483 | .5501 | .0487 |
| .23 | .0910 | .3885 | − .3680 | .2634 | 1.0434 | .73 | .2673 | .3056 | − .1428 | .5504 | .0265 |
| .24 | .0948 | .3876 | − .3653 | .2737 | 1.0302 | .74 | .2704 | .3034 | − .1373 | .5506 | .0043 |
| .25 | .0987 | .3867 | − .3625 | .2840 | 1.0165 | .75 | .2734 | .3011 | − .1318 | .5505 | − .0176 |
| .26 | .1026 | .3857 | − .3596 | .2941 | 1.0024 | .76 | .2764 | .2989 | − .1262 | .5502 | − .0394 |
| .27 | .1064 | .3847 | − .3566 | .3040 | 0.9878 | .77 | .2794 | .2966 | − .1207 | .5497 | − .0611 |
| .28 | .1103 | .3836 | − .3535 | .3138 | 0.9727 | .78 | .2823 | .2943 | − .1153 | .5490 | − .0825 |
| .29 | .1141 | .3825 | − .3504 | .3235 | 0.9572 | .79 | .2852 | .2920 | − .1098 | .5481 | − .1037 |
| .30 | .1179 | .3814 | − .3471 | .3330 | 0.9413 | .80 | .2881 | .2897 | − .1043 | .5469 | − .1247 |
| .31 | .1217 | .3802 | − .3437 | .3423 | 0.9250 | .81 | .2910 | .2874 | − .0988 | .5456 | − .1455 |
| .32 | .1255 | .3790 | − .3402 | .3515 | 0.9082 | .82 | .2939 | .2850 | − .0934 | .5440 | − .1660 |
| .33 | .1293 | .3778 | − .3367 | .3605 | 0.8910 | .83 | .2967 | .2827 | − .0880 | .5423 | − .1862 |
| .34 | .1331 | .3765 | − .3330 | .3693 | 0.8735 | .84 | .2996 | .2803 | − .0825 | .5403 | − .2063 |
| .35 | .1368 | .3752 | − .3293 | .3779 | 0.8556 | .85 | .3023 | .2780 | − .0771 | .5381 | − .2260 |
| .36 | .1406 | .3739 | − .3255 | .3864 | 0.8373 | .86 | .3051 | .2756 | − .0718 | .5358 | − .2455 |
| .37 | .1443 | .3726 | − .3216 | .3947 | 0.8186 | .87 | .3079 | .2732 | − .0664 | .5332 | − .2646 |
| .38 | .1480 | .3712 | − .3176 | .4028 | 0.7996 | .88 | .3106 | .2709 | − .0611 | .5305 | − .2835 |
| .39 | .1517 | .3697 | − .3135 | .4107 | 0.7803 | .89 | .3133 | .2685 | − .0558 | .5276 | − .3021 |
| .40 | .1554 | .3683 | − .3094 | .4184 | 0.7607 | .90 | .3159 | .2661 | − .0506 | .5245 | − .3203 |
| .41 | .1591 | .3668 | − .3051 | .4259 | 0.7408 | .91 | .3186 | .2637 | − .0453 | .5212 | − .3383 |
| .42 | .1628 | .3653 | − .3008 | .4332 | 0.7206 | .92 | .3212 | .2613 | − .0401 | .5177 | − .3559 |
| .43 | .1664 | .3637 | − .2965 | .4403 | 0.7001 | .93 | .3238 | .2589 | − .0350 | .5140 | − .3731 |
| .44 | .1700 | .3621 | − .2920 | .4472 | 0.6793 | .94 | .3264 | .2565 | − .0299 | .5102 | − .3901 |
| .45 | .1736 | .3605 | − .2875 | .4539 | 0.6583 | .95 | .3289 | .2541 | − .0248 | .5062 | − .4066 |
| .46 | .1772 | .3589 | − .2830 | .4603 | 0.6371 | .96 | .3315 | .2516 | − .0197 | .5021 | − .4228 |
| .47 | .1808 | .3572 | − .2783 | .4666 | 0.6156 | .97 | .3340 | .2492 | − .0147 | .4978 | − .4387 |
| .48 | .1844 | .3555 | − .2736 | .4727 | 0.5940 | .98 | .3365 | .2468 | − .0098 | .4933 | − .4541 |
| .49 | .1879 | .3538 | − .2689 | .4785 | 0.5721 | .99 | .3389 | .2444 | − .0049 | .4887 | − .4692 |
| .50 | .1915 | .3521 | − .2641 | .4841 | 0.5501 | 1.00 | .3413 | .2420 | .0000 | .4839 | − .4839 |

213

## Normal Curve $\phi(x) = \dfrac{1}{\sqrt{2\pi}} e^{-\frac{x^2}{2}}$ (Continued)

| $t$ | Area | Ordinate $\phi(x)$ | Second derivative $\phi''(x)$ | Third derivative $\phi'''(x)$ | Fourth derivative $\phi^{iv}(x)$ | $t$ | Area | Ordinate $\phi(x)$ | Second derivative $\phi''(x)$ | Third derivative $\phi'''(x)$ | Fourth derivative $\phi^{iv}(x)$ |
|---|---|---|---|---|---|---|---|---|---|---|---|
| 1.00 | .3413 | .2420 | .0000 | .4839 | −.4839 | 1.50 | .4332 | .1295 | .1619 | .1457 | −.7043 |
| 1.01 | .3438 | .2396 | .0048 | .4790 | −.4983 | 1.51 | .4345 | .1276 | .1633 | .1387 | −.6994 |
| 1.02 | .3461 | .2371 | .0096 | .4740 | −.5122 | 1.52 | .4357 | .1257 | .1647 | .1317 | −.6942 |
| 1.03 | .3485 | .2347 | .0143 | .4688 | −.5257 | 1.53 | .4370 | .1238 | .1660 | .1248 | −.6888 |
| 1.04 | .3508 | .2323 | .0190 | .4635 | −.5389 | 1.54 | .4382 | .1219 | .1672 | .1180 | −.6831 |
| 1.05 | .3531 | .2299 | .0236 | .4580 | −.5516 | 1.55 | .4394 | .1200 | .1683 | .1111 | −.6772 |
| 1.06 | .3554 | .2275 | .0281 | .4524 | −.5639 | 1.56 | .4406 | .1182 | .1694 | .1044 | −.6710 |
| 1.07 | .3577 | .2251 | .0326 | .4467 | −.5758 | 1.57 | .4418 | .1163 | .1704 | .0977 | −.6646 |
| 1.08 | .3599 | .2227 | .0371 | .4409 | −.5873 | 1.58 | .4430 | .1145 | .1714 | .0911 | −.6580 |
| 1.09 | .3621 | .2203 | .0414 | .4350 | −.5984 | 1.59 | .4441 | .1127 | .1722 | .0846 | −.6511 |
| 1.10 | .3643 | .2179 | .0458 | .4290 | −.6091 | 1.60 | .4452 | .1109 | .1730 | .0781 | −.6441 |
| 1.11 | .3665 | .2155 | .0500 | .4228 | −.6193 | 1.61 | .4463 | .1092 | .1738 | .0717 | −.6368 |
| 1.12 | .3686 | .2131 | .0542 | .4166 | −.6292 | 1.62 | .4474 | .1074 | .1745 | .0654 | −.6293 |
| 1.13 | .3708 | .2107 | .0583 | .4102 | −.6386 | 1.63 | .4485 | .1057 | .1751 | .0591 | −.6216 |
| 1.14 | .3729 | .2083 | .0624 | .4038 | −.6476 | 1.64 | .4495 | .1040 | .1757 | .0529 | −.6138 |
| 1.15 | .3749 | .2059 | .0664 | .3973 | −.6561 | 1.65 | .4505 | .1023 | .1762 | .0468 | −.6057 |
| 1.16 | .3770 | .2036 | .0704 | .3907 | −.6643 | 1.66 | .4515 | .1006 | .1766 | .0408 | −.5975 |
| 1.17 | .3790 | .2012 | .0742 | .3840 | −.6720 | 1.67 | .4525 | .0989 | .1770 | .0349 | −.5891 |
| 1.18 | .3810 | .1989 | .0780 | .3772 | −.6792 | 1.68 | .4535 | .0973 | .1773 | .0290 | −.5806 |
| 1.19 | .3830 | .1965 | .0818 | .3704 | −.6861 | 1.69 | .4545 | .0957 | .1776 | .0233 | −.5720 |
| 1.20 | .3849 | .1942 | .0854 | .3635 | −.6926 | 1.70 | .4554 | .0941 | .1778 | .0176 | −.5632 |
| 1.21 | .3869 | .1919 | .0890 | .3566 | −.6986 | 1.71 | .4564 | .0925 | .1779 | .0120 | −.5542 |
| 1.22 | .3888 | .1895 | .0926 | .3496 | −.7042 | 1.72 | .4573 | .0909 | .1780 | .0065 | −.5452 |
| 1.23 | .3907 | .1872 | .0960 | .3425 | −.7094 | 1.73 | .4582 | .0893 | .1780 | .0011 | −.5360 |
| 1.24 | .3925 | .1849 | .0994 | .3354 | −.7141 | 1.74 | .4591 | .0878 | .1780 | −.0042 | −.5267 |
| 1.25 | .3944 | .1827 | .1027 | .3282 | −.7185 | 1.75 | .4599 | .0863 | .1780 | −.0094 | −.5173 |
| 1.26 | .3962 | .1804 | .1060 | .3210 | −.7224 | 1.76 | .4608 | .0848 | .1778 | −.0146 | −.5079 |
| 1.27 | .3980 | .1781 | .1092 | .3138 | −.7259 | 1.77 | .4616 | .0833 | .1777 | −.0196 | −.4983 |
| 1.28 | .3997 | .1759 | .1123 | .3065 | −.7291 | 1.78 | .4625 | .0818 | .1774 | −.0245 | −.4887 |
| 1.29 | .4015 | .1736 | .1153 | .2992 | −.7318 | 1.79 | .4633 | .0804 | .1772 | −.0294 | −.4789 |
| 1.30 | .4032 | .1714 | .1182 | .2918 | −.7341 | 1.80 | .4641 | .0790 | .1769 | −.0341 | −.4692 |
| 1.31 | .4049 | .1692 | .1211 | .2845 | −.7361 | 1.81 | .4649 | .0775 | .1765 | −.0388 | −.4593 |
| 1.32 | .4066 | .1669 | .1239 | .2771 | −.7376 | 1.82 | .4656 | .0761 | .1761 | −.0433 | −.4494 |
| 1.33 | .4082 | .1647 | .1267 | .2697 | −.7388 | 1.83 | .4664 | .0748 | .1756 | −.0477 | −.4395 |
| 1.34 | .4099 | .1626 | .1293 | .2624 | −.7395 | 1.84 | .4671 | .0734 | .1751 | −.0521 | −.4295 |
| 1.35 | .4115 | .1604 | .1319 | .2550 | −.7399 | 1.85 | .4678 | .0721 | .1746 | −.0563 | −.4195 |
| 1.36 | .4131 | .1582 | .1344 | .2476 | −.7400 | 1.86 | .4686 | .0707 | .1740 | −.0605 | −.4095 |
| 1.37 | .4147 | .1561 | .1369 | .2402 | −.7396 | 1.87 | .4693 | .0694 | .1734 | −.0645 | −.3995 |
| 1.38 | .4162 | .1540 | .1392 | .2328 | −.7389 | 1.88 | .4700 | .0681 | .1727 | −.0685 | −.3894 |
| 1.39 | .4177 | .1518 | .1415 | .2254 | −.7378 | 1.89 | .4706 | .0669 | .1720 | −.0723 | −.3793 |
| 1.40 | .4192 | .1497 | .1437 | .2180 | −.7364 | 1.90 | .4713 | .0656 | .1713 | −.0761 | −.3693 |
| 1.41 | .4207 | .1476 | .1459 | .2107 | −.7347 | 1.91 | .4719 | .0644 | .1705 | −.0797 | −.3592 |
| 1.42 | .4222 | .1456 | .1480 | .2033 | −.7326 | 1.92 | .4726 | .0632 | .1697 | −.0832 | −.3492 |
| 1.43 | .4236 | .1435 | .1500 | .1960 | −.7301 | 1.93 | .4732 | .0620 | .1688 | −.0867 | −.3392 |
| 1.44 | .4251 | .1415 | .1519 | .1887 | −.7274 | 1.94 | .4738 | .0608 | .1679 | −.0900 | −.3292 |
| 1.45 | .4265 | .1394 | .1537 | .1815 | −.7243 | 1.95 | .4744 | .0596 | .1670 | −.0933 | −.3192 |
| 1.46 | .4279 | .1374 | .1555 | .1742 | −.7209 | 1.96 | .4750 | .0584 | .1661 | −.0964 | −.3093 |
| 1.47 | .4292 | .1354 | .1572 | .1670 | −.7172 | 1.97 | .4756 | .0573 | .1651 | −.0994 | −.2994 |
| 1.48 | .4306 | .1334 | .1588 | .1599 | −.7132 | 1.98 | .4762 | .0562 | .1641 | −.1024 | −.2895 |
| 1.49 | .4319 | .1315 | .1604 | .1528 | −.7089 | 1.99 | .4767 | .0551 | .1630 | −.1052 | −.2797 |
| 1.50 | .4332 | .1295 | .1619 | .1457 | −.7043 | 2.00 | .4773 | .0540 | .1620 | −.1080 | −.2700 |

## Normal Curve $\phi(x) = \dfrac{1}{\sqrt{2\pi}} e^{-\frac{x^2}{2}}$ (Continued)

| $t$ | Area | Ordinate $\phi(x)$ | Second derivative $\phi''(x)$ | Third derivative $\phi'''(x)$ | Fourth derivative $\phi^{iv}(x)$ | $t$ | Area | Ordinate $\phi(x)$ | Second derivative $\phi''(x)$ | Third derivative $\phi'''(x)$ | Fourth derivative $\phi^{iv}(x)$ |
|---|---|---|---|---|---|---|---|---|---|---|---|
| **2.00** | .4773 | .0540 | .1620 | −.1080 | −.2700 | **2.50** | .4938 | .0175 | .0920 | −.1424 | .0800 |
| 2.01 | .4778 | .0529 | .1609 | −.1106 | −.2603 | 2.51 | .4940 | .0171 | .0906 | −.1416 | .0836 |
| 2.02 | .4783 | .0519 | .1598 | −.1132 | −.2506 | 2.52 | .4941 | .0167 | .0892 | −.1408 | .0871 |
| 2.03 | .4788 | .0508 | .1586 | −.1157 | −.2411 | 2.53 | .4943 | .0163 | .0878 | −.1399 | .0905 |
| 2.04 | .4793 | .0498 | .1575 | −.1180 | −.2316 | 2.54 | .4945 | .0159 | .0864 | −.1389 | .0937 |
| **2.05** | .4798 | .0488 | .1563 | −.1203 | −.2222 | **2.55** | .4946 | .0155 | .0850 | −.1380 | .0968 |
| 2.06 | .4803 | .0478 | .1550 | −.1225 | −.2129 | 2.56 | .4948 | .0151 | .0836 | −.1370 | .0998 |
| 2.07 | .4808 | .0468 | .1538 | −.1245 | −.2036 | 2.57 | .4949 | .0147 | .0823 | −.1360 | .1027 |
| 2.08 | .4812 | .0459 | .1526 | −.1265 | −.1945 | 2.58 | .4951 | .0143 | .0809 | −.1350 | .1054 |
| 2.09 | .4817 | .0449 | 1513 | −.1284 | −.1854 | 2.59 | .4952 | .0139 | .0796 | −.1339 | .1080 |
| **2.10** | .4821 | .0440 | .1500 | −.1302 | −.1765 | **2.60** | .4953 | .0136 | .0782 | −.1328 | .1105 |
| 2.11 | .4826 | .0431 | .1487 | −.1320 | −.1676 | 2.61 | .4955 | .0132 | .0769 | −.1317 | .1129 |
| 2.12 | .4830 | .0422 | .1474 | −.1336 | −.1588 | 2.62 | .4956 | .0129 | .0756 | −.1305 | .1152 |
| 2.13 | .4834 | .0413 | .1460 | −.1351 | −.1502 | 2.63 | .4957 | .0126 | .0743 | −.1294 | .1173 |
| 2.14 | .4838 | .0404 | .1446 | −.1366 | −.1416 | 2.64 | .4959 | .0122 | .0730 | −.1282 | .1194 |
| **2.15** | .4842 | .0396 | .1433 | −.1380 | −.1332 | **2.65** | .4960 | .0119 | .0717 | −.1270 | .1213 |
| 2.16 | .4846 | .0387 | .1419 | −.1393 | −.1249 | 2.66 | .4961 | .0116 | .0705 | −.1258 | .1231 |
| 2.17 | .4850 | .0379 | .1405 | −.1405 | −.1167 | 2.67 | .4962 | .0113 | .0692 | −.1245 | .1248 |
| 2.18 | .4854 | .0371 | .1391 | −.1416 | −.1086 | 2.68 | .4963 | .0110 | .0680 | −.1233 | .1264 |
| 2.19 | .4857 | .0363 | .1377 | −.1426 | −.1006 | 2.69 | .4964 | .0107 | .0668 | −.1220 | .1279 |
| **2.20** | .4861 | .0355 | .1362 | −.1436 | −.0927 | **2.70** | .4965 | .0104 | .0656 | −.1207 | .1293 |
| 2.21 | .4865 | .0347 | .1348 | −.1445 | −.0850 | 2.71 | .4966 | .0101 | .0644 | −.1194 | .1306 |
| 2.22 | .4868 | .0339 | .1333 | −.1453 | −.0774 | 2.72 | .4967 | .0099 | .0632 | −.1181 | .1317 |
| 2.23 | .4871 | .0332 | .1319 | −.1460 | −.0700 | 2.73 | .4968 | .0096 | .0620 | −.1168 | .1328 |
| 2.24 | .4875 | .0325 | .1304 | −.1467 | −.0626 | 2.74 | .4969 | .0094 | .0608 | −.1154 | .1338 |
| **2.25** | .4878 | .0317 | .1289 | −.1473 | −.0554 | **2.75** | .4970 | .0091 | .0597 | −.1141 | .1347 |
| 2.26 | .4881 | .0310 | .1275 | −.1478 | −.0484 | 2.76 | .4971 | .0089 | .0585 | −.1127 | .1356 |
| 2.27 | .4884 | .0303 | .1260 | −.1483 | −.0414 | 2.77 | .4972 | .0086 | .0574 | −.1114 | .1363 |
| 2.28 | .4887 | .0297 | .1245 | −.1486 | −.0346 | 2.78 | .4973 | .0084 | .0563 | −.1100 | .1369 |
| 2.29 | .4890 | .0290 | .1230 | −.1490 | −.0279 | 2.79 | .4974 | .0081 | .0552 | −.1087 | .1375 |
| **2.30** | .4893 | .0283 | .1215 | −.1492 | −.0214 | **2.80** | .4974 | .0079 | .0541 | −.1073 | .1379 |
| 2.31 | .4896 | .0277 | .1200 | −.1494 | −.0150 | 2.81 | .4975 | .0077 | .0531 | −.1059 | .1383 |
| 2.32 | .4898 | .0271 | .1185 | −.1495 | −.0088 | 2.82 | .4976 | .0075 | .0520 | −.1045 | .1386 |
| 2.33 | .4901 | .0264 | .1170 | −.1496 | −.0027 | 2.83 | .4977 | .0073 | .0510 | −.1031 | .1389 |
| 2.34 | .4904 | .0258 | .1155 | −.1496 | .0033 | 2.84 | .4977 | .0071 | .0500 | −.1017 | .1390 |
| **2.35** | .4906 | .0252 | .1141 | −.1495 | .0092 | **2.85** | .4978 | .0069 | .0490 | −.1003 | .1391 |
| 2.36 | .4909 | .0246 | .1126 | −.1494 | .0149 | 2.86 | .4979 | .0067 | .0480 | −.0990 | .1391 |
| 2.37 | .4911 | .0241 | .1111 | −.1492 | .0204 | 2.87 | .4980 | .0065 | .0470 | −.0976 | .1391 |
| 2.38 | .4913 | .0235 | .1096 | −.1490 | .0258 | 2.88 | .4980 | .0063 | .0460 | −.0962 | .1389 |
| 2.39 | .4916 | .0229 | .1081 | −.1487 | .0311 | 2.89 | .4981 | .0061 | .0451 | −.0948 | .1388 |
| **2.40** | .4918 | .0224 | .1066 | −.1483 | .0362 | **2.90** | .4981 | .0060 | .0441 | −.0934 | .1385 |
| 2.41 | .4920 | .0219 | .1051 | −.1480 | .0412 | 2.91 | .4982 | .0058 | .0432 | −.0920 | .1382 |
| 2.42 | .4922 | .0213 | .1036 | −.1475 | .0461 | 2.92 | .4983 | .0056 | .0423 | −.0906 | .1378 |
| 2.43 | .4925 | .0208 | .1022 | −.1470 | .0508 | 2.93 | .4983 | .0055 | .0414 | −.0893 | .1374 |
| 2.44 | .4927 | .0203 | .1007 | −.1465 | .0554 | 2.94 | .4984 | .0053 | .0405 | −.0879 | .1369 |
| **2.45** | .4929 | .0198 | .0992 | −.1459 | .0598 | **2.95** | .4984 | .0051 | .0396 | −.0865 | .1364 |
| 2.46 | .4931 | .0194 | .0978 | −.1453 | .0641 | 2.96 | .4985 | .0050 | .0388 | −.0852 | .1358 |
| 2.47 | .4932 | .0189 | .0963 | −.1446 | .0683 | 2.97 | .4985 | .0049 | .0379 | −.0838 | .1352 |
| 2.48 | .4934 | .0184 | .0949 | −.1439 | .0723 | 2.98 | .4986 | .0047 | .0371 | −.0825 | .1345 |
| 2.49 | .4936 | .0180 | .0935 | −.1432 | .0762 | 2.99 | .4986 | .0046 | .03€3 | −.0811 | .1337 |
| **2.50** | .4938 | .0175 | .0920 | −.1424 | .0800 | **3.00** | .4987 | .0044 | .0355 | −.0798 | .1330 |

# NORMAL CURVE OF ERROR

## Normal Curve $\phi(x) = \dfrac{1}{\sqrt{2\pi}} e^{-\frac{x^2}{2}}$ (Continued)

| $t$ | Area | Ordinate $\phi(x)$ | Second derivative $\phi''(x)$ | Third derivative $\phi'''(x)$ | Fourth derivative $\phi^{iv}(x)$ | $t$ | Area | Ordinate $\phi(x)$ | Second derivative $\phi''(x)$ | Third derivative $\phi'''(x)$ | Fourth derivative $\phi^{iv}(x)$ |
|---|---|---|---|---|---|---|---|---|---|---|---|
| 3.00 | .4987 | .0044 | .0355 | $-.0798$ | .1330 | 3.50 | .4998 | .0009 | .0098 | $-.0283$ | .0694 |
| 3.01 | .4987 | .0043 | .0347 | $-.0785$ | .1321 | 3.51 | .4998 | .0008 | .0095 | $-.0276$ | .0681 |
| 3.02 | .4987 | .0042 | .0339 | $-.0771$ | .1313 | 3.52 | .4998 | .0008 | .0093 | $-.0269$ | .0669 |
| 3.03 | .4988 | .0041 | .0331 | $-.0758$ | .1304 | 3.53 | .4998 | .0008 | .0090 | $-.0262$ | .0656 |
| 3.04 | .4988 | .0039 | .0324 | $-.0745$ | .1294 | 3.54 | .4998 | .0008 | .0087 | $-.0256$ | .0643 |
| 3.05 | .4989 | .0038 | .0316 | $-.0732$ | .1285 | 3.55 | .4998 | .0007 | .0085 | $-.0249$ | .0631 |
| 3.06 | .4989 | .0037 | .0309 | $-.0720$ | .1275 | 3.56 | .4998 | .0007 | .0082 | $-.0243$ | .0618 |
| 3.07 | .4989 | .0036 | .0302 | $-.0707$ | .1264 | 3.57 | .4998 | .0007 | .0080 | $-.0237$ | .0606 |
| 3.08 | .4990 | .0035 | .0295 | $-.0694$ | .1254 | 3.58 | .4998 | .0007 | .0078 | $-.0231$ | .0594 |
| 3.09 | .4990 | .0034 | .0288 | $-.0682$ | .1243 | 3.59 | .4998 | .0006 | .0075 | $-.0225$ | .0582 |
| 3.10 | .4990 | .0033 | .0281 | $-.0669$ | .1231 | 3.60 | .4998 | .0006 | .0073 | $-.0219$ | .0570 |
| 3.11 | .4991 | .0032 | .0275 | $-.0657$ | .1220 | 3.61 | .4999 | .0006 | .0071 | $-.0214$ | .0559 |
| 3.12 | .4991 | .0031 | .0268 | $-.0645$ | .1208 | 3.62 | .4999 | .0006 | .0069 | $-.0208$ | .0547 |
| 3.13 | .4991 | .0030 | .0262 | $-.0633$ | .1196 | 3.63 | .4999 | .0006 | .0067 | $-.0203$ | .0536 |
| 3.14 | .4992 | .0029 | .0256 | $-.0621$ | .1184 | 3.64 | .4999 | .0005 | .0065 | $-.0198$ | .0524 |
| 3.15 | .4992 | .0028 | .0249 | $-.0609$ | .1171 | 3.65 | .4999 | .0005 | .0063 | $-.0192$ | .0513 |
| 3.16 | .4992 | .0027 | .0243 | $-.0598$ | .1159 | 3.66 | .4999 | .0005 | .0061 | $-.0187$ | .0502 |
| 3.17 | .4992 | .0026 | .0237 | $-.0586$ | .1146 | 3.67 | .4999 | .0005 | .0059 | $-.0182$ | .0492 |
| 3.18 | .4993 | .0025 | .0232 | $-.0575$ | .1133 | 3.68 | .4999 | .0005 | .0057 | $-.0177$ | .0481 |
| 3.19 | .4993 | .0025 | .0226 | $-.0564$ | .1120 | 3.69 | .4999 | .0004 | .0056 | $-.0173$ | .0470 |
| 3.20 | .4993 | .0024 | .0220 | $-.0552$ | .1107 | 3.70 | .4999 | .0004 | .0054 | $-.0168$ | .0460 |
| 3.21 | .4993 | .0023 | .0215 | $-.0541$ | .1093 | 3.71 | .4999 | .0004 | .0052 | $-.0164$ | .0450 |
| 3.22 | .4994 | .0022 | .0210 | $-.0531$ | .1080 | 3.72 | .4999 | .0004 | .0051 | $-.0159$ | .0440 |
| 3.23 | .4994 | .0022 | .0204 | $-.0520$ | .1066 | 3.73 | .4999 | .0004 | .0049 | $-.0155$ | .0430 |
| 3.24 | .4994 | .0021 | .0199 | $-.0509$ | .1053 | 3.74 | .4999 | .0004 | .0048 | $-.0150$ | .0420 |
| 3.25 | .4994 | .0020 | .0194 | $-.0499$ | .1039 | 3.75 | .4999 | .0004 | .0046 | $-.0146$ | .0410 |
| 3.26 | .4994 | .0020 | .0189 | $-.0488$ | .1025 | 3.76 | .4999 | .0003 | .0045 | $-.0142$ | .0401 |
| 3.27 | .4995 | .0019 | .0184 | $-.0478$ | .1011 | 3.77 | .4999 | .0003 | .0043 | $-.0138$ | .0392 |
| 3.28 | .4995 | .0018 | .0180 | $-.0468$ | .0997 | 3.78 | .4999 | .0003 | .0042 | $-.0134$ | .0382 |
| 3.29 | .4995 | .0018 | .0175 | $-.0458$ | .0983 | 3.79 | .4999 | .0003 | .0041 | $-.0131$ | .0373 |
| 3.30 | .4995 | .0017 | .0170 | $-.0449$ | .0969 | 3.80 | .4999 | .0003 | .0039 | $-.0127$ | .0365 |
| 3.31 | .4995 | .0017 | .0166 | $-.0439$ | .0955 | 3.81 | .4999 | .0003 | .0038 | $-.0123$ | .0356 |
| 3.32 | .4996 | .0016 | .0162 | $-.0429$ | .0941 | 3.82 | .4999 | .0003 | .0037 | $-.0120$ | .0347 |
| 3.33 | .4996 | .0016 | .0157 | $-.0420$ | .0927 | 3.83 | .4999 | .0003 | .0036 | $-.0116$ | .0339 |
| 3.34 | .4996 | .0015 | .0153 | $-.0411$ | .0913 | 3.84 | .4999 | .0003 | .0034 | $-.0113$ | .0331 |
| 3.35 | .4996 | .0015 | .0149 | $-.0402$ | .0899 | 3.85 | .4999 | .0002 | .0033 | $-.0110$ | .0323 |
| 3.36 | .4996 | .0014 | .0145 | $-.0393$ | .0885 | 3.86 | .4999 | .0002 | .0032 | $-.0107$ | .0315 |
| 3.37 | .4996 | .0014 | .0141 | $-.0384$ | .0871 | 3.87 | .5000 | .0002 | .0031 | $-.0104$ | .0307 |
| 3.38 | .4996 | .0013 | .0138 | $-.0376$ | .0857 | 3.88 | .5000 | .0002 | .0030 | $-.0100$ | .0299 |
| 3.39 | .4997 | .0013 | .0134 | $-.0367$ | .0843 | 3.89 | .5000 | .0002 | .0029 | $-.0098$ | .0292 |
| 3.40 | .4997 | .0012 | .0130 | $-.0359$ | .0829 | 3.90 | .5000 | .0002 | .0028 | $-.0095$ | .0284 |
| 3.41 | .4997 | .0012 | .0127 | $-.0350$ | .0815 | 3.91 | .5000 | .0002 | .0027 | $-.0092$ | .0277 |
| 3.42 | .4997 | .0012 | .0123 | $-.0342$ | .0801 | 3.92 | .5000 | .0002 | .0026 | $-.0089$ | .0270 |
| 3.43 | .4997 | .0011 | .0120 | $-.0334$ | .0788 | 3.93 | .5000 | .0002 | .0026 | $-.0086$ | .0263 |
| 3.44 | .4997 | .0011 | .0116 | $-.0327$ | .0774 | 3.94 | .5000 | .0002 | .0025 | $-.0084$ | .0256 |
| 3.45 | .4997 | .0010 | .0113 | $-.0319$ | .0761 | 3.95 | .5000 | .0002 | .0024 | $-.0081$ | .0250 |
| 3.46 | .4997 | .0010 | .0110 | $-.0311$ | .0747 | 3.96 | .5000 | .0002 | .0023 | $-.0079$ | .0243 |
| 3.47 | .4997 | .0010 | .0107 | $-.0304$ | .0734 | 3.97 | .5000 | .0002 | .0022 | $-.0076$ | .0237 |
| 3.48 | .4998 | .0009 | .0104 | $-.0297$ | .0721 | 3.98 | .5000 | .0001 | .0022 | $-.0074$ | .0230 |
| 3.49 | .4998 | .0009 | .0101 | $-.0290$ | .0707 | 3.99 | .5000 | .0001 | .0021 | $-.0072$ | .0224 |
| 3.50 | .4998 | .0009 | .0098 | $-.0283$ | .0694 | 4.00 | .5000 | .0001 | .0020 | $-.0070$ | .0218 |

## Normal Curve $\phi(x) = \dfrac{1}{\sqrt{2\pi}}\,e^{-\frac{x^2}{2}}$ (Continued)

| $t$ | Area | Ordinate $\phi(x)$ | Second derivative $\phi''(x)$ | Third derivative $\phi'''(x)$ | Fourth derivative $\phi^{\mathrm{iv}}(x)$ | $t$ | Area | Ordinate $\phi(x)$ | Second derivative $\phi''(x)$ | Third derivative $\phi'''(x)$ | Fourth derivative $\phi^{\mathrm{iv}}(x)$ |
|---|---|---|---|---|---|---|---|---|---|---|---|
| **4.00** | .5000 | .0001 | .0020 | $-.0070$ | .0218 | **4.50** | .5000 | .0000 | .0003 | $-.0012$ | .0047 |
| 4.01 | .5000 | .0001 | .0019 | $-.0067$ | .0212 | 4.51 | .5000 | .0000 | .0003 | $-.0012$ | .0045 |
| 4.02 | .5000 | .0001 | .0019 | $-.0065$ | .0207 | 4.52 | .5000 | .0000 | .0003 | $-.0012$ | .0044 |
| 4.03 | .5000 | .0001 | .0018 | $-.0063$ | .0201 | 4.53 | .5000 | .0000 | .0003 | $-.0011$ | .0042 |
| 4.04 | .5000 | .0001 | .0018 | $-.0061$ | .0195 | 4.54 | .5000 | .0000 | .0003 | $-.0011$ | .0041 |
| **4.05** | .5000 | .0001 | .0017 | $-.0059$ | .0190 | **4.55** | .5000 | .0000 | .0003 | $-.0010$ | .0039 |
| 4.06 | .5000 | .0001 | .0016 | $-.0058$ | .0185 | 4.56 | .5000 | .0000 | .0002 | $-.0010$ | .0038 |
| 4.07 | .5000 | .0001 | .0016 | $-.0056$ | .0180 | 4.57 | .5000 | .0000 | .0002 | $-.0010$ | .0037 |
| 4.08 | .5000 | .0001 | .0015 | $-.0054$ | .0175 | 4.58 | .5000 | .0000 | .0002 | $-.0009$ | .0035 |
| 4.09 | .5000 | .0001 | .0015 | $-.0052$ | .0170 | 4.59 | .5000 | .0000 | .0002 | $-.0009$ | .0034 |
| **4.10** | .5000 | .0001 | .0014 | $-.0051$ | .0165 | **4.60** | .5000 | .0000 | .0002 | $-.0009$ | .0033 |
| 4.11 | .5000 | .0001 | .0014 | $-.0049$ | .0160 | 4.61 | .5000 | .0000 | .0002 | $-.0008$ | .0032 |
| 4.12 | .5000 | .0001 | .0013 | $-.0047$ | .0156 | 4.62 | .5000 | .0000 | .0002 | $-.0008$ | .0031 |
| 4.13 | .5000 | .0001 | .0013 | $-.0046$ | .0151 | 4.63 | .5000 | .0000 | .0002 | $-.0008$ | .0030 |
| 4.14 | .5000 | .0001 | .0012 | $-.0044$ | .0147 | 4.64 | .5000 | .0000 | .0002 | $-.0007$ | .0028 |
| **4.15** | .5000 | .0001 | .0012 | $-.0043$ | .0143 | **4.65** | .5000 | .0000 | .0002 | $-.0007$ | .0027 |
| 4.16 | .5000 | .0001 | .0011 | $-.0042$ | .0138 | 4.66 | .5000 | .0000 | .0002 | $-.0007$ | .0026 |
| 4.17 | .5000 | .0001 | .0011 | $-.0040$ | .0134 | 4.67 | .5000 | .0000 | .0002 | $-.0006$ | .0026 |
| 4.18 | .5000 | .0001 | .0011 | $-.0039$ | .0130 | 4.68 | .5000 | .0000 | .0002 | $-.0006$ | .0025 |
| 4.19 | .5000 | .0001 | .0010 | $-.0038$ | .0127 | 4.69 | .5000 | .0000 | .0001 | $-.0006$ | .0024 |
| **4.20** | .5000 | .0001 | .0010 | $-.0036$ | .0123 | **4.70** | .5000 | .0000 | .0001 | $-.0006$ | .0023 |
| 4.21 | .5000 | .0001 | .0009 | $-.0035$ | .0119 | 4.71 | .5000 | .0000 | .0001 | $-.0006$ | .0022 |
| 4.22 | .5000 | .0001 | .0009 | $-.0034$ | .0116 | 4.72 | .5000 | .0000 | .0001 | $-.0005$ | .0021 |
| 4.23 | .5000 | .0001 | .0009 | $-.0033$ | .0112 | 4.73 | .5000 | .0000 | .0001 | $-.0005$ | .0020 |
| 4.24 | .5000 | .0001 | .0009 | $-.0032$ | .0109 | 4.74 | .5000 | .0000 | .0001 | $-.0005$ | .0020 |
| **4.25** | .5000 | .0001 | .0008 | $-.0031$ | .0105 | **4.75** | .5000 | .0000 | .0001 | $-.0005$ | .0019 |
| 4.26 | .5000 | .0001 | .0008 | $-.0030$ | .0102 | 4.76 | .5000 | .0000 | .0001 | $-.0005$ | .0018 |
| 4.27 | .5000 | .0000 | .0008 | $-.0029$ | .0099 | 4.77 | .5000 | .0000 | .0001 | $-.0004$ | .0018 |
| 4.28 | .5000 | .0000 | .0007 | $-.0028$ | .0096 | 4.78 | .5000 | .0000 | .0001 | $-.0004$ | .0017 |
| 4.29 | .5000 | .0000 | .0007 | $-.0027$ | .0093 | 4.79 | .5000 | .0000 | .0001 | $-.0004$ | .0016 |
| **4.30** | .5000 | .0000 | .0007 | $-.0026$ | .0090 | **4.80** | .5000 | .0000 | .0001 | $-.0004$ | .0016 |
| 4.31 | .5000 | .0000 | .0007 | $-.0025$ | .0087 | 4.81 | .5000 | .0000 | .0001 | $-.0004$ | .0015 |
| 4.32 | .5000 | .0000 | .0006 | $-.0024$ | .0085 | 4.82 | .5000 | .0000 | .0001 | $-.0004$ | .0015 |
| 4.33 | .5000 | .0000 | .0006 | $-.0023$ | .0082 | 4.83 | .5000 | .0000 | .0001 | $-.0003$ | .0014 |
| 4.34 | .5000 | .0000 | .0006 | $-.0022$ | .0079 | 4.84 | .5000 | .0000 | .0001 | $-.0003$ | .0013 |
| **4.35** | .5000 | .0000 | .0006 | $-.0022$ | .0077 | **4.85** | .5000 | .0000 | .0001 | $-.0003$ | .0013 |
| 4.36 | .5000 | .0000 | .0005 | $-.0021$ | .0074 | 4.86 | .5000 | .0000 | .0001 | $-.0003$ | .0012 |
| 4.37 | .5000 | .0000 | .0005 | $-.0020$ | .0072 | 4.87 | .5000 | .0000 | .0001 | $-.0003$ | .0012 |
| 4.38 | .5000 | .0000 | .0005 | $-.0019$ | .0070 | 4.88 | .5000 | .0000 | .0001 | $-.0003$ | .0012 |
| 4.39 | .5000 | .0000 | .0005 | $-.0019$ | .0067 | 4.89 | .5000 | .0000 | .0001 | $-.0003$ | .0011 |
| **4.40** | .5000 | .0000 | .0005 | $-.0018$ | .0065 | **4.90** | .5000 | .0000 | .0001 | $-.0003$ | .0011 |
| 4.41 | .5000 | .0000 | .0004 | $-.0017$ | .0063 | 4.91 | .5000 | .0000 | .0001 | $-.0002$ | .0010 |
| 4.42 | .5000 | .0000 | .0004 | $-.0017$ | .0061 | 4.92 | .5000 | .0000 | .0001 | $-.0002$ | .0010 |
| 4.43 | .5000 | .0000 | .0004 | $-.0016$ | .0059 | 4.93 | .5000 | .0000 | .0001 | $-.0002$ | .0009 |
| 4.44 | .5000 | .0000 | .0004 | $-.0016$ | .0057 | 4.94 | .5000 | .0000 | .0001 | $-.0002$ | .0009 |
| **4.45** | .5000 | .0000 | .0004 | $-.0015$ | .0055 | **4.95** | .5000 | .0000 | .0000 | $-.0002$ | .0009 |
| 4.46 | .5000 | .0000 | .0004 | $-.0014$ | .0053 | 4.96 | .5000 | .0000 | .0000 | $-.0002$ | .0008 |
| 4.47 | .5000 | .0000 | .0004 | $-.0014$ | .0052 | 4.97 | .5000 | .0000 | .0000 | $-.0002$ | .0008 |
| 4.48 | .5000 | .0000 | .0003 | $-.0013$ | .0050 | 4.98 | .5000 | .0000 | .0000 | $-.0002$ | .0008 |
| 4.49 | .5000 | .0000 | .0003 | $-.0013$ | .0048 | 4.99 | .5000 | .0000 | .0000 | $-.0002$ | .0007 |
| **4.50** | .5000 | .0000 | .0003 | $-.0012$ | .0047 | | | | | | |

# TESTS OF SIGNIFICANCE

## "$t$" Test of Significance Between Two Sample Means
### ($\bar{x}_1$ and $\bar{x}_2$).

(Use Fisher's $t$ distribution)

Paired variates:

$$t = \frac{\bar{d}}{\sqrt{\dfrac{\Sigma(d_i - \bar{d})^2}{N(N-1)}}} \text{ with } N - 1 \text{ degrees of freedom}$$

where $\bar{d} = \bar{x}_1 - \bar{x}_2$
$d_1 = x_{11} - x_{21}$
$d_2 = x_{12} - x_{22}$ etc.
$N$ = sample size

Unpaired variates:

$$t = \frac{\bar{x}_1 - \bar{x}_2}{\sqrt{\dfrac{\Sigma_i(x_{1i} - \bar{x}_1)^2 + \Sigma_i(x_{2i} - \bar{x}_2)^2}{N_1 + N_2 - 2}\left(\dfrac{1}{N_1} + \dfrac{1}{N_2}\right)}}$$

with $N_1 + N_2 - 2$ degrees of freedom

where $N_1$ = size of sample 1
$N_2$ = size of sample 2

---

## Chi Square Table

The column headings "$P$" are probabilities, while the body of the table gives values of $\chi^2$; the left column the degrees of freedom. The probability of a value $\chi^2 \geqq$ than the value specified is thus obtained. For $n = 20$, $P(\chi^2 \geqq 10.851)$ the table gives .95, and accordingly by subtraction $P(\chi^2 \leqq 10.851)$ is .05.

---

## $F$ Test for Equality of Variances

$$F = \frac{\sigma_1^2}{\sigma_2^2}$$

where $\sigma_1^2$ = variance of sample with size $N_1$
$\sigma_2^2$ = variance of sample with size $N_2$
with $N_1 - 1$ = degrees of freedom for numerator
$N_2 - 1$ = degrees of freedom for denominator

(Use Snedecor's $F$ distribution)

# TABLE FOR $t$ TEST OF SIGNIFICANCE

$-t$　　$0$　　$+t$

| Degrees of freedom | *P = 0.9 | 0.8 | 0.7 | 0.6 | 0.5 | 0.4 |
|---|---|---|---|---|---|---|
| 1 | 0.158 | 0.325 | 0.510 | 0.727 | 1.000 | 1.376 |
| 2 | 0.142 | 0.289 | 0.445 | 0.617 | 0.816 | 1.061 |
| 3 | 0.137 | 0.277 | 0.424 | 0.584 | 0.765 | 0.978 |
| 4 | 0.134 | 0.271 | 0.414 | 0.569 | 0.741 | 0.941 |
| 5 | 0.132 | 0.267 | 0.408 | 0.559 | 0.727 | 0.920 |
| 6 | 0.131 | 0.265 | 0.404 | 0.553 | 0.718 | 0.906 |
| 7 | 0.130 | 0.263 | 0.402 | 0.549 | 0.711 | 0.896 |
| 8 | 0.130 | 0.262 | 0.399 | 0.546 | 0.706 | 0.889 |
| 9 | 0.129 | 0.261 | 0.398 | 0.543 | 0.703 | 0.883 |
| 10 | 0.129 | 0.260 | 0.397 | 0.542 | 0.700 | 0.879 |
| 11 | 0.129 | 0.260 | 0.396 | 0.540 | 0.697 | 0.876 |
| 12 | 0.128 | 0.259 | 0.395 | 0.539 | 0.695 | 0.873 |
| 13 | 0.128 | 0.259 | 0.394 | 0.538 | 0.694 | 0.870 |
| 14 | 0.128 | 0.258 | 0.393 | 0.537 | 0.692 | 0.868 |
| 15 | 0.128 | 0.258 | 0.393 | 0.536 | 0.691 | 0.866 |
| 16 | 0.128 | 0.258 | 0.392 | 0.535 | 0.690 | 0.865 |
| 17 | 0.128 | 0.257 | 0.392 | 0.534 | 0.689 | 0.863 |
| 18 | 0.127 | 0.257 | 0.392 | 0.534 | 0.688 | 0.862 |
| 19 | 0.127 | 0.257 | 0.391 | 0.533 | 0.688 | 0.861 |
| 20 | 0.127 | 0.257 | 0.391 | 0.533 | 0.687 | 0.860 |
| 21 | 0.127 | 0.257 | 0.391 | 0.532 | 0.686 | 0.859 |
| 22 | 0.127 | 0.256 | 0.390 | 0.532 | 0.686 | 0.858 |
| 23 | 0.127 | 0.256 | 0.390 | 0.532 | 0.685 | 0.858 |
| 24 | 0.127 | 0.256 | 0.390 | 0.531 | 0.685 | 0.857 |
| 25 | 0.127 | 0.256 | 0.390 | 0.531 | 0.684 | 0.856 |
| 26 | 0.127 | 0.256 | 0.390 | 0.531 | 0.684 | 0.856 |
| 27 | 0.127 | 0.256 | 0.389 | 0.531 | 0.684 | 0.855 |
| 28 | 0.127 | 0.256 | 0.389 | 0.530 | 0.683 | 0.855 |
| 29 | 0.127 | 0.256 | 0.389 | 0.530 | 0.683 | 0.854 |
| 30 | 0.127 | 0.256 | 0.389 | 0.530 | 0.683 | 0.854 |
| ∞ | 0.12566 | 0.25335 | 0.38532 | 0.52440 | 0.67449 | 0.84162 |

Reproduced from *Statistical Methods for Research Workers*, 6th ed., with the permission of the author, R. A. Fisher, and his publisher, Oliver and Boyd, Edinburgh.

* $P$ is the probability of having $t$ this large or larger in size by chance.

| Degrees of freedom | 0.3 | 0.2 | 0.1 | 0.05 | 0.02 | 0.01 |
|---|---|---|---|---|---|---|
| 1 | 1.963 | 3.078 | 6.314 | 12.706 | 31.821 | 63.357 |
| 2 | 1.386 | 1.886 | 2.920 | 4.303 | 6.965 | 9.925 |
| 3 | 1.250 | 1.638 | 2.353 | 3.182 | 4.541 | 5.841 |
| 4 | 1.190 | 1.533 | 2.132 | 2.776 | 3.747 | 4.604 |
| 5 | 1.156 | 1.476 | 2.015 | 2.571 | 3.365 | 4.032 |
| 6 | 1.134 | 1.440 | 1.943 | 2.447 | 3.143 | 3.707 |
| 7 | 1.119 | 1.415 | 1.895 | 2.365 | 2.998 | 3.499 |
| 8 | 1.108 | 1.397 | 1.860 | 2.306 | 2.896 | 3.355 |
| 9 | 1.100 | 1.383 | 1.833 | 2.262 | 2.821 | 3.250 |
| 10 | 1.093 | 1.372 | 1.812 | 2.228 | 2.764 | 3.169 |
| 11 | 1.088 | 1.363 | 1.796 | 2.201 | 2.718 | 3.106 |
| 12 | 1.083 | 1.356 | 1.782 | 2.179 | 2.681 | 3.055 |
| 13 | 1.079 | 1.350 | 1.771 | 2.160 | 2.650 | 3.012 |
| 14 | 1.076 | 1.345 | 1.761 | 2.145 | 2.624 | 2.977 |
| 15 | 1.074 | 1.341 | 1.753 | 2.131 | 2.602 | 2.947 |
| 16 | 1.071 | 1.337 | 1.746 | 2.120 | 2.583 | 2.921 |
| 17 | 1.069 | 1.333 | 1.740 | 2.110 | 2.567 | 2.898 |
| 18 | 1.067 | 1.330 | 1.734 | 2.101 | 2.552 | 2.878 |
| 19 | 1.066 | 1.328 | 1.729 | 2.093 | 2.539 | 2.861 |
| 20 | 1.064 | 1.325 | 1.725 | 2.086 | 2.528 | 2.845 |
| 21 | 1.063 | 1.323 | 1.721 | 2.080 | 2.518 | 2.831 |
| 22 | 1.061 | 1.321 | 1.717 | 2.074 | 2.508 | 2.819 |
| 23 | 1.060 | 1.319 | 1.714 | 2.069 | 2.500 | 2.807 |
| 24 | 1.059 | 1.318 | 1.711 | 2.064 | 2.492 | 2.797 |
| 25 | 1.058 | 1.316 | 1.708 | 2.060 | 2.485 | 2.787 |
| 26 | 1.058 | 1.315 | 1.706 | 2.056 | 2.479 | 2.779 |
| 27 | 1.057 | 1.314 | 1.703 | 2.052 | 2.473 | 2.771 |
| 28 | 1.056 | 1.313 | 1.701 | 2.048 | 2.467 | 2.763 |
| 29 | 1.055 | 1.311 | 1.699 | 2.045 | 2.462 | 2.756 |
| 30 | 1.055 | 1.310 | 1.697 | 2.042 | 2.457 | 2.750 |
| $\infty$ | 1.03643 | 1.28155 | 1.64485 | 1.95996 | 2.32634 | 2.57582 |

# $\chi^2$ TABLE

| Degrees of freedom | $P = 0.99$ | 0.98 | 0.95 | 0.90 | 0.80 | 0.70 |
|---|---|---|---|---|---|---|
| 1 | 0.000157 | 0.000628 | 0.00393 | 0.0158 | 0.0642 | 0.148 |
| 2 | 0.0201 | 0.0404 | 0.103 | 0.211 | 0.446 | 0.713 |
| 3 | 0.115 | 0.185 | 0.352 | 0.584 | 1.005 | 1.424 |
| 4 | 0.297 | 0.429 | 0.711 | 1.064 | 1.649 | 2.195 |
| 5 | 0.554 | 0.752 | 1.145 | 1.610 | 2.343 | 3.000 |
| 6 | 0.872 | 1.134 | 1.635 | 2.204 | 3.070 | 3.828 |
| 7 | 1.239 | 1.564 | 2.167 | 2.833 | 3.822 | 4.671 |
| 8 | 1.646 | 2.032 | 2.733 | 3.490 | 4.594 | 5.527 |
| 9 | 2.088 | 2.532 | 3.325 | 4.168 | 5.380 | 6.393 |
| 10 | 2.558 | 3.059 | 3.940 | 4.865 | 6.179 | 7.267 |
| 11 | 3.053 | 3.609 | 4.575 | 5.578 | 6.989 | 8.148 |
| 12 | 3.571 | 4.178 | 5.226 | 6.304 | 7.807 | 9.034 |
| 13 | 4.107 | 4.765 | 5.892 | 7.042 | 8.634 | 9.926 |
| 14 | 4.660 | 5.368 | 6.571 | 7.790 | 9.467 | 10.821 |
| 15 | 5.229 | 5.985 | 7.261 | 8.547 | 10.307 | 11.721 |
| 16 | 5.812 | 6.614 | 7.962 | 9.312 | 11.152 | 12.624 |
| 17 | 6.408 | 7.255 | 8.672 | 10.085 | 12.002 | 13.531 |
| 18 | 7.015 | 7.906 | 9.390 | 10.865 | 12.857 | 14.440 |
| 19 | 7.633 | 8.567 | 10.117 | 11.651 | 13.716 | 15.352 |
| 20 | 8.260 | 9.237 | 10.851 | 12.443 | 14.578 | 16.266 |
| 21 | 8.897 | 9.915 | 11.591 | 13.240 | 15.445 | 17.182 |
| 22 | 9.542 | 10.600 | 12.338 | 14.041 | 16.314 | 18.101 |
| 23 | 10.196 | 11.293 | 13.091 | 14.848 | 17.187 | 19.021 |
| 24 | 10.856 | 11.992 | 13.848 | 15.659 | 18.062 | 19.943 |
| 25 | 11.524 | 12.697 | 14.611 | 16.473 | 18.940 | 20.867 |
| 26 | 12.198 | 13.409 | 15.379 | 17.292 | 19.820 | 21.792 |
| 27 | 12.879 | 14.125 | 16.151 | 18.114 | 20.703 | 22.719 |
| 28 | 13.565 | 14.847 | 16.928 | 18.939 | 21.588 | 23.647 |
| 29 | 14.256 | 15.574 | 17.708 | 19.768 | 22.475 | 24.577 |
| 30 | 14.953 | 16.306 | 18.493 | 20.599 | 23.364 | 25.508 |

For degrees of freedom greater than 30, the expression $\sqrt{2\chi^2} - \sqrt{2n' - 1}$ may be used as a normal deviate with unit variance, where $n'$ is the number of degrees of freedom.

Reproduced from *Statistical Methods for Research Workers*, 6th ed., with the permission of the author, R. A. Fisher, and his publisher, Oliver and Boyd, Edinburgh.

| De-grees of free-dom | 0.50 | 0.30 | 0.20 | 0.10 | 0.05 | 0.02 | 0.01 |
|---|---|---|---|---|---|---|---|
| 1 | 0.455 | 1.074 | 1.642 | 2.706 | 3.841 | 5.412 | 6.635 |
| 2 | 1.386 | 2.408 | 3.219 | 4.605 | 5.991 | 7.824 | 9.210 |
| 3 | 2.366 | 3.665 | 4.642 | 6.251 | 7.815 | 9.837 | 11.341 |
| 4 | 3.357 | 4.878 | 5.989 | 7.779 | 9.488 | 11.668 | 13.277 |
| 5 | 4.351 | 6.064 | 7.289 | 9.236 | 11.070 | 13.388 | 15.086 |
| 6 | 5.348 | 7.231 | 8.558 | 10.645 | 12.592 | 15.033 | 16.812 |
| 7 | 6.346 | 8.383 | 9.803 | 12.017 | 14.067 | 16.622 | 18.475 |
| 8 | 7.344 | 9.524 | 11.030 | 13.362 | 15.507 | 18.168 | 20.090 |
| 9 | 8.343 | 10.656 | 12.242 | 14.684 | 16.919 | 19.679 | 21.666 |
| 10 | 9.342 | 11.781 | 13.442 | 15.987 | 18.307 | 21.161 | 23.209 |
| 11 | 10.341 | 12.899 | 14.631 | 17.275 | 19.675 | 22.618 | 24.725 |
| 12 | 11.340 | 14.011 | 15.812 | 18.549 | 21.026 | 24.054 | 26.217 |
| 13 | 12.340 | 15.119 | 16.985 | 19.812 | 22.362 | 25.472 | 27.688 |
| 14 | 13.339 | 16.222 | 18.151 | 21.064 | 23.685 | 26.873 | 29.141 |
| 15 | 14.339 | 17.322 | 19.311 | 22.307 | 24.996 | 28.259 | 30.578 |
| 16 | 15.338 | 18.418 | 20.465 | 23.542 | 26.296 | 29.633 | 32.000 |
| 17 | 16.338 | 19.511 | 21.615 | 24.769 | 27.587 | 30.995 | 33.409 |
| 18 | 17.338 | 20.601 | 22.760 | 25.989 | 28.869 | 32.346 | 34.805 |
| 19 | 18.338 | 21.689 | 23.900 | 27.204 | 30.144 | 33.687 | 36.191 |
| 20 | 19.337 | 22.775 | 25.038 | 28.412 | 31.410 | 35.020 | 37.566 |
| 21 | 20.337 | 23.858 | 26.171 | 29.615 | 32.671 | 36.343 | 38.932 |
| 22 | 21.337 | 24.939 | 27.301 | 30.813 | 33.924 | 37.659 | 40.289 |
| 23 | 22.337 | 26.018 | 28.429 | 32.007 | 35.172 | 38.968 | 41.638 |
| 24 | 23.337 | 27.096 | 29.553 | 33.196 | 36.415 | 40.270 | 42.980 |
| 25 | 24.337 | 28.172 | 30.675 | 34.382 | 37.652 | 41.566 | 44.314 |
| 26 | 25.336 | 29.246 | 31.795 | 35.563 | 38.885 | 42.856 | 45.642 |
| 27 | 26.336 | 30.319 | 32.912 | 36.741 | 40.113 | 44.140 | 46.963 |
| 28 | 27.336 | 31.391 | 34.027 | 37.916 | 41.337 | 45.419 | 48.278 |
| 29 | 28.336 | 32.461 | 35.139 | 39.087 | 42.557 | 46.693 | 49.588 |
| 30 | 29.336 | 33.530 | 36.250 | 40.256 | 43.773 | 47.962 | 50.892 |

*5 % (Roman Type) and 1 % (Bold-Face Type)

| Degrees of freedom for lesser mean square | Degrees of freedom for greater mean square | | | | | | | | | | | |
|---|---|---|---|---|---|---|---|---|---|---|---|---|
| | 1 | 2 | 3 | 4 | 5 | 6 | 7 | 8 | 9 | 10 | 11 | 12 |
| 1 | 161 | 200 | 216 | 225 | 230 | 234 | 237 | 239 | 241 | 242 | 243 | 244 |
| | **4052** | **4999** | **5403** | **5625** | **5764** | **5859** | **5928** | **5981** | **6022** | **6056** | **6082** | **6106** |
| 2 | 18.51 | 19.00 | 19.16 | 19.25 | 19.30 | 19.33 | 19.36 | 19.37 | 19.38 | 19.39 | 19.40 | 19.41 |
| | **98.49** | **99.01** | **99.17** | **99.25** | **99.30** | **99.33** | **99.34** | **99.36** | **99.38** | **99.40** | **99.41** | **99.42** |
| 3 | 10.13 | 9.55 | 9.28 | 9.12 | 9.01 | 8.94 | 8.88 | 8.84 | 8.81 | 8.78 | 8.76 | 8.74 |
| | **34.12** | **30.81** | **29.46** | **28.71** | **28.24** | **27.91** | **27.67** | **27.49** | **27.34** | **27.23** | **27.13** | **27.05** |
| 4 | 7.71 | 6.94 | 6.59 | 6.39 | 6.26 | 6.16 | 6.09 | 6.04 | 6.00 | 5.96 | 5.93 | 5.91 |
| | **21.20** | **18.00** | **16.69** | **15.98** | **15.52** | **15.21** | **14.98** | **14.80** | **14.66** | **14.54** | **14.45** | **14.37** |
| 5 | 6.61 | 5.79 | 5.41 | 5.19 | 5.05 | 4.95 | 4.88 | 4.82 | 4.78 | 4.74 | 4.70 | 4.68 |
| | **16.26** | **13.27** | **12.06** | **11.39** | **10.97** | **10.67** | **10.45** | **10.27** | **10.15** | **10.05** | **9.96** | **9.89** |
| 6 | 5.99 | 5.14 | 4.76 | 4.53 | 4.39 | 4.28 | 4.21 | 4.15 | 4.10 | 4.06 | 4.03 | 4.00 |
| | **13.74** | **10.92** | **9.78** | **9.15** | **8.75** | **8.47** | **8.26** | **8.10** | **7.98** | **7.87** | **7.79** | **7.72** |
| 7 | 5.59 | 4.74 | 4.35 | 4.12 | 3.97 | 3.87 | 3.79 | 3.73 | 3.68 | 3.63 | 3.60 | 3.57 |
| | **12.25** | **9.55** | **8.45** | **7.85** | **7.46** | **7.19** | **7.00** | **6.84** | **6.71** | **6.62** | **6.54** | **6.47** |
| 8 | 5.32 | 4.46 | 4.07 | 3.84 | 3.69 | 3.58 | 3.50 | 3.44 | 3.39 | 3.34 | 3.31 | 3.28 |
| | **11.26** | **8.65** | **7.59** | **7.01** | **6.63** | **6.37** | **6.19** | **6.03** | **5.91** | **5.82** | **5.74** | **5.67** |
| 9 | 5.12 | 4.26 | 3.86 | 3.63 | 3.48 | 3.37 | 3.29 | 3.23 | 3.18 | 3.13 | 3.10 | 3.07 |
| | **10.56** | **8.02** | **6.99** | **6.42** | **6.06** | **5.80** | **5.62** | **5.47** | **5.35** | **5.26** | **5.18** | **5.11** |
| 10 | 4.96 | 4.10 | 3.71 | 3.48 | 3.33 | 3.22 | 3.14 | 3.07 | 3.02 | 2.97 | 2.94 | 2.91 |
| | **10.04** | **7.56** | **6.55** | **5.99** | **5.64** | **5.39** | **5.21** | **5.06** | **4.95** | **4.85** | **4.78** | **4.71** |
| 11 | 4.84 | 3.98 | 3.59 | 3.36 | 3.20 | 3.09 | 3.01 | 2.95 | 2.90 | 2.86 | 2.82 | 2.79 |
| | **9.65** | **7.20** | **6.22** | **5.67** | **5.32** | **5.07** | **4.88** | **4.74** | **4.63** | **4.54** | **4.46** | **4.40** |
| 12 | 4.75 | 3.88 | 3.49 | 3.26 | 3.11 | 3.00 | 2.92 | 2.85 | 2.80 | 2.76 | 2.72 | 2.69 |
| | **9.33** | **6.93** | **5.95** | **5.41** | **5.06** | **4.82** | **4.65** | **4.50** | **4.39** | **4.30** | **4.22** | **4.16** |
| 13 | 4.67 | 3.80 | 3.41 | 3.18 | 3.02 | 2.92 | 2.84 | 2.77 | 2.72 | 2.67 | 2.63 | 2.60 |
| | **9.07** | **6.70** | **5.74** | **5.20** | **4.86** | **4.62** | **4.44** | **4.30** | **4.19** | **4.10** | **4.02** | **3.96** |
| 14 | 4.60 | 3.74 | 3.34 | 3.11 | 2.96 | 2.85 | 2.77 | 2.70 | 2.65 | 2.60 | 2.56 | 2.53 |
| | **8.86** | **6.51** | **5.56** | **5.03** | **4.69** | **4.46** | **4.28** | **4.14** | **4.03** | **3.94** | **3.86** | **3.80** |
| 15 | 4.54 | 3.68 | 3.29 | 3.06 | 2.90 | 2.79 | 2.70 | 2.64 | 2.59 | 2.55 | 2.51 | 2.48 |
| | **8.68** | **6.36** | **5.42** | **4.89** | **4.56** | **4.32** | **4.14** | **4.00** | **3.89** | **3.80** | **3.73** | **3.67** |
| 16 | 4.49 | 3.63 | 3.24 | 3.01 | 2.85 | 2.74 | 2.66 | 2.59 | 2.54 | 2.49 | 2.45 | 2.42 |
| | **8.53** | **6.23** | **5.29** | **4.77** | **4.44** | **4.20** | **4.03** | **3.89** | **3.78** | **3.69** | **3.61** | **3.55** |

Reprinted, by permission, from Snedecor, *Statistical Methods*, Collegiate Press, Iowa State College, Ames.
* This table gives values of *F* which one would expect to exceed by chance alone 5 % and 1 % of the time.

# EQUALITY OF VARIANCES

| Degrees of freedom for lesser mean square | Degrees of freedom for greater mean square | | | | | | | | | | | |
|---|---|---|---|---|---|---|---|---|---|---|---|---|
| | 14 | 16 | 20 | 24 | 30 | 40 | 50 | 75 | 100 | 200 | 500 | ∞ |
| 1 | 245 | 246 | 248 | 249 | 250 | 251 | 252 | 253 | 253 | 254 | 254 | 254 |
| | **6142** | **6169** | **6208** | **6234** | **6258** | **6286** | **6302** | **6323** | **6334** | **6352** | **6361** | **6366** |
| 2 | 19.42 | 19.43 | 19.44 | 19.45 | 19.46 | 19.47 | 19.47 | 19.48 | 19.49 | 19.49 | 19.50 | 19.50 |
| | **99.43** | **99.44** | **99.45** | **99.46** | **99.47** | **99.48** | **99.48** | **99.49** | **99.49** | **99.49** | **99.50** | **99.50** |
| 3 | 8.71 | 8.69 | 8.66 | 8.64 | 8.62 | 8.60 | 8.58 | 8.57 | 8.56 | 8.54 | 8.54 | 8.53 |
| | **26.92** | **26.83** | **26.69** | **26.60** | **26.50** | **26.41** | **26.30** | **26.27** | **26.23** | **26.18** | **26.14** | **26.12** |
| 4 | 5.87 | 5.84 | 5.80 | 5.77 | 5.74 | 5.71 | 5.70 | 5.68 | 5.66 | 5.65 | 5.64 | 5.63 |
| | **14.24** | **14.15** | **14.02** | **13.93** | **13.83** | **13.74** | **13.69** | **13.61** | **13.57** | **13.52** | **13.48** | **13.46** |
| 5 | 4.64 | 4.60 | 4.56 | 4.53 | 4.50 | 4.46 | 4.44 | 4.42 | 4.40 | 4.38 | 4.37 | 4.36 |
| | **9.77** | **9.68** | **9.55** | **9.47** | **9.38** | **9.29** | **9.24** | **9.17** | **9.13** | **9.07** | **9.04** | **9.02** |
| 6 | 3.96 | 3.92 | 3.87 | 3.84 | 3.81 | 3.77 | 3.75 | 3.72 | 3.71 | 3.69 | 3.68 | 3.67 |
| | **7.60** | **7.52** | **7.39** | **7.31** | **7.23** | **7.14** | **7.09** | **7.02** | **6.99** | **6.94** | **6.90** | **6.88** |
| 7 | 3.52 | 3.49 | 3.44 | 3.41 | 3.38 | 3.34 | 3.32 | 3.29 | 3.28 | 3.25 | 3.24 | 3.23 |
| | **6.35** | **6.27** | **6.15** | **6.07** | **5.98** | **5.90** | **5.85** | **5.78** | **5.75** | **5.70** | **5.67** | **5.65** |
| 8 | 3.23 | 3.20 | 3.15 | 3.12 | 3.08 | 3.05 | 3.03 | 3.00 | 2.98 | 2.96 | 2.94 | 2.93 |
| | **5.56** | **5.48** | **5.36** | **5.28** | **5.20** | **5.11** | **5.06** | **5.00** | **4.96** | **4.91** | **4.88** | **4.86** |
| 9 | 3.02 | 2.98 | 2.93 | 2.90 | 2.86 | 2.82 | 2.80 | 2.77 | 2.76 | 2.73 | 2.72 | 2.71 |
| | **5.00** | **4.92** | **4.80** | **4.73** | **4.64** | **4.56** | **4.51** | **4.45** | **4.41** | **4.36** | **4.33** | **4.31** |
| 10 | 2.86 | 2.82 | 2.77 | 2.74 | 2.70 | 2.67 | 2.64 | 2.61 | 2.59 | 2.56 | 2.55 | 2.54 |
| | **4.60** | **4.52** | **4.41** | **4.33** | **4.25** | **4.17** | **4.12** | **4.05** | **4.01** | **3.96** | **3.93** | **3.91** |
| 11 | 2.74 | 2.70 | 2.65 | 2.61 | 2.57 | 2.53 | 2.50 | 2.47 | 2.45 | 2.42 | 2.41 | 2.40 |
| | **4.29** | **4.21** | **4.10** | **4.02** | **3.94** | **3.86** | **3.80** | **3.74** | **3.70** | **3.66** | **3.62** | **3.60** |
| 12 | 2.64 | 2.60 | 2.54 | 2.50 | 2.46 | 2.42 | 2.40 | 2.36 | 2.35 | 2.32 | 2.31 | 2.30 |
| | **4.05** | **3.98** | **3.86** | **3.78** | **3.70** | **3.61** | **3.56** | **3.49** | **3.46** | **3.41** | **3.38** | **3.36** |
| 13 | 2.55 | 2.51 | 2.46 | 2.42 | 2.38 | 2.34 | 2.32 | 2.28 | 2.26 | 2.24 | 2.22 | 2.21 |
| | **3.85** | **3.78** | **3.67** | **3.59** | **3.51** | **3.42** | **3.37** | **3.30** | **3.27** | **3.21** | **3.18** | **3.16** |
| 14 | 2.48 | 2.44 | 2.39 | 2.35 | 2.31 | 2.27 | 2.24 | 2.21 | 2.19 | 2.16 | 2.14 | 2.13 |
| | **3.70** | **3.62** | **3.51** | **3.43** | **3.34** | **3.26** | **3.21** | **3.14** | **3.11** | **3.06** | **3.02** | **3.00** |
| 15 | 2.43 | 2.39 | 2.33 | 2.29 | 2.25 | 2.21 | 2.18 | 2.15 | 2.12 | 2.10 | 2.08 | 2.07 |
| | **3.56** | **3.48** | **3.36** | **3.29** | **3.20** | **3.12** | **3.07** | **3.00** | **2.97** | **2.92** | **2.89** | **2.87** |
| 16 | 2.37 | 2.33 | 2.28 | 2.24 | 2.20 | 2.16 | 2.13 | 2.09 | 2.07 | 2.04 | 2.02 | 2.01 |
| | **3.45** | **3.37** | **3.25** | **3.18** | **3.10** | **3.01** | **2.96** | **2.89** | **2.86** | **2.80** | **2.77** | **2.75** |

| Degrees of freedom for lesser mean square | Degrees of freedom for greater mean square | | | | | | | | | | | |
|---|---|---|---|---|---|---|---|---|---|---|---|---|
| | 1 | 2 | 3 | 4 | 5 | 6 | 7 | 8 | 9 | 10 | 11 | 12 |
| 17 | 4.45 | 3.59 | 3.20 | 2.96 | 2.81 | 2.70 | 2.62 | 2.55 | 2.50 | 2.45 | 2.41 | 2.38 |
| | **8.40** | **6.11** | **5.18** | **4.67** | **4.34** | **4.10** | **3.93** | **3.79** | **3.68** | **3.59** | **3.52** | **3.45** |
| 18 | 4.41 | 3.55 | 3.16 | 2.93 | 2.77 | 2.66 | 2.58 | 2.51 | 2.46 | 2.41 | 2.37 | 2.34 |
| | **8.28** | **6.01** | **5.09** | **4.58** | **4.25** | **4.01** | **3.85** | **3.71** | **3.60** | **3.51** | **3.44** | **3.37** |
| 19 | 4.38 | 3.52 | 3.13 | 2.90 | 2.74 | 2.63 | 2.55 | 2.48 | 2.43 | 2.38 | 2.34 | 2.31 |
| | **8.18** | **5.93** | **5.01** | **4.50** | **4.17** | **3.94** | **3.77** | **3.63** | **3.52** | **3.43** | **3.36** | **3.30** |
| 20 | 4.35 | 3.49 | 3.10 | 2.87 | 2.71 | 2.60 | 2.52 | 2.45 | 2.40 | 2.35 | 2.31 | 2.28 |
| | **8.10** | **5.85** | **4.94** | **4.43** | **4.10** | **3.87** | **3.71** | **3.56** | **3.45** | **3.37** | **3.30** | **3.23** |
| 21 | 4.32 | 3.47 | 3.07 | 2.84 | 2.68 | 2.57 | 2.49 | 2.42 | 2.37 | 2.32 | 2.28 | 2.25 |
| | **8.02** | **5.78** | **4.87** | **4.37** | **4.04** | **3.81** | **3.65** | **3.51** | **3.40** | **3.31** | **3.24** | **3.17** |
| 22 | 4.30 | 3.44 | 3.05 | 2.82 | 2.66 | 2.55 | 2.47 | 2.40 | 2.35 | 2.30 | 2.26 | 2.23 |
| | **7.94** | **5.72** | **4.82** | **4.31** | **3.99** | **3.76** | **3.59** | **3.45** | **3.35** | **3.26** | **3.18** | **3.12** |
| 23 | 4.28 | 3.42 | 3.03 | 2.80 | 2.64 | 2.53 | 2.45 | 2.38 | 2.32 | 2.28 | 2.24 | 2.20 |
| | **7.88** | **5.66** | **4.76** | **4.26** | **3.94** | **3.71** | **3.54** | **3.41** | **3.30** | **3.21** | **3.14** | **3.07** |
| 24 | 4.26 | 3.40 | 3.01 | 2.78 | 2.62 | 2.51 | 2.43 | 2.36 | 2.30 | 2.26 | 2.22 | 2.18 |
| | **7.82** | **5.61** | **4.72** | **4.22** | **3.90** | **3.67** | **3.50** | **3.36** | **3.25** | **3.17** | **3.09** | **3.03** |
| 25 | 4.24 | 3.38 | 2.99 | 2.76 | 2.60 | 2.49 | 2.41 | 2.34 | 2.28 | 2.24 | 2.20 | 2.16 |
| | **7.77** | **5.57** | **4.68** | **4.18** | **3.86** | **3.63** | **3.46** | **3.32** | **3.21** | **3.13** | **3.05** | **2.99** |
| 26 | 4.22 | 3.37 | 2.89 | 2.74 | 2.59 | 2.47 | 2.39 | 2.32 | 2.27 | 2.22 | 2.18 | 2.15 |
| | **7.72** | **5.53** | **4.64** | **4.14** | **3.82** | **3.59** | **3.42** | **3.29** | **3.17** | **3.09** | **3.02** | **2.96** |
| 27 | 4.21 | 3.35 | 2.96 | 2.73 | 2.57 | 2.46 | 2.37 | 2.30 | 2.25 | 2.20 | 2.16 | 2.13 |
| | **7.68** | **5.49** | **4.60** | **4.11** | **3.79** | **3.56** | **3.39** | **3.26** | **3.14** | **3.06** | **2.98** | **2.93** |
| 28 | 4.20 | 3.34 | 2.95 | 2.71 | 2.56 | 2.44 | 2.36 | 2.29 | 2.24 | 2.19 | 2.15 | 2.12 |
| | **7.64** | **5.45** | **4.57** | **4.07** | **3.76** | **3.53** | **3.36** | **3.23** | **3.11** | **3.03** | **2.95** | **2.90** |
| 29 | 4.18 | 3.33 | 2.93 | 2.70 | 2.54 | 2.43 | 2.35 | 2.28 | 2.22 | 2.18 | 2.14 | 2.10 |
| | **7.60** | **5.52** | **4.54** | **4.04** | **3.73** | **3.50** | **3.33** | **3.20** | **3.08** | **3.00** | **2.92** | **2.87** |
| 30 | 4.17 | 3.32 | 2.92 | 2.69 | 2.53 | 2.42 | 2.34 | 2.27 | 2.21 | 2.16 | 2.12 | 2.09 |
| | **7.56** | **5.39** | **4.51** | **4.02** | **3.70** | **3.47** | **3.30** | **3.17** | **3.06** | **2.98** | **2.90** | **2.84** |
| 32 | 4.15 | 3.30 | 2.90 | 2.67 | 2.51 | 2.40 | 2.32 | 2.25 | 2.19 | 2.14 | 2.10 | 2.07 |
| | **7.50** | **5.34** | **4.46** | **3.97** | **3.66** | **3.42** | **3.25** | **3.12** | **3.01** | **2.94** | **2.86** | **2.80** |
| 34 | 4.13 | 3.28 | 2.88 | 2.65 | 2.49 | 2.38 | 2.30 | 2.23 | 2.17 | 2.12 | 2.08 | 2.05 |
| | **7.44** | **5.29** | **4.42** | **3.93** | **3.61** | **3.38** | **3.21** | **3.08** | **2.97** | **2.89** | **2.82** | **2.76** |
| 36 | 4.11 | 3.26 | 2.86 | 2.63 | 2.48 | 2.36 | 2.28 | 2.21 | 2.15 | 2.10 | 2.06 | 2.03 |
| | **7.39** | **5.25** | **4.38** | **3.89** | **3.58** | **3.35** | **3.18** | **3.04** | **2.94** | **2.86** | **2.78** | **2.72** |
| 38 | 4.10 | 3.25 | 2.85 | 2.62 | 2.46 | 2.35 | 2.26 | 2.19 | 2.14 | 2.09 | 2.05 | 2.02 |
| | **7.35** | **5.21** | **4.34** | **3.86** | **3.54** | **3.32** | **3.15** | **3.02** | **2.91** | **2.82** | **2.75** | **2.69** |
| 40 | 4.08 | 3.23 | 2.84 | 2.61 | 2.45 | 2.34 | 2.25 | 2.18 | 2.12 | 2.07 | 2.04 | 2.00 |
| | **7.31** | **5.18** | **4.31** | **3.83** | **3.51** | **3.29** | **3.12** | **2.99** | **2.88** | **2.80** | **2.73** | **2.66** |
| 42 | 4.07 | 3.22 | 2.83 | 2.59 | 2.44 | 2.32 | 2.24 | 2.17 | 2.11 | 2.06 | 2.02 | 1.99 |
| | **7.27** | **5.15** | **4.29** | **3.80** | **3.49** | **3.26** | **3.10** | **2.96** | **2.86** | **2.77** | **2.70** | **2.64** |
| 44 | 4.06 | 3.21 | 2.82 | 2.58 | 2.43 | 2.31 | 2.23 | 2.16 | 2.10 | 2.05 | 2.01 | 1.98 |
| | **7.24** | **5.12** | **4.26** | **3.78** | **3.46** | **3.24** | **3.07** | **2.94** | **2.84** | **2.75** | **2.68** | **2.62** |

| Degrees of freedom for lesser mean square | Degrees of freedom for greater mean square | | | | | | | | | | | |
|---|---|---|---|---|---|---|---|---|---|---|---|---|
| | 14 | 16 | 20 | 24 | 30 | 40 | 50 | 75 | 100 | 200 | 500 | ∞ |
| 17 | 2.33 | 2.29 | 2.23 | 2.19 | 2.15 | 2.11 | 2.08 | 2.04 | 2.02 | 1.99 | 1.97 | 1.96 |
| | 3.35 | 3.27 | 3.16 | 3.08 | 3.00 | 2.92 | 2.86 | 2.79 | 2.76 | 2.70 | 2.67 | 2.65 |
| 18 | 2.29 | 2.25 | 2.19 | 2.15 | 2.11 | 2.07 | 2.04 | 2.00 | 1.98 | 1.95 | 1.93 | 1.92 |
| | 3.27 | 3.19 | 3.07 | 3.00 | 2.91 | 2.83 | 2.78 | 2.71 | 2.68 | 2.62 | 2.59 | 2.57 |
| 19 | 2.26 | 2.21 | 2.15 | 2.11 | 2.07 | 2.02 | 2.00 | 1.96 | 1.94 | 1.91 | 1.90 | 1.88 |
| | 3.19 | 3.12 | 3.00 | 2.92 | 2.84 | 2.76 | 2.70 | 2.63 | 2.60 | 2.54 | 2.51 | 2.49 |
| 20 | 2.23 | 2.18 | 2.12 | 2.08 | 2.04 | 1.99 | 1.96 | 1.92 | 1.90 | 1.87 | 1.85 | 1.84 |
| | 3.13 | 3.05 | 2.94 | 2.86 | 2.77 | 2.69 | 2.63 | 2.56 | 2.53 | 2.47 | 2.44 | 2.42 |
| 21 | 2.20 | 2.15 | 2.09 | 2.05 | 2.00 | 1.96 | 1.93 | 1.89 | 1.87 | 1.84 | 1.82 | 1.81 |
| | 3.07 | 2.99 | 2.88 | 2.80 | 2.72 | 2.63 | 2.58 | 2.51 | 2.47 | 2.42 | 2.38 | 2.36 |
| 22 | 2.18 | 2.13 | 2.07 | 2.03 | 1.98 | 1.93 | 1.91 | 1.87 | 1.84 | 1.81 | 1.80 | 1.78 |
| | 3.02 | 2.94 | 2.83 | 2.75 | 2.67 | 2.58 | 2.53 | 2.46 | 2.42 | 2.37 | 2.33 | 2.31 |
| 23 | 2.14 | 2.10 | 2.04 | 2.00 | 1.96 | 1.91 | 1.88 | 1.84 | 1.82 | 1.79 | 1.77 | 1.76 |
| | 2.97 | 2.89 | 2.78 | 2.70 | 2.62 | 2.53 | 2.48 | 2.41 | 2.37 | 2.32 | 2.28 | 2.26 |
| 24 | 2.13 | 2.09 | 2.02 | 1.98 | 1.94 | 1.89 | 1.86 | 1.82 | 1.80 | 1.76 | 1.74 | 1.73 |
| | 2.93 | 2.85 | 2.74 | 2.66 | 2.58 | 2.49 | 2.44 | 2.36 | 2.33 | 2.27 | 2.23 | 2.21 |
| 25 | 2.11 | 2.06 | 2.00 | 1.96 | 1.92 | 1.87 | 1.84 | 1.80 | 1.77 | 1.74 | 1.72 | 1.71 |
| | 2.89 | 2.81 | 2.70 | 2.62 | 2.54 | 2.45 | 2.40 | 2.32 | 2.29 | 2.23 | 2.19 | 2.17 |
| 26 | 2.10 | 2.05 | 1.99 | 1.95 | 1.90 | 1.85 | 1.82 | 1.78 | 1.76 | 1.72 | 1.70 | 1.69 |
| | 2.86 | 2.77 | 2.66 | 2.58 | 2.50 | 2.41 | 2.36 | 2.28 | 2.25 | 2.19 | 2.15 | 2.13 |
| 27 | 2.08 | 2.03 | 1.97 | 1.93 | 1.88 | 1.84 | 1.80 | 1.76 | 1.74 | 1.71 | 1.68 | 1.67 |
| | 2.83 | 2.74 | 2.63 | 2.55 | 2.47 | 2.38 | 2.33 | 2.25 | 2.21 | 2.16 | 2.12 | 2.10 |
| 28 | 2.06 | 2.02 | 1.96 | 1.91 | 1.87 | 1.81 | 1.78 | 1.75 | 1.72 | 1.69 | 1.67 | 1.65 |
| | 2.80 | 2.71 | 2.60 | 2.52 | 2.44 | 2.35 | 2.30 | 2.22 | 2.18 | 2.13 | 2.09 | 2.06 |
| 29 | 2.05 | 2.00 | 1.94 | 1.90 | 1.85 | 1.80 | 1.77 | 1.73 | 1.71 | 1.68 | 1.65 | 1.64 |
| | 2.77 | 2.68 | 2.57 | 2.49 | 2.41 | 2.32 | 2.27 | 2.19 | 2.15 | 2.10 | 2.06 | 2.03 |
| 30 | 2.04 | 1.99 | 1.93 | 1.89 | 1.84 | 1.79 | 1.76 | 1.72 | 1.69 | 1.66 | 1.64 | 1.62 |
| | 2.74 | 2.66 | 2.55 | 2.47 | 2.38 | 2.29 | 2.24 | 2.16 | 2.13 | 2.07 | 2.03 | 2.01 |
| 32 | 2.02 | 1.97 | 1.91 | 1.86 | 1.82 | 1.76 | 1.74 | 1.69 | 1.67 | 1.64 | 1.61 | 1.59 |
| | 2.70 | 2.62 | 2.51 | 2.42 | 2.34 | 2.25 | 2.20 | 2.12 | 2.08 | 2.02 | 1.98 | 1.96 |
| 34 | 2.00 | 1.95 | 1.89 | 1.84 | 1.80 | 1.74 | 1.71 | 1.67 | 1.64 | 1.61 | 1.59 | 1.57 |
| | 2.66 | 2.58 | 2.47 | 2.38 | 2.30 | 2.21 | 2.15 | 2.08 | 2.04 | 1.98 | 1.94 | 1.91 |
| 36 | 1.89 | 1.93 | 1.87 | 1.82 | 1.78 | 1.72 | 1.69 | 1.65 | 1.62 | 1.59 | 1.56 | 1.55 |
| | 2.62 | 2.54 | 2.43 | 2.35 | 2.26 | 2.17 | 2.12 | 2.04 | 2.00 | 1.94 | 1.90 | 1.87 |
| 38 | 1.96 | 1.92 | 1.85 | 1.80 | 1.76 | 1.71 | 1.67 | 1.63 | 1.60 | 1.57 | 1.54 | 1.53 |
| | 2.59 | 2.51 | 2.40 | 2.32 | 2.22 | 2.14 | 2.08 | 2.00 | 1.97 | 1.90 | 1.86 | 1.84 |
| 40 | 1.95 | 1.90 | 1.84 | 1.79 | 1.74 | 1.69 | 1.66 | 1.61 | 1.59 | 1.55 | 1.53 | 1.51 |
| | 2.56 | 2.49 | 2.37 | 2.29 | 2.20 | 2.11 | 2.05 | 1.97 | 1.94 | 1.88 | 1.84 | 1.81 |
| 42 | 1.94 | 1.89 | 1.82 | 1.78 | 1.73 | 1.68 | 1.64 | 1.60 | 1.57 | 1.54 | 1.51 | 1.49 |
| | 2.54 | 2.46 | 2.35 | 2.26 | 2.17 | 2.08 | 2.02 | 1.94 | 1.91 | 1.85 | 1.80 | 1 78 |
| 44 | 1.92 | 1.88 | 1.81 | 1.76 | 1.72 | 1.66 | 1.63 | 1.58 | 1.56 | 1.52 | 1.50 | 1.48 |
| | 2.52 | 2.44 | 2.32 | 2.24 | 2.15 | 2.06 | 2.00 | 1.92 | 1.88 | 1.82 | 1.78 | 1.75 |

| Degrees of freedom for lesser mean square | Degrees of freedom for greater mean square | | | | | | | | | | | |
|---|---|---|---|---|---|---|---|---|---|---|---|---|
| | 1 | 2 | 3 | 4 | 5 | 6 | 7 | 8 | 9 | 10 | 11 | 12 |
| 46 | 4.05 | 3.20 | 2.81 | 2.57 | 2.42 | 2.30 | 2.22 | 2.14 | 2.09 | 2.04 | 2.00 | 1.97 |
| | **7.21** | **5.10** | **4.24** | **3.76** | **3.44** | **3.22** | **3.05** | **2.92** | **2.82** | **2.73** | **2.66** | **2.60** |
| 48 | 4.04 | 3.19 | 2.80 | 2.56 | 2.41 | 2.30 | 2.21 | 2.14 | 2.08 | 2.03 | 1.99 | 1.96 |
| | **7.19** | **5.08** | **4.22** | **3.74** | **3.42** | **3.20** | **3.04** | **2.90** | **2.80** | **2.71** | **2.64** | **2.58** |
| 50 | 4.03 | 3.18 | 2.79 | 2.56 | 2.40 | 2.29 | 2.20 | 2.13 | 2.07 | 2.02 | 1.98 | 1.95 |
| | **7.17** | **5.06** | **4.20** | **3.72** | **3.41** | **3.18** | **3.02** | **2.88** | **2.78** | **2.70** | **2.62** | **2.56** |
| 55 | 4.02 | 3.17 | 2.78 | 2.54 | 2.38 | 2.27 | 2.18 | 2.11 | 2.05 | 2.00 | 1.97 | 1.93 |
| | **7.12** | **5.01** | **4.16** | **3.68** | **3.37** | **3.15** | **2.98** | **2.85** | **2.75** | **2.66** | **2.59** | **2.53** |
| 60 | 4.00 | 3.15 | 2.76 | 2.52 | 2.37 | 2.25 | 2.17 | 2.10 | 2.04 | 1.99 | 1.95 | 1.92 |
| | **7.08** | **4.98** | **4.13** | **3.65** | **3.34** | **3.12** | **2.95** | **2.82** | **2.72** | **2.63** | **2.56** | **2.50** |
| 65 | 3.99 | 3.14 | 2.75 | 2.51 | 2.36 | 2.24 | 2.15 | 2.08 | 2.02 | 1.98 | 1.94 | 1.90 |
| | **7.04** | **4.95** | **4.10** | **3.62** | **3.31** | **3.09** | **2.93** | **2.79** | **2.70** | **2.61** | **2.54** | **2.47** |
| 70 | 3.98 | 3.13 | 2.74 | 2.50 | 2.35 | 2.32 | 2.14 | 2.07 | 2.01 | 1.97 | 1.93 | 1.89 |
| | **7.01** | **4.92** | **4.08** | **3.60** | **3.29** | **3.07** | **2.91** | **2.77** | **2.67** | **2.59** | **2.51** | **2.45** |
| 80 | 3.96 | 3.11 | 2.72 | 2.48 | 2.33 | 2.21 | 2.12 | 2.05 | 1.99 | 1.95 | 1.91 | 1.88 |
| | **6.96** | **4.88** | **4.04** | **3.56** | **3.25** | **3.04** | **2.87** | **2.74** | **2.64** | **2.55** | **2.48** | **2.41** |
| 100 | 3.94 | 3.09 | 2.70 | 2.46 | 2.30 | 2.19 | 2.10 | 2.03 | 1.97 | 1.92 | 1.88 | 1.85 |
| | **6.90** | **4.82** | **3.98** | **3.51** | **3.20** | **2.99** | **2.82** | **2.69** | **2.59** | **2.51** | **2.43** | **2.36** |
| 125 | 3.92 | 3.07 | 2.68 | 2.44 | 2.29 | 2.17 | 2.08 | 2.01 | 1.95 | 1.90 | 1.86 | 1.83 |
| | **6.84** | **4.78** | **3.94** | **3.47** | **3.17** | **2.95** | **2.79** | **2.65** | **2.56** | **2.47** | **2.40** | **2.33** |
| 150 | 3.91 | 3.06 | 2.67 | 2.43 | 2.27 | 2.16 | 2.07 | 2.00 | 1.94 | 1.89 | 1.85 | 1.82 |
| | **6.81** | **4.75** | **3.91** | **3.44** | **3.13** | **2.92** | **2.76** | **2.62** | **2.53** | **2.44** | **2.37** | **2.30** |
| 200 | 3.89 | 3.04 | 2.65 | 2.41 | 2.26 | 2.14 | 2.05 | 1.98 | 1.92 | 1.87 | 1.83 | 1.80 |
| | **6.76** | **4.71** | **3.88** | **3.41** | **3.11** | **2.90** | **2.73** | **2.60** | **2.50** | **2.41** | **2.34** | **2.28** |
| 400 | 3.86 | 3.02 | 2.62 | 2.39 | 2.23 | 2.12 | 2.03 | 1.96 | 1.90 | 1.85 | 1.81 | 1.78 |
| | **6.70** | **4.66** | **3.83** | **3.36** | **3.06** | **2.85** | **2.69** | **2.55** | **2.46** | **2.37** | **2.29** | **2.23** |
| 1000 | 3.85 | 3.00 | 2.61 | 2.38 | 2.22 | 2.10 | 2.02 | 1.95 | 1.89 | 1.84 | 1.80 | 1.76 |
| | **6.66** | **4.62** | **3.80** | **3.34** | **3.04** | **2.82** | **2.66** | **2.53** | **2.43** | **2.34** | **2.26** | **2.20** |
| ∞ | 3.84 | 2.99 | 2.60 | 2.37 | 2.21 | 2.09 | 2.01 | 1.94 | 1.88 | 1.83 | 1.79 | 1.75 |
| | **6.64** | **4.60** | **3.78** | **3.32** | **3.02** | **2.80** | **2.64** | **2.51** | **2.41** | **2.32** | **2.24** | **2.13** |

| Degrees of freedom for lesser mean square | Degrees of freedom for greater mean square | | | | | | | | | | | |
|---|---|---|---|---|---|---|---|---|---|---|---|---|
| | 14 | 16 | 20 | 24 | 30 | 40 | 50 | 75 | 100 | 200 | 500 | ∞ |
| 46 | 1.91 **2.50** | 1.87 **2.42** | 1.80 **2.30** | 1.75 **2.22** | 1.71 **2.13** | 1.65 **2.04** | 1.62 **1.98** | 1.57 **1.90** | 1.54 **1.86** | 1.51 **1.80** | 1.48 **1.76** | 1.46 **1.72** |
| 48 | 1.90 **2.48** | 1.86 **2.40** | 1.79 **2.28** | 1.74 **2.20** | 1.70 **2.11** | 1.64 **2.02** | 1.61 **1.96** | 1.56 **1.88** | 1.53 **1.84** | 1.50 **1.78** | 1.47 **1.73** | 1.45 **1.70** |
| 50 | 1.90 **2.46** | 1.85 **2.39** | 1.78 **2.26** | 1.74 **2.18** | 1.69 **2.10** | 1.63 **2.00** | 1.60 **1.94** | 1.55 **1.86** | 1.52 **1.82** | 1.48 **1.76** | 1.46 **1.71** | 1.44 **1.68** |
| 55 | 1.88 **2.43** | 1.83 **2.35** | 1.76 **2.23** | 1.72 **2.15** | 1.67 **2.06** | 1.61 **1.96** | 1.58 **1.90** | 1.52 **1.82** | 1.50 **1.78** | 1.46 **1.71** | 1.43 **1.66** | 1.41 **1.64** |
| 60 | 1.86 **2.40** | 1.81 **2.32** | 1.75 **2.20** | 1.70 **2.12** | 1.65 **2.03** | 1.59 **1.93** | 1.56 **1.87** | 1.50 **1.79** | 1.48 **1.74** | 1.44 **1.68** | 1.41 **1.63** | 1.39 **1.60** |
| 65 | 1.85 **2.37** | 1.80 **2.30** | 1.73 **2.18** | 1.68 **2.09** | 1.63 **2.00** | 1.57 **1.90** | 1.54 **1.84** | 1.49 **1.76** | 1.46 **1.71** | 1.42 **1.64** | 1.39 **1.60** | 1.37 **1.56** |
| 70 | 1.84 **2.35** | 1.79 **2.28** | 1.72 **2.15** | 1.67 **2.07** | 1.62 **1.98** | 1.56 **1.88** | 1.53 **1.82** | 1.47 **1.74** | 1.45 **1.69** | 1.40 **1.62** | 1.37 **1.56** | 1.35 **1.53** |
| 80 | 1.82 **2.32** | 1.77 **2.24** | 1.70 **2.11** | 1.65 **2.03** | 1.60 **1.94** | 1.54 **1.84** | 1.51 **1.78** | 1.45 **1.70** | 1.42 **1.65** | 1.38 **1.57** | 1.35 **1.52** | 1.32 **1.49** |
| 100 | 1.79 **2.26** | 1.75 **2.19** | 1.68 **2.06** | 1.63 **1.98** | 1.57 **1.89** | 1.51 **1.79** | 1.48 **1.73** | 1.42 **1.64** | 1.39 **1.59** | 1.34 **1.51** | 1.30 **1.46** | 1.28 **1.43** |
| 125 | 1.77 **2.23** | 1.72 **2.15** | 1.65 **2.03** | 1.60 **1.94** | 1.55 **1.85** | 1.49 **1.75** | 1.45 **1.68** | 1.39 **1.59** | 1.36 **1.54** | 1.31 **1.46** | 1.27 **1.40** | 1.25 **1.37** |
| 150 | 1.76 **2.20** | 1.71 **2.12** | 1.64 **2.00** | 1.59 **1.91** | 1.54 **1.83** | 1.47 **1.72** | 1.44 **1.66** | 1.37 **1.56** | 1.34 **1.51** | 1.29 **1.43** | 1.25 **1.37** | 1.22 **1.33** |
| 200 | 1.74 **1.17** | 1.69 **2.09** | 1.62 **1.97** | 1.57 **1.88** | 1.52 **1.79** | 1.45 **1.69** | 1.42 **1.62** | 1.35 **1.53** | 1.32 **1.48** | 1.26 **1.39** | 1.22 **1.33** | 1.19 **1.28** |
| 400 | 1.72 **2.12** | 1.67 **2.04** | 1.60 **1.92** | 1.54 **1.84** | 1.49 **1.74** | 1.42 **1.64** | 1.38 **1.57** | 1.32 **1.47** | 1.28 **1.42** | 1.22 **1.32** | 1.16 **1.24** | 1.13 **1.19** |
| 1000 | 1.70 **2.09** | 1.65 **2.01** | 1.58 **1.89** | 1.53 **1.81** | 1.47 **1.71** | 1.41 **1.61** | 1.36 **1.54** | 1.30 **1.44** | 1.26 **1.38** | 1.19 **1.28** | 1.13 **1.19** | 1.08 **1.11** |
| ∞ | 1.69 **2.07** | 1.64 **1.99** | 1.57 **1.87** | 1.52 **1.79** | 1.46 **1.69** | 1.40 **1.59** | 1.35 **1.52** | 1.28 **1.41** | 1.24 **1.36** | 1.17 **1.25** | 1.11 **1.15** | 1.00 **1.00** |

# COMPLETE ELLIPTIC INTEGRALS

$$K = \int_0^{\pi/2} \frac{d\Phi}{\sqrt{1 - k^2 \sin^2 \Phi}}.$$

$$E = \int_0^{\pi/2} \sqrt{1 - k^2 \sin^2 \Phi} \cdot d\Phi = E\left(k, \frac{\pi}{2}\right)$$

| $\sin^{-1} k$ | $K$ | $\log K$ | $\sin^{-1} k$ | $K$ | $\log K$ |
|---|---|---|---|---|---|
| **0°** | 1.5708 | 0.196120 | **40°** | 1.7868 | 0.252068 |
| 1 | 1.5709 | 0.196153 | 41 | 1.7992 | 0.255085 |
| 2 | 1.5713 | 0.196252 | 42 | 1.8122 | 0.258197 |
| 3 | 1.5719 | 0.196418 | 43 | 1.8256 | 0.261406 |
| 4 | 1.5727 | 0.196649 | 44 | 1.8396 | 0.264716 |
| **5** | 1.5738 | 0.196947 | **45** | 1.8541 | 0.268127 |
| 6 | 1.5751 | 0.197312 | 46 | 1.8691 | 0.271644 |
| 7 | 1.5767 | 0.197743 | 47 | 1.8848 | 0.275267 |
| 8 | 1.5785 | 0.198241 | 48 | 1.9011 | 0.279001 |
| 9 | 1.5805 | 0.198806 | 49 | 1.9180 | 0.282848 |
| **10** | 1.5828 | 0.199438 | **50** | 1.9356 | 0.286811 |
| 11 | 1.5854 | 0.200137 | 51 | 1.9539 | 0.290895 |
| 12 | 1.5882 | 0.200904 | 52 | 1.9729 | 0.295101 |
| 13 | 1.5913 | 0.201740 | 53 | 1.9927 | 0.299435 |
| 14 | 1.5946 | 0.202643 | 54 | 2.0133 | 0.303901 |
| **15** | 1.5981 | 0.203615 | **55** | 2.0347 | 0.308504 |
| 16 | 1.6020 | 0.204657 | 56 | 2.0571 | 0.313247 |
| 17 | 1.6061 | 0.205768 | 57 | 2.0804 | 0.318138 |
| 18 | 1.6105 | 0.206948 | 58 | 2.1047 | 0.323182 |
| 19 | 1.6151 | 0.208200 | 59 | 2.1300 | 0.328384 |
| **20** | 1.6200 | 0.209522 | **60** | 2.1565 | 0.333753 |
| 21 | 1.6252 | 0.210916 | 61 | 2.1842 | 0.339295 |
| 22 | 1.6307 | 0.212382 | 62 | 2.2132 | 0.345020 |
| 23 | 1.6365 | 0.213921 | 63 | 2.2435 | 0.350936 |
| 24 | 1.6426 | 0.215533 | 64 | 2.2754 | 0.357053 |
| **25** | 1.6490 | 0.217219 | **65** | 2.3088 | 0.363384 |
| 26 | 1.6557 | 0.218981 | 66 | 2.3439 | 0.369940 |
| 27 | 1.6627 | 0.220818 | 67 | 2.3809 | 0.376736 |
| 28 | 1.6701 | 0.222732 | 68 | 2.4198 | 0.383787 |
| 29 | 1.6777 | 0.224723 | 69 | 2.4610 | 0.391112 |
| **30** | 1.6858 | 0.226793 | **70** | 2.5046 | 0.398730 |
| 31 | 1.6941 | 0.228943 | 71 | 2.5507 | 0.406665 |
| 32 | 1.7028 | 0.231173 | 72 | 2.5998 | 0.414943 |
| 33 | 1.7119 | 0.233485 | 73 | 2.6521 | 0.423596 |
| 34 | 1.7214 | 0.235880 | 74 | 2.7081 | 0.432660 |
| **35** | 1.7312 | 0.238359 | **75** | 2.7681 | 0.442176 |
| 36 | 1.7415 | 0.240923 | 76 | 2.8327 | 0.452196 |
| 37 | 1.7522 | 0.243575 | 77 | 2.9026 | 0.462782 |
| 38 | 1.7633 | 0.246315 | 78 | 2.9786 | 0.474008 |
| 39 | 1.7748 | 0.249146 | 79 | 3.0617 | 0.485967 |
| **40** | 1.7868 | 0.252068 | **80** | 3.1534 | 0.498777 |

| $\sin^{-1} k$ | $K$ | $\log K$ | $\sin^{-1} k$ | $K$ | $\log K$ |
|---|---|---|---|---|---|
| **80°** | 3.1534 | 0.498777 | **85°** | 3.8317 | 0.583396 |
| 81 | 3.2553 | 0.512591 | 86 | 4.0528 | 0.607751 |
| 82 | 3.3699 | 0.527613 | 87 | 4.3387 | 0.637355 |
| 83 | 3.5004 | 0.544120 | 88 | 4.7427 | 0.676027 |
| 84 | 3.6519 | 0.562514 | 89 | 5.4349 | 0.735192 |
| **85** | 3.8317 | 0.583396 | **90** | ∞ | ∞ |

Values of $K$ for $\sin^{-1} k = 85°$ to $89°$ by 0.1° and $89°$ to $90°$ by minutes.

| $\sin^{-1} k$ | $K$ | $\log K$ | $\sin^{-1} k$ | | $K$ | $\log K$ |
|---|---|---|---|---|---|---|
| **85.0°** | 3.832 | 0.58343 | **89°** | **0'** | 5.435 | 0.73520 |
| 85.1 | 3.852 | 0.58569 | 89 | 2 | 5.469 | 0.73791 |
| 85.2 | 3.872 | 0.58794 | 89 | 4 | 5.504 | 0.74068 |
| 85.3 | 3.893 | 0.59028 | 89 | 6 | 5.540 | 0.74351 |
| 85.4 | 3.914 | 0.59262 | 89 | 8 | 5.578 | 0.74648 |
| **85.5** | 3.936 | 0.59506 | 89 | **10** | 5.617 | 0.74950 |
| 85.6 | 3.958 | 0.59748 | 89 | 12 | 5.658 | 0.75266 |
| 85.7 | 3.981 | 0.59999 | 89 | 14 | 5.700 | 0.75587 |
| 85.8 | 4.004 | 0.60249 | 89 | 16 | 5.745 | 0.75929 |
| 85.9 | 4.028 | 0.60509 | 89 | 18 | 5.791 | 0.76275 |
| **86.0** | 4.053 | 0.60778 | 89 | **20** | 5.840 | 0.76641 |
| 86.1 | 4.078 | 0.61045 | 89 | 22 | 5.891 | 0.77019 |
| 86.2 | 4.104 | 0.61321 | 89 | 24 | 5.946 | 0.77422 |
| 86.3 | 4.130 | 0.61595 | 89 | 26 | 6.003 | 0.77837 |
| 86.4 | 4.157 | 0.61878 | 89 | 28 | 6.063 | 0.78269 |
| **86.5** | 4.185 | 0.62170 | 89 | **30** | 6.128 | 0.78732 |
| 86.6 | 4.214 | 0.62469 | 89 | 32 | 6.197 | 0.79218 |
| 86.7 | 4.244 | 0.62778 | 89 | 34 | 6.271 | 0.79734 |
| 86.8 | 4.274 | 0.63083 | 89 | 36 | 6.351 | 0.80284 |
| 86.9 | 4.306 | 0.63407 | 89 | 38 | 6.438 | 0.80875 |
| **87.0** | 4.339 | 0.63739 | 89 | **40** | 6.533 | 0.81511 |
| 87.1 | 4.372 | 0.64068 | 89 | 41 | 6.584 | 0.81849 |
| 87.2 | 4.407 | 0.64414 | 89 | 42 | 6.639 | 0.82210 |
| 87.3 | 4.444 | 0.64777 | 89 | 43 | 6.696 | 0.82582 |
| 87.4 | 4.481 | 0.65137 | 89 | 44 | 6.756 | 0.82969 |
| **87.5** | 4.520 | 0.65514 | 89 | **45** | 6.821 | 0.83385 |
| 87.6 | 4.562 | 0.65916 | 89 | 46 | 6.890 | 0.83822 |
| 87.7 | 4.603 | 0.66304 | 89 | 47 | 6.964 | 0.84286 |
| 87.8 | 4.648 | 0.66727 | 89 | 48 | 7.044 | 0.84782 |
| 87.9 | 4.694 | 0.67154 | 89 | 49 | 7.131 | 0.85315 |
| **88.0** | 4.743 | 0.67605 | 89 | **50** | 7.226 | 0.85890 |
| 88.1 | 4.794 | 0.68070 | 89 | 51 | 7.332 | 0.86522 |
| 88.2 | 4.848 | 0.68556 | 89 | 52 | 7.449 | 0.87210 |
| 88.3 | 4.905 | 0.69064 | 89 | 53 | 7.583 | 0.87984 |
| 88.4 | 4.965 | 0.69592 | 89 | 54 | 7.737 | 0.88857 |
| **88.5** | 5.030 | 0.70157 | 89 | **55** | 7.919 | 0.89867 |
| 88.6 | 5.099 | 0.70749 | 89 | 56 | 8.143 | 0.91078 |
| 88.7 | 5.173 | 0.71374 | 89 | 57 | 8.430 | 0.92583 |
| 88.8 | 5.253 | 0.72041 | 89 | 58 | 8.836 | 0.94626 |
| 88.9 | 5.340 | 0.72754 | 89 | 59 | 9.529 | 0.97905 |
| **89.0** | 5.435 | 0.73520 | **90** | **0** | ∞ | ∞ |

# COMPLETE ELLIPTIC INTEGRALS (Continued)

| sin⁻¹ k | E | log E | sin⁻¹ k | E | log E |
|---|---|---|---|---|---|
| **0°** | 1.5708 | 0.196120 | **45°** | 1.3506 | 0.130541 |
| 1 | 1.5707 | 0.196087 | 46 | 1.3418 | 0.127690 |
| 2 | 1.5703 | 0.195988 | 47 | 1.3329 | 0.124788 |
| 3 | 1.5697 | 0.195822 | 48 | 1.3238 | 0.121836 |
| 4 | 1.5689 | 0.195591 | 49 | 1.3147 | 0.118836 |
| **5** | 1.5678 | 0.195293 | **50** | 1.3055 | 0.115790 |
| 6 | 1.5665 | 0.194930 | 51 | 1.2963 | 0.112698 |
| 7 | 1.5649 | 0.194500 | 52 | 1.2870 | 0.109563 |
| 8 | 1.5632 | 0.194004 | 53 | 1.2776 | 0.106386 |
| 9 | 1.5611 | 0.193442 | 54 | 1.2681 | 0.103169 |
| **10** | 1.5589 | 0.192815 | **55** | 1.2587 | 0.099915 |
| 11 | 1.5564 | 0.192121 | 56 | 1.2492 | 0.096626 |
| 12 | 1.5537 | 0.191362 | 57 | 1.2397 | 0.093303 |
| 13 | 1.5507 | 0.190537 | 58 | 1.2301 | 0.089950 |
| 14 | 1.5476 | 0.189646 | 59 | 1.2206 | 0.086569 |
| **15** | 1.5442 | 0.188690 | **60** | 1.2111 | 0.083164 |
| 16 | 1.5405 | 0.187668 | 61 | 1.2015 | 0.079738 |
| 17 | 1.5367 | 0.186581 | 62 | 1.1920 | 0.076293 |
| 18 | 1.5326 | 0.185428 | 63 | 1.1826 | 0.072834 |
| 19 | 1.5283 | 0.184210 | 64 | 1.1732 | 0.069364 |
| **20** | 1.5238 | 0.182928 | **65** | 1.1638 | 0.065889 |
| 21 | 1.5191 | 0.181580 | 66 | 1.1545 | 0.062412 |
| 22 | 1.5141 | 0.180168 | 67 | 1.1453 | 0.058937 |
| 23 | 1.5090 | 0.178691 | 68 | 1.1362 | 0.055472 |
| 24 | 1.5037 | 0.177150 | 69 | 1.1272 | 0.052020 |
| **25** | 1.4981 | 0.175545 | **70** | 1.1184 | 0.048589 |
| 26 | 1.4924 | 0.173876 | 71 | 1.1096 | 0.045183 |
| 27 | 1.4864 | 0.172144 | 72 | 1.1011 | 0.041812 |
| 28 | 1.4803 | 0.170348 | 73 | 1.0927 | 0.038481 |
| 29 | 1.4740 | 0.168489 | 74 | 1.0844 | 0.035200 |
| **30** | 1.4675 | 0.166567 | **75** | 1.0764 | 0.031976 |
| 31 | 1.4608 | 0.164583 | 76 | 1.0686 | 0.028819 |
| 32 | 1.4539 | 0.162537 | 77 | 1.0611 | 0.025740 |
| 33 | 1.4469 | 0.160429 | 78 | 1.0538 | 0.022749 |
| 34 | 1.4397 | 0.158261 | 79 | 1.0468 | 0.019858 |
| **35** | 1.4323 | 0.156031 | **80** | 1.0401 | 0.017081 |
| 36 | 1.4248 | 0.153742 | 81 | 1.0338 | 0.014432 |
| 37 | 1.4171 | 0.151393 | 82 | 1.0278 | 0.011927 |
| 38 | 1.4092 | 0.148985 | 83 | 1.0223 | 0.009584 |
| 39 | 1.4013 | 0.146519 | 84 | 1.0172 | 0.007422 |
| **40** | 1.3931 | 0.143995 | **85** | 1.0127 | 0.005465 |
| 41 | 1.3849 | 0.141414 | 86 | 1.0086 | 0.003740 |
| 42 | 1.3765 | 0.138778 | 87 | 1.0053 | 0.002278 |
| 43 | 1.3680 | 0.136086 | 88 | 1.0026 | 0.001121 |
| 44 | 1.3594 | 0.133340 | 89 | 1.0008 | 0.000326 |
| **45** | 1.3506 | 0.130541 | **90** | 1.0000 | 0.000000 |

# ELLIPTIC INTEGRALS OF THE FIRST AND SECOND KIND

An elliptic integral has the form $\int R(x, \sqrt{f(x)}\, dx$, where $R$ represents a rational function and $f(x) = a + bx + cx^2 + dx^3 + ex^4$, an algebraic function of the third or fourth degree.

1. Elliptic integrals of the *first kind* are represented by

$$F(k, \phi) = \int_0^\phi \frac{d\Phi}{\sqrt{1 - k^2 \sin^2 \Phi}}$$

$$= \int_0^x \frac{d\xi}{\sqrt{(1 - \xi^2)(1 - k^2\xi^2)}}, \quad x = \sin \phi,\, k^2 < 1.$$

2. Elliptic integrals of the second kind are represented by

$$E(k, \phi) = \int_0^\phi \sqrt{1 - k^2 \sin^2 \Phi}\, d\Phi$$

$$= \int_0^x \frac{\sqrt{1 - k^2\xi^2}}{\sqrt{1 - \xi^2}}\, d\xi, \quad x = \sin \phi,\, k^2 < 1.$$

3. Elliptic integrals of the third kind are represented as

$$\pi(k, n, \phi) = \int_0^\phi \frac{d\Phi}{(1 + n \sin^2 \Phi) \sqrt{1 - k^2 \sin^2 \Phi}},$$
$$k^2 < 1,\, n \text{ an integer.}$$

Elliptic integrals of the third kind are also represented as

$$\pi_1(k, n, x) = \int_0^x \frac{d\xi}{(1 + n\xi^2) \sqrt{(1 - \xi^2)(1 - k^2\xi^2)}},$$
$$x = \sin \phi,\, k^2 < 1,\, n \text{ an integer.}$$

4. The complete integrals are

$$K = F\left(k, \frac{\pi}{2}\right) = \frac{\pi}{2}\left[ 1 + \left(\frac{1}{2}\right)^2 k^2 + \left(\frac{3}{2 \cdot 4}\right)^2 k^4 \right.$$
$$\left. + \left(\frac{3 \cdot 5}{2 \cdot 4 \cdot 6}\right)^2 k^6 + \cdots \right]$$

$$E = E\left(k, \frac{\pi}{2}\right) = \frac{\pi}{2}\left[ 1 - \left(\frac{1}{2^2}\right) k^2 - \left(\frac{3^2}{2^2 \cdot 4^2}\right)\frac{k^4}{3} \right.$$
$$\left. - \left(\frac{3^2 \cdot 5^2}{2^2 \cdot 4^2 \cdot 6^2}\right)\frac{k^6}{5} - \left(\frac{3^2 \cdot 5^2 \cdot 7^2}{2^2 \cdot 4^2 \cdot 6^2 \cdot 8^2}\right)\frac{k^8}{7} - \cdots \right].$$

$$K' = F\left(\sqrt{1 - k^2}, \frac{\pi}{2}\right), \quad E' = E\left(\sqrt{1 - k^2}, \frac{\pi}{2}\right)$$

5. The following relation holds between $K, K', E, E'$, namely

$$KE' + EK' - KK' = \frac{\pi}{2}$$

234

## ELLIPTIC INTEGRALS OF THE FIRST AND SECOND KIND (Continued)

6. To evaluate elliptic integrals for values outside the range contained in the following tables, the following relations are useful

$$F(k, \pi) = 2K; \ E(k, \pi) = 2E$$

$$F(k, \phi + m\pi) = mF(k, \pi) + F(k, \phi) = 2mK + F(k, \phi)$$
$$m = 0, 1, 2, 3, \ldots$$

$$E(k, \phi + m\pi) = mE(k, \pi) + E(k, \phi) = 2mE + E(k, \phi)$$
$$m = 0, 1, 2, 3, \ldots$$

7. If $u = F(k, \phi) = \displaystyle\int_0^\phi \frac{d\Phi}{\sqrt{1 - k^2 \sin^2 \Phi}}$     $(k^2 < 1)$,

= elliptic integral of the first kind.

$$u = \int_0^x \frac{dx}{\sqrt{(1 - \xi^2)(1 - k^2\xi^2)}},$$
$$\text{where } x = \sin \phi.$$

$\phi$ is called the amplitude of $u$ or am $u$.
$k$ is called the modulus.

$$k' = \sqrt{1 - k^2} = \text{the complementary modulus.}$$

$$\sin \phi = \text{sn } u = x \qquad \tan \phi = \text{tn } u = \frac{x}{\sqrt{1 - x^2}}.$$

$\cos \phi = \text{cn } u = \sqrt{1 - x^2}$.      $\Delta\phi = \text{dn } u = \sqrt{1 - k^2x^2}$.
am $0 = 0$.                       sn $0 = 0$.
cn $0 = 1$.                       dn $0 = 1$.
am $(-u) = -$am $u$.        sn $(-u) = -$sn $u$.
cn $(-u) = $ cn $u$.         dn $(-u) = $ dn $u$.

tn $(-u) = -$tn $u$.
$\text{sn}^2 u + \text{cn}^2 u = 1$.
$\text{dn}^2 u + k^2 \text{sn}^2 u = 1$.
$\text{dn}^2 u - k^2 \text{cn}^2 u = 1 - k^2 = k'^2$.

# ELLIPTIC INTEGRALS OF THE FIRST KIND: $F(k, \phi)$

$$F(k, \phi) = \int_0^\phi \frac{d\Phi}{\sqrt{1 - k^2 \sin^2 \Phi}}, \qquad \theta = \sin^{-1} k$$

| $\phi$ \ $\theta$ | 5° | 10° | 15° | 20° | 25° | 30° | 35° | 40° | 45° |
|---|---|---|---|---|---|---|---|---|---|
| 1° | 0.0175 | 0.0175 | 0.0175 | 0.0175 | 0.0175 | 0.0175 | 0.0175 | 0.0175 | 0.0175 |
| 2° | 0.0349 | 0.0349 | 0.0349 | 0.0349 | 0.0349 | 0.0349 | 0.0349 | 0.0349 | 0.0349 |
| 3° | 0.0524 | 0.0524 | 0.0524 | 0.0524 | 0.0524 | 0.0524 | 0.0524 | 0.0524 | 0.0524 |
| 4° | 0.0698 | 0.0698 | 0.0698 | 0.0698 | 0.0698 | 0.0698 | 0.0698 | 0.0698 | 0.0698 |
| 5° | 0.0873 | 0.0873 | 0.0873 | 0.0873 | 0.0873 | 0.0873 | 0.0873 | 0.0873 | 0.0873 |
| 6° | 0.1047 | 0.1047 | 0.1047 | 0.1047 | 0.1048 | 0.1048 | 0.1048 | 0.1048 | 0.1048 |
| 7° | 0.1222 | 0.1222 | 0.1222 | 0.1222 | 0.1222 | 0.1222 | 0.1223 | 0.1223 | 0.1223 |
| 8° | 0.1396 | 0.1396 | 0.1397 | 0.1397 | 0.1397 | 0.1397 | 0.1398 | 0.1398 | 0.1399 |
| 9° | 0.1571 | 0.1571 | 0.1571 | 0.1572 | 0.1572 | 0.1572 | 0.1573 | 0.1573 | 0.1574 |
| 10° | 0.1745 | 0.1746 | 0.1746 | 0.1746 | 0.1747 | 0.1748 | 0.1748 | 0.1749 | 0.1750 |
| 11° | 0.1920 | 0.1920 | 0.1921 | 0.1921 | 0.1922 | 0.1923 | 0.1924 | 0.1925 | 0.1926 |
| 12° | 0.2095 | 0.2095 | 0.2095 | 0.2096 | 0.2097 | 0.2098 | 0.2099 | 0.2101 | 0.2102 |
| 13° | 0.2269 | 0.2270 | 0.2270 | 0.2271 | 0.2272 | 0.2274 | 0.2275 | 0.2277 | 0.2279 |
| 14° | 0.2444 | 0.2444 | 0.2445 | 0.2446 | 0.2448 | 0.2450 | 0.2451 | 0.2453 | 0.2456 |
| 15° | 0.2618 | 0.2619 | 0.2620 | 0.2621 | 0.2623 | 0.2625 | 0.2628 | 0.2630 | 0.2633 |
| 16° | 0.2793 | 0.2794 | 0.2795 | 0.2797 | 0.2799 | 0.2802 | 0.2804 | 0.2808 | 0.2811 |
| 17° | 0.2967 | 0.2968 | 0.2970 | 0.2972 | 0.2975 | 0.2978 | 0.2981 | 0.2985 | 0.2989 |
| 18° | 0.3142 | 0.3143 | 0.3145 | 0.3148 | 0.3151 | 0.3154 | 0.3159 | 0.3163 | 0.3167 |
| 19° | 0.3317 | 0.3318 | 0.3320 | 0.3323 | 0.3327 | 0.3331 | 0.3336 | 0.3341 | 0.3347 |
| 20° | 0.3491 | 0.3493 | 0.3495 | 0.3499 | 0.3503 | 0.3508 | 0.3514 | 0.3520 | 0.3526 |
| 21° | 0.3666 | 0.3668 | 0.3671 | 0.3675 | 0.3680 | 0.3685 | 0.3692 | 0.3699 | 0.3706 |
| 22° | 0.3840 | 0.3842 | 0.3846 | 0.3851 | 0.3856 | 0.3863 | 0.3871 | 0.3879 | 0.3887 |
| 23° | 0.4015 | 0.4017 | 0.4021 | 0.4027 | 0.4033 | 0.4041 | 0.4049 | 0.4059 | 0.4068 |
| 24° | 0.4190 | 0.4192 | 0.4197 | 0.4203 | 0.4210 | 0.4219 | 0.4229 | 0.4239 | 0.4250 |
| 25° | 0.4364 | 0.4367 | 0.4372 | 0.4379 | 0.4387 | 0.4397 | 0.4408 | 0.4420 | 0.4433 |
| 26° | 0.4539 | 0.4542 | 0.4548 | 0.4556 | 0.4565 | 0.4576 | 0.4588 | 0.4602 | 0.4616 |
| 27° | 0.4714 | 0.4717 | 0.4724 | 0.4732 | 0.4743 | 0.4755 | 0.4769 | 0.4784 | 0.4800 |
| 28° | 0.4888 | 0.4893 | 0.4899 | 0.4909 | 0.4921 | 0.4934 | 0.4950 | 0.4967 | 0.4985 |
| 29° | 0.5063 | 0.5068 | 0.5075 | 0.5086 | 0.5099 | 0.5114 | 0.5132 | 0.5150 | 0.5170 |
| 30° | 0.5238 | 0.5243 | 0.5251 | 0.5263 | 0.5277 | 0.5294 | 0.5313 | 0.5334 | 0.5356 |
| 31° | 0.5412 | 0.5418 | 0.5427 | 0.5440 | 0.5456 | 0.5475 | 0.5496 | 0.5519 | 0.5543 |
| 32° | 0.5587 | 0.5593 | 0.5603 | 0.5617 | 0.5635 | 0.5656 | 0.5679 | 0.5704 | 0.5731 |
| 33° | 0.5762 | 0.5769 | 0.5780 | 0.5795 | 0.5814 | 0.5837 | 0.5862 | 0.5890 | 0.5920 |
| 34° | 0.5937 | 0.5944 | 0.5956 | 0.5973 | 0.5994 | 0.6018 | 0.6046 | 0.6077 | 0.6109 |
| 35° | 0.6111 | 0.6119 | 0.6133 | 0.6151 | 0.6173 | 0.6200 | 0.6231 | 0.6264 | 0.6300 |
| 36° | 0.6286 | 0.6295 | 0.6309 | 0.6329 | 0.6353 | 0.6383 | 0.6416 | 0.6452 | 0.6491 |
| 37° | 0.6461 | 0.6470 | 0.6486 | 0.6507 | 0.6534 | 0.6565 | 0.6602 | 0.6641 | 0.6684 |
| 38° | 0.6636 | 0.6646 | 0.6662 | 0.6685 | 0.6714 | 0.6749 | 0.6788 | 0.6831 | 0.6877 |
| 39° | 0.6810 | 0.6821 | 0.6839 | 0.6864 | 0.6895 | 0.6932 | 0.6975 | 0.7021 | 0.7071 |
| 40° | 0.6985 | 0.6997 | 0.7016 | 0.7043 | 0.7076 | 0.7116 | 0.7162 | 0.7213 | 0.7267 |
| 41° | 0.7160 | 0.7173 | 0.7193 | 0.7222 | 0.7258 | 0.7301 | 0.7350 | 0.7405 | 0.7463 |
| 42° | 0.7335 | 0.7348 | 0.7370 | 0.7401 | 0.7440 | 0.7486 | 0.7539 | 0.7598 | 0.7661 |
| 43° | 0.7510 | 0.7524 | 0.7548 | 0.7580 | 0.7622 | 0.7671 | 0.7728 | 0.7791 | 0.7859 |
| 44° | 0.7685 | 0.7700 | 0.7725 | 0.7760 | 0.7804 | 0.7857 | 0.7918 | 0.7986 | 0.8059 |
| 45° | 0.7859 | 0.7876 | 0.7903 | 0.7940 | 0.7987 | 0.8044 | 0.8109 | 0.8181 | 0.8260 |

# ELLIPTIC INTEGRALS OF THE FIRST KIND: $F(k, \phi)$
## (Continued)

$$F(k, \phi) = \int_0^\phi \frac{d\Phi}{\sqrt{1 - k^2 \sin^2 \Phi}}, \qquad \theta = \sin^{-1} k$$

| $\phi$ \ $\theta$ | 50° | 55° | 60° | 65° | 70° | 75° | 80° | 85° | 90° |
|---|---|---|---|---|---|---|---|---|---|
| 1° | 0.0175 | 0.0175 | 0.0175 | 0.0175 | 0.0175 | 0.0175 | 0.0175 | 0.0175 | 0.0175 |
| 2° | 0.0349 | 0.0349 | 0.0349 | 0.0349 | 0.0349 | 0.0349 | 0.0349 | 0.0349 | 0.0349 |
| 3° | 0.0524 | 0.0524 | 0.0524 | 0.0524 | 0.0524 | 0.0524 | 0.0524 | 0.0524 | 0.0524 |
| 4° | 0.0698 | 0.0699 | 0.0699 | 0.0699 | 0.0699 | 0.0699 | 0.0699 | 0.0699 | 0.0699 |
| 5° | 0.0873 | 0.0873 | 0.0873 | 0.0874 | 0.0874 | 0.0874 | 0.0874 | 0.0874 | 0.0874 |
| 6° | 0.1048 | 0.1048 | 0.1049 | 0.1049 | 0.1049 | 0.1049 | 0.1049 | 0.1049 | 0.1049 |
| 7° | 0.1224 | 0.1224 | 0.1224 | 0.1224 | 0.1224 | 0.1225 | 0.1225 | 0.1225 | 0.1225 |
| 8° | 0.1399 | 0.1399 | 0.1400 | 0.1400 | 0.1400 | 0.1401 | 0.1401 | 0.1401 | 0.1401 |
| 9° | 0.1575 | 0.1575 | 0.1576 | 0.1576 | 0.1577 | 0.1577 | 0.1577 | 0.1577 | 0.1577 |
| 10° | 0.1751 | 0.1751 | 0.1752 | 0.1753 | 0.1753 | 0.1754 | 0.1754 | 0.1754 | 0.1754 |
| 11° | 0.1927 | 0.1928 | 0.1929 | 0.1930 | 0.1930 | 0.1931 | 0.1931 | 0.1932 | 0.1932 |
| 12° | 0.2103 | 0.2105 | 0.2106 | 0.2107 | 0.2108 | 0.2109 | 0.2109 | 0.2110 | 0.2110 |
| 13° | 0.2280 | 0.2282 | 0.2284 | 0.2285 | 0.2286 | 0.2287 | 0.2288 | 0.2288 | 0.2289 |
| 14° | 0.2458 | 0.2460 | 0.2462 | 0.2464 | 0.2465 | 0.2466 | 0.2467 | 0.2468 | 0.2468 |
| 15° | 0.2636 | 0.2638 | 0.2641 | 0.2643 | 0.2645 | 0.2646 | 0.2647 | 0.2648 | 0.2648 |
| 16° | 0.2814 | 0.2817 | 0.2820 | 0.2823 | 0.2825 | 0.2827 | 0.2828 | 0.2829 | 0.2830 |
| 17° | 0.2993 | 0.2997 | 0.3000 | 0.3003 | 0.3006 | 0.3008 | 0.3010 | 0.3011 | 0.3012 |
| 18° | 0.3172 | 0.3177 | 0.3181 | 0.3185 | 0.3188 | 0.3191 | 0.3193 | 0.3194 | 0.3195 |
| 19° | 0.3352 | 0.3357 | 0.3362 | 0.3367 | 0.3371 | 0.3374 | 0.3377 | 0.3378 | 0.3379 |
| 20° | 0.3533 | 0.3539 | 0.3545 | 0.3550 | 0.3555 | 0.3559 | 0.3561 | 0.3563 | 0.3564 |
| 21° | 0.3714 | 0.3721 | 0.3728 | 0.3734 | 0.3740 | 0.3744 | 0.3747 | 0.3749 | 0.3750 |
| 22° | 0.3896 | 0.3904 | 0.3912 | 0.3919 | 0.3926 | 0.3931 | 0.3935 | 0.3937 | 0.3938 |
| 23° | 0.4078 | 0.4088 | 0.4097 | 0.4105 | 0.4113 | 0 4119 | 0.4123 | 0.4126 | 0.4127 |
| 24° | 0.4261 | 0.4272 | 0.4283 | 0.4292 | 0.4301 | 0.4308 | 0.4313 | 0.4316 | 0.4317 |
| 25° | 0.4446 | 0.4458 | 0.4470 | 0.4481 | 0.4490 | 0.4498 | 0.4504 | 0.4508 | 0.4509 |
| 26° | 0.4630 | 0.4645 | 0.4658 | 0.4670 | 0.4681 | 0.4690 | 0.4697 | 0.4701 | 0.4702 |
| 27° | 0.4816 | 0.4832 | 0.4847 | 0.4861 | 0.4873 | 0.4884 | 0.4891 | 0.4896 | 0.4897 |
| 28° | 0.5003 | 0.5021 | 0.5038 | 0.5053 | 0.5067 | 0.5079 | 0.5087 | 0.5092 | 0.5094 |
| 29° | 0.5190 | 0.5210 | 0.5229 | 0.5247 | 0.5262 | 0.5275 | 0.5285 | 0.5291 | 0.5293 |
| 30° | 0.5379 | 0.5401 | 0.5422 | 0.5442 | 0.5459 | 0.5474 | 0.5484 | 0.5491 | 0.5493 |
| 31° | 0.5568 | 0.5593 | 0.5617 | 0.5639 | 0.5658 | 0.5674 | 0.5686 | 0.5693 | 0.5696 |
| 32° | 0.5759 | 0.5786 | 0.5812 | 0.5837 | 0.5858 | 0.5876 | 0.5889 | 0.5898 | 0.5900 |
| 33° | 0.5950 | 0.5980 | 0.6010 | 0.6037 | 0.6060 | 0.6080 | 0.6095 | 0.6104 | 0.6107 |
| 34° | 0.6143 | 0.6176 | 0.6208 | 0.6238 | 0.6265 | 0.6287 | 0.6303 | 0.6313 | 0.6317 |
| 35° | 0.6336 | 0.6373 | 0.6408 | 0.6441 | 0.6471 | 0.6495 | 0.6513 | 0.6525 | 0.6528 |
| 36° | 0.6531 | 0.6571 | 0.6610 | 0.6647 | 0.6679 | 0.6706 | 0.6726 | 0.6739 | 0.6743 |
| 37° | 0.6727 | 0.6771 | 0.6814 | 0.6854 | 0.6890 | 0.6919 | 0.6941 | 0.6955 | 0.6960 |
| 38° | 0.6925 | 0.6973 | 0.7019 | 0.7063 | 0.7102 | 0.7135 | 0.7159 | 0.7175 | 0.7180 |
| 39° | 0.7123 | 0.7176 | 0.7227 | 0.7275 | 0.7318 | 0.7353 | 0.7380 | 0.7397 | 0.7403 |
| 40° | 0.7323 | 0.7380 | 0.7436 | 0.7488 | 0.7535 | 0.7575 | 0.7604 | 0.7623 | 0.7629 |
| 41° | 0.7524 | 0.7586 | 0.7647 | 0.7704 | 0.7756 | 0.7799 | 0.7831 | 0.7852 | 0.7859 |
| 42° | 0.7727 | 0.7794 | 0.7860 | 0.7922 | 0.7979 | 0.8026 | 0.8062 | 0.8084 | 0.8092 |
| 43° | 0.7931 | 0.8004 | 0.8075 | 0.8143 | 0.8204 | 0.8256 | 0.8295 | 0.8320 | 0.8328 |
| 44° | 0.8136 | 0.8215 | 0.8293 | 0.8367 | 0.8433 | 0.8490 | 0.8533 | 0.8560 | 0.8569 |
| 45° | 0.8343 | 0.8428 | 0.8512 | 0.8592 | 0.8665 | 0.8727 | 0.8774 | 0.8804 | 0.8814 |

$$F(k, \phi) = \int_0^\phi \frac{d\Phi}{\sqrt{1 - k^2 \sin^2 \Phi}}, \qquad \theta = \sin^{-1} k$$

| $\phi$ \ $\theta$ | 5° | 10° | 15° | 20° | 25° | 30° | 35° | 40° | 45° |
|---|---|---|---|---|---|---|---|---|---|
| 46° | 0.8034 | 0.8052 | 0.8080 | 0.8120 | 0.8170 | 0.8230 | 0.8300 | 0.8378 | 0.8462 |
| 47° | 0.8209 | 0.8227 | 0.8258 | 0.8300 | 0.8353 | 0.8418 | 0.8492 | 0.8575 | 0.8666 |
| 48° | 0.8384 | 0.8403 | 0.8436 | 0.8480 | 0.8537 | 0.8606 | 0.8685 | 0.8773 | 0.8870 |
| 49° | 0.8559 | 0.8579 | 0.8614 | 0.8661 | 0.8721 | 0.8794 | 0.8878 | 0.8972 | 0.9076 |
| 50° | 0.8734 | 0.8756 | 0.8792 | 0.8842 | 0.8905 | 0.8982 | 0.9072 | 0.9173 | 0.9283 |
| 51° | 0.8909 | 0.8932 | 0.8970 | 0.9023 | 0.9090 | 0.9172 | 0.9267 | 0.9374 | 0.9491 |
| 52° | 0.9084 | 0.9108 | 0.9148 | 0.9204 | 0.9275 | 0.9361 | 0.9462 | 0.9575 | 0.9701 |
| 53° | 0.9259 | 0.9284 | 0.9326 | 0.9385 | 0.9460 | 0.9551 | 0.9658 | 0.9778 | 0.9912 |
| 54° | 0.9434 | 0.9460 | 0.9505 | 0.9567 | 0.9646 | 0.9742 | 0.9855 | 0.9982 | 1.0124 |
| 55° | 0.9609 | 0.9637 | 0.9683 | 0.9748 | 0.9832 | 0.9933 | 1.0052 | 1.0187 | 1.0337 |
| 56° | 0.9784 | 0.9813 | 0.9862 | 0.9930 | 1.0018 | 1.0125 | 1.0250 | 1.0393 | 1.0552 |
| 57° | 0.9959 | 0.9989 | 1.0041 | 1.0112 | 1.0204 | 1.0317 | 1.0449 | 1.0600 | 1.0768 |
| 58° | 1.0134 | 1.0166 | 1.0219 | 1.0295 | 1.0391 | 1.0509 | 1.0648 | 1.0807 | 1.0985 |
| 59° | 1.0309 | 1.0342 | 1.0398 | 1.0477 | 1.0578 | 1.0702 | 1.0848 | 1.1016 | 1.1204 |
| 60° | 1.0484 | 1.0519 | 1.0577 | 1.0660 | 1.0766 | 1.0896 | 1.1049 | 1.1226 | 1.1424 |
| 61° | 1.0659 | 1.0695 | 1.0757 | 1.0843 | 1.0953 | 1.1089 | 1.1250 | 1.1436 | 1.1646 |
| 62° | 1.0834 | 1.0872 | 1.0936 | 1.1026 | 1.1141 | 1.1284 | 1.1452 | 1.1648 | 1.1868 |
| 63° | 1.1009 | 1.1049 | 1.1115 | 1.1209 | 1.1330 | 1.1478 | 1.1655 | 1.1860 | 1.2093 |
| 64° | 1.1184 | 1.1225 | 1.1295 | 1.1392 | 1.1518 | 1.1674 | 1.1859 | 1.2073 | 1.2318 |
| 65° | 1.1359 | 1.1402 | 1.1474 | 1.1575 | 1.1707 | 1.1869 | 1.2063 | 1.2288 | 1.2545 |
| 66° | 1.1534 | 1.1579 | 1.1654 | 1.1759 | 1.1896 | 1.2065 | 1.2267 | 1.2503 | 1.2773 |
| 67° | 1.1709 | 1.1756 | 1.1833 | 1.1943 | 1.2085 | 1.2262 | 1.2472 | 1.2719 | 1.3002 |
| 68° | 1.1884 | 1.1932 | 1.2013 | 1.2127 | 1.2275 | 1.2458 | 1.2678 | 1.2936 | 1.3232 |
| 69° | 1.2059 | 1.2109 | 1.2193 | 1.2311 | 1.2465 | 1.2655 | 1.2885 | 1.3154 | 1.3464 |
| 70° | 1.2234 | 1.2286 | 1.2373 | 1.2495 | 1.2655 | 1.2853 | 1.3092 | 1.3372 | 1.3697 |
| 71° | 1.2410 | 1.2463 | 1.2553 | 1.2680 | 1.2845 | 1.3051 | 1.3209 | 1.3592 | 1.3931 |
| 72° | 1.2585 | 1.2640 | 1.2733 | 1.2864 | 1.3036 | 1.3249 | 1.3507 | 1.3812 | 1.4167 |
| 73° | 1.2760 | 1.2817 | 1.2913 | 1.3049 | 1.3226 | 1.3448 | 1.3715 | 1.4033 | 1.4403 |
| 74° | 1.2935 | 1.2994 | 1.3093 | 1.3234 | 1.3417 | 1.3647 | 1.3924 | 1.4254 | 1.4640 |
| 75° | 1.3110 | 1.3171 | 1.3273 | 1.3418 | 1.3608 | 1.3846 | 1.4134 | 1.4477 | 1.4879 |
| 76° | 1.3285 | 1.3348 | 1.3454 | 1.3603 | 1.3800 | 1.4045 | 1.4344 | 1.4700 | 1.5118 |
| 77° | 1.3460 | 1.3525 | 1.3634 | 1.3788 | 1.3991 | 1.4245 | 1.4554 | 1.4923 | 1.5359 |
| 78° | 1.3636 | 1.3702 | 1.3814 | 1.3974 | 1.4183 | 1.4445 | 1.4765 | 1.5147 | 1.5600 |
| 79° | 1.3811 | 1.3879 | 1.3995 | 1.4159 | 1.4374 | 1.4645 | 1.4976 | 1.5372 | 1.5842 |
| 80° | 1.3986 | 1.4056 | 1.4175 | 1.4344 | 1.4566 | 1.4846 | 1.5187 | 1.5597 | 1.6085 |
| 81° | 1.4161 | 1.4234 | 1.4356 | 1.4530 | 1.4758 | 1.5046 | 1.5399 | 1.5823 | 1.6328 |
| 82° | 1.4336 | 1.4411 | 1.4536 | 1.4715 | 1.4950 | 1.5247 | 1.5611 | 1.6049 | 1.6572 |
| 83° | 1.4512 | 1.4588 | 1.4717 | 1.4901 | 1.5143 | 1.5448 | 1.5823 | 1.6276 | 1.6817 |
| 84° | 1.4687 | 1.4765 | 1.4897 | 1.5086 | 1.5335 | 1.5649 | 1.6035 | 1.6502 | 1.7062 |
| 85° | 1.4862 | 1.4942 | 1.5078 | 1.5272 | 1.5527 | 1.5850 | 1.6248 | 1.6730 | 1.7308 |
| 86° | 1.5037 | 1.5120 | 1.5259 | 1.5457 | 1.5720 | 1.6052 | 1.6461 | 1.6957 | 1.7554 |
| 87° | 1.5212 | 1.5297 | 1.5439 | 1.5643 | 1.5912 | 1.6253 | 1.6673 | 1.7184 | 1.7801 |
| 88° | 1.5388 | 1.5474 | 1.5620 | 1.5829 | 1.6105 | 1.6454 | 1.6886 | 1.7412 | 1.8047 |
| 89° | 1.5563 | 1.5651 | 1.5801 | 1.6015 | 1.6297 | 1.6656 | 1.7099 | 1.7640 | 1.8294 |
| 90° | 1.5738 | 1.5828 | 1.5981 | 1.6200 | 1.6490 | 1.6858 | 1.7312 | 1.7868 | 1.8541 |

# ELLIPTIC INTEGRALS OF THE FIRST KIND: $F(k, \phi)$
## (Continued)

$$F(k, \phi) = \int_0^\phi \frac{d\Phi}{\sqrt{1 - k^2 \sin^2 \Phi}}, \qquad \theta = \sin^{-1} k$$

| $\phi$ \ $\theta$ | 50° | 55° | 60° | 65° | 70° | 75° | 80° | 85° | 90° |
|---|---|---|---|---|---|---|---|---|---|
| 46° | 0.8552 | 0.8643 | 0.8734 | 0.8821 | 0.8900 | 0.8968 | 0.9019 | 0.9052 | 0.9063 |
| 47° | 0.8761 | 0.8860 | 0.8958 | 0.9053 | 0.9139 | 0.9212 | 0.9269 | 0.9304 | 0.9316 |
| 48° | 0.8973 | 0.9079 | 0.9185 | 0.9287 | 0.9381 | 0.9461 | 0.9523 | 0.9561 | 0.9575 |
| 49° | 0.9186 | 0.9300 | 0.9415 | 0.9525 | 0.9627 | 0.9714 | 0.9781 | 0.9824 | 0.9838 |
| 50° | 0.9401 | 0.9523 | 0.9647 | 0.9766 | 0.9876 | 0.9971 | 1.0044 | 1.0091 | 1.0107 |
| 51° | 0.9617 | 0.9748 | 0.9881 | 1.0010 | 1.0130 | 1.0233 | 1.0313 | 1.0364 | 1.0381 |
| 52° | 0.9835 | 0.9976 | 1.0118 | 1.0258 | 1.0387 | 1.0499 | 1.0587 | 1.0642 | 1.0662 |
| 53° | 1.0055 | 1.0205 | 1.0359 | 1.0509 | 1.0649 | 1.0771 | 1.0866 | 1.0927 | 1.0948 |
| 54° | 1.0277 | 1.0437 | 1.0602 | 1.0764 | 1.0915 | 1.1048 | 1.1152 | 1.1219 | 1.1242 |
| 55° | 1.0500 | 1.0672 | 1.0848 | 1.1022 | 1.1186 | 1.1331 | 1.1444 | 1.1517 | 1.1542 |
| 56° | 1.0725 | 1.0908 | 1.1097 | 1.1285 | 1.1462 | 1.1619 | 1.1743 | 1.1823 | 1.1851 |
| 57° | 1.0952 | 1.1147 | 1.1349 | 1.1551 | 1.1743 | 1.1914 | 1.2049 | 1.2136 | 1.2167 |
| 58° | 1.1180 | 1.1389 | 1.1605 | 1.1822 | 1.2030 | 1.2215 | 1.2362 | 1.2458 | 1.2492 |
| 59° | 1.1411 | 1.1632 | 1.1864 | 1.2097 | 1.2321 | 1.2522 | 1.2684 | 1.2789 | 1.2826 |
| 60° | 1.1643 | 1.1879 | 1.2125 | 1.2376 | 1.2619 | 1.2837 | 1.3014 | 1.3129 | 1.3170 |
| 61° | 1.1877 | 1.2128 | 1.2392 | 1.2660 | 1.2922 | 1.3159 | 1.3352 | 1.3480 | 1.3524 |
| 62° | 1.2113 | 1.2379 | 1.2661 | 1.2949 | 1.3231 | 1.3490 | 1.3701 | 1.3841 | 1.3890 |
| 63° | 1.2351 | 1.2633 | 1.2933 | 1.3242 | 1.3547 | 1.3828 | 1.4059 | 1.4214 | 1.4268 |
| 64° | 1.2591 | 1.2890 | 1.3209 | 1.3541 | 1.3870 | 1.4175 | 1.4429 | 1.4599 | 1.4659 |
| 65° | 1.2833 | 1.3149 | 1.3489 | 1.3844 | 1.4199 | 1.4532 | 1.4810 | 1.4998 | 1.5065 |
| 66° | 1.3076 | 1.3411 | 1.3773 | 1.4153 | 1.4536 | 1.4898 | 1.5203 | 1.5411 | 1.5485 |
| 67° | 1.3321 | 1.3675 | 1.4060 | 1.4467 | 1.4880 | 1.5274 | 1.5610 | 1.5840 | 1.5923 |
| 68° | 1.3568 | 1.3942 | 1.4351 | 1.4786 | 1.5232 | 1.5661 | 1.6030 | 1.6287 | 1.6379 |
| 69° | 1.3817 | 1.4212 | 1.4646 | 1.5111 | 1.5591 | 1.6059 | 1.6466 | 1.6752 | 1.6856 |
| 70° | 1.4068 | 1.4484 | 1.4944 | 1.5441 | 1.5959 | 1.6468 | 1.6918 | 1.7237 | 1.7354 |
| 71° | 1.4320 | 1.4759 | 1.5246 | 1.5777 | 1.6335 | 1.6891 | 1.7388 | 1.7745 | 1.7877 |
| 72° | 1.4574 | 1.5036 | 1.5552 | 1.6118 | 1.6720 | 1.7326 | 1.7876 | 1.8277 | 1.8427 |
| 73° | 1.4830 | 1.5315 | 1.5862 | 1.6465 | 1.7113 | 1.7774 | 1.8384 | 1.8837 | 1.9008 |
| 74° | 1.5087 | 1.5597 | 1.6175 | 1.6818 | 1.7516 | 1.8237 | 1.8915 | 1.9427 | 1.9623 |
| 75° | 1.5345 | 1.5882 | 1.6492 | 1.7176 | 1.7927 | 1.8715 | 1.9468 | 2.0050 | 2.0276 |
| 76° | 1.5606 | 1.6168 | 1.6812 | 1.7540 | 1.8347 | 1.9207 | 2.0047 | 2.0711 | 2.0973 |
| 77° | 1.5867 | 1.6457 | 1.7136 | 1.7909 | 1.8777 | 1.9716 | 2.0653 | 2.1414 | 2.1721 |
| 78° | 1.6130 | 1.6748 | 1.7462 | 1.8284 | 1.9215 | 2.0240 | 2.1288 | 2.2164 | 2.2528 |
| 79° | 1.6394 | 1.7040 | 1.7792 | 1.8664 | 1.9663 | 2.0781 | 2.1954 | 2.2969 | 2.3404 |
| 80° | 1.6660 | 1.7335 | 1.8125 | 1.9048 | 2.0119 | 2.1339 | 2.2653 | 2.3836 | 2.4362 |
| 81° | 1.6926 | 1.7631 | 1.8461 | 1.9438 | 2.0584 | 2.1913 | 2.3387 | 2.4775 | 2.5421 |
| 82° | 1.7193 | 1.7929 | 1.8799 | 1.9831 | 2.1057 | 2.2504 | 2.4157 | 2.5795 | 2.6603 |
| 83° | 1.7462 | 1.8228 | 1.9140 | 2.0229 | 2.1537 | 2.3110 | 2.4965 | 2.6911 | 2.7942 |
| 84° | 1.7731 | 1.8528 | 1.9482 | 2.0630 | 2.2024 | 2.3731 | 2.5811 | 2.8136 | 2.9487 |
| 85° | 1.8001 | 1.8830 | 1.9826 | 2.1035 | 2.2518 | 2.4366 | 2.6694 | 2.9487 | 3.1313 |
| 86° | 1.8271 | 1.9132 | 2.0172 | 2.1442 | 2.3017 | 2.5013 | 2.7612 | 3.0978 | 3.3547 |
| 87° | 1.8542 | 1.9435 | 2.0519 | 2.1852 | 2.3520 | 2.5670 | 2.8561 | 3.2620 | 3.6425 |
| 88° | 1.8813 | 1.9739 | 2.0867 | 2.2263 | 2.4026 | 2.6336 | 2.9537 | 3.4412 | 4.0481 |
| 89° | 1.9084 | 2.0043 | 2.1216 | 2.2675 | 2.4535 | 2.7007 | 3.0530 | 3.6328 | 4.7413 |
| 90° | 1.9356 | 2.0347 | 2.1565 | 2.3088 | 2.5046 | 2.7681 | 3.1534 | 3.8317 | —— |

# ELLIPTIC INTEGRALS OF THE SECOND KIND: $E(k, \phi)$

$$E(k, \phi) = \int_0^\phi \sqrt{(1 - k^2 \sin^2 \Phi)}\, d\Phi, \qquad \theta = \sin^{-1} k$$

| φ＼θ | 5° | 10° | 15° | 20° | 25° | 30° | 35° | 40° | 45° |
|---|---|---|---|---|---|---|---|---|---|
| **1°** | 0.0175 | 0.0175 | 0.0175 | 0.0175 | 0.0175 | 0.0175 | 0.0175 | 0.0175 | 0.0175 |
| 2° | 0.0349 | 0.0349 | 0.0349 | 0.0349 | 0.0349 | 0.0349 | 0.0349 | 0.0349 | 0.0349 |
| 3° | 0.0524 | 0.0524 | 0.0524 | 0.0524 | 0.0524 | 0.0524 | 0.0524 | 0.0523 | 0.0523 |
| 4° | 0.0698 | 0.0698 | 0.0698 | 0.0698 | 0.0698 | 0.0698 | 0.0698 | 0.0698 | 0.0698 |
| 5° | 0.0873 | 0.0873 | 0.0873 | 0.0873 | 0.0872 | 0.0872 | 0.0872 | 0.0872 | 0.0872 |
| **6°** | 0.1047 | 0.1047 | 0.1047 | 0.1047 | 0.1047 | 0.1047 | 0.1047 | 0.1046 | 0.1046 |
| 7° | 0.1222 | 0.1222 | 0.1222 | 0.1221 | 0.1221 | 0.1221 | 0.1221 | 0.1220 | 0.1220 |
| 8° | 0.1396 | 0.1396 | 0.1396 | 0.1396 | 0.1395 | 0.1395 | 0.1395 | 0.1394 | 0.1394 |
| 9° | 0.1571 | 0.1571 | 0.1570 | 0.1570 | 0.1570 | 0.1569 | 0.1569 | 0.1568 | 0.1568 |
| 10° | 0.1745 | 0.1745 | 0.1745 | 0.1744 | 0.1744 | 0.1743 | 0.1742 | 0.1742 | 0.1741 |
| **11°** | 0.1920 | 0.1920 | 0.1919 | 0.1918 | 0.1918 | 0.1917 | 0.1916 | 0.1915 | 0.1914 |
| 12° | 0.2094 | 0.2094 | 0.2093 | 0.2093 | 0.2092 | 0.2091 | 0.2089 | 0.2088 | 0.2087 |
| 13° | 0.2269 | 0.2268 | 0.2268 | 0.2267 | 0.2265 | 0.2264 | 0.2263 | 0.2261 | 0.2259 |
| 14° | 0.2443 | 0.2443 | 0.2442 | 0.2441 | 0.2439 | 0.2437 | 0.2436 | 0.2433 | 0.2431 |
| 15° | 0.2618 | 0.2617 | 0.2616 | 0.2615 | 0.2613 | 0.2611 | 0.2608 | 0.2606 | 0.2603 |
| **16°** | 0.2792 | 0.2791 | 0.2790 | 0.2788 | 0.2786 | 0.2784 | 0.2781 | 0.2778 | 0.2775 |
| 17° | 0.2967 | 0.2966 | 0.2964 | 0.2962 | 0.2959 | 0.2956 | 0.2953 | 0.2949 | 0.2946 |
| 18° | 0.3141 | 0.3140 | 0.3138 | 0.3136 | 0.3133 | 0.3129 | 0.3125 | 0.3121 | 0.3116 |
| 19° | 0.3316 | 0.3314 | 0.3312 | 0.3309 | 0.3305 | 0.3301 | 0.3296 | 0.3291 | 0.3286 |
| 20° | 0.3490 | 0.3489 | 0.3486 | 0.3483 | 0.3478 | 0.3473 | 0.3468 | 0.3462 | 0.3456 |
| **21°** | 0.3665 | 0.3663 | 0.3660 | 0.3656 | 0.3651 | 0.3645 | 0.3639 | 0.3632 | 0.3625 |
| 22° | 0.3839 | 0.3837 | 0.3834 | 0.3829 | 0.3823 | 0.3817 | 0.3809 | 0.3802 | 0.3793 |
| 23° | 0.4013 | 0.4011 | 0.4007 | 0.4002 | 0.3996 | 0.3988 | 0.3980 | 0.3971 | 0.3961 |
| 24° | 0.4188 | 0.4185 | 0.4181 | 0.4175 | 0.4168 | 0.4159 | 0.4150 | 0.4139 | 0.4129 |
| 25° | 0.4362 | 0.4359 | 0.4354 | 0.4348 | 0.4339 | 0.4330 | 0.4319 | 0.4308 | 0.4296 |
| **26°** | 0.4537 | 0.4533 | 0.4528 | 0.4520 | 0.4511 | 0.4500 | 0.4488 | 0.4475 | 0.4462 |
| 27° | 0.4711 | 0.4707 | 0.4701 | 0.4693 | 0.4682 | 0.4670 | 0.4657 | 0.4643 | 0.4628 |
| 28° | 0.4886 | 0.4881 | 0.4874 | 0.4865 | 0.4854 | 0.4840 | 0.4825 | 0.4809 | 0.4793 |
| 29° | 0.5060 | 0.5055 | 0.5048 | 0.5037 | 0.5025 | 0.5010 | 0.4993 | 0.4975 | 0.4957 |
| 30° | 0.5234 | 0.5229 | 0.5221 | 0.5209 | 0.5195 | 0.5179 | 0.5161 | 0.5141 | 0.5120 |
| **31°** | 0.5409 | 0.5403 | 0.5394 | 0.5381 | 0.5366 | 0.5348 | 0.5327 | 0.5306 | 0.5283 |
| 32° | 0.5583 | 0.5577 | 0.5567 | 0.5553 | 0.5536 | 0.5516 | 0.5494 | 0.5470 | 0.5446 |
| 33° | 0.5757 | 0.5751 | 0.5740 | 0.5725 | 0.5706 | 0.5684 | 0.5660 | 0.5634 | 0.5607 |
| 34° | 0.5932 | 0.5924 | 0.5912 | 0.5896 | 0.5876 | 0.5852 | 0.5826 | 0.5797 | 0.5768 |
| 35° | 0.6106 | 0.6098 | 0.6085 | 0.6067 | 0.6045 | 0.6019 | 0.5991 | 0.5960 | 0.5928 |
| **36°** | 0.6280 | 0.6272 | 0.6258 | 0.6238 | 0.6214 | 0.6186 | 0.6155 | 0.6122 | 0.6087 |
| 37° | 0.6455 | 0.6445 | 0.6430 | 0.6409 | 0.6383 | 0.6353 | 0.6319 | 0.6283 | 0.6245 |
| 38° | 0.6629 | 0.6619 | 0.6602 | 0.6580 | 0.6552 | 0.6519 | 0.6483 | 0.6444 | 0.6403 |
| 39° | 0.6803 | 0.6792 | 0.6775 | 0.6750 | 0.6720 | 0.6685 | 0.6646 | 0.6604 | 0.6559 |
| 40° | 0.6977 | 0.6966 | 0.6947 | 0.6921 | 0.6888 | 0.6851 | 0.6808 | 0.6763 | 0.6715 |
| **41°** | 0.7152 | 0.7139 | 0.7119 | 0.7091 | 0.7056 | 0.7016 | 0.6970 | 0.6921 | 0.6870 |
| 42° | 0.7326 | 0.7313 | 0.7291 | 0.7261 | 0.7224 | 0.7180 | 0.7132 | 0.7079 | 0.7024 |
| 43° | 0.7500 | 0.7486 | 0.7463 | 0.7431 | 0.7391 | 0.7345 | 0.7293 | 0.7237 | 0.7178 |
| 44° | 0.7674 | 0.7659 | 0.7634 | 0.7600 | 0.7558 | 0.7508 | 0.7453 | 0.7393 | 0.7330 |
| 45° | 0.7849 | 0.7832 | 0.7806 | 0.7770 | 0.7725 | 0.7672 | 0.7613 | 0.7549 | 0.7482 |

$$E(k, \phi) = \int_0^\phi \sqrt{(1 - k^2 \sin^2 \Phi)} \, d\Phi, \qquad \theta = \sin^{-1} k$$

| $\phi$ \ $\theta$ | 50° | 55° | 60° | 65° | 70° | 75° | 80° | 85° | 90° |
|---|---|---|---|---|---|---|---|---|---|
| 1° | 0.0175 | 0.0175 | 0.0175 | 0.0175 | 0.0175 | 0.0175 | 0.0175 | 0.0175 | 0.0175 |
| 2° | 0.0349 | 0.0349 | 0.0349 | 0.0349 | 0.0349 | 0.0349 | 0.0349 | 0.0349 | 0.0349 |
| 3° | 0.0523 | 0.0523 | 0.0523 | 0.0523 | 0.0523 | 0.0523 | 0.0523 | 0.0523 | 0.0523 |
| 4° | 0.0698 | 0.0698 | 0.0698 | 0.0698 | 0.0698 | 0.0698 | 0.0698 | 0.0698 | 0.0698 |
| 5° | 0.0872 | 0.0872 | 0.0872 | 0.0872 | 0.0872 | 0.0872 | 0.0872 | 0.0872 | 0.0872 |
| 6° | 0.1046 | 0.1046 | 0.1046 | 0.1046 | 0.1046 | 0.1045 | 0.1045 | 0.1045 | 0.1045 |
| 7° | 0.1220 | 0.1220 | 0.1219 | 0.1219 | 0.1219 | 0.1219 | 0.1219 | 0.1219 | 0.1219 |
| 8° | 0.1394 | 0.1393 | 0.1393 | 0.1393 | 0.1392 | 0.1392 | 0.1392 | 0.1392 | 0.1392 |
| 9° | 0.1567 | 0.1566 | 0.1566 | 0.1566 | 0.1565 | 0.1565 | 0.1565 | 0.1564 | 0.1564 |
| 10° | 0.1740 | 0.1739 | 0.1739 | 0.1738 | 0.1738 | 0.1737 | 0.1737 | 0.1737 | 0.1736 |
| 11° | 0.1913 | 0.1912 | 0.1911 | 0.1910 | 0.1909 | 0.1909 | 0.1908 | 0.1908 | 0.1908 |
| 12° | 0.2085 | 0.2084 | 0.2083 | 0.2082 | 0.2081 | 0.2080 | 0.2080 | 0.2079 | 0.2079 |
| 13° | 0.2258 | 0.2256 | 0.2254 | 0.2253 | 0.2252 | 0.2251 | 0.2250 | 0.2250 | 0.2250 |
| 14° | 0.2429 | 0.2427 | 0.2425 | 0.2424 | 0.2422 | 0.2421 | 0.2420 | 0.2419 | 0.2419 |
| 15° | 0.2601 | 0.2598 | 0.2596 | 0.2594 | 0.2592 | 0.2590 | 0.2589 | 0.2588 | 0.2588 |
| 16° | 0.2771 | 0.2768 | 0.2765 | 0.2763 | 0.2761 | 0.2759 | 0.2757 | 0.2757 | 0.2756 |
| 17° | 0.2942 | 0.2938 | 0.2935 | 0.2932 | 0.2929 | 0.2927 | 0.2925 | 0.2924 | 0.2924 |
| 18° | 0.3112 | 0.3107 | 0.3103 | 0.3099 | 0.3096 | 0.3094 | 0.3092 | 0.3091 | 0.3090 |
| 19° | 0.3281 | 0.3276 | 0.3271 | 0.3267 | 0.3263 | 0.3260 | 0.3258 | 0.3256 | 0.3256 |
| 20° | 0.3450 | 0.3444 | 0.3438 | 0.3433 | 0.3429 | 0.3425 | 0.3422 | 0.3421 | 0.3420 |
| 21° | 0.3618 | 0.3611 | 0.3604 | 0.3598 | 0.3593 | 0.3589 | 0.3586 | 0.3584 | 0.3584 |
| 22° | 0.3785 | 0.3777 | 0.3770 | 0.3763 | 0.3757 | 0.3752 | 0.3749 | 0.3747 | 0.3746 |
| 23° | 0.3952 | 0.3943 | 0.3935 | 0.3927 | 0.3920 | 0.3915 | 0.3911 | 0.3908 | 0.3907 |
| 24° | 0.4118 | 0.4108 | 0.4098 | 0.4090 | 0.4082 | 0.4076 | 0.4071 | 0.4068 | 0.4067 |
| 25° | 0.4284 | 0.4272 | 0.4261 | 0.4251 | 0.4243 | 0.4236 | 0.4230 | 0.4227 | 0.4226 |
| 26° | 0.4449 | 0.4436 | 0.4423 | 0.4412 | 0.4402 | 0.4394 | 0.4389 | 0.4385 | 0.4384 |
| 27° | 0.4613 | 0.4598 | 0.4584 | 0.4572 | 0.4561 | 0.4552 | 0.4545 | 0.4541 | 0.4540 |
| 28° | 0.4776 | 0.4760 | 0.4744 | 0.4730 | 0.4718 | 0.4708 | 0.4701 | 0.4696 | 0.4695 |
| 29° | 0.4938 | 0.4920 | 0.4903 | 0.4887 | 0.4874 | 0.4863 | 0.4855 | 0.4850 | 0.4848 |
| 30° | 0.5100 | 0.5080 | 0.5061 | 0.5044 | 0.5029 | 0.5016 | 0.5007 | 0.5002 | 0.5000 |
| 31° | 0.5261 | 0.5239 | 0.5218 | 0.5199 | 0.5182 | 0.5169 | 0.5159 | 0.5152 | 0.5150 |
| 32° | 0.5421 | 0.5396 | 0.5373 | 0.5352 | 0.5334 | 0.5319 | 0.5308 | 0.5301 | 0.5299 |
| 33° | 0.5580 | 0.5553 | 0.5528 | 0.5505 | 0.5485 | 0.5468 | 0.5456 | 0.5449 | 0.5446 |
| 34° | 0.5738 | 0.5709 | 0.5681 | 0.5656 | 0.5634 | 0.5616 | 0.5603 | 0.5595 | 0.5592 |
| 35° | 0.5895 | 0.5863 | 0.5833 | 0.5806 | 0.5782 | 0.5762 | 0.5748 | 0.5739 | 0.5736 |
| 36° | 0.6051 | 0.6017 | 0.5984 | 0.5954 | 0.5928 | 0.5907 | 0.5891 | 0.5881 | 0.5878 |
| 37° | 0.6207 | 0.6169 | 0.6134 | 0.6101 | 0.6073 | 0.6050 | 0.6032 | 0.6022 | 0.6018 |
| 38° | 0.6361 | 0.6321 | 0.6282 | 0.6247 | 0.6216 | 0.6191 | 0.6172 | 0.6160 | 0.6157 |
| 39° | 0.6515 | 0.6471 | 0.6429 | 0.6391 | 0.6357 | 0.6330 | 0.6310 | 0.6297 | 0.6293 |
| 40° | 0.6667 | 0.6620 | 0.6575 | 0.6533 | 0.6497 | 0.6468 | 0.6446 | 0.6432 | 0.6428 |
| 41° | 0.6818 | 0.6767 | 0.6719 | 0.6674 | 0.6636 | 0.6604 | 0.6580 | 0.6566 | 0.6561 |
| 42° | 0.6969 | 0.6914 | 0.6862 | 0.6814 | 0.6772 | 0.6738 | 0.6712 | 0.6697 | 0.6691 |
| 43° | 0.7118 | 0.7059 | 0.7003 | 0.6952 | 0.6907 | 0.6870 | 0.6843 | 0.6826 | 0.6820 |
| 44° | 0.7266 | 0.7204 | 0.7144 | 0.7088 | 0.7040 | 0.7000 | 0.6971 | 0.6953 | 0.6947 |
| 45° | 0.7414 | 0.7346 | 0.7282 | 0.7223 | 0.7171 | 0.7129 | 0.7097 | 0.7078 | 0.7071 |

# ELLIPTIC INTEGRALS OF THE SECOND KIND: $E(k, \phi)$
## (Continued)

$$E(k, \phi) = \int_0^\phi \sqrt{(1 - k^2 \sin^2 \Phi)} \, d\Phi, \qquad \theta = \sin^{-1} k$$

| $\phi$ \ $\theta$ | 5° | 10° | 15° | 20° | 25° | 30° | 35° | 40° | 45° |
|---|---|---|---|---|---|---|---|---|---|
| **46°** | 0.8023 | 0.8006 | 0.7977 | 0.7939 | 0.7891 | 0.7835 | 0.7772 | 0.7704 | 0.7633 |
| 47° | 0.8197 | 0.8179 | 0.8149 | 0.8108 | 0.8057 | 0.7998 | 0.7931 | 0.7858 | 0.7782 |
| 48° | 0.8371 | 0.8352 | 0.8320 | 0.8277 | 0.8223 | 0.8160 | 0.8089 | 0.8012 | 0.7931 |
| 49° | 0.8545 | 0.8525 | 0.8491 | 0.8446 | 0.8389 | 0.8322 | 0.8247 | 0.8165 | 0.8079 |
| 50° | 0.8719 | 0.8698 | 0.8663 | 0.8614 | 0.8554 | 0.8483 | 0.8404 | 0.8317 | 0.8227 |
| **51°** | 0.8894 | 0.8871 | 0.8834 | 0.8783 | 0.8719 | 0.8644 | 0.8560 | 0.8469 | 0.8373 |
| 52° | 0.9068 | 0.9044 | 0.9004 | 0.8951 | 0.8884 | 0.8805 | 0.8716 | 0.8620 | 0.8518 |
| 53° | 0.9242 | 0.9217 | 0.9175 | 0.9119 | 0.9048 | 0.8965 | 0.8872 | 0.8770 | 0.8663 |
| 54° | 0.9416 | 0.9389 | 0.9345 | 0.9287 | 0.9212 | 0.9125 | 0.9026 | 0.8919 | 0.8806 |
| 55° | 0.9590 | 0.9562 | 0.9517 | 0.9454 | 0.9376 | 0.9284 | 0.9181 | 0.9068 | 0.8949 |
| **56°** | 0.9764 | 0.9735 | 0.9687 | 0.9622 | 0.9540 | 0.9443 | 0.9335 | 0.9216 | 0.9091 |
| 57° | 0.9938 | 0.9908 | 0.9858 | 0.9789 | 0.9703 | 0.9602 | 0.9488 | 0.9363 | 0.9232 |
| 58° | 1.0112 | 1.0080 | 1.0028 | 0.9956 | 0.9866 | 0.9760 | 0.9641 | 0.9510 | 0.9372 |
| 59° | 1.0286 | 1.0253 | 1.0198 | 1.0123 | 1.0029 | 1.9918 | 0.9793 | 0.9656 | 0.9511 |
| 60° | 1.0460 | 1.0426 | 1.0368 | 1.0290 | 1.0191 | 1.0076 | 0.9945 | 0.9801 | 0.9650 |
| **61°** | 1.0634 | 1.0598 | 1.0538 | 1.0456 | 1.0354 | 1.0233 | 1.0096 | 0.9946 | 0.9787 |
| 62° | 1.0808 | 1.0771 | 1.0708 | 1.0623 | 1.0516 | 1.0389 | 1.0246 | 1.0090 | 0.9924 |
| 63° | 1.0982 | 1.0943 | 1.0878 | 1.0789 | 1.0678 | 1.0546 | 1.0397 | 1.0233 | 1.0060 |
| 64° | 1.1156 | 1.1115 | 1.1048 | 1.0955 | 1.0839 | 1.0702 | 1.0547 | 1.0376 | 1.0195 |
| 65° | 1.1330 | 1.1288 | 1.1218 | 1.1121 | 1.1001 | 1.0858 | 1.0696 | 1.0518 | 1.0329 |
| **66°** | 1.1504 | 1.1460 | 1.1387 | 1.1287 | 1.1162 | 1.1013 | 1.0845 | 1.0660 | 1.0463 |
| 67° | 1.1678 | 1.1632 | 1.1557 | 1.1453 | 1.1323 | 1.1168 | 1.0993 | 1.0801 | 1.0596 |
| 68° | 1.1852 | 1.1805 | 1.1726 | 1.1618 | 1.1483 | 1.1323 | 1.1141 | 1.0941 | 1.0728 |
| 69° | 1.2026 | 1.1977 | 1.1896 | 1.1784 | 1.1644 | 1.1478 | 1.1289 | 1.1081 | 1.0859 |
| 70° | 1.2200 | 1.2149 | 1.2065 | 1.1949 | 1.1804 | 1.1632 | 1.1436 | 1.1221 | 1.0990 |
| **71°** | 1.2374 | 1.2321 | 1.2234 | 1.2114 | 1.1964 | 1.1786 | 1.1583 | 1.1359 | 1.1120 |
| 72° | 1.2548 | 1.2493 | 1.2403 | 1.2280 | 1.2124 | 1.1939 | 1.1729 | 1.1498 | 1.1250 |
| 73° | 1.2722 | 1.2666 | 1.2573 | 1.2445 | 1.2284 | 1.2093 | 1.1875 | 1.1636 | 1.1379 |
| 74° | 1.2896 | 1.2838 | 1.2742 | 1.2609 | 1.2443 | 1.2246 | 1.2021 | 1.1773 | 1.1507 |
| 75° | 1.3070 | 1.3010 | 1.2911 | 1.2774 | 1.2603 | 1.2399 | 1.2167 | 1.1910 | 1.1635 |
| **76°** | 1.3244 | 1.3182 | 1.3080 | 1.2939 | 1.2762 | 1.2552 | 1.2312 | 1.2047 | 1.1762 |
| 77° | 1.3418 | 1.3354 | 1.3249 | 1.3104 | 1.2921 | 1.2704 | 1.2457 | 1.2183 | 1.1889 |
| 78° | 1.3592 | 1.3526 | 1.3417 | 1.3268 | 1.3080 | 1.2856 | 1.2601 | 1.2319 | 1.2015 |
| 79° | 1.3765 | 1.3698 | 1.3586 | 1.3432 | 1.3239 | 1.3009 | 1.2746 | 1.2454 | 1.2141 |
| 80° | 1.3939 | 1.3870 | 1.3755 | 1.3597 | 1.3398 | 1.3161 | 1.2890 | 1.2590 | 1.2266 |
| **81°** | 1.4113 | 1.4042 | 1.3924 | 1.3761 | 1.3556 | 1.3312 | 1.3034 | 1.2725 | 1.2391 |
| 82° | 1.4287 | 1.4214 | 1.4093 | 1.3925 | 1.3715 | 1.3464 | 1.3177 | 1.2859 | 1.2516 |
| 83° | 1.4461 | 1.4386 | 1.4261 | 1.4090 | 1.3873 | 1.3616 | 1.3321 | 1.2994 | 1.2640 |
| 84° | 1.4635 | 1.4558 | 1.4430 | 1.4254 | 1.4032 | 1.3767 | 1.3464 | 1.3128 | 1.2765 |
| 85° | 1.4809 | 1.4729 | 1.4598 | 1.4418 | 1.4190 | 1.3919 | 1.3608 | 1.3262 | 1.2889 |
| **86°** | 1.4983 | 1.4901 | 1.4767 | 1.4582 | 1.4348 | 1.4070 | 1.3751 | 1.3396 | 1.3012 |
| 87° | 1.5156 | 1.5073 | 1.4936 | 1.4746 | 1.4507 | 1.4221 | 1.3894 | 1.3530 | 1.3136 |
| 88° | 1.5330 | 1.5245 | 1.5104 | 1.4910 | 1.4665 | 1.4372 | 1.4037 | 1.3664 | 1.3260 |
| 89° | 1.5504 | 1.5417 | 1.5273 | 1.5074 | 1.4823 | 1.4523 | 1.4180 | 1.3798 | 1.3383 |
| 90° | 1.5678 | 1.5589 | 1.5442 | 1.5238 | 1.4981 | 1.4675 | 1.4323 | 1.3931 | 1.3506 |

# ELLIPTIC INTEGRALS OF THE SECOND KIND: $E(k, \phi)$
## (Continued)

$$E(k, \phi) = \int_0^\phi \sqrt{(1 - k^2 \sin^2 \Phi)} \, d\Phi, \qquad \theta = \sin^{-1} k$$

| $\phi$ \ $\theta$ | 50° | 55° | 60° | 65° | 70° | 75° | 80° | 85° | 90° |
|---|---|---|---|---|---|---|---|---|---|
| **46°** | 0.7560 | 0.7488 | 0.7419 | 0.7356 | 0.7301 | 0.7255 | 0.7221 | 0.7200 | 0.7193 |
| 47° | 0.7705 | 0.7628 | 0.7555 | 0.7488 | 0.7429 | 0.7380 | 0.7344 | 0.7321 | 0.7314 |
| 48° | 0.7849 | 0.7768 | 0.7690 | 0.7618 | 0.7555 | 0.7502 | 0.7464 | 0.7440 | 0.7431 |
| 49° | 0.7992 | 0.7905 | 0.7822 | 0.7746 | 0.7679 | 0.7623 | 0.7581 | 0.7556 | 0.7547 |
| 50° | 0.8134 | 0.8042 | 0.7954 | 0.7872 | 0.7801 | 0.7741 | 0.7697 | 0.7670 | 0.7660 |
| **51°** | 0.8275 | 0.8177 | 0.8084 | 0.7997 | 0.7921 | 0.7858 | 0.7811 | 0.7781 | 0.7771 |
| 52° | 0.8414 | 0.8311 | 0.8212 | 0.8120 | 0.8039 | 0.7972 | 0.7922 | 0.7891 | 0.7880 |
| 53° | 0.8553 | 0.8444 | 0.8339 | 0.8241 | 0.8155 | 0.8084 | 0.8031 | 0.7998 | 0.7986 |
| 54° | 0.8690 | 0.8575 | 0.8464 | 0.8361 | 0.8270 | 0.8194 | 0.8137 | 0.8102 | 0.8090 |
| 55° | 0.8827 | 0.8705 | 0.8588 | 0.8479 | 0.8382 | 0.8302 | 0.8242 | 0.8204 | 0.8192 |
| **56°** | 0.8962 | 0.8834 | 0.8710 | 0.8595 | 0.8493 | 0.8408 | 0.8344 | 0.8304 | 0.8290 |
| 57° | 0.9096 | 0.8961 | 0.8831 | 0.8709 | 0.8601 | 0.8511 | 0.8443 | 0.8401 | 0.8387 |
| 58° | 0.9230 | 0.9088 | 0.8950 | 0.8822 | 0.8707 | 0.8612 | 0.8540 | 0.8496 | 0.8480 |
| 59° | 0.9362 | 0.9213 | 0.9068 | 0.8932 | 0.8812 | 0.8711 | 0.8635 | 0.8588 | 0.8572 |
| 60° | 0.9493 | 0.9336 | 0.9184 | 0.9042 | 0.8914 | 0.8808 | 0.8728 | 0.8677 | 0.8660 |
| **61°** | 0.9623 | 0.9459 | 0.9299 | 0.9149 | 0.9015 | 0.8903 | 0.8817 | 0.8764 | 0.8746 |
| 62° | 0.9752 | 0.9580 | 0.9412 | 0.9254 | 0.9113 | 0.8995 | 0.8905 | 0.8849 | 0.8829 |
| 63° | 0.9880 | 0.9700 | 0.9524 | 0.9358 | 0.9210 | 0.9085 | 0.8990 | 0.8930 | 0.8910 |
| 64° | 1.0007 | 0.9818 | 0.9634 | 0.9460 | 0.9304 | 0.9173 | 0.9072 | 0.9009 | 0.8988 |
| 65° | 1.0133 | 0.9936 | 0.9743 | 0.9561 | 0.9397 | 0.9258 | 0.9152 | 0.9086 | 0.9063 |
| **66°** | 1.0258 | 1.0052 | 0.9850 | 0.9659 | 0.9487 | 0.9341 | 0.9230 | 0.9159 | 0.9135 |
| 67° | 1.0383 | 1.0167 | 0.9956 | 0.9756 | 0.9576 | 0.9422 | 0.9305 | 0.9230 | 0.9205 |
| 68° | 1.0506 | 1.0281 | 1.0061 | 0.9852 | 0.9662 | 0.9501 | 0.9377 | 0.9299 | 0.9272 |
| 69° | 1.0628 | 1.0394 | 1.0164 | 0.9946 | 0.9747 | 0.9578 | 0.9447 | 0.9364 | 0.9336 |
| 70° | 1.0750 | 1.0506 | 1.0266 | 1.0038 | 0.9830 | 0.9652 | 0.9514 | 0.9427 | 0.9397 |
| **71°** | 1.0871 | 1.0617 | 1.0367 | 1.0129 | 0.9911 | 0.9724 | 0.9579 | 0.9487 | 0.9455 |
| 72° | 1.0991 | 1.0727 | 1.0467 | 1.0218 | 0.9990 | 0.9794 | 0.9642 | 0.9544 | 0.9511 |
| 73° | 1.1110 | 1.0836 | 1.0565 | 1.0306 | 1.0067 | 0.9862 | 0.9702 | 0.9599 | 0.9563 |
| 74° | 1.1228 | 1.0944 | 1.0662 | 1.0392 | 1.0143 | 0.9928 | 0.9759 | 0.9650 | 0.9613 |
| 75° | 1.1346 | 1.1051 | 1.0759 | 1.0477 | 1.0217 | 0.9992 | 0.9814 | 0.9699 | 0.9659 |
| **76°** | 1.1463 | 1.1158 | 1.0854 | 1.0561 | 1.0290 | 1.0053 | 0.9867 | 0.9745 | 0.9703 |
| 77° | 1.1580 | 1.1263 | 1.0948 | 1.0643 | 1.0361 | 1.0113 | 0.9917 | 0.9789 | 0.9744 |
| 78° | 1.1695 | 1.1368 | 1.1041 | 1.0724 | 1.0430 | 1.0171 | 0.9965 | 0.9829 | 0.9781 |
| 79° | 1.1811 | 1.1472 | 1.1133 | 1.0805 | 1.0498 | 1.0228 | 1.0011 | 0.9867 | 0.9816 |
| 80° | 1.1926 | 1.1576 | 1.1225 | 1.0884 | 1.0565 | 1.0282 | 1.0054 | 0.9902 | 0.9848 |
| **81°** | 1.2040 | 1.1678 | 1.1316 | 1.0962 | 1.0630 | 1.0335 | 1.0096 | 0.9935 | 0.9877 |
| 82° | 1.2154 | 1.1781 | 1.1406 | 1.1040 | 1.0695 | 1.0387 | 1.0135 | 0.9965 | 0.9903 |
| 83° | 1.2267 | 1.1883 | 1.1495 | 1.1116 | 1.0758 | 1.0437 | 1.0173 | 0.9992 | 0.9925 |
| 84° | 1.2381 | 1.1984 | 1.1584 | 1.1192 | 1.0821 | 1.0486 | 1.0209 | 1.0017 | 0.9945 |
| 85° | 1.2493 | 1.2085 | 1.1673 | 1.1267 | 1.0882 | 1.0534 | 1.0244 | 1.0039 | 0.9962 |
| **86°** | 1.2606 | 1.2186 | 1.1761 | 1.1342 | 1.0944 | 1.0581 | 1.0277 | 1.0060 | 0.9976 |
| 87° | 1.2719 | 1.2286 | 1.1848 | 1.1417 | 1.1004 | 1.0628 | 1.0309 | 1.0078 | 0.9986 |
| 88° | 1.2831 | 1.2386 | 1.1936 | 1.1491 | 1.1064 | 1.0673 | 1.0340 | 1.0095 | 0.9994 |
| 89° | 1.2943 | 1.2487 | 1.2023 | 1.1565 | 1.1124 | 1.0719 | 1.0371 | 1.0111 | 0.9998 |
| 90° | 1.3055 | 1.2587 | 1.2111 | 1.1638 | 1.1184 | 1.0764 | 1.0401 | 1.0127 | 1.0000 |

If $n$ is prime the mantissa of its logarithm is given.

| $n$ | 0 | 1 | 2 | 3 | 4 |
|---|---|---|---|---|---|
| 0 | ·········· | | **3010300** | **4771213** | $2^2$ |
| 1 | $2 \cdot 5$ | **0413927** | $2^2 \cdot 3$ | **1139434** | $2 \cdot 7$ |
| 2 | $2^2 \cdot 5$ | $3 \cdot 7$ | $2 \cdot 11$ | **3617278** | $2^3 \cdot 3$ |
| 3 | $2 \cdot 3 \cdot 5$ | **4913617** | $2^5$ | $3 \cdot 11$ | $2 \cdot 17$ |
| 4 | $2^3 \cdot 5$ | **6127839** | $2 \cdot 3 \cdot 7$ | **6334685** | $2^2 \cdot 11$ |
| 5 | $2 \cdot 5^2$ | $3 \cdot 17$ | $2^2 \cdot 13$ | **7242759** | $2 \cdot 3^3$ |
| 6 | $2^2 \cdot 3 \cdot 5$ | **7853298** | $2 \cdot 31$ | $3^2 \cdot 7$ | $2^6$ |
| 7 | $2 \cdot 5 \cdot 7$ | **8512583** | $2^3 \cdot 3^2$ | **8633229** | $2 \cdot 37$ |
| 8 | $2^4 \cdot 5$ | $3^4$ | $2 \cdot 41$ | **9190781** | $2^2 \cdot 3 \cdot 7$ |
| 9 | $2 \cdot 3^2 \cdot 5$ | $7 \cdot 13$ | $2^2 \cdot 23$ | $3 \cdot 31$ | $2 \cdot 47$ |
| 10 | $2^2 \cdot 5^2$ | **0043214** | $2 \cdot 3 \cdot 17$ | **0128372** | $2^3 \cdot 13$ |
| 11 | $2 \cdot 5 \cdot 11$ | $3 \cdot 37$ | $2^4 \cdot 7$ | **0530784** | $2 \cdot 3 \cdot 19$ |
| 12 | $2^3 \cdot 3 \cdot 5$ | $11^2$ | $2 \cdot 61$ | $3 \cdot 41$ | $2^2 \cdot 31$ |
| 13 | $2 \cdot 5 \cdot 13$ | **1172713** | $2^2 \cdot 3 \cdot 11$ | $7 \cdot 19$ | $2 \cdot 67$ |
| 14 | $2^2 \cdot 5 \cdot 7$ | $3 \cdot 47$ | $2 \cdot 71$ | $11 \cdot 13$ | $2^4 \cdot 3^2$ |
| 15 | $2 \cdot 3 \cdot 5^2$ | **1789769** | $2^3 \cdot 19$ | $3^2 \cdot 17$ | $2 \cdot 7 \cdot 11$ |
| 16 | $2^5 \cdot 5$ | $7 \cdot 23$ | $2 \cdot 3^4$ | **2121876** | $2^2 \cdot 41$ |
| 17 | $2 \cdot 5 \cdot 17$ | $3^2 \cdot 19$ | $2^2 \cdot 43$ | **2380461** | $2 \cdot 3 \cdot 29$ |
| 18 | $2^2 \cdot 3^2 \cdot 5$ | **2576786** | $2 \cdot 7 \cdot 13$ | $3 \cdot 61$ | $2^3 \cdot 23$ |
| 19 | $2 \cdot 5 \cdot 19$ | **2810334** | $2^6 \cdot 3$ | **2855573** | $2 \cdot 97$ |
| 20 | $2^3 \cdot 5^2$ | $3 \cdot 67$ | $2 \cdot 101$ | $7 \cdot 29$ | $2^2 \cdot 3 \cdot 17$ |
| 21 | $2 \cdot 3 \cdot 5 \cdot 7$ | **3242825** | $2^2 \cdot 53$ | $3 \cdot 71$ | $2 \cdot 107$ |
| 22 | $2^2 \cdot 5 \cdot 11$ | $13 \cdot 17$ | $2 \cdot 3 \cdot 37$ | **3483049** | $2^5 \cdot 7$ |
| 23 | $2 \cdot 5 \cdot 23$ | $3 \cdot 7 \cdot 11$ | $2^3 \cdot 29$ | **3673559** | $2 \cdot 3^2 \cdot 13$ |
| 24 | $2^4 \cdot 3 \cdot 5$ | **3820170** | $2 \cdot 11^2$ | $3^5$ | $2^2 \cdot 61$ |
| 25 | $2 \cdot 5^3$ | **3996737** | $2^2 \cdot 3^2 \cdot 7$ | $11 \cdot 23$ | $2 \cdot 127$ |
| 26 | $2^2 \cdot 5 \cdot 13$ | $3^2 \cdot 29$ | $2 \cdot 131$ | **4199557** | $2^3 \cdot 3 \cdot 11$ |
| 27 | $2 \cdot 3^3 \cdot 5$ | **4329693** | $2^4 \cdot 17$ | $3 \cdot 7 \cdot 13$ | $2 \cdot 137$ |
| 28 | $2^3 \cdot 5 \cdot 7$ | **4487063** | $2 \cdot 3 \cdot 47$ | **4517864** | $2^2 \cdot 71$ |
| 29 | $2 \cdot 5 \cdot 29$ | $3 \cdot 97$ | $2^2 \cdot 73$ | **4668676** | $2 \cdot 3 \cdot 7^2$ |
| 30 | $2^2 \cdot 3 \cdot 5^2$ | $7 \cdot 43$ | $2 \cdot 151$ | $3 \cdot 101$ | $2^4 \cdot 19$ |
| 31 | $2 \cdot 5 \cdot 31$ | **4927604** | $2^3 \cdot 3 \cdot 13$ | **4955443** | $2 \cdot 157$ |
| 32 | $2^6 \cdot 5$ | $3 \cdot 107$ | $2 \cdot 7 \cdot 23$ | $17 \cdot 19$ | $2^2 \cdot 3^4$ |
| 33 | $2 \cdot 3 \cdot 5 \cdot 11$ | **5198280** | $2^2 \cdot 83$ | $3^2 \cdot 37$ | $2 \cdot 167$ |
| 34 | $2^2 \cdot 5 \cdot 17$ | $11 \cdot 31$ | $2 \cdot 3^2 \cdot 19$ | $7^3$ | $2^3 \cdot 43$ |
| 35 | $2 \cdot 5^2 \cdot 7$ | $3^3 \cdot 13$ | $2^5 \cdot 11$ | **5477747** | $2 \cdot 3 \cdot 59$ |
| 36 | $2^3 \cdot 3^2 \cdot 5$ | $19^2$ | $2 \cdot 181$ | $3 \cdot 11^2$ | $2^2 \cdot 7 \cdot 13$ |
| 37 | $2 \cdot 5 \cdot 37$ | $7 \cdot 53$ | $2^2 \cdot 3 \cdot 31$ | **5717088** | $2 \cdot 11 \cdot 17$ |
| 38 | $2^2 \cdot 5 \cdot 19$ | $3 \cdot 127$ | $2 \cdot 191$ | **5831988** | $2^7 \cdot 3$ |
| 39 | $2 \cdot 3 \cdot 5 \cdot 13$ | $17 \cdot 23$ | $2^3 \cdot 7^2$ | $3 \cdot 131$ | $2 \cdot 197$ |
| 40 | $2^4 \cdot 5^2$ | **6031444** | $2 \cdot 3 \cdot 67$ | $13 \cdot 31$ | $2^2 \cdot 101$ |
| 41 | $2 \cdot 5 \cdot 41$ | $3 \cdot 137$ | $2^2 \cdot 103$ | $7 \cdot 59$ | $2 \cdot 3^2 \cdot 23$ |
| 42 | $2^2 \cdot 3 \cdot 5 \cdot 7$ | **6242821** | $2 \cdot 211$ | $3^2 \cdot 47$ | $2^3 \cdot 53$ |
| 43 | $2 \cdot 5 \cdot 43$ | **6344773** | $2^4 \cdot 3^3$ | **6364879** | $2 \cdot 7 \cdot 31$ |
| 44 | $2^3 \cdot 5 \cdot 11$ | $3^2 \cdot 7^2$ | $2 \cdot 13 \cdot 17$ | **6464037** | $2^2 \cdot 3 \cdot 37$ |
| 45 | $2 \cdot 3^2 \cdot 5^2$ | $11 \cdot 41$ | $2^2 \cdot 113$ | $3 \cdot 151$ | $2 \cdot 227$ |
| 46 | $2^2 \cdot 5 \cdot 23$ | **6637009** | $2 \cdot 3 \cdot 7 \cdot 11$ | **6655810** | $2^4 \cdot 29$ |
| 47 | $2 \cdot 5 \cdot 47$ | $3 \cdot 157$ | $2^3 \cdot 59$ | $11 \cdot 43$ | $2 \cdot 3 \cdot 79$ |
| 48 | $2^5 \cdot 3 \cdot 5$ | $13 \cdot 37$ | $2 \cdot 241$ | $3 \cdot 7 \cdot 23$ | $2^2 \cdot 11^2$ |
| 49 | $2 \cdot 5 \cdot 7^2$ | **6910815** | $2^2 \cdot 3 \cdot 41$ | $17 \cdot 29$ | $2 \cdot 13 \cdot 19$ |
| 50 | $2^2 \cdot 5^3$ | $3 \cdot 167$ | $2 \cdot 251$ | **7015680** | $2^3 \cdot 3^2 \cdot 7$ |

# FACTORS AND PRIMES (Continued)

If $n$ is not prime its prime factors are given.

| $n$ | 5 | 6 | 7 | 8 | 9 |
|---|---|---|---|---|---|
| 0 | 6989700 | $2 \cdot 3$ | 8450980 | $2^3$ | $3^2$ |
| 1 | $3 \cdot 5$ | $2^4$ | 2304489 | $2 \cdot 3^2$ | 2787536 |
| 2 | $5^2$ | $2 \cdot 13$ | $3^3$ | $2^2 \cdot 7$ | 4623980 |
| 3 | $5 \cdot 7$ | $2^2 \cdot 3^2$ | 5682017 | $2 \cdot 19$ | $3 \cdot 13$ |
| 4 | $3^2 \cdot 5$ | $2 \cdot 23$ | 6720979 | $2^4 \cdot 3$ | $7^2$ |
| 5 | $5 \cdot 11$ | $2^3 \cdot 7$ | $3 \cdot 19$ | $2 \cdot 29$ | 7708520 |
| 6 | $5 \cdot 13$ | $2 \cdot 3 \cdot 11$ | 8260748 | $2^2 \cdot 17$ | $3 \cdot 23$ |
| 7 | $3 \cdot 5^2$ | $2^2 \cdot 19$ | $7 \cdot 11$ | $2 \cdot 3 \cdot 13$ | 8976271 |
| 8 | $5 \cdot 17$ | $2 \cdot 43$ | $3 \cdot 29$ | $2^3 \cdot 11$ | 9493900 |
| 9 | $5 \cdot 19$ | $2^5 \cdot 3$ | 9867717 | $2 \cdot 7^2$ | $3^2 \cdot 11$ |
| 10 | $3 \cdot 5 \cdot 7$ | $2 \cdot 53$ | 0293838 | $2^2 \cdot 3^3$ | 0374265 |
| 11 | $5 \cdot 23$ | $2^2 \cdot 29$ | $3^2 \cdot 13$ | $2 \cdot 59$ | $7 \cdot 17$ |
| 12 | $5^3$ | $2 \cdot 3^2 \cdot 7$ | 1038037 | $2^7$ | $3 \cdot 43$ |
| 13 | $3^3 \cdot 5$ | $2^3 \cdot 17$ | 1367206 | $2 \cdot 3 \cdot 23$ | 1430148 |
| 14 | $5 \cdot 29$ | $2 \cdot 73$ | $3 \cdot 7^2$ | $2^2 \cdot 37$ | 1731863 |
| 15 | $5 \cdot 31$ | $2^2 \cdot 3 \cdot 13$ | 1958997 | $2 \cdot 79$ | $3 \cdot 53$ |
| 16 | $3 \cdot 5 \cdot 11$ | $2 \cdot 83$ | 2227165 | $2^3 \cdot 3 \cdot 7$ | $13^2$ |
| 17 | $5^2 \cdot 7$ | $2^4 \cdot 11$ | $3 \cdot 59$ | $2 \cdot 89$ | 2528530 |
| 18 | $5 \cdot 37$ | $2 \cdot 3 \cdot 31$ | $11 \cdot 17$ | $2^2 \cdot 47$ | $3^3 \cdot 7$ |
| 19 | $3 \cdot 5 \cdot 13$ | $2^2 \cdot 7^2$ | 2944662 | $2 \cdot 3^2 \cdot 11$ | 2988531 |
| 20 | $5 \cdot 41$ | $2 \cdot 103$ | $3^2 \cdot 23$ | $2^4 \cdot 13$ | $11 \cdot 19$ |
| 21 | $5 \cdot 43$ | $2^3 \cdot 3^3$ | $7 \cdot 31$ | $2 \cdot 109$ | $3 \cdot 73$ |
| 22 | $3^2 \cdot 5^2$ | $2 \cdot 113$ | 3560259 | $2^2 \cdot 3 \cdot 19$ | 3598355 |
| 23 | $5 \cdot 47$ | $2^2 \cdot 59$ | $3 \cdot 79$ | $2 \cdot 7 \cdot 17$ | 3783979 |
| 24 | $5 \cdot 7^2$ | $2 \cdot 3 \cdot 41$ | $13 \cdot 19$ | $2^3 \cdot 31$ | $3 \cdot 83$ |
| 25 | $3 \cdot 5 \cdot 17$ | $2^8$ | 4099331 | $2 \cdot 3 \cdot 43$ | $7 \cdot 37$ |
| 26 | $5 \cdot 53$ | $2 \cdot 7 \cdot 19$ | $3 \cdot 89$ | $2^2 \cdot 67$ | 4297523 |
| 27 | $5^2 \cdot 11$ | $2^2 \cdot 3 \cdot 23$ | 4424798 | $2 \cdot 139$ | $3^2 \cdot 31$ |
| 28 | $3 \cdot 5 \cdot 19$ | $2 \cdot 11 \cdot 13$ | $7 \cdot 41$ | $2^5 \cdot 3^2$ | $17^2$ |
| 29 | $5 \cdot 59$ | $2^3 \cdot 37$ | $3^3 \cdot 11$ | $2 \cdot 149$ | $13 \cdot 23$ |
| 30 | $5 \cdot 61$ | $2 \cdot 3^2 \cdot 17$ | 4871384 | $2^2 \cdot 7 \cdot 11$ | $3 \cdot 103$ |
| 31 | $3^2 \cdot 5 \cdot 7$ | $2^2 \cdot 79$ | 5010593 | $2 \cdot 3 \cdot 53$ | $11 \cdot 29$ |
| 32 | $5^2 \cdot 13$ | $2 \cdot 163$ | $3 \cdot 109$ | $2^3 \cdot 41$ | $7 \cdot 47$ |
| 33 | $5 \cdot 67$ | $2^4 \cdot 3 \cdot 7$ | 5276299 | $2 \cdot 13^2$ | $3 \cdot 113$ |
| 34 | $3 \cdot 5 \cdot 23$ | $2 \cdot 173$ | 5403295 | $2^2 \cdot 3 \cdot 29$ | 5428254 |
| 35 | $5 \cdot 71$ | $2^2 \cdot 89$ | $3 \cdot 7 \cdot 11$ | $2 \cdot 179$ | 5550944 |
| 36 | $5 \cdot 73$ | $2 \cdot 3 \cdot 61$ | 5646661 | $2^4 \cdot 23$ | $3^2 \cdot 41$ |
| 37 | $3 \cdot 5^3$ | $2^3 \cdot 47$ | $13 \cdot 29$ | $2 \cdot 3^3 \cdot 7$ | 5786392 |
| 38 | $5 \cdot 7 \cdot 11$ | $2 \cdot 193$ | $3^2 \cdot 43$ | $2^2 \cdot 97$ | 5899496 |
| 39 | $5 \cdot 79$ | $2^2 \cdot 3^2 \cdot 11$ | 5987905 | $2 \cdot 199$ | $3 \cdot 7 \cdot 19$ |
| 40 | $3^4 \cdot 5$ | $2 \cdot 7 \cdot 29$ | $11 \cdot 37$ | $2^3 \cdot 3 \cdot 17$ | 6117233 |
| 41 | $5 \cdot 83$ | $2^5 \cdot 13$ | $3 \cdot 139$ | $2 \cdot 11 \cdot 19$ | 6222140 |
| 42 | $5^2 \cdot 17$ | $2 \cdot 3 \cdot 71$ | $7 \cdot 61$ | $2^2 \cdot 107$ | $3 \cdot 11 \cdot 13$ |
| 43 | $3 \cdot 5 \cdot 29$ | $2^2 \cdot 109$ | $19 \cdot 23$ | $2 \cdot 3 \cdot 73$ | 6424645 |
| 44 | $5 \cdot 89$ | $2 \cdot 223$ | $3 \cdot 149$ | $2^6 \cdot 7$ | 6522463 |
| 45 | $5 \cdot 7 \cdot 13$ | $2^3 \cdot 3 \cdot 19$ | 6599162 | $2 \cdot 229$ | $3^3 \cdot 17$ |
| 46 | $3 \cdot 5 \cdot 31$ | $2 \cdot 233$ | 6693169 | $2^2 \cdot 3^2 \cdot 13$ | $7 \cdot 67$ |
| 47 | $5^2 \cdot 19$ | $2^2 \cdot 7 \cdot 17$ | $3^2 \cdot 53$ | $2 \cdot 239$ | 6803355 |
| 48 | $5 \cdot 97$ | $2 \cdot 3^5$ | 6875290 | $2^3 \cdot 61$ | $3 \cdot 163$ |
| 49 | $3^2 \cdot 5 \cdot 11$ | $2^4 \cdot 31$ | $7 \cdot 71$ | $2 \cdot 3 \cdot 83$ | 6981005 |
| 50 | $5 \cdot 101$ | $2 \cdot 11 \cdot 23$ | $3 \cdot 13^2$ | $2^2 \cdot 127$ | 7067178 |

| $n$ | 0 | 1 | 2 | 3 | 4 |
|---|---|---|---|---|---|
| **50** | $2^2 \cdot 5^3$ | $3 \cdot 167$ | $2 \cdot 251$ | **7015680** | $2^3 \cdot 3^2 \cdot 7$ |
| 51 | $2 \cdot 3 \cdot 5 \cdot 17$ | $7 \cdot 73$ | $2^9$ | $3^3 \cdot 19$ | $2 \cdot 257$ |
| 52 | $2^3 \cdot 5 \cdot 13$ | **7168377** | $2 \cdot 3^2 \cdot 29$ | **7185017** | $2^2 \cdot 131$ |
| 53 | $2 \cdot 5 \cdot 53$ | $3^2 \cdot 59$ | $2^2 \cdot 7 \cdot 19$ | $13 \cdot 41$ | $2 \cdot 3 \cdot 89$ |
| 54 | $2^2 \cdot 3^3 \cdot 5$ | **7331973** | $2 \cdot 271$ | $3 \cdot 181$ | $2^5 \cdot 17$ |
| **55** | $2 \cdot 5^2 \cdot 11$ | $19 \cdot 29$ | $2^3 \cdot 3 \cdot 23$ | $7 \cdot 79$ | $2 \cdot 277$ |
| 56 | $2^4 \cdot 5 \cdot 7$ | $3 \cdot 11 \cdot 17$ | $2 \cdot 281$ | **7505084** | $2^2 \cdot 3 \cdot 47$ |
| 57 | $2 \cdot 3 \cdot 5 \cdot 19$ | **7566361** | $2^2 \cdot 11 \cdot 13$ | $3 \cdot 191$ | $2 \cdot 7 \cdot 41$ |
| 58 | $2^2 \cdot 5 \cdot 29$ | $7 \cdot 83$ | $2 \cdot 3 \cdot 97$ | $11 \cdot 53$ | $2^3 \cdot 73$ |
| 59 | $2 \cdot 5 \cdot 59$ | $3 \cdot 197$ | $2^4 \cdot 37$ | **7730547** | $2 \cdot 3^3 \cdot 11$ |
| **60** | $2^3 \cdot 3 \cdot 5^2$ | **7788745** | $2 \cdot 7 \cdot 43$ | $3^2 \cdot 67$ | $2^2 \cdot 151$ |
| 61 | $2 \cdot 5 \cdot 61$ | $13 \cdot 47$ | $2 \cdot 3^2 \cdot 17$ | **7874605** | $2 \cdot 307$ |
| 62 | $2^2 \cdot 5 \cdot 31$ | $3^3 \cdot 23$ | $2 \cdot 311$ | $7 \cdot 89$ | $2^4 \cdot 3 \cdot 13$ |
| 63 | $2 \cdot 3^2 \cdot 5 \cdot 7$ | **8000294** | $2^3 \cdot 79$ | $3 \cdot 211$ | $2 \cdot 317$ |
| 64 | $2^7 \cdot 5$ | **8068580** | $2 \cdot 3 \cdot 107$ | **8082110** | $2^2 \cdot 7 \cdot 23$ |
| **65** | $2 \cdot 5^2 \cdot 13$ | $3 \cdot 7 \cdot 31$ | $2^2 \cdot 163$ | **8149132** | $2 \cdot 3 \cdot 109$ |
| 66 | $2^2 \cdot 3 \cdot 5 \cdot 11$ | **8202015** | $2 \cdot 331$ | $3 \cdot 13 \cdot 17$ | $2^3 \cdot 83$ |
| 67 | $2 \cdot 5 \cdot 67$ | $11 \cdot 61$ | $2^5 \cdot 3 \cdot 7$ | **8280151** | $2 \cdot 337$ |
| 68 | $2^3 \cdot 5 \cdot 17$ | $3 \cdot 227$ | $2 \cdot 11 \cdot 31$ | **8344207** | $2^2 \cdot 3^2 \cdot 19$ |
| 69 | $2 \cdot 3 \cdot 5 \cdot 23$ | **8394780** | $2^2 \cdot 173$ | $3^2 \cdot 7 \cdot 11$ | $2 \cdot 347$ |
| **70** | $2^2 \cdot 5^2 \cdot 7$ | **8457180** | $2 \cdot 3^3 \cdot 13$ | $19 \cdot 37$ | $2^6 \cdot 11$ |
| 71 | $2 \cdot 5 \cdot 71$ | $3^2 \cdot 79$ | $2^3 \cdot 89$ | $23 \cdot 31$ | $2 \cdot 3 \cdot 7 \cdot 17$ |
| 72 | $2^4 \cdot 3^2 \cdot 5$ | $7 \cdot 103$ | $2 \cdot 19^2$ | $3 \cdot 241$ | $2^2 \cdot 181$ |
| 73 | $2 \cdot 5 \cdot 73$ | $17 \cdot 43$ | $2^2 \cdot 3 \cdot 61$ | **8651040** | $2 \cdot 367$ |
| 74 | $2^2 \cdot 5 \cdot 37$ | $3 \cdot 13 \cdot 19$ | $2 \cdot 7 \cdot 53$ | **8709888** | $2^3 \cdot 3 \cdot 31$ |
| **75** | $2 \cdot 3 \cdot 5^3$ | **8756399** | $2^4 \cdot 47$ | $3 \cdot 251$ | $2 \cdot 13 \cdot 29$ |
| 76 | $2^3 \cdot 5 \cdot 19$ | **8813847** | $2 \cdot 3 \cdot 127$ | $7 \cdot 109$ | $2 \cdot 191$ |
| 77 | $2 \cdot 5 \cdot 7 \cdot 11$ | $3 \cdot 257$ | $2^2 \cdot 193$ | **8881795** | $2 \cdot 3^2 \cdot 43$ |
| 78 | $2^2 \cdot 3 \cdot 5 \cdot 13$ | $11 \cdot 71$ | $2 \cdot 17 \cdot 23$ | $3^3 \cdot 29$ | $2^4 \cdot 7^2$ |
| 79 | $2 \cdot 5 \cdot 79$ | $7 \cdot 113$ | $2^3 \cdot 3^2 \cdot 11$ | $13 \cdot 61$ | $2 \cdot 397$ |
| **80** | $2^5 \cdot 5^2$ | $3^2 \cdot 89$ | $2 \cdot 401$ | $11 \cdot 73$ | $2^2 \cdot 3 \cdot 67$ |
| 81 | $2 \cdot 3^4 \cdot 5$ | **9090209** | $2^2 \cdot 7 \cdot 29$ | $3 \cdot 271$ | $2 \cdot 11 \cdot 37$ |
| 82 | $2^2 \cdot 5 \cdot 41$ | **9143432** | $2 \cdot 3 \cdot 137$ | **9153998** | $2^3 \cdot 103$ |
| 83 | $2 \cdot 5 \cdot 83$ | $3 \cdot 277$ | $2^6 \cdot 13$ | $7^2 \cdot 17$ | $2 \cdot 3 \cdot 139$ |
| 84 | $2^3 \cdot 3 \cdot 5 \cdot 7$ | $29^2$ | $2 \cdot 421$ | $3 \cdot 281$ | $2^2 \cdot 211$ |
| **85** | $2 \cdot 5^2 \cdot 17$ | $23 \cdot 37$ | $2^2 \cdot 3 \cdot 71$ | **9309490** | $2 \cdot 7 \cdot 61$ |
| 86 | $2^2 \cdot 5 \cdot 43$ | $3 \cdot 7 \cdot 41$ | $2 \cdot 431$ | **9360108** | $2^5 \cdot 3^3$ |
| 87 | $2 \cdot 3 \cdot 5 \cdot 29$ | $13 \cdot 67$ | $2^3 \cdot 109$ | $3^2 \cdot 97$ | $2 \cdot 19 \cdot 23$ |
| 88 | $2^4 \cdot 5 \cdot 11$ | **9449759** | $2 \cdot 3^2 \cdot 7^2$ | **9459607** | $2^2 \cdot 13 \cdot 17$ |
| 89 | $2 \cdot 5 \cdot 89$ | $3^4 \cdot 11$ | $2^2 \cdot 223$ | $19 \cdot 47$ | $2 \cdot 3 \cdot 149$ |
| **90** | $2^2 \cdot 3^2 \cdot 5^2$ | $17 \cdot 53$ | $2 \cdot 11 \cdot 41$ | $3 \cdot 7 \cdot 43$ | $2^3 \cdot 113$ |
| 91 | $2 \cdot 5 \cdot 7 \cdot 13$ | **9595184** | $2^4 \cdot 3 \cdot 19$ | $11 \cdot 83$ | $2 \cdot 457$ |
| 92 | $2^3 \cdot 5 \cdot 23$ | $3 \cdot 307$ | $2 \cdot 461$ | $13 \cdot 71$ | $2^2 \cdot 3 \cdot 7 \cdot 11$ |
| 93 | $2 \cdot 3 \cdot 5 \cdot 31$ | $7^2 \cdot 19$ | $2^2 \cdot 233$ | $3 \cdot 311$ | $2 \cdot 467$ |
| 94 | $2^2 \cdot 5 \cdot 47$ | **9735896** | $2 \cdot 3 \cdot 157$ | $23 \cdot 41$ | $2^4 \cdot 59$ |
| **95** | $2 \cdot 5^2 \cdot 19$ | $3 \cdot 317$ | $2^3 \cdot 7 \cdot 17$ | **9790929** | $2 \cdot 3^2 \cdot 53$ |
| 96 | $2^6 \cdot 3 \cdot 5$ | $31^2$ | $2 \cdot 13 \cdot 37$ | $3^2 \cdot 107$ | $2^2 \cdot 241$ |
| 97 | $2 \cdot 5 \cdot 97$ | **9872192** | $2^2 \cdot 3^5$ | $7 \cdot 139$ | $2 \cdot 487$ |
| 98 | $2^2 \cdot 5 \cdot 7^2$ | $3^2 \cdot 109$ | $2 \cdot 491$ | **9925535** | $2^3 \cdot 3 \cdot 41$ |
| 99 | $2 \cdot 3^2 \cdot 5 \cdot 11$ | **9960737** | $2^5 \cdot 31$ | $3 \cdot 331$ | $2 \cdot 7 \cdot 71$ |
| **100** | $2^3 \cdot 5^3$ | $7 \cdot 11 \cdot 13$ | $2 \cdot 3 \cdot 167$ | $17 \cdot 59$ | $2^2 \cdot 251$ |

| $n$ | 5 | 6 | 7 | 8 | 9 |
|---|---|---|---|---|---|
| **50** | $5 \cdot 101$ | $2 \cdot 11 \cdot 23$ | $3 \cdot 13^2$ | $2^2 \cdot 127$ | **7067178** |
| 51 | $5 \cdot 103$ | $2^2 \cdot 3 \cdot 43$ | $11 \cdot 47$ | $2 \cdot 7 \cdot 37$ | $3 \cdot 173$ |
| 52 | $3 \cdot 5^2 \cdot 7$ | $2 \cdot 263$ | $17 \cdot 31$ | $2^4 \cdot 3 \cdot 11$ | $23^2$ |
| 53 | $5 \cdot 107$ | $2^3 \cdot 67$ | $3 \cdot 179$ | $2 \cdot 269$ | $7^2 \cdot 11$ |
| 54 | $5 \cdot 109$ | $2 \cdot 3 \cdot 7 \cdot 13$ | **7379873** | $2^2 \cdot 137$ | $3^2 \cdot 61$ |
| **55** | $3 \cdot 5 \cdot 37$ | $2^2 \cdot 139$ | **7458552** | $2 \cdot 3^2 \cdot 31$ | $13 \cdot 43$ |
| 56 | $5 \cdot 113$ | $2 \cdot 283$ | $3^4 \cdot 7$ | $2^3 \cdot 71$ | **7551123** |
| 57 | $5^2 \cdot 23$ | $2^6 \cdot 3^2$ | **7611758** | $2 \cdot 17^2$ | $3 \cdot 193$ |
| 58 | $3^2 \cdot 5 \cdot 13$ | $2 \cdot 293$ | **7686381** | $2^2 \cdot 3 \cdot 7^2$ | $19 \cdot 31$ |
| 59 | $5 \cdot 7 \cdot 17$ | $2^2 \cdot 149$ | $3 \cdot 199$ | $2 \cdot 13 \cdot 23$ | **7774268** |
| **60** | $5 \cdot 11^2$ | $2 \cdot 3 \cdot 101$ | **7831887** | $2^5 \cdot 19$ | $3 \cdot 7 \cdot 29$ |
| 61 | $3 \cdot 5 \cdot 41$ | $2^3 \cdot 7 \cdot 11$ | **7902852** | $2 \cdot 3 \cdot 103$ | **7916906** |
| 62 | $5^4$ | $2 \cdot 313$ | $3 \cdot 11 \cdot 19$ | $2^2 \cdot 157$ | $17 \cdot 37$ |
| 63 | $5 \cdot 127$ | $2^2 \cdot 3 \cdot 53$ | $7^2 \cdot 13$ | $2 \cdot 11 \cdot 29$ | $3^2 \cdot 71$ |
| 64 | $3 \cdot 5 \cdot 43$ | $2 \cdot 17 \cdot 19$ | **8109043** | $2^3 \cdot 3^4$ | $11 \cdot 59$ |
| **65** | $5 \cdot 131$ | $2^4 \cdot 41$ | $3^2 \cdot 73$ | $2 \cdot 7 \cdot 47$ | **8188854** |
| 66 | $5 \cdot 7 \cdot 19$ | $2 \cdot 3^2 \cdot 37$ | $23 \cdot 29$ | $2^2 \cdot 167$ | $3 \cdot 223$ |
| 67 | $3^3 \cdot 5^2$ | $2^2 \cdot 13^2$ | **8305887** | $2 \cdot 3 \cdot 113$ | $7 \cdot 97$ |
| 68 | $5 \cdot 137$ | $2 \cdot 7^3$ | $3 \cdot 229$ | $2^4 \cdot 43$ | $13 \cdot 53$ |
| 69 | $5 \cdot 139$ | $2^3 \cdot 3 \cdot 29$ | $17 \cdot 41$ | $2 \cdot 349$ | $3 \cdot 233$ |
| **70** | $3 \cdot 5 \cdot 47$ | $2 \cdot 353$ | $7 \cdot 101$ | $2^2 \cdot 3 \cdot 59$ | **8506462** |
| 71 | $5 \cdot 11 \cdot 13$ | $2^2 \cdot 179$ | $3 \cdot 239$ | $2 \cdot 359$ | **8567289** |
| 72 | $5^2 \cdot 29$ | $2 \cdot 3 \cdot 11^2$ | **8615344** | $2^3 \cdot 7 \cdot 13$ | $3^6$ |
| 73 | $3 \cdot 5 \cdot 7^2$ | $2^5 \cdot 23$ | $11 \cdot 67$ | $2 \cdot 3^2 \cdot 41$ | **8686444** |
| 74 | $5 \cdot 149$ | $2 \cdot 373$ | $3^2 \cdot 83$ | $2^2 \cdot 11 \cdot 17$ | $7 \cdot 107$ |
| **75** | $5 \cdot 151$ | $2^2 \cdot 3^3 \cdot 7$ | **8790959** | $2 \cdot 379$ | $3 \cdot 11 \cdot 23$ |
| 76 | $3^2 \cdot 5 \cdot 17$ | $2 \cdot 383$ | $13 \cdot 59$ | $2^6 \cdot 3$ | **8859263** |
| 77 | $5^2 \cdot 31$ | $2^3 \cdot 97$ | $3 \cdot 7 \cdot 37$ | $2 \cdot 389$ | $19 \cdot 41$ |
| 78 | $5 \cdot 157$ | $2 \cdot 3 \cdot 131$ | **8959747** | $2^2 \cdot 197$ | $3 \cdot 263$ |
| 79 | $3 \cdot 5 \cdot 53$ | $2^2 \cdot 199$ | **9014583** | $2 \cdot 3 \cdot 7 \cdot 19$ | $17 \cdot 47$ |
| **80** | $5 \cdot 7 \cdot 23$ | $2 \cdot 13 \cdot 31$ | $3 \cdot 269$ | $2^3 \cdot 101$ | **9079485** |
| 81 | $5 \cdot 163$ | $2^4 \cdot 3 \cdot 17$ | $19 \cdot 43$ | $2 \cdot 409$ | $3^2 \cdot 7 \cdot 13$ |
| 82 | $3 \cdot 5^2 \cdot 11$ | $2 \cdot 7 \cdot 59$ | **9175055** | $2^2 \cdot 3^2 \cdot 23$ | **9185545** |
| 83 | $5 \cdot 167$ | $2^2 \cdot 11 \cdot 19$ | $3^3 \cdot 31$ | $2 \cdot 419$ | **9237620** |
| 84 | $5 \cdot 13^2$ | $2 \cdot 3^2 \cdot 47$ | $7 \cdot 11^2$ | $2^4 \cdot 53$ | $3 \cdot 283$ |
| **85** | $3^2 \cdot 5 \cdot 19$ | $2^3 \cdot 107$ | **9329808** | $2 \cdot 3 \cdot 11 \cdot 13$ | **9339932** |
| 86 | $5 \cdot 173$ | $2 \cdot 433$ | $3 \cdot 17^2$ | $2^2 \cdot 7 \cdot 31$ | $11 \cdot 79$ |
| 87 | $5^3 \cdot 7$ | $2^2 \cdot 3 \cdot 73$ | **9429996** | $2 \cdot 439$ | $3 \cdot 293$ |
| 88 | $3 \cdot 5 \cdot 59$ | $2 \cdot 443$ | **9479236** | $2^3 \cdot 3 \cdot 37$ | $7 \cdot 127$ |
| 89 | $5 \cdot 179$ | $2^7 \cdot 7$ | $3 \cdot 13 \cdot 23$ | $2 \cdot 449$ | $29 \cdot 31$ |
| **90** | $5 \cdot 181$ | $2 \cdot 3 \cdot 151$ | **9576073** | $2^2 \cdot 227$ | $3^2 \cdot 101$ |
| 91 | $3 \cdot 5 \cdot 61$ | $2^2 \cdot 229$ | $7 \cdot 131$ | $2 \cdot 3^3 \cdot 17$ | **9633155** |
| 92 | $5^2 \cdot 37$ | $2 \cdot 463$ | $3^2 \cdot 103$ | $2^5 \cdot 29$ | **9680157** |
| 93 | $5 \cdot 11 \cdot 17$ | $2^3 \cdot 3^2 \cdot 13$ | **9717396** | $2 \cdot 7 \cdot 67$ | $3 \cdot 313$ |
| 94 | $3^3 \cdot 5 \cdot 7$ | $2 \cdot 11 \cdot 43$ | **9763500** | $2^2 \cdot 3 \cdot 79$ | $13 \cdot 73$ |
| **95** | $5 \cdot 191$ | $2^2 \cdot 239$ | $3 \cdot 11 \cdot 29$ | $2 \cdot 479$ | $7 \cdot 137$ |
| 96 | $5 \cdot 193$ | $2 \cdot 3 \cdot 7 \cdot 23$ | **9854265** | $2^3 \cdot 11^2$ | $3 \cdot 17 \cdot 19$ |
| 97 | $3 \cdot 5^2 \cdot 13$ | $2^4 \cdot 61$ | **9898946** | $2 \cdot 3 \cdot 163$ | $11 \cdot 89$ |
| 98 | $5 \cdot 197$ | $2 \cdot 17 \cdot 29$ | $3 \cdot 7 \cdot 47$ | $2^2 \cdot 13 \cdot 19$ | $23 \cdot 43$ |
| 99 | $5 \cdot 199$ | $2^2 \cdot 3 \cdot 83$ | **9986952** | $2 \cdot 499$ | $3^3 \cdot 37$ |
| **100** | $3 \cdot 5 \cdot 67$ | $2 \cdot 503$ | $19 \cdot 53$ | $2^4 \cdot 3^2 \cdot 7$ | **0038912** |

| $n$ | 0 | 1 | 2 | 3 | 4 |
|---|---|---|---|---|---|
| **100** | $2^3 \cdot 5^3$ | $7 \cdot 11 \cdot 13$ | $2 \cdot 3 \cdot 167$ | $17 \cdot 59$ | $2^2 \cdot 251$ |
| 101 | $2 \cdot 5 \cdot 101$ | $3 \cdot 337$ | $2^2 \cdot 11 \cdot 23$ | **0056094** | $2 \cdot 3 \cdot 13^2$ |
| 102 | $2^2 \cdot 3 \cdot 5 \cdot 17$ | **0090257** | $2 \cdot 7 \cdot 73$ | $3 \cdot 11 \cdot 31$ | $2^{10}$ |
| 103 | $2 \cdot 5 \cdot 103$ | **0132587** | $2^3 \cdot 3 \cdot 43$ | **0141003** | $2 \cdot 11 \cdot 47$ |
| 104 | $2^4 \cdot 5 \cdot 13$ | $3 \cdot 347$ | $2 \cdot 521$ | $7 \cdot 149$ | $2^2 \cdot 3^2 \cdot 29$ |
| **105** | $2 \cdot 3 \cdot 5^2 \cdot 7$ | **0216027** | $2^2 \cdot 263$ | $3^4 \cdot 13$ | $2 \cdot 17 \cdot 31$ |
| 106 | $2^2 \cdot 5 \cdot 53$ | **0257154** | $2 \cdot 3^2 \cdot 59$ | **0265333** | $2^3 \cdot 7 \cdot 19$ |
| 107 | $2 \cdot 5 \cdot 107$ | $3^2 \cdot 7 \cdot 17$ | $2^4 \cdot 67$ | $29 \cdot 37$ | $2 \cdot 3 \cdot 179$ |
| 108 | $2^3 \cdot 3^3 \cdot 5$ | $23 \cdot 47$ | $2 \cdot 541$ | $3 \cdot 19^2$ | $2^2 \cdot 271$ |
| 109 | $2 \cdot 5 \cdot 109$ | **0378248** | $2^2 \cdot 3 \cdot 7 \cdot 13$ | **0386202** | $2 \cdot 547$ |
| **110** | $2^2 \cdot 5^2 \cdot 11$ | $3 \cdot 367$ | $2 \cdot 19 \cdot 29$ | **0425755** | $2^4 \cdot 3 \cdot 23$ |
| 111 | $2 \cdot 3 \cdot 5 \cdot 37$ | $11 \cdot 101$ | $2^3 \cdot 139$ | $3 \cdot 7 \cdot 53$ | $2 \cdot 557$ |
| 112 | $2^5 \cdot 5 \cdot 7$ | $19 \cdot 59$ | $2 \cdot 3 \cdot 11 \cdot 17$ | **0503798** | $2^2 \cdot 281$ |
| 113 | $2 \cdot 5 \cdot 113$ | $3 \cdot 13 \cdot 29$ | $2^2 \cdot 283$ | $11 \cdot 103$ | $2 \cdot 3^4 \cdot 7$ |
| 114 | $2^2 \cdot 3 \cdot 5 \cdot 19$ | $7 \cdot 163$ | $2 \cdot 571$ | $3^2 \cdot 127$ | $2^3 \cdot 11 \cdot 13$ |
| **115** | $2 \cdot 5^2 \cdot 23$ | **0610753** | $2^7 \cdot 3^2$ | **0618293** | $2 \cdot 577$ |
| 116 | $2^3 \cdot 5 \cdot 29$ | $3^3 \cdot 43$ | $2 \cdot 7 \cdot 83$ | **0655797** | $2^2 \cdot 3 \cdot 97$ |
| 117 | $2 \cdot 3^2 \cdot 5 \cdot 13$ | **0685569** | $2^2 \cdot 293$ | $3 \cdot 17 \cdot 23$ | $2 \cdot 587$ |
| 118 | $2^2 \cdot 5 \cdot 59$ | **0722499** | $2 \cdot 3 \cdot 197$ | $7 \cdot 13^2$ | $2^5 \cdot 37$ |
| 119 | $2 \cdot 5 \cdot 7 \cdot 17$ | $3 \cdot 397$ | $2^3 \cdot 149$ | **0766404** | $2 \cdot 3 \cdot 199$ |
| **120** | $2^4 \cdot 3 \cdot 5^2$ | **0795430** | $2 \cdot 601$ | $3 \cdot 401$ | $2^2 \cdot 7 \cdot 43$ |
| 121 | $2 \cdot 5 \cdot 11^2$ | $7 \cdot 173$ | $2^2 \cdot 3 \cdot 101$ | **0838608** | $2 \cdot 607$ |
| 122 | $2^2 \cdot 5 \cdot 61$ | $3 \cdot 11 \cdot 37$ | $2 \cdot 13 \cdot 47$ | **0874265** | $2^3 \cdot 3^2 \cdot 17$ |
| 123 | $2 \cdot 3 \cdot 5 \cdot 41$ | **0902581** | $2^4 \cdot 7 \cdot 11$ | $3^2 \cdot 137$ | $2 \cdot 617$ |
| 124 | $2^3 \cdot 5 \cdot 31$ | $17 \cdot 73$ | $2 \cdot 3^3 \cdot 23$ | $11 \cdot 113$ | $2^2 \cdot 311$ |
| **125** | $2 \cdot 5^4$ | $3^2 \cdot 139$ | $2^2 \cdot 313$ | $7 \cdot 179$ | $2 \cdot 3 \cdot 11 \cdot 19$ |
| 126 | $2^2 \cdot 3^2 \cdot 5 \cdot 7$ | $13 \cdot 97$ | $2 \cdot 631$ | $3 \cdot 421$ | $2^4 \cdot 79$ |
| 127 | $2 \cdot 5 \cdot 127$ | $31 \cdot 41$ | $2^3 \cdot 3 \cdot 53$ | $19 \cdot 67$ | $2 \cdot 7^2 \cdot 13$ |
| 128 | $2^8 \cdot 5$ | $3 \cdot 7 \cdot 61$ | $2 \cdot 641$ | **1082267** | $2^2 \cdot 3 \cdot 107$ |
| 129 | $2 \cdot 3 \cdot 5 \cdot 43$ | **1109262** | $2^2 \cdot 17 \cdot 19$ | $3 \cdot 431$ | $2 \cdot 647$ |
| **130** | $2^2 \cdot 5^2 \cdot 13$ | **1142773** | $2 \cdot 3 \cdot 7 \cdot 31$ | **1149444** | $2^3 \cdot 163$ |
| 131 | $2 \cdot 5 \cdot 131$ | $3 \cdot 19 \cdot 23$ | $2^5 \cdot 41$ | $13 \cdot 101$ | $2 \cdot 3^2 \cdot 73$ |
| 132 | $2^3 \cdot 3 \cdot 5 \cdot 11$ | **1209028** | $2 \cdot 661$ | $3^3 \cdot 7^2$ | $2^2 \cdot 331$ |
| 133 | $2 \cdot 5 \cdot 7 \cdot 19$ | $11^3$ | $2^2 \cdot 3^2 \cdot 37$ | $31 \cdot 43$ | $2 \cdot 23 \cdot 29$ |
| 134 | $2^2 \cdot 5 \cdot 67$ | $3^2 \cdot 149$ | $2 \cdot 11 \cdot 61$ | $17 \cdot 79$ | $2^6 \cdot 3 \cdot 7$ |
| **135** | $2 \cdot 3^3 \cdot 5^2$ | $7 \cdot 193$ | $2^3 \cdot 13^2$ | $3 \cdot 11 \cdot 41$ | $2 \cdot 677$ |
| 136 | $2^4 \cdot 5 \cdot 17$ | **1338581** | $2 \cdot 3 \cdot 227$ | $29 \cdot 47$ | $2^2 \cdot 11 \cdot 31$ |
| 137 | $2 \cdot 5 \cdot 137$ | $3 \cdot 457$ | $2^2 \cdot 7^3$ | **1376705** | $2 \cdot 3 \cdot 229$ |
| 138 | $2^2 \cdot 3 \cdot 5 \cdot 23$ | **1401937** | $2 \cdot 691$ | $3 \cdot 461$ | $2^3 \cdot 173$ |
| 139 | $2 \cdot 5 \cdot 139$ | $13 \cdot 107$ | $2^4 \cdot 3 \cdot 29$ | $7 \cdot 199$ | $2 \cdot 17 \cdot 41$ |
| **140** | $2^3 \cdot 5^2 \cdot 7$ | $3 \cdot 467$ | $2 \cdot 701$ | $23 \cdot 61$ | $2^2 \cdot 3^2 \cdot 13$ |
| 141 | $2 \cdot 3 \cdot 5 \cdot 47$ | $17 \cdot 83$ | $2^2 \cdot 353$ | $3^2 \cdot 157$ | $2 \cdot 7 \cdot 101$ |
| 142 | $2^2 \cdot 5 \cdot 71$ | $7^2 \cdot 29$ | $2 \cdot 3^2 \cdot 79$ | **1532049** | $2^4 \cdot 89$ |
| 143 | $2 \cdot 5 \cdot 11 \cdot 13$ | $3^3 \cdot 53$ | $2^3 \cdot 179$ | **1562462** | $2 \cdot 3 \cdot 239$ |
| 144 | $2^5 \cdot 3^2 \cdot 5$ | $11 \cdot 131$ | $2 \cdot 7 \cdot 103$ | $3 \cdot 13 \cdot 37$ | $2^2 \cdot 19^2$ |
| **145** | $2 \cdot 5^2 \cdot 29$ | **1616674** | $2^2 \cdot 3 \cdot 11^2$ | **1622656** | $2 \cdot 727$ |
| 146 | $2^2 \cdot 5 \cdot 73$ | $3 \cdot 487$ | $2 \cdot 17 \cdot 43$ | $7 \cdot 11 \cdot 19$ | $2^3 \cdot 3 \cdot 61$ |
| 147 | $2 \cdot 3 \cdot 5 \cdot 7^2$ | **1676127** | $2^6 \cdot 23$ | $3 \cdot 491$ | $2 \cdot 11 \cdot 67$ |
| 148 | $2^3 \cdot 5 \cdot 37$ | **1705551** | $2 \cdot 3 \cdot 13 \cdot 19$ | **1711412** | $2^2 \cdot 7 \cdot 53$ |
| 149 | $2 \cdot 5 \cdot 149$ | $3 \cdot 7 \cdot 71$ | $2^2 \cdot 373$ | **1740598** | $2 \cdot 3^2 \cdot 83$ |
| **150** | $2^2 \cdot 3 \cdot 5^3$ | $19 \cdot 79$ | $2 \cdot 751$ | $3^2 \cdot 167$ | $2^5 \cdot 47$ |

| $n$ | 5 | 6 | 7 | 8 | 9 |
|---|---|---|---|---|---|
| **100** | $3 \cdot 5 \cdot 67$ | $2 \cdot 503$ | $19 \cdot 53$ | $2^4 \cdot 3^2 \cdot 7$ | **0038912** |
| 101 | $5 \cdot 7 \cdot 29$ | $2^3 \cdot 127$ | $3^2 \cdot 113$ | $2 \cdot 509$ | **0081742** |
| 102 | $5^2 \cdot 41$ | $2 \cdot 3^3 \cdot 19$ | $13 \cdot 79$ | $2^2 \cdot 257$ | $3 \cdot 7^3$ |
| 103 | $3^2 \cdot 5 \cdot 23$ | $2^2 \cdot 7 \cdot 37$ | $17 \cdot 61$ | $2 \cdot 3 \cdot 173$ | **0166155** |
| 104 | $5 \cdot 11 \cdot 19$ | $2 \cdot 523$ | $3 \cdot 349$ | $2^3 \cdot 131$ | **0207755** |
| **105** | $5 \cdot 211$ | $2^5 \cdot 3 \cdot 11$ | $7 \cdot 151$ | $2 \cdot 23^2$ | $3 \cdot 353$ |
| 106 | $3 \cdot 5 \cdot 71$ | $2 \cdot 13 \cdot 41$ | $11 \cdot 97$ | $2^2 \cdot 3 \cdot 89$ | **0289777** |
| 107 | $5^2 \cdot 43$ | $2^2 \cdot 269$ | $3 \cdot 359$ | $2 \cdot 7^2 \cdot 11$ | $13 \cdot 83$ |
| 108 | $5 \cdot 7 \cdot 31$ | $2 \cdot 3 \cdot 181$ | **0362295** | $2^6 \cdot 17$ | $3^2 \cdot 11^2$ |
| 109 | $3 \cdot 5 \cdot 73$ | $2^3 \cdot 137$ | **0402066** | $2 \cdot 3^2 \cdot 61$ | $7 \cdot 157$ |
| **110** | $5 \cdot 13 \cdot 17$ | $2 \cdot 7 \cdot 79$ | $3^3 \cdot 41$ | $2^2 \cdot 277$ | **0449315** |
| 111 | $5 \cdot 223$ | $2^2 \cdot 3^2 \cdot 31$ | **0480532** | $2 \cdot 13 \cdot 43$ | $3 \cdot 373$ |
| 112 | $3^2 \cdot 5^3$ | $2 \cdot 563$ | $7^2 \cdot 23$ | $2^3 \cdot 3 \cdot 47$ | **0526939** |
| 113 | $5 \cdot 227$ | $2^4 \cdot 71$ | $3 \cdot 379$ | $2 \cdot 569$ | $17 \cdot 67$ |
| 114 | $5 \cdot 229$ | $2 \cdot 3 \cdot 191$ | $31 \cdot 37$ | $2^2 \cdot 7 \cdot 41$ | $3 \cdot 383$ |
| **115** | $3 \cdot 5 \cdot 7 \cdot 11$ | $2^2 \cdot 17^2$ | $13 \cdot 89$ | $2 \cdot 3 \cdot 193$ | $19 \cdot 61$ |
| 116 | $5 \cdot 233$ | $2 \cdot 11 \cdot 53$ | $3 \cdot 389$ | $2^4 \cdot 73$ | $7 \cdot 167$ |
| 117 | $5^2 \cdot 47$ | $2^3 \cdot 3 \cdot 7^2$ | $11 \cdot 107$ | $2 \cdot 19 \cdot 31$ | $3^2 \cdot 131$ |
| 118 | $3 \cdot 5 \cdot 79$ | $2 \cdot 593$ | **0744507** | $2^2 \cdot 3^3 \cdot 11$ | $29 \cdot 41$ |
| 119 | $5 \cdot 239$ | $2^2 \cdot 13 \cdot 23$ | $3^2 \cdot 7 \cdot 19$ | $2 \cdot 599$ | $11 \cdot 109$ |
| **120** | $5 \cdot 241$ | $2 \cdot 3^2 \cdot 67$ | $17 \cdot 71$ | $2^3 \cdot 151$ | $3 \cdot 13 \cdot 31$ |
| 121 | $3^5 \cdot 5$ | $2^6 \cdot 19$ | **0852906** | $2 \cdot 3 \cdot 7 \cdot 29$ | $23 \cdot 53$ |
| 122 | $5^2 \cdot 7^2$ | $2 \cdot 613$ | $3 \cdot 409$ | $2^2 \cdot 307$ | **0895519** |
| 123 | $5 \cdot 13 \cdot 19$ | $2^2 \cdot 3 \cdot 103$ | **0923697** | $2 \cdot 619$ | $3 \cdot 7 \cdot 59$ |
| 124 | $3 \cdot 5 \cdot 83$ | $2 \cdot 7 \cdot 89$ | $29 \cdot 43$ | $2^5 \cdot 3 \cdot 13$ | **0965624** |
| **125** | $5 \cdot 251$ | $2^3 \cdot 157$ | $3 \cdot 419$ | $2 \cdot 17 \cdot 37$ | **1000257** |
| 126 | $5 \cdot 11 \cdot 23$ | $2 \cdot 3 \cdot 211$ | $7 \cdot 181$ | $2^2 \cdot 317$ | $3^3 \cdot 47$ |
| 127 | $3 \cdot 5^2 \cdot 17$ | $2^2 \cdot 11 \cdot 29$ | **1061909** | $2 \cdot 3^2 \cdot 71$ | **1068705** |
| 128 | $5 \cdot 257$ | $2 \cdot 643$ | $3^2 \cdot 11 \cdot 13$ | $2^3 \cdot 7 \cdot 23$ | **1102529** |
| 129 | $5 \cdot 7 \cdot 37$ | $2^4 \cdot 3^4$ | **1129400** | $2 \cdot 11 \cdot 59$ | $3 \cdot 433$ |
| **130** | $3^2 \cdot 5 \cdot 29$ | $2 \cdot 653$ | **1162756** | $2^2 \cdot 3 \cdot 109$ | $7 \cdot 11 \cdot 17$ |
| 131 | $5 \cdot 263$ | $2^2 \cdot 7 \cdot 47$ | $3 \cdot 439$ | $2 \cdot 659$ | **1202448** |
| 132 | $5^2 \cdot 53$ | $2 \cdot 3 \cdot 13 \cdot 17$ | **1228709** | $2^4 \cdot 83$ | $3 \cdot 443$ |
| 133 | $3 \cdot 5 \cdot 89$ | $2^3 \cdot 167$ | $7 \cdot 191$ | $2 \cdot 3 \cdot 223$ | $13 \cdot 103$ |
| 134 | $5 \cdot 269$ | $2 \cdot 673$ | $3 \cdot 449$ | $2^2 \cdot 337$ | $19 \cdot 71$ |
| **135** | $5 \cdot 271$ | $2^2 \cdot 3 \cdot 113$ | $23 \cdot 59$ | $2 \cdot 7 \cdot 97$ | $3^2 \cdot 151$ |
| 136 | $3 \cdot 5 \cdot 7 \cdot 13$ | $2 \cdot 683$ | **1357685** | $2^3 \cdot 3^2 \cdot 19$ | $37^2$ |
| 137 | $5^3 \cdot 11$ | $2^5 \cdot 43$ | $3^4 \cdot 17$ | $2 \cdot 13 \cdot 53$ | $7 \cdot 197$ |
| 138 | $5 \cdot 277$ | $2 \cdot 3^2 \cdot 7 \cdot 11$ | $19 \cdot 73$ | $2^2 \cdot 347$ | $3 \cdot 463$ |
| 139 | $3^2 \cdot 5 \cdot 31$ | $2^2 \cdot 349$ | $11 \cdot 127$ | $2 \cdot 3 \cdot 233$ | **1458177** |
| **140** | $5 \cdot 281$ | $2 \cdot 19 \cdot 37$ | $3 \cdot 7 \cdot 67$ | $2^7 \cdot 11$ | **1489110** |
| 141 | $5 \cdot 283$ | $2^3 \cdot 3 \cdot 59$ | $13 \cdot 109$ | $2 \cdot 709$ | $3 \cdot 11 \cdot 43$ |
| 142 | $3 \cdot 5^2 \cdot 19$ | $2 \cdot 23 \cdot 31$ | **1544240** | $2^2 \cdot 3 \cdot 7 \cdot 17$ | **1550322** |
| 143 | $5 \cdot 7 \cdot 41$ | $2^2 \cdot 359$ | $3 \cdot 479$ | $2 \cdot 719$ | **1580608** |
| 144 | $5 \cdot 17^2$ | $2 \cdot 3 \cdot 241$ | **1604685** | $2^3 \cdot 181$ | $3^2 \cdot 7 \cdot 23$ |
| **145** | $3 \cdot 5 \cdot 97$ | $2^4 \cdot 7 \cdot 13$ | $31 \cdot 47$ | $2 \cdot 3^6$ | **1640553** |
| 146 | $5 \cdot 293$ | $2 \cdot 733$ | $3^2 \cdot 163$ | $2^2 \cdot 367$ | $13 \cdot 113$ |
| 147 | $5^2 \cdot 59$ | $2^2 \cdot 3^2 \cdot 41$ | $7 \cdot 211$ | $2 \cdot 739$ | $3 \cdot 17 \cdot 29$ |
| 148 | $3^3 \cdot 5 \cdot 11$ | $2 \cdot 743$ | **1723110** | $2^4 \cdot 3 \cdot 31$ | **1728947** |
| 149 | $5 \cdot 13 \cdot 23$ | $2^3 \cdot 11 \cdot 17$ | $3 \cdot 499$ | $2 \cdot 7 \cdot 107$ | **1758016** |
| **150** | $5 \cdot 7 \cdot 43$ | $2 \cdot 3 \cdot 251$ | $11 \cdot 137$ | $2^2 \cdot 13 \cdot 29$ | $3 \cdot 503$ |

# FACTORS AND PRIMES (Continued)

| $n$ | 0 | 1 | 2 | 3 | 4 |
|---|---|---|---|---|---|
| **150** | $2^2 \cdot 3 \cdot 5^3$ | $19 \cdot 79$ | $2 \cdot 751$ | $3^2 \cdot 167$ | $2^5 \cdot 47$ |
| 151 | $2 \cdot 5 \cdot 151$ | **1792665** | $2^3 \cdot 3^3 \cdot 7$ | $17 \cdot 89$ | $2 \cdot 757$ |
| 152 | $2^4 \cdot 5 \cdot 19$ | $3^2 \cdot 13^2$ | $2 \cdot 761$ | **1826999** | $2^2 \cdot 3 \cdot 127$ |
| 153 | $2 \cdot 3^2 \cdot 5 \cdot 17$ | **1849752** | $2^2 \cdot 383$ | $3 \cdot 7 \cdot 73$ | $2 \cdot 13 \cdot 59$ |
| 154 | $2^2 \cdot 5 \cdot 7 \cdot 11$ | $23 \cdot 67$ | $2 \cdot 3 \cdot 257$ | **1883659** | $2^3 \cdot 193$ |
| **155** | $2 \cdot 5^2 \cdot 31$ | $3 \cdot 11 \cdot 47$ | $2^4 \cdot 97$ | **1911715** | $2 \cdot 3 \cdot 7 \cdot 37$ |
| 156 | $2^3 \cdot 3 \cdot 5 \cdot 13$ | $7 \cdot 223$ | $2 \cdot 11 \cdot 71$ | $3 \cdot 521$ | $2^2 \cdot 17 \cdot 23$ |
| 157 | $2 \cdot 5 \cdot 157$ | **1961762** | $2^2 \cdot 3 \cdot 131$ | $11^2 \cdot 13$ | $2 \cdot 787$ |
| 158 | $2^2 \cdot 5 \cdot 79$ | $3 \cdot 17 \cdot 31$ | $2 \cdot 7 \cdot 113$ | **1994809** | $2^4 \cdot 3^2 \cdot 11$ |
| 159 | $2 \cdot 3 \cdot 5 \cdot 53$ | $37 \cdot 43$ | $2^3 \cdot 199$ | $3^3 \cdot 59$ | $2 \cdot 797$ |
| **160** | $2^6 \cdot 5^2$ | **2043913** | $2 \cdot 3^2 \cdot 89$ | $7 \cdot 229$ | $2^2 \cdot 401$ |
| 161 | $2 \cdot 5 \cdot 7 \cdot 23$ | $3^2 \cdot 179$ | $2^2 \cdot 13 \cdot 31$ | **2076344** | $2 \cdot 3 \cdot 269$ |
| 162 | $2^2 \cdot 3^4 \cdot 5$ | **2097830** | $2 \cdot 811$ | $3 \cdot 541$ | $2^3 \cdot 7 \cdot 29$ |
| 163 | $2 \cdot 5 \cdot 163$ | $7 \cdot 233$ | $2^5 \cdot 3 \cdot 17$ | $23 \cdot 71$ | $2 \cdot 19 \cdot 43$ |
| 164 | $2^3 \cdot 5 \cdot 41$ | $3 \cdot 547$ | $2 \cdot 821$ | $31 \cdot 53$ | $2^2 \cdot 3 \cdot 137$ |
| **165** | $2 \cdot 3 \cdot 5^2 \cdot 11$ | $13 \cdot 127$ | $2^2 \cdot 7 \cdot 59$ | $3 \cdot 19 \cdot 29$ | $2 \cdot 827$ |
| 166 | $2^2 \cdot 5 \cdot 83$ | $11 \cdot 151$ | $2 \cdot 3 \cdot 277$ | **2208922** | $2^7 \cdot 13$ |
| 167 | $2 \cdot 5 \cdot 167$ | $3 \cdot 557$ | $2^3 \cdot 11 \cdot 19$ | $7 \cdot 239$ | $2 \cdot 3^3 \cdot 31$ |
| 168 | $2^4 \cdot 3 \cdot 5 \cdot 7$ | $41^2$ | $2 \cdot 29^2$ | $3^2 \cdot 11 \cdot 17$ | $2^2 \cdot 421$ |
| 169 | $2 \cdot 5 \cdot 13^2$ | $19 \cdot 89$ | $2^2 \cdot 3^2 \cdot 47$ | **2286570** | $2 \cdot 7 \cdot 11^2$ |
| **170** | $2^2 \cdot 5^2 \cdot 17$ | $3^5 \cdot 7$ | $2 \cdot 23 \cdot 37$ | $13 \cdot 131$ | $2^3 \cdot 3 \cdot 71$ |
| 171 | $2 \cdot 3^2 \cdot 5 \cdot 19$ | $29 \cdot 59$ | $2^4 \cdot 107$ | $3 \cdot 571$ | $2 \cdot 857$ |
| 172 | $2^3 \cdot 5 \cdot 43$ | **2357809** | $2 \cdot 3 \cdot 7 \cdot 41$ | **2362853** | $2^2 \cdot 431$ |
| 173 | $2 \cdot 5 \cdot 173$ | $3 \cdot 577$ | $2^2 \cdot 433$ | **2387986** | $2 \cdot 3 \cdot 17^2$ |
| 174 | $2^2 \cdot 3 \cdot 5 \cdot 29$ | **2407988** | $2 \cdot 13 \cdot 67$ | $3 \cdot 7 \cdot 83$ | $2^4 \cdot 109$ |
| **175** | $2 \cdot 5^3 \cdot 7$ | $17 \cdot 103$ | $2^3 \cdot 3 \cdot 73$ | **2437819** | $2 \cdot 877$ |
| 176 | $2^5 \cdot 5 \cdot 11$ | $3 \cdot 587$ | $2 \cdot 881$ | $41 \cdot 43$ | $2^2 \cdot 3^2 \cdot 7^2$ |
| 177 | $2 \cdot 3 \cdot 5 \cdot 59$ | $7 \cdot 11 \cdot 23$ | $2^2 \cdot 443$ | $3^2 \cdot 197$ | $2 \cdot 887$ |
| 178 | $2^2 \cdot 5 \cdot 89$ | $13 \cdot 137$ | $2 \cdot 3^4 \cdot 11$ | **2511513** | $2^3 \cdot 223$ |
| 179 | $2 \cdot 5 \cdot 179$ | $3^2 \cdot 199$ | $2^3 \cdot 7$ | $11 \cdot 163$ | $2 \cdot 3 \cdot 13 \cdot 23$ |
| **180** | $2^3 \cdot 3^2 \cdot 5^2$ | **2555137** | $2 \cdot 17 \cdot 53$ | $3 \cdot 601$ | $2^2 \cdot 11 \cdot 41$ |
| 181 | $2 \cdot 5 \cdot 181$ | **2579185** | $2^2 \cdot 3 \cdot 151$ | $7^2 \cdot 37$ | $2 \cdot 907$ |
| 182 | $2^2 \cdot 5 \cdot 7 \cdot 13$ | $3 \cdot 607$ | $2 \cdot 911$ | **2607867** | $2^5 \cdot 3 \cdot 19$ |
| 183 | $2 \cdot 3 \cdot 5 \cdot 61$ | **2626883** | $2^3 \cdot 229$ | $3 \cdot 13 \cdot 47$ | $2 \cdot 7 \cdot 131$ |
| 184 | $2^4 \cdot 5 \cdot 23$ | $7 \cdot 263$ | $2 \cdot 3 \cdot 307$ | $19 \cdot 97$ | $2^2 \cdot 461$ |
| **185** | $2 \cdot 5^2 \cdot 37$ | $3 \cdot 617$ | $2^2 \cdot 463$ | $17 \cdot 109$ | $2 \cdot 3^2 \cdot 103$ |
| 186 | $2^3 \cdot 3 \cdot 5 \cdot 31$ | **2697464** | $2 \cdot 7^2 \cdot 19$ | $3^4 \cdot 23$ | $2^3 \cdot 233$ |
| 187 | $2 \cdot 5 \cdot 11 \cdot 17$ | **2720738** | $2^4 \cdot 3^2 \cdot 13$ | **2725378** | $2 \cdot 937$ |
| 188 | $2^3 \cdot 5 \cdot 47$ | $3^2 \cdot 11 \cdot 19$ | $2 \cdot 941$ | $7 \cdot 269$ | $2^2 \cdot 3 \cdot 157$ |
| 189 | $2 \cdot 3^3 \cdot 5 \cdot 7$ | $31 \cdot 61$ | $2^2 \cdot 11 \cdot 43$ | $3 \cdot 631$ | $2 \cdot 947$ |
| **190** | $2^2 \cdot 5^2 \cdot 19$ | **2789821** | $2 \cdot 3 \cdot 317$ | $11 \cdot 173$ | $2^4 \cdot 7 \cdot 17$ |
| 191 | $2 \cdot 5 \cdot 191$ | $3 \cdot 7^2 \cdot 13$ | $2^3 \cdot 239$ | **2817150** | $2 \cdot 3 \cdot 11 \cdot 29$ |
| 192 | $2^7 \cdot 3 \cdot 5$ | $17 \cdot 113$ | $2 \cdot 31^2$ | $3 \cdot 641$ | $2^2 \cdot 13 \cdot 37$ |
| 193 | $2 \cdot 5 \cdot 193$ | **2857823** | $2^2 \cdot 3 \cdot 7 \cdot 23$ | **2862319** | $2 \cdot 967$ |
| 194 | $2^2 \cdot 5 \cdot 97$ | $3 \cdot 647$ | $2 \cdot 971$ | $29 \cdot 67$ | $2^3 \cdot 3^5$ |
| **195** | $2 \cdot 3 \cdot 5^2 \cdot 13$ | **2902573** | $2^5 \cdot 61$ | $3^2 \cdot 7 \cdot 31$ | $2 \cdot 977$ |
| 196 | $2^2 \cdot 5 \cdot 7^2$ | $37 \cdot 53$ | $2 \cdot 3^2 \cdot 109$ | $13 \cdot 151$ | $2^2 \cdot 491$ |
| 197 | $2 \cdot 5 \cdot 197$ | $3^3 \cdot 73$ | $2^2 \cdot 17 \cdot 29$ | **2951271** | $2 \cdot 3 \cdot 7 \cdot 47$ |
| 198 | $2^2 \cdot 3^2 \cdot 5 \cdot 11$ | $7 \cdot 283$ | $2 \cdot 991$ | $3 \cdot 661$ | $2^6 \cdot 31$ |
| 199 | $2 \cdot 5 \cdot 199$ | $11 \cdot 181$ | $2^3 \cdot 3 \cdot 83$ | **2995073** | $2 \cdot 997$ |
| **200** | $2^4 \cdot 5^3$ | $3 \cdot 23 \cdot 29$ | $2 \cdot 7 \cdot 11 \cdot 13$ | **3016809** | $2^2 \cdot 3 \cdot 167$ |

| $n$ | 5 | 6 | 7 | 8 | 9 |
|---|---|---|---|---|---|
| **150** | $5 \cdot 7 \cdot 43$ | $2 \cdot 3 \cdot 251$ | $11 \cdot 137$ | $2^2 \cdot 13 \cdot 29$ | $3 \cdot 503$ |
| 151 | $3 \cdot 5 \cdot 101$ | $2^2 \cdot 379$ | $37 \cdot 41$ | $2 \cdot 3 \cdot 11 \cdot 23$ | $7^2 \cdot 31$ |
| 152 | $5^2 \cdot 61$ | $2 \cdot 7 \cdot 109$ | $3 \cdot 509$ | $2^3 \cdot 191$ | $11 \cdot 139$ |
| 153 | $5 \cdot 307$ | $2^9 \cdot 3$ | $29 \cdot 53$ | $2 \cdot 769$ | $3^4 \cdot 19$ |
| 154 | $3 \cdot 5 \cdot 103$ | $2 \cdot 773$ | $7 \cdot 13 \cdot 17$ | $2^2 \cdot 3^2 \cdot 43$ | **1900514** |
| **155** | $5 \cdot 311$ | $2^2 \cdot 389$ | $3^2 \cdot 173$ | $2 \cdot 19 \cdot 41$ | **1928461** |
| 156 | $5 \cdot 313$ | $2 \cdot 3^3 \cdot 29$ | **1950690** | $2^5 \cdot 7^2$ | $3 \cdot 523$ |
| 157 | $3^2 \cdot 5^2 \cdot 7$ | $2^3 \cdot 197$ | $19 \cdot 83$ | $2 \cdot 3 \cdot 263$ | **1983821** |
| 158 | $5 \cdot 317$ | $2 \cdot 13 \cdot 61$ | $3 \cdot 23^2$ | $2^2 \cdot 397$ | $7 \cdot 227$ |
| 159 | $5 \cdot 11 \cdot 29$ | $2^2 \cdot 3 \cdot 7 \cdot 19$ | **2033049** | $2 \cdot 17 \cdot 47$ | $3 \cdot 13 \cdot 41$ |
| **160** | $3 \cdot 5 \cdot 107$ | $2 \cdot 11 \cdot 73$ | **2060159** | $2^3 \cdot 3 \cdot 67$ | **2065560** |
| 161 | $5 \cdot 17 \cdot 19$ | $2^4 \cdot 101$ | $3 \cdot 7^2 \cdot 11$ | $2 \cdot 809$ | **2092468** |
| 162 | $5^3 \cdot 13$ | $2 \cdot 3 \cdot 271$ | **2113876** | $2^2 \cdot 11 \cdot 37$ | $3^2 \cdot 181$ |
| 163 | $3 \cdot 5 \cdot 109$ | $2^2 \cdot 409$ | **2140487** | $2 \cdot 3^2 \cdot 7 \cdot 13$ | $11 \cdot 149$ |
| 164 | $5 \cdot 7 \cdot 47$ | $2 \cdot 823$ | $3^3 \cdot 61$ | $2^4 \cdot 103$ | $17 \cdot 97$ |
| **165** | $5 \cdot 331$ | $2^3 \cdot 3^2 \cdot 23$ | **2193225** | $2 \cdot 829$ | $3 \cdot 7 \cdot 79$ |
| 166 | $3^2 \cdot 5 \cdot 37$ | $2 \cdot 7^2 \cdot 17$ | **2219356** | $2^2 \cdot 3 \cdot 139$ | **2224563** |
| 167 | $5^2 \cdot 67$ | $2^2 \cdot 419$ | $3 \cdot 13 \cdot 43$ | $2 \cdot 839$ | $23 \cdot 73$ |
| 168 | $5 \cdot 337$ | $2 \cdot 3 \cdot 281$ | $7 \cdot 241$ | $2^3 \cdot 211$ | $3 \cdot 563$ |
| 169 | $3 \cdot 5 \cdot 113$ | $2^5 \cdot 53$ | **2296818** | $2 \cdot 3 \cdot 283$ | **2301934** |
| **170** | $5 \cdot 11 \cdot 31$ | $2 \cdot 853$ | $3 \cdot 569$ | $2^2 \cdot 7 \cdot 61$ | **2327421** |
| 171 | $5 \cdot 7^3$ | $2^2 \cdot 3 \cdot 11 \cdot 13$ | $17 \cdot 101$ | $2 \cdot 859$ | $3^2 \cdot 191$ |
| 172 | $3 \cdot 5^2 \cdot 23$ | $2 \cdot 863$ | $11 \cdot 157$ | $2^6 \cdot 3^3$ | $7 \cdot 13 \cdot 19$ |
| 173 | $5 \cdot 347$ | $2^3 \cdot 7 \cdot 31$ | $3^2 \cdot 193$ | $2 \cdot 11 \cdot 79$ | $37 \cdot 47$ |
| 174 | $5 \cdot 349$ | $2 \cdot 3^2 \cdot 97$ | **2422929** | $2^2 \cdot 19 \cdot 23$ | $3 \cdot 11 \cdot 53$ |
| **175** | $3^3 \cdot 5 \cdot 13$ | $2^2 \cdot 439$ | $7 \cdot 251$ | $2 \cdot 3 \cdot 293$ | **2452658** |
| 176 | $5 \cdot 353$ | $2 \cdot 883$ | $3 \cdot 19 \cdot 31$ | $2^3 \cdot 13 \cdot 17$ | $29 \cdot 61$ |
| 177 | $5^2 \cdot 71$ | $2^4 \cdot 3 \cdot 37$ | **2496874** | $2 \cdot 7 \cdot 127$ | $3 \cdot 593$ |
| 178 | $3 \cdot 5 \cdot 7 \cdot 17$ | $2 \cdot 19 \cdot 47$ | **2521246** | $2^2 \cdot 3 \cdot 149$ | **2526103** |
| 179 | $5 \cdot 359$ | $2^2 \cdot 449$ | $3 \cdot 599$ | $2 \cdot 29 \cdot 31$ | $7 \cdot 257$ |
| **180** | $5 \cdot 19^2$ | $2 \cdot 3 \cdot 7 \cdot 43$ | $13 \cdot 139$ | $2^4 \cdot 113$ | $3^3 \cdot 67$ |
| 181 | $3 \cdot 5 \cdot 11^2$ | $2^3 \cdot 227$ | $23 \cdot 79$ | $2 \cdot 3^2 \cdot 101$ | $17 \cdot 107$ |
| 182 | $5^2 \cdot 73$ | $2 \cdot 11 \cdot 83$ | $3^2 \cdot 7 \cdot 29$ | $2^2 \cdot 457$ | $31 \cdot 59$ |
| 183 | $5 \cdot 367$ | $2^2 \cdot 3^3 \cdot 17$ | $11 \cdot 167$ | $2 \cdot 919$ | $3 \cdot 613$ |
| 184 | $3^2 \cdot 5 \cdot 41$ | $2 \cdot 13 \cdot 71$ | **2664669** | $2^3 \cdot 3 \cdot 7 \cdot 11$ | $43^2$ |
| **185** | $5 \cdot 7 \cdot 53$ | $2^6 \cdot 29$ | $3 \cdot 619$ | $2 \cdot 929$ | $11 \cdot 13^2$ |
| 186 | $5 \cdot 373$ | $2 \cdot 3 \cdot 311$ | **2711443** | $2^2 \cdot 467$ | $3 \cdot 7 \cdot 89$ |
| 187 | $3 \cdot 5^4$ | $2^2 \cdot 7 \cdot 67$ | **2734643** | $2 \cdot 3 \cdot 313$ | **2739268** |
| 188 | $5 \cdot 13 \cdot 29$ | $2 \cdot 23 \cdot 41$ | $3 \cdot 17 \cdot 37$ | $2^5 \cdot 59$ | **2762320** |
| 189 | $5 \cdot 379$ | $2^3 \cdot 3 \cdot 79$ | $7 \cdot 271$ | $2 \cdot 13 \cdot 73$ | $3^2 \cdot 211$ |
| **190** | $3 \cdot 5 \cdot 127$ | $2 \cdot 953$ | **2803507** | $2^2 \cdot 3^2 \cdot 53$ | $23 \cdot 83$ |
| 191 | $5 \cdot 383$ | $2^2 \cdot 479$ | $3^3 \cdot 71$ | $2 \cdot 7 \cdot 137$ | $19 \cdot 101$ |
| 192 | $5^2 \cdot 7 \cdot 11$ | $2 \cdot 3^2 \cdot 107$ | $41 \cdot 47$ | $2^3 \cdot 241$ | $3 \cdot 643$ |
| 193 | $3^2 \cdot 5 \cdot 43$ | $2^4 \cdot 11^2$ | $13 \cdot 149$ | $2 \cdot 3 \cdot 17 \cdot 19$ | $7 \cdot 277$ |
| 194 | $5 \cdot 389$ | $2 \cdot 7 \cdot 139$ | $3 \cdot 11 \cdot 59$ | $2^2 \cdot 487$ | **2898118** |
| **195** | $5 \cdot 17 \cdot 23$ | $2^2 \cdot 3 \cdot 163$ | $19 \cdot 103$ | $2 \cdot 11 \cdot 89$ | $3 \cdot 653$ |
| 196 | $3 \cdot 5 \cdot 131$ | $2 \cdot 983$ | $7 \cdot 281$ | $2^4 \cdot 3 \cdot 41$ | $11 \cdot 179$ |
| 197 | $5^2 \cdot 79$ | $2^3 \cdot 13 \cdot 19$ | $3 \cdot 659$ | $2 \cdot 23 \cdot 43$ | **2964458** |
| 198 | $5 \cdot 397$ | $2 \cdot 3 \cdot 331$ | **2981979** | $2^2 \cdot 7 \cdot 71$ | $3^2 \cdot 13 \cdot 17$ |
| 199 | $3 \cdot 5 \cdot 7 \cdot 19$ | $2^2 \cdot 499$ | **3003781** | $2 \cdot 3^3 \cdot 37$ | **3008128** |
| **200** | $5 \cdot 401$ | $2 \cdot 17 \cdot 59$ | $3^2 \cdot 223$ | $2^3 \cdot 251$ | $7^2 \cdot 41$ |

# FACTORS AND PRIMES (Continued)

## EXTENDED TABLES OF FACTORS AND PRIMES

The following procedure makes possible the determination of a number between 2009 and 19,949 as being either prime, or if not, what its factors will be. It is herewith included with the kind permission of its author, Professor Leonard Caners.

The following symbols will be used:

$N$ is the number whose factors, if any, are to be determined.
$A$ is $N$ with the last digit dropped. Thus if $N = 17,873$, $A = 1787$.
$R$ is the range and is the integral part of the square root of $N$ with its last two digits dropped. Thus $R$ of $17,873 = 13$.
$K$ is the key number and is found in the table below.
$P_1$ is a possible factor corresponding to $K$.
The twin series are given in the table for the sake of completeness but are not written down in actual practice.
There are two steps as outlined below.

### Step I

| $N$ | $K$ | $P_1$ | Series | Procedure |
|---|---|---|---|---|
| Any number ending in 1, 3, 7, or 9, within limits stated above | $A - R$ | $10R +$ last digit | $K + n; P_1 - 10n$ $n = 0, 1, \ldots, 2R + 1$ | Beginning with $K$ read table of Factors and Primes from left to right and look for corresponding possible factors |

### Step II

| $N$ ending in | $K$ | $P_1$ | Series | Procedure |
|---|---|---|---|---|
| 1 | $(A - 2) - 3R$ | $10R + 7$ | $K + 3n; P_1 - 10n$ $n = 0, 1, \ldots, 2R + 1$ | Same as in Step I except that only every *third* entry in table of Factors and Primes is examined for corresponding possible factors |
| 3 | $A - 3R$ | $10R + 1$ | $n = 0, 1, \ldots, 2R + 1$ | |
| 7 | $(A - 2) - 3R$ | $10R + 9$ | $n = 0, 1, \ldots, 2R + 1$ | |
| 9 | $A - 3R$ | $10R + 3$ | $n = 0, 1, \ldots, 2R + 1$ | |

As an example consider 7519. Using tables on preceding pages proceed as follows:

Step I

From Table $N = 7519$; $A = 751$; $R = 8$, $K = 743$; $P_1 = 89$ and the series obtained:

| | |
|---|---|
| 743 | 89 |
| 744 | 79 |
| 745 | 69 |
| 746 | 59 |
| 751 | 9 |
| 752 | 1 |
| 753 | 11 |
| 760 | 81 |

Examining the Table of Factors and Primes beginning with 743 note whether 743 has 89 as a factor; whether 744 has 79 as a factor, etc. Then continue to read from left to right keeping in mind the possible factors 69, 59, . . . 81.

Since none are found one concludes that 7519 has no factors within the given range ending in 9 or 1.

Step II

From Table $K = 727$ and $P_1 = 83$; the series obtained is:

| | |
|---|---|
| 727 | 83 |
| 730 | 73 |
| 733 | 63 |
| 751 | 3 |
| 754 | 7 |
| 778 | 87 |

Proceed exactly as in Step I. Begin with 727 and note whether it has 83 as a factor. Thereafter examine every *third* entry for the remaining corresponding possible factors 73, 63 . . . 3, 7, . . . 87. Since 730 yields the factor 73 one concludes that 73 is the factor of 7519. By division 7519 = $73 \times 103$. Had no factor been found in either Step I or Step II the conclusion would be that the number under consideration was prime.

Proof for Step I

Let $N$ end in 1. Then, if $N$ has a factor ending in 1, write

$$(10a + 1)(10b + 1) = N = 10A + 1$$
$$10ab + a + b = A$$

or

$$b(10a + 1) = (A - a)$$

This proves that any factor $10a + 1$ of $N$ is also a factor of $A - a$. Let $a = (R - n)$, then $(10a + 1)$ becomes $(10R + 1) - 10n$

and $(A - a)$ becomes $(A - R) + n$, i.e., $P_1 - 10n$ and $K + n$ respectively as given in the table. Since $P_1 - 10n$ becomes a number ending in 9 when $P_1 < 10n$, all possible factors ending in 9 are also provided for.

The proof for Step II is similar. For possible factors ending in 3 or 7 write

$$(10a + 7)(10b + 3) = N = 10A + 1.$$

By identical reasoning this results in $P_1 - 10n$ and $K + 3n$ respectively given in the table. This completes the proof for numbers ending in 1.

Identical reasoning establishes the key numbers and series for ending in 3, 7, or 9.

# CALCULUS

## Differentials

$d\,(au) = a\,du$

$d\,(u + v - w) = du + dv - dw$

$d\,(uv) = u\,dv + v\,du$

$d\left(\dfrac{u}{v}\right) = \dfrac{v\,du - u\,dv}{v^2}$

$d(u^n) = nu^{n-1}\,du$

$d(u^v) = vu^{v-1}\,du + u^v(\log_e u)\,dv$

$d\,(e^u) = e^u\,du$

$d(e^{au}) = ae^{au}\,du$

$d\,(a^u) = a^u(\log_e a)\,du$

$d\,(\log_e u) = u^{-1}du$

$d\,(\log_a u) = u^{-1}(\log_a e)\,du$

$d\,(u^u) = u^u(1 + \log_e u)\,du$

---

$d\,\sin u = \cos u\,du$

$d\,\cos u = -\sin u\,du$

$d\,\tan u = \sec^2 u\,du$

$d\,\cot u = -\csc^2 u\,du$

$d\,\sec u = \tan u \sec u\,du$

$d\,\csc u = -\cot u \cdot \csc u\,du$

$d\,\text{vers } u = \sin u\,du$

$d\,\sin^{-1} u = (1 - u^2)^{-\frac{1}{2}}\,du$

$d\,\cos^{-1} u = -(1 - u^2)^{-\frac{1}{2}}du$

$d\,\tan^{-1} u = (1 + u^2)^{-1}du$

$d\,\cot^{-1} u = -(1 + u^2)^{-1}du$

$d\,\sec^{-1} u = u^{-1}(u^2 - 1)^{-\frac{1}{2}}du$

$d\,\csc^{-1} u = -u^{-1}(u^2 - 1)^{-\frac{1}{2}}du$

$d\,\sinh u = \cosh u\,du$

$d\,\cosh u = \sinh u\,du$

$d\,\tanh u = \operatorname{sech}^2 u\,du$

$d\,\coth u = -\operatorname{csch}^2 u\,du$

$d\,\operatorname{sech} u = -\operatorname{sech} u \tanh u\,du$

$d\,\operatorname{csch} u = -\operatorname{csch} u \coth u\,du$

$d\,\text{vers}^{-1} u = (2u - u^2)^{-\frac{1}{2}}\,du$

$d\,\sinh^{-1} u = (u^2 + 1)^{-\frac{1}{2}}du$

$d\,\cosh^{-1} u = (u^2 - 1)^{-\frac{1}{2}}\,du$

$d\,\tanh^{-1} u = (1 - u^2)^{-1}\,du$

$d\,\coth^{-1} u = -(u^2 - 1)^{-1}du$

$d\,\operatorname{sech}^{-1} u = -u^{-1}(1 - u^2)^{-\frac{1}{2}}\,du$

$d\,\operatorname{csch}^{-1} u = -u^{-1}(u^2 + 1)^{-\frac{1}{2}}du$

## TABLE OF INTEGRALS

The following points should be observed when using this table.

1. A constant of integration is to be supplied with the answers for indefinite integrals.

2. Logarithmic expressions are to base $e = 2.71828 \cdots$, unless otherwise specified, and are to be evaluated for the absolute value of the arguments involved therein.

*3. All angles are measured in radians, and inverse trigonometric functions represent principal angles.

4. If the application of a formula produces either a zero denominator or a radical involving the unit $i = \sqrt{-1}$ in the result, there is always available another form of the answer which avoids this difficulty. In many of the results, the excluded values are specified, but when such are omitted it is presumed that one can tell what these should be, especially when difficulties of the type herein mentioned are obtained.

### ELEMENTARY FORMS

**1.** $\int a \, dx = ax.$

**2.** $\int a \cdot f(x) dx = a \int f(x) dx.$

**3.** $\int \phi(y) dx = \int \frac{\phi(y)}{y'} \, dy,$ where $y' = dy/dx$.

**4.** $\int (u + v) \, dx = \int u \, dx + \int v \, dx,$ where $u$ and $v$ are any functions of $x$.

**5.** $\int u \, dv = u \int dv - \int v \, du = uv - \int v \, du.$

**6.** $\int u \frac{dv}{dx} \, dx = uv - \int v \frac{du}{dx} \, dx.$

**7.** $\int x^n \, dx = \frac{x^{n+1}}{n + 1},$ except $n = -1$.

**8.** $\int \frac{f'(x) \, dx}{f(x)} = \log f(x),$ $[d f(x) = f'(x) \, dx].$

**9.** $\int \frac{dx}{x} = \log x,$ or $\log (-x)$.

**10.** $\int \frac{f'(x) \, dx}{2 \sqrt{f(x)}} = \sqrt{f(x)},$ $[d f(x) = f'(x) \, dx].$

**11.** $\int e^x \, dx = e^x.$

**12.** $\int e^{ax} \, dx = e^{ax}/a.$

* See index for table "Inverse Trigonometric Functions.

**13.** $\int b^{ax} dx = \dfrac{b^{ax}}{a \log b}$.

**14.** $\int \log x \, dx = x \log x - x$.

**15.** $\int a^x \log a \, dx = a^x$.

**16.** $\int \dfrac{dx}{a^2 + x^2} = \dfrac{1}{a} \tan^{-1}\left(\dfrac{x}{a}\right)$, or $-\dfrac{1}{a} \cot^{-1}\left(\dfrac{x}{a}\right)$.

**17.** $\int \dfrac{dx}{a^2 - x^2} = \dfrac{1}{a} \tanh^{-1}\left(\dfrac{x}{a}\right)$, or $\dfrac{1}{2a} \log \dfrac{a + x}{a - x}$.

**18.** $\int \dfrac{dx}{x^2 - a^2} = -\dfrac{1}{a} \coth^{-1}\left(\dfrac{x}{a}\right)$, or $\dfrac{1}{2a} \log \dfrac{x - a}{x + a}$.

**19.** $\int \dfrac{dx}{\sqrt{a^2 - x^2}} = \sin^{-1}\left(\dfrac{x}{a}\right)$, or $-\cos^{-1}\left(\dfrac{x}{a}\right)$.

**20.** $\int \dfrac{dx}{\sqrt{x^2 \pm a^2}} = \log\left(x + \sqrt{x^2 \pm a^2}\right)$.

**21.** $\int \dfrac{dx}{x \sqrt{x^2 - a^2}} = \dfrac{1}{a} \cos^{-1}\left(\dfrac{a}{x}\right)$.

**22.** $\int \dfrac{dx}{x \sqrt{a^2 \pm x^2}} = -\dfrac{1}{a} \log\left(\dfrac{a + \sqrt{a^2 \pm x^2}}{x}\right)$.

**23.** $\int \dfrac{dx}{x \sqrt{a + bx}} = \dfrac{2}{\sqrt{-a}} \tan^{-1} \sqrt{\dfrac{a + bx}{-a}}$, or

$\dfrac{-2}{\sqrt{a}} \tanh^{-1} \sqrt{\dfrac{a + bx}{a}}$, or $\dfrac{1}{\sqrt{a}} \log \dfrac{\sqrt{a + bx} - \sqrt{a}}{\sqrt{a + bx} + \sqrt{a}}$.

### FORMS CONTAINING $(a + bx)$

**24.** $\int (a + bx)^n dx = \dfrac{(a + bx)^{n+1}}{(n + 1)b}$, except $n = -1$.

**25.** $\int x (a + bx)^n dx = \dfrac{1}{b^2(n + 2)} (a + bx)^{n+2}$

$- \dfrac{a}{b^2(n + 1)} (a + bx)^{n+1}$, except $n = -1$ or $-2$.

**26.** $\int x^2 (a + bx)^n dx = \dfrac{1}{b^3}\left[\dfrac{(a + bx)^{n+3}}{n + 3} - 2a \dfrac{(a + bx)^{n+2}}{n + 2} + a^2 \dfrac{(a + bx)^{n+1}}{n + 1}\right]$.

**27.** $\int x^m (a + bx)^n \, dx = \dfrac{x^{m+1} (a + bx)^n}{m + n + 1} + \dfrac{an}{m + n + 1}$
$$\int x^m (a + bx)^{n-1} \, dx.$$

**28.** $\int x^m (a + bx)^n \, dx = \dfrac{1}{a(n + 1)} \left[ -x^{m+1}(a + bx)^{n+1} \right.$
$$\left. + (m + n + 2) \int x^m (a + bx)^{n+1} \, dx \right].$$

**29.** $\int \dfrac{dx}{a + bx} = \dfrac{1}{b} \log (a + bx).$

**30.** $\int \dfrac{dx}{(a + bx)^2} = - \dfrac{1}{b(a + bx)}.$

**31.** $\int \dfrac{dx}{(a + bx)^3} = - \dfrac{1}{2 b (a + bx)^2}.$

**32.** $\int \dfrac{x \, dx}{a + bx} = \dfrac{1}{b^2} [a + bx - a \log (a + bx)].$

**33.** $\int \dfrac{x \, dx}{(a + bx)^2} = \dfrac{1}{b^2} \left[ \log (a + bx) + \dfrac{a}{a + bx} \right].$

**34.** $\int \dfrac{x \, dx}{(a + bx)^3} = \dfrac{1}{b^2} \left[ - \dfrac{1}{a + bx} + \dfrac{a}{2(a + bx)^2} \right].$

**35.** $\int \dfrac{x \, dx}{(a + bx)^n} = \dfrac{1}{b^2} \left[ \dfrac{-1}{(n - 2)(a + bx)^{n-2}} \right.$
$$\left. + \dfrac{a}{(n - 1)(a + bx)^{n-1}} \right], n \neq 1, 2.$$

**36.** $\int \dfrac{x^2 \, dx}{a + bx} = \dfrac{1}{b^3} \left[ \dfrac{1}{2} (a + bx)^2 - \right.$
$$\left. 2 a (a + bx) + a^2 \log (a + bx) \right].$$

**37.** $\int \dfrac{x^2 \, dx}{(a + bx)^2} = \dfrac{1}{b^3} \left[ a + bx - 2 a \log (a + bx) - \dfrac{a^2}{a + bx} \right].$

**38.** $\int \dfrac{x^2 \, dx}{(a + bx)^3} = \dfrac{1}{b^3} \left[ \log (a + bx) + \dfrac{2a}{a + bx} - \dfrac{a^2}{2(a + bx)^2} \right].$

**39.** $\int \dfrac{x^2 \, dx}{(a + bx)^n} = \dfrac{1}{b^3} \left[ \dfrac{-1}{(n - 3)(a + bx)^{n-3}} \right.$
$$\left. + \dfrac{2a}{(n - 2)(a + bx)^{n-2}} - \dfrac{a^2}{(n - 1)(a + bx)^{n-1}} \right], n \neq 1, 2, 3.$$

**40.** $\int \dfrac{dx}{x(a + bx)} = - \dfrac{1}{a} \log \dfrac{a + bx}{x}.$

**41.** $\int \dfrac{dx}{x(a + bx)^2} = \dfrac{1}{a(a + bx)} - \dfrac{1}{a^2} \log \dfrac{a + bx}{x}.$

## INTEGRALS (Continued)

**42.** $\displaystyle\int \frac{dx}{x^2(a + bx)} = -\frac{1}{ax} + \frac{b}{a^2} \log \frac{a + bx}{x}.$

**43.** $\displaystyle\int \frac{dx}{x^2(a + bx)^2} = -\frac{a + 2bx}{a^2x\,(a + bx)} + \frac{2b}{a^3} \log \frac{a + bx}{x}.$

### FORMS CONTAINING $c^2 \pm x^2,\ x^2 - c^2$

**44.** $\displaystyle\int \frac{dx}{c^2 + x^2} = \frac{1}{c} \tan^{-1} \frac{x}{c},\ \text{or}\ \frac{1}{c} \sin^{-1} \frac{x}{\sqrt{c^2 + x^2}}.$

**45.** $\displaystyle\int \frac{dx}{c^2 - x^2} = \frac{1}{2c} \log \frac{c + x}{c - x},\ \text{or}\ \frac{1}{c} \tanh^{-1} \left(\frac{x}{c}\right).$

**46.** $\displaystyle\int \frac{dx}{x^2 - c^2} = \frac{1}{2c} \log \frac{x - c}{x + c},\ \text{or}\ -\frac{1}{c} \coth^{-1} \left(\frac{x}{c}\right).$

### FORMS CONTAINING $a + bx$ AND $a' + b'x$

**47.** $\displaystyle\int \frac{dx}{(a + bx)(a' + b'x)} = \frac{1}{ab' - a'b} \cdot \log \left(\frac{a' + b'x}{a + bx}\right).$

**48.** $\displaystyle\int \frac{x\,dx}{(a + bx)(a' + b'x)} = \frac{1}{ab' - a'b} \left[\frac{a}{b} \log (a + bx) \right.$
$$\left. - \frac{a'}{b'} \log (a' + b'x)\right].$$

**49.** $\displaystyle\int \frac{dx}{(a + bx)^2(a' + b'x)} = \frac{1}{ab' - a'b} \left(\frac{1}{a + bx} + \frac{b'}{ab' - a'b}\right.$
$$\left. \log \frac{a' + b'x}{a + bx}\right).$$

**50.** $\displaystyle\int \frac{x\,dx}{(a + bx)^2(a' + b'x)} = \frac{-a}{b(ab' - a'b)(a + bx)}$
$$- \frac{a'}{(ab' - a'b)^2} \log \frac{a' + b'x}{a + bx}.$$

**51.** $\displaystyle\int \frac{x^2\,dx}{(a + bx)^2(a' + b'x)} = \frac{a^2}{b^2(ab' - a'b)(a + bx)} +$
$$\frac{1}{(ab' - a'b)^2} \left[\frac{a'^2}{b'} \log (a' + b'x) + \frac{a(ab' - 2\,a'b)}{b^2} \log (a + bx)\right].$$

**52.** $\displaystyle\int \frac{dx}{(a + bx)^n(a' + b'x)^m} = \frac{1}{(m - 1)(ab' - a'b)}$
$$\left(\frac{-1}{(a + bx)^{n-1}(a' + b'x)^{m-1}} - (m + n - 2)b\right.$$
$$\left. \int \frac{dx}{(a + bx)^n(a' + b'x)^{m-1}}\right).$$

**53.** $\displaystyle\int \frac{a + bx}{a' + b'x}\,dx = \frac{bx}{b'} + \frac{ab' - a'b}{b'^2} \log (a' + b'x).$

259

**54.** $\displaystyle\int \frac{(a + bx)^m dx}{(a' + b'x)^n} = -\frac{1}{(n - 1)(ab' - a'b)}\left[\frac{(a + bx)^{m+1}}{(a' + b'x)^{n-1}}\right.$

$$\left. + b(n - m - 2)\int \frac{(a + bx)^m\, dx}{(a' + b'x)^{n-1}}\right]$$

$$= -\frac{1}{b'(n - m - 1)}\left[\frac{(a + bx)^m}{(a' + b'x)^{n-1}}\right.$$

$$\left. + m(ab' - a'b)\int \frac{(a + bx)^{m-1}dx}{(a' + b'x)^n}\right]$$

$$= -\frac{-1}{(n - 1)b'}\left[\frac{(a + bx)^m}{(a' + b'x)^{n-1}} - mb\int \frac{(a + bx)^{m-1}dx}{(a' + b'x)^{n-1}}\right].$$

FORMS CONTAINING $\sqrt{a + bx} = \sqrt{u}$ AND $\sqrt{a' + b'x} = \sqrt{v}$
WITH $k = ab' - a'b$

**55.** $\displaystyle\int \sqrt{uv}\, dx = \frac{k + 2\, bv}{4\, bb'} \sqrt{uv} - \frac{k^2}{8\, bb'}\int \frac{dx}{\sqrt{uv}}.$

**56.** $\displaystyle\int \frac{dx}{v\sqrt{u}} = \frac{1}{\sqrt{kb'}} \log \frac{b'\sqrt{u} - \sqrt{kb'}}{b'\sqrt{u} + \sqrt{kb'}},$ or

$$\frac{2}{\sqrt{-kb'}} \tan^{-1} \frac{b'\sqrt{u}}{\sqrt{-kb'}}.$$

**57.** $\displaystyle\int \frac{dx}{\sqrt{uv}} = \frac{2}{\sqrt{bb'}} \log (\sqrt{bb'u} + b\sqrt{v}),$ or

$$\frac{2}{\sqrt{bb'}} \tanh^{-1} \sqrt{\frac{b'u}{bv}}, \ = \frac{2}{\sqrt{-bb'}} \tan^{-1} \sqrt{\frac{-b'u}{bv}}, \text{ or}$$

$$\frac{-1}{\sqrt{-bb'}} \sin^{-1} \frac{2bb'x + a'b + ab'}{|k|}.$$

**58.** $\displaystyle\int \frac{x\, dx}{\sqrt{uv}} = \frac{\sqrt{uv}}{bb'} - \frac{ab' + a'b}{2bb'}\int \frac{dx}{\sqrt{uv}}.$

**59.** $\displaystyle\int \frac{dx}{v\sqrt{uv}} = -\frac{2\sqrt{u}}{k\sqrt{v}}.$

**60.** $\displaystyle\int \frac{\sqrt{v}\, dx}{\sqrt{u}} = \frac{1}{b}\sqrt{uv} - \frac{k}{2b}\int \frac{dx}{\sqrt{uv}}.$

**61.** $\displaystyle\int v^m \sqrt{u}\, dx = \frac{1}{(2m + 3)b'}\left(2v^{m+1}\sqrt{u} + k\int \frac{v^m dx}{\sqrt{u}}\right).$

**62.** $\displaystyle\int \frac{dx}{v^m\sqrt{u}} = -\frac{1}{(m - 1)k}\left(\frac{\sqrt{u}}{v^{m-1}} + \left(m - \frac{3}{2}\right)b\right.$

$$\left. \int \frac{dx}{v^{m-1}\sqrt{u}}\right).$$

FORMS CONTAINING $(a + bx^n)$

**63.** $\int \dfrac{dx}{a + bx^2} = \dfrac{1}{\sqrt{ab}} \tan^{-1} \dfrac{x\sqrt{ab}}{a}.$

**64.** $\int \dfrac{dx}{a + bx^2} = \dfrac{1}{2\sqrt{-ab}} \log \dfrac{a + x\sqrt{-ab}}{a - x\sqrt{-ab}},$ or

$$\dfrac{1}{\sqrt{-ab}} \tanh^{-1} \dfrac{x\sqrt{-ab}}{a}.$$

**65.** $\int \dfrac{xdx}{a + bx^2} = \dfrac{1}{2b} \log \left( x^2 + \dfrac{a}{b} \right).$

**66.** $\int \dfrac{x^2\,dx}{a + bx^2} = \dfrac{x}{b} - \dfrac{a}{b} \int \dfrac{dx}{a + bx^2}.$

**67.** $\int \dfrac{dx}{(a + bx^2)^2} = \dfrac{x}{2a(a + bx^2)} + \dfrac{1}{2a} \int \dfrac{dx}{a + bx^2}.$

**68.** $\int \dfrac{dx}{(a + bx^2)^{m+1}} = \dfrac{1}{2ma} \dfrac{x}{(a + bx^2)^m} + \dfrac{2m - 1}{2\,ma}$
$$\int \dfrac{dx}{(a + bx^2)^m}.$$

**69.** $\int \dfrac{xdx}{(a + bx^2)^{m+1}} = \dfrac{1}{2} \int \dfrac{dz}{(a + bz)^{m+1}},$ $\qquad [z = x^2].$

**70.** $\int \dfrac{x^2dx}{(a + bx^2)^{m+1}} = \dfrac{-x}{2\,mb(a + bx^2)^m} + \dfrac{1}{2\,mb} \int \dfrac{dx}{(a + bx^2)^m}.$

**71.** $\int \dfrac{dx}{x(a + bx^2)} = \dfrac{1}{2a} \log \dfrac{x^2}{a + bx^2}.$

**72.** $\int \dfrac{dx}{x^2(a + bx^2)} = -\dfrac{1}{ax} - \dfrac{b}{a} \int \dfrac{dx}{a + bx^2}.$

**73.** $\int \dfrac{dx}{x(a + bx^2)^{m+1}} = \dfrac{1}{2am(a + bx^2)^m} + \dfrac{1}{a} \int \dfrac{dx}{x(a + bx^2)^m}$
$$m \neq 0.$$

**74.** $\int \dfrac{dx}{x^2(a + bx^2)^{m+1}} = \dfrac{1}{a} \int \dfrac{dx}{x^2(a + bx^2)^m} - \dfrac{b}{a}$
$$\int \dfrac{dx}{(a + bx^2)^{m+1}}.$$

**75.** $\int \dfrac{dx}{a + bx^3} = \dfrac{k}{3a} \left[ \dfrac{1}{2} \log \dfrac{(k + x)^2}{k^2 - kx + x^2} + \sqrt{3} \tan^{-1} \right.$
$$\left. \dfrac{2x - k}{k\sqrt{3}} \right], \ [bk^3 = a].$$

**76.** $\int \dfrac{xdx}{a + bx^3} = \dfrac{1}{3bk} \left[ \dfrac{1}{2} \log \dfrac{k^2 - kx + x^2}{(k + x)^2} + \sqrt{3} \tan^{-1} \right.$
$$\left. \dfrac{2x - k}{k\sqrt{3}} \right], \ [bk^3 = a].$$

**77.** $\int \dfrac{dx}{x(a + bx^n)} = \dfrac{1}{an} \log \dfrac{x^n}{a + bx^n}.$

**78.** $\int \dfrac{dx}{(a + bx^n)^{m+1}} = \dfrac{1}{a} \int \dfrac{dx}{(a + bx^n)^m} - \dfrac{b}{a} \int \dfrac{x^n dx}{(a + bx^n)^{m+1}}.$

**79.** $\int \dfrac{x^m dx}{(a + bx^n)^{p+1}} = \dfrac{1}{b} \int \dfrac{x^{m-n}dx}{(a + bx^n)^p} - \dfrac{a}{b} \int \dfrac{x^{m-n}dx}{(a + bx^n)^{p+1}}.$

**80.** $\int \dfrac{dx}{x^m(a + bx^n)^{p+1}} = \dfrac{1}{a} \int \dfrac{dx}{x^m(a + bx^n)^p} - \dfrac{b}{a}$
$$\int \dfrac{dx}{x^{m-n}(a + bx^n)^{p+1}}.$$

**81.** $\int x^m(a + bx^n)^p dx = \dfrac{x^{m-n+1}(a + bx^n)^{p+1}}{b(np + m + 1)} -$
$$\dfrac{a(m - n + 1)}{b(np + m + 1)} \int x^{m-n}(a + bx^n)^p \, dx.$$

**82.** $\int x^m(a + bx^n)^p \, dx = \dfrac{x^{m+1}(a + bx^n)^p}{np + m + 1} +$
$$\dfrac{anp}{np + m + 1} \int x^m(a + bx^n)^{p-1} \, dx.$$

**83.** $\int x^{m-1}(a + bx^n)^p \, dx = \dfrac{1}{b(m + np)} \Big[ x^{m-n}(a + bx^n)^{p+1} -$
$$(m - n) \, a \int x^{m-n-1}(a + bx^n)^p \, dx \Big].$$

**84.** $\int x^{m-1}(a + bx^n)^p \, dx = \dfrac{1}{m + np} \Big[ x^m(a + bx^n)^p +$
$$npa \int x^{m-1}(a + bx^n)^{p-1} \, dx \Big].$$

**85.** $\int x^{m-1}(a + bx^n)^p \, dx = \dfrac{1}{ma} \Big[ x^m(a + bx^n)^{p+1} - (m +$
$$np + n)b \int x^{m+n-1}(a + bx^n)^p \, dx \Big].$$

**86.** $\int x^{m-1}(a + bx^n)^p \, dx = \dfrac{1}{an(p + 1)} \Big[ - x^m(a + bx^n)^{p+1} +$
$$(m + np + n) \int x^{m-1}(a + bx^n)^{p+1} \, dx \Big].$$

FORMS CONTAINING $(a + bx + cx^2)$
$X = a + bx + cx^2$ and $q = 4ac - b^2$

**87.** $\int \dfrac{dx}{X} = \dfrac{2}{\sqrt{q}} \tan^{-1} \dfrac{2 cx + b}{\sqrt{q}}.$

**88.** $\int \dfrac{dx}{X} = \dfrac{-2}{\sqrt{-q}} \tanh^{-1} \dfrac{2 cx + b}{\sqrt{-q}}.$

**89.** $\int \dfrac{dx}{X} = \dfrac{1}{\sqrt{-q}} \log \dfrac{2\,cx + b - \sqrt{-q}}{2\,cx + b + \sqrt{-q}}.$

**90.** $\int \dfrac{dx}{X^2} = \dfrac{2\,cx + b}{qX} + \dfrac{2c}{q} \int \dfrac{dx}{X}.$

**91.** $\int \dfrac{dx}{X^3} = \dfrac{2\,cx + b}{q} \left( \dfrac{1}{2\,X^2} + \dfrac{3c}{qX} \right) + \dfrac{6c^2}{q^2} \int \dfrac{dx}{X}.$

**92.** $\int \dfrac{dx}{X^{n+1}} = \dfrac{2\,cx + b}{nqX^n} + \dfrac{2\,(2n-1)\,c}{qn} \int \dfrac{dx}{X^n}.$

**93.** $\int \dfrac{x\,dx}{X} = \dfrac{1}{2c} \log X - \dfrac{b}{2c} \int \dfrac{dx}{X}.$

**94.** $\int \dfrac{x\,dx}{X^2} = - \dfrac{bx + 2a}{qX} - \dfrac{b}{q} \int \dfrac{dx}{X}.$

**95.** $\int \dfrac{x\,dx}{X^{n+1}} = - \dfrac{2\,a + bx}{nqX^n} - \dfrac{b\,(2n-1)}{nq} \int \dfrac{dx}{X^n}.$

**96.** $\int \dfrac{x^2}{X} dx = \dfrac{x}{c} - \dfrac{b}{2\,c^2} \log X + \dfrac{b^2 - 2\,ac}{2\,c^2} \int \dfrac{dx}{X}.$

**97.** $\int \dfrac{x^2}{X^2} dx = \dfrac{(b^2 - 2\,ac)x + ab}{cqX} + \dfrac{2\,a}{q} \int \dfrac{dx}{X}.$

**98.** $\int \dfrac{x^m\,dx}{X^{n+1}} = - \dfrac{x^{m-1}}{(2n-m+1)cX^n} - \dfrac{n-m+1}{2n-m+1} \cdot \dfrac{b}{c}$
$$\int \dfrac{x^{m-1}\,dx}{X^{n+1}} + \dfrac{m-1}{2n-m+1} \cdot \dfrac{a}{c} \int \dfrac{x^{m-2}\,dx}{X^{n+1}}.$$

**99.** $\int \dfrac{dx}{xX} = \dfrac{1}{2a} \log \dfrac{x^2}{X} - \dfrac{b}{2\,a} \int \dfrac{dx}{X}.$

**100.** $\int \dfrac{dx}{x^2X} = \dfrac{b}{2\,a^2} \log \dfrac{X}{x^2} - \dfrac{1}{ax} + \left( \dfrac{b^2}{2\,a^2} - \dfrac{c}{a} \right) \int \dfrac{dx}{X}.$

**101.** $\int \dfrac{dx}{xX^n} = \dfrac{1}{2a(n-1)X^{n-1}} - \dfrac{b}{2a} \int \dfrac{dx}{X^n} + \dfrac{1}{a} \int \dfrac{dx}{xX^{n-1}}.$

**102.** $\int \dfrac{dx}{x^mX^{n+1}} = - \dfrac{1}{(m-1)ax^{m-1}X^n} - \dfrac{n+m-1}{m-1} \cdot \dfrac{b}{a}$
$$\int \dfrac{dx}{x^{m-1}X^{n+1}} - \dfrac{2n+m-1}{m-1} \cdot \dfrac{c}{a} \int \dfrac{dx}{x^{m-2}X^{n+1}}.$$

### FORMS CONTAINING $\sqrt{a + bx}$

**103.** $\int \sqrt{a + bx}\, dx = \dfrac{2}{3b} \sqrt{(a + bx)^3}.$

**104.** $\int x \sqrt{a + bx}\, dx = - \dfrac{2(2a - 3\,bx) \sqrt{(a + bx)^3}}{15\,b^2}.$

**105.** $\int x^2 \sqrt{a + bx}\, dx$

$$= \frac{2(8\,a^2 - 12\,abx + 15\,b^2x^2)\sqrt{(a+bx)^3}}{105\,b^3}.$$

**106.** $\int x^m \sqrt{a + bx}\, dx = \dfrac{2}{b(2m+3)}\left[ x^m \sqrt{(a+bx)^3} \right.$

$$\left. - ma \int x^{m-1} \sqrt{a+bx}\, dx \right].$$

**107.** $\int \dfrac{\sqrt{a+bx}}{x}\, dx = 2\sqrt{a+bx} + a\int \dfrac{dx}{x\sqrt{a+bx}}.$

(see No. 114 and No. 115).

**108.** $\int \dfrac{\sqrt{a+bx}}{x^2}\, dx = -\dfrac{\sqrt{a+bx}}{x} + \dfrac{b}{2}\int \dfrac{dx}{x\sqrt{a+bx}}.$

(see No. 114 and No. 115).

**109.** $\int \dfrac{\sqrt{a+bx}}{x^m} = -\dfrac{1}{(m-1)a}\left[ \dfrac{\sqrt{(a+bx)^3}}{x^{m-1}} \right.$

$$\left. + \dfrac{(2m-5)b}{2} \int \dfrac{\sqrt{a+bx}\, dx}{x^{m-1}} \right] \qquad m \neq 1.$$

**110.** $\int \dfrac{dx}{\sqrt{a+bx}} = \dfrac{2\sqrt{a+bx}}{b}.$

**111.** $\int \dfrac{x\,dx}{\sqrt{a+bx}} = -\dfrac{2(2a-bx)}{3\,b^2}\sqrt{a+bx}.$

**112.** $\int \dfrac{x^2\,dx}{\sqrt{a+bx}} = \dfrac{2(8\,a^2 - 4\,abx + 3\,b^2x^2)}{15\,b^3}\sqrt{a+bx}.$

**113.** $\int \dfrac{x^m\,dx}{\sqrt{a+bx}} = \dfrac{2x^m\sqrt{a+bx}}{(2m+1)b} - \dfrac{2ma}{(2m+1)b}\int \dfrac{x^{m-1}dx}{\sqrt{a+bx}}.$

**114.** $\int \dfrac{dx}{x\sqrt{a+bx}} = \dfrac{1}{\sqrt{a}}\log\left( \dfrac{\sqrt{a+bx} - \sqrt{a}}{\sqrt{a+bx} + \sqrt{a}} \right), a > 0$ } See #23

**115.** $\int \dfrac{dx}{x\sqrt{a+bx}} = \dfrac{-2}{\sqrt{a}}\tanh^{-1}\sqrt{\dfrac{a+bx}{a}}, \qquad a > 0$ } for $a < 0$

**116.** $\int \dfrac{dx}{x^2\sqrt{a+bx}} = -\dfrac{\sqrt{a+bx}}{ax} - \dfrac{b}{2\,a}\int \dfrac{dx}{x\sqrt{a+bx}}.$

**117.** $\int \dfrac{dx}{x^n\sqrt{a+bx}} = -\dfrac{\sqrt{a+bx}}{(n-1)ax^{n-1}} - \dfrac{(2n-3)b}{(2n-2)a}$

$$\int \dfrac{dx}{x^{n-1}\sqrt{a+bx}}.$$

**118.** $\int (a + bx)^{\pm n/2} dx = \dfrac{2\,(a + bx)^{\frac{2 \pm n}{2}}}{b(2 \pm n)}.$

**119.** $\int x(a + bx)^{\pm n/2} dx = \dfrac{2}{b^2}\left[ \dfrac{(a + bx)^{\frac{4 \pm n}{2}}}{4 \pm n} - \dfrac{a\,(a + bx)^{\frac{2 \pm n}{2}}}{2 \pm n} \right].$

**120.** $\int \dfrac{dx}{x(a + bx)^{m/2}} = \dfrac{1}{a} \int \dfrac{dx}{x(a + bx)^{\frac{m-2}{2}}} - \dfrac{b}{a} \int \dfrac{dx}{(a + bx)^{m/2}}.$

**121.** $\int \dfrac{(a + bx)^{n/2} dx}{x} = b \int (a + bx)^{\frac{n-2}{2}} dx + a$

$$\int \dfrac{(a + bx)^{\frac{n-2}{2}}}{x}\, dx.$$

**122.** $\int f(x,\ \sqrt{a + bx})\, dx = \dfrac{2}{b} \int f\left( \dfrac{z^2 - a}{b},\, z \right) z\,dz$

$$(z^2 = a + bx).$$

### Forms Containing $\sqrt{x^2 \pm a^2}$

**123.** $\int \sqrt{x^2 \pm a^2}\, dx = \tfrac{1}{2}[x\,\sqrt{x^2 \pm a^2}$

$$\pm\, a^2 \log\,(x + \sqrt{x^2 \pm a^2})].$$

**124.** $\int \dfrac{dx}{\sqrt{x^2 \pm a^2}} = \log\,(x + \sqrt{x^2 \pm a^2}).$

**125.** $\int \dfrac{dx}{x\,\sqrt{x^2 - a^2}} = \dfrac{1}{a} \cos^{-1}\left( \dfrac{a}{x} \right),\ \text{or}\ \dfrac{1}{a} \sec^{-1}\left( \dfrac{x}{a} \right).$

**126.** $\int \dfrac{dx}{x\,\sqrt{x^2 + a^2}} = -\dfrac{1}{a} \log\left( \dfrac{a + \sqrt{x^2 + a^2}}{x} \right).$

**127.** $\int \dfrac{\sqrt{x^2 + a^2}}{x}\, dx = \sqrt{x^2 + a^2} - a \log\left( \dfrac{a + \sqrt{x^2 + a^2}}{x} \right).$

**128.** $\int \dfrac{\sqrt{x^2 - a^2}}{x}\, dx = \sqrt{x^2 - a^2} - a \cos^{-1}\dfrac{a}{x}.$

**129.** $\int \dfrac{x\, dx}{\sqrt{x^2 \pm a^2}} = \sqrt{x^2 \pm a^2}.$

**130.** $\int x\,\sqrt{x^2 \pm a^2}\, dx = \tfrac{1}{3}\,\sqrt{(x^2 \pm a^2)^3}.$

**131.** $\int \sqrt{(x^2 \pm a^2)^3}\, dx = \dfrac{1}{4}\left[ x\,\sqrt{(x^2 \pm a^2)^3} \pm \dfrac{3\,a^2 x}{2}\right.$

$$\left. \sqrt{x^2 \pm a^2} + \dfrac{3\,a^4}{2} \log\,(x + \sqrt{x^2 \pm a^2}) \right].$$

**132.** $\displaystyle\int \frac{dx}{\sqrt{(x^2 \pm a^2)^3}} = \frac{\pm x}{a^2 \sqrt{x^2 \pm a^2}}.$

**133.** $\displaystyle\int \frac{x\,dx}{\sqrt{(x^2 \pm a^2)^3}} = \frac{-1}{\sqrt{x^2 \pm a^2}}.$

**134.** $\displaystyle\int x \sqrt{(x^2 \pm a^2)^3}\,dx = \tfrac{1}{5} \sqrt{(x^2 \pm a^2)^5}.$

**135.** $\displaystyle\int x^2 \sqrt{x^2 \pm a^2}\,dx = \frac{x}{4} \sqrt{(x^2 \pm a^2)^3} \mp \frac{a^2}{8} x \sqrt{x^2 \pm a^2} -$
$$\frac{a^4}{8} \log (x + \sqrt{x^2 \pm a^2}).$$

**136.** $\displaystyle\int x^3 \sqrt{x^2 + a^2}\,dx = (\tfrac{1}{5}x^2 - \tfrac{2}{15}a^2) \sqrt{(a^2 + x^2)^3}.$

**137.** $\displaystyle\int x^3 \sqrt{x^2 - a^2}\,dx = \frac{1}{5} \sqrt{(x^2 - a^2)^5} + \frac{a^2}{3} \sqrt{(x^2 - a^2)^3}.$

**138.** $\displaystyle\int \frac{x^2\,dx}{\sqrt{x^2 \pm a^2}} = \frac{x}{2} \sqrt{x^2 \pm a^2} \mp \frac{a^2}{2} \log (x + \sqrt{x^2 \pm a^2}).$

**139.** $\displaystyle\int \frac{x^3\,dx}{\sqrt{x^2 \pm a^2}} = \frac{1}{3} \sqrt{(x^2 \pm a^2)^3} \mp a^2 \sqrt{x^2 \pm a^2}.$

**140.** $\displaystyle\int \frac{dx}{x^2 \sqrt{x^2 \pm a^2}} = \mp \frac{\sqrt{x^2 \pm a^2}}{a^2 x}.$

**141.** $\displaystyle\int \frac{dx}{x^3 \sqrt{x^2 + a^2}} = - \frac{\sqrt{x^2 + a^2}}{2a^2 x^2} + \frac{1}{2a^3} \log \frac{a + \sqrt{x^2 + a^2}}{x}.$

**142.** $\displaystyle\int \frac{dx}{x^3 \sqrt{x^2 - a^2}} = \frac{\sqrt{x^2 - a^2}}{2a^2 x^2} + \frac{1}{2a^3} \arccos \frac{a}{x}.$

**143.** $\displaystyle\int x^2 \sqrt{(x^2 \pm a^2)^3}\,dx = \frac{x}{6} \sqrt{(x^2 \pm a^2)^5}$
$$\mp \frac{a^2 x}{24} \sqrt{(x^2 \pm a^2)^3} - \frac{a^4 x}{16} \sqrt{x^2 \pm a^2}$$
$$\mp \frac{a^6}{16} \log (x + \sqrt{x^2 \pm a^2}).$$

**144.** $\displaystyle\int x^3 \sqrt{(x^2 \pm a^2)^3}\,dx = \frac{1}{7} \sqrt{(x^2 \pm a^2)^7} \mp \frac{a^2}{5} \sqrt{(x^2 \pm a^2)^5}.$

**145.** $\displaystyle\int \frac{\sqrt{x^2 \pm a^2}\,dx}{x^2} = - \frac{\sqrt{x^2 \pm a^2}}{x} + \log (x + \sqrt{x^2 \pm a^2}).$

**146.** $\displaystyle\int \frac{\sqrt{x^2 + a^2}}{x^3}\,dx = - \frac{\sqrt{x^2 + a^2}}{2x^2} - \frac{1}{2a} \log \frac{a + \sqrt{x^2 + a^2}}{x}.$

**147.** $\displaystyle\int \frac{\sqrt{x^2 - a^2}}{x^3}\,dx = - \frac{\sqrt{x^2 - a^2}}{2x^2} + \frac{1}{2a} \arccos \frac{a}{x}.$

**148.** $\int \dfrac{x^2 dx}{\sqrt{(x^2 \pm a^2)^3}} = \dfrac{-x}{\sqrt{x^2 \pm a^2}} + \log(x + \sqrt{x^2 \pm a^2})$.

**149.** $\int \dfrac{x^3 dx}{\sqrt{(x^2 \pm a^2)^3}} = \sqrt{x^2 \pm a^2} \pm \dfrac{a^2}{\sqrt{x^2 \pm a^2}}$.

**150.** $\int \dfrac{dx}{x\sqrt{(x^2 + a^2)^3}} = \dfrac{1}{a^2 \sqrt{x^2 + a^2}} -$

$$\dfrac{1}{a^3} \log \dfrac{a + \sqrt{x^2 + a^2}}{x}.$$

**151.** $\int \dfrac{dx}{x\sqrt{(x^2 - a^2)^3}} = -\dfrac{1}{a^2 \sqrt{x^2 - a^2}} - \dfrac{1}{a^3} \text{arc cos } \dfrac{a}{x}$.

**152.** $\int \dfrac{dx}{x^2 \sqrt{(x^2 \pm a^2)^3}} = -\dfrac{1}{a^4}\left[ \dfrac{\sqrt{x^2 \pm a^2}}{x} + \dfrac{x}{\sqrt{x^2 \pm a^2}} \right]$.

**153.** $\int \dfrac{dx}{x^3 \sqrt{(x^2 + a^2)^3}} = -\dfrac{1}{2a^2 x^2 \sqrt{x^2 + a^2}} - \dfrac{3}{2a^4 \sqrt{x^2 + a^2}}$

$$+ \dfrac{3}{2a^5} \log \dfrac{a + \sqrt{x^2 + a^2}}{x}.$$

**154.** $\int \dfrac{dx}{x^3 \sqrt{(x^2 - a^2)^3}} = \dfrac{1}{2a^2 x^2 \sqrt{x^2 - a^2}} - \dfrac{3}{2a^4 \sqrt{x^2 - a^2}}$

$$- \dfrac{3}{2a^5} \text{arc cos } \dfrac{a}{x}.$$

**155.** $\int f(x, \sqrt{x^2 + a^2})\, dx = a \int f(a \tan u, a \sec u) \sec^2 u\, du$

$$(x = a \tan u).$$

**156.** $\int f(x, \sqrt{x^2 - a^2})\, dx = a \int f(a \sec u, a \tan u)$

$$\sec u \tan u\, du \qquad (x = a \sec u).$$

FORMS CONTAINING $\sqrt{a^2 - x^2}$

**157.** $\int \sqrt{a^2 - x^2}\, dx = \dfrac{1}{2}\left[ x\sqrt{a^2 - x^2} + a^2 \sin^{-1}\left(\dfrac{x}{a}\right) \right]$.

**158.** $\int \dfrac{dx}{\sqrt{a^2 - x^2}} = \sin^{-1}\left(\dfrac{x}{a}\right), \text{ or } -\cos^{-1}\left(\dfrac{x}{a}\right) \Big]$.

**159.** $\dfrac{dx}{x\sqrt{a^2 - x^2}} = -\dfrac{1}{a} \log\left(\dfrac{a + \sqrt{a^2 - x^2}}{x}\right)$.

**160.** $\int \dfrac{\sqrt{a^2 - x^2}}{x}\, dx = \sqrt{a^2 - x^2} - a \log\left(\dfrac{a + \sqrt{a^2 - x^2}}{x}\right)$.

**161.** $\int \dfrac{x\, dx}{\sqrt{a^2 - x^2}} = -\sqrt{a^2 - x^2}$.

**162.** $\int x\sqrt{a^2 - x^2}\, dx = -\dfrac{1}{3}\sqrt{(a^2 - x^2)^3}$.

## INTEGRALS (Continued)

**163.** $\int \sqrt{(a^2 - x^2)^3}\, dx = \dfrac{1}{4}\Big[ x \sqrt{(a^2 - x^2)^3} + \dfrac{3\, a^2 x}{2}$
$$\sqrt{a^2 - x^2} + \dfrac{3\, a^4}{2} \sin^{-1} \dfrac{x}{a}\Big].$$

**164.** $\int \dfrac{dx}{\sqrt{(a^2 - x^2)^3}} = \dfrac{x}{a^2 \sqrt{a^2 - x^2}}.$

**165.** $\int \dfrac{x\, dx}{\sqrt{(a^2 - x^2)^3}} = \dfrac{1}{\sqrt{a^2 - x^2}}.$

**166.** $\int x \sqrt{(a^2 - x^2)^3}\, dx = -\tfrac{1}{5} \sqrt{(a^2 - x^2)^5}.$

**167.** $\int x^2 \sqrt{a^2 - x^2}\, dx = -\dfrac{x}{4} \sqrt{(a^2 - x^2)^3} + \dfrac{a^2}{8}$
$$\Big( x \sqrt{a^2 - x^2} + a^2 \sin^{-1} \dfrac{x}{a}\Big).$$

**168.** $\int x^3 \sqrt{a^2 - x^2}\, dx = (-\tfrac{1}{5}x^2 - \tfrac{2}{15}a^2) \sqrt{(a^2 - x^2)^3}.$

**169.** $\int x^2 \sqrt{(a^2 - x^2)^3}\, dx = -\dfrac{1}{6} x \sqrt{(a^2 - x^2)^5}$
$$+ \dfrac{a^2 x}{24} \sqrt{(a^2 - x^2)^3} + \dfrac{a^4 x}{16} \sqrt{a^2 - x^2} + \dfrac{a^6}{16} \arcsin \dfrac{x}{a}.$$

**170.** $\int x^3 \sqrt{(a^2 - x^2)^3}\, dx = \dfrac{1}{7} \sqrt{(a^2 - x^2)^7} - \dfrac{a^2}{5} \sqrt{(a^2 - x^2)^5}.$

**171.** $\int \dfrac{x^2\, dx}{\sqrt{a^2 - x^2}} = -\dfrac{x}{2} \sqrt{a^2 - x^2} + \dfrac{a^2}{2} \sin^{-1} \dfrac{x}{a}.$

**172.** $\int \dfrac{dx}{x^2 \sqrt{a^2 - x^2}} = -\dfrac{\sqrt{a^2 - x^2}}{a^2 x}.$

**173.** $\int \dfrac{\sqrt{a^2 - x^2}}{x^2}\, dx = -\dfrac{\sqrt{a^2 - x^2}}{x} - \sin^{-1} \dfrac{x}{a}.$

**173a.** $\int \dfrac{\sqrt{a^2 - x^2}}{x^3}\, dx = -\dfrac{\sqrt{a^2 - x^2}}{2x^2} + \dfrac{1}{2a} \log \dfrac{a + \sqrt{a^2 - x^2}}{x}.$

**174.** $\int \dfrac{x^2\, dx}{\sqrt{(a^2 - x^2)^3}} = \dfrac{x}{\sqrt{a^2 - x^2}} - \sin^{-1} \dfrac{x}{a}.$

**175.** $\int \dfrac{x^3 dx}{\sqrt{a^2 - x^2}} = -\dfrac{2}{3} (a^2 - x^2)^{\frac{3}{2}} - x^2(a^2 - x^2)^{\frac{1}{2}}$

**176.** $\int \dfrac{x^3 dx}{\sqrt{(a^2 - x^2)^3}} = 2(a^2 - x^2)^{\frac{1}{2}} + \dfrac{x^2}{(a^2 - x^2)^{\frac{1}{2}}}$

**177.** $\int \dfrac{dx}{x^3 \sqrt{a^2 - x^2}} = -\dfrac{\sqrt{a^2 - x^2}}{2a^2 x^2} - \dfrac{1}{2a^3} \log \dfrac{a + \sqrt{a^2 - x^2}}{x}.$

**177a.** $\int \dfrac{dx}{x \sqrt{(a^2 - x^2)^3}} = \dfrac{1}{a^2 \sqrt{a^2 - x^2}} - \dfrac{1}{a^3} \log \dfrac{a + \sqrt{a^2 - x^2}}{x}$

**178.** $\int \dfrac{dx}{x^2 \sqrt{(a^2-x^2)^3}} = \dfrac{1}{a^4}\left[ -\dfrac{\sqrt{a^2-x^2}}{x} + \dfrac{x}{\sqrt{a^2-x^2}} \right].$

**179.** $\int \dfrac{dx}{x^3 \sqrt{(a^2-x^2)^3}} = -\dfrac{1}{2a^2 x^2 \sqrt{a^2-x^2}} + \dfrac{3}{2a^4 \sqrt{a^2-x^2}}$
$$- \dfrac{3}{2a^5}\log \dfrac{a+\sqrt{a^2+x^2}}{x}.$$

**180.** $\int f(x, \sqrt{a^2-x^2})\, dx = a \int f\,(a\sin u,\, a\cos u)\cos u\, du$
$$(x = a\sin u).$$

FORMS CONTAINING $\sqrt{a+bx+cx^2}$

$$X = a + bx + cx^2,\ q = 4ac - b^2,\ \text{and}\ k = \dfrac{4c}{q}.$$

**181.** $\int \dfrac{dx}{\sqrt{X}} = \dfrac{1}{\sqrt{c}}\log\left(\sqrt{X} + x\sqrt{c} + \dfrac{b}{2\sqrt{c}}\right),\quad$ if $c > 0$.

**182.** $\int \dfrac{dx}{\sqrt{X}} = \dfrac{1}{\sqrt{c}}\sinh^{-1}\left(\dfrac{2cx+b}{\sqrt{4ac-b^2}}\right),\quad$ if $c > 0$.

**183.** $\int \dfrac{dx}{\sqrt{X}} = \dfrac{1}{\sqrt{-c}}\sin^{-1}\left(\dfrac{-2cx-b}{\sqrt{b^2-4ac}}\right),\quad$ if $c < 0$.

**184.** $\int \dfrac{dx}{X\sqrt{X}} = \dfrac{2(2cx+b)}{q\sqrt{X}}.$

**185.** $\int \dfrac{dx}{X^2\sqrt{X}} = \dfrac{2(2cx+b)}{3q\sqrt{X}}\left(\dfrac{1}{X} + 2k\right).$

**186.** $\int \dfrac{dx}{X^n\sqrt{X}} = \dfrac{2(2cx+b)\sqrt{X}}{(2n-1)qX^n} + \dfrac{2k(n-1)}{2n-1}$
$$\int \dfrac{dx}{X^{n-1}\sqrt{X}}.$$

**187.** $\int \sqrt{X}\, dx = \dfrac{(2cx+b)\sqrt{X}}{4c} + \dfrac{1}{2k}\int \dfrac{dx}{\sqrt{X}}.$

**188.** $\int X\sqrt{X}\, dx = \dfrac{(2cx+b)\sqrt{X}}{8c}\left(X + \dfrac{3}{2k}\right)$
$$+ \dfrac{3}{8k^2}\int \dfrac{dx}{\sqrt{X}}.$$

**189.** $\int X^2\sqrt{X}\, dx = \dfrac{(2cx+b)\sqrt{X}}{12c}\left(X^2 + \dfrac{5X}{4k} + \right.$
$$\left. \dfrac{15}{8k^2}\right) + \dfrac{5}{16k^3}\int \dfrac{dx}{\sqrt{X}}.$$

**190.** $\int X^n \sqrt{X}\, dx = \dfrac{(2\,cx + b)\, X^n \sqrt{X}}{4(n+1)c} + \dfrac{2n+1}{2(n+1)\,k} \int \dfrac{X^n dx}{\sqrt{X}}.$

**191.** $\int \dfrac{x\, dx}{\sqrt{X}} = \dfrac{\sqrt{X}}{c} - \dfrac{b}{2\,c} \int \dfrac{dx}{\sqrt{X}}.$

**192.** $\int \dfrac{x\, dx}{X \sqrt{X}} = -\dfrac{2\,(bx + 2a)}{q \sqrt{X}}.$

**193.** $\int \dfrac{x\, dx}{X^n \sqrt{X}} = -\dfrac{\sqrt{X}}{(2n-1)\, cX^n} - \dfrac{b}{2\,c} \int \dfrac{dx}{X^n \sqrt{X}}.$

**194.** $\int \dfrac{x^2\, dx}{\sqrt{X}} = \left( \dfrac{x}{2\,c} - \dfrac{3\,b}{4\,c^2} \right) \sqrt{X} + \dfrac{3\,b^2 - 4\,ac}{8\,c^2} \int \dfrac{dx}{\sqrt{X}}.$

**195.** $\int \dfrac{x^2\, dx}{X \sqrt{X}} = \dfrac{(2\,b^2 - 4\,ac)x + 2\,ab}{cq \sqrt{X}} + \dfrac{1}{c} \int \dfrac{dx}{\sqrt{X}}.$

**196.** $\int \dfrac{x^2\, dx}{X^n \sqrt{X}} = \dfrac{(2\,b^2 - 4\,ac)x + 2\,ab}{(2n-1)\, cq\, X^{n-1} \sqrt{X}} +$
$\qquad\qquad \dfrac{4\,ac + (2\,n - 3)b^2}{(2n-1)\, cq} \int \dfrac{dx}{X^{n-1} \sqrt{X}}.$

**197.** $\int \dfrac{x^3\, dx}{\sqrt{X}} = \left( \dfrac{x^2}{3\,c} - \dfrac{5\,bx}{12\,c^2} + \dfrac{5\,b^2}{8\,c^3} - \dfrac{2\,a}{3\,c^2} \right) \sqrt{X} +$
$\qquad\qquad \left( \dfrac{3}{4}\dfrac{ab}{c^2} - \dfrac{5\,b^3}{16\,c^3} \right) \int \dfrac{dx}{\sqrt{X}}.$

**198.** $\int x \sqrt{X}\, dx = \dfrac{X \sqrt{X}}{3\,c} - \dfrac{b}{2\,c} \int \sqrt{X}\, dx.$

**199.** $\int x\, X \sqrt{X}\, dx = \dfrac{X^2 \sqrt{X}}{5\,c} - \dfrac{b}{2\,c} \int X \sqrt{X}\, dx.$

**200.** $\int \dfrac{x\, X^n\, dx}{\sqrt{X}} = \dfrac{X^n \sqrt{X}}{(2n+1)c} - \dfrac{b}{2\,c} \int \dfrac{X^n dx}{\sqrt{X}}.$

**201.** $\int x^2 \sqrt{X}\, dx = \left( x - \dfrac{5\,b}{6\,c} \right) \dfrac{X \sqrt{X}}{4\,c} + \dfrac{5\,b^2 - 4\,ac}{16\,c^2} \int \sqrt{X}\, dx.$

**202.** $\int \dfrac{dx}{x \sqrt{X}} = -\dfrac{1}{\sqrt{a}} \log \left( \dfrac{\sqrt{X} + \sqrt{a}}{x} + \dfrac{b}{2 \sqrt{a}} \right),$
$\qquad\qquad\qquad\qquad\qquad$ if $a > 0.$

**203.** $\int \dfrac{dx}{x \sqrt{X}} = \dfrac{1}{\sqrt{-a}} \sin^{-1} \left( \dfrac{bx + 2\,a}{x \sqrt{b^2 - 4\,ac}} \right),$ $\qquad$ if $a < 0.$

## INTEGRALS (Continued)

**204.** $\int \dfrac{dx}{x\sqrt{X}} = -\dfrac{2\sqrt{X}}{bx},$          if $a = 0.$

**205.** $\int \dfrac{dx}{x^2\sqrt{X}} = -\dfrac{\sqrt{X}}{ax} - \dfrac{b}{2a} \int \dfrac{dx}{x\sqrt{X}}.$

**206.** $\int \dfrac{\sqrt{X}\,dx}{x} = \sqrt{X} + \dfrac{b}{2} \int \dfrac{dx}{\sqrt{X}} + a \int \dfrac{dx}{x\sqrt{X}}.$

**207.** $\int \dfrac{\sqrt{X}\,dx}{x^2} = -\dfrac{\sqrt{X}}{x} + \dfrac{b}{2} \int \dfrac{dx}{x\sqrt{X}} + c \int \dfrac{dx}{\sqrt{X}}.$

FORMS INVOLVING $\sqrt{2ax - x^2}$

**208.** $\int \sqrt{2ax - x^2}\,dx = \frac{1}{2}[(x - a)\sqrt{2ax - x^2} + a^2 \sin^{-1}(x - a)/a].$

**209.** $\int \dfrac{dx}{\sqrt{2ax - x^2}} = \cos^{-1}\left(\dfrac{a - x}{a}\right) = 2\sin^{-1}\dfrac{\sqrt{x}}{2a}.$

**210.** $\int x^n \sqrt{2ax - x^2}\,dx = -\dfrac{x^{n-1}(2ax - x^2)^{\frac{3}{2}}}{n + 2}$

$\qquad\qquad + \dfrac{(2n + 1)a}{n + 2} \int x^{n-1}\sqrt{2ax - x^2}\,dx \quad n \neq -2.$

**211.** $\int \dfrac{\sqrt{2ax - x^2}}{x^n}\,dx = \dfrac{(2ax - x^2)^{\frac{3}{2}}}{(3 - 2n)ax^n}$

$\qquad\qquad + \dfrac{n - 3}{(2n - 3)a} \int \dfrac{\sqrt{2ax - x^2}}{x^{n-1}}\,dx \quad n \neq \dfrac{3}{2}.$

**212.** $\int \dfrac{x^n dx}{\sqrt{2ax - x^2}} = \dfrac{-x^{n-1}\sqrt{2ax - x^2}}{n}$

$\qquad\qquad + \dfrac{a(2n - 1)}{n} \int \dfrac{x^{n-1}}{\sqrt{2ax - x^2}}\,dx \quad n \neq 0.$

**213.** $\int \dfrac{dx}{x^n \sqrt{2ax - x^2}} = \dfrac{\sqrt{2ax - x^2}}{a(1 - 2n)x^n}$

$\qquad\qquad + \dfrac{n - 1}{(2n - 1)a} \int \dfrac{dx}{x^{n-1}\sqrt{2ax - x^2}} \quad n \neq \dfrac{1}{2}.$

**214.** $\int \dfrac{dx}{(2ax - x^2)^{\frac{3}{2}}} = \dfrac{x - a}{a^2\sqrt{2ax - x^2}}.$

**215.** $\int \dfrac{x\,dx}{(2ax - x^2)^{\frac{3}{2}}} = \dfrac{x}{a\sqrt{2ax - x^2}}.$

**216.** $\int \dfrac{dx}{\sqrt{2ax + x^2}} = \log(x + a + \sqrt{2ax + x^2}).$

## INTEGRALS (Continued)

### Miscellaneous Algebraic Forms

**217.** $\displaystyle\int \sqrt{ax^2 + c}\, dx = \frac{x}{2}\sqrt{ax^2 + c} + \frac{c}{2\sqrt{a}}\log\left(x\sqrt{a} + \sqrt{ax^2 + c}\right),\quad [a > 0].$

$\displaystyle\qquad = \frac{x}{2}\sqrt{ax^2 + c} + \frac{c}{2\sqrt{-a}}\sin^{-1}\left(x\sqrt{\frac{-a}{c}}\right),\quad [a < 0].$

**218.** $\displaystyle\int \frac{dx}{\sqrt{a + bx}\cdot\sqrt{a' + b'x}} = \frac{2}{\sqrt{-bb'}}\tan^{-1}\sqrt{\frac{-b'(a + bx)}{b(a' + b'x)}}.$

**219.** $\displaystyle\int \sqrt{\frac{1 + x}{1 - x}}\, dx = \sin^{-1} x - \sqrt{1 - x^2}.$

**220.** $\displaystyle\int \frac{dx}{\sqrt{a \pm 2bx + cx^2}} = \frac{1}{\sqrt{c}}\log\left(\pm b + cx + \sqrt{c}\sqrt{a \pm 2bx + cx^2}\right).$

**221.** $\displaystyle\int \frac{dx}{\sqrt{a \pm 2bx - cx^2}} = \frac{1}{\sqrt{c}}\sin^{-1}\frac{cx \mp b}{\sqrt{b^2 + ac}}.$

**222.** $\displaystyle\int \frac{x\,dx}{\sqrt{a \pm 2bx + cx^2}} = \frac{1}{c}\sqrt{a \pm 2bx + cx^2}$

$\displaystyle\qquad \mp \frac{b}{\sqrt{c^3}}\log\left(\pm b + cx + \sqrt{c}\sqrt{a \pm 2bx + cx^2}\right).$

**223.** $\displaystyle\int \frac{x\,dx}{\sqrt{a \pm 2bx - cx^2}} = -\frac{1}{c}\sqrt{a \pm 2bx - cx^2} \pm$

$\displaystyle\qquad \frac{b}{\sqrt{c^3}}\sin^{-1}\frac{cx \mp b}{\sqrt{b^2 + ac}}.$

### Forms Involving Trigonometric Functions

**224.** $\displaystyle\int \sin x\, dx = -\cos x,\text{ or versin } x.$

**225.** $\displaystyle\int \cos x\, dx = \sin x,\text{ or } -\text{coversin } x.$

**226.** $\displaystyle\int \tan x\, dx = -\log\cos x.$

**227.** $\displaystyle\int \cot x\, dx = \log\sin x.$

**228.** $\displaystyle\int \sec x\, dx = \log(\sec x + \tan x) = \log\tan\left(\frac{\pi}{4} + \frac{x}{2}\right).$

**229.** $\displaystyle\int \csc x\, dx = \log(\csc x - \cot x) = \log\tan\frac{x}{2}.$

**230.** $\displaystyle\int \sin^2 x\, dx = -\tfrac{1}{2}\cos x \sin x + \tfrac{1}{2}x = \tfrac{1}{2}x - \tfrac{1}{4}\sin 2x.$

**231.** $\displaystyle\int \sin^3 x \, dx = -\tfrac{1}{3} \cos x \, (\sin^2 x + 2).$

**232.** $\displaystyle\int \sin^n x \, dx = -\frac{\sin^{n-1} x \cos x}{n} + \frac{n-1}{n} \int \sin^{n-2} x \, dx.$

**233.** $\displaystyle\int \cos^2 x \, dx = \tfrac{1}{2} \sin x \cos x + \tfrac{1}{2} x = \tfrac{1}{2} x + \tfrac{1}{4} \sin 2 x.$

**234.** $\displaystyle\int \cos^3 x \, dx = \tfrac{1}{3} \sin x \, (\cos^2 x + 2).$

**235.** $\displaystyle\int \cos^n x \, dx = \frac{1}{n} \cos^{n-1} x \sin x + \frac{n-1}{n} \int \cos^{n-2} x \, dx.$

**236.** $\displaystyle\int \sin \frac{x}{a} \, dx = - a \cos \frac{x}{a}.$

**237.** $\displaystyle\int \cos \frac{x}{a} \, dx = a \sin \frac{x}{a}.$

**238.** $\displaystyle\int \sin (a + bx) \, dx = - \frac{1}{b} \cos (a + bx).$

**239.** $\displaystyle\int \cos (a + bx) \, dx = \frac{1}{b} \sin (a + bx).$

**240.** $\displaystyle\int \frac{dx}{\sin x} = \int \csc x \, dx = \log (\csc x - \cot x)$
$$= -\frac{1}{2} \log \frac{1 + \cos x}{1 - \cos x} = \log \tan \frac{x}{2}.$$

**241.** $\displaystyle\int \frac{dx}{\cos x} = \int \sec x \, dx = \log (\sec x + \tan x)$
$$= \frac{1}{2} \log \left( \frac{1 + \sin x}{1 - \sin x} \right) = \log \tan \left( \frac{\pi}{4} + \frac{x}{2} \right).$$

**242.** $\displaystyle\int \frac{dx}{\cos^2 x} = \int \sec^2 x \, dx = \tan x.$

**243.** $\displaystyle\int \frac{dx}{\cos^n x} = \frac{1}{n-1} \cdot \frac{\sin x}{\cos^{n-1} x} + \frac{n-2}{n-1} \int \frac{dx}{\cos^{n-2} x}.$

**244.** $\displaystyle\int \frac{dx}{1 \pm \sin x} = \mp \tan \left( \frac{\pi}{4} \mp \frac{x}{2} \right).$

**245.** $\displaystyle\int \frac{dx}{1 + \cos x} = \tan \frac{x}{2}.$

**246.** $\displaystyle\int \frac{dx}{1 - \cos x} = - \cot \frac{x}{2}.$

**247.** $\displaystyle\int \frac{dx}{a + b \sin x} = \frac{2}{\sqrt{a^2 - b^2}} \tan^{-1} \frac{a \tan \frac{1}{2} x + b}{\sqrt{a^2 - b^2}}$
$$= \frac{1}{\sqrt{b^2 - a^2}} \log \frac{a \tan \frac{1}{2} x + b - \sqrt{b^2 - a^2}}{a \tan \frac{1}{2} x + b + \sqrt{b^2 - a^2}}.$$

**248.** $\displaystyle\int \frac{dx}{a + b \cos x} = \frac{2}{\sqrt{a^2 - b^2}} \tan^{-1} \frac{\sqrt{a^2 - b^2} \tan \frac{1}{2} x}{a + b}$

$$= \frac{1}{\sqrt{b^2 - a^2}} \log \left( \frac{\sqrt{b^2 - a^2} \tan \frac{1}{2} x + a + b}{\sqrt{b^2 - a^2} \tan \frac{1}{2} x - a - b} \right).$$

**249.** $\displaystyle\int \frac{dx}{a + b \sin x + c \cos x}$

$$= \begin{cases} \dfrac{1}{\sqrt{b^2 + c^2 - a^2}} \log \dfrac{b - \sqrt{b^2 + c^2 - a^2} + (a - c) \tan \dfrac{x}{2}}{b + \sqrt{b^2 + c^2 - a^2} + (a - c) \tan \dfrac{x}{2}} \\ \qquad\qquad\qquad\qquad\qquad \text{if } a^2 < b^2 + c^2. \\[2em] \dfrac{2}{\sqrt{a^2 - b^2 - c^2}} \tan^{-1} \dfrac{b + (a - c) \tan \dfrac{x}{2}}{\sqrt{a^2 - b^2 - c^2}} \\ \qquad\qquad\qquad\qquad\qquad \text{if } a^2 > b^2 + c^2. \end{cases}$$

**250.** $\displaystyle\int \sqrt{1 - \cos x}\, dx = -2\sqrt{2} \cos \frac{x}{2}.$

**251.** $\displaystyle\int \sqrt{1 + \cos x}\, dx = 2\sqrt{2} \sin \frac{x}{2}.$

**252.** $\displaystyle\int \sin mx \sin nx\, dx = \frac{\sin (m - n) x}{2(m - n)} - \frac{\sin (m + n) x}{2(m + n)},$
$$[m^2 \neq n^2].$$

**253.** $\displaystyle\int x \sin^2 x\, dx = \frac{x^2}{4} - \frac{x \sin 2x}{4} - \frac{\cos 2x}{8}.$

**254.** $\displaystyle\int x^2 \sin^2 x\, dx = \frac{x^3}{6} - \left( \frac{x^2}{4} - \frac{1}{8} \right) \sin 2x - \frac{x \cos 2x}{4}.$

**255.** $\displaystyle\int x \sin^3 x\, dx = \frac{x \cos 3x}{12} - \frac{\sin 3x}{36} - \frac{3}{4} x \cos x + \frac{3}{4} \sin x.$

**256.** $\displaystyle\int \sin^4 x\, dx = \frac{3x}{8} - \frac{\sin 2x}{4} + \frac{\sin 4x}{32}.$

**257.** $\displaystyle\int \cos mx \cos nx\, dx = \frac{\sin (m - n)x}{2(m - n)} + \frac{\sin (m + n)x}{2(m + n)},$
$$[m^2 \neq n^2].$$

**258.** $\displaystyle\int x \cos^2 x\, dx = \frac{x^2}{4} + \frac{x \sin 2x}{4} + \frac{\cos 2x}{8}.$

**259.** $\displaystyle\int x^2 \cos^2 x\, dx = \frac{x^3}{6} + \left( \frac{x^2}{4} - \frac{1}{8} \right) \sin 2x + \frac{x \cos 2x}{4}.$

**260.** $\displaystyle\int x \cos^3 x\, dx = \frac{x \sin 3x}{12} + \frac{\cos 3x}{36} + \frac{3}{4} x \sin x + \frac{3}{4} \cos x.$

**261.** $\int \cos^4 x \, dx = \dfrac{3x}{8} + \dfrac{\sin 2x}{4} + \dfrac{\sin 4x}{32}.$

**262.** $\int \dfrac{\sin x \, dx}{x^m} = -\dfrac{\sin x}{(m-1)\,x^{m-1}} + \dfrac{1}{m-1} \int \dfrac{\cos x \, dx}{x^{m-1}}.$

**263.** $\int \dfrac{\cos x \, dx}{x^m} = -\dfrac{\cos x}{(m-1)x^{m-1}} - \dfrac{1}{m-1} \int \dfrac{\sin x \, dx}{x^{m-1}}.$

**264.** $\int \tan^3 x \, dx = \tfrac{1}{2} \tan^2 x + \log \cos x.$

**265.** $\int \tan^4 x \, dx = \tfrac{1}{3} \tan^3 x - \tan x + x.$

**265a.** $\int \tan^n x \, dx = \dfrac{\tan^{n-1} x}{n-1} - \int \tan^{n-2} x \, dx, \qquad [n \neq 1].$

**266.** $\int \cot^3 x \, dx = -\tfrac{1}{2} \cot^2 x - \log \sin x.$

**267.** $\int \cot^4 x \, dx = -\tfrac{1}{3} \cot^3 x + \cot x + x.$

**268.** $\int \cot^n x \, dx = -\dfrac{\cot^{n-1} x}{n-1} - \int \cot^{n-2} x \, dx, \qquad [n \neq 1].$

**269.** $\int \sin x \cos x \, dx = \tfrac{1}{2} \sin^2 x.$

**270.** $\int \sin mx \cos nx \, dx = -\dfrac{\cos (m-n)x}{2(m-n)} - \dfrac{\cos (m+n)x}{2(m+n)}.$

**271.** $\int \sin^2 x \cos^2 x \, dx = -\tfrac{1}{8}(\tfrac{1}{4} \sin 4x - x).$

**272.** $\int \sin x \cos^m x \, dx = -\dfrac{\cos^{m+1} x}{m+1}.$

**273.** $\int \sin^m x \cos x \, dx = \dfrac{\sin^{m+1} x}{m+1}.$

**274.** $\int \cos^m x \sin^n x \, dx = \dfrac{\cos^{m-1} x \sin^{n+1} x}{m+n} +$
$$\dfrac{m-1}{m+n} \int \cos^{m-2} x \sin^n x \, dx.$$

**275.** $\int \cos^m x \sin^n x \, dx = -\dfrac{\sin^{n-1} x \cos^{m+1} x}{m+n} +$
$$\dfrac{n-1}{m+n} \int \cos^m x \sin^{n-2} x \, dx.$$

**276.** $\int \dfrac{\cos^m x \, dx}{\sin^n x} = -\dfrac{\cos^{m+1} x}{(n-1)\sin^{n-1} x} -$
$$\dfrac{m-n+2}{n-1} \int \dfrac{\cos^m x \, dx}{\sin^{n-2} x},$$

**277.** $\int \dfrac{\cos^m x \, dx}{\sin^n x} = \dfrac{\cos^{m-1} x}{(m-n)\sin^{n-1} x} + \dfrac{m-1}{m-n} \int \dfrac{\cos^{m-2} x \, dx}{\sin^n x}.$

**278.** $\int \dfrac{\sin^m x\, dx}{\cos^n x} = -\int \dfrac{\cos^m \left(\dfrac{\pi}{2} - x\right) d \left(\dfrac{\pi}{2} - x\right)}{\sin^n \left(\dfrac{\pi}{2} - x\right)}.$

**279.** $\int \dfrac{\sin x\, dx}{\cos^2 x} = \dfrac{1}{\cos x} = \sec x.$

**280.** $\int \dfrac{\sin^2 x\, dx}{\cos x} = -\sin x + \log \tan \left(\dfrac{\pi}{4} + \dfrac{x}{2}\right).$

**281.** $\int \dfrac{\cos x\, dx}{\sin^2 x} = \dfrac{-1}{\sin x} = -\operatorname{cosec} x.$

**282.** $\int \dfrac{dx}{\sin x \cos x} = \log \tan x.$

**283.** $\int \dfrac{dx}{\sin x \cos^2 x} = \dfrac{1}{\cos x} + \log \tan \dfrac{x}{2}.$

**284.** $\int \dfrac{dx}{\sin x \cos^n x} = \dfrac{1}{(n-1)\cos^{n-1} x} + \int \dfrac{dx}{\sin x \cos^{n-2} x},$
$$[n \neq 1].$$

**285.** $\int \dfrac{dx}{\sin^2 x \cos x} = -\dfrac{1}{\sin x} + \log \tan \left(\dfrac{\pi}{4} + \dfrac{x}{2}\right).$

**286.** $\int \dfrac{dx}{\sin^2 x \cos^2 x} = -2 \cot 2x.$

**287.** $\int \dfrac{dx}{\sin^m x \cos^n x} = -\dfrac{1}{m-1} \cdot \dfrac{1}{\sin^{m-1} x \cdot \cos^{n-1} x} +$
$$\dfrac{m+n-2}{m-1} \int \dfrac{dx}{\sin^{m-2} x \cdot \cos^n x}.$$

**288.** $\int \dfrac{dx}{\sin^m x} = -\dfrac{1}{m-1} \cdot \dfrac{\cos x}{\sin^{m-1} x} + \dfrac{m-2}{m-1} \int \dfrac{dx}{\sin^{m-2} x}.$

**289.** $\int \dfrac{dx}{\sin^2 x} = -\cot x.$

---

**290.** $\int \tan^2 x\, dx = \tan x - x.$

**291.** $\int \tan^n x\, dx = \dfrac{\tan^{n-1} x}{n-1} - \int \tan^{n-2} x\, dx.$

**292.** $\int \cot^2 x\, dx = -\cot x - x.$

**293.** $\int \cot^n x\, dx = -\dfrac{\cot^{n-1} x}{n-1} - \int \cot^{n-2} x\, dx.$

**294.** $\int \sec^2 x\, dx = \tan x.$

**295.** $\displaystyle\int \sec^n x \, dx = \int \frac{dx}{\cos^n x} = \frac{1}{n-1} \frac{\sin x}{\cos^{n-1} x}$
$$+ \frac{n-2}{n-1} \int \frac{dx}{\cos^{n-2} x}.$$

**296.** $\displaystyle\int \csc^2 x \, dx = -\cot x.$

**297.** $\displaystyle\int \csc^n x \, dx = \int \frac{dx}{\sin^n x} = -\frac{1}{n-1} \frac{\cos x}{\sin^{n-1} x}$
$$+ \frac{n-2}{n-1} \int \frac{dx}{\sin^{n-2} x}.$$

---

**298.** $\displaystyle\int x \sin x \, dx = \sin x - x \cos x.$

**299.** $\displaystyle\int x^2 \sin x \, dx = 2\,x \sin x - (x^2 - 2) \cos x.$

**300.** $\displaystyle\int x^3 \sin x \, dx = (3\,x^2 - 6) \sin x - (x^3 - 6\,x) \cos x.$

**301.** $\displaystyle\int x^m \sin x \, dx = -x^m \cos x + m \int x^{m-1} \cos x \, dx.$

**302.** $\displaystyle\int x \cos x \, dx = \cos x + x \sin x.$

**303.** $\displaystyle\int x^2 \cos x \, dx = 2\,x \cos x + (x^2 - 2) \sin x.$

**304.** $\displaystyle\int x^3 \cos x \, dx = (3\,x^2 - 6) \cos x + (x^3 - 6\,x) \sin x.$

**305.** $\displaystyle\int x^m \cos x \, dx = x^m \sin x - m \int x^{m-1} \sin x \, dx.$

**306.** $\displaystyle\int \frac{\sin x}{x} \, dx = x - \frac{x^3}{3 \cdot 3!} + \frac{x^5}{5 \cdot 5!} - \frac{x^7}{7 \cdot 7!} + \frac{x^9}{9 \cdot 9!} \cdots$

**307.** $\displaystyle\int \frac{\cos x}{x} \, dx = \log x - \frac{x^2}{2 \cdot 2!} + \frac{x^4}{4 \cdot 4!} - \frac{x^6}{6 \cdot 6!} + \frac{x^8}{8 \cdot 8!} \cdots$

FORMS INVOLVING INVERSE TRIGONOMETRIC FUNCTIONS

**308.** $\displaystyle\int \sin^{-1} x \, dx = x \sin^{-1} x + \sqrt{1 - x^2}.$

**309.** $\displaystyle\int \cos^{-1} x \, dx = x \cos^{-1} x - \sqrt{1 - x^2}.$

**310.** $\displaystyle\int \tan^{-1} x \, dx = x \tan^{-1} x - \tfrac{1}{2} \log (1 + x^2).$

**311.** $\displaystyle\int \cot^{-1} x \, dx = x \cot^{-1} x + \tfrac{1}{2} \log (1 + x^2).$

**312.** $\displaystyle\int \sec^{-1} x \, dx = x \sec^{-1} x - \log (x + \sqrt{x^2 - 1}).$

**313.** $\displaystyle\int \csc^{-1} x \, dx = x \csc^{-1} x + \log (x + \sqrt{x^2 - 1}).$

# INTEGRALS (Continued)

**314.** $\int \text{vers}^{-1} x \, dx = (x - 1) \text{vers}^{-1} x + \sqrt{2x - x^2}.$

**315.** $\int \sin^{-1} \dfrac{x}{a} \, dx = x \sin^{-1} \dfrac{x}{a} + \sqrt{a^2 - x^2}.$

**316.** $\int \cos^{-1} \dfrac{x}{a} \, dx = x \cos^{-1} \dfrac{x}{a} - \sqrt{a^2 - x^2}.$

**317.** $\int \tan^{-1} \dfrac{x}{a} \, dx = x \tan^{-1} \dfrac{x}{a} - \dfrac{a}{2} \log (a^2 + x^2).$

**318.** $\int \cot^{-1} \dfrac{x}{a} \, dx = x \cot^{-1} \dfrac{x}{a} + \dfrac{a}{2} \log (a^2 + x^2).$

**319.** $\int (\sin^{-1} x)^2 \, dx = x (\sin^{-1} x)^2 - 2x + 2 \sqrt{1 - x^2} (\sin^{-1} x).$

**320.** $\int (\cos^{-1} x)^2 \, dx = x (\cos^{-1} x)^2 - 2x - 2 \sqrt{1 - x^2} (\cos^{-1} x).$

**321.** $\int x \cdot \sin^{-1} x \, dx = \tfrac{1}{4}[(2 x^2 - 1) \sin^{-1} x + x \sqrt{1 - x^2}].$

**321a.** $\int x \cos^{-1} x \, dx = \tfrac{1}{4}[(2x^2 - 1) \cos^{-1} x - x \sqrt{1 - x^2}].$

**322.** $\int x^n \sin^{-1} x \, dx = \dfrac{x^{n+1} \sin^{-1} x}{n + 1} - \dfrac{1}{n + 1} \int \dfrac{x^{n+1} \, dx}{\sqrt{1 - x^2}}.$

**323.** $\int x^n \cos^{-1} x \, dx = \dfrac{x^{n+1} \cos^{-1} x}{n + 1} + \dfrac{1}{n + 1} \int \dfrac{x^{n+1} \, dx}{\sqrt{1 - x^2}}.$

**324.** $\int x^n \tan^{-1} x \, dx = \dfrac{x^{n+1} \tan^{-1} x}{n + 1} - \dfrac{1}{n + 1} \int \dfrac{x^{n+1} \, dx}{1 + x^2}.$

**325.** $\int \dfrac{\sin^{-1} x \, dx}{x^2} = \log \left( \dfrac{1 - \sqrt{1 - x^2}}{x} \right) - \dfrac{\sin^{-1} x}{x}.$

**326.** $\int \dfrac{\tan^{-1} x \, dx}{x^2} = \log x - \dfrac{1}{2} \log (1 + x^2) - \dfrac{\tan^{-1} x}{x}.$

## Forms Involving Trigonometric Substitutions

**327.** $\int f(\sin x) \, dx = 2 \int f\left(\dfrac{2z}{1 + z^2}\right) \cdot \dfrac{dz}{1 + z^2}; \left(z = \tan \dfrac{x}{2}\right).$

**328.** $\int f(\cos x) \, dx = 2 \int f\left(\dfrac{1 - z^2}{1 + z^2}\right) \dfrac{dz}{1 + z^2}; \left(z = \tan \dfrac{x}{2}\right).$

**329.** $\int f(\sin x) \, dx = \int f(u) \dfrac{du}{\sqrt{1 - u^2}}; (u = \sin x).$

**330.** $\int f(\cos x) \, dx = - \int f(u) \dfrac{du}{\sqrt{1 - u^2}}; (u = \cos x).$

**331.** $\int f(\sin x, \cos x) \, dx = \int f(u, \sqrt{1 - u^2}) \dfrac{du}{\sqrt{1 - u^2}};$
$(u = \sin x).$

**332.** $\int f(\sin x, \cos x)\, dx = 2 \int f\left(\dfrac{2z}{1+z^2}, \dfrac{1-z^2}{1+z^2}\right) \dfrac{dz}{1+z^2};$
$$\left(z = \tan \frac{x}{2}\right).$$

**333.** $\int \dfrac{dx}{a+b\tan x} = \dfrac{1}{a^2+b^2}\,[ax + b\log(a\cos x + b\sin x)].$

**334.** $\int \dfrac{dx}{a+b\cot x} = \dfrac{1}{a^2+b^2}\,[ax - b\log(a\sin x + b\cos x)].$

### Logarithmic Forms

**335.** $\int \log x\, dx = x\log x - x.$

**336.** $\int x\log x\, dx = \dfrac{x^2}{2}\log x - \dfrac{x^2}{4}.$

**337.** $\int x^2\log x\, dx = \dfrac{x^3}{3}\log x - \dfrac{x^3}{9}.$

**338.** $\int x^p\log(ax)\, dx = \dfrac{x^{p+1}}{p+1}\log(ax) - \dfrac{x^{p+1}}{(p+1)^2}\quad [p \neq -1].$

**339.** $\int (\log x)^2\, dx = x\,(\log x)^2 - 2x\log x + 2x.$

**340.** $\int (\log x)^n\, dx = x\,(\log x)^n - n\int (\log x)^{n-1}\, dx\quad [n \neq -1].$

**341.** $\int \dfrac{(\log x)^n}{x}\, dx = \dfrac{1}{n+1}\,(\log x)^{n+1}.$

**342.** $\int \dfrac{dx}{\log x} = \log(\log x) + \log x + \dfrac{(\log x)^2}{2\cdot 2!} + \dfrac{(\log x)^3}{3\cdot 3!} + \cdots$

**343.** $\int \dfrac{dx}{x\log x} = \log(\log x).$

**344.** $\int \dfrac{dx}{x\,(\log x)^n} = -\dfrac{1}{(n-1)\,(\log x)^{n-1}}.$

**345.** $\int \dfrac{x^m\, dx}{(\log x)^n} = -\dfrac{x^{m+1}}{(n-1)\,(\log x)^{n-1}} + \dfrac{m+1}{n-1}\int \dfrac{x^m\, dx}{(\log x)^{n-1}}.$

**346.** $\int x^m\log x\, dx = x^{m+1}\left[\dfrac{\log x}{m+1} - \dfrac{1}{(m+1)^2}\right].$

**347.** $\int x^m\,(\log x)^n\, dx = \dfrac{x^{m+1}\,(\log x)^n}{m+1} - \dfrac{n}{m+1}\int x^m\,(\log x)^{n-1}\, dx,\; [m, n \neq -1].$

**348.** $\int \sin \log x \, dx = \frac{1}{2}x \sin \log x - \frac{1}{2}x \cos \log x.$

**349.** $\int \cos \log x \, dx = \frac{1}{2}x \sin \log x + \frac{1}{2}x \cos \log x.$

### Exponential Forms

**350.** $\int e^x \, dx = e^x.$

**351.** $\int e^{-x} \, dx = -e^{-x}.$

**352.** $\int e^{ax} \, dx = \dfrac{e^{ax}}{a}.$

**353.** $\int x \, e^{ax} \, dx = \dfrac{e^{ax}}{a^2}(ax - 1).$

**354.** $\int x^m \, e^{ax} \, dx = \dfrac{x^m \, e^{ax}}{a} - \dfrac{m}{a} \int x^{m-1} \, e^{ax} \, dx.$

**355.** $\int \dfrac{e^{ax} \, dx}{x} = \log x + \dfrac{ax}{1!} + \dfrac{a^2x^2}{2 \cdot 2!} + \dfrac{a^3x^3}{3 \cdot 3!} + \cdots$

**356.** $\int \dfrac{e^{ax}}{x^m} \, dx = -\dfrac{1}{m-1} \dfrac{e^{ax}}{x^{m-1}} + \dfrac{a}{m-1} \int \dfrac{e^{ax}}{x^{m-1}} \, dx.$

**357.** $\int e^{ax} \log x \, dx = \dfrac{e^{ax} \log x}{a} - \dfrac{1}{a} \int \dfrac{e^{ax}}{x} \, dx.$

**358.** $\int e^{ax} \cdot \sin px \, dx = \dfrac{e^{ax}(a \sin px - p \cos px)}{a^2 + p^2}.$

**359.** $\int e^{ax} \cdot \cos px \, dx = \dfrac{e^{ax}(a \cos px + p \sin px)}{a^2 + p^2}.$

**360.** $\int \dfrac{dx}{1 + e^x} = x - \log(1 + e^x) = \log \dfrac{e^x}{1 + e^x}.$

**361.** $\int \dfrac{dx}{a + be^{px}} = \dfrac{x}{a} - \dfrac{1}{ap} \log(a + be^{px}).$

**362.** $\int \dfrac{dx}{ae^{mx} + be^{-mx}} = \dfrac{1}{m \sqrt{ab}} \tan^{-1}\left(e^{mx} \sqrt{\dfrac{a}{b}}\right).$

**363.** $\int e^{ax} \sin^n bx \, dx = \dfrac{1}{a^2 + n^2b^2}\Big((a \sin bx - nb \cos bx)$
$e^{ax} \sin^{n-1} bx + n(n-1)b^2 \int e^{ax} \sin^{n-2} bx \cdot dx\Big).$

**364.** $\int e^{ax} \cos^n bx \, dx = \dfrac{1}{a^2 + n^2b^2}\Big((a \cos bx + nb \sin bx)$
$e^{ax} \cos^{n-1} bx + n(n-1)b^2 \int e^{ax} \cos^{n-2} bx \, dx\Big).$

### Hyperbolic Forms

**365.** $\int \sinh x \, dx = \cosh x.$

**366.** $\int \cosh x \, dx = \sinh x.$

**367.** $\int \tanh x \, dx = \log \cosh x.$

**368.** $\int \coth x \, dx = \log \sinh x.$

**369.** $\int \operatorname{sech} x \, dx = 2 \tan^{-1}(e^x) = \tan^{-1}(\sinh x).$

**370.** $\int \operatorname{csch} x \, dx = \log \tanh \left(\dfrac{x}{2}\right).$

**371.** $\int x \sinh x \, dx = x \cosh x - \sinh x.$

**372.** $\int x \cosh x \, dx = x \sinh x - \cosh x.$

**373.** $\int \operatorname{sech} x \tanh x \, dx = -\operatorname{sech} x.$

**374.** $\int \operatorname{csch} x \coth x \, dx = -\operatorname{csch} x.$

**375.** $\int \sinh^2 x \, dx = \dfrac{\sinh 2x}{4} - \dfrac{x}{2}.$

**376.** $\int \tanh^2 x \, dx = x - \tanh x.$

**377.** $\int \operatorname{sech}^2 x \, dx = \tanh x.$

**378.** $\int \cosh^2 x \, dx = \dfrac{\sinh 2x}{4} + \dfrac{x}{2}.$

**379.** $\int \operatorname{ctnh}^2 x \, dx = x - \operatorname{ctnh} x.$

**380.** $\int \operatorname{csch}^2 x \, dx = -\operatorname{ctnh} x.$

**381.** $\int \sinh mx \sinh nx \, dx = \dfrac{\sinh (m+n)x}{2(m+n)}$
$$- \dfrac{\sinh (m-n)x}{2(m-n)} \qquad m^2 \neq n^2.$$

**382.** $\int \cosh mx \cosh nx \, dx = \dfrac{\sinh (m+n)x}{2(m+n)}$
$$+ \dfrac{\sinh (m-n)x}{2(m-n)} \qquad m^2 \neq n^2.$$

**383.** $\int \sinh mx \cosh mx\, dx = \dfrac{\cosh (m + n)x}{2(m + n)}$
$$+ \dfrac{\cosh (m - n)x}{2(m - n)} \qquad m^2 \neq n^2.$$

**384.** $\int \text{arc sinh}\, \dfrac{x}{a}\, dx = x\, \text{arc sinh}\, \dfrac{x}{a} - \sqrt{x^2 + a^2}.$

**385.** $\int x\, \text{arc sinh}\, \dfrac{x}{a}\, dx = \left(\dfrac{x^2}{2} + \dfrac{a^2}{4}\right) \text{arc sinh}\, \dfrac{x}{a} - \dfrac{x}{4} \sqrt{x^2 + a^2}.$

**386.** $\int \text{arc cosh}\, \dfrac{x}{a}\, dx = x\, \text{arc cosh}\, \dfrac{x}{a} - \sqrt{x^2 - a^2},$
$$\left[\text{arc cosh}\, \dfrac{x}{a} > 0\right].$$
$$= x\, \text{arc cosh}\, \dfrac{x}{a} + \sqrt{x^2 - a^2}, \left[\text{arc cosh}\, \dfrac{x}{a} < 0\right].$$

**387.** $\int \text{arc tanh}\, \dfrac{x}{a}\, dx = x\, \text{arc tanh}\, \dfrac{x}{a} + \dfrac{a}{2} \log (a^2 - x^2).$

**388.** $\int x\, \text{arc tanh}\, \dfrac{x}{a}\, dx = \dfrac{x^2 - a^2}{2}\, \text{arc tanh}\, \dfrac{x}{a} + \dfrac{ax}{2}.$

## DEFINITE INTEGRALS

**389.** $\displaystyle\int_0^\infty x^{n-1} e^{-x}\, dx = \int_0^1 \left(\log \dfrac{1}{x}\right)^{n-1} dx = \Gamma(n).$
(Gamma function).

**390.** $\Gamma(n)$ is finite if $n > 0$, $\Gamma(n + 1) = n\Gamma(n).$

**391.** $\Gamma(n) \cdot \Gamma(1 - n) = \dfrac{\pi}{\sin n\pi}.$

**392.** $\Gamma(n) = (n - 1)!$ if $n = $ integer $> 0.$

**393.** $\Gamma\left(\tfrac{1}{2}\right) = \sqrt{\pi}.$

**394.** $\Gamma\left(n + \dfrac{1}{2}\right) = \dfrac{1 \cdot 3 \cdot 5 \cdot 7 \cdots (2n - 1)}{2^n} \sqrt{\pi},$ where $n$ is an integer and $> 0.$

(See values of $\Gamma(n)$ at end of integral table)

**395.** $\displaystyle\int_0^1 x^{m-1}(1 - x)^{n-1}\, dx = \mathrm{B}(m,n).$ (Beta function).

**396.** $\mathrm{B}(m,n) = \mathrm{B}(n,m) = \dfrac{\Gamma(m)\Gamma(n)}{\Gamma(m + n)},$ where $m$ and $n$ are any positive real numbers.

**397.** $\displaystyle\int_0^1 x^{m-1} (1 - x)^{n-1}\, dx = \int_0^\infty \dfrac{x^{m-1}\, dx}{(1 + x)^{m+n}} = \dfrac{\Gamma(m)\, \Gamma(n)}{\Gamma(m + n)}.$

**398.** $\displaystyle\int_1^\infty \dfrac{dx}{x^m} = \dfrac{1}{m - 1},$ $\qquad\qquad [m > 1].$

**399.** $\displaystyle\int_0^\infty \frac{dx}{(1+x)x^p} = \pi \csc p\pi,$ $\qquad\qquad [p < 1].$

**400.** $\displaystyle\int_0^\infty \frac{dx}{(1-x)x^p} = -\pi \cot p\pi,$ $\qquad\qquad [p < 1].$

**401.** $\displaystyle\int_0^\infty \frac{x^{p-1}\,dx}{1+x} = \frac{\pi}{\sin p\pi},$ $\qquad\qquad [0 < p < 1].$

**402.** $\displaystyle\int_0^\infty \frac{x^{m-1}\,dx}{1+x^n} = \frac{\pi}{n \sin \dfrac{m\pi}{n}},$ $\qquad\qquad [0 < m < n].$

**403.** $\displaystyle\int_0^\infty \frac{dx}{(1+x)\sqrt{x}} = \pi.$

**404.** $\displaystyle\int_0^\infty \frac{a\,dx}{a^2+x^2} = \frac{\pi}{2},$ if $a > 0$; $0$, if $a = 0$; $-\dfrac{\pi}{2}$, if $a < 0$.

**405.** $\displaystyle\int_0^{\pi/2} \sin^n x\,dx = \int_0^{\pi/2} \cos^n x\,dx$

$\qquad\quad = \dfrac{1 \cdot 3 \cdot 5 \,\cdots\, (n-1)}{2 \cdot 4 \cdot 6 \,\cdots\, (n)} \cdot \dfrac{\pi}{2},$ $\quad$ [$n$ an even integer],

$\qquad\quad = \dfrac{2 \cdot 4 \cdot 6 \,\cdots\, (n-1)}{1 \cdot 3 \cdot 5 \cdot 7 \,\cdots\, n},$ $\qquad$ [$n$ an odd integer],

$\qquad\quad = \dfrac{1}{2}\sqrt{\pi}\, \dfrac{\Gamma\left(\dfrac{n+1}{2}\right)}{\Gamma\left(\dfrac{n}{2}+1\right)},$ $\qquad\qquad$ [$n > -1$].

**406.** $\displaystyle\int_0^\infty \frac{\sin mx\,dx}{x} = \frac{\pi}{2},$ if $m > 0$; $0$, if $m = 0$; $-\dfrac{\pi}{2}$, if $m < 0$.

**407.** $\displaystyle\int_0^\infty \frac{\cos x\,dx}{x} = \infty \cdot$

**408.** $\displaystyle\int_0^\infty \frac{\tan x\,dx}{x} = \frac{\pi}{2}.$

**409.** $\displaystyle\int_0^\pi \sin kx \cdot \sin mx\,dx = \int_0^\pi \cos kx \cdot \cos mx\,dx = 0,$

$\qquad\qquad\qquad\qquad [k \neq m;\, m, k = \text{integers}].$

**410.** $\displaystyle\int_0^\infty \frac{\sin x \cos mx\,dx}{x} = 0,$ if $m < -1$ or $m > 1,$

$\qquad\qquad = \dfrac{\pi}{4},$ if $m = \pm 1;\; = \dfrac{\pi}{2},$ if $m^2 < 1.$

**411.** $\displaystyle\int_0^\pi \sin^2 mx\,dx = \int_0^\pi \cos^2 mx\,dx = \frac{\pi}{2}\cdot$

**412.** $\displaystyle\int_0^\infty \frac{\sin^2 x\,dx}{x^2} = \frac{\pi}{2}.$

**413.** $\int_0^\infty \dfrac{\cos mx}{1 + x^2}\, dx = \dfrac{\pi}{2} e^{-m},$ $\qquad\qquad$ $[m > 0].$

$\qquad\qquad\qquad = \dfrac{\pi}{2} e^{m},$ $\qquad\qquad\qquad$ $[m < 0].$

**414.** $\int_0^\infty \cos (x^2)\, dx = \int_0^\infty \sin (x^2)\, dx = \dfrac{1}{2} \sqrt{\dfrac{\pi}{2}}.$

**415.** $\int_0^\infty \dfrac{\sin x\, dx}{\sqrt{x}} = \int_0^\infty \dfrac{\cos x\, dx}{\sqrt{x}} = \sqrt{\dfrac{\pi}{2}}.$

**416.** $\int_0^{\pi/2} \dfrac{dx}{1 + a \cos x} = \dfrac{\cos^{-1} a}{\sqrt{1 - a^2}},$ $\qquad$ $[a < 1].$

**417.** $\int_0^{2\pi} \dfrac{dx}{1 + a \cos x} = \dfrac{2\pi}{\sqrt{1 - a^2}},$ $\qquad$ $[a^2 < 1].$

**418.** $\int_0^\infty \dfrac{\cos ax - \cos bx}{x}\, dx = \log \dfrac{b}{a}.$

**419.** $\int_0^{\pi/2} \dfrac{dx}{a^2 \sin^2 x + b^2 \cos^2 x} = \dfrac{\pi}{2ab}.$

**420.** $\int_0^{\pi/2} \sin^{n-1} x \cos^{m-1} x\, dx = \dfrac{1}{2} \mathrm{B} \left(\dfrac{n}{2}, \dfrac{m}{2}\right),$

$\qquad\qquad\qquad\qquad\qquad$ *m* and *n* positive integers.

**421.** $\int_0^\infty e^{-ax}\, dx = \dfrac{1}{a},$ $\qquad\qquad\qquad$ $[a > 0].$

**422.** $\int_0^\infty x^n\, e^{-ax}\, dx = \dfrac{\Gamma(n + 1)}{a^{n+1}},$ $\qquad$ $[n > -1, a > 0],$

$\qquad\qquad\qquad = \dfrac{n!}{a^{n+1}},$ $\qquad$ $[n \text{ pos. integ.}, a > 0].$

**423.** $\int_0^\infty e^{-a^2 x^2}\, dx = \dfrac{1}{2a} \sqrt{\pi} = \dfrac{1}{2a} \Gamma \left(\dfrac{1}{2}\right),$ $\qquad$ $[a > 0].$

**424.** $\int_0^\infty x e^{-x^2}\, dx = \tfrac{1}{2}.$

**425.** $\int_0^\infty x^2 e^{-x^2}\, dx = \dfrac{\sqrt{\pi}}{4}.$

**426.** $\int_0^\infty x^{2n}\, e^{-ax^2}\, dx = \dfrac{1 \cdot 3 \cdot 5 \cdots (2n - 1)}{2^{n+1} a^n} \sqrt{\dfrac{\pi}{a}}.$

**427.** $\int_0^\infty e^{(-x^2 - a^2/x^2)}\, dx = \dfrac{e^{-2a} \sqrt{\pi}}{2}.$

**428.** $\int_0^\infty e^{-nx} \sqrt{x}\, dx = \dfrac{1}{2n} \sqrt{\dfrac{\pi}{n}}.$

**429.** $\int_0^\infty \dfrac{e^{-nx}}{\sqrt{x}}\, dx = \sqrt{\dfrac{\pi}{n}}.$

### DEFINITE INTEGRALS (Continued)

**430.** $\int_0^\infty e^{-ax} \cos mx\, dx = \dfrac{a}{a^2 + m^2},$ $\qquad [a > 0].$

**431.** $\int_0^\infty e^{-ax} \sin mx\, dx = \dfrac{m}{a^2 + m^2},$ $\qquad [a > 0].$

**432.** $\int_0^\infty e^{-a^2x^2} \cos bx\, dx = \dfrac{\sqrt{\pi} \cdot e^{-b^2/4a^2}}{2a},$ $\qquad [a > 0].$

**433.** $\int_0^1 (\log x)^n\, dx = (-1)^n \cdot n!.$

**434.** $\int_0^1 \left(\log \dfrac{1}{x}\right)^{\frac{1}{2}} dx = \dfrac{\sqrt{\pi}}{2}.$

**435.** $\int_0^1 \left(\log \dfrac{1}{x}\right)^{-\frac{1}{2}} dx = \sqrt{\pi}.$

**436.** $\int_0^1 \left(\log \dfrac{1}{x}\right)^n dx = n!.$

**437.** $\int_0^1 x \log (1 - x)\, dx = -\dfrac{3}{4}.$

**438.** $\int_0^1 x \log (1 + x)\, dx = \dfrac{1}{4}.$

**439.** $\int_0^1 \dfrac{\log x}{1 + x}\, dx = -\dfrac{\pi^2}{12}.$

**440.** $\int_0^1 \dfrac{\log x}{1 - x}\, dx = -\dfrac{\pi^2}{6}.$

**441.** $\int_0^1 \dfrac{\log x}{1 - x^2}\, dx = -\dfrac{\pi^2}{8}.$

**442.** $\int_0^1 \log \left(\dfrac{1 + x}{1 - x}\right) \cdot \dfrac{dx}{x} = \dfrac{\pi^2}{4}.$

**443.** $\int_0^1 \dfrac{\log x\, dx}{\sqrt{1 - x^2}} = -\dfrac{\pi}{2} \log 2.$

**444.** $\int_0^1 x^m \left[\log \left(\dfrac{1}{x}\right)\right]^n dx = \dfrac{\Gamma(n + 1)}{(m + 1)^{n+1}},$
$\qquad\qquad$ if $m + 1 > 0,\ n + 1 > 0.$

**445.** $\int_0^1 \dfrac{(x^p - x^q)\, dx}{\log x} = \log \left(\dfrac{p + 1}{q + 1}\right),$
$\qquad\qquad\qquad [p + 1 > 0,\ q + 1 > 0].$

**446.** $\int_0^1 \dfrac{dx}{\sqrt{\log \left(\dfrac{1}{x}\right)}} = \sqrt{\pi}.$

**447.** $\int_0^\infty \log \left(\dfrac{e^x + 1}{e^x - 1}\right) dx = \dfrac{\pi^2}{4}.$

285

## DEFINITE INTEGRALS (Continued)

**448.** $\int_0^{\pi/2} \log \sin x \, dx = \int_0^{\pi/2} \log \cos x \, dx = -\frac{\pi}{2} \log 2.$

**449.** $\int_0^{\pi/2} \log \sec x \, dx = \int_0^{\pi/2} \log \csc x \, dx = \frac{\pi}{2} \log 2.$

**450.** $\int_0^{\pi} x \log \sin x \, dx = -\frac{\pi^2}{2} \log 2.$

**451.** $\int_0^{\pi/2} \sin x \log \sin x \, dx = \log 2 - 1.$

**452.** $\int_0^{\pi/2} \log \tan x \, dx = 0.$

**453.** $\int_0^{\pi} \log (a \pm b \cos x) \, dx = \pi \log \left( \frac{a + \sqrt{a^2 - b^2}}{2} \right),$

$$[a \geqq b].$$

**454.** $\int_0^{\infty} \frac{dx}{\cosh ax} = \frac{\pi}{2a}.$

**455.** $\int_0^{\infty} \frac{x \, dx}{\sinh ax} = \frac{\pi^2}{4a^2}.$

**456.** $\int_0^{\infty} e^{-ax} \cosh bx \, dx = \frac{a}{a^2 - b^2} \qquad\qquad a > 0.$

**457.** $\int_0^{\infty} e^{-ax} \sinh bx \, dx = \frac{b}{a^2 - b^2} \qquad\qquad a > 0.$

**458.** $\int_{+\infty}^{1} \frac{e^{-xu}}{u} \, du = \gamma + \log x - x + \frac{x^2}{2 \cdot 2!} - \frac{x^3}{3 \cdot 3!}$

$\qquad + \frac{x^4}{4 \cdot 4!} - \cdots$, where $\gamma = \lim\limits_{z \to \infty} \left( 1 + \frac{1}{2} + \frac{1}{3} \right.$

$\qquad + \cdots + \frac{1}{z} - \log z \Big) = 0.5772157 \cdots, 0 < x < \infty.$

**459.** $\int_0^{\pi/2} \frac{dx}{\sqrt{1 - k^2 \sin^2 x}} = \frac{\pi}{2} \left[ 1 + \left( \frac{1}{2} \right)^2 k^2 + \left( \frac{1 \cdot 3}{2 \cdot 4} \right)^2 k^4 \right.$

$\qquad\qquad \left. + \left( \frac{1 \cdot 3 \cdot 5}{2 \cdot 4 \cdot 6} \right)^2 k^6 + \cdots \right]$, if $k^2 < 1.$

**460.** $\int_0^{\pi/2} \sqrt{1 - k^2 \sin^2 x} \, dx = \frac{\pi}{2} \left[ 1 - \left( \frac{1}{2} \right)^2 k^2 \right.$

$\qquad\qquad \left. - \left( \frac{1 \cdot 3}{2 \cdot 4} \right)^2 \frac{k^4}{3} - \left( \frac{1 \cdot 3 \cdot 5}{2 \cdot 4 \cdot 6} \right)^2 \frac{k^6}{5} - \cdots \right]$, if $k^2 < 1.$

**461.** $\int_0^{\infty} e^{-x} \log x \, dx = -\gamma = -0.5772157 \cdots$

**462.** $\int_0^{\infty} \left( \frac{1}{1 - e^{-x}} - \frac{1}{x} \right) e^{-x} dx = \gamma = 0.5772157 \cdots$

$\qquad\qquad\qquad\qquad\qquad$ [Euler's Constant].

**463.** $\int_0^{\infty} \frac{1}{x} \left( \frac{1}{1 + x} - e^{-x} \right) dx = \gamma = 0.5772157 \cdots$

# *GAMMA FUNCTION

Values of $\Gamma(n) = \int_0^\infty e^{-x}x^{n-1}dx$; $\Gamma(n+1) = n\Gamma(n)$

| $n$ | $\Gamma(n)$ | $n$ | $\Gamma(n)$ | $n$ | $\Gamma(n)$ | $n$ | $\Gamma(n)$ |
|------|---------|------|---------|------|---------|------|---------|
| 1.00 | 1.00000 | 1.25 | .90640 | 1.50 | .88623 | 1.75 | .91906 |
| 1.01 | .99433 | 1.26 | .90440 | 1.51 | .88659 | 1.76 | .92137 |
| 1.02 | .98884 | 1.27 | .90250 | 1.52 | .88704 | 1.77 | .92376 |
| 1.03 | .98355 | 1.28 | .90072 | 1.53 | .88757 | 1.78 | .92623 |
| 1.04 | .97844 | 1.29 | .89904 | 1.54 | .88818 | 1.79 | .92877 |
| 1.05 | .97350 | 1.30 | .89747 | 1.55 | .88887 | 1.80 | .93138 |
| 1.06 | .96874 | 1.31 | .89600 | 1.56 | .88964 | 1.81 | .93408 |
| 1.07 | .96415 | 1.32 | .89464 | 1.57 | .89049 | 1.82 | .93685 |
| 1.08 | .95973 | 1.33 | .89338 | 1.58 | .89142 | 1.83 | .93969 |
| 1.09 | .95546 | 1.34 | .89222 | 1.59 | .89243 | 1.84 | .94261 |
| 1.10 | .95135 | 1.35 | .89115 | 1.60 | .89352 | 1.85 | .94561 |
| 1.11 | .94739 | 1.36 | .89018 | 1.61 | .89468 | 1.86 | .94869 |
| 1.12 | .94359 | 1.37 | .88931 | 1.62 | .89592 | 1.87 | .95184 |
| 1.13 | .93993 | 1.38 | .88854 | 1.63 | .89724 | 1.88 | .95507 |
| 1.14 | .93642 | 1.39 | .88785 | 1.64 | .89864 | 1.89 | .95838 |
| 1.15 | .93304 | 1.40 | .88726 | 1.65 | .90012 | 1.90 | .96177 |
| 1.16 | .92980 | 1.41 | .88676 | 1.66 | .90167 | 1.91 | .96523 |
| 1.17 | .92670 | 1.42 | .88636 | 1.67 | .90330 | 1.92 | .96878 |
| 1.18 | .92373 | 1.43 | .88604 | 1.68 | .90500 | 1.93 | .97240 |
| 1.19 | .92088 | 1.44 | .88580 | 1.69 | .90678 | 1.94 | .97610 |
| 1.20 | .91817 | 1.45 | .88565 | 1.70 | .90864 | 1.95 | .97988 |
| 1.21 | .91558 | 1.46 | .88560 | 1.71 | .91057 | 1.96 | .98374 |
| 1.22 | .91311 | 1.47 | .88563 | 1.72 | .91258 | 1.97 | .98768 |
| 1.23 | .91075 | 1.48 | .88575 | 1.73 | .91466 | 1.98 | .99171 |
| 1.24 | .90852 | 1.49 | .88595 | 1.74 | .91683 | 1.99 | .99581 |
|  |  |  |  |  |  | 2.00 | 1.00000 |

\* For large positive values of $x$, $\Gamma(x)$ approximates the asymptotic series

$$x^x e^{-x} \sqrt{\frac{2\pi}{x}} \left[ 1 + \frac{1}{12x} + \frac{1}{288x^2} - \frac{139}{51840x^3} - \frac{571}{2488320x^4} + \cdots \right].$$

# BESSEL FUNCTIONS $J_0(x)$ AND $J_1(x)$

$$J_0(x) = 1 - \left(\frac{x}{2}\right)^2 + \frac{\left(\frac{x}{2}\right)^4}{1^2 \cdot 2^2} - \frac{\left(\frac{x}{2}\right)^6}{1^2 \cdot 2^2 \cdot 3^2} + - \cdots$$

$$J_1(x) = -J_0{}^1(x) = \frac{x}{2} - \frac{\left(\frac{x}{2}\right)^3}{1^2 \cdot 2} + \frac{\left(\frac{x}{2}\right)^5}{1^2 \cdot 2^2 \cdot 3} - + \cdots$$

$$J_n(x) = \sum_{k=0}^{\infty} \frac{(-1)^k X^{n+2k}}{2^{n+2k} k! (n+k)!} \qquad (n = 0, 1, 2, 3, \ldots)$$

| $x$ | $J_0(x)$ | $J_1(x)$ | $x$ | $J_0(x)$ | $J_1(x)$ | $x$ | $J_0(x)$ | $J_1(x)$ |
|---|---|---|---|---|---|---|---|---|
| **0.0** | 1.0000 | .0000 | **5.0** | $-.1776$ | $-.3276$ | **10.0** | $-.2459$ | .0435 |
| 0.1 | .9975 | .0499 | 5.1 | $-.1443$ | $-.3371$ | 10.1 | $-.2490$ | .0184 |
| 0.2 | .9900 | .0995 | 5.2 | $-.1103$ | $-.3432$ | 10.2 | $-.2496$ | $-.0066$ |
| 0.3 | .9776 | .1483 | 5.3 | $-.0758$ | $-.3460$ | 10.3 | $-.2477$ | $-.0313$ |
| 0.4 | .9604 | .1960 | 5.4 | $-.0412$ | $-.3453$ | 10.4 | $-.2434$ | $-.0555$ |
| **0.5** | .9385 | .2423 | **5.5** | $-.0068$ | $-.3414$ | **10.5** | $-.2366$ | $-.0789$ |
| 0.6 | .9120 | .2867 | 5.6 | .0270 | $-.3343$ | 10.6 | $-.2276$ | $-.1012$ |
| 0.7 | .8812 | .3290 | 5.7 | .0599 | $-.3241$ | 10.7 | $-.2164$ | $-.1224$ |
| 0.8 | .8463 | .3688 | 5.8 | .0917 | $-.3110$ | 10.8 | $-.2032$ | $-.1422$ |
| 0.9 | .8075 | .4059 | 5.9 | .1220 | $-.2951$ | 10.9 | $-.1881$ | $-.1603$ |
| **1.0** | .7652 | .4401 | **6.0** | .1506 | $-.2767$ | **11.0** | $-.1712$ | $-.1768$ |
| 1.1 | .7196 | .4709 | 6.1 | .1773 | $-.2559$ | 11.1 | $-.1528$ | $-.1913$ |
| 1.2 | .6711 | .4983 | 6.2 | .2017 | $-.2329$ | 11.2 | $-.1330$ | $-.2039$ |
| 1.3 | .6201 | .5220 | 6.3 | .2238 | $-.2081$ | 11.3 | $-.1121$ | $-.2143$ |
| 1.4 | .5669 | .5419 | 6.4 | .2433 | $-.1816$ | 11.4 | $-.0902$ | $-.2225$ |
| **1.5** | .5118 | .5579 | **6.5** | .2601 | $-.1538$ | **11.5** | $-.0677$ | $-.2284$ |
| 1.6 | .4554 | .5699 | 6.6 | .2740 | $-.1250$ | 11.6 | $-.0446$ | $-.2320$ |
| 1.7 | .3980 | .5778 | 6.7 | .2851 | $-.0953$ | 11.7 | $-.0213$ | $-.2333$ |
| 1.8 | .3400 | .5815 | 6.8 | .2931 | $-.0652$ | 11.8 | .0020 | $-.2323$ |
| 1.9 | .2818 | .5812 | 6.9 | .2981 | $-.0349$ | 11.9 | .0250 | $-.2290$ |
| **2.0** | .2239 | .5767 | **7.0** | .3001 | $-.0047$ | **12.0** | .0477 | $-.2234$ |
| 2.1 | .1666 | .5683 | 7.1 | .2991 | .0252 | 12.1 | .0697 | $-.2157$ |
| 2.2 | .1104 | .5560 | 7.2 | .2951 | .0543 | 12.2 | .0908 | $-.2060$ |
| 2.3 | .0555 | .5399 | 7.3 | .2882 | .0826 | 12.3 | .1108 | $-.1943$ |
| 2.4 | .0025 | .5202 | 7.4 | .2786 | .1096 | 12.4 | .1296 | $-.1807$ |
| **2.5** | $-.0484$ | .4971 | **7.5** | .2663 | .1352 | **12.5** | .1469 | $-.1655$ |
| 2.6 | $-.0968$ | .4708 | 7.6 | .2516 | .1592 | 12.6 | .1626 | $-.1487$ |
| 2.7 | $-.1424$ | .4416 | 7.7 | .2346 | .1813 | 12.7 | .1766 | $-.1307$ |
| 2.8 | $-.1850$ | .4097 | 7.8 | .2154 | .2014 | 12.8 | .1887 | $-.1114$ |
| 2.9 | $-.2243$ | .3754 | 7.9 | .1944 | .2192 | 12.9 | .1988 | $-.0912$ |
| **3.0** | $-.2601$ | .3391 | **8.0** | .1717 | .2346 | **13.0** | .2069 | $-.0703$ |
| 3.1 | $-.2921$ | .3009 | 8.1 | .1475 | .2476 | 13.1 | .2129 | $-.0489$ |
| 3.2 | $-.3202$ | .2613 | 8.2 | .1222 | .2580 | 13.2 | .2167 | $-.0271$ |
| 3.3 | $-.3443$ | .2207 | 8.3 | .0960 | .2657 | 13.3 | .2183 | $-.0052$ |
| 3.4 | $-.3643$ | .1792 | 8.4 | .0692 | .2708 | 13.4 | .2177 | .0166 |
| **3.5** | $-.3801$ | .1374 | **8.5** | .0419 | .2731 | **13.5** | .2150 | .0380 |
| 3.6 | $-.3918$ | .0955 | 8.6 | .0146 | .2728 | 13.6 | .2101 | .0590 |
| 3.7 | $-.3992$ | .0538 | 8.7 | $-.0125$ | .2697 | 13.7 | .2032 | .0791 |
| 3.8 | $-.4026$ | .0128 | 8.8 | $-.0392$ | .2641 | 13.8 | .1943 | .0984 |
| 3.9 | $-.4018$ | $-.0272$ | 8.9 | $-.0653$ | .2559 | 13.9 | .1836 | .1165 |
| **4.0** | $-.3971$ | $-.0660$ | **9.0** | $-.0903$ | .2453 | **14.0** | .1711 | .1334 |
| 4.1 | $-.3887$ | $-.1033$ | 9.1 | $-.1142$ | .2324 | 14.1 | .1570 | .1488 |
| 4.2 | $-.3766$ | $-.1386$ | 9.2 | $-.1367$ | .2174 | 14.2 | .1414 | .1626 |
| 4.3 | $-.3610$ | $-.1719$ | 9.3 | $-.1577$ | .2004 | 14.3 | .1245 | .1747 |
| 4.4 | $-.3423$ | $-.2028$ | 9.4 | $-.1768$ | .1816 | 14.4 | .1065 | .1850 |
| **4.5** | $-.3205$ | $-.2311$ | **9.5** | $-.1939$ | .1613 | **14.5** | .0875 | .1934 |
| 4.6 | $-.2961$ | $-.2566$ | 9.6 | $-.2090$ | .1395 | 14.6 | .0679 | .1999 |
| 4.7 | $-.2693$ | $-.2791$ | 9.7 | $-.2218$ | .1166 | 14.7 | .0476 | .2043 |
| 4.8 | $-.2404$ | $-.2985$ | 9.8 | $-.2323$ | .0928 | 14.8 | .0271 | .2066 |
| 4.9 | $-.2097$ | $-.3147$ | 9.9 | $-.2403$ | .0684 | 14.9 | .0064 | .2069 |

$J_0(x) = 0;\ x = 2.405,\ 5.520,\ 8.654,\ 11.792,\ 14.931,\ 18.071,\ 21.212,\ 24.352.$
$J_1(x) = 0;\ x = 3.832,\ 7.016,\ 10.173,\ 13.324,\ 16.471,\ 19.616.$

# BESSEL FUNCTIONS FOR SPHERICAL COORDINATES

$$j_n(x) = \sqrt{\pi/2x}\, J_{n+\frac{1}{2}}(x), \qquad n_n(x) = \sqrt{\pi/2x}\, N_{n+\frac{1}{2}}(x)$$

| $x$ | $j_0(x)$ | $n_0(x)$ | $j_1(x)$ | $n_1(x)$ | $j_2(x)$ | $n_2(x)$ |
|---|---|---|---|---|---|---|
| 0.0 | 1.0000 | $-\infty$ | 0.0000 | $-\infty$ | 0.0000 | $-\infty$ |
| 0.1 | 0.9983 | $-9.9500$ | 0.0333 | $-100.50$ | 0.0007 | $-3005.0$ |
| 0.2 | 0.9933 | $-4.9003$ | 0.0664 | $-25.495$ | 0.0027 | $-377.52$ |
| 0.4 | 0.9735 | $-2.3027$ | 0.1312 | $-6.7302$ | 0.0105 | $-48.174$ |
| 0.6 | 0.9411 | $-1.3756$ | 0.1929 | $-3.2337$ | 0.0234 | $-14.793$ |
| 0.8 | 0.8967 | $-0.8709$ | 0.2500 | $-1.9853$ | 0.0408 | $-6.5740$ |
| 1.0 | 0.8415 | $-0.5403$ | 0.3012 | $-1.3818$ | 0.0620 | $-3.6050$ |
| 1.2 | 0.7767 | $-0.3020$ | 0.3453 | $-1.0283$ | 0.0865 | $-2.2689$ |
| 1.4 | 0.7039 | $-0.1214$ | 0.3814 | $-0.7906$ | 0.1133 | $-1.5728$ |
| 1.6 | 0.6247 | $+0.0183$ | 0.4087 | $-0.6133$ | 0.1416 | $-1.1682$ |
| 1.8 | 0.5410 | 0.1262 | 0.4268 | $-0.4709$ | 0.1703 | $-0.9111$ |
| 2.0 | 0.4546 | 0.2081 | 0.4354 | $-0.3506$ | 0.1985 | $-0.7340$ |
| 2.2 | 0.3675 | 0.2675 | 0.4346 | $-0.2459$ | 0.2251 | $-0.6028$ |
| 2.4 | 0.2814 | 0.3072 | 0.4245 | $-0.1534$ | 0.2492 | $-0.4990$ |
| 2.6 | 0.1983 | 0.3296 | 0.4058 | $-0.0715$ | 0.2700 | $-0.4121$ |
| 2.8 | 0.1196 | 0.3365 | 0.3792 | $+0.0005$ | 0.2867 | $-0.3359$ |
| 3.0 | $+0.0470$ | 0.3300 | 0.3457 | 0.0630 | 0.2986 | $-0.2670$ |
| 3.2 | $-0.0182$ | 0.3120 | 0.3063 | 0.1157 | 0.3054 | $-0.2035$ |
| 3.4 | $-0.0752$ | 0.2844 | 0.2623 | 0.1588 | 0.3066 | $-0.1442$ |
| 3.6 | $-0.1229$ | 0.2491 | 0.2150 | 0.1921 | 0.3021 | $-0.0890$ |
| 3.8 | $-0.1610$ | 0.2082 | 0.1658 | 0.2158 | 0.2919 | $-0.0378$ |
| 4.0 | $-0.1892$ | 0.1634 | 0.1161 | 0.2300 | 0.2763 | $+0.0091$ |
| 4.2 | $-0.2075$ | 0.1167 | 0.0673 | 0.2353 | 0.2556 | 0.0514 |
| 4.4 | $-0.2163$ | 0.0699 | $+0.0207$ | 0.2321 | 0.2304 | 0.0884 |
| 4.6 | $-0.2160$ | $+0.0244$ | $-0.0226$ | 0.2213 | 0.2013 | 0.1200 |
| 4.8 | $-0.2075$ | $-0.0182$ | $-0.0615$ | 0.2037 | 0.1691 | 0.1456 |
| 5.0 | $-0.1918$ | $-0.0567$ | $-0.0951$ | 0.1804 | 0.1347 | 0.1650 |
| 5.2 | $-0.1699$ | $-0.0901$ | $-0.1228$ | 0.1526 | 0.0991 | 0.1781 |
| 5.4 | $-0.1431$ | $-0.1175$ | $-0.1440$ | 0.1213 | 0.0631 | 0.1850 |
| 5.6 | $-0.1127$ | $-0.1385$ | $-0.1586$ | 0.0880 | $+0.0278$ | 0.1856 |
| 5.8 | $-0.0801$ | $-0.1527$ | $-0.1665$ | 0.0538 | $-0.0060$ | 0.1805 |
| 6.0 | $-0.0466$ | $-0.1600$ | $-0.1678$ | $+0.0199$ | $-0.0373$ | 0.1700 |
| 6.2 | $-0.0134$ | $-0.1607$ | $-0.1629$ | $-0.0125$ | $-0.0654$ | 0.1547 |
| 6.4 | $+0.0182$ | $-0.1552$ | $-0.1523$ | $-0.0425$ | $-0.0896$ | 0.1353 |
| 6.6 | 0.0472 | $-0.1440$ | $-0.1368$ | $-0.0690$ | $-0.1094$ | 0.1126 |
| 6.8 | 0.0727 | $-0.1278$ | $-0.1172$ | $-0.0915$ | $-0.1243$ | 0.0875 |
| 7.0 | 0.0939 | $-0.1077$ | $-0.0943$ | $-0.1092$ | $-0.1343$ | 0.0609 |
| 7.2 | 0.1102 | $-0.0845$ | $-0.0692$ | $-0.1220$ | $-0.1391$ | 0.0337 |
| 7.4 | 0.1215 | $-0.0593$ | $-0.0429$ | $-0.1294$ | $-0.1388$ | $+0.0068$ |
| 7.6 | 0.1274 | $-0.0331$ | $-0.0163$ | $-0.1317$ | $-0.1338$ | $-0.0189$ |
| 7.8 | 0.1280 | $-0.0069$ | $+0.0095$ | $-0.1289$ | $-0.1244$ | $-0.0427$ |
| 8.0 | 0.1237 | $+0.0182$ | 0.0336 | $-0.1214$ | $-0.1111$ | $-0.0637$ |

Taken from Vibration and Sound with the permission of Philip Morse, author, and McGraw-Hill Book Company, Inc., publisher.

# HYPERBOLIC BESSEL FUNCTIONS

$$I_m(z) = i^{-m}J_m(iz)$$

| $z$ | $I_0(z)$ | $I_1(z)$ | $I_2(z)$ |
|---|---|---|---|
| 0.0 | 1.0000 | 0.0000 | 0.0000 |
| 0.1 | 1.0025 | 0.0501 | 0.0012 |
| 0.2 | 1.0100 | 0.1005 | 0.0050 |
| 0.4 | 1.0404 | 0.2040 | 0.0203 |
| 0.6 | 1.0921 | 0.3137 | 0.0464 |
| 0.8 | 1.1665 | 0.4329 | 0.0843 |
| 1.0 | 1.2661 | 0.5652 | 0.1358 |
| 1.2 | 1.3937 | 0.7147 | 0.2026 |
| 1.4 | 1.5534 | 0.8861 | 0.2876 |
| 1.6 | 1.7500 | 1.0848 | 0.3940 |
| 1.8 | 1.9895 | 1.3172 | 0.5260 |
| 2.0 | 2.2796 | 1.5906 | 0.6890 |
| 2.2 | 2.6292 | 1.9141 | 0.8891 |
| 2.4 | 3.0492 | 2.2981 | 1.1111 |
| 2.6 | 3.5532 | 2.7554 | 1.4338 |
| 2.8 | 4.1574 | 3.3011 | 1.7994 |
| 3.0 | 4.8808 | 3.9534 | 2.2452 |
| 3.2 | 5.7472 | 4.7343 | 2.7884 |
| 3.4 | 6.7848 | 5.6701 | 3.4495 |
| 3.6 | 8.0278 | 6.7926 | 4.2538 |
| 3.8 | 9.5169 | 8.1405 | 5.2323 |
| 4.0 | 11.302 | 9.7594 | 6.4224 |
| 4.2 | 13.443 | 11.705 | 7.8683 |
| 4.4 | 16.010 | 14.046 | 9.6259 |
| 4.6 | 19.097 | 16.863 | 11.761 |
| 4.8 | 22.794 | 20.253 | 14.355 |
| 5.0 | 27.240 | 24.335 | 17.505 |
| 5.2 | 32.584 | 29.254 | 21.332 |
| 5.4 | 39.010 | 35.181 | 25.980 |
| 5.6 | 46.738 | 42.327 | 31.621 |
| 5.8 | 56.039 | 50.945 | 38.472 |
| 6.0 | 67.235 | 61.341 | 46.788 |
| 6.2 | 80.717 | 73.888 | 56.882 |
| 6.4 | 96.963 | 89.025 | 69.143 |
| 6.6 | 116.54 | 107.31 | 84.021 |
| 6.8 | 140.14 | 129.38 | 102.08 |
| 7.0 | 168.59 | 156.04 | 124.01 |
| 7.2 | 202.92 | 188.25 | 150.63 |
| 7.4 | 244.34 | 227.17 | 182.94 |
| 7.6 | 294.33 | 274.22 | 222.17 |
| 7.8 | 354.68 | 331.10 | 269.79 |
| 8.0 | 427.57 | 399.87 | 327.60 |

Taken from Vibration and Sound with the permission of Philip Morse, author, and McGraw-Hill Book Company, Inc., publisher.

# SINE, COSINE, AND EXPONENTIAL INTEGRALS

$$Si(x) = \int_0^x \frac{\sin v}{v} \, dv; \qquad Ci(x) = \int_\infty^x \frac{\cos v}{v} \, dv;$$

$$Ei(x) = \int_{-\infty}^x \frac{e^v}{v} \, dv; \qquad -Ei(-x) = \int_x^\infty \frac{e^{-v}}{v} \, dv$$

| $x$ | $Si(x)$ | $Ci(x)$ | $Ei(x)$ | $-Ei(-x)$ |
|---|---|---|---|---|
| 0.0 | 0.00000 | $-\infty$ | $-\infty$ | $+\infty$ |
| 0.1 | 0.09994 | $-1.72787$ | $-1.62281$ | 1.82292 |
| 0.2 | .19956 | $-1.04221$ | $-\,.82176$ | 1.22265 |
| 0.3 | .29850 | $-\,.64917$ | $-\,.30267$ | .90568 |
| 0.4 | .39646 | $-\,.37881$ | .10477 | .70238 |
| 0.5 | .49311 | $-\,.17778$ | .45422 | .55977 |
| 0.6 | .58813 | $-\,.02227$ | .76988 | .45438 |
| 0.7 | .68122 | .10051 | 1.06491 | .37377 |
| 0.8 | .77210 | .19828 | 1.34740 | .31060 |
| 0.9 | .86047 | .27607 | 1.62281 | .26018 |
| 1.0 | .94608 | .33740 | 1.89512 | .21938 |
| 1.1 | 1.02869 | .38487 | 2.16738 | .18599 |
| 1.2 | 1.10805 | .42046 | 2.44209 | .15841 |
| 1.3 | 1.18396 | .44574 | 2.72140 | .13545 |
| 1.4 | 1.25623 | .46201 | 3.00721 | .11622 |
| 1.5 | 1.32468 | .47036 | 3.30129 | .10002 |
| 1.6 | 1.38918 | .47173 | 3.60532 | .08631 |
| 1.7 | 1.44959 | .46697 | 3.92096 | .07465 |
| 1.8 | 1.50582 | .45681 | 4.24987 | .06471 |
| 1.9 | 1.55778 | .44194 | 4.59371 | .05620 |
| 2.0 | 1.60541 | .42298 | 4.95423 | .04890 |
| 2.1 | 1.64870 | .40051 | 5.33324 | .04261 |
| 2.2 | 1.68762 | .37507 | 5.73261 | .03719 |
| 2.3 | 1.72221 | .34718 | 6.15438 | .03250 |
| 2.4 | 1.75249 | .31729 | 6.60067 | .02844 |
| 2.5 | 1.77852 | .28587 | 7.07377 | .02491 |
| 2.6 | 1.80039 | .25334 | 7.57611 | .02185 |
| 2.7 | 1.81821 | .22008 | 8.11035 | .01918 |
| 2.8 | 1.83210 | .18649 | 8.67930 | .01686 |
| 2.9 | 1.84219 | .15290 | 9.28602 | .01482 |
| 3.0 | 1.84865 | .11963 | 9.93383 | .01305 |
| 3.1 | 1.85166 | .08699 | 10.6263 | .01149 |
| 3.2 | 1.85140 | .05526 | 11.3673 | .01013 |
| 3.3 | 1.84808 | .02468 | 12.1610 | .00894 |
| 3.4 | 1.84191 | $-\,.00452$ | 13.0121 | .00789 |
| 3.5 | 1.83313 | $-\,.03213$ | 13.9254 | .00697 |
| 3.6 | 1.82195 | $-\,.05797$ | 14.9063 | .00616 |
| 3.7 | 1.80862 | $-\,.08190$ | 15.9606 | .00545 |
| 3.8 | 1.79339 | $-\,.10378$ | 17.0948 | .00482 |
| 3.9 | 1.77650 | $-\,.12350$ | 18.3157 | .00427 |
| 4.0 | 1.75820 | $-\,.14098$ | 19.6309 | .00378 |
| 4.1 | 1.73874 | $-\,.15617$ | 21.0485 | .00335 |
| 4.2 | 1.71837 | $-\,.16901$ | 22.5774 | .00297 |
| 4.3 | 1.69732 | $-\,.17951$ | 24.2274 | .00263 |
| 4.4 | 1.67583 | $-\,.18766$ | 26.0090 | .00234 |
| 4.5 | 1.65414 | $-\,.19349$ | 27.9337 | .00207 |
| 4.6 | 1.63246 | $-\,.19705$ | 30.0141 | .00184 |
| 4.7 | 1.61101 | $-\,.19839$ | 32.2639 | .00164 |
| 4.8 | 1.58998 | $-\,.19760$ | 34.6979 | .00145 |
| 4.9 | 1.56956 | $-\,.19478$ | 37.3325 | .00129 |
| 5.0 | 1.54993 | $-\,.19003$ | 40.1853 | .00115 |
| 5.1 | 1.53125 | $-\,.18348$ | 43.2757 | .00102 |
| 5.2 | 1.51367 | $-\,.17525$ | 46.6249 | .00091 |
| 5.3 | 1.49731 | $-\,.16551$ | 50.2557 | .00081 |
| 5.4 | 1.48230 | $-\,.15439$ | 54.1935 | .00072 |

| $x$ | $Si(x)$ | $Ci(x)$ | $Ei(x)$ | $-Ei(-x)$ |
|---|---|---|---|---|
| 5.5 | 1.46872 | − .14205 | 58.4655 | .00064 |
| 5.6 | 1.45667 | − .12867 | 63.1018 | .00057 |
| 5.7 | 1.44620 | − .11441 | 68.1350 | .00051 |
| 5.8 | 1.43736 | − .09944 | 73.6008 | .00045 |
| 5.9 | 1.43018 | − .08393 | 79.5382 | .00040 |
| 6.0 | 1.42469 | − .06806 | 85.9898 | .00036 |
| 6.1 | 1.42087 | − .05198 | 93.0020 | .00032 |
| 6.2 | 1.41871 | − .03587 | 100.626 | .00029 |
| 6.3 | 1.41817 | − .01988 | 108.916 | .00026 |
| 6.4 | 1.41922 | − .00418 | 117.935 | .00023 |
| 6.5 | 1.42179 | + .01110 | 127.747 | .00020 |
| 6.6 | 1.42582 | + .02582 | 138.426 | .00018 |
| 6.7 | 1.43121 | .03986 | 150.050 | .00016 |
| 6.8 | 1.43787 | .05308 | 162.707 | .00014 |
| 6.9 | 1.44570 | .06539 | 176.491 | .00013 |
| 7.0 | 1.45460 | .07670 | 191.505 | .00012 |
| 7.1 | 1.46443 | .08691 | 207.863 | .00010 |
| 7.2 | 1.47509 | .09596 | 225.688 | .00009 |
| 7.3 | 1.48644 | .10379 | 245.116 | .00008 |
| 7.4 | 1.49834 | .11036 | 266.296 | .00007 |
| 7.5 | 1.51068 | .11563 | 289.388 | .00007 |
| 7.6 | 1.52331 | .11960 | 314.572 | .00006 |
| 7.7 | 1.53611 | .12225 | 342.040 | .00005 |
| 7.8 | 1.54894 | .12359 | 372.006 | .00005 |
| 7.9 | 1.56167 | .12364 | 404.701 | .00004 |
| 8.0 | 1.57419 | .12243 | 440.380 | .00004 |
| 8.1 | 1.58637 | .12002 | 479.322 | .00003 |
| 8.2 | 1.59810 | .11644 | 521.831 | .00003 |
| 8.3 | 1.60928 | .11177 | 568.242 | .00003 |
| 8.4 | 1.61981 | .10607 | 618.919 | 00002 |
| 8.5 | 1.62960 | .09943 | 674.264 | .00002 |
| 8.6 | 1.63857 | .09194 | 734.714 | .00002 |
| 8.7 | 1.64665 | .08368 | 800.749 | .00002 |
| 8.8 | 1.65379 | .07476 | 872.895 | .00002 |
| 8.9 | 1.65993 | .06528 | 951.728 | .00001 |
| 9.0 | 1.66504 | .05535 | 1037.88 | .00001 |
| 9.1 | 1.66908 | .04507 | 1132.04 | .00001 |
| 9.2 | 1.67205 | .03455 | 1234.96 | .00001 |
| 9.3 | 1.67393 | .02391 | 1347.48 | .00001 |
| 9.4 | 1.67473 | .01325 | 1470.51 | .00001 |
| 9.5 | 1.67446 | .00268 | 1605.03 | .00001 |
| 9.6 | 1.67316 | − .00771 | 1752.14 | .00001 |
| 9.7 | 1.67084 | − .01780 | 1913.05 | .00001 |
| 9.8 | 1.66757 | − .02752 | 2089.05 | .00001 |
| 9.9 | 1.66338 | − .03676 | 2281.58 | .00000 |
| 10.0 | 1.65835 | − .04546 | 2492.23 | .00000 |
| 10.5 | 1.62294 | − .07828 | 3883.74 | .00000 |
| 11.0 | 1.57831 | − .08956 | 6071.41 | .00000 |
| 11.5 | 1.53572 | − .07857 | 9518.20 | .00000 |
| 12.0 | 1.50497 | − .04978 | 14959.5 | .00000 |
| 12.5 | 1.49234 | − .01141 | 23565.1 | .00000 |
| 13.0 | 1.49936 | + .02676 | 37197.7 | .00000 |
| 13.5 | 1.52291 | + .05576 | 58827.0 | .00000 |
| 14.0 | 1.55621 | .06940 | 93193.0 | .00000 |
| 14.5 | 1.59072 | .06554 | 147866. | .00000 |
| 15.0 | 1.61819 | .04628 | 234956. | .00000 |

# LAPLACE AND FOURIER TRANSFORMS

## LAPLACE TRANSFORMS

These tables of Operations and Transforms were taken from "Modern Operational Mathematics in Engineering" by permission from the author, R. V. Churchill, and the publisher, McGraw-Hill Book Company, Inc.

The operational method for solving differential equations makes use of the Laplace transformation which associates a given function $F(t)$ with a second function $f(s)$, so that

$$f(s) = L\{F(t)\} = \int_0^\infty e^{-st} F(t)\, dt,$$

where $t$ = a real variable, $F(t)$ = a real function of $t$; $F(t) = 0$, $t < 0$; $f(s)$ = a function of $s$; $s$ = a complex variable; and $e = 2.71828 \ldots$

$f(s)$ is called the Laplace transform of $F(t)$.

$F(t)$ can also be expressed as follows:

$$F(t) = \frac{1}{2\pi i} \int_{a-i\infty}^{a+i\infty} e^{st} f(s)\, ds,$$

where $a$ is chosen to the right of any singularity of $f(s)$.

## FOURIER TRANSFORMS

For a sectionally continuous function $F(x)$ over a finite interval of the variable $x$, in which the origin and a unit of length have been so chosen that the end points of the interval for $x$ become $x = 0$ and $x = \pi$, the Fourier finite sine and cosine transforms for $F(x)$ are defined and symbolized respectively as follows:

$$S\{F(x)\} = \int_0^\pi F(x) \sin nx\, dx = f_s(n) \qquad (n = 1, 2, \cdots)$$

$$C\{F(x)\} = \int_0^\pi F(x) \cos nx\, dx = f_c(n) \qquad (n = 1, 2, \cdots)$$

If the interval for $F(x)$ is defined so that the end points are $x = 0$ and $x = l$, the substitution $\alpha = \dfrac{\pi x}{l}$ makes possible the use of these tables with

$$\int_0^l F(x) \sin \frac{n\pi x}{l}\, dx = \frac{l}{\pi} S\left\{ F\left( \frac{lx}{\pi} \right) \right\}$$

$$\int_0^l F(x) \cos \frac{nx}{l}\, dx = \frac{l}{\pi} C\left\{ F\left( \frac{lx}{\pi} \right) \right\}$$

Thus if $F(x) = x$ for interval $(0,l)$

$$\int_0^l x \sin \frac{n\pi x}{l}\, dx = \frac{l}{\pi} S\left\{ \frac{l}{\pi} x \right\} = \frac{l^2}{\pi^2} S\{x\} = \frac{l^2}{\pi^2} \frac{(-1)^{n+1}}{n}$$

$$(n = 1, 2, \cdots)$$

# LAPLACE OPERATIONS

| | $F(t)$ | $f(s)$ |
|---|---|---|
| 1 | $F(t)$ | $\int_0^\infty e^{-st}F(t)\,dt$ |
| 2 | $AF(t) + BG(t)$ | $Af(s) + Bg(s)$ |
| 3 | $F'(t)$ | $sf(s) - F(+0)$ |
| 4 | $F^{(n)}(t)$ | $s^n f(s) - s^{n-1}F(+0)$ $-\, s^{n-2}F'(+0) - \cdots$ $-\, F^{(n-1)}(+0)$ |
| 5 | $\int_0^t F(\tau)\,d\tau$ | $\dfrac{1}{s}f(s)$ |
| 6 | $\int_0^t \int_0^\tau F(\lambda)\,d\lambda\,d\tau$ | $\dfrac{1}{s^2}f(s)$ |
| 7 | $\int_0^t F_1(t - \tau)F_2(\tau)\,d\tau = F_1 * F_2$ | $f_1(s)f_2(s)$ |
| 8 | $tF(t)$ | $-f'(s)$ |
| 9 | $t^n F(t)$ | $(-1)^n f^{(n)}(s)$ |
| 10 | $\dfrac{1}{t}F(t)$ | $\int_s^\infty f(x)\,dx$ |
| 11 | $e^{at}F(t)$ | $f(s - a)$ |
| 12 | $F(t - b)$, where $F(t) = 0$ when $t < 0$ | $e^{-bs}f(s)$ |
| 13 | $\dfrac{1}{c}F\left(\dfrac{t}{c}\right)$ | $f(cs)$ |
| 14 | $\dfrac{1}{c}e^{\frac{bt}{c}}F\left(\dfrac{t}{c}\right)$ | $f(cs - b)$ |
| 15 | $F(t + a) = F(t)$ | $\dfrac{\int_0^a e^{-st}F(t)\,dt}{1 - e^{-as}}$ |
| 16 | $F(t + a) = -F(t)$ | $\dfrac{\int_0^a e^{-st}F(t)\,dt}{1 + e^{-as}}$ |
| 17 | $F_1(t)$, the half-wave rectification of $F(t)$ in No. 16 | $\dfrac{f(s)}{1 - e^{-as}}$ |
| 18 | $F_2(t)$, the full-wave rectification of $F(t)$ in No. 16 | $f(s)\coth\dfrac{as}{2}$ |
| 19 | $\displaystyle\sum_1^m \dfrac{p(a_n)}{q'(a_n)}e^{a_n t}$ | $\dfrac{p(s)}{q(s)}$, $q(s) = (s - a_1)(s - a_2)$ $\cdots (s - a_m)$ |
| 20 | $e^{at}\displaystyle\sum_{n=1}^r \dfrac{\phi^{(r-n)}(a)}{(r - n)!}\dfrac{t^{n-1}}{(n - 1)!} + \cdots$ | $\dfrac{p(s)}{q(s)} = \dfrac{\phi(s)}{(s - a)^r}$ |

## LAPLACE TRANSFORMS

| | $f(s)$ | $F(t)$ |
|---|---|---|
| 1 | $\dfrac{1}{s}$ | $1$ |
| 2 | $\dfrac{1}{s^2}$ | $t$ |
| 3 | $\dfrac{1}{s^n}$ $(n = 1, 2, \cdots)$ | $\dfrac{t^{n-1}}{(n-1)!}$ |
| 4 | $\dfrac{1}{\sqrt{s}}$ | $\dfrac{1}{\sqrt{\pi t}}$ |
| 5 | $s^{-\frac{3}{2}}$ | $2\sqrt{\dfrac{t}{\pi}}$ |
| 6 | $s^{-(n+\frac{1}{2})}$ $(n = 1, 2, \cdots)$ | $\dfrac{2^n t^{n-\frac{1}{2}}}{1 \cdot 3 \cdot 5 \cdots (2n-1)\sqrt{\pi}}$ |
| 7 | $\dfrac{\Gamma(k)}{s^k}$ $(k > 0)$ | $t^{k-1}$ |
| 8 | $\dfrac{1}{s-a}$ | $e^{at}$ |
| 9 | $\dfrac{1}{(s-a)^2}$ | $te^{at}$ |
| 10 | $\dfrac{1}{(s-a)^n}$ $(n = 1, 2, \cdots)$ | $\dfrac{1}{(n-1)!}t^{n-1}e^{at}$ |
| 11 | $\dfrac{\Gamma(k)}{(s-a)^k}$ $(k > 0)$ | $t^{k-1}e^{at}$ |
| 12* | $\dfrac{1}{(s-a)(s-b)}$ | $\dfrac{1}{a-b}(e^{at} - e^{bt})$ |
| 13* | $\dfrac{s}{(s-a)(s-b)}$ | $\dfrac{1}{a-b}(ae^{at} - be^{bt})$ |
| 14* | $\dfrac{1}{(s-a)(s-b)(s-c)}$ | $-\dfrac{(b-c)e^{at} + (c-a)e^{bt} + (a-b)e^{ct}}{(a-b)(b-c)(c-a)}$ |
| 15 | $\dfrac{1}{s^2 + a^2}$ | $\dfrac{1}{a}\sin at$ |
| 16 | $\dfrac{s}{s^2 + a^2}$ | $\cos at$ |
| 17 | $\dfrac{1}{s^2 - a^2}$ | $\dfrac{1}{a}\sinh at$ |
| 18 | $\dfrac{s}{s^2 - a^2}$ | $\cosh at$ |
| 19 | $\dfrac{1}{s(s^2 + a^2)}$ | $\dfrac{1}{a^2}(1 - \cos at)$ |
| 20 | $\dfrac{1}{s^2(s^2 + a^2)}$ | $\dfrac{1}{a^3}(at - \sin at)$ |
| 21 | $\dfrac{1}{(s^2 + a^2)^2}$ | $\dfrac{1}{2a^3}(\sin at - at\cos at)$ |
| 22 | $\dfrac{s}{(s^2 + a^2)^2}$ | $\dfrac{t}{2a}\sin at$ |
| 23 | $\dfrac{s^2}{(s^2 + a^2)^2}$ | $\dfrac{1}{2a}(\sin at + at\cos at)$ |

* Here $a$, $b$, and (in 14) $c$ represent distinct constants.

| | $f(s)$ | $F(t)$ |
|---|---|---|
| 24 | $\dfrac{s^2 - a^2}{(s^2 + a^2)^2}$ | $t \cos at$ |
| 25 | $\dfrac{s}{(s^2 + a^2)(s^2 + b^2)}$ $(a^2 \neq b^2)$ | $\dfrac{\cos at - \cos bt}{b^2 - a^2}$ |
| 26 | $\dfrac{1}{(s - a)^2 + b^2}$ | $\dfrac{1}{b} e^{at} \sin bt$ |
| 27 | $\dfrac{s - a}{(s - a)^2 + b^2}$ | $e^{at} \cos bt$ |
| 28 | $\dfrac{3a^2}{s^3 + a^3}$ | $e^{-at} - e^{\frac{at}{2}} \left( \cos \dfrac{at \sqrt{3}}{2} \right.$ $\left. - \sqrt{3} \sin \dfrac{at \sqrt{3}}{2} \right)$ |
| 29 | $\dfrac{4a^3}{s^4 + 4a^4}$ | $\sin at \cosh at - \cos at \sinh at$ |
| 30 | $\dfrac{s}{s^4 + 4a^4}$ | $\dfrac{1}{2a^2} \sin at \sinh at$ |
| 31 | $\dfrac{1}{s^4 - a^4}$ | $\dfrac{1}{2a^3} (\sinh at - \sin at)$ |
| 32 | $\dfrac{s}{s^4 - a^4}$ | $\dfrac{1}{2a^2} (\cosh at - \cos at)$ |
| 33 | $\dfrac{8a^3 s^2}{(s^2 + a^2)^3}$ | $(1 + a^2 t^2) \sin at - at \cos at$ |
| 34* | $\dfrac{1}{s} \left( \dfrac{s - 1}{s} \right)^n$ | $L_n(t) = \dfrac{e^t}{n!} \dfrac{d^n}{dt^n} (t^n e^{-t})$ |
| 35 | $\dfrac{s}{(s - a)^{\frac{3}{2}}}$ | $\dfrac{1}{\sqrt{\pi t}} e^{at} (1 + 2at)$ |
| 36 | $\sqrt{s - a} - \sqrt{s - b}$ | $\dfrac{1}{2 \sqrt{\pi t^3}} (e^{bt} - e^{at})$ |
| 37 | $\dfrac{1}{\sqrt{s} + a}$ | $\dfrac{1}{\sqrt{\pi t}} - a e^{a^2 t} \operatorname{erfc} (a \sqrt{t})$ |
| 38 | $\dfrac{\sqrt{s}}{s - a^2}$ | $\dfrac{1}{\sqrt{\pi t}} + a e^{a^2 t} \operatorname{erf} (a \sqrt{t})$ |
| 39 | $\dfrac{\sqrt{s}}{s + a^2}$ | $\dfrac{1}{\sqrt{\pi t}} - \dfrac{2a}{\sqrt{\pi}} e^{-a^2 t} \displaystyle\int_0^{a\sqrt{t}} e^{\lambda^2} \, d\lambda$ |
| 40 | $\dfrac{1}{\sqrt{s} (s - a^2)}$ | $\dfrac{1}{a} e^{a^2 t} \operatorname{erf} (a \sqrt{t})$ |
| 41 | $\dfrac{1}{\sqrt{s} (s + a^2)}$ | $\dfrac{2}{a \sqrt{\pi}} e^{-a^2 t} \displaystyle\int_0^{a\sqrt{t}} e^{\lambda^2} \, d\lambda$ |
| 42 | $\dfrac{b^2 - a^2}{(s - a^2)(b + \sqrt{s})}$ | $e^{a^2 t} [b - a \operatorname{erf} (a \sqrt{t})]$ $- b e^{b^2 t} \operatorname{erfc} (b \sqrt{t})$ |
| 43 | $\dfrac{1}{\sqrt{s} (\sqrt{s} + a)}$ | $e^{a^2 t} \operatorname{erfc} (a \sqrt{t})$ |
| 44 | $\dfrac{1}{(s + a) \sqrt{s + b}}$ | $\dfrac{1}{\sqrt{b - a}} e^{-at} \operatorname{erf} (\sqrt{b - a} \sqrt{t})$ |

* $L_n(t)$ is the Laguerre polynomial of degree $n$.

| | $f(s)$ | $F(t)$ |
|---|---|---|
| 45 | $\dfrac{b^2 - a^2}{\sqrt{s}\,(s - a^2)(\sqrt{s} + b)}$ | $e^{a^2t}\left[\dfrac{b}{a}\,\mathrm{erf}\,(a\,\sqrt{t}) - 1\right]$ $+ e^{b^2t}\,\mathrm{erfc}\,(b\,\sqrt{t})$ |
| 46* | $\dfrac{(1 - s)^n}{s^{n+\frac{1}{2}}}$ | $\dfrac{n!}{(2n)!\,\sqrt{\pi t}}\,H_{2n}(\sqrt{t})$ |
| 47 | $\dfrac{(1 - s)^n}{s^{n+\frac{3}{2}}}$ | $-\dfrac{n!}{\sqrt{\pi}\,(2n + 1)!}\,H_{2n+1}(\sqrt{t})$ |
| 48† | $\dfrac{\sqrt{s + 2a}}{\sqrt{s}} - 1$ | $ae^{-at}[I_1(at) + I_0(at)]$ |
| 49 | $\dfrac{1}{\sqrt{s + a}\,\sqrt{s + b}}$ | $e^{-\frac{1}{2}(a+b)t}I_0\left(\dfrac{a - b}{2}t\right)$ |
| 50 | $\dfrac{\Gamma(k)}{(s + a)^k\,(s + b)^k}\ (k > 0)$ | $\sqrt{\pi}\left(\dfrac{t}{a - b}\right)^{k-\frac{1}{2}}e^{-\frac{1}{2}(a+b)t}$ $I_{k-\frac{1}{2}}\left(\dfrac{a - b}{2}t\right)$ |
| 51 | $\dfrac{1}{(s + a)^{\frac{1}{2}}(s + b)^{\frac{3}{2}}}$ | $te^{-\frac{1}{2}(a+b)t}\left[I_0\left(\dfrac{a - b}{2}t\right)\right.$ $\left. + I_1\left(\dfrac{a - b}{2}t\right)\right]$ |
| 52 | $\dfrac{\sqrt{s + 2a} - \sqrt{s}}{\sqrt{s + 2a} + \sqrt{s}}$ | $\dfrac{1}{t}\,e^{-at}I_1(at)$ |
| 53 | $\dfrac{(a - b)^k}{(\sqrt{s + a} + \sqrt{s + b})^{2k}}\ (k > 0)$ | $\dfrac{k}{t}\,e^{-\frac{1}{2}(a+b)t}I_k\left(\dfrac{a - b}{2}t\right)$ |
| 54 | $\dfrac{(\sqrt{s + a} + \sqrt{s})^{-2\nu}}{\sqrt{s}\sqrt{s + a}}\ (\nu > -1)$ | $\dfrac{1}{a^\nu}\,e^{-\frac{1}{2}at}I_\nu\left(\dfrac{1}{2}at\right)$ |
| 55 | $\dfrac{1}{\sqrt{s^2 + a^2}}$ | $J_0(at)$ |
| 56 | $\dfrac{(\sqrt{s^2 + a^2} - s)^\nu}{\sqrt{s^2 + a^2}}\ (\nu > -1)$ | $a^\nu J_\nu(at)$ |
| 57 | $\dfrac{1}{(s^2 + a^2)^k}\ (k > 0)$ | $\dfrac{\sqrt{\pi}}{\Gamma(k)}\left(\dfrac{t}{2a}\right)^{k-\frac{1}{2}}J_{k-\frac{1}{2}}(at)$ |
| 58 | $(\sqrt{s^2 + a^2} - s)^k(k > 0)$ | $\dfrac{ka^k}{t}\,J_k(at)$ |
| 59 | $\dfrac{(s - \sqrt{s^2 - a^2})^\nu}{\sqrt{s^2 - a^2}}\ (\nu > -1)$ | $a^\nu I_\nu(at)$ |
| 60 | $\dfrac{1}{(s^2 - a^2)^k}\ (k > 0)$ | $\dfrac{\sqrt{\pi}}{\Gamma(k)}\left(\dfrac{t}{2a}\right)^{k-\frac{1}{2}}I_{k-\frac{1}{2}}(at)$ |
| 61 | $\dfrac{e^{-ks}}{s}$ | $S_k(t) = \begin{cases} 0 \text{ when } 0 < t < k \\ 1 \text{ when } t > k \end{cases}$ |
| 62 | $\dfrac{e^{-ks}}{s^2}$ | $\begin{cases} 0 \quad \text{ when } 0 < t < k \\ t - k \text{ when } t > k \end{cases}$ |

* $H_n(x)$ is the Hermite polynomial, $H_n(x) = e^{x^2}\dfrac{d^n}{dx^n}\,(e^{-x^2})$.

† $I_n(x) = i^{-n}J_n(ix)$, where $J_n$ is Bessel's function of the first kind.

| | $f(s)$ | $F(t)$ |
|---|---|---|
| 63 | $\dfrac{e^{-ks}}{s^\mu}$ $(\mu > 0)$ | $\begin{cases} 0 & \text{when } 0 < t < k \\ \dfrac{(t-k)^{\mu-1}}{\Gamma(\mu)} & \text{when } t > k \end{cases}$ |
| 64 | $\dfrac{1 - e^{-ks}}{s}$ | $\begin{cases} 1 \text{ when } 0 < t < k \\ 0 \text{ when } t > k \end{cases}$ |
| 65 | $\dfrac{1}{s(1 - e^{-ks})} = \dfrac{1 + \coth \frac{1}{2}ks}{2s}$ | $S(k, t) = n$ when $(n-1)k < t < nk(n = 1, 2, \cdots)$ |
| 66 | $\dfrac{1}{s(e^{ks} - a)}$ | $\begin{cases} 0 & \text{when } 0 < t < k \\ 1 + a + a^2 + \cdots + a^{n-1} \\ \quad \text{when } nk < t < (n+1)k \\ \qquad (n = 1, 2, \cdots) \end{cases}$ |
| 67 | $\dfrac{1}{s} \tanh ks$ | $M(2k, t) = (-1)^{n-1}$ when $2k(n-1) < t < 2kn$ $(n = 1, 2, \cdots)$ |
| 68 | $\dfrac{1}{s(1 + e^{-ks})}$ | $\dfrac{1}{2} M(k, t) + \dfrac{1}{2} = \dfrac{1 - (-1)^n}{2}$ when $(n-1)k < t < nk$ |
| 69* | $\dfrac{1}{s^2} \tanh ks$ | $H(2k, t)$ |
| 70 | $\dfrac{1}{s \sinh ks}$ | $2S(2k, t + k) - 2 = 2(n-1)$ when $(2n-3)k < t < (2n-1)k$ $(t > 0)$ |
| 71 | $\dfrac{1}{s \cosh ks}$ | $M(2k, t + 3k) + 1 = 1 + (-1)^n$ when $(2n-3)k < t < (2n-1)k$ $(t > 0)$ |
| 72 | $\dfrac{1}{s} \coth ks$ | $2S(2k, t) - 1 = 2n - 1$ when $2k(n-1) < t < 2kn$ |
| 73 | $\dfrac{k}{s^2 + k^2} \coth \dfrac{\pi s}{2k}$ | $\lvert \sin kt \rvert$ |
| 74 | $\dfrac{1}{(s^2 + 1)(1 - e^{-\pi s})}$ | $\begin{cases} \sin t \text{ when } (2n-2)\pi \\ \quad < t < (2n-1)\pi \\ 0 \quad \text{when } (2n-1)\pi \\ \quad < t < 2n\pi \end{cases}$ |
| 75 | $\dfrac{1}{s} e^{-\frac{k}{s}}$ | $J_0(2 \sqrt{kt})$ |
| 76 | $\dfrac{1}{\sqrt{s}} e^{-\frac{k}{s}}$ | $\dfrac{1}{\sqrt{\pi t}} \cos 2 \sqrt{kt}$ |
| 77 | $\dfrac{1}{\sqrt{s}} e^{\frac{k}{s}}$ | $\dfrac{1}{\sqrt{\pi t}} \cosh 2 \sqrt{kt}$ |
| 78 | $\dfrac{1}{s^{\frac{3}{2}}} e^{-\frac{k}{s}}$ | $\dfrac{1}{\sqrt{\pi k}} \sin 2 \sqrt{kt}$ |
| 79 | $\dfrac{1}{s^{\frac{3}{2}}} e^{\frac{k}{s}}$ | $\dfrac{1}{\sqrt{\pi k}} \sinh 2 \sqrt{kt}$ |
| 80 | $\dfrac{1}{s^\mu} e^{-\frac{k}{s}}$ $(\mu > 0)$ | $\left(\dfrac{t}{k}\right)^{\frac{\mu-1}{2}} J_{\mu-1}(2 \sqrt{kt})$ |

* $H(2k,t) = k + (r - k)(-1)^n$ where $t = 2kn + r$; $0 \leq r < 2k$; $n = 0, 1, 2, \ldots$.

| | $f(s)$ | $F(t)$ |
|---|---|---|
| 81 | $\dfrac{1}{s^{\mu}} e^{\frac{k}{s}} \ (\mu > 0)$ | $\left(\dfrac{t}{k}\right)^{\frac{\mu-1}{2}} I_{\mu-1}(2\sqrt{kt})$ |
| 82 | $e^{-k\sqrt{s}} \ (k > 0)$ | $\dfrac{k}{2\sqrt{\pi t^3}} \exp\left(-\dfrac{k^2}{4t}\right)$ |
| 83 | $\dfrac{1}{s} e^{-k\sqrt{s}} \ (k \geqq 0)$ | $\operatorname{erfc}\left(\dfrac{k}{2\sqrt{t}}\right)$ |
| 84 | $\dfrac{1}{\sqrt{s}} e^{-k\sqrt{s}} \ (k \geqq 0)$ | $\dfrac{1}{\sqrt{\pi t}} \exp\left(-\dfrac{k^2}{4t}\right)$ |
| 85 | $s^{-\frac{3}{2}} e^{-k\sqrt{s}} \ (k \geqq 0)$ | $2\sqrt{\dfrac{t}{\pi}} \exp\left(-\dfrac{k^2}{4t}\right)$ $\qquad - k \operatorname{erfc}\left(\dfrac{k}{2\sqrt{t}}\right)$ |
| 86 | $\dfrac{a e^{-k\sqrt{s}}}{s(a + \sqrt{s})} \ (k \geqq 0)$ | $-e^{ak}e^{a^2 t} \operatorname{erfc}\left(a\sqrt{t} + \dfrac{k}{2\sqrt{t}}\right)$ $\qquad + \operatorname{erfc}\left(\dfrac{k}{2\sqrt{t}}\right)$ |
| 87 | $\dfrac{e^{-k\sqrt{s}}}{\sqrt{s}\,(a + \sqrt{s})} \ (k \geqq 0)$ | $e^{ak}e^{a^2 t} \operatorname{erfc}\left(a\sqrt{t} + \dfrac{k}{2\sqrt{t}}\right)$ |
| 88 | $\dfrac{e^{-k\sqrt{s(s+a)}}}{\sqrt{s(s+a)}}$ | $\begin{cases} 0 & \text{when } 0 < t < k \\ e^{-\frac{1}{2}at}I_0(\tfrac{1}{2}a\sqrt{t^2-k^2}) & \text{when } t > k \end{cases}$ |
| 89 | $\dfrac{e^{-k\sqrt{s^2+a^2}}}{\sqrt{s^2+a^2}}$ | $\begin{cases} 0 & \text{when } 0 < t < k \\ J_0(a\sqrt{t^2-k^2}) & \text{when } t > k \end{cases}$ |
| 90 | $\dfrac{e^{-k\sqrt{s^2-a^2}}}{\sqrt{s^2-a^2}}$ | $\begin{cases} 0 & \text{when } 0 < t < k \\ I_0(a\sqrt{t^2-k^2}) & \text{when } t > k \end{cases}$ |
| 91 | $\dfrac{e^{-k(\sqrt{s^2+a^2}-s)}}{\sqrt{s^2+a^2}} \ (k \geqq 0)$ | $J_0(a\sqrt{t^2+2kt})$ |
| 92 | $e^{-ks} - e^{-k\sqrt{s^2+a^2}}$ | $\begin{cases} 0 & \text{when } 0 < t < k \\ \dfrac{ak}{\sqrt{t^2-k^2}} J_1(a\sqrt{t^2-k^2}) & \\ & \text{when } t > k \end{cases}$ |
| 93 | $e^{-k\sqrt{s^2-a^2}} - e^{-ks}$ | $\begin{cases} 0 & \text{when } 0 < t < k \\ \dfrac{ak}{\sqrt{t^2-k^2}} I_1(a\sqrt{t^2-k^2}) & \\ & \text{when } t > k \end{cases}$ |
| 94 | $\dfrac{a^{\nu}e^{-k\sqrt{s^2+a^2}}}{\sqrt{s^2+a^2}\,(\sqrt{s^2+a^2}+s)^{\nu}}$ $(\nu > -1)$ | $\begin{cases} 0 & \text{when } 0 < t < k \\ \left(\dfrac{t-k}{t+k}\right)^{\frac{1}{2}\nu} J_{\nu}(a\sqrt{t^2-k^2}) & \\ & \text{when } t > k \end{cases}$ |
| 95 | $\dfrac{1}{s} \log s$ | $\Gamma'(1) - \log t \quad [\Gamma'(1) = -0.5772]$ |

| | $f(s)$ | $F(t)$ |
|---|---|---|
| 96 | $\dfrac{1}{s^k} \log s \ (k > 0)$ | $t^{k-1} \left\{ \dfrac{\Gamma'(k)}{[\Gamma(k)]^2} - \dfrac{\log t}{\Gamma(k)} \right\}$ |
| 97 | $\dfrac{\log s}{s - a} \ (a > 0)$ | $e^{at}[\log a - \text{Ei}(-at)]$ |
| 98 | $\dfrac{\log s}{s^2 + 1}$ | $\cos t \ \text{Si}(t) - \sin t \ \text{Ci}(t)$ |
| 99 | $\dfrac{s \log s}{s^2 + 1}$ | $- \sin t \ \text{Si}(t) - \cos t \ \text{Ci}(t)$ |
| 100 | $\dfrac{1}{s} \log (1 + ks) \ (k > 0)$ | $- \text{Ei} \left( - \dfrac{t}{k} \right)$ |
| 101 | $\log \dfrac{s - a}{s - b}$ | $\dfrac{1}{t} (e^{bt} - e^{at})$ |
| 102 | $\dfrac{1}{s} \log (1 + k^2 s^2)$ | $-2\text{Ci} \left( \dfrac{t}{k} \right)$ |
| 103 | $\dfrac{1}{s} \log (s^2 + a^2) \ (a > 0)$ | $2 \log a - 2\text{Ci}(at)$ |
| 104 | $\dfrac{1}{s^2} \log (s^2 + a^2) \ (a > 0)$ | $\dfrac{2}{a} [at \log a + \sin at - at \ \text{Ci}(at)]$ |
| 105 | $\log \dfrac{s^2 + a^2}{s^2}$ | $\dfrac{2}{t} (1 - \cos at)$ |
| 106 | $\log \dfrac{s^2 - a^2}{s^2}$ | $\dfrac{2}{t} (1 - \cosh at)$ |
| 107 | $\arctan \dfrac{k}{s}$ | $\dfrac{1}{t} \sin kt$ |
| 108 | $\dfrac{1}{s} \arctan \dfrac{k}{s}$ | $\text{Si}(kt)$ |
| 109 | $e^{k^2 s^2} \text{erfc}\,(ks) \ (k > 0)$ | $\dfrac{1}{k \sqrt{\pi}} \exp \left( - \dfrac{t^2}{4k^2} \right)$ |
| 110 | $\dfrac{1}{s} e^{k^2 s^2} \text{erfc}\,(ks) \ (k > 0)$ | $\text{erf} \left( \dfrac{t}{2k} \right)$ |
| 111 | $e^{ks} \text{erfc}\,(\sqrt{ks}) \ (k > 0)$ | $\dfrac{\sqrt{k}}{\pi \sqrt{t} \,(t + k)}$ |
| 112 | $\dfrac{1}{\sqrt{s}} \text{erfc}\,(\sqrt{ks})$ | $\begin{cases} 0 & \text{when } 0 < t < k \\ (\pi t)^{-\frac{1}{2}} & \text{when } t > k \end{cases}$ |
| 113 | $\dfrac{1}{\sqrt{s}} e^{ks} \text{erfc}\,(\sqrt{ks}) \ (k > 0)$ | $\dfrac{1}{\sqrt{\pi(t + k)}}$ |
| 114 | $\text{erf} \left( \dfrac{k}{\sqrt{s}} \right)$ | $\dfrac{1}{\pi t} \sin (2k \sqrt{t})$ |
| 115 | $\dfrac{1}{\sqrt{s}} e^{\frac{k^2}{s}} \text{erfc} \left( \dfrac{k}{\sqrt{s}} \right)$ | $\dfrac{1}{\sqrt{\pi t}} e - 2k\sqrt{t}$ |
| 116* | $K_0(ks)$ | $\begin{cases} 0 & \text{when } 0 < t < k \\ (t^2 - k^2)^{-\frac{1}{2}} & \text{when } t > k \end{cases}$ |
| 117 | $K_0(k \sqrt{s})$ | $\dfrac{1}{2t} \exp \left( - \dfrac{k^2}{4t} \right)$ |

* $K_n(x)$ is Bessel's function of the second kind for the imaginary argument.

300

| | $f(s)$ | $F(t)$ |
|---|---|---|
| 118 | $\dfrac{1}{s} e^{ks} K_1(ks)$ | $\dfrac{1}{k} \sqrt{t(t + 2k)}$ |
| 119 | $\dfrac{1}{\sqrt{s}} K_1(k\sqrt{s})$ | $\dfrac{1}{k} \exp\left(-\dfrac{k^2}{4t}\right)$ |
| 120 | $\dfrac{1}{\sqrt{s}} e^{\frac{k}{s}} K_0\left(\dfrac{k}{s}\right)$ | $\dfrac{2}{\sqrt{\pi t}} K_0(2\sqrt{2kt})$ |
| 121 | $\pi e^{-ks} I_0(ks)$ | $\begin{cases} [t(2k-t)]^{-\frac{1}{2}} & \text{when } 0 < t < 2k \\ 0 & \text{when } t > 2k \end{cases}$ |
| 122* | $e^{-ks} I_1(ks)$ | $\begin{cases} \dfrac{k-t}{\pi k \sqrt{t(2k-t)}} & \text{when } 0 < t < 2k \\ 0 & \text{when } t > 2k \end{cases}$ |

**\*** Several additional transforms, especially those involving other Bessel functions, can be found in the tables by G. A. Campbell and R. M. Foster, "Fourier Integrals for Practical Applications," or N. W. McLachlan and P. Humbert, "Formulaire pour le calcul symbolique." In the tables by Campbell and Foster, only those entries containing the condition $0 < g$ or $k < g$, where $g$ is our $t$, are Laplace transforms.

## FOURIER TRANSFORMS
### FINITE SINE TRANSFORMS

| | $f_s(n)$ | $F(x)$ |
|---|---|---|
| 1 | $f_s(n) = \displaystyle\int_0^\pi F(x) \sin nx\, dx$ $(n = 1, 2, \cdots)$ | $F(x)$ |
| 2 | $(-1)^{n+1} f_s(n)$ | $F(\pi - x)$ |
| 3 | $\dfrac{1}{n}$ | $\dfrac{\pi - x}{\pi}$ |
| 4 | $\dfrac{(-1)^{n+1}}{n}$ | $\dfrac{x}{\pi}$ |
| 5 | $\dfrac{1 - (-1)^n}{n}$ | $1$ |
| 6 | $\dfrac{2}{n^2} \sin \dfrac{n\pi}{2}$ | $\begin{cases} x & \text{when } 0 < x < \pi/2 \\ \pi - x & \text{when } \pi/2 < x < \pi \end{cases}$ |
| 7 | $\dfrac{(-1)^{n+1}}{n^3}$ | $\dfrac{x(\pi^2 - x^2)}{6\pi}$ |
| 8 | $\dfrac{1 - (-1)^n}{n^3}$ | $\dfrac{x(\pi - x)}{2}$ |
| 9 | $\dfrac{\pi^2(-1)^{n-1}}{n} - \dfrac{2[1 - (-1)^n]}{n^3}$ | $x^2$ |
| 10 | $\pi(-1)^n \left(\dfrac{6}{n^3} - \dfrac{\pi^2}{n}\right)$ | $x^3$ |
| 11 | $\dfrac{n}{n^2 + c^2} [1 - (-1)^n e^{c\pi}]$ | $e^{cx}$ |
| 12 | $\dfrac{n}{n^2 + c^2}$ | $\dfrac{\sinh c(\pi - x)}{\sinh c\pi}$ |

# FOURIER TRANSFORMS (Continued)

| | $f_s(n)$ | $F(x)$ |
|---|---|---|
| 13 | $\dfrac{n}{n^2 - k^2}$ $(k \neq 0, 1, 2, \cdots)$ | $\dfrac{\sin k(\pi - x)}{\sin k\pi}$ |
| 14 | $\begin{cases} \dfrac{\pi}{2} \text{ when } n = m & (m = 1, 2, \cdots) \\ 0 \text{ when } n \neq m \end{cases}$ | $\sin mx$ |
| 15 | $\dfrac{n}{n^2 - k^2}[1 - (-1)^n \cos k\pi]$ $(k \neq 1, 2, \cdots)$ | $\cos kx$ |
| 16 | $\begin{cases} \dfrac{n}{n^2 - m^2}[1 - (-1)^{n+m}] \\ \qquad \text{when } n \neq m = 1, 2, \cdots \\ 0 \qquad \text{when } n = m \end{cases}$ | $\cos mx$ |
| 17 | $\dfrac{n}{(n^2 - k^2)^2}$ $(k \neq 0, 1, 2, \cdots)$ | $\dfrac{\pi \sin kx}{2k \sin^2 k\pi} - \dfrac{x \cos k(\pi - x)}{2k \sin k\pi}$ |
| 18 | $\dfrac{b^n}{n}$ $(|b| \leqq 1)$ | $\dfrac{2}{\pi} \arctan \dfrac{b \sin x}{1 - b \cos x}$ |
| 19 | $\dfrac{1 - (-1)^n}{n} b^n$ $(|b| \leqq 1)$ | $\dfrac{2}{\pi} \arctan \dfrac{2b \sin x}{1 - b^2}$ |

## FINITE COSINE TRANSFORMS

| | $f_c(n)$ | $F(x)$ |
|---|---|---|
| 1 | $f_c(n) = \displaystyle\int_0^\pi F(x) \cos nx \, dx$ $(n = 0, 1, 2, \cdots)$ | $F(x)$ |
| 2 | $(-1)^n f_c(n)$ | $F(\pi - x)$ |
| 3 | $0$ when $n = 1, 2, \cdots$ ; $f_c(0) = \pi$ | $1$ |
| 4 | $\dfrac{2}{n} \sin \dfrac{n\pi}{2}$ ; $f_c(0) = 0$ | $\begin{cases} \ \ 1 \text{ when } 0 < x < \pi/2 \\ -1 \text{ when } \pi/2 < x < \pi \end{cases}$ |
| 5 | $-\dfrac{1 - (-1)^n}{n^2}$ ; $f_c(0) = \dfrac{\pi^2}{2}$ | $x$ |
| 6 | $\dfrac{(-1)^n}{n^2}$ ; $f_c(0) = \dfrac{\pi^2}{6}$ | $\dfrac{x^2}{2\pi}$ |
| 7 | $\dfrac{1}{n^2}$ ; $f_c(0) = 0$ | $\dfrac{(\pi - x)^2}{2\pi} - \dfrac{\pi}{6}$ |
| 8 | $3\pi^2 \dfrac{(-1)^n}{n^2} - 6 \dfrac{1 - (-1)^n}{n^4}$ ; $f_c(0) = \dfrac{\pi^4}{4}$ | $x^3$ |
| 9 | $\dfrac{(-1)^n e^{c\pi} - 1}{n^2 + c^2}$ | $\dfrac{1}{c} e^{cx}$ |
| 10 | $\dfrac{1}{n^2 + c^2}$ | $\dfrac{\cosh c(\pi - x)}{c \sinh c\pi}$ |
| 11 | $\dfrac{k}{n^2 - k^2}[(-1)^n \cos \pi k - 1]$ $(k \neq 0, 1, 2, \cdots)$ | $\sin kx$ |
| 12 | $\dfrac{(-1)^{n+m} - 1}{n^2 - m^2}$ ; $f_c(m) = 0$ $(m = 1, 2, \cdots)$ | $\dfrac{1}{m} \sin mx$ |
| 13 | $\dfrac{1}{n^2 - k^2}$ $(k \neq 0, 1, 2, \cdots)$ | $-\dfrac{\cos k(\pi - x)}{k \sin k\pi}$ |
| 14 | $0$ when $n = 1, 2, \cdots$ ; $f_c(m) = \dfrac{\pi}{2}$ $(m = 1, 2, \cdots)$ | $\cos mx$ |

The following functions appear among the entries of the preceding tables on transforms.

| Function | Definition | Name |
|---|---|---|
| $Ei(x)$ | $\int_{-\infty}^{x} \dfrac{e^v}{v}\, dv$; or sometimes defined as $-Ei(-x) = \int_{x}^{\infty} \dfrac{e^{-v}}{v}\, dv$ | See index for Sine, Cosine, and Exponential Integral tables |
| $Si(x)$ | $\int_{0}^{x} \dfrac{\sin v}{v}\, dv$ | See index for Sine, Cosine, and Exponential Integral tables |
| $Ci(x)$ | $\int_{\infty}^{x} \dfrac{\cos v}{v}\, dv$; or sometimes defined as negative of this integral | See index for Sine, Cosine, and Exponential Integral tables |
| $erf(x)$ | $\dfrac{2}{\sqrt{\pi}} \int_{0}^{x} e^{-v^2}\, dv$ | Error function |
| $erfc(x)$ | $1 - erf(x) = \dfrac{2}{\sqrt{\pi}} \int_{x}^{\infty} e^{-v^2}\, dv$ | Complementary function to error function |
| $L_n(x)$ | $\dfrac{e^x}{n!} \dfrac{d^n}{dx^n} (x^n e^{-x})$, $n = 0, 1, \cdots$ | Laguerre polynomial of degree $n$ |

# DIFFERENTIAL EQUATIONS
## Special Formulas

Certain types of differential equations occur sufficiently often to justify the use of formulas for the corresponding particular solutions. The following set of tables I to XIV covers all first-second and $n$'th order ordinary linear differential equations with constant coefficients for which the right members are of the form $P(x)e^{rx} \sin sx$ or $P(x)e^{rx} \cos sx$ where $r$ and $s$ are constants and $P(x)$ is a polynomial of degree $n$.

When the right member of a reducible partial linear differential equation with constant coefficients is not zero, particular solutions for certain types of right members are contained in tables XV to XXI. In these tables both $F$ and $P$ are used to denote polynomials, and it is assumed that no denominator is zero. In any formula the roles of $x$ and $y$ may be reversed throughout, changing a formula in which $x$ dominates to one in which $y$ dominates. Tables XIX, XX, XXI are applicable whether the equations are reducible or not. The symbol $\binom{m}{n}$ stands for $\dfrac{m!}{(m-n)!n!}$ and is the $n+1$ st coefficient in the expansion of $(a+b)^m$. Also $0! = 1$ by definition.

The tables as herewith given are those contained in the text Differential Equations by Ginn and Company (1955) and are published with their kind permission and that of the author, Professor Frederick H. Steen.

**TABLE I: $(D - a)y = R$**

| $R$ | $y_p$ |
|---|---|
| 1. $e^{rx}$ | $\dfrac{e^{rx}}{r-a}$ |
| 2. $\sin sx$* | $-\dfrac{a\sin sx + s\cos sx}{a^2+s^2} = -\dfrac{1}{\sqrt{a^2+s^2}}\sin\left(sx+\tan^{-1}\dfrac{s}{a}\right)$ |
| 3. $P(x)$ | $-\dfrac{1}{a}\left[P(x) + \dfrac{P'(x)}{a} + \dfrac{P''(x)}{a^2} + \cdots + \dfrac{P^{(n)}(x)}{a^n}\right]$ |
| 4. $e^{rx}\sin sx$* | Replace $a$ by $a-r$ in formula 2 and multiply by $e^{rx}$. |
| 5. $P(x)e^{rx}$ | Replace $a$ by $a-r$ in formula 3 and multiply by $e^{rx}$. |
| 6. $P(x)\sin sx$* | $-\sin sx\left[\dfrac{a}{a^2+s^2}P(x) + \dfrac{a^2-s^2}{(a^2+s^2)^2}P'(x) + \dfrac{a^3-3as^2}{(a^2+s^2)^3}P''(x) + \cdots \right.$ $\left. + \dfrac{a^k - \binom{k}{2}a^{k-2}s^2 + \binom{k}{4}a^{k-4}s^4 - \cdots}{(a^2+s^2)^k}P^{(k-1)}(x) + \cdots\right]$ $-\cos sx\left[\dfrac{s}{a^2+s^2}P(x) + \dfrac{2as}{(a^2+s^2)^2}P'(x) + \dfrac{3a^2s-s^3}{(a^2+s^2)^3}P''(x) + \cdots \right.$ $\left. + \dfrac{\binom{k}{1}a^{k-1}s - \binom{k}{3}a^{k-3}s^3 + \cdots}{(a^2+s^2)^k}P^{(k-1)}(x) + \cdots\right]$ |
| 7. $P(x)e^{rx}\sin sx$* | Replace $a$ by $a-r$ in formula 6 and multiply by $e^{rx}$. |
| 8. $e^{ax}$ | $xe^{ax}$ |
| 9. $e^{ax}\sin sx$* | $-\dfrac{e^{ax}\cos sx}{s}$ |
| 10. $P(x)e^{ax}$ | $e^{ax}\displaystyle\int P(x)\,dx$ |
| 11. $P(x)e^{ax}\sin sx$* | $\dfrac{e^{ax}\sin sx}{s}\left[\dfrac{P'(x)}{s} - \dfrac{P'''(x)}{s^3} + \dfrac{P^{v}(x)}{s^5} - \cdots\right] - \dfrac{e^{ax}\cos sx}{s}\left[P(x) - \dfrac{P''(x)}{s^2} + \dfrac{P^{iv}(x)}{s^4} - \cdots\right]$ |

* For $\cos sx$ in $R$ replace "sin" by "cos" and "cos" by "− sin" in $y_p$.

$$D^n = \dfrac{d^n}{dx^n} \qquad \binom{m}{n} = \dfrac{m!}{(m-n)!\,n!} \qquad 0! = 1$$

## TABLE II: $(D-a)^2 y = R$

| R | $y_p$ |
|---|---|
| 12. $e^{rx}$ | $\dfrac{e^{rx}}{(r-a)^2}$ |
| 13. $\sin sx^*$ | $\dfrac{1}{(a^2+s^2)^2}[(a^2-s^2)\sin sx + 2as\cos sx] = \dfrac{1}{a^2+s^2}\sin\left(sx+\tan^{-1}\dfrac{2as}{a^2-s^2}\right)$ |
| 14. $P(x)$ | $\dfrac{1}{a^2}\left[P(x)+\dfrac{2P'(x)}{a}+\dfrac{3P''(x)}{a^2}+\cdots+\dfrac{(n+1)P^{(n)}(x)}{a^n}\right]$ |
| 15. $e^{rx}\sin sx^*$ | Replace $a$ by $a-r$ in formula 13 and multiply by $e^{rx}$. |
| 16. $P(x)e^{rx}$ | Replace $a$ by $a-r$ in formula 14 and multiply by $e^{rx}$. |
| 17. $P(x)\sin sx^*$ | $\sin sx\left[\dfrac{a^2-s^2}{(a^2+s^2)^2}P(x)+2\dfrac{a^3-3as^2}{(a^2+s^2)^3}P'(x)+3\dfrac{a^4-6a^2s^2+s^4}{(a^2+s^2)^4}P''(x)+\cdots\right.$ $\left.+(k-1)\dfrac{a^k-\binom{k}{2}a^{k-2}s^2+\binom{k}{4}a^{k-4}s^4-\cdots}{(a^2+s^2)^k}P^{(k-2)}(x)+\cdots\right]$ $+\cos sx\left[\dfrac{2as}{(a^2+s^2)^2}P(x)+2\dfrac{3a^2s-s^3}{(a^2+s^2)^3}P'(x)+3\dfrac{4a^3s-4as^3}{(a^2+s^2)^4}P''(x)+\cdots\right.$ $\left.+(k-1)\dfrac{\binom{k}{1}a^{k-1}s-\binom{k}{3}a^{k-3}s^3+\cdots}{(a^2+s^2)^k}P^{(k-2)}(x)+\cdots\right]$ |
| 18. $P(x)e^{rx}\sin sx^*$ | Replace $a$ by $a-r$ in formula 17 and multiply by $e^{rx}$. |
| 19. $e^{ax}$ | $\frac{1}{2}x^2 e^{ax}$ |
| 20. $e^{ax}\sin sx^*$ | $-\dfrac{e^{ax}\sin sx}{s^2}$ |
| 21. $P(x)e^{ax}$ | $e^{ax}\displaystyle\iint P(x)dx\,dx$ |
| 22. $P(x)e^{ax}\sin sx^*$ | $\dfrac{e^{ax}\sin sx}{s^2}\left[P(x)-\dfrac{3P''(x)}{s^2}+\dfrac{5P^{\mathrm{iv}}(x)}{s^4}-\dfrac{7P^{\mathrm{vi}}(x)}{s^6}+\cdots\right]$ $-\dfrac{e^{ax}\cos sx}{s^2}\left[\dfrac{2P'(x)}{s}-\dfrac{4P'''(x)}{s^3}+\dfrac{6P^{\mathrm{v}}(x)}{s^5}-\cdots\right]$ |

\* For cos $sx$ in $R$ replace "sin" by "cos" and "cos" by "− sin" in $y_p$.

# DIFFERENTIAL EQUATIONS (Continued)

## TABLE III: $(D^2 + q)y = R$

| $R$ | $y_p$ |
|---|---|
| 23. $e^{rx}$ | $\dfrac{e^{rx}}{r^2+q}$ |
| 24. $\sin sx$* | $\dfrac{\sin sx}{-s^2+q}$ |
| 25. $P(x)$ | $\dfrac{1}{q}\left[P(x) - \dfrac{P''(x)}{q} + \dfrac{P^{iv}(x)}{q^2} - \cdots + (-1)^k \dfrac{P^{(2k)}(x)}{q^k}\cdots\right]$ |
| 26. $e^{rx}\sin sx$* | $\dfrac{e^{rx}\sin sx - 2\,rs\,e^{rx}\cos sx}{(r^2-s^2+q)^2+(2rs)^2} = \dfrac{e^{rx}}{\sqrt{(r^2-s^2+q)^2+(2rs)^2}}\sin\left[sx - \tan^{-1}\dfrac{2rs}{r^2-s^2+q}\right]$ |
| 27. $P(x)e^{rx}$ | $\dfrac{e^{rx}}{r^2+q}\left[P(x) - \dfrac{2r}{r^2+q}P'(x) + \dfrac{3r^2-q}{(r^2+q)^2}P''(x) - \dfrac{4r^3-4qr}{(r^2+q)^3}P'''(x) + \cdots \right.$ $\left. + (-1)^{k-1}\dfrac{\binom{k}{1}r^{k-1} - \binom{k}{3}r^{k-3}q + \binom{k}{5}r^{k-5}q^2 - \cdots}{(r^2+q)^{k-1}}P^{(k-1)}(x) + \cdots\right]$ |
| 28. $P(x)\sin sx$* | $\dfrac{\sin sx}{(-s^2+q)}\left[P(x) - \dfrac{3s^2+q}{(-s^2+q)^2}P''(x) + \dfrac{5s^4+10s^2q+q^2}{(-s^2+q)^4}P^{iv}(x) + \cdots \right.$ $\left. + (-1)^k\dfrac{\binom{2k+1}{1}s^{2k} + \binom{2k+1}{3}s^{2k-2}q + \binom{2k+1}{5}s^{2k-4}q^2 + \cdots}{(-s^2+q)^{2k}}P^{(2k)}(x) + \cdots\right]$ $- \dfrac{s\cos sx}{(-s^2+q)}\left[\dfrac{2P'(x)}{(-s^2+q)} - \dfrac{4s^2+4q}{(-s^2+q)^3}P'''(x) + \cdots \right.$ $\left. + (-1)^{k+1}\dfrac{\binom{2k}{1}s^{2k-2} + \binom{2k}{3}s^{2k-4}q + \cdots}{(-s^2+q)^{2k-1}}P^{(2k-1)}(x) + \cdots\right]$ |

## TABLE IV: $(D^2 + b^2)y = R$

| $R$ | $y_p$ |
|---|---|
| 29. $\sin bx$* | $-\dfrac{x\cos bx}{2b}$ |
| 30. $P(x)\sin bx$* | $\dfrac{x\sin bx}{(2b)^2}\left[P(x) - \dfrac{P''(x)}{(2b)^2} + \dfrac{P^{iv}(x)}{(2b)^4} - \cdots\right] - \dfrac{\cos bx}{2b}\int\left[P(x) - \dfrac{P''(x)}{(2b)^2} + \cdots\right]dx$ |

* For cos $sx$ in $R$ replace "sin" by "cos" and "cos" by "$-$sin" in $y_p$.

# DIFFERENTIAL EQUATIONS (Continued)

## TABLE V: $(D^2 + pD + q)y = R$

| $R$ | $y_p$ |
|---|---|
| 31. $e^{rx}$ | $\dfrac{e^{rx}}{r^2+pr+q}$ |
| 32. $\sin sx$ * | $\dfrac{(q-s^2)\sin sx - ps\cos sx}{(q-s^2)^2+(ps)^2} = \dfrac{1}{\sqrt{(q-s^2)^2+(ps)^2}}\sin\left(sx - \tan^{-1}\dfrac{ps}{q-s^2}\right)$ |
| 33. $P(x)$ | $\dfrac{1}{q}\left[P(x) - \dfrac{p}{q}P'(x) + \dfrac{p^2-q}{q^2}P''(x) - \dfrac{p^3-2pq}{q^3}P'''(x) + \cdots\right.$ $\left.+ (-1)^n \dfrac{p^n - \binom{n-1}{1}p^{n-2}q + \binom{n-2}{2}p^{n-4}q^2 - \cdots}{q^n}P^{(n)}(x)\right]$ |
| 34. $e^{rx}\sin sx$ * | Replace $p$ by $p+2r$, $q$ by $q+pr+r^2$ in formula 32 and multiply by $e^{rx}$. |
| 35. $P(x)e^{rx}$ | Replace $p$ by $p+2r$, $q$ by $q+pr+r^2$ in formula 33 and multiply by $e^{rx}$. |

## TABLE VI: $(D-b)(D-a)y = R$

| $R$ | |
|---|---|
| 36. $P(x)\sin sx$ * | $\dfrac{\sin sx}{b-a}\left[\left(\dfrac{a}{a^2+s^2} - \dfrac{b}{b^2+s^2}\right)P(x) + \left(\dfrac{a^2-s^2}{(a^2+s^2)^2} - \dfrac{b^2-s^2}{(b^2+s^2)^2}\right)P'(x)\right.$ $\left. + \left(\dfrac{a^3-3as^2}{(a^2+s^2)^3} - \dfrac{b^3-3bs^2}{(b^2+s^2)^3}\right)P''(x) + \cdots\right]$ $+ \dfrac{\cos sx}{b-a}\left[\left(\dfrac{s}{a^2+s^2} - \dfrac{s}{b^2+s^2}\right)P(x) + \left(\dfrac{2as}{(a^2+s^2)^2} - \dfrac{2bs}{(b^2+s^2)^2}\right)P'(x)\right.$ $\left. + \left(\dfrac{3a^2s-s^3}{(a^2+s^2)^3} - \dfrac{3b^2s-s^3}{(b^2+s^2)^3}\right)P''(x) + \cdots\right]^\dagger$ |
| 37. $P(x)e^{rx}\sin sx$ * | Replace $a$ by $a-r$, $b$ by $b-r$ in formula 36 and multiply by $e^{rx}$. |
| 38. $P(x)e^{ax}$ | $\dfrac{e^{ax}}{a-b}\left[\iint P(x)\,dx + \dfrac{P(x)}{b-a} + \dfrac{P'(x)}{(b-a)^2} + \dfrac{P''(x)}{(b-a)^3} + \cdots + \dfrac{P^{(n)}(x)}{(b-a)^{n+1}}\right]$ |

\* For $\cos sx$ in $R$ replace "sin" by "cos" and "cos" by "$-$ sin" in $y_p$.
† For additional terms, compare with formula 6.

## TABLE VII: $(D^2 - 2aD + a^2 + b^2)y = R$

| R | $y_p$ |
|---|---|
| 39. $P(x)\sin sx$* | $\dfrac{\sin sx}{2b}\left[\left(\dfrac{s+b}{a^2+(s+b)^2} - \dfrac{s-b}{a^2+(s-b)^2}\right)P(x) + \left(\dfrac{2a(s+b)}{[a^2+(s+b)^2]^2} - \dfrac{2a(s-b)}{[a^2+(s-b)^2]^2}\right)P'(x)\right.$ $\left. + \left(\dfrac{3a^2(s+b)-(s+b)^3}{[a^2+(s+b)^2]^3} - \dfrac{3a^2(s-b)-(s-b)^3}{[a^2+(s-b)^2]^3}\right)P''(x) + \cdots\right]$ $- \dfrac{\cos sx}{2b}\left[\left(\dfrac{a}{a^2+(s+b)^2} - \dfrac{a}{a^2+(s-b)^2}\right)P(x) + \left(\dfrac{a^2-(s+b)^2}{[a^2+(s+b)^2]^2} - \dfrac{a^2-(s-b)^2}{[a^2+(s-b)^2]^2}\right)P'(x)\right.$ $\left. + \left(\dfrac{a^3-3a(s+b)^2}{[a^2+(s+b)^2]^3} - \dfrac{a^3-3a(s-b)^2}{[a^2+(s-b)^2]^3}\right)P''(x) + \cdots\right]^\dagger$ |
| 40. $P(x)e^{rx}\sin sx$* | Replace $a$ by $a - r$ in formula 39 and multiply by $e^{rx}$. |
| 41. $P(x)e^{ax}$ | $\dfrac{e^{ax}}{b^2}\left[P(x) - \dfrac{P''(x)}{b^2} + \dfrac{P^{iv}(x)}{b^4} - \cdots\right]$ |
| 42. $e^{ax}\sin sx$* | $\dfrac{e^{ax}\sin sx}{-s^2+b^2}$ |
| 43. $e^{ax}\sin bx$* | $-\dfrac{xe^{ax}\cos bx}{2b}$ |
| 44. $P(x)e^{ax}\sin bx$* | $\dfrac{e^{ax}\sin bx}{(2b)^2}\left[P(x) - \dfrac{P''(x)}{(2b)^2} + \dfrac{P^{iv}(x)}{(2b)^4} - \cdots\right] - \dfrac{e^{ax}\cos bx}{2b}\int\left[\int\left[P(x) - \dfrac{P''(x)}{(2b)^2} + \dfrac{P^{iv}(x)}{(2b)^4} - \cdots\right]dx\right]$ |

## TABLE VIII: $f(D)y = [D^n + a_{n-1}D^{n-1} + \cdots + a_1D + a_0]y = R$

| R | $y_p$ |
|---|---|
| 45. $e^{rx}]$ | $\dfrac{e^{rx}}{f(r)}$ |
| 46. $\sin sx$* | $\dfrac{[a_0 - a_2s^2 + a_4s^4 - \cdots]\sin sx - [a_1s - a_3s^3 + a_5s^5 + \cdots]\cos sx}{[a_0 - a_2s^2 + a_4s^4 - \cdots]^2 + [a_1s - a_3s^3 + a_5s^5 - \cdots]^2}$ |

* For cos $sx$ in R replace "sin" by "cos" and "cos" by "− sin" in $y_p$.
† For additional terms, compare with formula 6.

## TABLE IX: $f(D^2)y = R$

| $R$ | $y_p$ |
|---|---|
| 47. $\sin sx$* | $\dfrac{\sin sx}{f(-s^2)} = \dfrac{\sin sx}{a_0 - a_2 s^2 + \cdots \pm s^{2n}}$ |

## TABLE X: $(D - a)^n = R$

| $R$ | $y_p$ |
|---|---|
| 48. $e^x$ | $\dfrac{e^{rx}}{(r-a)^n}$ |
| 49. $\sin sx$* | $\dfrac{(-1)^n}{(a^2+s^2)^n}\left\{\left[a^n - \binom{n}{2}a^{n-2}s^2 + \binom{n}{4}a^{n-4}s^4 - \cdots\right]\sin sx + 1\left[\binom{n}{1}a^{n-1}s - \binom{n}{3}a^{n-3}s^3 + \cdots\right]\cos sx\right\}$ |
| 50. $P(x)$ | $\dfrac{(-1)^{\bar n}}{a^n}\left[P(x) + \binom{n}{1}\dfrac{P'(x)}{a} + \binom{n+1}{2}\dfrac{P''(x)}{a^2} + \binom{n+2}{3}\dfrac{P'''(x)}{a^3} + \cdots\right]$ |
| 51. $e^x \sin sx$* | Replace $a$ by $a - r$ in formula 49 and multiply by $e^{rx}$. |
| 52. $e^{rx}P(x)$ | Replace $a$ by $a - r$ in formula 50 and multiply by $e^{rx}$. |
| 53. $P(x)\sin sx$* | $(-1)^n \sin sx\left[A_n P(x) + \binom{n}{1}A_{n+1}P'(x) + \binom{n+1}{2}A_{n+2}P''(x) + \binom{n+2}{3}A_{n+3}P'''(x) + \cdots\right]$ $+ (-1)^n \cos sx\left[B_n P(x) + \binom{n}{1}B_{n+1}P'(x) + \binom{n+1}{2}B_{n+2}P''(x) + \binom{n+2}{3}B_{n+3}P'''(x) + \cdots\right]$ |

$$A_1 = \frac{a}{a^2 + s^2}, \quad A_2 = \frac{a^2 - s^2}{(a^2 + s^2)^2}, \quad \cdots, \quad A_k = \frac{a^k - \binom{k}{2}a^{k-2}s^2 + \binom{k}{4}a^{k-4}s^4 - \cdots}{(a^2 + s^2)^k}$$

$$B_1 = \frac{s}{a^2 + s^2}, \quad B_2 = \frac{2as}{(a^2 + s^2)^2}, \quad \cdots, \quad B_k = \frac{\binom{k}{1}a^{k-1}s - \binom{k}{3}a^{k-3}s^3 + \cdots}{(a^2 + s^2)^k}$$

| $R$ | $y_p$ |
|---|---|
| 54. $P(x)e^{rx}\sin sx$* | Replace $a$ by $a - r$ in formula 53 and multiply by $e^{rx}$. |
| 55. $e^{ax}P(x)$ | $e^{ax}\displaystyle\int\int\cdots\int P(x)dx^n$ |

* For cos $sx$ in $R$ replace "sin" by "cos" and "cos" by "− sin" in $y_p$.

## TABLE X: $(D-a)^n = R$ (Continued)

| $R$ | $y_p$ |
|---|---|
| 56. $P(x)e^{ax}\sin sx$* | $(-1)^{\frac{n-1}{2}}\dfrac{e^{ax}\sin sx}{s^n}\left[\binom{n}{n-1}\dfrac{P'(x)}{s} - \binom{n+2}{n-1}\dfrac{P'''(x)}{s^3} + \binom{n+4}{n-1}\dfrac{P^{v}(x)}{s^5} - \cdots\right]$ $+ (-1)^{\frac{n+1}{2}}\dfrac{e^{ax}\cos sx}{s^n}\left[\binom{n-1}{n-1}P(x) - \binom{n+1}{n-1}\dfrac{P''(x)}{s^2} + \binom{n+3}{n-1}\dfrac{P^{iv}(x)}{s^4} - \cdots\right]$ [n odd] $(-1)^{\frac{n}{2}}\dfrac{e^{ax}\sin sx}{s^n}\left[\binom{n-1}{n-1}P(x) - \binom{n+1}{n-1}\dfrac{P''(x)}{s^2} + \binom{n+3}{n-1}\dfrac{P^{iv}(x)}{s^4} - \cdots\right]$ $+ (-1)^{\frac{n}{2}}\dfrac{e^{ax}\cos sx}{s^n}\left[\binom{n}{n-1}\dfrac{P'(x)}{s} - \binom{n+2}{n-1}\dfrac{P'''(x)}{s^3} + \binom{n+4}{n-1}\dfrac{P^{v}(x)}{s^5} - \cdots\right]$ [n even] |

## TABLE XI: $(D-a)^n f(D)y = R$

| | |
|---|---|
| 57. $e^{ax}$ | $\dfrac{x^n}{n!}\cdot\dfrac{e^{ax}}{f(a)}$ |

## TABLE XII: $(D^2+q)^n y = R$

| | |
|---|---|
| 58. $e^{rx}$ | $e^{rx}/(r^2+q)^n$ |
| 59. $\sin sx$* | $\sin sx/(q-s^2)^n$ |
| 60. $P(x)$ | $\dfrac{1}{q^n}\left[P(x) - \binom{n}{1}\dfrac{P''(x)}{q} + \binom{n+1}{2}\dfrac{P^{iv}(x)}{q^2} - \binom{n+2}{3}\dfrac{P^{vi}(x)}{q^3} + \cdots\right]$ |
| 61. $e^{rx}\sin sx$* | $\dfrac{e^{rx}}{(A^2+B^2)^n}\{[A^n - \binom{n}{2}A^{n-2}B^2 + \binom{n}{4}A^{n-4}B^4 + \cdots]\sin sx - [\binom{n}{1}A^{n-1}B - \binom{n}{3}A^{n-3}B^3 + \cdots]\cos sx\}$ $A = r^2 - s^2 + q$, $B = 2rs$ |

* For cos $sx$ in $R$ replace "sin" by "cos" and "cos" by "— sin" in $y_p$.

**TABLE XIII:** $(D^2 + b^2)^n y = R$

| $R$ | $y_p$ |
|---|---|
| 62. $\sin bx$* | $(-1)^{\frac{n+1}{2}} \dfrac{x^n \cos bx}{n!(2b)^n}$ (n odd), $\quad (-1)^{\frac{n}{2}} \dfrac{x^n \sin bx}{n!(2b)^n}$ (n even) |

**TABLE XIV:** $(D^n - q)y = R$

| 63. $e^{rx}$ | $e^{rx}/(r^n - q)$ |
|---|---|
| 64. $P(x)$ | $-\dfrac{1}{q}\left[P(x) + \dfrac{P^{(n)}(x)}{q} + \dfrac{P^{(2n)}(x)}{q^2} + \cdots\right]$ |
| 65. $\sin sx$* | $-\dfrac{q \sin sx + (-1)^{\frac{n-1}{2}} s^n \cos sx}{q^2 + s^{2n}}$ (n odd), $\quad \dfrac{\sin sx}{(-s^2)^{n/2} - q}$ (n even) |
| 66. $e^{rx}\sin sx$* | $\dfrac{Ae^{rx}\sin sx - Be^{rx}\cos sx}{A^2 + B^2} = \dfrac{e^{rx}}{\sqrt{A^2 + B^2}}\sin\left(sx - \tan^{-1}\dfrac{B}{A}\right)$ |

$$A = [r^n - \binom{n}{2}r^{n-2}s^2 + \binom{n}{4}r^{n-4}s^4 - \cdots] - q, \qquad B = [\binom{n}{1}r^{n-1}s - \binom{n}{3}r^{n-3}s^3 + \cdots]$$

**TABLE XV:** $(D_x + mD_y)z = R$

| $R$ | $z_p$ |
|---|---|
| 67. $e^{ax+by}$ | $\dfrac{e^{ax+by}}{a+mb}$ |
| 68. $f(ax + by)$ | $\dfrac{\int f(u)du}{a + mb}, \quad u = ax + by$ |
| 69. $f(y - mx)$ | $xf(y - mx)$ |
| 70. $\phi(x, y)f(y - mx)$ | $f(y - mx)\int\phi(x, a + mx)dx \quad (a = y - mx$ after integration) |

* For $\cos sx$ in $R$ replace "sin" by "cos" and "cos" by "-sin" in $y_p$.

312

## TABLE XVI: $(D_x + mD_y - k)z = R$

| R | $z_p$ |
|---|---|
| 71. $e^{ax+by}$ | $\dfrac{e^{ax+by}}{a+mb-k}$ |
| 72. $\sin(ax+by)$* | $-\dfrac{(a+bm)\cos(ax+by)+k\sin(ax+by)}{(a+bm)^2+k^2}$ |
| 73. $e^{\alpha x+\beta y}\sin(ax+by)$* | Replace $k$ in 72 by $k-\alpha-m\beta$ and multiply by $e^{\alpha x+\beta y}$ |
| 74. $e^{xk}f(ax+by)$ | $\dfrac{e^{kx}\int f(u)du}{a+mb}$, $u = ax+by$ |
| 75. $f(y-mx)$ | $-\dfrac{f(y-mx)}{k}$ |
| 76. $P(x)f(y-mx)$ | $-\dfrac{1}{k}f(y-mx)\left[P(x)+\dfrac{P'(x)}{k}+\dfrac{P''(x)}{k^2}+\cdots+\dfrac{P^{(n)}(x)}{k^n}\right]$ |
| 77. $e^{kx}f(y-mx)$ | $xe^{kx}f(y-mx)$ |

## TABLE XVII: $(D_x + mD_y)^n z = R$

| R | |
|---|---|
| 78. $e^{ax+by}$ | $\dfrac{e^{ax+by}}{(a+mb)^n}$ |
| 79. $f(ax+by)$ | $\dfrac{\int\int\cdots\int f(u)du^n}{(a+mb)^n}$, $u=ax+by$ |
| 80. $f(y-mx)$ | $\dfrac{x^n}{n!}f(y-mx)$ |
| 81. $\phi(x,y)f(y+mx)$ | $f(y-mx)\int\int\cdots\int\phi(x, a+mx)dx^n$ $(a = y-mx$ after integration) |

\* For $(ax+by)$ replace "sin" by "cos," and "cos" by "—sin" in $z_p$.

$$D_x=\frac{\partial}{\partial x}; \quad D_y=\frac{\partial}{\partial y}; \quad D_x^kD_y^r=\frac{\partial^{k+r}}{\partial_x^k\partial_y^r}$$

313

## TABLE XVIII: $(D_x + mD_y - k)^n z = R$

| $R$ | $z_p$ |
|---|---|
| 82. $e^{ax+by}$ | $\dfrac{e^{ax+by}}{(a+mb-k)^n}$ |
| 83. $f(y-mx)$ | $\dfrac{(-1)^n f(y-mx)}{k^n}$ |
| 84. $P(x)f(y-mx)$ | $\dfrac{(-1)^n}{k^n}f(y-mx)\left[P(x) + \binom{n}{1}\dfrac{P'(x)}{k} + \binom{n+1}{2}\dfrac{P''(x)}{k^2} + \binom{n+2}{3}\dfrac{P'''(x)}{k^3} + \cdots\right]$ |
| 85. $e^{kx}f(ax+by)$ | $\dfrac{e^{kx}f\cdots ff(u)du^n}{(a+mb)^n}$, $u = ax + by$ |
| 86. $e^{kx}f(y-mx)$ | $\dfrac{x^n}{n!}e^{kx}f(y-mx)$ |

## TABLE XIX: $[D_x^n + a_1 D_x^{n-1}D_y + a_2 D_x^{n-2}D_y^2 + \cdots + a^n D_y^n]z = R$

| $R$ | $z_p$ |
|---|---|
| 87. $e^{ax+by}$ | $\dfrac{e^{ax+by}}{a^n + a_1 a^{n-1}b + a_2 a^{n-2}b^2 + \cdots + a_n b^n}$ |
| 88. $f(ax+by)$ | $\dfrac{f\int\cdots\int f(u)du^n}{a^n + a_1 a^{n-1}b + a_2 a^{n-2}b^2 + \cdots + a^n b^n}$, $u = ax + by$ |

## TABLE XX: $F(D_x, D_y)z = R$

| $R$ | $z_p$ |
|---|---|
| 89. $e^{ax+by}$ | $\dfrac{e^{ax+by}}{F(a, b)}$  1 |

## TABLE XXI: $F(D_x^2, D_xD_y, D_y^2)z = R$

| $R$ | $z_p$ |
|---|---|
| 90. $\sin(ax+by)$* | $\dfrac{\sin(ax+by)}{F(-a^2, -ab, -b^2)}$ |

* For $\cos(ax+by)$ replace "sin" by "cos," and "cos" by "— sin" in $z_p$.

# DIFFERENTIAL EQUATIONS (Continued)

The following examples illustrate the use of the tables.

EXAMPLE 1. Solve $(D^2 - 4)y = \sin 3x$.
Substitution of $q = -4$, $s = 3$ in formula 24 gives

$$y_p = \frac{\sin 3x}{-9 - 4},$$

wherefore the general solution is

$$y = c_1 e^{2x} + c_2 e^{-2x} - \frac{\sin 3x}{13}.$$

EXAMPLE 2. Obtain a particular solution of $(D^2 - 4D + 5)y = x^2 e^{3x} \sin x$.

Applying formula 40 with $a = 2$, $b = 1$, $r = 3$, $s = 1$, $P(x) = x^2$, $s + b = 2$, $s - b = 0$, $a - r = -1$, $(a - r)^2 + (s + b)^2 = 5$, $(a - r)^2 + (s - b)^2 = 1$, we have

$$y_p = \frac{e^{3x} \sin x}{2} \left[ \left( \frac{2}{5} - \frac{0}{1} \right) x^2 + \left( \frac{2 \cdot -1 \cdot 2}{25} - \frac{2 \cdot -1 \cdot 0}{1} \right) 2x \right.$$
$$\left. + \left( \frac{3 \cdot 1 \cdot 2 - 2^3}{125} - \frac{3 \cdot 1 \cdot 0 - 0}{1} \right) 2 \right]$$
$$- \frac{e^{3x} \cos x}{2} \left[ \left( \frac{-1}{5} - \frac{-1}{1} \right) x^2 + \left( \frac{1 - 4}{25} - \frac{1 - 0}{1} \right) 2x \right.$$
$$\left. + \left( \frac{-1 - 3 \cdot -1 \cdot 4}{125} - \frac{-1 - 3 \cdot -1 \cdot 0}{1} \right) 2 \right]$$
$$= (\tfrac{1}{5}x^2 - \tfrac{4}{25}x - \tfrac{2}{125})e^{3x} \sin x + (-\tfrac{2}{5}x^2 + \tfrac{28}{25}x - \tfrac{136}{125})e^{3x} \cos x.$$

The special formulas effect a very considerable saving of time in problems of this type.

EXAMPLE 3. Obtain a particular solution of $(D^2 - 4D + 5)y = x^2 e^{2x} \cos x$. (Compare with Example 2.)

Formula 40 is not applicable here since for this equation $r = a$, $s = b$, wherefore the denominator $(a - r)^2 + (s - b)^2 = 0$. We turn instead to formula 44. Substituting $a = 2$, $b = 1$, $P(x) = x^2$ and replacing sin by cos, cos by $-$ sin, we obtain

$$y_p = \frac{e^{2x} \cos x}{4} (x^2 - \tfrac{3}{4}) + \frac{e^{2x} \sin x}{2} \int (x^2 - \tfrac{1}{2})dx$$
$$= \left( \frac{x^2}{4} - \frac{1}{8} \right) e^{2x} \cos x + \left( \frac{x^3}{6} - \frac{x}{4} \right) e^{2x} \sin x,$$

which is the required solution.

## DIFFERENTIAL EQUATIONS (Continued)

EXAMPLE 4. Find $z_p$ for $(D_x - 3D_y)z = \ln (y + 3x)$.

Referring to Table XV we note that formula 69 (not 68) is applicable. This gives

$$z_p = x \ln (y + 3x).$$

It is easily seen that $-\dfrac{y}{3} \ln (y + 3x)$ would serve equally well.

EXAMPLE 5. Solve $(D_x + 2D_y - 4)z = y \cos (y - 2x)$.

Since $R$ in formula 76 contains a polynomial in $x$, not $y$, we rewrite the given equation in the form

$$(D_y + \tfrac{1}{2}D_x - 2)z = \tfrac{1}{2}y \cos (y - 2x).$$

Then

$$z_c = e^{2y}F(x - \tfrac{1}{2}y) = e^{2y}f(2x - y),$$

and by the formula

$$z_p = -\tfrac{1}{2} \cos (y - 2x) \cdot \left( \frac{y}{2} + \frac{\frac{1}{2}}{2} \right)$$
$$= -\tfrac{1}{8}(2y + 1) \cos (y - 2x).$$

EXAMPLE 6. Find $z_p$ for $(D_x + 4D_y)^3z = (2x - y)^2$.

Using formula 79, we obtain

$$z_p = \frac{\int\int\int u^2 du^3}{[2 + 4(-1)]^3} = \frac{u^5}{5 \cdot 4 \cdot 3 \cdot (-8)} = -\frac{(2x - y)^5}{480}.$$

EXAMPLE 7. Find $z_p$ for $(D_x{}^3 + 5D_x{}^2D_y - 7D_x + 4)z = e^{2x+3y}$.

By formula 87

$$z_p = \frac{e^{2x+3y}}{2^3 + 5 \cdot 2^2 \cdot 3 - 7 \cdot 2 + 4} = \frac{e^{2x+3y}}{58}.$$

EXAMPLE 8. Find $z_p$ for

$$(D_x{}^4 + 6D_x{}^3D_y + D_xD_y + D_y{}^2 + 9)z = \sin (3x + 4y).$$

Since every term in the left member is of *even* degree in the two operators $D_x$ and $D_y$, formula 90 is applicable.

It gives

$$z_p = \frac{\sin (3x + 4y)}{(-9)^2 + 6(-9)(-12) + (-12) + (-16) + 9}$$
$$= \frac{\sin (3x + 4y)}{710}$$

# ALGEBRA

## Factors and Expansions

$(a \pm b)^2 = a^2 \pm 2ab + b^2.$
$(a \pm b)^3 = a^3 \pm 3a^2b + 3ab^2 \pm b^3.$
$(a \pm b)^4 = a^4 \pm 4a^3b + 6a^2b^2 \pm 4ab^3 + b^4.$
$a^2 - b^2 = (a - b)(a + b).$
$a^2 + b^2 = (a + b\sqrt{-1})(a - b\sqrt{-1}).$
$a^3 - b^3 = (a - b)(a^2 + ab + b^2).$
$a^3 + b^3 = (a + b)(a^2 - ab + b^2).$
$a^4 + b^4 = (a^2 + ab\sqrt{2} + b^2)(a^2 - ab\sqrt{2} + b^2).$
$a^n - b^n = (a - b)(a^{n-1} + a^{n-2}b + \ldots + b^{n-1}).$
$a^n - b^n = (a + b)(a^{n-1} - a^{n-2}b + \ldots - b^{n-1}),$
$$\text{for even values of } n.$$
$a^n + b^n = (a + b)(a^{n-1} - a^{n-2}b + \ldots + b^{n-1}),$
$$\text{for odd values of } n.$$
$a^4 + a^2b^2 + b^4 = (a^2 + ab + b^2)(a^2 - ab + b^2).$
$(a + b + c)^2 = a^2 + b^2 + c^2 + 2ab + 2ac + 2bc.$
$(a + b + c)^3 = a^3 + b^3 + c^3 + 3a^2(b + c) + 3b^2(a + c) +$
$$3c^2(a + b) + 6abc.$$
$(a + b + c + d + \ldots)^2 = a^2 + b^2 + c^2 + d^2 + \ldots +$
$2a(b + c + d + \ldots) + 2b(c + d + \ldots) + 2c(d + \ldots) + \ldots$
*See also under Series*

## Powers and Roots

$a^x \times a^y = a^{(x+y)}.$    $a^0 = 1 \text{ [if } a \neq 0].$  $(ab)^x = a^x b^x.$

$\dfrac{a^x}{a^y} = a^{(x-y)}.$    $a^{-x} = \dfrac{1}{a^x}.$    $\left(\dfrac{a}{b}\right)^x = \dfrac{a^x}{b^x}.$

$(a^x)^y = a^{xy}.$    $a^{\frac{1}{x}} = \sqrt[x]{a}.$    $\sqrt[x]{ab} = \sqrt[x]{a}\,\sqrt[x]{b}.$

$\sqrt[x]{\sqrt[y]{a}} = \sqrt[xy]{a}.$    $a^{\frac{x}{y}} = \sqrt[y]{a^x}.$    $\sqrt[x]{\dfrac{a}{b}} = \dfrac{\sqrt[x]{a}}{\sqrt[x]{b}}.$

## Proportion

If    $\dfrac{a}{b} = \dfrac{c}{d},$    then    $\dfrac{a + b}{b} = \dfrac{c + d}{d},$

$\dfrac{a - b}{b} = \dfrac{c - d}{d},$    $\dfrac{a - b}{a + b} = \dfrac{c - d}{c + d}.$

317

# ALGEBRA (Continued)

## SUM OF POWERS OF INTEGERS, $\sum_{k=1}^{n} k^m$

$(m = 1, 2, 3, 4); 1 \leq n \leq 40$

| $n$ | $\Sigma k$ | $\Sigma k^2$ | $\Sigma k^3$ | $\Sigma k^4$ |
|---|---|---|---|---|
| 1 | 1 | 1 | 1 | 1 |
| 2 | 3 | 5 | 9 | 17 |
| 3 | 6 | 14 | 36 | 98 |
| 4 | 10 | 30 | 100 | 354 |
| 5 | 15 | 55 | 225 | 979 |
| 6 | 21 | 91 | 441 | 2275 |
| 7 | 28 | 140 | 784 | 4676 |
| 8 | 36 | 204 | 1296 | 8772 |
| 9 | 45 | 285 | 2025 | 15333 |
| 10 | 55 | 385 | 3025 | 25333 |
| 11 | 66 | 506 | 4356 | 39974 |
| 12 | 78 | 650 | 6084 | 60710 |
| 13 | 91 | 819 | 8281 | 89271 |
| 14 | 105 | 1015 | 11025 | 127687 |
| 15 | 120 | 1240 | 14400 | 178312 |
| 16 | 136 | 1496 | 18496 | 243848 |
| 17 | 153 | 1785 | 23409 | 327369 |
| 18 | 171 | 2109 | 29241 | 432345 |
| 19 | 190 | 2470 | 36100 | 562666 |
| 20 | 210 | 2870 | 44100 | 722666 |
| 21 | 231 | 3311 | 53361 | 917147 |
| 22 | 253 | 3795 | 64009 | 1151403 |
| 23 | 276 | 4324 | 76176 | 1431244 |
| 24 | 300 | 4900 | 90000 | 1763020 |
| 25 | 325 | 5525 | 105625 | 2153645 |
| 26 | 351 | 6201 | 123201 | 2610621 |
| 27 | 378 | 6930 | 142884 | 3142062 |
| 28 | 406 | 7714 | 164836 | 3756718 |
| 29 | 435 | 8555 | 189225 | 4463999 |
| 30 | 465 | 9455 | 216225 | 5273999 |
| 31 | 496 | 10416 | 246016 | 6197520 |
| 32 | 528 | 11440 | 278784 | 7246096 |
| 33 | 561 | 12529 | 314721 | 8432017 |
| 34 | 595 | 13685 | 354025 | 9768353 |
| 35 | 630 | 14910 | 396900 | 11268978 |
| 36 | 666 | 16206 | 443556 | 12948504 |
| 37 | 703 | 17575 | 494209 | 14822755 |
| 38 | 741 | 19019 | 549081 | 16907891 |
| 39 | 780 | 20540 | 608400 | 19221332 |
| 40 | 820 | 22140 | 672400 | 21781332 |

## ALGEBRA—(Continued)
## SUMS OF NUMBERS

The sum of the first $n$ numbers,—

$$\Sigma(n) = 1 + 2 + 3 + 4 + 5 \ldots + n = \frac{n(n+1)}{2}$$

The sum of the squares of the first $n$ numbers,

$$\Sigma(n^2) = 1^2 + 2^2 + 3^2 + 4^2 + 5^2 \ldots + n^2 = \frac{n(n+1)(2n+1)}{6}$$

The sum of the cubes of the first $n$ numbers,

$$\Sigma(n^3) = 1^3 + 2^3 + 3^3 + 4^3 + 5^3 \ldots + n^3 = \frac{n^2(n+1)^2}{4}$$

## ARITHMETICAL PROGRESSION

If $a$ is the first term; $l$, the last term; $d$, the common difference; $n$, the number of terms and $s$, the sum of $n$ terms,—

$$l = a + (n-1)d \qquad s = \frac{n}{2}(a+l)$$

$$s = \frac{n}{2}\left\{ 2a + (n-1)d \right\}$$

## GEOMETRICAL PROGRESSION

If $a$ is the first term; $l$, the last term; $r$, the common ratio; $n$, the number of terms and $s$, the sum of $n$ terms,—

$$l = ar^{n-1} \qquad\qquad s = a\frac{(1-r^n)}{1-r}$$

$$s = a\frac{(r^n-1)}{r-1} \qquad\qquad s = \frac{lr-a}{r-1}$$

If $n$ is infinity and $r^2$ less than unity,—

$$s = \frac{a}{1-r}$$

## FACTORIALS

$$\underline{|n} = n! = e^{-n}n^n\sqrt{2\pi n}, \text{ approximately.}$$

## PERMUTATIONS

If $M$ denote the number of permutations of $n$ things taken $p$ at a time,—

$$M = n(n-1)(n-2) \ldots (n-p+1)$$

## COMBINATIONS

If $M$ denote the number of combinations of $n$ things taken $p$ at a time,—

$$M = \frac{n(n-1)(n-2) \ldots (n-p+1)}{p!}$$

$$M = \frac{n!}{p!(n-p)!}$$

# ALGEBRA (Continued)

## Quadratic Equations

**Any** quadratic equation may be reduced to the form, —
$$ax^2 + bx + c = 0$$

Then $x = \dfrac{-b \pm \sqrt{b^2 - 4ac}}{2a}.$

If $a$, $b$, and $c$, are real, then
if $b^2 - 4ac$ is positive, the roots are real and unequal;
if $b^2 - 4ac$ is zero, the roots are real and equal;
if $b^2 - 4ac$ is negative, the roots are imaginary and unequal;
$a$, $b$, and $c$, are rational.

## Cubic Equations

A cubic equation, $y^3 + py^2 + qy + r = 0$ may be reduced to
the form, —
$$x^3 + ax + b = 0$$

by substituting for $y$ the value, $\left( x - \dfrac{p}{3} \right)$. Here

$a = \frac{1}{3}(3q - p^2)$ and $b = \frac{1}{27}(2p^3 - 9pq + 27r)$.
For solution let, —

$$A = \sqrt[3]{-\frac{b}{2} + \sqrt{\frac{b^2}{4} + \frac{a^3}{27}}}, \qquad B = \sqrt[3]{-\frac{b}{2} - \sqrt{\frac{b^2}{4} + \frac{a^3}{27}}},$$

then the values of $x$ will be given by,

$$x = A + B, \quad -\frac{A + B}{2} + \frac{A - B}{2}\sqrt{-3}, \quad -\frac{A + B}{2} - \frac{A - B}{2}\sqrt{-3}$$

If $\dfrac{b^2}{4} + \dfrac{a^3}{27} > 0,$ there will be one real root and two conjugate imaginary roots.

If $\dfrac{b^2}{4} + \dfrac{a^3}{27} = 0,$ there will be three real roots of which two at least are equal

If $\dfrac{b^2}{4} + \dfrac{a^3}{27} < 0,$ there will be three real and unequal roots.

In the last case a trigonometric solution is useful. Compute
the value of the angle $\phi$ in the expression, —

$$\cos \phi = -\frac{b}{2} \div \sqrt{\left( -\frac{a^3}{27} \right)},$$

then $x$ will have the following values:—

$$2\sqrt{-\frac{a}{3}} \cos \frac{\phi}{3}, \qquad 2\sqrt{-\frac{a}{3}} \cos\left( \frac{\phi}{3} + 120° \right),$$

$$2\sqrt{-\frac{a}{3}} \cos\left( \frac{\phi}{3} + 240° \right).$$

## PARTIAL FRACTIONS

Compiled by Professor M. D. Prince

This section applies only to rational algebraic fractions with numerator of lower degree than the denominator. Improper fractions can be reduced to proper fractions by long division.

Every fraction may be expressed as the sum of component fractions whose denominators are factors of the denominator of the original fraction.

Let $N(x)$ = numerator, a polynomial of the form

$$n_0 + n_1x + n_2x^2 + \cdots + n_ix^i$$

I. *Non-repeated Linear Factors*

$$\frac{N(x)}{(x-a)G(x)} = \frac{A}{x-a} + \frac{F(x)}{G(x)}$$

$$A = \left[\frac{N(x)}{G(x)}\right]x = a$$

$F(x)$ determined by methods discussed in the following sections. Example:

$$\frac{x^2+3}{x(x-2)(x^2+2x+4)} = \frac{A}{x} + \frac{B}{x-2} + \frac{F(x)}{x^2+2x+4}$$

$$A = \left[\frac{x^2+3}{(x-2)(x^2+2x+4)}\right]x = 0 = -\frac{3}{8}$$

$$B = \left[\frac{x^2+3}{x(x^2+2x+4)}\right]x = 2 = \frac{4+3}{2(4+4+4)} = \frac{7}{24}$$

II. *Repeated Linear Factors*

$$\frac{N(x)}{x^mG(x)} = \frac{A_0}{x^m} + \frac{A_1}{x^{m-1}} + \cdots + \frac{A_{m-1}}{x} + \frac{F(x)}{G(x)}$$

$$F(x) = f_0 + f_1x + f_2x^2 + \cdots, \quad G(x) = g_0 + g_1x + g_2x^2 + \cdots$$

$$A_0 = \frac{n_0}{g_0}, \quad A_1 = \frac{n_1 - A_0g_1}{g_0}, \quad A_2 = \frac{n_2 - A_0g_2 - A_1g_1}{g_0}$$

General term: $A_k = \dfrac{1}{g_0}\left[n_k - \displaystyle\sum_{i=0}^{k-1} A_ig_{k-i}\right]$

$$*m = 1 \begin{cases} f_0 = n_1 - A_0g_1 \\ f_1 = n_2 - A_0g_2 \\ f_j = n_{j+1} - A_0g_{j+1} \end{cases}$$

$$m = 2 \begin{cases} f_0 = n_2 - A_0g_2 - A_1g_1 \\ f_1 = n_3 - A_0g_3 - A_1g_2 \\ f_j = n_{j+2} - [A_0g_{j+2} + A_1g_{j+1}] \end{cases}$$

$$m = 3 \begin{cases} f_0 = n_3 - A_0g_3 - A_1g_2 - A_2g_1 \\ f_1 = n_3 - A_0g_4 - A_1g_3 - A_2g_2 \\ f_j = n_{j+3} - [A_0g_{j+3} + A_1g_{j+2} + A_2g_{j+1}] \end{cases}$$

* Note: If $G(x)$ contains linear factors, $F(x)$ may be determined by previous section I.

$$\text{any } m: \quad f_j = n_{m+j} - \sum_{i=0}^{m-1} A_i g_{m+j-i}$$

Example: $\dfrac{x^2 + 1}{x^3(x^2 - 3x + 6)} = \dfrac{A_0}{x^3} + \dfrac{A_1}{x^2} + \dfrac{A_2}{x} + \dfrac{f_1 x + f_0}{x^2 - 3x + 6}$

$A_0 = \dfrac{1}{6}, \qquad A_1 = \dfrac{0 - (\frac{1}{6})(-3)}{6} = \dfrac{1}{12},$

$$A_2 = \dfrac{1 - (\frac{1}{6})(1) - (\frac{1}{12})(-3)}{6} = \tfrac{13}{72}$$

$m = 3, \qquad f_0 = 0 - \tfrac{1}{6}(0) - \tfrac{1}{12}(1) - \tfrac{13}{72}(-3) = \tfrac{11}{24}$

$\qquad\qquad f_1 = 0 - \tfrac{1}{6}(0) - \tfrac{1}{12}(0) - \tfrac{13}{72}(1) = -\tfrac{13}{72}$

## III. *Repeated Linear Factors*

$$\frac{N(x)}{(x - a)^m G(x)} = \frac{A_0}{(x - a)^m} + \frac{A_1}{(x - a)^{m-1}} + \cdots$$
$$+ \frac{A_{m-1}}{(x - a)} + \frac{F(x)}{G(x)}$$

Change to form $\dfrac{N'(y)}{y^m G'(y)}$ by substitution of $x = y + a$. Resolve into partial fractions in terms of $y$ as described in Section II. Then express in terms of $x$ by substitution $y = x - a$.

Example: $\dfrac{x - 3}{(x - 2)^2(x^2 + x + 1)}$. Let $x - 2 = y$, $x = y + 2$

$\dfrac{(y + 2) - 3}{y^2[(y + 2)^2 + (y + 2) + 1]} = \dfrac{y - 1}{y^2(y^2 + 5y + 7)}$

$$= \frac{A_0}{y^2} + \frac{A_1}{y} + \frac{f_1 y + f_0}{y^2 + 5y + 7}$$

$$A_0 = -\tfrac{1}{7} \qquad A_1 = \frac{1 - (-\frac{1}{7})(5)}{7} = \frac{12}{49}$$

$(m = 2)$

$f_0 = 0 - (-\tfrac{1}{7})(1) - (\tfrac{12}{49})(5) = -\tfrac{53}{49}$

$f_1 = 0 - (-\tfrac{1}{7})(0) - (\tfrac{12}{49})(1) = -\tfrac{12}{49}$

$$\therefore \frac{y - 1}{y^2(y^2 + 5y + 7)} = \frac{-\frac{1}{7}}{y^2} + \frac{\frac{12}{49}}{y} + \frac{-\frac{12}{49}y - \frac{53}{49}}{y^2 + 5y + 7}$$

Let $y = x - 2$, then

$$\frac{x - 3}{(x - 2)^2(x^2 + x + 1)} = \frac{-\frac{1}{7}}{(x - 2)^2} + \frac{\frac{12}{35}}{(x - 2)}$$
$$+ \frac{-\frac{12}{49}(x - 2) - \frac{53}{49}}{x^2 + x + 1} = -\frac{1}{7(x - 2)^2} + \frac{12}{35(x - 2)}$$
$$+ \frac{-12x - 29}{49(x^2 + x + 1)}$$

**IV.** *Repeated Linear Factors*

Alternative method of determining coefficients:

$$\frac{N(x)}{(x-a)^m G(x)} = \frac{A_0}{(x-a)^m} + \cdots + \frac{A_k}{(x-a)^{m-k}} + \cdots$$
$$+ \frac{A_{m-1}}{x-a} + \frac{F(x)}{G(x)}$$

$$A_k = \frac{1}{k!}\left\{D_x^k\left[\frac{N(x)}{G(x)}\right]\right\}x = a$$

Where $D_x^k$ is the differentiating operator, and the derivative of zero order is defined as:

$$D_x^0 u = u.$$

---

**V.** *Factors of Higher Degree*

Factors of higher degree have the corresponding numerators indicated.

$$\frac{N(x)}{(x^2+h_1x+h_0)G(x)} = \frac{a_1x+a_0}{x^2+h_1x+h_0} + \frac{F(x)}{G(x)}$$

$$\frac{N(x)}{(x^2+h_1x+h_0)^2 G(x)} = \frac{a_1x+a_0}{(x^2+h_1x+h_0)^2}$$
$$+ \frac{b_1x+b_0}{(x^2+h_1x+h_0)} + \frac{F(x)}{G(x)}$$

$$\frac{N(x)}{(x^3+h_2x^2+h_1x+h_0)G(x)} = \frac{a_2x^2+a_1x+a_0}{x^3+h_2x^2+h_1x+h_0} + \frac{F(x)}{G(x)}$$

etc.

Problems of this type are determined first by solving for the coefficients due to linear factors as shown above, and then determining the remaining coefficients by the general methods given below.

**VI.** *General Methods for Evaluating Coefficients*

1. $\dfrac{N(x)}{D(x)} = \dfrac{N(x)}{G(x)H(x)L(x)} = \dfrac{A(x)}{G(x)} + \dfrac{B(x)}{H(x)} + \dfrac{C(x)}{L(x)} + \cdots$

Multiply both sides of equation by $D(x)$ to clear fractions. Then collect terms, equate like powers of $x$, and solve the resulting simultaneous equations for the unknown coefficients.

2. Clear fractions as above. Then let $x$ assume certain convenient values ($x = 1, 0, -1, \ldots$). Solve the resulting equations for the unknown coefficients.

3. $\qquad\qquad \dfrac{N(x)}{G(x)H(x)} = \dfrac{A(x)}{G(x)} + \dfrac{B(x)}{H(x)}$

Then $\qquad \dfrac{N(x)}{G(x)H(x)} - \dfrac{A(x)}{G(x)} = \dfrac{B(x)}{H(x)}$

If $A(x)$ can be determined, such as by Method I, then $B(x)$ can be found as above.

## APPROXIMATIONS

If $a$ and $b$ are small quantities, the following relations are approximately true,—

$$(1 \pm a)^m = 1 \pm ma,$$
$$(1 \pm a)^m (1 \pm b)^n = 1 \pm ma \pm nb.$$

If $n$ is nearly equal to $m$,

$$\sqrt{mn} = \frac{n+m}{2}, \text{ approximately.}$$

If $\theta$ is a very small angle expressed in radians,—

$$\frac{\sin \theta}{\theta} = 1 \text{ and } \frac{\tan \theta}{\theta} = 1, \text{ approximately.}$$

## SERIES

The expression in parentheses following certain of the series indicates the region of convergence. If not otherwise indicated it is to be understood that the series converges for all finite values of $x$.

### BINOMIAL

$$(x+y)^n = x^n + nx^{n-1}y + \frac{n(n-1)}{2!} x^{n-2}y^2$$
$$+ \frac{n(n-1)(n-2)}{3!} x^{(n-3)} y^3 + \ldots . (y^2 < x^2)$$

$$(1 \pm x)^n = 1 \pm nx + \frac{n(n-1)x^2}{2!} \pm \frac{n(n-1)(n-2)x^3}{3!} + \ldots \text{etc.}$$
$$(x^2 < 1)$$

$$(1 \pm x)^{-n} = 1 \mp nx + \frac{n(n+1)x^2}{2!} \mp \frac{n(n+1)(n+2)x^3}{3!} + \ldots \text{etc.}$$
$$(x^2 < 1)$$

$$(1 \pm x)^{-1} = 1 \mp x + x^2 \mp x^3 + x^4 \mp x^5 + \ldots \qquad (x^2 < 1)$$
$$(1 \pm x)^{-2} = 1 \mp 2x + 3x^2 \mp 4x^3 + 5x^4 \mp 6x^5 + \ldots \qquad (x^2 < 1)$$

### REVERSION OF SERIES

Let a series be represented by

$$y = a_1x + a_2x^2 + a_3x^3 + a_4x^4 + a_5x^5 + a_6x^6 + \cdots \quad (a_1 \neq 0)$$

to find the coefficients of the series

$$x = A_1y + A_2y^2 + A_3y^3 + A_4y^4 + \cdots$$

$$A_1 = \frac{1}{a_1} \qquad A_2 = -\frac{a_2}{a_1^3} \qquad A_3 = \frac{1}{a_1^5}(2a_2^2 - a_1a_3)$$

$$A_4 = \frac{1}{a_1^7}(5a_1a_2a_3 - a_1^2a_4 - 5a_2^3)$$

$$A_5 = \frac{1}{a_1^9}(6a_1^2a_2a_4 + 3a_1^2a_3^2 + 14a_2^4 - a_1^3a_5 - 21a_1a_2^2a_3)$$

$$A_6 = \frac{1}{a_1^{11}}(7a_1^3a_2a_5 + 7a_1^3a_3a_4 + 84a_1a_2^3a_3 - a_1^4a_6$$
$$- 28a_1^2a_2^2a_4$$
$$- 28a_1^2a_2a_3^2$$
$$- 42a_2^5)$$

$$A_7 = \frac{1}{a_1^{13}} (8a_1^4a_2a_6 + 8a_1^4a_3a_5 + 4a_1^4a_4^2 + 120a_1^2a_2^3a_4$$
$$+ 180a_1^2a_2^2a_3^2 + 132a_2^6 - a_1^5a_7$$
$$- 36a_1^3a_2^2a_5 - 72a_1^3a_2a_3a_4 - 12a_1^3a_3^3 - 330a_1a_2^4a_3)$$

### TAYLOR'S SERIES

$$f(x + h) = f(x) + hf'(x) + \frac{h^2}{2!}f''(x) + \frac{h^3}{3!}f'''(x) + \cdots$$
$$= f(h) + xf'(h) + \frac{x^2}{2!}f''(h) + \frac{x^3}{3!}f'''(h) + \cdots$$

### MACLAURIN'S SERIES

$$f(x) = f(o) + xf'(o) + \frac{x^2}{2!}f''(o) + \frac{x^3}{3!}f'''(o) + \cdots$$

### EXPONENTIAL

$$e = 1 + \frac{1}{1} + \frac{1}{2!} + \frac{1}{3!} + \frac{1}{4!} + \cdots \quad \text{(all real values of } x\text{)}$$
$$e^x = 1 + x + \frac{x^2}{2!} + \frac{x^3}{3!} + \frac{x^4}{4!} + \cdots \quad \text{(all real values of } x\text{)}$$
$$a^x = 1 + x \log_e a + \frac{(x \log a)^2}{2!} + \frac{(x \log a)^3}{3!} + \cdots$$

### LOGARITHMIC

$$\log_e x = \frac{x-1}{x} + \frac{1}{2}\left(\frac{x-1}{x}\right)^2 + \frac{1}{3}\left(\frac{x-1}{x}\right)^3 + \cdots$$
$$(x > \tfrac{1}{2})$$
$$\log_e x = (x-1) - \tfrac{1}{2}(x-1)^2 + \tfrac{1}{3}(x-1)^3 - \cdots$$
$$(2 > x > 0)$$
$$\log_e x = 2\left[\frac{x-1}{x+1} + \frac{1}{3}\left(\frac{x-1}{x+1}\right)^3 + \frac{1}{5}\left(\frac{x-1}{x+1}\right)^5 + \cdots\right]$$
$$(x > 0)$$
$$\log_e(1+x) = x - \tfrac{1}{2}x^2 + \tfrac{1}{3}x^3 - \tfrac{1}{4}x^4 + \cdots \quad (-1 < x < 1)$$
$$\log_e(n+1) - \log_e(n-1) = 2\left[\frac{1}{n} + \frac{1}{3n^3} + \frac{1}{5n^5} + \cdots\right]$$
$$\log_e(a+x) = \log_e a + 2\left[\frac{x}{2a+x} + \frac{1}{3}\left(\frac{x}{2a+x}\right)^3 + \frac{1}{5}\left(\frac{x}{2a+x}\right)^5 + \cdots\right]$$
$$(a > 0, \ -a < x < +\infty)$$

### TRIGONOMETRIC

$$\sin x = x - \frac{x^3}{3!} + \frac{x^5}{5!} - \frac{x^7}{7!} + \cdots \qquad \text{(all real values of } x\text{)}$$

$$\cos x = 1 - \frac{x^2}{2!} + \frac{x^4}{4!} - \frac{x^6}{6!} + \cdots \qquad \text{(all real values of } x\text{)}$$

$$\tan x = x + \frac{x^3}{3} + \frac{2x^5}{15} + \frac{17x^7}{315} + \frac{62x^9}{2835} + \cdots \qquad \left(x^2 < \frac{\pi^2}{4}\right)$$

$$\sin^{-1} x = x + \frac{x^3}{6} + \frac{1}{2}\cdot\frac{3}{4}\cdot\frac{x^5}{5} + \frac{1}{2}\cdot\frac{3}{4}\cdot\frac{5}{6}\cdot\frac{x^7}{7} + \cdots \qquad (x^2 < 1)$$

$$\tan^{-1} x = x - \tfrac{1}{3}x^3 + \tfrac{1}{5}x^5 - \tfrac{1}{7}x^7 + \cdots \qquad (x^2 < 1)$$

$$= \frac{\pi}{2} - \frac{1}{x} + \frac{1}{3x^3} - \frac{1}{5x^5} + \cdots \qquad (x^2 > 1)$$

$$\log_e \sin x = \log_e x - \frac{x^2}{6} - \frac{x^4}{180} - \frac{x^6}{2835} - \cdots \qquad (x^2 < \pi^2)$$

$$\log_e \cos x = -\frac{x^2}{2} - \frac{x^4}{12} - \frac{x^6}{45} - \frac{17x^8}{2520} - \cdots \qquad \left(x^2 < \frac{\pi^2}{4}\right)$$

$$\log_e \tan x = \log_e x + \frac{x^2}{3} + \frac{7x^4}{90} + \frac{62x^6}{2835} + \cdots \qquad \left(x^2 < \frac{\pi^2}{4}\right)$$

$$e^{\sin x} = 1 + x + \frac{x^2}{2!} - \frac{3x^4}{4!} - \frac{8x^5}{5!} - \frac{3x^6}{6!} + \frac{56x^7}{7!} + \cdots$$

$$e^{\cos x} = e\left(1 - \frac{x^2}{2!} + \frac{4x^4}{4!} - \frac{31x^6}{6!} + \cdots\right)$$

$$e^{\tan x} = 1 + x + \frac{x^2}{2!} + \frac{3x^3}{3!} + \frac{9x^4}{4!} + \frac{37x^5}{5!} + \cdots \qquad \left(x^2 < \frac{\pi^2}{4}\right)$$

## FOURIER SERIES

$$f(x) = \frac{a_0}{2} + a_1 \cos \frac{2\pi x}{T} + a_2 \cos \frac{4\pi x}{T} + \cdots$$
$$+ a_m \cos \frac{2\pi m x}{T} + \cdots + b_1 \sin \frac{2\pi x}{T} + b_2 \sin \frac{4\pi x}{T}$$
$$+ b_3 \sin \frac{6\pi x}{T} + \cdots + b_n \sin \frac{2\pi n x}{T} + \cdots,$$

where

$$a_0 = \frac{2}{T}\int_c^{c+T} f(x)dx, \quad a_m = \frac{2}{T}\int_c^{c+T} f(x) \cos \frac{2\pi m x}{T} dx, \quad b_n = \frac{2}{T}\int_c^{c+T} f(x) \sin \frac{2\pi n x}{T} dx,$$ and $f(x + T) = f(x)$, with $c$ and $T$ constants.

### Auxiliary Formulas for Fourier Series

$$1 = \frac{4}{\pi} \left[ \sin \frac{\pi x}{k} + \frac{1}{3} \sin \frac{3\pi x}{k} + \frac{1}{5} \sin \frac{5\pi x}{k} + \cdots \right] \quad [0 < x < k]$$

$$x = \frac{2k}{\pi} \left[ \sin \frac{\pi x}{k} - \frac{1}{2} \sin \frac{2\pi x}{k} + \frac{1}{3} \sin \frac{3\pi x}{k} - \cdots \right] \quad [-k < x < k]$$

$$x = \frac{k}{2} - \frac{4k}{\pi^2} \left[ \cos \frac{\pi x}{k} + \frac{1}{3^2} \cos \frac{3\pi x}{k} + \frac{1}{5^2} \cos \frac{5\pi x}{k} + \cdot \right] [0 < x < k]$$

$$x^2 = \frac{2k^2}{\pi^3} \left[ \left( \frac{\pi^2}{1} - \frac{4}{1} \right) \sin \frac{\pi x}{k} - \frac{\pi^2}{2} \sin \frac{2\pi x}{k} + \left( \frac{\pi^2}{3} - \frac{4}{3^3} \right) \sin \frac{3\pi x}{k} \right.$$
$$\left. - \frac{\pi^2}{4} \sin \frac{4\pi x}{k} + \left( \frac{\pi^2}{5} - \frac{4}{5^3} \right) \sin \frac{5\pi x}{k} + \cdots \right] \quad [0 < x < k]$$

$$x^2 = \frac{k^2}{3} - \frac{4k^2}{\pi^2} \left[ \cos \frac{\pi x}{k} - \frac{1}{2^2} \cos \frac{2\pi x}{k} + \frac{1}{3^2} \cos \frac{3\pi x}{k} \right.$$
$$\left. - \frac{1}{4^2} \cos \frac{4\pi x}{k} + \cdots \right] [-k < x < k]$$

$$1 - \frac{1}{3} + \frac{1}{5} - \frac{1}{7} + \cdots = \frac{\pi}{4}$$

$$1 + \frac{1}{2^2} + \frac{1}{3^2} + \frac{1}{4^2} + \cdots = \frac{\pi^2}{6} = B_1 \pi^2$$

$$1 - \frac{1}{2^2} + \frac{1}{3^2} - \frac{1}{4^2} + \cdots = \frac{\pi^2}{12} = \frac{B_1 \pi^2}{2}$$

$$1 + \frac{1}{3^2} + \frac{1}{5^2} + \frac{1}{7^2} + \cdots = \frac{\pi^2}{8} = \frac{3B_1 \pi^2}{4}$$

$$\frac{1}{2^2} + \frac{1}{4^2} + \frac{1}{6^2} + \frac{1}{8^2} + \cdots = \frac{\pi^2}{24} = \frac{B_2 \pi^4}{90}$$

In the above $B_1$, $B_2$ . . . represent the Bernoulli Numbers.

### Bernoulli Numbers and Euler Numbers

The sequence of numbers $E_1$, $E_2$, $E_3$, . . . obtained from

$$E_n = \frac{(2n)!}{(2n-2)!2!} E_{n-1} - \frac{(2n)!}{(2n-4)!4!} E_{n-2} + \cdots + (-1)^{n-1}$$

are called Euler Numbers. Thus $E_1 = 1$, $E_2 = 5$, $E_3 = 61$, $E_4 = 1385$, $E_5 = 50{,}521$, . . . .

In the above $0! = 1$ and $E_0 = 1$ by definition.

The sequence of numbers $B_1$, $B_2$, $B_3$, $B_4$, . . . obtained from

$$B_n = \frac{2n}{2^{2n}(2^{2n}-1)} \left[ \frac{(2n-1)!}{(2n-2)!1!} E_{n-1} - \frac{(2n-1)!}{(2n-4)!3!} E_{n-2} \right.$$
$$\left. + \cdots + (-1)^{n-1} \right]$$

are called Bernoulli numbers. Thus

$$B_1 = \tfrac{1}{6}, \qquad B_2 = \tfrac{1}{30}, \qquad B_3 = \tfrac{1}{42}, \qquad B_4 = \tfrac{1}{30}, \qquad B_5 = \tfrac{5}{66}, \ \ldots$$

$$B_n = \frac{(2n)!}{\pi^{2n} 2^{2n-1}} \left[ 1 + \frac{1}{2^{2n}} + \frac{1}{3^{2n}} + \frac{1}{4^{2n}} + \cdots \right]$$

$$B_n = \frac{(2n)!}{\pi^{2n}(2^{2n-1} - 1)} \left[ 1 - \frac{1}{2^{2n}} + \frac{1}{3^{2n}} - \frac{1}{4^{2n}} + \cdots \right]$$

$$B_n = \frac{2(2n)!}{\pi^{2n}(2^{2n} - 1)} \left[ 1 + \frac{1}{3^{2n}} + \frac{1}{5^{2n}} + \frac{1}{7^{2n}} + \cdots \right]$$

$$E_n = \frac{2^{2n+2}(2n)!}{\pi^{2n+1}} \left[ 1 - \frac{1}{3^{2n+1}} + \frac{1}{5^{2n+1}} + \frac{1}{7^{2n+1}} + \cdots \right]$$

# ALGEBRA (Continued)
## VECTOR ANALYSIS
### Definitions

Any quantity which is completely determined by its magnitude is called a *scalar*. Examples of such are mass, density, temperature, etc. Any quantity which is completely determined by its magnitude and direction is called a *vector*. Examples of such are velocity, acceleration, force, etc. A vector quantity is represented by a directed line segment, the length of which represents the magnitude of the vector. A vector quantity is usually represented by a bold-faced letter such as $\mathbf{V}$. Two vectors $\mathbf{V}_1$ and $\mathbf{V}_2$ are equal to one another if they have equal magnitudes and are acting in the same directions. A negative vector, written as $-\mathbf{V}$, is one which acts in the opposite direction to $\mathbf{V}$, but is of equal magnitude to it. If we represent the magnitude of $\mathbf{V}$ by $v$, we write $|\mathbf{V}| = v$. A vector parallel to $\mathbf{V}$, but equal to the reciprocal of its magnitude is written as $\mathbf{V}^{-1}$ or as $\dfrac{1}{\mathbf{V}}$.

The unit vector $\dfrac{\mathbf{V}}{|\mathbf{V}|}$ $(\mathbf{V} \neq 0)$ is the one which has the same direction as $\mathbf{V}$, but has a magnitude of 1. (Sometimes represented as $\mathbf{V}^0$.)

### Vector Algebra

The vector sum of $\mathbf{V}_1$ and $\mathbf{V}_2$ is represented by $\mathbf{V}_1 + \mathbf{V}_2$. The vector sum of $\mathbf{V}_1$ and $-\mathbf{V}_2$, or the difference of the vector $\mathbf{V}_2$ from $\mathbf{V}_1$ is represented by $\mathbf{V}_1 - \mathbf{V}_2$.

If $r$ is a scalar, then $r\mathbf{V} = \mathbf{V}r$, and represents a vector $r$ times the magnitude of $\mathbf{V}$, in the same direction as $\mathbf{V}$ if $r$ is positive, and in the opposite direction if $r$ is negative. If $r$ and $s$ are scalars, $\mathbf{V}_1$, $\mathbf{V}_2$, $\mathbf{V}_3$, vectors, then the following rules of scalars and vectors hold:

$$\mathbf{V}_1 + \mathbf{V}_2 = \mathbf{V}_2 + \mathbf{V}_1$$
$$(r + s)\mathbf{V}_1 = r\mathbf{V}_1 + s\mathbf{V}_1; \qquad r(\mathbf{V}_1 + \mathbf{V}_2) = r\mathbf{V}_1 + r\mathbf{V}_2$$
$$\mathbf{V}_1 + (\mathbf{V}_2 + \mathbf{V}_3) = (\mathbf{V}_1 + \mathbf{V}_2) + \mathbf{V}_3 = \mathbf{V}_1 + \mathbf{V}_2 + \mathbf{V}_3$$

If $\mathbf{V}_1$ is a vector in space, and $a_1$, $b_1$, $c_1$, the respective magnitudes of the projections of the vector along the coordinate $Ox$, $Oy$, $Oz$ axes, then

$\mathbf{V}_1 = a_1\mathbf{i} + b_1\mathbf{j} + c_1\mathbf{k}$, where $\mathbf{i}$, $\mathbf{j}$, $\mathbf{k}$ are respectively the unit vectors along $Ox$, $Oy$, and $Oz$. Its magnitude is

$$|\mathbf{V}_1| = \sqrt{a_1{}^2 + b_1{}^2 + c_1{}^2},$$

and its direction cosines satisfy the proportion

$$a_1 : b_1 : c_1 = \cos \alpha : \cos \beta : \cos \gamma.$$

Thus, if $\mathbf{V}_1 = a_1\mathbf{i} + b_1\mathbf{j} + c_1\mathbf{k}$ and $\mathbf{V}_2 = a_2\mathbf{i} + b_2\mathbf{j} + c_2\mathbf{k}$,
Then $\mathbf{V}_1 + \mathbf{V}_2 = (a_1 + a_2)\mathbf{i} + (b_1 + b_2)\mathbf{j} + (c_1 + c_2)\mathbf{k}$

### The Scalar, Dot, or Inner Product of Two Vectors $V_1$ and $V_2$

This product is represented as $V_1 \cdot V_2$ and is defined to be equal to $|V_1| \, |V_2| \cos \theta$, where $\theta$ is the angle from $V_1$ to $V_2$, i.e.,

$$V_1 \cdot V_2 = |V_1| \, |V_2| \cos \theta$$

The following rules apply for this product:

$$V_1 \cdot V_2 = a_1 a_2 + b_1 b_2 + c_1 c_2 = V_2 \cdot V_1$$

It should be noted that scalar multiplication is commutative.

If $V_1 = V_2$, then $V_1 \cdot V_2 = |V_1|^2$
$$(V_1 + V_2) \cdot V_3 = V_1 \cdot V_3 + V_2 \cdot V_3$$
$$V_1 \cdot (V_2 + V_3) = V_1 \cdot V_2 + V_1 \cdot V_3$$
$$i \cdot i = j \cdot j = k \cdot k = 1; \quad i \cdot j = j \cdot k = k \cdot i = 0$$

### The Vector or Cross Product of Vectors $V_1$ and $V_2$

This product is represented as $V_1 \times V_2$ and is defined to be equal to $|V_1| \, |V_2| \, (\sin \theta) l$, where $\theta$ is the angle from $V_1$ to $V_2$ and $l$ is a unit vector perpendicular to the plane of $V_1$ and $V_2$ and so directed that a right-handed screw driven in the direction of $l$ would carry $V_1$ into $V_2$, i.e.,

$$V_1 \times V_2 = |V_1| \, |V_2| \, (\sin \theta) l$$

The following rules apply for vector products:

$$V_1 \times V_2 = -V_2 \times V_1$$
$$V_1 \times (V_2 + V_3) = V_1 \times V_2 + V_1 \times V_3$$
$$(V_1 + V_2) \times V_3 = V_1 \times V_3 + V_2 \times V_3$$
$$V_1 \times (V_2 \times V_3) = V_2(V_3 \cdot V_1) - V_3(V_1 \cdot V_2)$$
$$i \times i = j \times j = k \times k = 0.1 \text{ (zero vector)}$$
$$= 0$$
$$i \times j = k, \quad j \times k = i, \quad k \times i = j$$

If $V_1 = a_1 i + b_1 j + c_1 k$, $\quad V_2 = a_2 i + b_2 j + c_2 k$,
$V_3 = a_3 i + b_3 j + c_3 k$,

then

$$V_1 \times V_2 = \begin{vmatrix} i & j & k \\ a_1 & b_1 & c_1 \\ a_2 & b_2 & c_2 \end{vmatrix} = (b_1 c_2 - b_2 c_1)i + (c_1 a_2 - c_2 a_1)j + (a_1 b_2 - a_2 b_1)k$$

It should be noted that, since $V_1 \times V_2 = -V_2 \times V_1$, the vector product is not commutative.

$$V_1 \cdot (V_2 \times V_3) = (V_1 \times V_2) \cdot V_3 = V_2 \cdot (V_3 \times V_1)$$

$$= (V_1 V_2 V_3) = \begin{vmatrix} a_1 & b_1 & c_1 \\ a_2 & b_2 & c_2 \\ a_3 & b_3 & c_3 \end{vmatrix}$$

which is equal to the volume of a parallelepiped whose three determining edges are $V_1$, $V_2$, $V_3$.

### Differentiation of Vectors

If $V_1 = a_1\mathbf{i} + b_1\mathbf{j} + c_1\mathbf{k}$, and $V_2 = a_2\mathbf{i} + b_2\mathbf{j} + c_2\mathbf{k}$, and if $V_1$ and $V_2$ are functions of the scalar $t$, then

$$\frac{d}{dt}(V_1 + V_2 + \cdots) = \frac{dV_1}{dt} + \frac{dV_2}{dt} + \cdots,$$

where $\dfrac{dV_1}{dt} = \dfrac{da_1}{dt}\mathbf{i} + \dfrac{db_1}{dt}\mathbf{j} + \dfrac{dc_1}{dt}\mathbf{k}$, etc.

$$\frac{d}{dt}(V_1 \cdot V_2) = \frac{dV_1}{dt} \cdot V_2 + V_1 \cdot \frac{dV_2}{dt}$$

$$\frac{d}{dt}(V_1 \times V_2) = \frac{dV_1}{dt} \times V_2 + V_1 \times \frac{dV_2}{dt}$$

### Differential Operators—Rectangular Coordinates

By definition

$$\nabla \equiv \text{del} \equiv \mathbf{i}\,\frac{\partial}{\partial x} + \mathbf{j}\,\frac{\partial}{\partial y} + \mathbf{k}\,\frac{\partial}{\partial z}$$

$$\nabla^2 \equiv \text{Laplacian} \equiv \frac{\partial^2}{\partial x^2} + \frac{\partial^2}{\partial y^2} + \frac{\partial^2}{\partial z^2}$$

If $S$ is a scalar function, then

$$\nabla S \equiv \text{grad } S \equiv \frac{\partial S}{\partial x}\mathbf{i} + \frac{\partial S}{\partial y}\mathbf{j} + \frac{\partial S}{\partial z}\mathbf{k}$$

The *distributive* law holds for finding a gradient. Thus if $S$ and $T$ are scalar functions

$$\nabla(S + T) = \nabla S + \nabla T$$

The *associative* law becomes the rule for differentiating a product:

$$\nabla(ST) = S\nabla T + T\nabla S$$

If $V$ is a vector function with the magnitudes of the components parallel to the three coordinate axes $V_x$, $V_y$, $V_z$, then

$$\nabla \cdot V \equiv \text{div } V \equiv \frac{\partial V_x}{\partial x} + \frac{\partial V_y}{\partial y} + \frac{\partial V_z}{\partial z}$$

The divergence obeys the distributive law. Thus, if $\mathbf{V}$ and $\mathbf{U}$ are vector functions, then

$$\nabla \cdot (\mathbf{V} + \mathbf{U}) = \nabla \cdot \mathbf{V} + \nabla \cdot \mathbf{U}$$

$$\nabla \times \mathbf{V} \equiv \operatorname{curl} \mathbf{V} \equiv \operatorname{rot} \mathbf{V} \equiv \begin{vmatrix} \mathbf{i} & \mathbf{j} & \mathbf{k} \\ \dfrac{\partial}{\partial x} & \dfrac{\partial}{\partial y} & \dfrac{\partial}{\partial z} \\ V_x & V_y & V_z \end{vmatrix}$$

The operator $\nabla$ can be used more than once. The number of possibilities where $\nabla$ is used twice are

$$\nabla \cdot (\nabla \theta) \equiv \operatorname{div} \operatorname{grad} \theta$$
$$\nabla \times (\nabla \theta) \equiv \operatorname{curl} \operatorname{grad} \theta$$
$$\nabla(\nabla \cdot \mathbf{V}) \equiv \operatorname{grad} \operatorname{div} \mathbf{V}$$
$$\nabla \cdot (\nabla \times \mathbf{V}) \equiv \operatorname{div} \operatorname{curl} \mathbf{V}$$
$$\nabla \times (\nabla \times \mathbf{V}) \equiv \operatorname{curl} \operatorname{curl} \mathbf{V}$$

Thus: $\operatorname{div} \operatorname{grad} S \equiv \nabla \cdot (\nabla S) \equiv \text{Laplacian } S \equiv \nabla^2 S$

$$\equiv \frac{\partial^2 S}{\partial x^2} + \frac{\partial^2 S}{\partial y^2} + \frac{\partial^2 S}{\partial z^2}$$

$$\operatorname{curl} \operatorname{grad} S \equiv 0; \qquad \operatorname{curl} \operatorname{curl} \mathbf{V} \equiv \operatorname{grad} \operatorname{div} \mathbf{V} - \nabla^2 \mathbf{V};$$
$$\operatorname{div} \operatorname{curl} \mathbf{V} \equiv 0$$

### Green's Theorem

Let $\mathbf{F}$ be a vector function and $v$ a volume bounded by a surface $s$, then

$$\iiint_{(v)} \operatorname{div} \mathbf{F} \, dv = \iiint_{(v)} \nabla \cdot \mathbf{F} \, dv = \iint_{(s)} \mathbf{F} \cdot ds,$$

where the integrations are to be carried out over the volume $v$ and the surface $s$.

### Stokes Theorem

Let $\mathbf{F}$ be a vector function and $s$ a surface bounded by a simple closed curve $c$, then

$$\int_{(c)} \mathbf{F} \cdot d\mathbf{1} = \iint_{(s)} (\nabla \times \mathbf{F}) \cdot ds = \iint_{(s)} \operatorname{curl} \mathbf{F} \cdot ds,$$

where the integrations are to be carried out over the curve $c$ and the surface $s$. It should be noted that

$$d\mathbf{1} = dx \, \mathbf{i} + dy \, \mathbf{j} + dz \, \mathbf{k}$$

The theorem implies that the line integral of $\mathbf{F}$ over the contour $c$ equals the surface integral of $\nabla \times \mathbf{F}$ over a surface $s$ which is bounded by $c$.

# ALGEBRA (Continued)

## MISCELLANEOUS

### The Sum ($\Sigma$, = Sigma) and Product ($\Pi$, = Pi) Notations

$\Sigma$ denotes the **sum,** and $\Pi$, the **product** of all quantities of a given collection. In particular,

$$\sum_{i=m}^{m+n} x_i \text{ means } x_m + x_{m+1} + \ldots + x_{m+n}, (n+1 \text{ terms in all}),$$

$$\prod_{i=m}^{m+n} x_i \text{ means } x_m x_{m+1} \ldots x_{m+n}, (n+1 \text{ factors in all}).$$

For indicated **range,** $R$, (such as $m \leq i \leq m+n$), one may write $\sum_R x_i$, $\prod_R x_i$, respectively. Where the range is clear from the context one writes $\Sigma x_i$, $\Pi x_i$, or even $\Sigma x$, $\Pi x$, respectively. For $c$ a constant and for $x_i$ and $y_i$ with common range (say of $n$ elements),

$$\Sigma c x_i = c \Sigma x_i, \ \Sigma(x_i + y_i) = \Sigma x_i + \Sigma y_i, \ \Sigma(x_i + c) = nc + \Sigma x_i$$

### Special Numerical Relations

(i) For range, $i = 1, 2, \ldots, n$, with $x_i = i$.
$\Sigma x_i = n(n+1)/2, \ \Sigma(2x_i - 1) = n^2,$
$\Sigma x_i^2 = n(n+1)(2n+1)/6.$
$\Sigma x_i^3 = (\Sigma x_i)^2, \ \Sigma x_i^4 = (\Sigma x_i^2)[6(\Sigma x_i) - 1]/5.$
$\Pi(c+1-x_i) = c^{(n)}, \ \Pi x_i = n^{(n)} = n!$ (**"factorial** $n$**"**).
Hence $n! = n \cdot (n-1)!$ $0!$ is defined to be 1.
**Stirling's formula** (used for $n$ large),

$$\sqrt{2n\pi}(n/e)^n < n! < \sqrt{2n\pi}(n/e)^n\left(1 + \frac{1}{12n-1}\right),$$
$$(\pi = 3.14159 \ldots, e = 2.71828 \ldots).$$

$n!/(n-m)!$ gives the number of **permutations of $n$ distinct things taken $m$ at a time.**

(ii) For range, $i = -\left(\dfrac{n-1}{2}\right), \ -\left(\dfrac{n-1}{2}\right) + 1, \ldots,$
$$\left(\dfrac{n-1}{2}\right) - 1, \left(\dfrac{n-1}{2}\right), \text{ with}$$

$x_i = i$ (whether $n$ is odd or even),

$$\sum x_i = \sum x_i^3 = 0, \ \sum x_i^2 = \frac{n(n^2-1)}{12}, \ \sum x_i^4 = \frac{3n^2-7}{20}\sum x_i^2.$$

(iii) The Binomial Coefficients, $\binom{n}{m}$.

$\binom{n}{m} = n!/[(n-m)!m!]$, for integers $m$, $n$, $0 \leq m \leq n$. $\binom{n}{0} = \binom{n}{n} = 1$.

$(x+c)^n = \sum_r \binom{n}{r} x^{n-r} c^r$, $(0 \leq r \leq n)$, the binomial expansion. $\binom{n}{m}$ gives also the number of **combinations of $n$ distinct things taken $m$ at a time.**

$\binom{n}{m} + \binom{n}{m+1} = \binom{n+1}{m+1}$, **recursion relation** for binomial coefficients.

$$\binom{n}{n-m} = \binom{n}{m}, \quad \sum_r (-1)^r \binom{n}{r} = 0, \quad \sum_r \binom{n}{r}^2 = \binom{2n}{n}, \quad \sum_{s=m}^{n} \binom{s}{m} = \binom{n+1}{m+1}.$$

### Table of Binomial Coefficients

| $n$ | $\binom{n}{0}$ | $\binom{n}{1}$ | $\binom{n}{2}$ | $\binom{n}{3}$ | $\binom{n}{4}$ | $\binom{n}{5}$ | $\binom{n}{6}$ | $\binom{n}{7}$ | $\binom{n}{8}$ | $\binom{n}{9}$ | $\binom{n}{10}$ |
|---|---|---|---|---|---|---|---|---|---|---|---|
| 0 | 1 | | | | | | | | | | |
| 1 | 1 | 1 | | | | | | | | | |
| 2 | 1 | 2 | 1 | | | | | | | | |
| 3 | 1 | 3 | 3 | 1 | | | | | | | |
| 4 | 1 | 4 | 6 | 4 | 1 | | | | | | |
| 5 | 1 | 5 | 10 | 10 | 5 | 1 | | | | | |
| 6 | 1 | 6 | 15 | 20 | 15 | 6 | 1 | | | | |
| 7 | 1 | 7 | 21 | 35 | 35 | 21 | 7 | 1 | | | |
| 8 | 1 | 8 | 28 | 56 | 70 | 56 | 28 | 8 | 1 | | |
| 9 | 1 | 9 | 36 | 84 | 126 | 126 | 84 | 36 | 9 | 1 | |
| 10 | 1 | 10 | 45 | 120 | 210 | 252 | 210 | 120 | 45 | 10 | 1 |
| 11 | 1 | 11 | 55 | 165 | 330 | 462 | 462 | 330 | 165 | 55 | 11 |
| 12 | 1 | 12 | 66 | 220 | 495 | 792 | 924 | 792 | 495 | 220 | 66 |
| 13 | 1 | 13 | 78 | 286 | 715 | 1287 | 1716 | 1716 | 1287 | 715 | 286 |
| 14 | 1 | 14 | 91 | 364 | 1001 | 2002 | 3003 | 3432 | 3003 | 2002 | 1001 |
| 15 | 1 | 15 | 105 | 455 | 1365 | 3003 | 5005 | 6435 | 6435 | 5005 | 3003 |
| 16 | 1 | 16 | 120 | 560 | 1820 | 4368 | 8008 | 11440 | 12870 | 11440 | 8008 |
| 17 | 1 | 17 | 136 | 680 | 2380 | 6188 | 12376 | 19448 | 24310 | 24310 | 19448 |
| 18 | 1 | 18 | 153 | 816 | 3060 | 8568 | 18564 | 31824 | 43758 | 48620 | 43758 |
| 19 | 1 | 19 | 171 | 969 | 3876 | 11628 | 27132 | 50388 | 75582 | 92378 | 92378 |
| 20 | 1 | 20 | 190 | 1140 | 4845 | 15504 | 38760 | 77520 | 125970 | 167960 | 184756 |

NOTE: $\binom{n}{m} = \dfrac{n(n-1)(n-2) \ldots (n-m+1)}{m(m-1)(m-2) \ldots 3.2.1}$: $\binom{n}{0} = 1$; $\binom{n}{1} = n$.

For coefficients missing from the above table, use the relation

$$\binom{n}{m} = \binom{n}{n-m}, \text{ e.g. } \binom{20}{11} = \binom{20}{9} = 167960.$$

### Finite Differences

For equi-spaced arguments $x_i$, and associated $y_i$, the successive advancing $y$-differences are, $\Delta^0 y_i = y_i$, $\Delta y_i = y_{i+1} - y_i$, $\Delta^2 y_i = \Delta y_{i+1} - \Delta y_i = y_{i+2} - 2y_{i+1} + y_i$, ..., $\Delta^m y_i = \Delta^{m-1} y_{i+1} - \Delta^{m-1} y_i = \sum_r (-1)^r \binom{m}{r} y_{i+m-r}$. With arbitrary origin $A$ and class-interval length, $x_{i+1} - x_i = h$, using $u_i = (x_i - A)/h$, write $y(u_i)$ for $y_i$. Then if for some fixed $m$, for the portion of the table considered, the values of $\Delta^{m+1} y_i$ be zero (or approximately, if these be regarded as negligible) **Newton's formula** gives

$$y(u) = \sum \frac{u^{(r)}}{r!} \Delta^r y(0) = y(0) + u\Delta y(0) + \frac{u(u-1)}{1 \cdot 2} \Delta^2 y(0)$$
$$+ \cdots + \frac{u(u-1) \ldots (u-m+1)}{m!} \Delta^m y(0).$$

This formula reduces to an identity for $u = u_0, u_1, \ldots, u_n$, $(u_i = i)$, and may be used to interpolate for intermediate values.

Example. Given

| $x$ | -4, | -2, | 0, | 2, | 4, | 6, | 8, ... |
|---|---|---|---|---|---|---|---|
| $y$ | 10, | 14, | 30, | 64, | 122, | 210, | 334, ... |

to find a value for $y$ when $x = 10$, and when $x = 1$. Suppose for some reason $A$ has been taken at $x = 2$. The work may be arranged as follows:

| $u$ | $x$ | $y$ | $\Delta$ | $\Delta^2$ | $\Delta^3$ | $\Delta^4$ |
|---|---|---|---|---|---|---|
| -3 | -4 | 10 | | | | |
| | | | 4 | | | |
| -2 | -2 | 14 | | 12 | | |
| | | | 16 | | 6 | |
| -1 | 0 | 30 | | 18 | | 0 |
| | | | 34 | | 6 | |
| 0 | 2 | 64 | | 24 | | 0 |
| | | | 58 | | 6 | |
| 1 | 4 | 122 | | 30 | | 0 |
| | | | 88 | | 6 | |
| 2 | 6 | 210 | | 36 | | — |
| | | | 124 | | — | |
| 3 | 8 | 334 | | — | | — |
| | | | — | | — | |
| — | — | — | | — | | — |

$$y(u) = 64 + 58u + 30\frac{u(u-1)}{1 \cdot 2} + 6\frac{u(u-1)(u-2)}{1 \cdot 2 \cdot 3}$$
$$= 64 + 58u + 15u(u-1) + u(u-1)(u-2).$$

At $x = 10$, $u = 4$. Substituting $u = 4$, one has $y|_{x-10} = 500$.
At $x = 1$, $u = -\frac{1}{2}$. Substituting $u = -\frac{1}{2}$, one has $y|_{x-1} = 44\frac{5}{8}$.

# STATISTICS
## Central Measures

**Here** the range of $i$ is from 1 to $n$. With each value $x_i$ is associated a weighting factor $f_i \geq 0$ (such as the frequency, the probability, the mass, the reliability, or other multiplier).

$N$, the **total weight**, $= \Sigma f_i$.

$\bar{x}$, the **arithmetic mean**, $= \Sigma f_i x_i / N = \Sigma f_i x_i / \Sigma f_i$.

$GM$, the **geometric mean** (available when each $x_i$ is positive), $= \sqrt[N]{\Pi x_i{}^{f_i}}$. $\log GM = \Sigma f_i \log x_i / N$.

$Mo$, the **mode**, $=$ value among $(x_1, \ldots, x_n)$ having maximum associated $f_i$ (usually obtained by interpolating after the data are graduated). For unweighted items, $x_i$, a mode is a value about which the values of $x_i$ cluster most densely.

$RMS$, the **root-mean-square**, $= \sqrt{\Sigma f_i x_i{}^2 / N}$.

$Md$, the **median** (see below). For unweighted items, the median is the value, equaled or exceeded by exactly half of the values $x_i$ in the given list. In case of a central pair, the median is usually taken as the arithmetic mean of this pair.

$Mm$, the **mid-mean** (see below). For unweighted items, the mid-mean is the arithmetic mean of the half-list obtained upon dropping out the highest quarter and lowest quarter of the items.

Cum $f|_X$, the value of "cumulative $f$" at $X$, $= \displaystyle\sum_{x_i < X} f_i$ (interpolation being used for $X$ if necessary).

## The M-Tiles

For **ungrouped data**, $X$ is called the $r$th **m-tile** (or $r$th **m-tile mark**) $(r = 0, 1, \ldots, m)$ if simultaneously, $\displaystyle\sum_{x_i < X} f_i / N \leq r / m$, and $\displaystyle\sum_{x_i > X} f_i / N \leq (m - r) / m$. In particular the zeroth $m$-tile is **min**, the minimal value among the list $(x_1, \ldots, x_n)$, and the $m$th $m$-tile is **max**, the maximal value among the list.

For **grouped data**, the $r$th $m$-tile mark, $X$, is such that
$$\text{Cum } f|_X = Nr/m, \quad (r = 0, 1, 2, \ldots, m).$$
$$\text{Cum } f|_{\min} = 0, \qquad \text{Cum } f|_{\max} = N.$$

In particular, certain intermediate $(0 < r < m)$ $m$-tile marks are named as follows:

| $m$ | $r = 1$ | 2 | 3 |
|---|---|---|---|
| 2 | $Md$ (median) | | |
| 3 | $T_1$ (lower tertile) | $T_2$ (upper tertile) | |
| 4 | $Q_1$ (lower quartile) | $Md$ | $Q_3$ (upper quartile) |
| 10 | $D_1$ (first decile) | $D_2$ | $D_3$ etc. |
| 100 | $PC_1$ (first percentile) | $PC_2$ | $PC_3$ etc. |

## STATISTICS (Continued)

The term "rth m-tile" $(r = 1, \ldots, m)$ is also used to denote the class interval extending from the $(r-1)$st to $r$th m-tile mark as defined above.

$Mm$, the mid-mean, =

$$2 \sum_{Q_1 \leq x_i \leq Q_3} f_i x_i / N = \sum_{Q_1 \leq x_i \leq Q_3} f_i x_i / \sum_{Q_1 \leq x_i \leq Q_3} f_i.$$

When each $x_i$ is positive, and not all are equal, one always has $0 < \min < GM < \bar{x} < RMS < \max$.

For moderately-skewed distributions, one has approximately $Mo - \bar{x} = 3(Md - \bar{x})$, or $3Md = Mo + 2\bar{x}$.

### Measures of Dispersion and Skewness

Here $A$ is an arbitrary reference value, usually a convenient integral measure near $\bar{x}$.

$\nu_k$, $k$th moment about $A$, $= \Sigma f_i(x_i - A)^k / N$, $(k = 0, 1, \ldots)$.
$\nu_0 = 1$, $\nu_1 = \bar{x} - A$. $\nu_2$ as function of $A$ is minimum for $A = \bar{x}$.

$\mu_k$, $k$th moment about $\bar{x}$, $= \Sigma f_i(x_i - \bar{x})^k / N$, $(k = 0, 1, \ldots)$.

$$\mu_0 = 1,$$
$$\mu_1 = 0,$$
$$\mu_2 = \nu_2 - \nu_1^2 \ (\mu_2 = \text{variance}),$$
$$\mu_3 = \nu_3 - 3\nu_1\nu_2 + 2\nu_1^3,$$
$$\mu_4 = \nu_4 - 4\nu_1\nu_3 + 6\nu_1^2\nu_2 - 3\nu_1^4.$$
$$\beta_1 = \mu_3^2 / \mu_2^3, \ \beta_2 = \mu_4 / \mu_2^2.$$

$\sigma$, standard deviation, $= \sqrt{\mu_2}$.

$\alpha_3/2$, momental skewness; $\alpha_3 = \sqrt{\beta_1} = \mu_3/\sigma^3$.

$(\alpha_4 - 3)/2$, kurtosis; $\alpha_4 = \beta_2$.

$MD$, mean deviation (from the mean), $= \Sigma f_i |x_i - \bar{x}| / N$
$$= 2 \left[ \bar{x} \sum_{x_i < \bar{x}} f_i - \sum_{x_i < \bar{x}} f_i x_i \right] / N. \qquad \text{(This latter form is convenient for computation.)}$$

$s$, quartile deviation, $= |Q_3 - Q_1|/2$.

$P.E.$, probable error, $= 0.6745\sigma$.

$V$, coefficient of variation, $= 100\sigma/\bar{x} \%$.

Pearson's measure of skewness $= (\bar{x} - Mo)/\sigma$. (Usually approximately $\alpha_3/2$.)

Bowley's measure of skewness $= (Q_3 - 2Md + Q_1)/(2s)$.

(Bowley's measure of skewness lies between $-1$ and $+1$.)

## The Class Interval

$$\Delta x_i = x_{i+1} - x_i.$$

For equi-spaced arguments, $\Delta x_i = h$, the **length of the class interval**, $x_i$ is the mid-value or **class mark**. The interval from $x_i - (h/2)$ to $x_i + (h/2)$ is the **class interval** with these as given **initial** and **terminal** end values.

$$u_i = (x_i - A)/h.$$
$$\bar{u} = \Sigma f_i u_i / N, \ \bar{x} = h\bar{u} + A.$$
$$(\mu_k)_x = h^k(\mu_k)_u, \ (k = 0, 1, \ldots).$$
$$\sigma_u^2 = [\Sigma f_i u_i^2/N] - \bar{u}^2, \ \sigma_x = h\sigma_u.$$
$$(\beta_1)_x = (\beta_1)_u, \ (\beta_2)_x = (\beta_2)_u.$$

**Sheppard's corrections** (to correct approximately for the error due to treating all elements in a given class interval of length $h$ as though concentrated at the class mark).

For $\mu_0, \mu_1, \mu_3$, no corrections.

In $x$-units,

corrected $(\mu_2)_x =$ uncorrected $(\mu_2)_x - h^2/12$,

corrected $(\mu_4)_x =$ uncorrected $(\mu_4)_x - h^2$ uncorrected $(\mu_2)_x/2 + 7h^4/240$.

In $u$-units, replace $h$ by 1 in the formulae given above.

## Least Squares

The **normal equations** for finding coefficients, $a_0, a_1, \ldots, a_m$, in fitting a curve of the form $y = a_0 + a_1 x + \ldots + a_m x^m$ to data $(X_i, Y_i)$, $i = 1, \ldots, n$, $(n > m)$, are $m + 1$ in number as follows:

$$\Sigma Y_i = a_0 n + a_1 \Sigma X_i + a_2 \Sigma X_i^2 + \ldots + a_m \Sigma X_i^m,$$
$$\Sigma X_i Y_i = a_0 \Sigma X_i + a_1 \Sigma X_i^2 + a_2 \Sigma X_i^3 + \ldots + a_m \Sigma X_i^{m+1},$$

$$\Sigma X_i^m Y_i = a_0 \Sigma X_i^m + a_1 \Sigma X_i^{m+1} + a_2 \Sigma X_i^{m+2} + \ldots + a_m \Sigma X_i^{2m},$$

**Deviation** from fitted curve,

$$d_i = Y_i - (a_0 + a_1 X_i + \ldots + a_m X_i^m).$$

$$\Sigma d_i^2 = \Sigma Y_i^2 - (a_0 \Sigma Y_i + a_1 \Sigma X_i Y_i + \ldots + a_m \Sigma X_i^m Y_i).$$

For $z = ab^x$, use $y = \log z$, $a_0 = \log a$, $a_1 = \log b$.

For $z = at^p$, use $y = \log z$, $a_0 = \log a$, $a_1 = p$, $x = \log t$.

$S_y$, **standard error of estimate**, = root-mean-square of the $y$-deviations about a fitted curve = $\sqrt{\Sigma d_i^2/n}$.

## Simple Correlation

### Product Moment Method

Given $n$ equi-spaced measurements $X_i$, $i = 1, 2, \ldots, n$, with $h = X_{i+1} - X_i$, $x_i = X_i - \bar{X}$; and $m$ equi-spaced measurements $Y_j$, $j = 1, 2, \ldots, m$, with $k = Y_{j+1} - Y_j$, $y_j = Y_j - \bar{Y}$; and a weight (frequency, probability, etc.) $e_{ij}$ $(\geq 0)$, associated with $(X_i, Y_i)$. Here $e_{ij}$ is an entry in the table.

$$f_i = \sum_j e_{ij}, \; g_j = \sum_i e_{ij}.$$

$$N = \sum_{ij} e_{ij} = \sum_i f_i = \sum_j g_j. \quad \text{(Check)}$$

$$\bar{x} = \sum_{ij} e_{ij} X_i / N = \sum_i f_i X_i / N; \; \bar{y} = \sum_{ij} e_{ij} Y_j / N = \sum_j g_j Y_j / N.$$

Let $A$ and $B$ be arbitrary reference values, usually convenient integral measures near $\overline{X}$ and $\overline{Y}$, respectively.

$$u_i = (X_i - A)/h, \; v_j = (Y_j - B)/k;$$

$$\bar{u} = \Sigma f_i u_i / N, \; \overline{X} = h\bar{u} + A, \; \bar{v} = \Sigma g_j v_j / N, \; \overline{Y} = k\bar{v} + B.$$

$$\left. \begin{array}{l} \sigma_u^2 = (\mu_2)_u = (\Sigma f_i u_i^2 / N) - \bar{u}^2, \; \sigma_x = h\sigma_u. \\ \sigma_v^2 = (\mu_2)_v = (\Sigma g_j v_j^2)/N - \bar{v}^2, \; \sigma_y = k\sigma_v. \end{array} \right\} \begin{array}{l} \text{Apply Sheppard's} \\ \text{corrections.} \end{array}$$

$$U_j = \sum_i e_{ij} u_i, \; V_i = \sum_j e_{ij} v_j, \; P = \sum u_i V_i = \sum v_j U_j, \quad \text{(Check)}$$

$$p_{uv} = \sum_{ij} e_{ij} (u_i - \bar{u})(v_j - \bar{v})/N$$

$$= (P/N) - \overline{uv}.$$

$$p_{xy} = hk p_{uv}.$$

$r = p_{uv}/(\sigma_u \sigma_v) = p_{xy}/(\sigma_x \sigma_y)$ (**product-moment**) **coefficient of correlation.** In every case $-1 \le r \le 1$.

$$Y - \overline{Y} = r\frac{\sigma_y}{\sigma_x}(X - \overline{X}), \text{ or } y = r\frac{\sigma_y}{\sigma_x}x, \text{ regression line of } y \text{ on } x.$$

$$X - \overline{X} = r\frac{\sigma_x}{\sigma_y}(Y - \overline{Y}), \text{ or } x = r\frac{\sigma_x}{\sigma_y}y, \text{ regression line of } x \text{ on } y.$$

## Example of Computation for Product-Moment Coefficient of Correlation

| $v_j$ \ $u_i$ | $y_j$ \ $x_i$ | -3 / 12 | -2 / 16 | -1 / 20 | 0 / 24 | 1 / 28 | 2 / 32 | $g_j$ | $g_j v_j$ | $g_j v_j^2$ | $U_j \left(-\sum_i e_{ij} u_i\right)$ | $v_j U_j$ |
|---|---|---|---|---|---|---|---|---|---|---|---|---|
| 2 | 21 | | | 1 | 5 | 7 | 1 | 14 | 28 | 56 | 8 | 16 |
| 1 | 18 | | 1 | 3 | 7 | 5 | 2 | 18 | 18 | 18 | 4 | 4 |
| 0 | 15 | | 2 | 3 | 4 | 1 | | 10 | 0 | 0 | 0 | 0 |
| -1 | 12 | | 3 | 1 | 1 | | | 5 | -5 | 5 | -7 | 7 |
| -2 | 9 | 2 | 1 | | | | | 3 | -6 | 12 | -8 | 16 |
| $f_i$ | | 2 | 7 | 8 | 17 | 13 | 3 | 50 | 35 | 91 | | 43 |
| $f_i u_i$ | | -6 | -14 | -8 | 0 | 13 | 6 | -9 | | | | |
| $f_i u_i^2$ | | 18 | 28 | 8 | 0 | 13 | 12 | 79 | | | | |
| $V_i \left(-\sum_j e_{ij} v_j\right)$ | | -4 | -4 | 4 | | 19 | 4 | | | | | |
| $u_i V_i$ | | 12 | 8 | -4 | 0 | 19 | 8 | 43 | | | | |

$A = 24, B = 15,$
$h = 4, k = 3,$
$N = \Sigma f_i = \Sigma g_j = 50,$
$\Sigma f_i u_i = -9, \; \Sigma g_j v_j = 35,$
$\Sigma f_i u_i^2 = 79, \; \Sigma g_j v_j^2 = 91,$
$P = \Sigma u_i V_i = \Sigma v_j U_j = 43.$

$\bar{u} = -\frac{9}{50} = -.18 \qquad \bar{v} = \frac{35}{50} = .70$
$\sigma_u^2 = (\frac{79}{50}) - (-.18)^2 = .083 = 1.46, \qquad \sigma_u = 1.21$
$\sigma_v^2 = (\frac{91}{50}) - (.70)^2 = .083 = 1.247. \qquad \sigma_v = 1.117$
$p_{uv} = (\frac{43}{50}) - (-.18)(.70) = +0.986$

$r = +0.986/(1.21 \times 1.117) = +.730.$ \qquad Ans. $r = +.730$

### Rank Difference Method

Given $n$ corresponding pairs of measured items $(X_i, Y_i)$, $(i = 1, \ldots, n)$. Let $(u_i, v_i)$ be the corresponding rank numbers. Here $u_i = 1$ for the largest $X_i$, 2 for the next largest $X_i$, etc., and similarly $v_i = 1$ for the largest $Y_i$, 2 for the next largest $Y_i$, etc. $\rho = 1 - \dfrac{6\,\Sigma(u_i - v_i)^2}{n(n^2 - 1)}$, (rank difference) coefficient of correlation. In every case $-1 \leq \rho \leq 1$. Check: $\Sigma(u_i - v_i) = 0$.

**Example of Computation for Rank-Difference Coefficient of Correlation**

| $X_i$ | $Y_i$ | $u_i$ | $v_i$ | $u_i - v_i$ | $(u_i - v_i)^2$ | |
|---|---|---|---|---|---|---|
| 76 | 52 | 3 | 1 | $+2$ | 4 | Check: $\Sigma(u_i - v_i) = 0.$ |
| 66 | 34 | 8 | 9 | $-1$ | 1 | |
| 63 | 32 | 10 | 10 | 0 | 0 | |
| 74 | 45 | 4 | 4 | 0 | 0 | $\rho = 1 - \dfrac{6 \times 62}{10(10^2 - 1)}$ |
| 79 | 50 | 1 | 2 | $-1$ | 1 | |
| 69 | 37 | 7 | 7 | 0 | 0 | |
| 77 | 35 | 2 | 8 | $-6$ | 36 | $= +0.63$ |
| 65 | 42 | 9 | 5 | $+4$ | 16 | |
| 71 | 40 | 6 | 6 | 0 | 0 | Ans. $\rho = +.63$ |
| 73 | 48 | 5 | 3 | $+2$ | 4 | |
| $N = 10$ | | | | 0 | 62 | |

### Probability

If among $a + b$ equi-probable and mutually exclusive events, $a$ are regarded as favorable and $b$ unfavorable, then for a single trial

$p$, probability of favorable outcome, $= \dfrac{a}{a + b}$,

$q$, probability of unfavorable outcome, $= 1 - p = \dfrac{b}{a + b}$.

The successive terms in the binomial expansion $(p + q)^n = \sum_r \binom{n}{r} p^{n-r} q^r$ give the respective probabilities that in $n$ trials, the

event will be favorable exactly $n - r$ times, $r = 0, \ldots, n$.

The mean number of favorable events is $np$, of unfavorable, $nq$; the standard deviation is $\sigma = \sqrt{npq}$, $\alpha_3 = (p - q)/\sigma$ (the positive direction being that of increasing unfavorability).

**Normal curve** ($x$ measured in $\sigma$-units from the mean, and with area $= 1$):

$$y = \frac{1}{\sqrt{2\pi}} e^{-x^2/2} = 0.3989 e^{-x^2/2}.$$

$MD$ (mean deviation from the mean) $= \sigma\sqrt{2/\pi} = 0.7979\sigma$.
$s$ (quartile deviation from the mean) $= 0.6745\sigma = 0.845\ MD$.

Percentage areas, under normal curve, for successive class intervals measured from the mean:

Multiples of $\sigma$: 34 %, 14 %, 2 %.
Multiples of $s$: 25 %, 16 %, 7 %, 2 %.

**Normal surface** ($x$ measured in $\sigma_x$-units $y$ in $\sigma_y$-units from their means),

$$z = \frac{1}{2\pi\sqrt{1-\gamma^2}}e^{-(x^2-2rxy+y^2)/[2(1-r^2)]}.$$

*Goodness of Fit. For a universe of objects falling into $n$ mutually exclusive classes with class marks, $x_i(i = 1, 2, \ldots, n)$, let $p_i$ be the probability for the $i$th class. Given a sample of $N$ items, with $f_i$ items in the $i$th class ($\Sigma f_i = N$), the probability that a random sample of $N$ items gives no better fit, expressed in terms of $n$ and $\chi^2$ ("Chi square"), $= \Sigma(f_i - Np_i)^2/(Np_i)$, is given by a table, portions of which are as follows:

**Probability that a Random Sample Gives no Better Fit**

| $\chi^2$ / $n$ | 1 | 2 | 3 | 4 | 6 | 8 | 10 | 15 | 20 |
|---|---|---|---|---|---|---|---|---|---|
| 3 | .607 | .368 | .223 | .135 | .050 | .018 | .007 | .001 | .000 |
| 4 | .801 | .572 | .392 | .261 | .112 | .046 | .019 | .002 | .000 |
| 5 | .910 | .736 | .558 | .406 | .199 | .092 | .040 | .005 | .000 |
| 6 | .963 | .849 | .700 | .549 | .306 | .156 | .075 | .010 | .001 |
| 7 | .986 | .920 | .809 | .677 | .423 | .238 | .125 | .020 | .003 |
| 8 | .995 | .960 | .885 | .780 | .540 | .333 | .189 | .036 | .006 |
| 9 | .998 | .981 | .934 | .857 | .647 | .433 | .265 | .059 | .010 |
| 10 | .999 | .991 | .964 | .911 | .740 | .534 | .350 | .091 | .018 |
| 11 | 1.000 | .996 | .981 | .947 | .815 | .629 | .440 | .132 | .029 |
| 12 | 1.000 | .998 | .991 | .970 | .873 | .713 | .530 | .182 | .045 |

| $\chi^2$ / $n$ | 8 | 10 | 12 | 14 | 16 | 18 | 20 | 25 | 30 |
|---|---|---|---|---|---|---|---|---|---|
| 10 | .534 | .350 | .213 | .122 | .067 | .035 | .018 | .003 | .000 |
| 11 | .629 | .440 | .285 | .173 | .100 | .055 | .029 | .005 | .001 |
| 12 | .713 | .530 | .363 | .233 | .141 | .082 | .045 | .009 | .002 |
| 13 | .785 | .616 | .446 | .301 | .191 | .116 | .067 | .015 | .003 |
| 14 | .844 | .694 | .528 | .374 | .249 | .158 | .095 | .023 | .005 |
| 15 | .889 | .762 | .606 | .450 | .313 | .207 | .130 | .035 | .008 |
| 16 | .924 | .820 | .679 | .526 | .382 | .263 | .172 | .050 | .012 |
| 17 | .949 | .867 | .744 | .599 | .453 | .324 | .220 | .070 | .018 |
| 18 | .967 | .904 | .800 | .667 | .524 | .389 | .274 | .095 | .026 |
| 19 | .979 | .932 | .847 | .729 | .593 | .456 | .333 | .125 | .037 |
| 20 | .987 | .953 | .886 | .784 | .657 | .522 | .395 | .161 | .052 |

* See index for $t$ Test and $F$ Test Tables.

# MENSURATION FORMULÆ

## Plane Figures Bounded by Straight Lines

The **area of a triangle** whose base is $b$ and altitude $h$

$$= \frac{hb}{2}.$$

The area of a **triangle** with angles $A$, $B$, and $C$ and sides opposite $a$, $b$, and $c$, respectively

$$= \tfrac{1}{2}ab \sin C.$$

or
$$= \sqrt{s(s-a)(s-b)(s-c)},$$
where $s = \tfrac{1}{2}(a + b + c)$.

A **rectangle** with sides $a$ and $b$ has an area $= ab$.

The area of a **parallelogram** with side $b$ and the perpendicular distance to the parallel side $h$

$$= bh.$$

The area of a **parallelogram** with sides $a$ and $b$ and the included angle $\theta$

$$= ab \sin \theta.$$

The area of a **rhombus** with diagonals $c$ and $d$,

$$= \tfrac{1}{2}cd.$$

The area of a **trapezoid** whose parallel sides are $a$ and $b$ and altitude $h$

$$= \tfrac{1}{2}(a + b)h.$$

The area of any **quadrilateral** with diagonals $a$ and $b$ and the angle between them $\theta$

$$= \tfrac{1}{2}ab \sin \theta.$$

The area of a **regular polygon** with $n$ sides, each of length $l$,

$$= \tfrac{1}{4}nl^2 \cot \frac{180°}{n}.$$

For a regular polygon of $n$ sides, each side of length $l$, the radius of the **inscribed circle**,

$$= \frac{l}{2} \cot \frac{180°}{n}.$$

The radius of the **circumscribed circle**,

$$= \frac{l}{2} \operatorname{cosec} \frac{180°}{n}.$$

### Area, Radius of Inscribed and Circumscribed Circles for Regular Polygons

$l$ = length of one side.

| Name. | Number of sides. | Area. | Radius of inscribed circle. | Radius of circumscribed circle. |
|---|---|---|---|---|
| Triangle, equilateral.......... | 3 | $0.43301l^2$ | $0.28867l$ | $0.57735l$ |
| Square.......... | 4 | $1.00000l^2$ | $0.50000l$ | $0.70710l$ |
| Pentagon........ | 5 | $1.72048l^2$ | $0.68819l$ | $0.85065l$ |
| Hexagon........ | 6 | $2.59808l^2$ | $0.86602l$ | $1.0000l$ |
| Heptagon....... | 7 | $3.63391l^2$ | $1.0383l$ | $1.1523l$ |
| Octagon......... | 8 | $4.82843l^2$ | $1.2071l$ | $1.3065l$ |
| Nonagon........ | 9 | $6.18182l^2$ | $1.3737l$ | $1.4619l$ |
| Decagon........ | 10 | $7.69421l^2$ | $1.5388l$ | $1.6180l$ |
| Undecagon...... | 11 | $9.36564l^2$ | $1.7028l$ | $1.7747l$ |
| Dodecagon...... | 12 | $11.19615l^2$ | $1.8660l$ | $1.9318l$ |

**Radius of circle inscribed in any triangle,** whose sides are $a$, $b$, and $c$, where $s = \frac{1}{2}(a + b + c)$ is given by $r$

$$= \frac{\sqrt{s(s - a)(s - b)(s - c)}}{s}.$$

The radius of the **circumscribed** circle is given by $R$

$$= \frac{abc}{4\sqrt{s(s - a)(s - b)(s - c)}}.$$

The **perimeter of a polygon inscribed in a circle** of radius $r$, where $n$ is the number of sides,

$$= 2nr \sin \frac{\pi}{n}. \qquad (\pi \text{ radians} = 180°)$$

The area of the **inscribed** polygon,

$$= \tfrac{1}{2}nr^2 \sin \frac{2\pi}{n}.$$

**The perimeter of a polygon circumscribed about a circle of** radius $r$, number of sides $n$

$$= 2nr \tan \frac{\pi}{n}.$$

The area of the **circumscribed** polygon

$$= nr^2 \tan \frac{\pi}{n}.$$

### Plane Figures Bounded by Curved Lines

The **circumference of a circle** whose radius is $r$ and diameter $d (d = 2r)$

$$= 2\pi r = \pi d. \qquad (\pi = 3.14159)$$

The **area of a circle**

$$= \pi r^2 = \tfrac{1}{4}\pi d^2 = .7854 d^2.$$

The **length of an arc** of a circle for an arc of $\theta$ degrees

$$= \frac{\pi r \theta}{180}.$$

NOTE.—In this and following similar formulæ $r$ denotes the radius of the circle, ($OC$, Fig. 1).

For an arc of $\theta$ radians the length $s$

$$= r\theta.$$

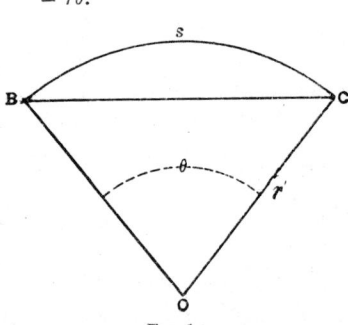

FIG. 1.

The **length of a chord** subtending an angle $\theta$.

$$= 2r \sin \tfrac{1}{2}\theta.$$

The **area of a sector** where $\theta$ is the angle between the radii in degrees

$$= \frac{\pi r^2 \theta}{360}.$$

If $s$ is the length of the arc, the area of the sector

$$= \frac{sr}{2}.$$

The **area of a segment** where $\theta$ is the angle between the two radii in degrees

$$= \frac{\pi r^2 \theta}{360} - \frac{r^2 \sin \theta}{2} \qquad \begin{bmatrix} \theta° = 180° - [2\sin^{-1}(x/r)] \\ x = \perp \text{ dist. center to chord} \end{bmatrix}$$

344

If $\theta$ is in radians the area $= \frac{1}{2}r^2(\theta - \sin \theta)$.

The **area of the segment of a circle**

$$= \frac{\pi r^2}{2} - \left[ x\sqrt{r^2 - x^2} + r^2 \sin^{-1}\left(\frac{x}{r}\right) \right]$$

where $r$ is the radius of the circle and $x$ the perpendicular distance of the chord from the center. The principal angle must be used in this formula.

The **area of the ring** between two circles of radius $r_1$ and $r_2$, one of which encloses the other,

$$= \pi(r_1 + r_2)\,(r_1 - r_2).$$

The two circles are not necessarily concentric.

**Area of the sector of an annulus.** (Fig. 2.)—If angle $GOH = \theta$ and the lines $GO$ and $JO = r_1$ and $r_2$ respectively, the area $GHIJ = \frac{1}{2}\theta\,(r_1 + r_2)\,(r_1 - r_2)$.

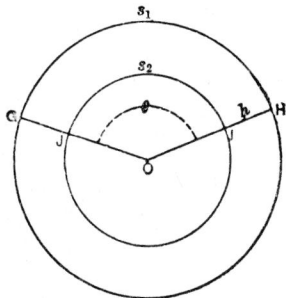

Fig. 2.

If $s_1$ = the length of the arc $GH$ and $s_2$ = the arc $JI$ and $h = HI = r_1 - r_2$, the area $GHIJ = \frac{1}{2}h(s_1 + s_2)$.

The **circumference of an ellipse** whose semiaxes are $a$ and $b$ $= 2\pi\sqrt{\dfrac{a^2+b^2}{2}}$ (approx.) $= 4aE$ exactly. See tables of elliptic integrals for $E$, using $k = \dfrac{\sqrt{a^2 - b^2}}{a}$

The **area of an ellipse** $= \pi ab$.

The length of the **arc of a parabola**, as arc $SPQ$ in Fig. 3, where $x = PR$, and $y = QR$

$$\sqrt{4x^2 + y^2} + \frac{y^2}{2x} \log_e \frac{2x + \sqrt{4x^2 + y^2}}{y}$$

The **area of the section of the parabola** $PQRS$, $= \frac{4}{3}xy$.

## MENSURATION FORMULAE (Continued)

### Solids Bounded by Planes

The **lateral area of a regular prism** = perimeter of a right section × the length.

The **volume of a regular prism** = area of base × the altitude.

The **lateral area of a regular pyramid,** slant height $l$, length of one side of base $a$, and a number of sides $n$,

$$= \tfrac{1}{2}nal.$$

The **volume of a pyramid** = $\tfrac{1}{3}$ area of base × altitude.

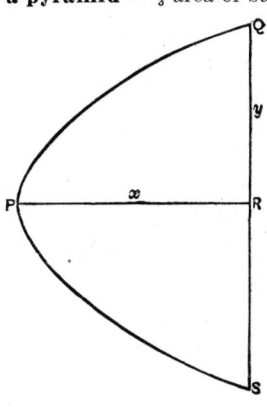

Fig. 3.

### Surface and Volume of Regular Polyhedra

Surface and volume of regular polyhedra in terms of the length of one edge $l$.

| Name. | Nature of surface. | Surface. | Volume. |
|---|---|---|---|
| Tetrahedron... | 4 equilateral triangles | $1.73205l^2$ | $0.11785l^3$ |
| Hexahedron or cube........ | 6 squares.......... | $6.00000l^2$ | $1.00000l^3$ |
| Octahedron.... | 8 equilateral triangles | $3.46410l^2$ | $0.47140l^3$ |
| Dodecahedron. | 12 pentagons......... | $20.64573l^2$ | $7.66312l^3$ |
| Icosahedron... | 20 equilateral triangles | $8.66025l^2$ | $2.18170l^3$ |

### Solids Bounded by Curved Surfaces

The **surface of a sphere** of radius $r$ and diameter $d(= 2r)$

$$= 4\pi r^2 = \pi d^2 = 12.57r^2.$$

The **volume of a sphere**

$$= \tfrac{4}{3}\pi r^3 = \tfrac{1}{6}\pi d^3 = 4.189r^3.$$

346

The **area of a lune** on the surface of a sphere of radius $r$, included between two great circles whose inclination is $\theta$ radians.

$$= 2r^2\theta.$$

The **area of a spherical triangle** whose angles are $A$, $B$, and $C$ (radians) on a sphere of radius $r$

$$= (A + B + C - \pi)r^2.$$

The **area of a spherical polygon** of $n$ sides where $\theta$ is the sum of its angles in radians

$$= [\theta - (n - 2)\pi]r^2.$$

The area of the curved surface of a **spherical segment** of height $h$, radius of sphere $r$

$$= 2\pi\, rh.$$

The **volume of a spherical segment,** data as above

$$= \tfrac{1}{3}\pi h^2\,(3r - h).$$

If $a$ = radius of the base of the segment, the volume

$$= \tfrac{1}{6}\pi h(h^2 + 3a^2).$$

The **curved surface of a right cylinder where** $r$ = the radius of the base and $h$, the altitude,

$$= 2\pi rh.$$

The **volume of a cylinder,** data as above,

$$= \pi r^2 h.$$

The **curved surface of a right cone** whose altitude is $h$ and radius of base $r$

$$= \pi r\,\sqrt{r^2 + h^2}.$$

The **volume of a cone,** data as above,

$$= \frac{\pi}{3}\, r^2 h = 1.047\, r^2 h.$$

The **curved surface of the frustum of a right cone,** radius of base $r_1$, of top $r_2$ and altitude $h$,

$$= \pi(r_1 + r_2)\,\sqrt{h^2 + (r_1 - r_2)^2}.$$

The **volume of the frustum of a cone,** data as above,

$$= \pi\,\frac{h}{3}\,(r_1^2 + r_1 r_2 + r_2^2).$$

The **oblate spheroid** is formed by the rotation of an ellipse about its minor axis. If $a$ and $b$ are the major and minor semi-axes respectively, and $\epsilon$ the eccentricity, the surface

$$= 2\pi a^2 + \pi\,\frac{b^2}{\epsilon}\,\log_e\frac{1 + \epsilon}{1 - \epsilon},$$

and volume $= \tfrac{4}{3}\pi a^2 b.$

347

## MENSURATION FORMULAE (Continued)

The prolate spheroid is formed by the rotation of an ellipse about its major axis ($2a$), data as above.

Surface $\qquad = 2\pi b^2 + 2\pi \dfrac{ab}{\epsilon} \sin^{-1}\epsilon,$

volume $\qquad = \frac{4}{3}\pi ab^2.$

## SIMPSON'S RULE FOR IRREGULAR AREAS

Divide the area into an even number ($2m$) of panels by means of $2m+1$ parallel lines, drawn at constant distance $h$ apart; and denote the lengths of the intercepted segments by $y_0, y_1 \ldots, y_{2m-1}, y_{2m}$. The first and last of these may be zero. The area will then be

$$A = \tfrac{1}{3}h[(y_0 + y_{2m}) + 4(y_1 + y_3 + \ldots + y_{2m-1}) + 2(y_2 + y_4 + \ldots + y_{2m-2})]$$

While the formula is exact in many simple cases, ordinarily the formula provides only an approximation, for which the accuracy increases with an increase in the number of divisions. Simpson's Rule may be applied to finding volumes, if the measures $y_0, y_1 \ldots, y_{2m}$ be interpreted as the areas of parallel plane sections at constant distance $h$ apart.

## PRISMOIDAL FORMULA

As a special case where $m=1$, and H, ($=2h$) is the distance between two limiting parallel planes, one has for the volume of a solid figure,

$$V = \tfrac{1}{6}H(S_0 + 4S_1 + S_2).$$

Here $S_0$ and $S_2$ are the cross-sectional areas in these limiting planes (lower and upper bases, respectively), and $S_1$ is the cross section of the mid-section. The formula is exact for the cone, sphere, ellipsoid, and prismoid.

# TRIGONOMETRIC FORMULAE

## TRIGONOMETRIC FUNCTIONS IN A RIGHT-ANGLED TRIANGLE

If $A$, $B$, and $C$ are the vertices ($C$ the right angle), and $a$, $b$, and $h$ the sides opposite respectively,

$$\text{sine } A = \sin A = \frac{a}{h}, \qquad \text{cosine } A = \cos A = \frac{b}{h},$$

$$\text{tangent } A = \tan A = \frac{a}{b}, \quad \text{cotangent } A = \cot A = \text{ctn } A = \frac{b}{a},$$

$$\text{secant } A = \sec A = \frac{h}{b}, \qquad \text{cosecant } A = \csc A = \frac{h}{a}.$$

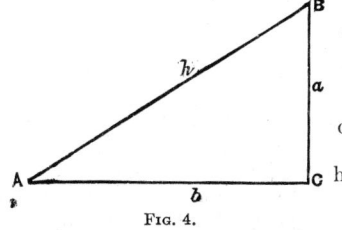

exsecant $A$ = exsec $A$ = sec $A$ − 1

versine $A$ = vers $A$ = 1 − cos $A$

coversine $A$ = covers $A$ = 1 − sin $A$

haversine $A$ = hav $A$ = $\frac{1}{2}$ vers $A$

Fig. 4.

## RELATIONS BETWEEN DEGREE OF ACCURACY OF COMPUTED LENGTHS AND ANGLES

When solving a triangle for any of its parts the following should be observed:

| Length to | (requires) Angle to: |
|---|---|
| 2 significant digits | nearest 30′ = 0.5° |
| 3 significant digits | nearest 05′ = 0.083° |
| 4 significant digits | nearest 01′ = 0.0167° |
| 5 significant digits | nearest 0.1′ = 0.00167° |

## SIGNS AND LIMITS OF VALUE ASSUMED BY THE FUNCTIONS

| Function | Quadrant I | | Quadrant II | | Quadrant III | | Quadrant IV | |
|---|---|---|---|---|---|---|---|---|
| | Sign | Value | Sign | Value | Sign | Value | Sign | Value |
| sin | + | 0 to 1 | + | 1 to 0 | − | 0 to 1 | − | 1 to 0 |
| cos | + | 1 to 0 | − | 0 to 1 | − | 1 to 0 | + | 0 to 1 |
| tan | + | 0 to ∞ | − | ∞ to 0 | + | 0 to ∞ | − | ∞ to 0 |
| cot | + | ∞ to 0 | − | 0 to ∞ | + | ∞ to 0 | − | 0 to ∞ |
| sec | + | 1 to ∞ | − | ∞ to 1 | − | 1 to ∞ | + | ∞ to 1 |
| cosec | + | ∞ to 1 | + | 1 to ∞ | − | ∞ to 1 | − | 1 to ∞ |

## GRAPHS OF THE TRIGONOMETRIC FUNCTIONS

$y = \sin x$

| $x$ | $y$ | Point |
|---|---|---|
| 0 | 0 | $P_0(0, 0)$ |
| $\frac{\pi}{6} = .52$ | .50 | $P_1(.52, .50)$ |
| $\frac{\pi}{4} = .79$ | .71 | $P_2(.79, .71)$ |
| $\frac{\pi}{3} = 1.05$ | .87 | $P_3(1.05, .87)$ |
| $\frac{\pi}{2} = 1.57$ | 1 | $P_4(1.57, 1)$ |
| $\pi = 3.14$ | 0 | $P_5(3.14, 0)$ |
| $\frac{3\pi}{2} = 4.71$ | $-1$ | $P_6(4.71, -1)$ |
| $2\pi = 6.28$ | 0 | $P_7(6.28, 0)$ |

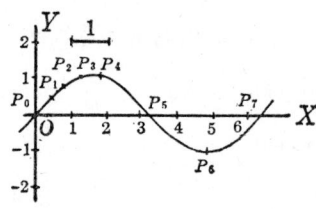

$y = \cos x$

| $x$ | $y$ | Point |
|---|---|---|
| 0 | 1 | $P_0(0, 1)$ |
| $\frac{\pi}{6} = .52$ | .87 | $P_1(.52, .87)$ |
| $\frac{\pi}{4} = .79$ | .71 | $P_2(.79, .71)$ |
| $\frac{\pi}{3} = 1.05$ | .5 | $P_3(1.05, .5)$ |
| $\frac{\pi}{2} = 1.57$ | 0 | $P_4(1.57, 0)$ |
| $\pi = 3.14$ | $-1$ | $P_5(3.14, -1)$ |
| $\frac{3\pi}{2} = 4.71$ | 0 | $P_6(4.71, 0)$ |
| $2\pi = 6.28$ | 1 | $P_7(6.28, 1)$ |

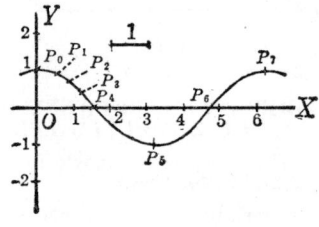

$y = \tan x$

| $x$ | $y$ | Point |
|---|---|---|
| 0 | 0 | $P_0(0, 0)$ |
| $\frac{\pi}{4}$ | 1 | $P_1(.79, 1)$ |
| $\frac{\pi}{2}$ | $\infty$ | .......... |
| $\frac{3\pi}{4}$ | $-1$ | $P_3(2.36, -1)$ |
| $\pi$ | 0 | $P_4(3.14, 0)$ |
| $\frac{5\pi}{4}$ | 1 | $P_5(3.93, 1)$ |
| $\frac{3\pi}{2}$ | $\infty$ | .......... |
| $2\pi$ | 0 | $P_6(6.28, 0)$ |

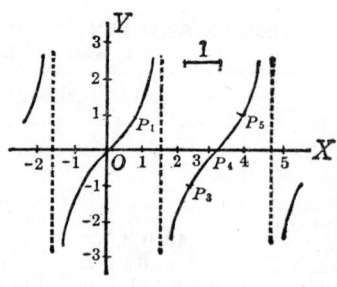

| $y = \cot x$ | | |
|---|---|---|
| $x$ | $y$ | Point |
| $0$ | $\pm \infty$ | .......... |
| $\frac{\pi}{4}$ | $1$ | $P_1(.79, 1)$ |
| $\frac{\pi}{2}$ | $0$ | $P_2(1.57, 0)$ |
| $\frac{3\pi}{4}$ | $-1$ | $P_3(2.36, -1)$ |
| $\pi$ | $\pm \infty$ | .......... |

| $y = \sec x$ | | |
|---|---|---|
| $x$ | $y$ | Point |
| $0$ | $1$ | $P_0(0, 1)$ |
| $\frac{\pi}{4}$ | $\sqrt{2}$ | $P_1(.79, 1.4)$ |
| $\frac{\pi}{2}$ | $\pm \infty$ | .......... |
| $\pi$ | $-1$ | $P_2(3.14, -1)$ |

| $y = \csc x$ | | |
|---|---|---|
| $x$ | $y$ | Point |
| $0$ | $\pm \infty$ | .......... |
| $\frac{\pi}{4}$ | $\sqrt{2}$ | $P_1(.79, 1.4)$ |
| $\frac{\pi}{2}$ | $1$ | $P_2(1.57, 1)$ |
| $\pi$ | $\pm \infty$ | .......... |

351

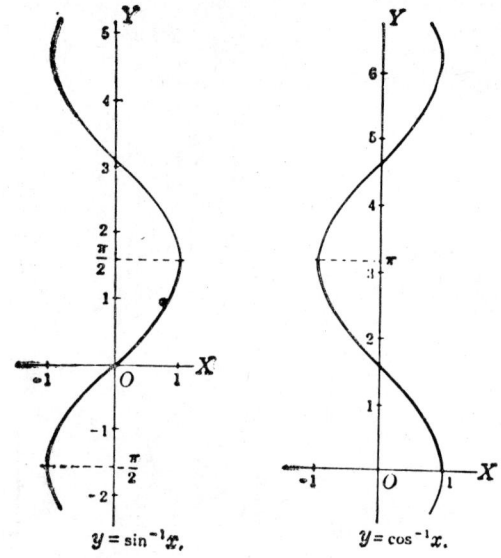

$y = \sin^{-1}x.$　　　　$y = \cos^{-1}x.$

## VALUE OF THE FUNCTIONS OF VARIOUS ANGLES

|        | 0°       | 30°                    | 45°                       | 60°                    | 90°      | 180°     | 270°     |
|--------|----------|------------------------|---------------------------|------------------------|----------|----------|----------|
| sin    | 0        | $\frac{1}{2}$          | $\frac{1}{2}\sqrt{2}$     | $\frac{1}{2}\sqrt{3}$  | 1        | 0        | −1       |
| cos    | 1        | $\frac{1}{2}\sqrt{3}$  | $\frac{1}{2}\sqrt{2}$     | $\frac{1}{2}$          | 0        | −1       | 0        |
| tan    | 0        | $\frac{1}{3}\sqrt{3}$  | 1                         | $\sqrt{3}$             | ∞        | 0        | ∞        |
| cot    | ∞        | $\sqrt{3}$             | 1                         | $\frac{1}{3}\sqrt{3}$  | 0        | ∞        | 0        |
| sec    | 1        | $\frac{2\sqrt{3}}{3}$  | $\sqrt{2}$                | 2                      | ∞        | −1       | ∞        |
| cosec  | ∞        | 2                      | $\sqrt{2}$                | $\frac{2\sqrt{3}}{3}$  | 1        | ∞        | −1       |

## EXPONENTIAL DEFINITIONS OF CIRCULAR FUNCTIONS

$$\sin x = \frac{1}{2i}(e^{ix} - e^{-ix})$$
$$(i^2 = -1)$$
$$\cos x = \frac{e^{ix} + e^{-ix}}{2}$$
$$\tan x = \frac{e^{ix} - e^{-ix}}{ie^{ix} + ie^{-ix}}$$

$$\operatorname{cosec} x = \frac{2i}{e^{ix} - e^{-ix}}$$
$$\sec x = \frac{2}{e^{ix} + e^{-ix}}$$
$$\cot x = \frac{ie^{ix} + ie^{-ix}}{e^{ix} - e^{-ix}}$$

## RELATIONS OF THE FUNCTIONS

$$\sin x = \frac{1}{\operatorname{cosec} x}.$$
$$\cos x = \frac{1}{\sec x}.$$
$$\tan x = \frac{1}{\cot x} = \frac{\sin x}{\cos x}.$$
$$\cot x = \frac{1}{\tan x} = \frac{\cos x}{\sin x}.$$
$$*\sin x = \pm\sqrt{1 - \cos^2 x}.$$
$$\tan x = \pm\sqrt{\sec^2 x - 1}.$$
$$\cot x = \pm\sqrt{\operatorname{cosec}^2 x - 1}.$$
$$\sin x = \cos(90° - x) = \sin(180° - x).$$

$$\operatorname{cosec} x = \frac{1}{\sin x}.$$
$$\sec x = \frac{1}{\cos x}.$$
$$\sin^2 x + \cos^2 x = 1.$$
$$1 + \tan^2 x = \sec^2 x.$$
$$1 + \cot^2 x = \operatorname{cosec}^2 x.$$
$$\cos x = \pm\sqrt{1 - \sin^2 x}.$$
$$\sec x = \pm\sqrt{\tan^2 x + 1}.$$
$$\operatorname{cosec} x = \pm\sqrt{\cot^2 x + 1}.$$

---

* The sign in front of radical depends on quadrant in which $x$ falls.

$\cos x = \sin (90° - x) = - \cos (180° - x)$.

$\tan x = \cot (90° - x) = - \tan (180° - x)$.

$\cot x = \tan (90° - x) = - \cot (180° - x)$.

$\operatorname{cosec} x = \cot \dfrac{x}{2} - \cot x$.

## FUNCTIONS OF SUMS OF ANGLES

$\sin (x \pm y) = \sin x \cos y \pm \cos x \sin y$.

$\cos (x \pm y) = \cos x \cos y \mp \sin x \sin y$.

$\tan (x \pm y) = \dfrac{\tan x \pm \tan y}{1 \mp \tan x \tan y}$.

## FUNCTIONS OF MULTIPLE ANGLES

$\sin 2x = 2 \sin x \cos x$.

$\cos 2x = \cos^2 x - \sin^2 x = 2 \cos^2 x - 1 = 1 - 2 \sin^2 x$.

$\sin 3x = 3 \sin x - 4 \sin^3 x$.

$\cos 3x = 4 \cos^3 x - 3 \cos x$.

$\sin 4x = 8 \cos^3 x \sin x - 4 \cos x \sin x$.

$\cos 4x = 8 \cos^4 x - 8 \cos^2 x + 1$.

$\sin 5x = 5 \sin x - 20 \sin^3 x + 16 \sin^5 x$.

$\cos 5x = 16 \cos^5 x - 20 \cos^3 x + 5 \cos x$.

$\sin 6x = 32 \cos^5 x \sin x - 32 \cos^3 x \sin x + 6 \cos x \sin x$.

$\cos 6x = 32 \cos^6 x - 48 \cos^4 x + 18 \cos^2 x - 1$.

$\tan 2x = \dfrac{2 \tan x}{1 - \tan^2 x}$.

$\cot 2x = \dfrac{\cot^2 x - 1}{2 \cot x}$.

$\tan 3x = \dfrac{3 \tan x - \tan^3 x}{1 - 3 \tan^2 x}$.

*$\sin \frac{1}{2}x = \pm \sqrt{\dfrac{1 - \cos x}{2}}$.

$\cos \frac{1}{2}x = \pm \sqrt{\dfrac{1 + \cos x}{2}}$.

$\tan \frac{1}{2}x = \pm \sqrt{\dfrac{1 - \cos x}{1 + \cos x}} = \dfrac{1 - \cos x}{\sin x} = \dfrac{\sin x}{1 + \cos x}$.

---

* The sign in front of radical depends on quadrant in which $\dfrac{x}{2}$ falls.

## MISCELLANEOUS RELATIONS

$\sin x \pm \sin y = 2 \sin \frac{1}{2} (x \pm y) \cdot \cos \frac{1}{2} (x \mp y).$

$\cos x + \cos y = 2 \cos \frac{1}{2} (x + y) \cdot \cos \frac{1}{2} (x - y).$

$\cos x - \cos y = -2 \sin \frac{1}{2} (x + y) \cdot \sin \frac{1}{2} (x - y).$

$\tan x \pm \tan y = \dfrac{\sin (x \pm y)}{\cos x \cdot \cos y}.$  $\cot x \pm \cot y = \dfrac{\pm \sin (x \pm y)}{\sin x \cdot \sin y}.$

$\dfrac{1 + \tan x}{1 - \tan x} = \tan (45° + x).$  $\dfrac{\cot x + 1}{\cot x - 1} = \cot (45° - x)$

$\dfrac{\sin x \pm \sin y}{\cos x + \cos y} = \tan \frac{1}{2} (x \pm y).$

$\dfrac{\sin x \pm \sin y}{\cos x - \cos y} = -\cot \frac{1}{2} (x \mp y).$

$\dfrac{\sin x + \sin y}{\sin x - \sin y} = \dfrac{\tan \frac{1}{2} (x + y)}{\tan \frac{1}{2} (x - y)}.$

$\sin^2 x - \sin^2 y = \sin (x + y) \cdot \sin (x - y).$

$\cos^2 x - \cos^2 y = -\sin (x + y) \sin (x - y).$

$\cos^2 x - \sin^2 y = \cos (x + y) \cos (x - y).$

## INVERSE TRIGONOMETRIC FUNCTIONS

The following table lists each of the six inverse trigonometric functions together with the interval of its principal value:

| Function | Interval containing principal value | |
|---|---|---|
| | $x$ positive or zero | $x$ negative |
| $y = \sin^{-1} x$ and $\tan^{-1} x$.. | $0 \leqq y \leqq \pi/2$ | $-\pi/2 \leqq y < 0$ |
| $y = \cos^{-1} x$ and $\cot^{-1} x$.. | $0 \leqq y \leqq \pi/2$ | $\pi/2 < y \leqq \pi$ |
| $y = \sec^{-1} x$ and $\csc^{-1} x$.. | $0 \leqq y \leqq \pi/2$ | $-\pi \leqq y \leqq -\pi/2$ |

Usually the first letter in "arc" or the name of the inverse trigonometric functions is capitalized if the principal value is desired. Thus

$$\text{Arc} \sin \frac{1}{2} = \text{Sin}^{-1} \frac{1}{2} = \frac{\pi}{6},$$

while 
$$\text{arc} \sin \frac{1}{2} = \frac{\pi}{6} + 2\pi n \text{ or } \frac{5\pi}{6} + 2\pi n$$

In the calculus both for differentiation and integral formulas, capitalization is not adhered to strictly, but principal values are always understood for inverse trigonometric functions when used unless specifically stated otherwise.

## RELATIONS BETWEEN SIDES AND ANGLES OF ANY PLANE TRIANGLE

In a triangle with angles $A$, $B$, and $C$ and sides opposite $a$, $b$, and $c$ respectively,

$$\frac{a}{\sin A} = \frac{b}{\sin B} = \frac{c}{\sin C} = \text{diameter of the circumscribed circle.}$$

$$a^2 = b^2 + c^2 - 2bc \cos A.$$

$$a = b \cos C + c \cos B.$$

$$\cos A = \frac{b^2 + c^2 - a^2}{2bc}.$$

$$\tan \frac{A - B}{2} = \frac{a - b}{a + b} \cot \frac{C}{2}.$$

$$\sin A = \frac{2}{bc} \sqrt{s(s-a)\ (s-b)\ (s-c)},$$

where $s = \frac{1}{2}(a+b+c)$ and $r = \sqrt{\dfrac{(s-a)\ (s-b)\ (s-c)}{s}}$,

$$\sin \frac{A}{2} = \sqrt{\frac{(s-b)\ (s-c)}{bc}}.$$

$$\cos \frac{A}{2} = \sqrt{\frac{s(s-a)}{bc}}.$$

$$\tan \frac{A}{2} = \sqrt{\frac{(s-b)\ (s-c)}{s(s-a)}} = \frac{r}{s-a}.$$

$$\frac{a+b}{a-b} = \frac{\sin A + \sin B}{\sin A - \sin B} = \frac{\tan \frac{1}{2}(A+B)}{\tan \frac{1}{2}(A-B)} = \frac{\cot \frac{1}{2}C}{\tan \frac{1}{2}(A-B)}.$$

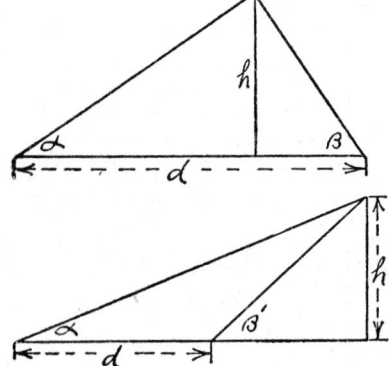

$$h = d\frac{\sin \alpha \sin \beta}{\sin (\alpha + \beta)} = \frac{d}{\cot \alpha + \cot \beta}$$

Similarly

$$h = d\frac{\sin \alpha \sin \beta'}{\sin (\beta' - \alpha)} = \frac{d}{\cot \alpha - \cot \beta'}$$

Fig. 5.

# TRIGONOMETRIC FORMULAE (Continued)

## RELATIONS IN ANY SPHERICAL TRIANGLE

If $A$, $B$ and $C$ be the three angles and $a$, $b$, and $c$ the opposite sides,

$$\frac{\sin A}{\sin a} = \frac{\sin B}{\sin b} = \frac{\sin C}{\sin c}.$$

$$\cos a = \cos b \cos c + \sin b \sin c \cos A = \frac{\cos b \cos (c \pm \theta)}{\cos \theta}.$$

where $\quad \tan \theta = \tan b \cos A.$

$$\cos A = -\cos B \cos C + \sin B \sin C \cos a.$$

$$\sin \tfrac{1}{2} A = \sqrt{\frac{\sin (s-b) \sin (s-c)}{\sin b \sin c}}.$$

where $\quad s = \tfrac{1}{2}(a+b+c).$

$$\cos \tfrac{1}{2} A = \sqrt{\frac{\sin s \sin (s-a)}{\sin b \sin c}}.$$

$$\tan \tfrac{1}{2} A = \frac{r}{\sin (s-a)}.$$

where $\quad r = \sqrt{\dfrac{\sin (s-a) \sin (s-b) \sin (s-c)}{\sin s}}.$

$$\cos \tfrac{1}{2} a = \sqrt{\frac{\cos (S-B) \cos (S-C)}{\sin B \sin C}}.$$

where $\quad S = \tfrac{1}{2}(A + B + C).$

$$\sin \tfrac{1}{2} a = \sqrt{-\frac{\cos S \cos (S-A)}{\sin B \sin C}}.$$

$$\tan \tfrac{1}{2} a = R \cos (S-A)$$

where $\quad R = \sqrt{\dfrac{-\cos S}{\cos (S-A) \cos (S-B) \cos (S-C)}}.$

$$\frac{\tan \dfrac{a+b}{2}}{\tan \dfrac{c}{2}} = \frac{\cos \dfrac{A-B}{2}}{\cos \dfrac{A+B}{2}}, \qquad \frac{\tan \dfrac{A+B}{2}}{\cot \dfrac{C}{2}} = \frac{\cos \dfrac{a-b}{2}}{\cos \dfrac{a+b}{2}},$$

$$\frac{\tan \dfrac{a-b}{2}}{\tan \dfrac{c}{2}} = \frac{\sin \dfrac{A-B}{2}}{\sin \dfrac{A+B}{2}}, \qquad \frac{\tan \dfrac{A-B}{2}}{\cot \dfrac{C}{2}} = \frac{\sin \dfrac{a-b}{2}}{\sin \dfrac{a+b}{2}}.$$

$$\operatorname{hav} a = \operatorname{hav} (b-c) + \sin b \sin c \operatorname{hav} A$$

$$\operatorname{hav} A = \frac{\sqrt{\operatorname{hav} [a + (b-c)] \operatorname{hav} [a - (b-c)]}}{\sin b \sin c}$$

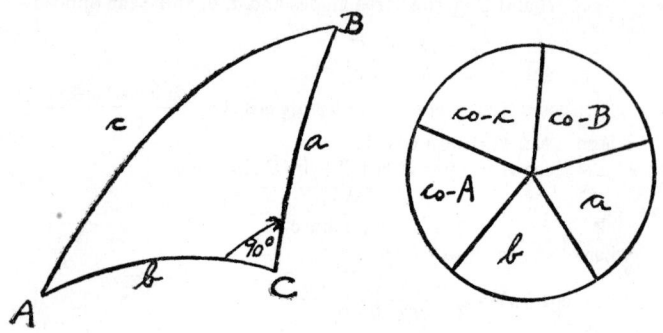

Take the five parts, *excluding the right angle* and consider them to be in a circular arrangement.

Attach a "Co" to the two angles and the hypotenuse, meaning "Complement of A" etc. Then:

1. The sine of the middle part equals the product of the tangents of the adjacent parts.

2. The sine of the middle part equals the product of the cosines of the opposite parts. The following rules for determining the quadrant of a calculated part apply:

1. A leg and the angle opposite it are always of the same quadrant.

2. If the hypotenuse is less than 90°, the legs are of the same quadrant. If the hypotenuse is greater than 90°, the legs are of opposite quadrants.

# ANALYTICAL GEOMETRY

**The distance between two points** $x_1$, $y_1$, and $x_2$, $y_2$,—rectangular coördinates:

$$d = \sqrt{(x_2 - x_1)^2 + (y_2 - y_1)^2}$$

For polar coördinates and points $r_1$, $\theta_1$, and $r_2$, $\theta_2$:

$$d = \sqrt{r_1{}^2 + r_2{}^2 - 2r_1r_2 \cos (\theta_1 - \theta_2)}$$

**The area of a triangle** whose vertices are $x_1$, $y_1$; $x_2$, $y_2$, and $x_3$, $y_3$:

$$A = \tfrac{1}{2}|x_1y_2 - x_2y_1 + x_2y_3 - x_3y_2 + x_3y_1 - x_1y_3|$$

For polar coördinates and vertices, $r_1$, $\theta_1$; $r_2$, $\theta_2$, and $r_3$, $\theta_3$:

$$A = \tfrac{1}{2}\{r_1r_2 \sin (\theta_2 - \theta_1) + r_2r_3 \sin (\theta_3 - \theta_2) + r_3r_1 \sin (\theta_1 - \theta_3)\}$$

**The equation of a straight line** where $m$ is the tangent of the angle of inclination and $c$, the distance of intersection with the $Y$ axis from the origin:

$$y = mx + c$$

If a line of slope $m$ passes through the point $x_1$, $y_1$ its equation is:

$$y - y_1 = m(x - x_1)$$

The equation of a line through the points $x_1$, $y_1$, and $x_2$, $y_2$ is:

$$\frac{y - y_1}{y_2 - y_1} = \frac{x - x_1}{x_2 - x_1}$$

If the intercepts on the $X$ and $Y$ axes are $a$ and $b$ respectively, the equation is:

$$\frac{x}{a} + \frac{y}{b} = 1$$

If the length of the perpendicular from the origin is $p$ and its angle of inclination $\theta$ the equation is:

$$x \cos \theta + y \sin \theta = p$$

General equation of the straight line:

$Ax + By + C = 0$, where slope $m = \dfrac{-A}{B}$; $x$-intercept $a = \dfrac{-C}{A}$; $y$-intercept $b = \dfrac{-C}{B}$.

**The equation of a circle** whose center is at $a$, $b$, and whose radius is $c$:

$$(x - a)^2 + (y - b)^2 = c^2$$

If the origin is at the center:

$$x^2 + y^2 = c^2$$

The polar equation of a circle with the origin on the circumference and its center at point $c$, $\alpha$:

$$r = 2c \cos (\theta - \alpha).$$

If the origin is not on the circumference, the radius $a$ and the center at $l$, $\alpha$, the equation becomes

$$a^2 = r^2 + l^2 - 2rl \cos (\theta - \alpha).$$

The equation of a parabola with the origin at the vertex, where $f$ is the distance from the focus to the vertex:

$$y^2 = 4fx$$

If $p$ is the semi-latus rectum ($=2f$) the equation is:

$$y^2 = 2px$$

The polar equation where the pole is at the focus and $p$ the semi-latus rectum is:

$$r = \frac{p}{1 - \cos \theta}$$

If the pole is at the vertex and $p$ as above:

$$r = \frac{2p \cos \theta}{\sin^2 \theta}$$

The equation of the ellipse with the origin at the center and semi-axes $a$ and $b$:

$$\frac{x^2}{a^2} + \frac{y^2}{b^2} = 1$$

Polar equation where the pole is at the center:

$$r^2 = \frac{a^2 b^2}{a^2 \sin^2 \theta + b^2 \cos^2 \theta}$$

The equation of the hyperbola with the origin at the center, semi-axes $a$ and $b$:

$$\frac{x^2}{a^2} - \frac{y^2}{b^2} = 1$$

Polar equation, pole at center:

$$r^2 = \frac{a^2 b^2}{a^2 \sin^2 \theta - b^2 \cos^2 \theta}$$

## TRANSFORMATION OF COORDINATES

### Rectangular System

(1) Translation only of axes parallel to themselves.

The coordinates of new origin with respect to old axes: $x = h$, $y = k$. Primed letters designate new coordinates.

$$x' = x - h \qquad x = x' + h$$
$$y' = y - k \qquad y = y' + k$$

(2) Rotation of axes with fixed origin.

$$\text{Angle of rotation} = \theta$$
$$x' = x \cos \theta + y \sin \theta \qquad x = x' \cos \theta - y' \sin \theta$$
$$y' = y \cos \theta - x \sin \theta \qquad y = y' \cos \theta + x' \sin \theta$$

(3) Origin translated and axes rotated.

Symbols same as above

$$x' = (x - h) \cos \theta + (y - k) \sin \theta$$
$$y' = (y - k) \cos \theta - (x - h) \sin \theta$$
$$x = x' \cos \theta - y' \sin \theta + h$$
$$y = y' \cos \theta + x' \sin \theta + k$$

### Relation between Rectangular and Polar Coordinates

$$x = r \cos \theta \qquad r = \sqrt{x^2 + y^2} \qquad \sin \theta = \frac{y}{\sqrt{x^2 + y^2}}$$

$$y = r \sin \theta \qquad \theta = \tan^{-1} \frac{y}{x} \qquad \cos \theta = \frac{x}{\sqrt{x^2 + y^2}}$$

### Rotation of Polar Axes through Angle $\theta$

$$x' = r \cos \alpha$$
$$y' = r \sin \alpha$$
$$x = r \cos (\alpha + \theta)$$
$$y = r \sin (\alpha + \theta)$$

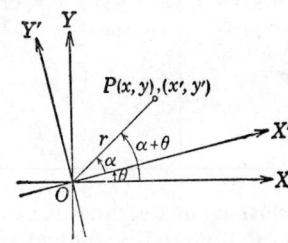

## TRANSFORMATION OF COORDINATES (Continued)
## SOLID ANALYTICAL GEOMETRY
### Space Coordinates

1. Rectangular System $x$, $y$, $z$.
2. Cylindrical System $r$, $\theta$, $z$.
3. Spherical System $\rho$, $\theta$, $\phi$.   In certain situations it is desireable to interchange the symbols $\phi$ for $\theta$ and vice versa.
4. Polar Space System $\rho$, $\alpha$, $\beta$, $\gamma$.

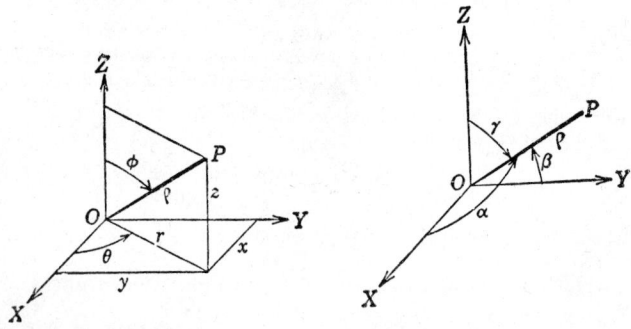

### Relations of Coordinates of Systems in Terms of $x$, $y$, $z$

| Cylindrical | Spherical | Polar Space |
|---|---|---|
| $r = \sqrt{x^2 + y^2}$ | $\rho = \sqrt{x^2 + y^2 + z^2}$ | $\rho = \sqrt{x^2 + y^2 + z^2}$ |
| $\theta = \tan^{-1}\dfrac{y}{x}$ | $\theta = \tan^{-1}\dfrac{y}{x}$ | $\alpha = \cos^{-1}\left(\dfrac{x}{\sqrt{x^2+y^2+z^2}}\right)$ |
| $z = z$ | $\phi = \cos^{-1}\left(\dfrac{z}{\sqrt{x^2+y^2+z^2}}\right)$ | $\beta = \cos^{-1}\left(\dfrac{y}{\sqrt{x^2+y^2+z^2}}\right)$ |
| | | $\gamma = \cos^{-1}\left(\dfrac{z}{\sqrt{x^2+y^2+z^2}}\right)$ |

### Relations of Rectangular Coordinates $(x, y, z)$ in Terms of Cylindrical, Spherical and Polar Space Coordinates

| Cylindrical | Spherical | Polar Space |
|---|---|---|
| $x = r \cos \theta$ | $x = \rho \sin \phi \cos \theta$ | $x = \rho \cos \alpha$ |
| $y = r \sin \theta$ | $y = \rho \sin \phi \sin \theta$ | $y = \rho \cos \beta$ |
| $z = z$ | $z = \rho \cos \phi$ | $z = \rho \cos \gamma$ |

## TRANSFORMATION OF COORDINATES (Continued)

### TRANSFORMATION OF RECTANGULAR SPACE COORDINATES FOR TRANSLATION WITHOUT ROTATION

Coordinates of new origin are $(h, k, l)$ in terms of the old coordinates. New coordinates are $(x', y', z')$

$$
\begin{aligned}
x' &= x - h & x &= x' + h \\
y' &= y - k & y &= y' + k \\
z' &= z - l & z &= z' + l
\end{aligned}
$$

For rotation only about the origin where $\lambda_1, \mu_1, \nu_1$; $\lambda_2, \mu_2, \nu_2$ and $\lambda_3, \mu_3, \nu_3$ are the direction cosines of the new axes with respect to the old axes. The coordinates of point P are $(x, y, z)$ referred to the original axes and $(x', y', z')$ referred to the new rotated axes.

$$
\begin{aligned}
x' &= \lambda_1 x + \mu_1 y + \nu_1 z \\
y' &= \lambda_2 x + \mu_2 y + \nu_2 z \\
z' &= \lambda_3 x + \mu_3 y + \nu_3 z \\
x &= \lambda_1 x' + \lambda_2 y' + \lambda_3 z' \\
y &= \mu_1 x' + \mu_2 y' + \mu_3 z' \\
z &= \nu_1 x' + \nu_2 y' + \nu_3 z'
\end{aligned}
$$

# HYPERBOLIC FUNCTIONS

### Definitions

An hyperbolic function represents a relation between the coordinates of a given point on the arc of a rectangular hyperbola.

If O is the center, A the vertex, and P any point of the hyperbola APB,

$OM = x,$
$MP = y,$
$OA = a.$

The function $u$ may be defined by the following relation,

FIG. 6.

$$u = \frac{2 \times \text{Area } OAP}{OA^2}$$

The hyperbolic sine of $u = \sinh u = y/a$.
The hyperbolic cosine of $u = \cosh u = x/a$.

## Exponential Definitions of Hyperbolic Functions and Their Power Series

$$\sinh u = \frac{e^u - e^{-u}}{2} = \frac{1}{2}(e^u - e^{-u}) = u + \frac{u^3}{3!} + \frac{u^5}{5!} + \cdots$$

$$\cosh u = \frac{e^u + e^{-u}}{2} = \frac{1}{2}(e^u + e^{-u}) = 1 + \frac{u^2}{2!} + \frac{u^4}{4!} + \cdots$$

$$\tanh u = \frac{e^u - e^{-u}}{e^u + e^{-u}} = u - \frac{u^3}{3} + \frac{2u^5}{15} - \frac{17u^7}{315} + \cdots$$
$$\left( u^2 < \frac{1}{4}\pi^2 \right).$$

$$\sinh^{-1} u = u - \frac{1}{2} \cdot \frac{u^3}{3} + \frac{1 \cdot 3}{2 \cdot 4} \cdot \frac{u^5}{5} - \frac{1 \cdot 3 \cdot 5}{2 \cdot 4 \cdot 6} \cdot \frac{u^7}{7} + \cdots$$
$$(u^2 < 1).$$

$$\sinh^{-1} u = \log 2u + \frac{1}{2} \cdot \frac{1}{2u^2} - \frac{1 \cdot 3}{2 \cdot 4} \cdot \frac{1}{4u^4} + \frac{1 \cdot 3 \cdot 5}{2 \cdot 4 \cdot 6} \cdot \frac{1}{6u^6} - \cdots$$
$$(u^2 > 1).$$

$$\cosh^{-1} u = \log 2u - \frac{1}{2} \cdot \frac{1}{2u^2} - \frac{1 \cdot 3}{2 \cdot 4} \cdot \frac{1}{4u^4} - \frac{1 \cdot 3 \cdot 5}{2 \cdot 4 \cdot 6} \cdot \frac{1}{6u^6} - \cdots$$
$$(u^2 > 1).$$

$$\tanh^{-1} u = u + \frac{u^3}{3} + \frac{u^5}{5} + \frac{u^7}{7} + \cdots \qquad (u^2 < 1).$$

$$\tanh u = \frac{\sinh u}{\cosh u}. \qquad \text{sech } u = \frac{1}{\cosh u}.$$

$$\coth u = \frac{1}{\tanh u}. \qquad \text{csch } u = \frac{1}{\sinh u}.$$

364

# HYPERBOLIC FUNCTIONS (Continued)

## Relations of the Functions

$$\sinh x = -\sinh(-x). \qquad \text{sech } x = \text{sech}(-x).$$
$$\cosh x = \cosh(-x). \qquad \text{csch } x = -\text{csch}(-x).$$
$$\tanh x = -\tanh(-x). \qquad \coth x = -\coth(-x).$$

$$\sinh x = \frac{2\tanh \frac{1}{2}x}{1 - \tanh^2 \frac{1}{2}x} = \frac{\tanh x}{\sqrt{1 - \tanh^2 x}}.$$

$$\cosh x = \frac{1 + \tanh^2 \frac{1}{2}x}{1 - \tanh^2 \frac{1}{2}x} = \frac{1}{\sqrt{1 - \tanh^2 x}}.$$

$$\cosh^2 x - \sinh^2 x = 1.$$

$$\tanh x = \sqrt{1 - \text{sech}^2 x}. \qquad \text{sech } x = \sqrt{1 - \tanh^2 x}.$$
$$\coth x = \sqrt{\text{csch}^2 x + 1}. \qquad \text{csch } x = \sqrt{\coth^2 x - 1}.$$

$$\sinh(\tfrac{1}{2}x) = \sqrt{\tfrac{1}{2}(\cosh x - 1)}.$$
$$\cosh(\tfrac{1}{2}x) = \sqrt{\tfrac{1}{2}(\cosh x + 1)}.$$
$$\tanh(\tfrac{1}{2}x) = (\cosh x - 1) \div \sinh x = \sinh x \div (\cosh x + 1).$$
$$\sinh(2x) = 2\sinh x \cosh x.$$
$$\cosh(2x) = \cosh^2 x + \sinh^2 x = 2\cosh^2 x - 1 = 1 + 2\sinh^2 x$$
$$\tanh(2x) = 2\tanh x \div (1 + \tanh^2 x).$$
$$\sinh 3x = 3\sinh x + 4\sinh^3 x.$$
$$\cosh 3x = 4\cosh^3 x - 3\cosh x.$$
$$\tanh 3x = (3\tanh x + \tanh^3 x) \div (1 + 3\tanh^2 x).$$
$$\sinh(x \pm y) = \sinh x \cdot \cosh y \pm \cosh x \cdot \sinh y.$$
$$\cosh(x \pm y) = \cosh x \cdot \cosh y \pm \sinh x \cdot \sinh y.$$
$$\tanh(x \pm y) = (\tanh x \pm \tanh y) \div (1 \pm \tanh x \cdot \tanh y).$$
$$\sinh x + \sinh y = 2\sinh \tfrac{1}{2}(x + y) \cdot \cosh \tfrac{1}{2}(x - y).$$
$$\sinh x - \sinh y = 2\cosh \tfrac{1}{2}(x + y) \cdot \sinh \tfrac{1}{2}(x - y).$$
$$\cosh x + \cosh y = 2\cosh \tfrac{1}{2}(x + y) \cdot \cosh \tfrac{1}{2}(x - y).$$
$$\cosh x - \cosh y = 2\sinh \tfrac{1}{2}(x + y) \cdot \sinh \tfrac{1}{2}(x - y).$$

$$\sinh x + \cosh x = \frac{1 + \tanh \frac{1}{2}x}{1 - \tanh \frac{1}{2}x}$$

$$\tanh x \pm \tanh y = \frac{\sinh(x \pm y)}{\cosh x \cosh y}.$$

$$\coth x \pm \coth y = \pm\frac{\sinh(x \pm y)}{\sinh x \sinh y}.$$

## Inverse Functions

$$\sinh^{-1} x = \log(x + \sqrt{x^2 + 1}) = \int \frac{dx}{\sqrt{x^2 + 1}} =$$
$$\cosh^{-1} \sqrt{x^2 + 1}.$$

# HYPERBOLIC FUNCTIONS (Continued)

$$\cosh^{-1} x = \log (x + \sqrt{x^2 - 1}) = \int \frac{dx}{\sqrt{x^2 - 1}} =$$
$$\sinh^{-1} \sqrt{x^2 - 1},$$

$$\tanh^{-1} x = \frac{1}{2} \log (1 + x) - \frac{1}{2} \log (1 - x) = \int \frac{dx}{1 - x^2}.$$

$$\coth^{-1} x = \frac{1}{2} \log (1 + x) - \frac{1}{2} \log (x - 1) = \int \frac{dx}{1 - x^2}.$$

$$\operatorname{sech}^{-1} x = \log \left( \frac{1}{x} + \sqrt{\frac{1}{x^2} - 1} \right) = -\int \frac{dx}{x\sqrt{1 - x^2}}.$$

$$\operatorname{csch}^{-1} x = \log \left( \frac{1}{x} + \sqrt{\frac{1}{x^2} + 1} \right) = -\int \frac{dx}{x\sqrt{x^2 + 1}}.$$

## Relations to Circular Functions

$$\sinh x = -i \sin ix. \qquad \sinh ix = i \sin x.$$
$$\cosh x = \cos ix. \qquad \cosh ix = \cos x.$$
$$\tanh x = -i \tan ix. \qquad \tanh ix = i \tan x.$$

If $x = \log \tan \left( \dfrac{\pi}{4} + \dfrac{\theta}{2} \right) = \log (\sec \theta + \tan \theta)$,

$$\theta = \text{the \textbf{gudermannian} of } x = \operatorname{gd} x.$$

$$\sinh x = \tan \operatorname{gd} x. \qquad \tanh x = \sin \operatorname{gd} x.$$
$$\cosh x = \sec \operatorname{gd} x. \qquad \tanh \tfrac{1}{2} x = \tan \tfrac{1}{2} \operatorname{gd} x.$$

$$\frac{d \operatorname{gd} x}{dx} = \operatorname{sech} x.$$

Integrals involving the hyperbolic functions will be found in the table of integrals.

# COMPLETE ELLIPTIC INTEGRALS

$$K = \int_0^{\pi/2} \frac{d\Phi}{\sqrt{1 - k^2 \sin^2 \Phi}} = F\left(k, \frac{\pi}{2}\right)$$

$$E = \int_0^{\pi/2} \sqrt{1 - k^2 \sin^2 \Phi}\, d\Phi = E\left(k, \frac{\pi}{2}\right)$$

See index for other elliptic integral tables.

# INTEREST TABLES

## SIMPLE INTEREST

If $P$ is the principal placed at interest at a rate $i$ (expressed as a decimal), for a period of $n$ years
The **amount,**

$$A = P(1 + ni)$$

**Present value,**

$$P = \frac{A}{1 + ni}$$

## COMPOUND INTEREST

At interest compounded annually the **amount,—**

$$A = P(1 + i)^n$$

At interest compounded $q$ times per year,—

$$A = P\left(1 + \frac{i}{q}\right)^{nq}$$

At interest compounded annually the **present value,—**

$$P = \frac{A}{(1 + i)^n} = A(1 + i)^{-n} = Av^n. \qquad v = \frac{1}{1 + i}$$

At interest compounded $q$ times per year,—

$$P = A\left(1 + \frac{i}{q}\right)^{-nq}$$

The **amount of an annuity of 1 per annum,—**

$$s_{\overline{n}|} \text{ at } i = \frac{(1 + i)^n - 1}{i}$$

The **present value of an annuity,—**

$$a_{\overline{n}|} \text{ at } i = \frac{1 - (1 + i)^{-n}}{i}$$

The **annuity whose present value is 1,—**

$$\frac{1}{a_{\overline{n}|} \text{ at } i} = \frac{1}{s_{\overline{n}|}} + i = \frac{i}{(1 - v^n)}$$

**Compound amount of 1 for fractional periods,—$(1 + i)^{1/p}$**

**Nominal rate** convertible $p$ times per year equivalent to effective rate $i$,—

$$j_p = p[(1 + i)^{1/p} - 1]$$

**Amount for year** of $p$ deposits of $1/p$, $p$ times per year,—$i/j_p$

## THE NUMBER OF EACH DAY OF THE YEAR

| Day of Mo. | Jan. | Feb. | Mar. | Apr. | May | Jun. | Jul. | Aug. | Sep. | Oct. | Nov. | Dec. | Day of Mo. |
|---|---|---|---|---|---|---|---|---|---|---|---|---|---|
| 1 | 1 | 32 | 60 | 91 | 121 | 152 | 182 | 213 | 244 | 274 | 305 | 335 | 1 |
| 2 | 2 | 33 | 61 | 92 | 122 | 153 | 183 | 214 | 245 | 275 | 306 | 336 | 2 |
| 3 | 3 | 34 | 62 | 93 | 123 | 154 | 184 | 215 | 246 | 276 | 307 | 337 | 3 |
| 4 | 4 | 35 | 63 | 94 | 124 | 155 | 185 | 216 | 247 | 277 | 308 | 338 | 4 |
| 5 | 5 | 36 | 64 | 95 | 125 | 156 | 186 | 217 | 248 | 278 | 309 | 339 | 5 |
| 6 | 6 | 37 | 65 | 96 | 126 | 157 | 187 | 218 | 249 | 279 | 310 | 340 | 6 |
| 7 | 7 | 38 | 66 | 97 | 127 | 158 | 188 | 219 | 250 | 280 | 311 | 341 | 7 |
| 8 | 8 | 39 | 67 | 98 | 128 | 159 | 189 | 220 | 251 | 281 | 312 | 342 | 8 |
| 9 | 9 | 40 | 68 | 99 | 129 | 160 | 190 | 221 | 252 | 282 | 313 | 343 | 9 |
| 10 | 10 | 41 | 69 | 100 | 130 | 161 | 191 | 222 | 253 | 283 | 314 | 344 | 10 |
| 11 | 11 | 42 | 70 | 101 | 131 | 162 | 192 | 223 | 254 | 284 | 315 | 345 | 11 |
| 12 | 12 | 43 | 71 | 102 | 132 | 163 | 193 | 224 | 255 | 285 | 316 | 346 | 12 |
| 13 | 13 | 44 | 72 | 103 | 133 | 164 | 194 | 225 | 256 | 286 | 317 | 347 | 13 |
| 14 | 14 | 45 | 73 | 104 | 134 | 165 | 195 | 226 | 257 | 287 | 318 | 348 | 14 |
| 15 | 15 | 46 | 74 | 105 | 135 | 166 | 196 | 227 | 258 | 288 | 319 | 349 | 15 |
| 16 | 16 | 47 | 75 | 106 | 136 | 167 | 197 | 228 | 259 | 289 | 320 | 350 | 16 |
| 17 | 17 | 48 | 76 | 107 | 137 | 168 | 198 | 229 | 260 | 290 | 321 | 351 | 17 |
| 18 | 18 | 49 | 77 | 108 | 138 | 169 | 199 | 230 | 261 | 291 | 322 | 352 | 18 |
| 19 | 19 | 50 | 78 | 109 | 139 | 170 | 200 | 231 | 262 | 292 | 323 | 353 | 19 |
| 20 | 20 | 51 | 79 | 110 | 140 | 171 | 201 | 232 | 263 | 293 | 324 | 354 | 20 |
| 21 | 21 | 52 | 80 | 111 | 141 | 172 | 202 | 233 | 264 | 294 | 325 | 355 | 21 |
| 22 | 22 | 53 | 81 | 112 | 142 | 173 | 203 | 234 | 265 | 295 | 326 | 356 | 22 |
| 23 | 23 | 54 | 82 | 113 | 143 | 174 | 204 | 235 | 266 | 296 | 327 | 357 | 23 |
| 24 | 24 | 55 | 83 | 114 | 144 | 175 | 205 | 236 | 267 | 297 | 328 | 358 | 24 |
| 25 | 25 | 56 | 84 | 115 | 145 | 176 | 206 | 237 | 268 | 298 | 329 | 359 | 25 |
| 26 | 26 | 57 | 85 | 116 | 146 | 177 | 207 | 238 | 269 | 299 | 330 | 360 | 26 |
| 27 | 27 | 58 | 86 | 117 | 147 | 178 | 208 | 239 | 270 | 300 | 331 | 361 | 27 |
| 28 | 28 | 59 | 87 | 118 | 148 | 179 | 209 | 240 | 271 | 301 | 332 | 362 | 28 |
| 29 | 29 | * | 88 | 119 | 149 | 180 | 210 | 241 | 272 | 302 | 333 | 363 | 29 |
| 30 | 30 |  | 89 | 120 | 150 | 181 | 211 | 242 | 273 | 303 | 334 | 364 | 30 |
| 31 | 31 |  | 90 |  | 151 |  | 212 | 243 |  | 304 |  | 365 | 31 |

* In leap years, after February 28, add 1 to the tabulated number.

## AMOUNT AT COMPOUND INTEREST $(1 + i)^n$

The following table gives the amount after a term of $n$ years on unit original principal at rate of interest $i$.

| Years $n$ | Rate $i$ | | | | |
|---|---|---|---|---|---|
| | .0025($\frac{1}{4}$ %) | .004167($\frac{5}{12}$ %) | .005($\frac{1}{2}$ %) | .005833($\frac{7}{12}$ %) | .0075($\frac{3}{4}$ %) |
| 1 | 1.00250000 | 1.00416667 | 1.00500000 | 1.00583333 | 1.00750000 |
| 2 | 1.00500625 | 1.00835069 | 1.01002500 | 1.01170069 | 1.01505625 |
| 3 | 1.00751877 | 1.01255216 | 1.01507513 | 1.01760228 | 1.02266917 |
| 4 | 1.01003756 | 1.01677112 | 1.02015050 | 1.02353830 | 1.03033919 |
| 5 | 1.01256266 | 1.02100767 | 1.02525125 | 1.02950894 | 1.03806673 |
| 6 | 1.01509406 | 1.02526187 | 1.03037751 | 1.03551440 | 1.04585224 |
| 7 | 1.01763180 | 1.02953379 | 1.03552940 | 1.04155490 | 1.05369613 |
| 8 | 1.02017588 | 1.03382352 | 1.04070704 | 1.04763064 | 1.06159885 |
| 9 | 1.02272632 | 1.03813111 | 1.04591058 | 1.05374182 | 1.06956084 |
| 10 | 1.02528313 | 1.04245666 | 1.05114013 | 1.05988865 | 1.07758255 |
| 11 | 1.02784634 | 1.04680023 | 1.05639583 | 1.06607133 | 1.08566441 |
| 12 | 1.03041596 | 1.05116190 | 1.06167781 | 1.07229008 | 1.09380690 |
| 13 | 1.03299200 | 1.05554174 | 1.06698620 | 1.07854511 | 1.10201045 |
| 14 | 1.03557448 | 1.05993983 | 1.07232113 | 1.08483662 | 1.11027553 |
| 15 | 1.03816341 | 1.06435625 | 1.07768274 | 1.09116483 | 1.11860259 |
| 16 | 1.04075882 | 1.06879106 | 1.08307115 | 1.09752996 | 1.12699211 |
| 17 | 1.04336072 | 1.07324436 | 1.08848651 | 1.10393222 | 1.13544455 |
| 18 | 1.04596912 | 1.07771621 | 1.09392894 | 1.11037182 | 1.14396039 |
| 19 | 1.04858404 | 1.08220670 | 1.09939858 | 1.11684899 | 1.15254009 |
| 20 | 1.05120550 | 1.08671589 | 1.10489558 | 1.12336395 | 1.16118414 |
| 21 | 1.05383352 | 1.09124387 | 1.11042006 | 1.12991669 | 1.16989302 |
| 22 | 1.05646810 | 1.09579072 | 1.11597216 | 1.13650808 | 1.17866722 |
| 23 | 1.05910927 | 1.10035652 | 1.12155202 | 1.14313771 | 1.18750723 |
| 24 | 1.06175704 | 1.10494134 | 1.12715978 | 1.14980602 | 1.19641353 |
| 25 | 1.06441144 | 1.10954526 | 1.13279558 | 1.15651322 | 1.20538663 |
| 26 | 1.06707247 | 1.11416836 | 1.13845955 | 1.16325955 | 1.21442703 |
| 27 | 1.06974015 | 1.11881073 | 1.14415185 | 1.17004523 | 1.22353523 |
| 28 | 1.07241450 | 1.12347244 | 1.14987261 | 1.17687049 | 1.23271175 |
| 29 | 1.07509553 | 1.12815358 | 1.15562197 | 1.18373557 | 1.24195709 |
| 30 | 1.07778327 | 1.13285422 | 1.16140008 | 1.19064069 | 1.25127176 |
| 31 | 1.08047773 | 1.13757444 | 1.16720708 | 1.19758610 | 1.26065630 |
| 32 | 1.08317892 | 1.14231434 | 1.17304312 | 1.20457202 | 1.27011122 |
| 33 | 1.08588687 | 1.14707398 | 1.17890833 | 1.21159869 | 1.27963706 |
| 34 | 1.08860159 | 1.15185346 | 1.18480288 | 1.21866634 | 1.28923434 |
| 35 | 1.09132309 | 1.15665284 | 1.19072689 | 1.22577523 | 1.29890359 |
| 36 | 1.09405140 | 1.16147223 | 1.19668052 | 1.23292559 | 1.30864537 |
| 37 | 1.09678653 | 1.16631170 | 1.20266393 | 1.24011765 | 1.31846021 |
| 38 | 1.09952850 | 1.17117133 | 1.20867725 | 1.24735167 | 1.32834866 |
| 39 | 1.10227732 | 1.17605121 | 1.21472063 | 1.25462789 | 1.33831128 |
| 40 | 1.10503301 | 1.18095142 | 1.22079424 | 1.26194655 | 1.34834861 |
| 41 | 1.10779559 | 1.18587206 | 1.22689821 | 1.26930791 | 1.35846123 |
| 42 | 1.11056508 | 1.19081319 | 1.23303270 | 1.27671220 | 1.36864969 |
| 43 | 1.11334149 | 1.19577491 | 1.23919786 | 1.28415969 | 1.37891456 |
| 44 | 1.11612485 | 1.20075731 | 1.24539385 | 1.29165062 | 1.38925642 |
| 45 | 1.11891516 | 1.20576046 | 1.25162082 | 1.29918525 | 1.39967584 |
| 46 | 1.12171245 | 1.21078446 | 1.25787892 | 1.30676383 | 1.41017341 |
| 47 | 1.12451673 | 1.21582940 | 1.26416832 | 1.31438662 | 1.42074971 |
| 48 | 1.12732802 | 1.22089536 | 1.27048916 | 1.32205388 | 1.43140533 |
| 49 | 1.13014634 | 1.22598242 | 1.27684161 | 1.32976586 | 1.44214087 |
| 50 | 1.13297171 | 1.23109068 | 1.28322581 | 1.33752283 | 1.45295693 |

## AMOUNT AT COMPOUND INTEREST $(1 + i)^n$
(Continued)

| Years n | Rate i | | | | |
|---|---|---|---|---|---|
| | .0025($\frac{1}{4}$ %) | .004167($\frac{5}{12}$ %) | .005($\frac{1}{2}$ %) | .005833($\frac{7}{12}$ %) | .0075($\frac{3}{4}$ %) |
| **50** | 1.13297171 | 1.23109068 | 1.28322581 | 1.33752283 | 1.45295693 |
| 51 | 1.13580414 | 1.23622022 | 1.28964194 | 1.34532504 | 1.46385411 |
| 52 | 1.13864365 | 1.24137114 | 1.29609015 | 1.35317277 | 1.47483301 |
| 53 | 1.14149026 | 1.24654352 | 1.30257060 | 1.36106628 | 1.48589426 |
| 54 | 1.14434398 | 1.25173745 | 1.30908346 | 1.36900583 | 1.49703847 |
| **55** | 1.14720484 | 1.25695302 | 1.31562887 | 1.37699170 | 1.50826626 |
| 56 | 1.15007285 | 1.26219033 | 1.32220702 | 1.38502415 | 1.51957825 |
| 57 | 1.15294804 | 1.26744946 | 1.32881805 | 1.39310346 | 1.53097509 |
| 58 | 1.15583041 | 1.27273050 | 1.33546214 | 1.40122990 | 1.54245740 |
| 59 | 1.15871998 | 1.27803354 | 1.34213946 | 1.40940374 | 1.55402583 |
| **60** | 1.16161678 | 1.28335868 | 1.34885015 | 1.41762526 | 1.56568103 |
| 61 | 1.16452082 | 1.28870601 | 1.35559440 | 1.42589474 | 1.57742363 |
| 62 | 1.16743213 | 1.29407561 | 1.36237238 | 1.43421246 | 1.58925431 |
| 63 | 1.17035071 | 1.29946760 | 1.36918424 | 1.44257870 | 1.60117372 |
| 64 | 1.17327658 | 1.30488204 | 1.37603016 | 1.45099374 | 1.61318252 |
| **65** | 1.17620977 | 1.31031905 | 1.38291031 | 1.45945787 | 1.62528139 |
| 66 | 1.17915030 | 1.31577872 | 1.38982486 | 1.46797138 | 1.63747100 |
| 67 | 1.18209817 | 1.32126113 | 1.39677399 | 1.47653454 | 1.64975203 |
| 68 | 1.18505342 | 1.32676638 | 1.40375785 | 1.48514766 | 1.66212517 |
| 69 | 1.18801605 | 1.33229458 | 1.41077664 | 1.49381102 | 1.67459111 |
| **70** | 1.19098609 | 1.33784580 | 1.41783053 | 1.50252492 | 1.68715055 |
| 71 | 1.19396356 | 1.34342016 | 1.42491968 | 1.51128965 | 1.69980418 |
| 72 | 1.19694847 | 1.34901774 | 1.43204428 | 1.52010550 | 1.71255271 |
| 73 | 1.19994084 | 1.35463865 | 1.43920450 | 1.52897279 | 1.72539685 |
| 74 | 1.20294069 | 1.36028298 | 1.44640052 | 1.53789179 | 1.73833733 |
| 75 | 1.20594804 | 1.36595082 | 1.45363252 | 1.54686283 | 1.75137486 |
| 76 | 1.20896291 | 1.37164229 | 1.46090069 | 1.55588620 | 1.76451017 |
| 77 | 1.21198532 | 1.37735746 | 1.46820519 | 1.56496220 | 1.77774400 |
| 78 | 1.21501528 | 1.38309645 | 1.47554622 | 1.57409115 | 1.79107708 |
| 79 | 1.21805282 | 1.38885935 | 1.48292395 | 1.58327334 | 1.80451015 |
| **80** | 1.22109795 | 1.39464627 | 1.49033857 | 1.59250910 | 1.81804398 |
| 81 | 1.22415070 | 1.40045729 | 1.49779026 | 1.60179874 | 1.83167931 |
| 82 | 1.22721108 | 1.40629253 | 1.50527921 | 1.61114257 | 1.84541691 |
| 83 | 1.23027910 | 1.41215209 | 1.51280561 | 1.62054090 | 1.85925753 |
| 84 | 1.23335480 | 1.41803605 | 1.52036964 | 1.62999405 | 1.87320196 |
| **85** | 1.23643819 | 1.42394454 | 1.52797148 | 1.63950235 | 1.88725098 |
| 86 | 1.23952928 | 1.42987764 | 1.53561134 | 1.64906612 | 1.90140536 |
| 87 | 1.24262811 | 1.43583546 | 1.54328940 | 1.65868567 | 1.91566590 |
| 88 | 1.24573468 | 1.44181811 | 1.55100585 | 1.66836134 | 1.93003339 |
| 89 | 1.24884901 | 1.44782568 | 1.55876087 | 1.67809344 | 1.94450865 |
| **90** | 1.25197114 | 1.45385829 | 1.56655468 | 1.68788232 | 1.95909246 |
| 91 | 1.25510106 | 1.45991603 | 1.57438745 | 1.69772830 | 1.97378565 |
| 92 | 1.25823882 | 1.46599902 | 1.58225939 | 1.70763172 | 1.98858905 |
| 93 | 1.26138441 | 1.47210735 | 1.59017069 | 1.71759290 | 2.00350346 |
| 94 | 1.26453787 | 1.47824113 | 1.59812154 | 1.72761219 | 2.01852974 |
| **95** | 1.26769222 | 1.48440047 | 1.60611215 | 1.73768993 | 2.03366871 |
| 96 | 1.27086847 | 1.49058547 | 1.61414271 | 1.74782646 | 2.04892123 |
| 97 | 1.27404564 | 1.49679624 | 1.62221342 | 1.75802211 | 2.06428814 |
| 98 | 1.27723075 | 1.50303289 | 1.63032449 | 1.76827724 | 2.07977030 |
| 99 | 1.28042383 | 1.50929553 | 1.63847611 | 1.77859219 | 2.09536858 |
| **100** | 1.28362489 | 1.51558426 | 1.64666849 | 1.78896731 | 2.11108384 |

# AMOUNT AT COMPOUND INTEREST $(1 + i)^n$
## (Continued)

| Years n | Rate i | | | | |
|---|---|---|---|---|---|
| | .01(1 %) | .01125(1⅛ %) | .0125(1¼ %) | .015(1½ %) | .0175(1¾ %) |
| 1 | 1.01000000 | 1.01125000 | 1.01250000 | 1.01500000 | 1.01750000 |
| 2 | 1.02010000 | 1.02262656 | 1.02515625 | 1.03022500 | 1.03530626 |
| 3 | 1.03030100 | 1.03413111 | 1.03797070 | 1.04567838 | 1.05342411 |
| 4 | 1.04060401 | 1.04576509 | 1.05094534 | 1.06136355 | 1.07185903 |
| 5 | 1.05101005 | 1.05752994 | 1.06408215 | 1.07728400 | 1.09061656 |
| 6 | 1.06152015 | 1.06942716 | 1.07738318 | 1.09344326 | 1.10970235 |
| 7 | 1.07213535 | 1.08145821 | 1.09085047 | 1.10984491 | 1.12912215 |
| 8 | 1.08285671 | 1.09362462 | 1.10448610 | 1.12649259 | 1.14888178 |
| 9 | 1.09368527 | 1.10592789 | 1.11829218 | 1.14338998 | 1.16898721 |
| 10 | 1.10462213 | 1.11836958 | 1.13227083 | 1.16054083 | 1.18944449 |
| 11 | 1.11566835 | 1.13095124 | 1.14642422 | 1.17794894 | 1.21025977 |
| 12 | 1.12682503 | 1.14367444 | 1.16075452 | 1.19561817 | 1.23143931 |
| 13 | 1.13809328 | 1.15654078 | 1.17526395 | 1.21355244 | 1.25298950 |
| 14 | 1.14947421 | 1.16955186 | 1.18995475 | 1.23175573 | 1.27491682 |
| 15 | 1.16096896 | 1.18270932 | 1.20482932 | 1.25023207 | 1.29722786 |
| 16 | 1.17257864 | 1.19601480 | 1.21988955 | 1.26898555 | 1.31992935 |
| 17 | 1.18430443 | 1.20946997 | 1.23513817 | 1.28802033 | 1.34302811 |
| 18 | 1.19614748 | 1.22307650 | 1.25057739 | 1.30734064 | 1.36653111 |
| 19 | 1.20810895 | 1.23683611 | 1.26620961 | 1.32695075 | 1.39044540 |
| 20 | 1.22019004 | 1.25075052 | 1.28203723 | 1.34685501 | 1.41477820 |
| 21 | 1.23239194 | 1.26482146 | 1.29806270 | 1.36705783 | 1.43953681 |
| 22 | 1.24471586 | 1.27905071 | 1.31428848 | 1.38756370 | 1.46472871 |
| 23 | 1.25716302 | 1.29344003 | 1.33071709 | 1.40837715 | 1.49036146 |
| 24 | 1.26973465 | 1.30799123 | 1.34735105 | 1.42950281 | 1.51644279 |
| 25 | 1.28243200 | 1.32270613 | 1.36419294 | 1.45094535 | 1.54298054 |
| 26 | 1.29525631 | 1.33758657 | 1.38124535 | 1.47270953 | 1.56998269 |
| 27 | 1.30820888 | 1.35263442 | 1.39851092 | 1.49480018 | 1.59745739 |
| 28 | 1.32129097 | 1.36785156 | 1.41599230 | 1.51722218 | 1.62541290 |
| 29 | 1.33450388 | 1.38323989 | 1.43369221 | 1.53998051 | 1.65385762 |
| 30 | 1.34784892 | 1.39880134 | 1.45161336 | 1.56308022 | 1.68280013 |
| 31 | 1.36132740 | 1.41453785 | 1.46975853 | 1.58652642 | 1.71224913 |
| 32 | 1.37494068 | 1.43045140 | 1.48813051 | 1.61032432 | 1.74221349 |
| 33 | 1.38869009 | 1.44654398 | 1.50673214 | 1.63447918 | 1.77270223 |
| 34 | 1.40257699 | 1.46281760 | 1.52556629 | 1.65899637 | 1.80372452 |
| 35 | 1.41660276 | 1.47927430 | 1.54463587 | 1.68388132 | 1.83528970 |
| 36 | 1.43076878 | 1.49591613 | 1.56394382 | 1.70913954 | 1.86740727 |
| 37 | 1.44507647 | 1.51274519 | 1.58349312 | 1.73477663 | 1.90008689 |
| 38 | 1.45952724 | 1.52976357 | 1.60328678 | 1.76079828 | 1.93333841 |
| 39 | 1.47412251 | 1.54697341 | 1.62332787 | 1.78721025 | 1.96717184 |
| 40 | 1.48886373 | 1.56437687 | 1.64361946 | 1.81401841 | 2.00159734 |
| 41 | 1.50375237 | 1.58197611 | 1.66416471 | 1.84122868 | 2.03662530 |
| 42 | 1.51878989 | 1.59977334 | 1.68496677 | 1.86884712 | 2.07226624 |
| 43 | 1.53397779 | 1.61777079 | 1.70602885 | 1.89687982 | 2.10853090 |
| 44 | 1.54931757 | 1.63597071 | 1.72735421 | 1.92533302 | 2.14543019 |
| 45 | 1.56481075 | 1.65437538 | 1.74894614 | 1.95421301 | 2.18297522 |
| 46 | 1.58045885 | 1.67298710 | 1.77080797 | 1.98352621 | 2.22117728 |
| 47 | 1.59626344 | 1.69180821 | 1.79294306 | 2.01327910 | 2.26004789 |
| 48 | 1.61222608 | 1.71084105 | 1.81535485 | 2.04347829 | 2.29959872 |
| 49 | 1.62834834 | 1.73008801 | 1.83804679 | 2.07413046 | 2.33984170 |
| 50 | 1.64463182 | 1.74955150 | 1.86102237 | 2.10524242 | 2.38078893 |

## AMOUNT AT COMPOUND INTEREST $(1 + i)^n$
### (Continued)

| Years | Rate $i$ | | | | |
|---|---|---|---|---|---|
| $n$ | .01(1 %) | .01125(1⅛ %) | .0125(1¼ %) | .015(1½ %) | .0175(1¾ %) |
| 50 | 1.64463182 | 1.74955150 | 1.86102237 | 2.10524242 | 2.38078893 |
| 51 | 1.66107814 | 1.76923395 | 1.88428515 | 2.13682106 | 2.42245274 |
| 52 | 1.67768892 | 1.78913784 | 1.90783872 | 2.16887337 | 2.46484566 |
| 53 | 1.69446581 | 1.80926564 | 1.93168670 | 2.20140647 | 2.50798046 |
| 54 | 1.71141047 | 1.82961988 | 1.95583279 | 2.23442757 | 2.55187012 |
| 55 | 1.72852457 | 1.85020310 | 1.98028070 | 2.26794398 | 2.59652785 |
| 56 | 1.74580982 | 1.87101788 | 2.00503420 | 2.30196314 | 2.64196708 |
| 57 | 1.76326792 | 1.89206684 | 2.03009713 | 2.33649259 | 2.68820151 |
| 58 | 1.78090060 | 1.91335259 | 2.05547335 | 2.37153998 | 2.73524503 |
| 59 | 1.79870960 | 1.93487780 | 2.08116676 | 2.40711308 | 2.78311182 |
| 60 | 1.81669670 | 1.95664518 | 2.10718135 | 2.44321978 | 2.83181628 |
| 61 | 1.83486367 | 1.97865744 | 2.13352111 | 2.47986807 | 2.88137306 |
| 62 | 1.85321230 | 2.00091733 | 2.16019013 | 2.51706609 | 2.93179709 |
| 63 | 1.87174443 | 2.02342765 | 2.18719250 | 2.55482208 | 2.98310354 |
| 64 | 1.89046187 | 2.04619121 | 2.21453241 | 2.59314442 | 3.03530785 |
| 65 | 1.90936649 | 2.06921087 | 2.24221407 | 2.63204158 | 3.08842574 |
| 66 | 1.92846015 | 2.09248949 | 2.27024174 | 2.67152221 | 3.14247319 |
| 67 | 1.94774475 | 2.11602999 | 2.29861976 | 2.71159504 | 3.19746647 |
| 68 | 1.96722220 | 2.13983533 | 2.32735251 | 2.75226896 | 3.25342213 |
| 69 | 1.98689442 | 2.16390848 | 2.35644442 | 2.79355300 | 3.31035702 |
| 70 | 2.00676337 | 2.18825245 | 2.38589997 | 2.83545629 | 3.36828827 |
| 71 | 2.02683100 | 2.21287029 | 2.41572372 | 2.87798814 | 3.42723331 |
| 72 | 2.04709931 | 2.23776508 | 2.44592027 | 2.92115796 | 3.48720990 |
| 73 | 2.06757031 | 2.26293994 | 2.47649427 | 2.96497533 | 3.54823607 |
| 74 | 2.08824601 | 2.28839801 | 2.50745045 | 3.00944996 | 3.61033020 |
| 75 | 2.10912847 | 2.31414249 | 2.53879358 | 3.05459171 | 3.67351098 |
| 76 | 2.13021975 | 2.34017659 | 2.57052850 | 3.10041059 | 3.73779742 |
| 77 | 2.15152195 | 2.36650358 | 2.60266011 | 3.14691674 | 3.80320888 |
| 78 | 2.17303717 | 2.39312675 | 2.63519336 | 3.19412050 | 3.86976503 |
| 79 | 2.19476754 | 2.42004942 | 2.66813327 | 3.24203230 | 3.93748592 |
| 80 | 2.21671522 | 2.44727498 | 2.70148494 | 3.29066279 | 4.00639192 |
| 81 | 2.23888237 | 2.47480682 | 2.73525350 | 3.34002273 | 4.07650378 |
| 82 | 2.26127119 | 2.50264840 | 2.76944417 | 3.39012307 | 4.14784260 |
| 83 | 2.28388390 | 2.53080319 | 2.80406222 | 3.44097492 | 4.22042984 |
| 84 | 2.30672274 | 2.55927473 | 2.83911300 | 3.49258954 | 4.29428737 |
| 85 | 2.32978997 | 2.58806657 | 2.87460191 | 3.54497838 | 4.36943740 |
| 86 | 2.35308787 | 2.61718232 | 2.91053444 | 3.59815306 | 4.44590255 |
| 87 | 2.37661875 | 2.64662562 | 2.94691612 | 3.65212535 | 4.52370584 |
| 88 | 2.40038494 | 2.67640016 | 2.98375257 | 3.70690723 | 4.60287070 |
| 89 | 2.42438879 | 2.70650966 | 3.02104948 | 3.76251084 | 4.68342093 |
| 90 | 2.44863267 | 2.73695789 | 3.05881260 | 3.81894851 | 4.76538080 |
| 91 | 2.47311900 | 2.76774867 | 3.09704775 | 3.87623273 | 4.84877496 |
| 92 | 2.49785019 | 2.79888584 | 3.13576085 | 3.93437622 | 4.93362853 |
| 93 | 2.52282869 | 2.83037331 | 3.17495786 | 3.99339187 | 5.01996703 |
| 94 | 2.54805698 | 2.86221501 | 3.21464483 | 4.05329275 | 5.10781645 |
| 95 | 2.57353755 | 2.89441492 | 3.25482789 | 4.11409214 | 5.19720324 |
| 96 | 2.59927293 | 2.92697709 | 3.29551324 | 4.17580352 | 5.28815429 |
| 97 | 2.62526565 | 2.95990559 | 3.33670716 | 4.23844057 | 5.38069699 |
| 98 | 2.65151831 | 2.99320452 | 3.37841600 | 4.30201718 | 5.47485919 |
| 99 | 2.67803349 | 3.02687807 | 3.42064620 | 4.36654744 | 5.57066923 |
| 100 | 2.70481383 | 3.06093045 | 3.46340427 | 4.43204565 | 5.66815594 |

## AMOUNT AT COMPOUND INTEREST $(1 + i)^n$
(Continued)

| Years $n$ | Rate $i$ | | | | |
|---|---|---|---|---|---|
| | .02(2 %) | .0225(2¼ %) | .025(2½ %) | .0275(2¾ %) | .03(3 %) |
| 1 | 1.02000000 | 1.02250000 | 1.02500000 | 1.02750000 | 1.03000000 |
| 2 | 1.04040000 | 1.04550625 | 1.05062500 | 1.05575625 | 1.06090000 |
| 3 | 1.06120800 | 1.06903014 | 1.07689063 | 1.08478955 | 1.09272700 |
| 4 | 1.08243216 | 1.09308332 | 1.10381289 | 1.11462126 | 1.12550881 |
| 5 | 1.10408080 | 1.11767769 | 1.13140821 | 1.14527334 | 1.15927407 |
| 6 | 1.12616242 | 1.14282544 | 1.15969342 | 1.17676836 | 1.19405230 |
| 7 | 1.14868567 | 1.16853901 | 1.18868575 | 1.20912949 | 1.22987387 |
| 8 | 1.17165938 | 1.19483114 | 1.21840290 | 1.24238055 | 1.26677008 |
| 9 | 1.19509257 | 1.22171484 | 1.24886297 | 1.27654602 | 1.30477318 |
| 10 | 1.21899442 | 1.24920343 | 1.28008454 | 1.31165103 | 1.34391638 |
| 11 | 1.24337431 | 1.27731050 | 1.31208666 | 1.34772144 | 1.38423387 |
| 12 | 1.26824179 | 1.30604999 | 1.34488882 | 1.38478378 | 1.42576089 |
| 13 | 1.29360663 | 1.33543611 | 1.37851104 | 1.42286533 | 1.46853371 |
| 14 | 1.31947876 | 1.36548343 | 1.41297382 | 1.46199413 | 1.51258972 |
| 15 | 1.34586834 | 1.39620680 | 1.44829817 | 1.50219896 | 1.55796742 |
| 16 | 1.37278571 | 1.42762146 | 1.48450562 | 1.54350944 | 1.60470644 |
| 17 | 1.40024142 | 1.45974294 | 1.52161826 | 1.58595695 | 1.65284763 |
| 18 | 1.42824625 | 1.49258716 | 1.55965872 | 1.62956973 | 1.70243306 |
| 19 | 1.45681117 | 1.52617037 | 1.59865019 | 1.67438290 | 1.75350605 |
| 20 | 1.48594740 | 1.56050920 | 1.63861644 | 1.72042843 | 1.80611123 |
| 21 | 1.51566634 | 1.59562066 | 1.67958185 | 1.76774021 | 1.86029457 |
| 22 | 1.54597967 | 1.63152212 | 1.72157140 | 1.81635307 | 1.91610341 |
| 23 | 1.57689926 | 1.66823137 | 1.76461068 | 1.86630278 | 1.97358651 |
| 24 | 1.60843725 | 1.70576658 | 1.80872595 | 1.91762610 | 2.03279411 |
| 25 | 1.64060599 | 1.74414632 | 1.85394410 | 1.97036082 | 2.09377793 |
| 26 | 1.67341811 | 1.78338962 | 1.90029270 | 2.02454575 | 2.15659127 |
| 27 | 1.70688648 | 1.82351588 | 1.94780002 | 2.08022075 | 2.22128901 |
| 28 | 1.74102421 | 1.86454499 | 1.99649502 | 2.13742682 | 2.28792768 |
| 29 | 1.77584469 | 1.90649725 | 2.04640739 | 2.19620606 | 2.35656551 |
| 30 | 1.81136158 | 1.94939344 | 2.09756758 | 2.25660173 | 2.42726247 |
| 31 | 1.84758882 | 1.99325479 | 2.15000677 | 2.31865828 | 2.50008035 |
| 32 | 1.88454059 | 2.03810303 | 2.20375694 | 2.38242138 | 2.57508276 |
| 33 | 1.92223140 | 2.08396034 | 2.25885086 | 2.44793797 | 2.65233524 |
| 34 | 1.96067603 | 2.13084945 | 2.31532213 | 2.51525626 | 2.73190530 |
| 35 | 1.99988955 | 2.17879356 | 2.37320519 | 2.58442581 | 2.81386245 |
| 36 | 2.03988734 | 2.22781642 | 2.43253532 | 2.65549752 | 2.89827833 |
| 37 | 2.08068509 | 2.27794229 | 2.49334870 | 2.72852370 | 2.98522668 |
| 38 | 2.12229879 | 2.32919599 | 2.55568242 | 2.80355810 | 3.07478348 |
| 39 | 2.16474477 | 2.38160290 | 2.61957448 | 2.88065595 | 3.16702698 |
| 40 | 2.20803966 | 2.43518897 | 2.68506384 | 2.95987399 | 3.26203779 |
| 41 | 2.25220046 | 2.48998072 | 2.75219043 | 3.04127052 | 3.35989893 |
| 42 | 2.29724447 | 2.54600528 | 2.82099520 | 3.12490546 | 3.46069589 |
| 43 | 2.34318936 | 2.60329040 | 2.89152008 | 3.21084036 | 3.56451677 |
| 44 | 2.39005314 | 2.66186444 | 2.96380808 | 3.29913847 | 3.67145227 |
| 45 | 2.43785421 | 2.72175639 | 3.03790328 | 3.38986478 | 3.78159584 |
| 46 | 2.48661129 | 2.78299590 | 3.11385086 | 3.48308606 | 3.89504372 |
| 47 | 2.53634352 | 2.84561331 | 3.19169713 | 3.57887093 | 4.01189503 |
| 48 | 2.58707039 | 2.90963961 | 3.27148956 | 3.67728988 | 4.13225188 |
| 49 | 2.63881179 | 2.97510650 | 3.35327680 | 3.77841535 | 4.25621944 |
| 50 | 2.69158803 | 3.04204640 | 3.43710872 | 3.88232177 | 4.38390602 |

# AMOUNT AT COMPOUND INTEREST $(1 + i)^n$
## (Continued)

| Years | Rate $i$ | | | | |
|---|---|---|---|---|---|
| $n$ | .02(2 %) | .0225(2¼ %) | .025(2½ %) | .0275(2¾ %) | .03(3 %) |
| 50 | 2.69158803 | 3.04204640 | 3.43710872 | 3.88232177 | 4.38390602 |
| 51 | 2.74541979 | 3.11049244 | 3.52303644 | 3.98908562 | 4.51542320 |
| 52 | 2.80032819 | 3.18047852 | 3.61111235 | 4.09878547 | 4.65088590 |
| 53 | 2.85633475 | 3.25203929 | 3.70139016 | 4.21150208 | 4.79041247 |
| 54 | 2.91346144 | 3.32521017 | 3.79392491 | 4.32731838 | 4.93412485 |
| 55 | 2.97173067 | 3.40002740 | 3.88877303 | 4.44631964 | 5.08214859 |
| 56 | 3.03116529 | 3.47652802 | 3.98599236 | 4.56859343 | 5.23461305 |
| 57 | 3.09178859 | 3.55474990 | 4.08564217 | 4.69422975 | 5.39165144 |
| 58 | 3.15362436 | 3.63473177 | 4.18778322 | 4.82332107 | 5.55340098 |
| 59 | 3.21669685 | 3.71651324 | 4.29247780 | 4.95596239 | 5.72000301 |
| 60 | 3.28103079 | 3.80013479 | 4.39978975 | 5.09225136 | 5.89160310 |
| 61 | 3.34665140 | 3.88563782 | 4.50978449 | 5.23228827 | 6.06835120 |
| 62 | 3.41358443 | 3.97306467 | 4.62252910 | 5.37617620 | 6.25040173 |
| 63 | 3.48185612 | 4.06245862 | 4.73809233 | 5.52402105 | 6.43791379 |
| 64 | 3.55149324 | 4.15386394 | 4.85654464 | 5.67593162 | 6.63105120 |
| 65 | 3.62252311 | 4.24732588 | 4.97795826 | 5.83201974 | 6.82998273 |
| 66 | 3.69497357 | 4.34289071 | 5.10240721 | 5.99240029 | 7.03488222 |
| 67 | 3.76887304 | 4.44060576 | 5.22996739 | 6.15719130 | 7.24592868 |
| 68 | 3.84425050 | 4.54051939 | 5.36071658 | 6.32651406 | 7.46330654 |
| 69 | 3.92113551 | 4.64268107 | 5.49473449 | 6.50049319 | 7.68720574 |
| 70 | 3.99955822 | 4.74714140 | 5.63210286 | 6.67925676 | 7.91782191 |
| 71 | 4.07954939 | 4.85395208 | 5.77290543 | 6.86293632 | 8.15535657 |
| 72 | 4.16114038 | 4.96316600 | 5.91722806 | 7.05166706 | 8.40001727 |
| 73 | 4.24436318 | 5.07483723 | 6.06515876 | 7.24558791 | 8.65201778 |
| 74 | 4.32925045 | 5.18902107 | 6.21678773 | 7.44484158 | 8.91157832 |
| 75 | 4.41583546 | 5.30577405 | 6.37220743 | 7.64957472 | 9.17892567 |
| 76 | 4.50415216 | 5.42515396 | 6.53151261 | 7.85993802 | 9.45429344 |
| 77 | 4.59423521 | 5.54721993 | 6.69480043 | 8.07608632 | 9.73792224 |
| 78 | 4.68611991 | 5.67203237 | 6.86217044 | 8.29817869 | 10.0300599 |
| 79 | 4.77984231 | 5.79965310 | 7.03372470 | 8.52637861 | 10.3309617 |
| 80 | 4.87543916 | 5.93014530 | 7.20956782 | 8.76085402 | 10.6408906 |
| 81 | 4.97294794 | 6.06357357 | 7.38980701 | 9.00177751 | 10.9601173 |
| 82 | 5.07240690 | 6.20000397 | 7.57455219 | 9.24932639 | 11.2889208 |
| 83 | 5.17385504 | 6.33950406 | 7.76391509 | 9.50368286 | 11.6275884 |
| 84 | 5.27733214 | 6.48214290 | 7.95801389 | 9.76503414 | 11.9764161 |
| 85 | 5.38287878 | 6.62799112 | 8.15696424 | 10.0335726 | 12.3357085 |
| 86 | 5.49053636 | 6.77712092 | 8.36088834 | 10.3094958 | 12.7057798 |
| 87 | 5.60034708 | 6.92960614 | 8.56991055 | 10.5930070 | 13.0869532 |
| 88 | 5.71235402 | 7.08552228 | 8.78415832 | 10.8843147 | 13.4795618 |
| 89 | 5.82660110 | 7.24494653 | 9.00376228 | 11.1836333 | 13.8839487 |
| 90 | 5.94313313 | 7.40795782 | 9.22885633 | 11.4911832 | 14.3004671 |
| 91 | 6.06199579 | 7.57463688 | 9.45957774 | 11.8071908 | 14.7294811 |
| 92 | 6.18323570 | 7.74506621 | 9.69606718 | 12.1318885 | 15.1713656 |
| 93 | 6.30690042 | 7.91933020 | 9.93846886 | 12.4655154 | 15.6265065 |
| 94 | 6.43303843 | 8.09751512 | 10.1869306 | 12.8083171 | 16.0953017 |
| 95 | 6.56169920 | 8.27970921 | 10.4416038 | 13.1605458 | 16.5781608 |
| 96 | 6.69293318 | 8.46600267 | 10.7026439 | 13.5224608 | 17.0755056 |
| 97 | 6.82679184 | 8.65648773 | 10.9702100 | 13.8943285 | 17.5877708 |
| 98 | 6.96332768 | 8.85125871 | 11.2444653 | 14.2764226 | 18.1154039 |
| 99 | 7.10259423 | 9.05041203 | 11.5255769 | 14.6690242 | 18.6588660 |
| 100 | 7.24464612 | 9.25404630 | 11.8137164 | 15.0724223 | 19.2186320 |

# AMOUNT AT COMPOUND INTEREST $(1 + i)^n$
## (Continued)

| Years | Rate $i$ | | | | |
|---|---|---|---|---|---|
| $n$ | .035(3½ %) | .04(4 %) | .045(4½ %) | .05(5 %) | .055(5½ %) |
| 1 | 1.03500000 | 1.04000000 | 1.04500000 | 1.05000000 | 1.05500000 |
| 2 | 1.07122500 | 1.08160000 | 1.09202500 | 1.10250000 | 1.11302500 |
| 3 | 1.10871788 | 1.12486400 | 1.14116613 | 1.15762500 | 1.17424138 |
| 4 | 1.14752300 | 1.16985856 | 1.19251860 | 1.21550625 | 1.23882465 |
| 5 | 1.18768631 | 1.21665290 | 1.24618194 | 1.27628156 | 1.30696001 |
| 6 | 1.22925533 | 1.26531902 | 1.30226012 | 1.34009564 | 1.37884281 |
| 7 | 1.27227926 | 1.31593178 | 1.36086183 | 1.40710042 | 1.45467916 |
| 8 | 1.31680904 | 1.36856905 | 1.42210061 | 1.47745544 | 1.53468661 |
| 9 | 1.36289735 | 1.42331181 | 1.48609514 | 1.55132822 | 1.61909427 |
| 10 | 1.41059876 | 1.48024428 | 1.55296942 | 1.62889463 | 1.70814446 |
| 11 | 1.45996972 | 1.53945406 | 1.62285305 | 1.71033936 | 1.80209240 |
| 12 | 1.51106866 | 1.60103222 | 1.69588143 | 1.79585633 | 1.90120749 |
| 13 | 1.56395606 | 1.66507351 | 1.77219610 | 1.88564914 | 2.00577390 |
| 14 | 1.61869452 | 1.73167645 | 1.85194492 | 1.97993160 | 2.11609146 |
| 15 | 1.67534883 | 1.80094351 | 1.93528244 | 2.07892818 | 2.23247649 |
| 16 | 1.73398604 | 1.87298125 | 2.02237015 | 2.18287459 | 2.35526270 |
| 17 | 1.79467555 | 1.94790050 | 2.11337681 | 2.29201832 | 2.48480215 |
| 18 | 1.85748920 | 2.02581652 | 2.20847877 | 2.40661923 | 2.62146627 |
| 19 | 1.92250132 | 2.10684918 | 2.30786031 | 2.52695020 | 2.76564691 |
| 20 | 1.98978886 | 2.19112314 | 2.41171402 | 2.65329771 | 2.91775749 |
| 21 | 2.05943147 | 2.27876807 | 2.52024116 | 2.78596259 | 3.07823415 |
| 22 | 2.13151158 | 2.36991879 | 2.63365201 | 2.92526072 | 3.24753703 |
| 23 | 2.20611448 | 2.46471554 | 2.75216635 | 3.07152376 | 3.42615157 |
| 24 | 2.28332849 | 2.56330416 | 2.87601383 | 3.22509994 | 3.61458990 |
| 25 | 2.36324498 | 2.66583633 | 3.00543446 | 3.38635494 | 3.81339235 |
| 26 | 2.44595856 | 2.77246978 | 3.14067901 | 3.55567269 | 4.02312893 |
| 27 | 2.53156711 | 2.88336858 | 3.28200956 | 3.73345632 | 4.24440102 |
| 28 | 2.62017196 | 2.99870332 | 3.42969999 | 3.92012914 | 4.47784307 |
| 29 | 2.71187798 | 3.11865145 | 3.58403649 | 4.11613560 | 4.72412444 |
| 30 | 2.80679370 | 3.24339751 | 3.74531813 | 4.32194238 | 4.98395129 |
| 31 | 2.90503148 | 3.37313341 | 3.91385745 | 4.53803949 | 5.25806861 |
| 32 | 3.00670759 | 3.50805875 | 4.08998104 | 4.76494147 | 5.54726238 |
| 33 | 3.11194235 | 3.64838110 | 4.27403018 | 5.00318854 | 5.85236181 |
| 34 | 3.22086033 | 3.79431634 | 4.46636154 | 5.25334797 | 6.17424171 |
| 35 | 3.33359045 | 3.94608899 | 4.66734781 | 5.51601537 | 6.51382501 |
| 36 | 3.45026611 | 4.10393255 | 4.87737846 | 5.79181614 | 6.87208538 |
| 37 | 3.57102543 | 4.26808986 | 5.09686049 | 6.08140694 | 7.25005008 |
| 38 | 3.69601132 | 4.43881345 | 5.32621921 | 6.38547729 | 7.64880283 |
| 39 | 3.82537171 | 4.61636599 | 5.56589908 | 6.70475115 | 8.06948699 |
| 40 | 3.95925972 | 4.80102063 | 5.81636454 | 7.03998871 | 8.51330877 |
| 41 | 4.09783381 | 4.99306145 | 6.07810094 | 7.39198815 | 8.98154076 |
| 42 | 4.24125799 | 5.19278391 | 6.35161548 | 7.76158756 | 9.47552550 |
| 43 | 4.38970202 | 5.40049527 | 6.63743818 | 8.14966693 | 9.99667940 |
| 44 | 4.54334160 | 5.61651508 | 6.93612290 | 8.55715028 | 10.5464968 |
| 45 | 4.70235855 | 5.84117568 | 7.24824843 | 8.98500779 | 11.1265541 |
| 46 | 4.86694110 | 6.07482271 | 7.57441961 | 9.43425818 | 11.7385146 |
| 47 | 5.03728404 | 6.31781562 | 7.91526849 | 9.90597109 | 12.3841329 |
| 48 | 5.21358898 | 6.57052824 | 8.27145557 | 10.4012696 | 13.0652602 |
| 49 | 5.39606459 | 6.83334937 | 8.64367107 | 10.9213331 | 13.7838495 |
| 50 | 5.58492686 | 7.10668335 | 9.03263627 | 11.4673998 | 14.5419612 |

# AMOUNT AT COMPOUND INTEREST $(1 + i)^n$
## (Continued)

| Years | Rate $i$ | | | | |
|---|---|---|---|---|---|
| $n$ | .06(6 %) | .065(6½ %) | .07(7 %) | .075(7½) % | .08(8 %) |
| 1 | 1.06000000 | 1.06500000 | 1.07000000 | 1.07500000 | 1.08000000 |
| 2 | 1.12360000 | 1.13422500 | 1.14490000 | 1.15562500 | 1.16640000 |
| 3 | 1.19101600 | 1.20794963 | 1.22504300 | 1.24229688 | 1.25971200 |
| 4 | 1.26247696 | 1.28646635 | 1.31079601 | 1.33546914 | 1.36048896 |
| 5 | 1.33822558 | 1.37008666 | 1.40255173 | 1.43562933 | 1.46932808 |
| 6 | 1.41851911 | 1.45914230 | 1.50073035 | 1.54330153 | 1.58687432 |
| 7 | 1.50363026 | 1.55398655 | 1.60578148 | 1.65904914 | 1.71382427 |
| 8 | 1.59384807 | 1.65499567 | 1.71818618 | 1.78347783 | 1.85093021 |
| 9 | 1.68947896 | 1.76257039 | 1.83845921 | 1.91723866 | 1.99900463 |
| 10 | 1.79084770 | 1.87713747 | 1.96715136 | 2.06103156 | 2.15892500 |
| 11 | 1.89829856 | 1.99915140 | 2.10485195 | 2.21560893 | 2.33163900 |
| 12 | 2.01219647 | 2.12909624 | 2.25219159 | 2.38177960 | 2.51817012 |
| 13 | 2.13292826 | 2.26748750 | 2.40984500 | 2.56041307 | 2.71962373 |
| 14 | 2.26090396 | 2.41487418 | 2.57853415 | 2.75244405 | 2.93719362 |
| 15 | 2.39655819 | 2.57184101 | 2.75903154 | 2.95887735 | 3.17216911 |
| 16 | 2.54035168 | 2.73901067 | 2.95216375 | 3.18079315 | 3.42594264 |
| 17 | 2.69277279 | 2.91704637 | 3.15881521 | 3.41935264 | 3.70001805 |
| 18 | 2.85433915 | 3.10665438 | 3.37993228 | 3.67580409 | 3.99601950 |
| 19 | 3.02559950 | 3.30858691 | 3.61652754 | 3.95148940 | 4.31570106 |
| 20 | 3.20713547 | 3.52364506 | 3.86968446 | 4.24785110 | 4.66095714 |
| 21 | 3.39956360 | 3.75268199 | 4.14056237 | 4.56643993 | 5.03383372 |
| 22 | 3.60353742 | 3.99660632 | 4.43040174 | 4.90892293 | 5.43654041 |
| 23 | 3.81974966 | 4.25638573 | 4.74052986 | 5.27709215 | 5.87146365 |
| 24 | 4.04893464 | 4.53305081 | 5.07236695 | 5.67287406 | 6.34118070 |
| 25 | 4.29187072 | 4.82769911 | 5.42743264 | 6.09833961 | 6.84847520 |
| 26 | 4.54938296 | 5.14149955 | 5.80735292 | 6.55571508 | 7.39635321 |
| 27 | 4.82234594 | 5.47569702 | 6.21386763 | 7.04739371 | 7.98806147 |
| 28 | 5.11168670 | 5.83161733 | 6.64883836 | 7.57594824 | 8.62710639 |
| 29 | 5.41838790 | 6.21067245 | 7.11425705 | 8.14414436 | 9.31727490 |
| 30 | 5.74349117 | 6.61436616 | 7.61225504 | 8.75495519 | 10.0626569 |
| 31 | 6.08810064 | 7.04429996 | 8.14511290 | 9.41157683 | 10.8676694 |
| 32 | 6.45338668 | 7.50217946 | 8.71527080 | 10.1174451 | 11.7370830 |
| 33 | 6.84058988 | 7.98982113 | 9.32533975 | 10.8762535 | 12.6760496 |
| 34 | 7.25102528 | 8.50915950 | 9.97811354 | 11.6919725 | 13.6901336 |
| 35 | 7.68608679 | 9.06225487 | 10.6765815 | 12.5688704 | 14.7853443 |
| 36 | 8.14725200 | 9.65130143 | 11.4239422 | 13.5115357 | 15.9681718 |
| 37 | 8.63608712 | 10.2786360 | 12.2236181 | 14.5249009 | 17.2456256 |
| 38 | 9.15425235 | 10.9467474 | 13.0792714 | 15.6142684 | 18.6252756 |
| 39 | 9.70350749 | 11.6582859 | 13.9948204 | 16.7853386 | 20.1152977 |
| 40 | 10.2857179 | 12.4160745 | 14.9744578 | 18.0442390 | 21.7245215 |
| 41 | 10.9028610 | 13.2231194 | 16.0226699 | 19.3975569 | 23.4624832 |
| 42 | 11.5570327 | 14.0826221 | 17.1442568 | 20.8523737 | 25.3394819 |
| 43 | 12.2504546 | 14.9979926 | 18.3443548 | 22.4163017 | 27.3666404 |
| 44 | 12.9854819 | 15.9728621 | 19.6284596 | 24.0975243 | 29.5559717 |
| 45 | 13.7646108 | 17.0110981 | 21.0024518 | 25.9048386 | 31.9204494 |
| 46 | 14.5904875 | 18.1168195 | 22.4726234 | 27.8477015 | 34.4740853 |
| 47 | 15.4659167 | 19.2944128 | 24.0457070 | 29.9362791 | 37.2320122 |
| 48 | 16.3938717 | 20.5485496 | 25.7289065 | 32.1815001 | 40.2105731 |
| 49 | 17.3775040 | 21.8842053 | 27.5299300 | 34.5951126 | 43.4274190 |
| 50 | 18.4201543 | 23.3066787 | 29.4570251 | 37.1897460 | 46.9016125 |

## PRESENT VALUE $1/(1 + i)^n$

The following table gives the value of unit amount due in $n$ years at rate of interest $i$, compounded annually, $1/(1 + i)^n = v^n$.

| n | .0025($\frac{1}{4}$ %) | .004167($\frac{5}{12}$ %) | .005($\frac{1}{2}$ %) | .005833($\frac{7}{12}$ %) | .0075($\frac{3}{4}$ %) |
|---|---|---|---|---|---|
| 1 | .99750623 | .99585062 | .99502488 | .99420050 | .99255583 |
| 2 | .99501869 | .99171846 | .99007450 | .98843463 | .98516708 |
| 3 | .99253734 | .98760345 | .98514876 | .98270220 | .97783333 |
| 4 | .99006219 | .98350551 | .98024752 | .97700301 | .97055417 |
| 5 | .98759321 | .97942457 | .97537067 | .97133688 | .96332920 |
| 6 | .98513038 | .97536057 | .97051808 | .96570361 | .95615802 |
| 7 | .98267370 | .97131343 | .96568963 | .96010301 | .94904022 |
| 8 | .98022314 | .96728308 | .96088520 | .95453489 | .94197540 |
| 9 | .97777869 | .96326946 | .95610468 | .94899906 | .93496318 |
| 10 | .97534034 | .95927249 | .95134794 | .94349534 | .92800315 |
| 11 | .97290807 | .95529211 | .94661487 | .93802354 | .92109494 |
| 12 | .97048187 | .95132824 | .94190534 | .93258347 | .91423815 |
| 13 | .96806171 | .94738082 | .93721924 | .92717495 | .90743241 |
| 14 | .96564759 | .94344978 | .93255646 | .92179779 | .90067733 |
| 15 | .96323949 | .93953505 | .92791688 | .91645182 | .89397254 |
| 16 | .96083740 | .93563657 | .92330037 | .91113686 | .88731766 |
| 17 | .95844130 | .93175426 | .91870684 | .90585272 | .88071231 |
| 18 | .95605117 | .92788806 | .91413616 | .90059922 | .87415614 |
| 19 | .95366700 | .92403790 | .90958822 | .89537619 | .86764878 |
| 20 | .95128878 | .92020372 | .90506290 | .89018346 | .86118985 |
| 21 | .94891649 | .91638544 | .90056010 | .88502084 | .85477901 |
| 22 | .94655011 | .91258301 | .89607971 | .87988815 | .84841589 |
| 23 | .94418964 | .90879636 | .89162160 | .87478524 | .84210014 |
| 24 | .94183505 | .90502542 | .88718567 | .86971192 | .83583140 |
| 25 | .93948634 | .90127013 | .88277181 | .86466802 | .82960933 |
| 26 | .93714348 | .89753042 | .87837991 | .85965338 | .82343358 |
| 27 | .93480646 | .89380623 | .87400986 | .85466782 | .81730380 |
| 28 | .93247527 | .89009749 | .86966155 | .84971117 | .81121966 |
| 29 | .93014990 | .88640414 | .86533488 | .84478327 | .80518080 |
| 30 | .92783032 | .88272611 | .86102973 | .83988394 | .79918690 |
| 31 | .92551653 | .87906335 | .85674600 | .83501303 | .79323762 |
| 32 | .92320851 | .87541578 | .85248358 | .83017037 | .78733262 |
| 33 | .92090624 | .87178335 | .84824237 | .82535580 | .78147158 |
| 34 | .91860972 | .86816599 | .84402226 | .82056914 | .77565418 |
| 35 | .91631892 | .86456365 | .83982314 | .81581025 | .76988008 |
| 36 | .91403384 | .86097624 | .83564492 | .81107896 | .76414896 |
| 37 | .91175445 | .85740373 | .83148748 | .80637510 | .75846051 |
| 38 | .90948075 | .85384604 | .82735073 | .80169853 | .75281440 |
| 39 | .90721272 | .85030311 | .82323455 | .79704907 | .74721032 |
| 40 | .90495034 | .84677488 | .81913886 | .79242659 | .74164796 |
| 41 | .90269361 | .84326129 | .81506354 | .78783091 | .73612701 |
| 42 | .90044250 | .83976228 | .81100850 | .78326188 | .73064716 |
| 43 | .89819701 | .83627779 | .80697363 | .77871935 | .72520809 |
| 44 | .89595712 | .83280776 | .80295884 | .77420316 | .71980952 |
| 45 | .89372281 | .82935212 | .79896402 | .76971317 | .71445114 |
| 46 | .89149407 | .82591083 | .79498907 | .76524922 | .70913264 |
| 47 | .88927090 | .82248381 | .79103390 | .76081115 | .70385374 |
| 48 | .88705326 | .81907102 | .78709841 | .75639883 | .69861414 |
| 49 | .88484116 | .81567238 | .78318250 | .75201209 | .69341353 |
| 50 | .88263457 | .81228785 | .77928607 | .74765079 | .68825165 |

| Years | | | Rate $i$ | | |
|---|---|---|---|---|---|
| $n$ | .0025($\frac{1}{4}$ %) | .004167($\frac{5}{12}$ %) | .005($\frac{1}{2}$ %) | .005833($\frac{7}{12}$ %) | .0075($\frac{3}{4}$ %) |
| 50 | .88263457 | .81228785 | .77928607 | .74765079 | .68825165 |
| 51 | .88043349 | .80891736 | .77540902 | .74331479 | .68312819 |
| 52 | .87823790 | .80556086 | .77155127 | .73900393 | .67804286 |
| 53 | .87604778 | .80221828 | .76771270 | .73471808 | .67299540 |
| 54 | .87386312 | .79888957 | .76389324 | .73045708 | .66798551 |
| 55 | .87168391 | .79557468 | .76009277 | .72622079 | .66301291 |
| 56 | .86951013 | .79227354 | .75631122 | .72200907 | .65807733 |
| 57 | .86734178 | .78898610 | .75254847 | .71782178 | .65317849 |
| 58 | .86517883 | .78571230 | .74880445 | .71365877 | .64831612 |
| 59 | .86302128 | .78245208 | .74507906 | .70951990 | .64348995 |
| 60 | .86086911 | .77920539 | .74137220 | .70540504 | .63869970 |
| 61 | .85872230 | .77597217 | .73768378 | .70131404 | .63394511 |
| 62 | .85658085 | .77275237 | .73401371 | .69724677 | .62922592 |
| 63 | .85444474 | .76954593 | .73036190 | .69320308 | .62454185 |
| 64 | .85231395 | .76635279 | .72672826 | .68918285 | .61989266 |
| 65 | .85018848 | .76317291 | .72311269 | .68518593 | .61527807 |
| 66 | .84806831 | .76000621 | .71951512 | .68121219 | .61069784 |
| 67 | .84595343 | .75685266 | .71593544 | .67726150 | .60615170 |
| 68 | .84384382 | .75371219 | .71237357 | .67333372 | .60163940 |
| 69 | .84173947 | .75058476 | .70882943 | .66942872 | .59716070 |
| 70 | .83964037 | .74747030 | .70530291 | .66554637 | .59271533 |
| 71 | .83754650 | .74436876 | .70179394 | .66168653 | .58830306 |
| 72 | .83545786 | .74128009 | .69830243 | .65784908 | .58392363 |
| 73 | .83337442 | .73820424 | .69482829 | .65403388 | .57957681 |
| 74 | .83129618 | .73514115 | .69137143 | .65024081 | .57526234 |
| 75 | .82922312 | .73209078 | .68793177 | .64646973 | .57097999 |
| 76 | .82715523 | .72905306 | .68450923 | .64272053 | .56672952 |
| 77 | .82509250 | .72602794 | .68110371 | .63899306 | .56251069 |
| 78 | .82303491 | .72301537 | .67771513 | .63528723 | .55832326 |
| 79 | .82098246 | .72001531 | .67434342 | .63160288 | .55416701 |
| 80 | .81893512 | .71702770 | .67098847 | .62793989 | .55004170 |
| 81 | .81689289 | .71405248 | .66765022 | .62429816 | .54594710 |
| 82 | .81485575 | .71108960 | .66432858 | .62067754 | .54188297 |
| 83 | .81282369 | .70813902 | .66102346 | .61707792 | .53784911 |
| 84 | .81079670 | .70520069 | .65773479 | .61349917 | .53384527 |
| 85 | .80877476 | .70227454 | .65446248 | .60994118 | .52987123 |
| 86 | .80675787 | .69936054 | .65120644 | .60640382 | .52592678 |
| 87 | .80474600 | .69645863 | .64796661 | .60288698 | .52201169 |
| 88 | .80273915 | .69356876 | .64474290 | .59939064 | .51812575 |
| 89 | .80073731 | .69069088 | .64153522 | .59591437 | .51426873 |
| 90 | .79874046 | .68782495 | .63834350 | .59245836 | .51044043 |
| 91 | .79674859 | .68497090 | .63516766 | .58902240 | .50664063 |
| 92 | .79476168 | .68212870 | .63200763 | .58560636 | .50286911 |
| 93 | .79277973 | .67929829 | .62886331 | .58221014 | .49912567 |
| 94 | .79080273 | .67647962 | .62573464 | .57883361 | .49541009 |
| 95 | .78883065 | .67367265 | .62262153 | .57547666 | .49172217 |
| 96 | .78686349 | .67087733 | .61952391 | .57213918 | .48806171 |
| 97 | .78490124 | .66809361 | .61644170 | .56882106 | .48442850 |
| 98 | .78294388 | .66532143 | .61337483 | .56552218 | .48082233 |
| 99 | .78099140 | .66256076 | .61032321 | .56224243 | .47724301 |
| 100 | .77904379 | .65981155 | .60728678 | .55898171 | .47369033 |

## PRESENT VALUE $1/(1 + i)^n$ (Continued)

| Years $n$ | Rate $i$ .01(1 %) | .01125(1⅛ %) | .0125(1¼ %) | .015(1½ %) | .0175(1¾ %) |
|---|---|---|---|---|---|
| 1 | .99009901 | .98887515 | .98765432 | .98522167 | .98280098 |
| 2 | .98029605 | .97787407 | .97546106 | .97066175 | .96589777 |
| 3 | .97059015 | .96699537 | .96341833 | .95631699 | .94928528 |
| 4 | .96098034 | .95623770 | .95152428 | .94218423 | .93295851 |
| 5 | .95146569 | .94559970 | .93977706 | .92826033 | .91691254 |
| 6 | .94204524 | .93508005 | .92817488 | .91454219 | .90114254 |
| 7 | .93271805 | .92467743 | .91671593 | .90102679 | .88564378 |
| 8 | .92348322 | .91439054 | .90539845 | .88771112 | .87041157 |
| 9 | .91433982 | .90421808 | .89422069 | .87459224 | .85544135 |
| 10 | .90528695 | .89415880 | .88318093 | .86166723 | .84072860 |
| 11 | .89632372 | .88421142 | .87227746 | .84893323 | .82626889 |
| 12 | .88744923 | .87437470 | .86150860 | .83638742 | .81205788 |
| 13 | .87866260 | .86464742 | .85087269 | .82402702 | .79809128 |
| 14 | .86996297 | .85502835 | .84036809 | .81184928 | .78436490 |
| 15 | .86134947 | .84551629 | .82999318 | .79985150 | .77087459 |
| 16 | .85282126 | .83611005 | .81974635 | .78803104 | .75761631 |
| 17 | .84437749 | .82680846 | .80962602 | .77638526 | .74458605 |
| 18 | .83601731 | .81761034 | .79963064 | .76491159 | .73177990 |
| 19 | .82773992 | .80851455 | .78975866 | .75360747 | .71919401 |
| 20 | .81954447 | .79951995 | .78000855 | .74247042 | .70682458 |
| 21 | .81143017 | .79062542 | .77037881 | .73149795 | .69466789 |
| 22 | .80339621 | .78182983 | .76086796 | .72068763 | .68272028 |
| 23 | .79544179 | .77313210 | .75147453 | .71003708 | .67097817 |
| 24 | .78756613 | .76453112 | .74219707 | .69954392 | .65943800 |
| 25 | .77976844 | .75602583 | .73303414 | .68920583 | .64809632 |
| 26 | .77204796 | .74761516 | .72398434 | .67902052 | .63694970 |
| 27 | .76440392 | .73929806 | .71504626 | .66898574 | .62599479 |
| 28 | .75683557 | .73107348 | .70621853 | .65909925 | .61522829 |
| 29 | .74934215 | .72294040 | .69749978 | .64935887 | .60464697 |
| 30 | .74192292 | .71489780 | .68888867 | .63976243 | .59424764 |
| 31 | .73457715 | .70694467 | .68038387 | .63030781 | .58402716 |
| 32 | .72730411 | .69908002 | .67198407 | .62099292 | .57398247 |
| 33 | .72010307 | .69130287 | .66368797 | .61181568 | .56411053 |
| 34 | .71297334 | .68361223 | .65549429 | .60277407 | .55440839 |
| 35 | .70591420 | .67600715 | .64740177 | .59386608 | .54487311 |
| 36 | .69892495 | .66848667 | .63940916 | .58508974 | .53550183 |
| 37 | .69200490 | .66104986 | .63151522 | .57644309 | .52629172 |
| 38 | .68515337 | .65369578 | .62371873 | .56792423 | .51724002 |
| 39 | .67836967 | .64642352 | .61601850 | .55953126 | .50834400 |
| 40 | .67165314 | .63923216 | .60841334 | .55126232 | .49960098 |
| 41 | .66500311 | .63212080 | .60090206 | .54311559 | .49100834 |
| 42 | .65841892 | .62508855 | .59348352 | .53508925 | .48256348 |
| 43 | .65189992 | .61813454 | .58615656 | .52718153 | .47426386 |
| 44 | .64544546 | .61125789 | .57892006 | .51939067 | .46610699 |
| 45 | .63905492 | .60445774 | .57177290 | .51171494 | .45809040 |
| 46 | .63272764 | .59773324 | .56471397 | .50415265 | .45021170 |
| 47 | .62646301 | .59108355 | .55774219 | .49670212 | .44246850 |
| 48 | .62026041 | .58450784 | .55085649 | .48936170 | .43485848 |
| 49 | .61411921 | .57800528 | .54405579 | .48212975 | .42737934 |
| 50 | .60803882 | .57157506 | .53733905 | .47500468 | .42002883 |

# PRESENT VALUE $1/(1 + i)^n$ (Continued)

| Years | | | Rate $i$ | | |
|---|---|---|---|---|---|
| $n$ | .01(1 %) | .01125(1⅛ %) | .0125(1¼ %) | .015(1½ %) | .0175(1¾ %) |
| **50** | .60803882 | .57157506 | .53733905 | .47500468 | .42002883 |
| 51 | .60201864 | .56521637 | .53070524 | .46798491 | .41280475 |
| 52 | .59605806 | .55892843 | .52415332 | .46106887 | .40570492 |
| 53 | .59015649 | .55271044 | .51768229 | .45425505 | .39872719 |
| 54 | .58431336 | .54656162 | .51129115 | .44754192 | .39186947 |
| **55** | .57852808 | .54048120 | .50497892 | .44092800 | .38512970 |
| 56 | .57280008 | .53446843 | .49874461 | .43441182 | .37850585 |
| 57 | .56712879 | .52852256 | .49258727 | .42799194 | .37199592 |
| 58 | .56151365 | .52264282 | .48650594 | .42166694 | .36559796 |
| 59 | .55595411 | .51682850 | .48049970 | .41543541 | .35931003 |
| **60** | .55044962 | .51107887 | .47456760 | .40929597 | .35313025 |
| 61 | .54499962 | .50539319 | .46870874 | .40324726 | .34705676 |
| 62 | .53960358 | .49977077 | .46292222 | .39728794 | .34108772 |
| 63 | .53426097 | .49421090 | .45720713 | .39141669 | .33522135 |
| 64 | .52897126 | .48871288 | .45156259 | .38563221 | .32945587 |
| **65** | .52373392 | .48327602 | .44598775 | .37993321 | .32378956 |
| 66 | .51854844 | .47789965 | .44048173 | .37431843 | .31822069 |
| 67 | .51341429 | .47258309 | .43504368 | .36878663 | .31274761 |
| 68 | .50833099 | .46732568 | .42967277 | .36333658 | .30736866 |
| 69 | .50329801 | .46212675 | .42436817 | .35796708 | .30208222 |
| **70** | .49831486 | .45698566 | .41912905 | .35267692 | .29688670 |
| 71 | .49338105 | .45190177 | .41395462 | .34746495 | .29178054 |
| 72 | .48849609 | .44687443 | .40884407 | .34233000 | .28676221 |
| 73 | .48365949 | .44190302 | .40379661 | .33727093 | .28183018 |
| 74 | .47887078 | .43698692 | .39881147 | .33228663 | .27698298 |
| **75** | .47412949 | .43212551 | .39388787 | .32737599 | .27221914 |
| 76 | .46943514 | .42731818 | .38902506 | .32253793 | .26753724 |
| 77 | .46478726 | .42256433 | .38422228 | .31777136 | .26293586 |
| 78 | .46018541 | .41786337 | .37947879 | .31307523 | .25841362 |
| 79 | .45562912 | .41321470 | .37479387 | .30844850 | .25396916 |
| **80** | .45111794 | .40861775 | .37016679 | .30389015 | .24960114 |
| 81 | .44665142 | .40407194 | .36559683 | .29939916 | .24530825 |
| 82 | .44222913 | .39957670 | .36108329 | .29497454 | .24108919 |
| 83 | .43785063 | .39513148 | .35662547 | .29061531 | .23694269 |
| 84 | .43351547 | .39073570 | .35222268 | .28632050 | .23286751 |
| **85** | .42922324 | .38638882 | .34787426 | .28208917 | .22886242 |
| 86 | .42497350 | .38209031 | .34357951 | .27792036 | .22492621 |
| 87 | .42076585 | .37783961 | .33933779 | .27381316 | .22105770 |
| 88 | .41659985 | .37363621 | .33514843 | .26976666 | .21725572 |
| 89 | .41247510 | .36947956 | .33101080 | .26577996 | .21351914 |
| **90** | .40839119 | .36536916 | .32692425 | .26185218 | .20984682 |
| 91 | .40434771 | .36130448 | .32288814 | .25798245 | .20623766 |
| 92 | .40034427 | .35728503 | .31890187 | .25416990 | .20269057 |
| 93 | .39638046 | .35331029 | .31496481 | .25041369 | .19920450 |
| 94 | .39245590 | .34937976 | .31107636 | .24671300 | .19577837 |
| **95** | .38857020 | .34549297 | .30723591 | .24306699 | .19241118 |
| 96 | .38472297 | .34164941 | .30344287 | .23947487 | .18910190 |
| 97 | .38091383 | .33784861 | .29969666 | .23593583 | .18584953 |
| 98 | .37714241 | .33409010 | .29599670 | .23244909 | .18265310 |
| 99 | .37340832 | .33037340 | .29234242 | .22901389 | .17951165 |
| **100** | .36971121 | .32669805 | .28873326 | .22562944 | .17642422 |

## PRESENT VALUE $1/(1 + i)^n$ (Continued)

| Years $n$ | .02(2 %) | .0225(2¼ %) | .025(2½ %) | .0275(2¾ %) | .03(3 %) |
|---|---|---|---|---|---|
| | | | Rate $i$ | | |
| 1 | .98039216 | .97799511 | .97560976 | .97323601 | .97087379 |
| 2 | .96116878 | .95647444 | .95181440 | .94718833 | .94259591 |
| 3 | .94232233 | .93542732 | .92859941 | .92183779 | .91514166 |
| 4 | .92384543 | .91484335 | .90595064 | .89716573 | .88848705 |
| 5 | .90573081 | .89471232 | .88385429 | .87315400 | .86260878 |
| 6 | .88797138 | .87502427 | .86229687 | .84978491 | .83748426 |
| 7 | .87056018 | .85576946 | .84126524 | .82704128 | .81309151 |
| 8 | .85349037 | .83693835 | .82074657 | .80490635 | .78940923 |
| 9 | .83675527 | .81852161 | .80072836 | .78336385 | .76641673 |
| 10 | .82034830 | .80051013 | .78119840 | .76239791 | .74409391 |
| 11 | .80426304 | .78289499 | .76214478 | .74199310 | .72242128 |
| 12 | .78849318 | .76566748 | .74355589 | .72213440 | .70137988 |
| 13 | .77303253 | .74881905 | .72542038 | .70280720 | .68095134 |
| 14 | .75787502 | .73234137 | .70772720 | .68399728 | .66111781 |
| 15 | .74301473 | .71622628 | .69046556 | .66569078 | .64186195 |
| 16 | .72844581 | .70046580 | .67362493 | .64787424 | .62316694 |
| 17 | .71416256 | .68505212 | .65719506 | .63053454 | .60501645 |
| 18 | .70015937 | .66997763 | .64116591 | .61365892 | .58739461 |
| 19 | .68643076 | .65523484 | .62552772 | .59723496 | .57028603 |
| 20 | .67297133 | .64081647 | .61027094 | .58125057 | .55367575 |
| 21 | .65977582 | .62671538 | .59538629 | .56569398 | .53754928 |
| 22 | .64683904 | .61292457 | .58086467 | .55055375 | .52189250 |
| 23 | .63415592 | .59943724 | .56669724 | .53581874 | .50669175 |
| 24 | .62172149 | .58624668 | .55287535 | .52147809 | .49193374 |
| 25 | .60953087 | .57334639 | .53939059 | .50752126 | .47760557 |
| 26 | .59757928 | .56072997 | .52623472 | .49393796 | .46369473 |
| 27 | .58586204 | .54839117 | .51339973 | .48071821 | .45018906 |
| 28 | .57437455 | .53632388 | .50087778 | .46785227 | .43707675 |
| 29 | .56311231 | .52452213 | .48866125 | .45533068 | .42434636 |
| 30 | .55207089 | .51298008 | .47674269 | .44314421 | .41198676 |
| 31 | .54124597 | .50169201 | .46511481 | .43128391 | .39998715 |
| 32 | .53063330 | .49065233 | .45377055 | .41974103 | .38833703 |
| 33 | .52022873 | .47985558 | .44270298 | .40850708 | .37702625 |
| 34 | .51002817 | .46929641 | .43190534 | .39757380 | .36604490 |
| 35 | .50002761 | .45896960 | .42137107 | .38693314 | .35538340 |
| 36 | .49022315 | .44887002 | .41109372 | .37657727 | .34503243 |
| 37 | .48061093 | .43899268 | .40106705 | .36649856 | .33498294 |
| 38 | .47118719 | .42933270 | .39128492 | .35668959 | .32522615 |
| 39 | .46194822 | .41988528 | .38174139 | .34714316 | .31575355 |
| 40 | .45289042 | .41064575 | .37243062 | .33785222 | .30655684 |
| 41 | .44401021 | .40160954 | .36334695 | .32880995 | .29762800 |
| 42 | .43530413 | .39277216 | .35448483 | .32000968 | .28895922 |
| 43 | .42676875 | .38412925 | .34583886 | .31144495 | .28054294 |
| 44 | .41840074 | .37567653 | .33740376 | .30310944 | .27237178 |
| 45 | .41019680 | .36740981 | .32917440 | .29499702 | .26443862 |
| 46 | .40215373 | .35932500 | .32114576 | .28710172 | .25673653 |
| 47 | .39426836 | .35141809 | .31331294 | .27941773 | .24925876 |
| 48 | .38653761 | .34368518 | .30567116 | .27193940 | .24199880 |
| 49 | .37895844 | .33612242 | .29821576 | .26466122 | .23495029 |
| 50 | .37152788 | .32872608 | .29094221 | .25757783 | .22810708 |

## PRESENT VALUE $1/(1 + i)^n$ (Continued)

| Years | | | | | |
|---|---|---|---|---|---|
| | | | Rate $i$ | | |
| $n$ | .02(2 %) | .0225(2¼ %) | .025(2½ %) | .0275(2¾ %) | .03(3 %) |
| **50** | .37152788 | .32872608 | .29094221 | .25757783 | .22810708 |
| 51 | .36424302 | .32149250 | .28384606 | .25068402 | .22146318 |
| 52 | .35710100 | .31441810 | .27692298 | .24397471 | .21501280 |
| 53 | .35009902 | .30749936 | .27016876 | .23744497 | .20875029 |
| 54 | .34323433 | .30073287 | .26357928 | .23109000 | .20267019 |
| **55** | .33650425 | .29411528 | .25715052 | .22490511 | .19676717 |
| 56 | .32990613 | .28764330 | .25087855 | .21888575 | .19103609 |
| 57 | .32343738 | .28131374 | .24475956 | .21302749 | .18547193 |
| 58 | .31709547 | .27512347 | .23878982 | .20732603 | .18006984 |
| 59 | .31087791 | .26906940 | .23296568 | .20177716 | .17482508 |
| **60** | .30478227 | .26314856 | .22728359 | .19637679 | .16973309 |
| 61 | .29880614 | .25735801 | .22174009 | .19112097 | .16478941 |
| 62 | .29294720 | .25169487 | .21633179 | .18600581 | .15998972 |
| 63 | .28720314 | .24615635 | .21105541 | .18102755 | .15532982 |
| 64 | .28157170 | .24073971 | .20590771 | .17618253 | .15080565 |
| **65** | .27605069 | .23544226 | .20088557 | .17146718 | .14641325 |
| 66 | .27063793 | .23026138 | .19598593 | .16687804 | .14214879 |
| 67 | .26533130 | .22519450 | .19120578 | .16241172 | .13800853 |
| 68 | .26012873 | .22023912 | .18654223 | .15806493 | .13398887 |
| 69 | .25502817 | .21539278 | .18199241 | .15383448 | .13008628 |
| **70** | .25002761 | .21065309 | .17755358 | .14971726 | .12629736 |
| 71 | .24512511 | .20601769 | .17322300 | .14571023 | .12261880 |
| 72 | .24031874 | .20148429 | .16899805 | .14181044 | .11904737 |
| 73 | .23560661 | .19705065 | .16487615 | .13801503 | .11557998 |
| 74 | .23098687 | .19271458 | .16085478 | .13432119 | .11221357 |
| **75** | .22645771 | .18847391 | .15693149 | .13072622 | .10894521 |
| 76 | .22201737 | .18432657 | .15310389 | .12722747 | .10577205 |
| 77 | .21766408 | .18027048 | .14936965 | .12382235 | .10269131 |
| 78 | .21339616 | .17630365 | .14572649 | .12050837 | .09970030 |
| 79 | .20921192 | .17242411 | .14217218 | .11728309 | .09679641 |
| **80** | .20510973 | .16862993 | .13870457 | .11414412 | .09397710 |
| 81 | .20108797 | .16491925 | .13532153 | .11108917 | .09123990 |
| 82 | .19714507 | .16129022 | .13202101 | .10811598 | .08858243 |
| 83 | .19327948 | .15774105 | .12880098 | .10522237 | .08600236 |
| 84 | .18948968 | .15426997 | .12565949 | .10240620 | .08349743 |
| **85** | .18577420 | .15087528 | .12259463 | .09966540 | .08106547 |
| 86 | .18213157 | .14755528 | .11960452 | .09699795 | .07870434 |
| 87 | .17856036 | .14430835 | .11668733 | .09440190 | .07641198 |
| 88 | .17505918 | .14113286 | .11384130 | .09187533 | .07418639 |
| 89 | .17162665 | .13802724 | .11106468 | .08941638 | .07202562 |
| **90** | .16826142 | .13498997 | .10835579 | .08702324 | .06992779 |
| 91 | .16496217 | .13201953 | .10571296 | .08469415 | .06789105 |
| 92 | .16172762 | .12911445 | .10313460 | .08242740 | .06591364 |
| 93 | .15855649 | .12627331 | .10061912 | .08022131 | .06399383 |
| 94 | .15544754 | .12349468 | .09816500 | .07807427 | .06212993 |
| **95** | .15239955 | .12077719 | .09577073 | .07598469 | .06032032 |
| 96 | .14941132 | .11811950 | .09343486 | .07395104 | .05856342 |
| 97 | .14648169 | .11552029 | .09115596 | .07197181 | .05685769 |
| 98 | .14360950 | .11297828 | .08893264 | .07004556 | .05520164 |
| 99 | .14079363 | .11049221 | .08676355 | .06817086 | .05359383 |
| **100** | .13803297 | .10806084 | .08464737 | .06634634 | .05203284 |

## PRESENT VALUE $1/(1 + i)^n$ (Continued)

| Years n | Rate i | | | | |
|---|---|---|---|---|---|
| | .035(3½ %) | .04(4 %) | .045(4½ %) | .05(5 %) | .055(5½ %) |
| 1 | .96618357 | .96153846 | .95693780 | .95238095 | .94786730 |
| 2 | .93351070 | .92455621 | .91572995 | .90702948 | .89845242 |
| 3 | .90194271 | .88899636 | .87629660 | .86383760 | .85161366 |
| 4 | .87144223 | .85480419 | .83856134 | .82270247 | .80721674 |
| 5 | .84197317 | .82192711 | .80245105 | .78352617 | .76513435 |
| 6 | .81350064 | .79031453 | .76789574 | .74621540 | .72524583 |
| 7 | .78599096 | .75991781 | .73482846 | .71068133 | .68743681 |
| 8 | .75941156 | .73069021 | .70318513 | .67683936 | .65159887 |
| 9 | .73373097 | .70258674 | .67290443 | .64460892 | .61762926 |
| 10 | .70891881 | .67556417 | .64392768 | .61391325 | .58543058 |
| 11 | .68494571 | .64958093 | .61619874 | .58467929 | .55491050 |
| 12 | .66178330 | .62459705 | .58966386 | .55683742 | .52598152 |
| 13 | .63940415 | .60057409 | .56427164 | .53032135 | .49856068 |
| 14 | .61778179 | .57747508 | .53997286 | .50506795 | .47256937 |
| 15 | .59689062 | .55526450 | .51672044 | .48101710 | .44793305 |
| 16 | .57670591 | .53390818 | .49446932 | .45811152 | .42458109 |
| 17 | .55720378 | .51337325 | .47317639 | .43629669 | .40244653 |
| 18 | .53836114 | .49362812 | .45280037 | .41552065 | .38146590 |
| 19 | .52015569 | .47464242 | .43330179 | .39573396 | .36157906 |
| 20 | .50256588 | .45638695 | .41464286 | .37688948 | .34272896 |
| 21 | .48557090 | .43883360 | .39678743 | .35894236 | .32486158 |
| 22 | .46915063 | .42195539 | .37970089 | .34184987 | .30792567 |
| 23 | .45328563 | .40572633 | .36335013 | .32557131 | .29187267 |
| 24 | .43795713 | .39012147 | .34770347 | .31006791 | .27665656 |
| 25 | .42314699 | .37511680 | .33273060 | .29530277 | .26223370 |
| 26 | .40883767 | .36068923 | .31840248 | .28124073 | .24856275 |
| 27 | .39501224 | .34681657 | .30469137 | .26784832 | .23560450 |
| 28 | .38165434 | .33347747 | .29157069 | .25509364 | .22332181 |
| 29 | .36874815 | .32065141 | .27901502 | .24294632 | .21167944 |
| 30 | .35627841 | .30831867 | .26700002 | .23137745 | .20064402 |
| 31 | .34423035 | .29646026 | .25550241 | .22035947 | .19018390 |
| 32 | .33258971 | .28505794 | .24449991 | .20986617 | .18026910 |
| 33 | .32134271 | .27409417 | .23397121 | .19987254 | .17087119 |
| 34 | .31047605 | .26355209 | .22389589 | .19035480 | .16196321 |
| 35 | .29997686 | .25341547 | .21425444 | .18129029 | .15351963 |
| 36 | .28983272 | .24366872 | .20502817 | .17265741 | .14551624 |
| 37 | .28003161 | .23429685 | .19619921 | .16443563 | .13793008 |
| 38 | .27056194 | .22528543 | .18775044 | .15660536 | .13073941 |
| 39 | .26141250 | .21662061 | .17966549 | .14914797 | .12392362 |
| 40 | .25257247 | .20828904 | .17192870 | .14204568 | .11746314 |
| 41 | .24403137 | .20027793 | .16452507 | .13528160 | .11133947 |
| 42 | .23577910 | .19257493 | .15744026 | .12883962 | .10553504 |
| 43 | .22780590 | .18516820 | .15066054 | .12270440 | .10003322 |
| 44 | .22010231 | .17804635 | .14417276 | .11686133 | .09481822 |
| 45 | .21265924 | .17119841 | .13796437 | .11129651 | .08987509 |
| 46 | .20546787 | .16461386 | .13202332 | .10599668 | .08518965 |
| 47 | .19851968 | .15828256 | .12633810 | .10094921 | .08074849 |
| 48 | .19180645 | .15219476 | .12089771 | .09614211 | .07653885 |
| 49 | .18532024 | .14634112 | .11569158 | .09156391 | .07254867 |
| 50 | .17905337 | .14071262 | .11070965 | .08720373 | .06876652 |

| Years $n$ | Rate $i$ | | | | |
|---|---|---|---|---|---|
| | .06(6 %) | .065(6½ %) | .07(7 %) | .075(7½ %) | .08(8 %) |
| 1 | .94339623 | .93896714 | .93457944 | .93023256 | .92592593 |
| 2 | .88999644 | .88165928 | .87343873 | .86533261 | .85733882 |
| 3 | .83961928 | .82784909 | .81629788 | .80496057 | .79383224 |
| 4 | .79209366 | .77732309 | .76289521 | .74880053 | .73502985 |
| 5 | .74725817 | .72988084 | .71298618 | .69655863 | .68058320 |
| 6 | .70496054 | .68533412 | .66634222 | .64796152 | .63016963 |
| 7 | .66505711 | .64350621 | .62274974 | .60275490 | .58349040 |
| 8 | .62741237 | .60423119 | .58200910 | .56070223 | .54026888 |
| 9 | .59189846 | .56735323 | .54393374 | .52158347 | .50024897 |
| 10 | .55839478 | .53272604 | .50834929 | .48519393 | .46319349 |
| 11 | .52678753 | .50021224 | .47509280 | .45134319 | .42888286 |
| 12 | .49696936 | .46968285 | .44401196 | .41985413 | .39711376 |
| 13 | .46883902 | .44101676 | .41496445 | .39056198 | .36769792 |
| 14 | .44230096 | .41410025 | .38781724 | .36331347 | .34046104 |
| 15 | .41726506 | .38882652 | .36244602 | .33796602 | .31524170 |
| 16 | .39364628 | .36509533 | .33873460 | .31438699 | .29189047 |
| 17 | .37136442 | .34281251 | .31657439 | .29245302 | .27026895 |
| 18 | .35034379 | .32188969 | .29586392 | .27204932 | .25024903 |
| 19 | .33051301 | .30224384 | .27650833 | .25306913 | .23171206 |
| 20 | .31180473 | .28379703 | .25841900 | .23541315 | .21454821 |
| 21 | .29415540 | .26647608 | .24151309 | .21898897 | .19865575 |
| 22 | .27750510 | .25021228 | .22571317 | .20371067 | .18394051 |
| 23 | .26179726 | .23494111 | .21094688 | .18949830 | .17031528 |
| 24 | .24697855 | .22060198 | .19714662 | .17627749 | .15769934 |
| 25 | .23299863 | .20713801 | .18424918 | .16397906 | .14601790 |
| 26 | .21981003 | .19449579 | .17219549 | .15253866 | .13520176 |
| 27 | .20736795 | .18262515 | .16093037 | .14189643 | .12518682 |
| 28 | .19563014 | .17147902 | .15040221 | .13199668 | .11591372 |
| 29 | .18455674 | .16101316 | .14056282 | .12278761 | .10732752 |
| 30 | .17411013 | .15118607 | .13136712 | .11422103 | .09937733 |
| 31 | .16425484 | .14195875 | .12277301 | .10625212 | .09201605 |
| 32 | .15495740 | .13329460 | .11474113 | .09883918 | .08520005 |
| 33 | .14618622 | .12515925 | .10723470 | .09194343 | .07888893 |
| 34 | .13791153 | .11752042 | .10021934 | .08552877 | .07304531 |
| 35 | .13010522 | .11034781 | .09366294 | .07956164 | .06763454 |
| 36 | .12274077 | .10361297 | .08753546 | .07401083 | .06262458 |
| 37 | .11579318 | .09728917 | .08180884 | .06884729 | .05798572 |
| 38 | .10923885 | .09135134 | .07645686 | .06404399 | .05369048 |
| 39 | .10305552 | .08577590 | .07145501 | .05957580 | .04971341 |
| 40 | .09722219 | .08054075 | .06678038 | .05541935 | .04603093 |
| 41 | .09171905 | .07562512 | .06241157 | .05155288 | .04262123 |
| 42 | .08652740 | .07100950 | .05832857 | .04795617 | .03946411 |
| 43 | .08162962 | .06667559 | .05451268 | .04461039 | .03654084 |
| 44 | .07700908 | .06260619 | .05094643 | .04149804 | .03383411 |
| 45 | .07265007 | .05878515 | .04761349 | .03860283 | .03132788 |
| 46 | .06853781 | .05519733 | .04449859 | .03590961 | .02900730 |
| 47 | .06465831 | .05182848 | .04158747 | .03340428 | .02685861 |
| 48 | .06099840 | .04866524 | .03886679 | .03107375 | .02486908 |
| 49 | .05754566 | .04569506 | .03632410 | .02890582 | .02302693 |
| 50 | .05428836 | .04290616 | .03394776 | .02688913 | .02132123 |

## AMOUNT OF ANNUITY $[(1 + i)^n - 1]/i$

The following table gives the amount of an annuity of unit value per period after a term of $n$ periods at rate of interest of $i$ per period; usually indicated as $(s_{\overline{n}|}$ at $i)$.

| Years | | | Rate $i$ | | |
|---|---|---|---|---|---|
| $n$ | .0025($\frac{1}{4}$ %) | .004167($\frac{5}{12}$ %) | .005($\frac{1}{2}$ %) | .005833($\frac{7}{12}$ %) | .0075($\frac{3}{4}$ %) |
| 1 | 1.00000000 | 1.00000000 | 1.00000000 | 1.00000000 | 1.00000000 |
| 2 | 2.00250000 | 2.00416667 | 2.00500000 | 2.00583333 | 2.00750000 |
| 3 | 3.00750625 | 3.01251736 | 3.01502500 | 3.01753403 | 3.02255625 |
| 4 | 4.01502502 | 4.02506952 | 4.03010013 | 4.03513631 | 4.04522542 |
| 5 | 5.02506258 | 5.04184064 | 5.05025063 | 5.05867460 | 5.07556461 |
| 6 | 6.03762523 | 6.06284831 | 6.07550188 | 6.08818354 | 6.11363135 |
| 7 | 7.05271930 | 7.08811018 | 7.10587939 | 7.12369794 | 7.15948358 |
| 8 | 8.07035110 | 8.11764397 | 8.14140879 | 8.16525285 | 8.21317971 |
| 9 | 9.09052697 | 9.15146749 | 9.18211583 | 9.21288349 | 9.27477856 |
| 10 | 10.1132533 | 10.1895986 | 10.2280264 | 10.2666253 | 10.3443394 |
| 11 | 11.1385364 | 11.2320553 | 11.2791665 | 11.3265140 | 11.4219219 |
| 12 | 12.1663828 | 12.2788555 | 12.3355624 | 12.3925853 | 12.5075864 |
| 13 | 13.1967987 | 13.3300174 | 13.3972402 | 13.4648754 | 13.6013933 |
| 14 | 14.2297907 | 14.3855591 | 14.4642264 | 14.5434205 | 14.7034037 |
| 15 | 15.2653652 | 15.4454990 | 15.5365475 | 15.6282571 | 15.8136792 |
| 16 | 16.3035286 | 16.5098552 | 16.6142303 | 16.7194219 | 16.9322818 |
| 17 | 17.3442874 | 17.5786463 | 17.6973014 | 17.8169519 | 18.0592739 |
| 18 | 18.3876481 | 18.6518906 | 18.7857879 | 18.9208841 | 19.1947185 |
| 19 | 19.4336173 | 19.7296068 | 19.8797169 | 20.0312559 | 20.3386789 |
| 20 | 20.4822013 | 20.8118135 | 20.9791154 | 21.1481049 | 21.4912190 |
| 21 | 21.5334068 | 21.8985294 | 22.0840110 | 22.2714689 | 22.6524031 |
| 22 | 22.5872403 | 22.9897733 | 23.1944311 | 23.4013858 | 23.8222961 |
| 23 | 23.6437084 | 24.0855640 | 24.3104032 | 24.5378939 | 25.0009634 |
| 24 | 24.7028177 | 25.1859205 | 25.4319552 | 25.6810316 | 26.1884706 |
| 25 | 25.7645747 | 26.2908619 | 26.5591150 | 26.8308376 | 27.3848841 |
| 26 | 26.8289862 | 27.4004071 | 27.6919106 | 27.9873508 | 28.5902707 |
| 27 | 27.8960587 | 28.5145755 | 28.8303701 | 29.1506104 | 29.8046978 |
| 28 | 28.9657988 | 29.6333862 | 29.9745220 | 30.3206556 | 31.0282330 |
| 29 | 30.0382133 | 30.7568587 | 31.1243946 | 31.4975261 | 32.2609448 |
| 30 | 31.1133088 | 31.8850122 | 32.2800166 | 32.6812616 | 33.5029018 |
| 31 | 32.1910921 | 33.0178665 | 33.4414167 | 33.8719023 | 34.7541736 |
| 32 | 33.2715698 | 34.1554409 | 34.6086237 | 35.0694884 | 36.0148299 |
| 33 | 34.3547488 | 35.2977552 | 35.7816669 | 36.2740604 | 37.2849411 |
| 34 | 35.4406356 | 36.4448292 | 36.9605752 | 37.4856591 | 38.5645782 |
| 35 | 36.5292372 | 37.5966827 | 38.1453781 | 38.7043255 | 39.8538125 |
| 36 | 37.6205603 | 38.7533355 | 39.3361050 | 39.9301007 | 41.1527161 |
| 37 | 38.7146117 | 39.9148078 | 40.5327855 | 41.1630263 | 42.4613615 |
| 38 | 39.8113982 | 41.0811195 | 41.7354494 | 42.4031440 | 43.7798217 |
| 39 | 40.9109267 | 42.2522908 | 42.9441267 | 43.6504956 | 45.1081704 |
| 40 | 42.0132041 | 43.4283420 | 44.1588473 | 44.9051235 | 46.4464816 |
| 41 | 43.1182371 | 44.6092934 | 45.3796415 | 46.1670701 | 47.7948303 |
| 42 | 44.2260327 | 45.7951655 | 46.6065397 | 47.4363780 | 49.1532915 |
| 43 | 45.3365977 | 46.9859787 | 47.8395724 | 48.7130902 | 50.5219412 |
| 44 | 46.4499392 | 48.1817536 | 49.0787703 | 49.9972499 | 51.9008557 |
| 45 | 47.5660641 | 49.3825109 | 50.3241642 | 51.2889005 | 53.2901121 |
| 46 | 48.6849792 | 50.5882713 | 51.5757850 | 52.5880858 | 54.6897880 |
| 47 | 49.8066917 | 51.7990558 | 52.8336639 | 53.8948496 | 56.0999614 |
| 48 | 50.9312084 | 53.0148852 | 54.0978322 | 55.2092362 | 57.5207111 |
| 49 | 52.0585364 | 54.2357806 | 55.3683214 | 56.5312901 | 58.9521164 |
| 50 | 53.1886828 | 55.4617630 | 56.6451630 | 57.8610559 | 60.3942573 |

## AMOUNT OF ANNUITY $[(1 + i)^n - 1]/i$ (Continued)

| Years $n$ | .0025($\frac{1}{4}$%) | .004167($\frac{5}{12}$%) | .005($\frac{1}{2}$%) | .005833($\frac{7}{12}$%) | .0075($\frac{3}{4}$%) |
|---|---|---|---|---|---|
| 50 | 53.1886828 | 55.4617630 | 56.6451630 | 57.8610559 | 60.3942573 |
| 51 | 54.3216545 | 56.6928537 | 57.9283888 | 59.1985788 | 61.8472142 |
| 52 | 55.4574586 | 57.9290739 | 59.2180307 | 60.5439038 | 63.3110684 |
| 53 | 56.5961023 | 59.1704450 | 60.5141209 | 61.8970766 | 64.7859014 |
| 54 | 57.7375925 | 60.4169885 | 61.8166915 | 63.2581429 | 66.2717956 |
| 55 | 58.8819365 | 61.6687260 | 63.1257750 | 64.6271487 | 67.7688341 |
| 56 | 60.0291413 | 62.9256790 | 64.4414038 | 66.0041404 | 69.2271003 |
| 57 | 61.1792142 | 64.1878694 | 65.7636109 | 67.3891646 | 70.7966786 |
| 58 | 62.3321622 | 65.4553188 | 67.0924289 | 68.7822680 | 72.3276537 |
| 59 | 63.4879926 | 66.7280493 | 68.4278911 | 70.1834979 | 73.8701111 |
| 60 | 64.6467126 | 68.0060828 | 69.7700305 | 71.5929016 | 75.4241369 |
| 61 | 65.8083294 | 69.2894415 | 71.1188807 | 73.0105269 | 76.9898180 |
| 62 | 66.9728502 | 70.5781475 | 72.4744751 | 74.4364216 | 78.5672416 |
| 63 | 68.1402824 | 71.8722231 | 73.8368474 | 75.8706341 | 80.1564959 |
| 64 | 69.3106331 | 73.1716907 | 75.2060317 | 77.3132128 | 81.7576696 |
| 65 | 70.4839096 | 74.4765728 | 76.5820618 | 78.7642065 | 83.3708521 |
| 66 | 71.6601194 | 75.7868918 | 77.9649721 | 80.2236644 | 84.9961335 |
| 67 | 72.8392697 | 77.1026706 | 79.3547970 | 81.6916358 | 86.6336045 |
| 68 | 74.0213679 | 78.4239317 | 80.7515710 | 83.1681703 | 88.2833566 |
| 69 | 75.2064213 | 79.7506981 | 82.1553288 | 84.6533180 | 89.9454817 |
| 70 | 76.3944374 | 81.0829926 | 83.5661055 | 86.1471290 | 91.6200729 |
| 71 | 77.5854235 | 82.4208384 | 84.9839360 | 87.6496539 | 93.3072234 |
| 72 | 78.7793870 | 83.7642586 | 86.4088557 | 89.1609436 | 95.0070276 |
| 73 | 79.9763355 | 85.1132763 | 87.8409000 | 90.6810491 | 96.7195803 |
| 74 | 81.1762763 | 86.4679150 | 89.2801045 | 92.2100219 | 98.4449771 |
| 75 | 82.3792170 | 87.8281980 | 90.7265050 | 93.7479137 | 100.183314 |
| 76 | 83.5851651 | 89.1941488 | 92.1801375 | 95.2947765 | 101.934689 |
| 77 | 84.7941280 | 90.5657911 | 93.6410382 | 96.8506627 | 103.699199 |
| 78 | 86.0061133 | 91.9431485 | 95.1092434 | 98.4156249 | 105.476943 |
| 79 | 87.2211286 | 93.3262450 | 96.5847896 | 99.9897160 | 107.268021 |
| 80 | 88.4391814 | 94.7151044 | 98.0677136 | 101.572989 | 109.072531 |
| 81 | 89.6602793 | 96.1097506 | 99.5580521 | 103.165498 | 110.890575 |
| 82 | 90.8844300 | 97.5102079 | 101.055842 | 104.767297 | 112.722254 |
| 83 | 92.1116411 | 98.9165004 | 102.561122 | 106.378440 | 114.567671 |
| 84 | 93.3419202 | 100.328653 | 104.073927 | 107.998981 | 116.426928 |
| 85 | 94.5752750 | 101.746689 | 105.594297 | 109.628975 | 118.300130 |
| 86 | 95.8117132 | 103.170633 | 107.122268 | 111.268477 | 120.187381 |
| 87 | 97.0512425 | 104.600511 | 108.657880 | 112.917543 | 122.088787 |
| 88 | 98.2938706 | 106.036346 | 110.201169 | 114.576229 | 124.004453 |
| 89 | 99.5396053 | 107.478164 | 111.752175 | 116.244590 | 125.934486 |
| 90 | 100.788454 | 108.925990 | 113.310936 | 117.922684 | 127.878995 |
| 91 | 102.040425 | 110.379848 | 114.877490 | 119.610566 | 129.838087 |
| 92 | 103.295526 | 111.839764 | 116.451878 | 121.308294 | 131.811873 |
| 93 | 104.553765 | 113.305763 | 118.034137 | 123.015926 | 133.800462 |
| 94 | 105.815150 | 114.777871 | 119.624308 | 124.733519 | 135.803965 |
| 95 | 107.079688 | 116.256112 | 121.222430 | 126.461131 | 137.822495 |
| 96 | 108.347387 | 117.740512 | 122.828542 | 128.198821 | 139.856164 |
| 97 | 109.618255 | 119.231098 | 124.442684 | 129.946647 | 141.905085 |
| 98 | 110.892301 | 120.727894 | 126.064898 | 131.704670 | 143.969373 |
| 99 | 112.169532 | 122.230927 | 127.695222 | 133.472947 | 146.049143 |
| 100 | 113.449955 | 123.740222 | 129.333698 | 135.251539 | 148.144512 |

## AMOUNT OF ANNUITY $[(1 + i)^n - 1]/i$ (Continued)

| Years $n$ | Rate $i$ | | | | |
|---|---|---|---|---|---|
| | .01(1 %) | .01125(1⅛ %) | .0125(1¼ %) | .015(1½ %) | .0175(1¾ %) |
| 1 | 1.00000000 | 1.00000000 | 1.00000000 | 1.00000000 | 1.00000000 |
| 2 | 2.01000000 | 2.01125000 | 2.01250000 | 2.01500000 | 2.01750000 |
| 3 | 3.03010000 | 3.03387656 | 3.03765625 | 3.04522500 | 3.05280625 |
| 4 | 4.06040100 | 4.06800767 | 4.07562695 | 4.09090338 | 4.10623036 |
| 5 | 5.10100501 | 5.11377276 | 5.12657229 | 5.15226693 | 5.17808939 |
| 6 | 6.15201506 | 6.17130270 | 6.19065444 | 6.22955093 | 6.26870696 |
| 7 | 7.21353521 | 7.24072986 | 7.26803762 | 7.32299419 | 7.37840831 |
| 8 | 8.28567056 | 8.32218807 | 8.35888809 | 8.43283911 | 8.50753045 |
| 9 | 9.36852727 | 9.41581269 | 9.46337420 | 9.55933169 | 9.65641224 |
| 10 | 10.4622125 | 10.5217406 | 10.5816664 | 10.7027217 | 10.8253995 |
| 11 | 11.5668347 | 11.6401102 | 11.7139372 | 11.8632625 | 12.0148439 |
| 12 | 12.6825030 | 12.7710614 | 12.8603614 | 13.0412114 | 13.2251037 |
| 13 | 13.8093280 | 13.9147358 | 14.0211159 | 14.2368296 | 14.4565430 |
| 14 | 14.9474213 | 15.0712766 | 15.1963799 | 15.4503820 | 15.7095325 |
| 15 | 16.0968955 | 16.2408285 | 16.3863346 | 16.6821378 | 16.9844493 |
| 16 | 17.2578645 | 17.4235378 | 17.5911638 | 17.9323698 | 18.2816772 |
| 17 | 18.4304431 | 18.6195526 | 18.8110534 | 19.2013554 | 19.6016066 |
| 18 | 19.6147476 | 19.8290226 | 20.0461915 | 20.4893757 | 20.9446347 |
| 19 | 20.8108950 | 21.0520991 | 21.2967689 | 21.7967164 | 22.3111658 |
| 20 | 22.0190040 | 22.2889352 | 22.5629785 | 23.1236671 | 23.7016112 |
| 21 | 23.2391940 | 23.5396857 | 23.8450158 | 24.4705221 | 25.1163894 |
| 22 | 24.4715860 | 24.8045072 | 25.1430785 | 25.8375799 | 26.5559262 |
| 23 | 25.7163018 | 26.0835579 | 26.4573669 | 27.2251436 | 28.0206549 |
| 24 | 26.9734649 | 27.3769979 | 27.7880840 | 28.6335208 | 29.5110164 |
| 25 | 28.2431995 | 28.6849891 | 29.1354351 | 30.0630236 | 31.0274592 |
| 26 | 29.5256315 | 30.0076953 | 30.4996280 | 31.5139690 | 32.5704397 |
| 27 | 30.8208878 | 31.3452818 | 31.8808734 | 32.9866785 | 34.1404224 |
| 28 | 32.1290967 | 32.6979162 | 33.2793843 | 34.4814787 | 35.7378798 |
| 29 | 33.4503877 | 34.0657678 | 34.6953766 | 35.9987009 | 37.3632927 |
| 30 | 34.7848915 | 35.4490077 | 36.1290688 | 37.5386814 | 39.0171503 |
| 31 | 36.1327404 | 36.8478090 | 37.5806822 | 39.1017616 | 40.6999504 |
| 32 | 37.4940679 | 38.2623469 | 39.0504407 | 40.6882880 | 42.4121996 |
| 33 | 38.8690085 | 39.6927983 | 40.5385712 | 42.2986123 | 44.1544130 |
| 34 | 40.2576986 | 41.1393423 | 42.0453033 | 43.9330915 | 45.9271153 |
| 35 | 41.6602756 | 42.6021599 | 43.5708696 | 45.5920879 | 47.7308398 |
| 36 | 43.0768784 | 44.0814342 | 45.1155055 | 47.2759692 | 49.5661295 |
| 37 | 44.5076471 | 45.5773503 | 46.6794493 | 48.9851087 | 51.4335368 |
| 38 | 45.9527236 | 47.0900955 | 48.2629424 | 50.7198854 | 53.3336236 |
| 39 | 47.4122508 | 48.6198591 | 49.8662292 | 52.4806837 | 55.2669621 |
| 40 | 48.8863734 | 50.1668325 | 51.4895571 | 54.2678939 | 57.2341339 |
| 41 | 50.3752371 | 51.7312093 | 53.1331765 | 56.0819123 | 59.2357312 |
| 42 | 51.8789895 | 53.3131854 | 54.7973412 | 57.9231410 | 61.2723565 |
| 43 | 53.3977794 | 54.9129588 | 56.4823080 | 59.7919881 | 63.3446228 |
| 44 | 54.9317572 | 56.5307296 | 58.1883369 | 61.6888679 | 65.4531537 |
| 45 | 56.4810747 | 58.1667003 | 59.9156911 | 63.6142010 | 67.5985839 |
| 46 | 58.0458855 | 59.8210757 | 61.6646372 | 65.5684140 | 69.7815591 |
| 47 | 59.6263443 | 61.4940628 | 63.4354452 | 67.5519402 | 72.0027364 |
| 48 | 61.2226078 | 63.1858710 | 65.2283882 | 69.5652193 | 74.2627843 |
| 49 | 62.8348338 | 64.8967120 | 67.0437431 | 71.6086976 | 76.5623830 |
| 50 | 64.4631822 | 66.6268000 | 68.8817899 | 73.6828280 | 78.9022247 |

## AMOUNT OF ANNUITY $[(1 + i)^n - 1]/i$ (Continued)

| Years $n$ | .01(1 %) | .01125(1⅛ %) | .0125(1¼ %) | .015(1½ %) | .0175(1¾ %) |
|---|---|---|---|---|---|
| **50** | 64.4631822 | 66.6268000 | 68.8817899 | 73.6828280 | 78.9022247 |
| 51 | 66.1078140 | 68.3763515 | 70.7428123 | 75.7880705 | 81.2830136 |
| 52 | 67.7688921 | 70.1455855 | 72.6270974 | 77.9248915 | 83.7054663 |
| 53 | 69.4465811 | 71.9347233 | 74.5349361 | 80.0937649 | 86.1703120 |
| 54 | 71.1410469 | 73.7439890 | 76.4666228 | 82.2951714 | 88.6782925 |
| **55** | 72.8524573 | 75.5736088 | 78.4224556 | 84.5295989 | 91.2301626 |
| 56 | 74.5809819 | 77.4238119 | 80.4027363 | 86.7975429 | 93.8266904 |
| 57 | 76.3267917 | 79.2948298 | 82.4077705 | 89.0995061 | 96.4686575 |
| 58 | 78.0900597 | 81.1868966 | 84.4378676 | 91.4359987 | 99.1568590 |
| 59 | 79.8709603 | 83.1002492 | 86.4933410 | 93.8075386 | 101.892104 |
| **60** | 81.6696699 | 85.0351270 | 88.5745078 | 96.2146517 | 104.675216 |
| 61 | 83.4863666 | 86.9917722 | 90.6816891 | 98.6578715 | 107.507032 |
| 62 | 85.3212302 | 88.9704297 | 92.8152102 | 101.137740 | 110.388405 |
| 63 | 87.1744425 | 90.9713470 | 94.9754003 | 103.654806 | 113.320202 |
| 64 | 89.0461869 | 92.9947746 | 97.1625928 | 106.209628 | 116.303306 |
| **65** | 90.9366488 | 95.0409659 | 99.3771253 | 108.802772 | 119.338614 |
| 66 | 92.8460153 | 97.1101767 | 101.619339 | 111.434814 | 122.427039 |
| 67 | 94.7744755 | 99.2026662 | 103.889581 | 114.106336 | 125.569513 |
| 68 | 96.7222202 | 101.318696 | 106.188201 | 116.817931 | 128.766979 |
| 69 | 98.6894424 | 103.458532 | 108.515553 | 119.570200 | 132.020401 |
| **70** | 100.676337 | 105.622440 | 110.871998 | 122.363753 | 135.330758 |
| 71 | 102.683100 | 107.810692 | 113.257898 | 125.199209 | 138.699047 |
| 72 | 104.709931 | 110.023563 | 115.673621 | 128.077197 | 142.126280 |
| 73 | 106.757031 | 112.261328 | 118.119542 | 130.998355 | 145.613490 |
| 74 | 108.824601 | 114.524268 | 120.596036 | 133.963331 | 149.161726 |
| **75** | 110.912847 | 116.812666 | 123.103486 | 136.972781 | 152.772056 |
| 76 | 113.021975 | 119.126808 | 125.642280 | 140.027372 | 156.445567 |
| 77 | 115.152195 | 121.466985 | 128.212809 | 143.127783 | 160.183364 |
| 78 | 117.303717 | 123.833488 | 130.815469 | 146.274700 | 163.986573 |
| 79 | 119.476754 | 126.226615 | 133.450662 | 149.468820 | 167.856338 |
| **80** | 121.671522 | 128.646665 | 136.118795 | 152.710852 | 171.793824 |
| 81 | 123.888237 | 131.093940 | 138.820280 | 156.001515 | 175.800216 |
| 82 | 126.127119 | 133.568746 | 141.555534 | 159.341538 | 179.876720 |
| 83 | 128.388390 | 136.071395 | 144.324978 | 162.731661 | 184.024563 |
| 84 | 130.672274 | 138.602198 | 147.129040 | 166.172636 | 188.244992 |
| **85** | 132.978997 | 141.161473 | 149.968153 | 169.665226 | 192.539280 |
| 86 | 135.308787 | 143.749539 | 152.842755 | 173.210204 | 196.908717 |
| 87 | 137.661875 | 146.366722 | 155.753289 | 176.808357 | 201.354620 |
| 88 | 140.038494 | 149.013347 | 158.700206 | 180.460482 | 205.878326 |
| 89 | 142.438879 | 151.689747 | 161.683958 | 184.167390 | 210.481196 |
| **90** | 144.863267 | 154.396257 | 164.705008 | 187.929900 | 215.164617 |
| 91 | 147.311900 | 157.133215 | 167.763820 | 191.748849 | 219.929998 |
| 92 | 149.785019 | 159.900964 | 170.860868 | 195.625082 | 224.778773 |
| 93 | 152.282869 | 162.699849 | 173.996629 | 199.559458 | 229.712401 |
| 94 | 154.805698 | 165.530223 | 177.171587 | 203.552850 | 234.732369 |
| **95** | 157.353755 | 168.392438 | 180.386232 | 207.606142 | 239.840185 |
| 96 | 159.927293 | 171.286853 | 183.641059 | 211.720235 | 245.037388 |
| 97 | 162.526565 | 174.213830 | 186.936573 | 215.896038 | 250.325542 |
| 98 | 165.151831 | 177.173735 | 190.273280 | 220.134479 | 255.706239 |
| 99 | 167.803349 | 180.166940 | 193.651696 | 224.436496 | 261.181099 |
| **100** | 170.481383 | 183.193818 | 197.072342 | 228.803043 | 266.751768 |

## AMOUNT OF ANNUITY $[(1 + i)^n - 1]/i$ (Continued)

| $n$ | .02(2 %) | .0225(2¼ %) | .025(2½ %) | .0275(2¾ %) | .03(3 %) |
|---|---|---|---|---|---|
| | | | Rate $i$ | | |
| 1 | 1.00000000 | 1.00000000 | 1.00000000 | 1.00000000 | 1.00000000 |
| 2 | 2.02000000 | 2.02250000 | 2.02500000 | 2.02750000 | 2.03000000 |
| 3 | 3.06040000 | 3.06800625 | 3.07562500 | 3.08325625 | 3.09090000 |
| 4 | 4.12160800 | 4.13703639 | 4.15251563 | 4.16804580 | 4.18362700 |
| 5 | 5.20404016 | 5.23011971 | 5.25632852 | 5.28266706 | 5.30913581 |
| 6 | 6.30812096 | 6.34779740 | 6.38773673 | 6.42794040 | 6.46840988 |
| 7 | 7.43428338 | 7.49062284 | 7.54743015 | 7.60470876 | 7.66246218 |
| 8 | 8.58296905 | 8.65916186 | 8.73611590 | 8.81383825 | 8.89233605 |
| 9 | 9.75462843 | 9.85399300 | 9.95451880 | 10.0562188 | 10.1591061 |
| 10 | 10.9497210 | 11.0757078 | 11.2033818 | 11.3327648 | 11.4638793 |
| 11 | 12.1687154 | 12.3249113 | 12.4834663 | 12.6444159 | 12.8077957 |
| 12 | 13.4120897 | 13.6022218 | 13.7955530 | 13.9921373 | 14.1920296 |
| 13 | 14.6803315 | 14.9082718 | 15.1404418 | 15.3769211 | 15.6177904 |
| 14 | 15.9739382 | 16.2437079 | 16.5189528 | 16.7997864 | 17.0863242 |
| 15 | 17.2934169 | 17.6091913 | 17.9319267 | 18.2617805 | 18.5989139 |
| 16 | 18.6392853 | 19.0053981 | 19.3802248 | 19.7639795 | 20.1568813 |
| 17 | 20.0120710 | 20.4330196 | 20.8647304 | 21.3074889 | 21.7615877 |
| 18 | 21.4123124 | 21.8927625 | 22.2363487 | 22.8934449 | 23.4144354 |
| 19 | 22.8405586 | 23.3853497 | 23.9460074 | 24.5230146 | 25.1168684 |
| 20 | 24.2973698 | 24.9115200 | 25.5446576 | 26.1973975 | 26.8703745 |
| 21 | 25.7833132 | 26.4720292 | 27.1832741 | 27.9178259 | 28.6764857 |
| 22 | 27.2989835 | 28.0676499 | 28.8628559 | 29.6855661 | 30.5367803 |
| 23 | 28.8449632 | 29.6991720 | 30.5844273 | 31.5019192 | 32.4528837 |
| 24 | 30.4218625 | 31.3674034 | 32.3490380 | 33.3682220 | 34.4264702 |
| 25 | 32.0302997 | 33.0731700 | 34.1577639 | 35.2858481 | 36.4592643 |
| 26 | 33.6709057 | 34.8173163 | 36.0117080 | 37.2562089 | 38.5530423 |
| 27 | 35.3443238 | 36.6007059 | 37.9120007 | 39.2807547 | 40.7096335 |
| 28 | 37.0512103 | 38.4242218 | 39.8598008 | 41.3609754 | 42.9309225 |
| 29 | 38.7922345 | 40.2887668 | 41.8562958 | 43.4984022 | 45.2188502 |
| 30 | 40.5680792 | 42.1952640 | 43.9027032 | 45.6946083 | 47.5754157 |
| 31 | 42.3794408 | 44.1446575 | 46.0002707 | 47.9512100 | 50.0026782 |
| 32 | 44.2270296 | 46.1379123 | 48.1502775 | 50.2698683 | 52.5027585 |
| 33 | 46.1115702 | 48.1760153 | 50.3540344 | 52.6522897 | 55.0778413 |
| 34 | 48.0338016 | 50.2599756 | 52.6128853 | 55.1002277 | 57.7301765 |
| 35 | 49.9944776 | 52.3908251 | 54.9282074 | 57.6154839 | 60.4620818 |
| 36 | 51.9943672 | 54.5696186 | 57.3014126 | 60.1999097 | 63.2759443 |
| 37 | 54.0342545 | 56.7974351 | 59.7339479 | 62.8554072 | 66.1742226 |
| 38 | 56.1149396 | 59.0753774 | 62.2272966 | 65.5839309 | 69.1594493 |
| 39 | 58.2372384 | 61.4045733 | 64.7829791 | 68.3874890 | 72.2342328 |
| 40 | 60.4019832 | 63.7861762 | 67.4025535 | 71.2681450 | 75.4012597 |
| 41 | 62.6100228 | 66.2213652 | 70.0876174 | 74.2280190 | 78.6632975 |
| 42 | 64.8622233 | 68.7113459 | 72.8398078 | 77.2692895 | 82.0231965 |
| 43 | 67.1594678 | 71.2573512 | 75.6608030 | 80.3941950 | 85.4838923 |
| 44 | 69.5026571 | 73.8606416 | 78.5523231 | 83.6050353 | 89.0484091 |
| 45 | 71.8927103 | 76.5225060 | 81.5161312 | 86.9041738 | 92.7198614 |
| 46 | 74.3305645 | 79.2442624 | 84.5540344 | 90.2940386 | 96.5014572 |
| 47 | 76.8171758 | 82.0272583 | 87.6678853 | 93.7771246 | 100.396501 |
| 48 | 79.3535193 | 84.8728716 | 90.8595824 | 97.3559956 | 104.408396 |
| 49 | 81.9405897 | 87.7825113 | 94.1310720 | 101.033285 | 108.540648 |
| 50 | 84.5794015 | 90.7576178 | 97.4843488 | 104.811701 | 112.796867 |

## AMOUNT OF ANNUITY $[(1 + i)^n - 1]/i$ (Continued)

| Years $n$ | .02(2 %) | .0225(2¼ %) | .025(2½ %) | .0275(2¾ %) | 03(3 %) |
|---|---|---|---|---|---|
| **50** | 84.5794015 | 90.7576178 | 97.4843488 | 104.811701 | 112.796867 |
| 51 | 87.2709895 | 93.7996642 | 100.921458 | 108.694023 | 117.180773 |
| 52 | 90.0164093 | 96.9101566 | 104.444494 | 112.683108 | 121.696197 |
| 53 | 92.8167375 | 100.090635 | 108.055606 | 116.781894 | 126.347082 |
| 54 | 95.6730722 | 103.342674 | 111.756996 | 120.993396 | 131.137495 |
| **55** | 98.5865337 | 106.667885 | 115.550921 | 125.320714 | 136.071620 |
| 56 | 101.558264 | 110.067912 | 119.439694 | 129.767034 | 141.153768 |
| 57 | 104.589430 | 113.544440 | 123.425687 | 134.335627 | 146.388381 |
| 58 | 107.681218 | 117.099190 | 127.511329 | 139.029857 | 151.780033 |
| 59 | 110.834843 | 120.733922 | 131.699112 | 143.853178 | 157.333434 |
| **60** | 114.051539 | 124.450435 | 135.991590 | 148.809140 | 163.053437 |
| 61 | 117.332570 | 128.250570 | 140.391380 | 153.901392 | 168.945040 |
| 62 | 120.679222 | 132.136208 | 144.901164 | 159.133680 | 175.013391 |
| 63 | 124.092806 | 136.109272 | 149.523693 | 164.509856 | 181.263793 |
| 64 | 127.574062 | 140.171731 | 154.261786 | 170.033877 | 187.701707 |
| **65** | 131.126155 | 144.325595 | 159.118330 | 175.709809 | 194.332758 |
| 66 | 134.748679 | 148.572921 | 164.096289 | 181.541829 | 201.162741 |
| 67 | 138.443652 | 152.915811 | 169.198696 | 187.534229 | 208.197623 |
| 68 | 142.212525 | 157.356417 | 174.428663 | 193.691420 | 215.443551 |
| 69 | 146.056776 | 161.896937 | 179.789380 | 200.017934 | 222.906858 |
| **70** | 149.977911 | 166.539618 | 185.284114 | 206.518427 | 230.594064 |
| 71 | 153.977469 | 171.286759 | 190.916217 | 213.197684 | 238.511886 |
| 72 | 158.057019 | 176.140711 | 196.689122 | 220.060621 | 246.667243 |
| 73 | 162.218159 | 181.103877 | 202.606351 | 227.112288 | 255.067259 |
| 74 | 166.462522 | 186.178714 | 208.671509 | 234.357876 | 263.719277 |
| **75** | 170.791773 | 191.367735 | 214.888297 | 241.802717 | 272.630856 |
| 76 | 175.207608 | 196.673509 | 221.260504 | 249.452292 | 281.809781 |
| 77 | 179.711760 | 202.098663 | 227.792017 | 257.312230 | 291.264075 |
| 78 | 184.305996 | 207.645883 | 234.486818 | 265.388316 | 301.001997 |
| 79 | 188.992115 | 213.317916 | 241.348988 | 273.686495 | 311.032057 |
| **80** | 193.771958 | 219.117569 | 248.382713 | 282.212873 | 321.363019 |
| 81 | 198.647397 | 225.047714 | 255.592280 | 290.973727 | 332.003909 |
| 82 | 203.620345 | 231.111288 | 262.982087 | 299.975505 | 342.964026 |
| 83 | 208.692752 | 237.311292 | 270.556640 | 309.224831 | 354.252947 |
| 84 | 213.866607 | 243.650796 | 278.320556 | 318.728514 | 365.880536 |
| **85** | 219.143939 | 250.132939 | 286.278570 | 328.493548 | 377.856952 |
| 86 | 224.526818 | 256.760930 | 294.435534 | 338.527121 | 390.192660 |
| 87 | 230.017354 | 263.538051 | 302.796422 | 348.836617 | 402.898440 |
| 88 | 235.617701 | 270.467657 | 311.366333 | 359.429624 | 415.985393 |
| 89 | 241.330055 | 277.553179 | 320.150491 | 370.313938 | 429.464955 |
| **90** | 247.156656 | 284.798126 | 329.154253 | 381.497572 | 443.348904 |
| 91 | 253.099789 | 292.206083 | 338.383110 | 392.988755 | 457.649371 |
| 92 | 259.161785 | 299.780720 | 347.842687 | 404.795946 | 472.378852 |
| 93 | 265.345021 | 307.525786 | 357.538755 | 416.927834 | 487.550217 |
| 94 | 271.651921 | 315.445117 | 367.477223 | 429.393350 | 503.176724 |
| **95** | 278.084960 | 323.542632 | 377.664154 | 442.201667 | 519.272026 |
| 96 | 284.646659 | 331.822341 | 388.105758 | 455.362213 | 535.850186 |
| 97 | 291.339592 | 340.288344 | 398.808402 | 468.884673 | 552.925692 |
| 98 | 298.166384 | 348.944831 | 409.778612 | 482.779002 | 570.513463 |
| 99 | 305.129712 | 357.796090 | 421.023077 | 497.055424 | 588.628867 |
| **100** | 312.232306 | 366.846502 | 432.548654 | 511.724449 | 607.287733 |

## PRESENT VALUE OF ANNUITY $[1 - (1 + i)^{-n}]/i$

The following table gives the present value of an annuity of unit value per period for a term of $n$ periods at rate of interest $i$ per period; usually indicated as $a_{\overline{n}|}$ at $i$.

| Years | Rate $i$ | | | | |
|---|---|---|---|---|---|
| $n$ | .0025($\frac{1}{4}$%) | .004167($\frac{5}{12}$%) | .005($\frac{1}{2}$%) | .005833($\frac{7}{12}$%) | .0075($\frac{3}{4}$%) |
| 1 | 0.99750623 | 0.99585062 | 0.99502488 | 0.99420050 | 0.99255583 |
| 2 | 1.99252492 | 1.98756908 | 1.98509938 | 1.98263513 | 1.97772291 |
| 3 | 2.98506227 | 2.97517253 | 2.97024814 | 2.96533732 | 2.95555624 |
| 4 | 3.97512446 | 3.95867804 | 3.95049566 | 3.94234034 | 3.92611041 |
| 5 | 4.96271766 | 4.93810261 | 4.92586633 | 4.91367722 | 4.88943961 |
| 6 | 5.94784804 | 5.91346318 | 5.89638441 | 5.87938083 | 5.84559763 |
| 7 | 6.93052174 | 6.88477661 | 6.86207404 | 6.83948384 | 6.79463785 |
| 8 | 7.91074487 | 7.85205970 | 7.82295924 | 7.79401874 | 7.73661325 |
| 9 | 8.88852357 | 8.81532916 | 8.77906392 | 8.74301780 | 8.67157642 |
| 10 | 9.86386391 | 9.77460165 | 9.73041186 | 9.68651314 | 9.59957958 |
| 11 | 10.8367720 | 10.7298938 | 10.6770267 | 10.6245367 | 10.5206745 |
| 12 | 11.8072538 | 11.6812220 | 11.6189321 | 11.5571201 | 11.4349127 |
| 13 | 12.7753156 | 12.6286028 | 12.5561513 | 12.4842951 | 12.3423451 |
| 14 | 13.7409631 | 13.5720526 | 13.4887078 | 13.4060929 | 13.2430224 |
| 15 | 14.7042026 | 14.5115877 | 14.4166246 | 14.3225447 | 14.1369950 |
| 16 | 15.6650400 | 15.4472242 | 15.3399250 | 15.2336816 | 15.0243126 |
| 17 | 16.6234813 | 16.3789785 | 16.2586319 | 16.1395343 | 15.9050249 |
| 18 | 17.5795325 | 17.3068665 | 17.1727680 | 17.0401335 | 16.7791811 |
| 19 | 18.5331995 | 18.2309044 | 18.0823562 | 17.9355097 | 17.6468298 |
| 20 | 19.4844883 | 19.1511082 | 18.9874191 | 18.8256931 | 18.5080197 |
| 21 | 20.4334048 | 20.0674936 | 19.8879793 | 19.7107140 | 19.3627987 |
| 22 | 21.3799549 | 20.9800766 | 20.7840590 | 20.5906021 | 20.2112146 |
| 23 | 22.3241445 | 21.8888730 | 21.6756806 | 21.4653874 | 21.0533147 |
| 24 | 23.2659796 | 22.7938984 | 22.5628662 | 22.3350993 | 21.8891461 |
| 25 | 24.2054659 | 23.6951685 | 23.4456380 | 23.1997673 | 22.7187555 |
| 26 | 25.1426094 | 24.5926989 | 24.3240179 | 24.0594207 | 23.5421891 |
| 27 | 26.0774158 | 25.4865052 | 25.1980278 | 24.9140885 | 24.3594929 |
| 28 | 27.0098911 | 26.3766027 | 26.0676894 | 25.7637997 | 25.1707125 |
| 29 | 27.9400410 | 27.2630068 | 26.9330242 | 26.6085830 | 25.9758933 |
| 30 | 28.8678713 | 28.1457329 | 27.7940540 | 27.4484669 | 26.7750802 |
| 31 | 29.7933879 | 29.0247963 | 28.6508000 | 28.2834799 | 27.5683178 |
| 32 | 30.7165964 | 29.9002120 | 29.5032835 | 29.1136503 | 28.3556504 |
| 33 | 31.6375026 | 30.7719954 | 30.3515259 | 29.9390061 | 29.1371220 |
| 34 | 32.5561123 | 31.6401614 | 31.1955482 | 30.7595752 | 29.9127762 |
| 35 | 33.4724313 | 32.5047250 | 32.0353713 | 31.5753855 | 30.6826563 |
| 36 | 34.3864651 | 33.3657013 | 32.8710162 | 32.3864645 | 31.4468053 |
| 37 | 35.2982196 | 34.2231050 | 33.7025037 | 33.1928396 | 32.2052658 |
| 38 | 36.2077003 | 35.0769511 | 34.5298544 | 33.9945381 | 32.9580802 |
| 39 | 37.1149130 | 35.9272542 | 35.3530890 | 34.7915872 | 33.7052905 |
| 40 | 38.0198634 | 36.7740290 | 36.1722279 | 35.5840137 | 34.4469384 |
| 41 | 38.9225570 | 37.6172903 | 36.9872914 | 36.3718446 | 35.1830654 |
| 42 | 39.8229995 | 38.4570526 | 37.7982999 | 37.1551065 | 35.9137126 |
| 43 | 40.7211965 | 39.2933304 | 38.6052735 | 37.9338259 | 36.6389207 |
| 44 | 41.6171536 | 40.1261382 | 39.4082324 | 38.7080290 | 37.3587302 |
| 45 | 42.5108764 | 40.9554903 | 40.2071964 | 39.4777422 | 38.0731814 |
| 46 | 43.4023705 | 41.7814011 | 41.0021855 | 40.2429914 | 38.7823140 |
| 47 | 44.2916414 | 42.6038849 | 41.7932194 | 41.0038026 | 39.4861677 |
| 48 | 45.1786946 | 43.4229559 | 42.5803178 | 41.7602014 | 40.1847819 |
| 49 | 46.0635358 | 44.2386283 | 43.3635003 | 42.5122135 | 40.8781954 |
| 50 | 46.9461704 | 45.0509162 | 44.1427864 | 43.2598643 | 41.5664471 |

## AMOUNT OF ANNUITY $[(1 + i)^n - 1]/i$ (Continued)

| Years $n$ | Rate $i$ | | | | |
|---|---|---|---|---|---|
| | .06(6 %) | .065(6½ %) | .07(7 %) | .075(7½ %) | .08(8 %) |
| 1 | 1.00000000 | 1.00000000 | 1.00000000 | 1.00000000 | 1.00000000 |
| 2 | 2.06000000 | 2.06500000 | 2.07000000 | 2.07500000 | 2.08000000 |
| 3 | 3.18360000 | 3.19922500 | 3.21490000 | 3.23062500 | 3.24640000 |
| 4 | 4.37461600 | 4.40717463 | 4.43994300 | 4.47292188 | 4.50611200 |
| 5 | 5.63709296 | 5.69364098 | 5.75073901 | 5.80839102 | 5.86660096 |
| 6 | 6.97531854 | 7.06372764 | 7.15329074 | 7.24402034 | 7.33592904 |
| 7 | 8.39383765 | 8.52286994 | 8.65402109 | 8.78732187 | 8.92280336 |
| 8 | 9.89746791 | 10.0768565 | 10.2598026 | 10.4463710 | 10.6366276 |
| 9 | 11.4913160 | 11.7318522 | 11.9779887 | 12.2298488 | 12.4875578 |
| 10 | 13.1807949 | 13.4944225 | 13.8164480 | 14.1470875 | 14.4865625 |
| 11 | 14.9716426 | 15.3715600 | 15.7835993 | 16.2081191 | 16.6454875 |
| 12 | 16.8699412 | 17.3707114 | 17.8884513 | 18.4237280 | 18.9771265 |
| 13 | 18.8821377 | 19.4998076 | 20.1406429 | 20.8055076 | 21.4952966 |
| 14 | 21.0150659 | 21.7672951 | 22.5504879 | 23.3659207 | 24.2149203 |
| 15 | 23.2759699 | 24.1821693 | 25.1290220 | 26.1183647 | 27.1521139 |
| 16 | 25.6725281 | 26.7540103 | 27.8880536 | 29.0772421 | 30.3242830 |
| 17 | 28.2128798 | 29.4930210 | 30.8402173 | 32.2580352 | 33.7502257 |
| 18 | 30.9056525 | 32.4100674 | 33.9990325 | 35.6773879 | 37.4502437 |
| 19 | 33.7599917 | 35.5167218 | 37.3789648 | 39.3531919 | 41.4462632 |
| 20 | 36.7855912 | 38.8253087 | 40.9954923 | 43.3046813 | 45.7619643 |
| 21 | 39.9927267 | 42.3489537 | 44.8651763 | 47.5525324 | 50.4229214 |
| 22 | 43.3922903 | 46.1016357 | 49.0057392 | 52.1189724 | 55.4567552 |
| 23 | 46.9958277 | 50.0982420 | 53.4361409 | 57.0278953 | 60.8932956 |
| 24 | 50.8155774 | 54.3546278 | 58.1766708 | 62.3049874 | 66.7647592 |
| 25 | 54.8645120 | 58.8876786 | 63.2490377 | 67.9778615 | 73.1059400 |
| 26 | 59.1563827 | 63.7153777 | 68.6764704 | 74.0762011 | 79.9544151 |
| 27 | 63.7057657 | 68.8568772 | 74.4838233 | 80.6319162 | 87.3507684 |
| 28 | 68.5281116 | 74.3325743 | 80.6976909 | 87.6793099 | 95.3388298 |
| 29 | 73.6397983 | 80.1641916 | 87.3465293 | 95.2552582 | 103.965936 |
| 30 | 79.0581862 | 86.3748640 | 94.4607863 | 103.399403 | 113.283211 |
| 31 | 84.8016774 | 92.9892302 | 102.073041 | 112.154358 | 123.345868 |
| 32 | 90.8897780 | 100.033530 | 110.218154 | 121.565935 | 134.213537 |
| 33 | 97.3431647 | 107.535710 | 118.933425 | 131.683380 | 145.950620 |
| 34 | 104.183755 | 115.525531 | 128.258765 | 142.559633 | 158.626670 |
| 35 | 111.434780 | 124.034690 | 138.236878 | 154.251606 | 172.316804 |
| 36 | 119.120867 | 133.096945 | 148.913460 | 166.820476 | 187.102148 |
| 37 | 127.268119 | 142.748247 | 160.337402 | 180.332012 | 203.070320 |
| 38 | 135.904206 | 153.026883 | 172.561020 | 194.856913 | 220.315945 |
| 39 | 145.058458 | 163.973630 | 185.640292 | 210.471181 | 238.941221 |
| 40 | 154.761966 | 175.631916 | 199.635112 | 227.256520 | 259.056519 |
| 41 | 165.047684 | 188.047990 | 214.609570 | 245.300759 | 280.781040 |
| 42 | 175.950545 | 201.271110 | 230.632240 | 264.698315 | 304.243523 |
| 43 | 187.507577 | 215.353732 | 247.776496 | 285.550689 | 329.583005 |
| 44 | 199.758032 | 230.351725 | 266.120851 | 307.966991 | 356.949646 |
| 45 | 212.743514 | 246.324587 | 285.749311 | 332.064515 | 386.505617 |
| 46 | 226.508125 | 263.335685 | 306.751763 | 357.969354 | 418.426067 |
| 47 | 241.098612 | 281.452504 | 329.224386 | 385.817055 | 452.900152 |
| 48 | 256.564529 | 300.746917 | 353.270093 | 415.753334 | 490.132164 |
| 49 | 272.958401 | 321.295467 | 378.999000 | 447.934835 | 530.342737 |
| 50 | 290.335905 | 343.179672 | 406.528929 | 482.529947 | 573.770156 |

## AMOUNT OF ANNUITY $[(1 + i)^n - 1]/i$ (Continued)

| $n$ | .035(3½ %) | .04(4 %) | .045(4½ %) | .05(5 %) | .055(5½ %) |
|---|---|---|---|---|---|
| 1 | 1.00000000 | 1.00000000 | 1.00000000 | 1.00000000 | 1.00000000 |
| 2 | 2.03500000 | 2.04000000 | 2.04500000 | 2.05000000 | 2.05500000 |
| 3 | 3.10622500 | 3.12160000 | 3.13702500 | 3.15250000 | 3.16802500 |
| 4 | 4.21494288 | 4.24646400 | 4.27819113 | 4.31012500 | 4.34226638 |
| 5 | 5.36246588 | 5.41632256 | 5.47070973 | 5.52563125 | 5.58109103 |
| 6 | 6.55015218 | 6.63297546 | 6.71689166 | 6.80191281 | 6.88805103 |
| 7 | 7.77940751 | 7.89829448 | 8.01915179 | 8.14200845 | 8.26689384 |
| 8 | 9.05168677 | 9.21422626 | 9.38001362 | 9.54910888 | 9.72157300 |
| 9 | 10.3684958 | 10.5827953 | 10.8021142 | 11.0265643 | 11.2562595 |
| 10 | 11.7313932 | 12.0061071 | 12.2882094 | 12.5778925 | 12.8753538 |
| 11 | 13.1419919 | 13.4863514 | 13.8411788 | 14.2067872 | 14.5834982 |
| 12 | 14.6019616 | 15.0258055 | 15.4640318 | 15.9171265 | 16.3855907 |
| 13 | 16.1130303 | 16.6268377 | 17.1599133 | 17.7129828 | 18.2867981 |
| 14 | 17.6769864 | 18.2919112 | 18.9321094 | 19.5986320 | 20.2925720 |
| 15 | 19.2956809 | 20.0235876 | 20.7840543 | 21.5785636 | 22.4086635 |
| 16 | 20.9710297 | 21.8245311 | 22.7193367 | 23.6574918 | 24.6411400 |
| 17 | 22.7050157 | 23.6975124 | 24.7417069 | 25.8403664 | 26.9964027 |
| 18 | 24.4996913 | 25.6454129 | 26.8550837 | 28.1323847 | 29.4812048 |
| 19 | 26.3571805 | 27.6712294 | 29.0635625 | 30.5390039 | 32.1026711 |
| 20 | 28.2796818 | 29.7780786 | 31.3714228 | 33.0659541 | 34.8683180 |
| 21 | 30.2694707 | 31.9692017 | 33.7831368 | 35.7192508 | 37.7860755 |
| 22 | 32.3289022 | 34.2479698 | 36.3033780 | 38.5052144 | 40.8643097 |
| 23 | 34.4604137 | 36.6178886 | 38.9370300 | 41.4304751 | 44.1118467 |
| 24 | 36.6665282 | 39.0826041 | 41.6891963 | 44.5019989 | 47.5379983 |
| 25 | 38.9498567 | 41.6459083 | 44.5652101 | 47.7270988 | 51.1525882 |
| 26 | 41.3131017 | 44.3117446 | 47.5706446 | 51.1134538 | 54.9659805 |
| 27 | 43.7590602 | 47.0842144 | 50.7113236 | 54.6691264 | 58.9891094 |
| 28 | 46.2906273 | 49.9675830 | 53.9933332 | 58.4025828 | 63.2335105 |
| 29 | 48.9107993 | 52.9662863 | 57.4230332 | 62.3227119 | 67.7113535 |
| 30 | 51.6226773 | 56.0849378 | 61.0070697 | 66.4388475 | 72.4354780 |
| 31 | 54.4294710 | 59.3283353 | 64.7523878 | 70.7607899 | 77.4194293 |
| 32 | 57.3345025 | 62.7014687 | 68.6662452 | 75.2988294 | 82.6774979 |
| 33 | 60.3412101 | 66.2095274 | 72.7562263 | 80.0637708 | 88.2247603 |
| 34 | 63.4531524 | 69.8579085 | 77.0302565 | 85.0669594 | 94.0771221 |
| 35 | 66.6740127 | 73.6522249 | 81.4966180 | 90.3203074 | 100.251364 |
| 36 | 70.0076032 | 77.5983138 | 86.1639658 | 95.8363227 | 106.765189 |
| 37 | 73.4578693 | 81.7022464 | 91.0413443 | 101.628139 | 113.637274 |
| 38 | 77.0288947 | 85.9703363 | 96.1382048 | 107.709546 | 120.887324 |
| 39 | 80.7249060 | 90.4091497 | 101.464424 | 114.095023 | 128.536127 |
| 40 | 84.5502777 | 95.0255157 | 107.030323 | 120.799774 | 136.605614 |
| 41 | 88.5095375 | 99.8265363 | 112.846688 | 127.839763 | 145.118923 |
| 42 | 92.6073713 | 104.819598 | 118.924789 | 135.231751 | 154.100464 |
| 43 | 96.8486293 | 110.012382 | 125.276404 | 142.993339 | 163.575989 |
| 44 | 101.238331 | 115.412877 | 131.913842 | 151.143006 | 173.572669 |
| 45 | 105.781673 | 121.029392 | 138.849965 | 159.700156 | 184.119165 |
| 46 | 110.484031 | 126.870568 | 146.098214 | 168.685164 | 195.245719 |
| 47 | 115.350973 | 132.945390 | 153.672633 | 178.119422 | 206.984234 |
| 48 | 120.388257 | 139.263206 | 161.587902 | 188.025393 | 219.368367 |
| 49 | 125.601846 | 145.833734 | 169.859357 | 198.426663 | 232.433627 |
| 50 | 130.997910 | 152.667084 | 178.503028 | 209.347996 | 246.217476 |

## PRESENT VALUE OF ANNUITY $[1 - (1 + i)^{-n}]/i$
### (Continued)

| n | .0025(¼%) | .004167(₁₂%) | .005(½%) | .005833(₁₂%) | .0075(¾%) |
|---|---|---|---|---|---|
| **50** | 46.9461704 | 45.0509162 | 44.1427864 | 43.2598643 | 41.5664471 |
| 51 | 47.8266039 | 45.8598335 | 44.9181954 | 44.0031791 | 42.2495753 |
| 52 | 48.7048418 | 46.6653944 | 45.6897466 | 44.7421830 | 42.9276181 |
| 53 | 49.5808895 | 47.4676127 | 46.4574593 | 45.4769011 | 43.6006135 |
| 54 | 50.4547527 | 48.2665022 | 47.2213526 | 46.2073582 | 44.2685990 |
| **55** | 51.3264366 | 49.0620769 | 47.9814454 | 46.9335789 | 44.9316119 |
| 56 | 52.1959467 | 49.8543505 | 48.7377566 | 47.6555880 | 45.5896893 |
| 57 | 53.0632885 | 50.6433366 | 49.4903050 | 48.3734098 | 46.2428678 |
| 58 | 53.9284673 | 51.4290489 | 50.2391095 | 49.0870686 | 46.8911839 |
| 59 | 54.7914886 | 52.2115009 | 50.9841886 | 49.7965885 | 47.5346738 |
| **60** | 55.6523577 | 52.9907063 | 51.7255608 | 50.5019935 | 48.1733735 |
| 61 | 56.5110800 | 53.7666785 | 52.4632445 | 51.2033075 | 48.8073186 |
| 62 | 57.3676608 | 54.5394309 | 53.1972582 | 51.9005543 | 49.4365445 |
| 63 | 58.2221056 | 55.3089768 | 53.9276201 | 52.5937574 | 50.0610864 |
| 64 | 59.0744195 | 56.0753296 | 54.6543484 | 53.2829402 | 50.6809791 |
| **65** | 59.9246080 | 56.8385025 | 55.3774611 | 53.9681262 | 51.2962571 |
| 66 | 60.7726763 | 57.5985087 | 56.0969762 | 54.6493384 | 51.9069550 |
| 67 | 61.6186297 | 58.3553614 | 56.8129117 | 55.3265999 | 52.5131067 |
| 68 | 62.4624736 | 59.1090736 | 57.5252852 | 55.9999336 | 53.1147461 |
| 69 | 63.3042130 | 59.8596583 | 58.2341147 | 56.6693623 | 53.7119068 |
| **70** | 64.1438534 | 60.6071286 | 58.9394176 | 57.3349087 | 54.3046221 |
| 71 | 64.9813999 | 61.3514974 | 59.6412115 | 57.9965952 | 54.8929252 |
| 72 | 65.8168577 | 62.0927775 | 60.3395139 | 58.6544443 | 55.4768488 |
| 73 | 66.6502322 | 62.8309817 | 61.0343422 | 59.3084781 | 56.0564256 |
| 74 | 67.4815283 | 63.5661229 | 61.7257137 | 59.9587190 | 56.6316879 |
| **75** | 68.3107515 | 64.2982136 | 62.4136454 | 60.6051887 | 57.2026679 |
| 76 | 69.1379067 | 65.0272667 | 63.0981547 | 61.2479092 | 57.7693975 |
| 77 | 69.9629992 | 65.7532946 | 63.7792584 | 61.8869023 | 58.3319081 |
| 78 | 70.7860341 | 66.4763100 | 64.4569735 | 62.5221895 | 58.8902314 |
| 79 | 71.6070166 | 67.1963253 | 65.1313169 | 63.1537924 | 59.4443984 |
| **80** | 72.4259517 | 67.9133530 | 65.8023054 | 63.7817323 | 59.9944401 |
| 81 | 73.2428446 | 68.6274055 | 66.4699556 | 64.4060304 | 60.5403872 |
| 82 | 74.0577003 | 69.3384951 | 67.1342842 | 65.0267080 | 61.0822702 |
| 83 | 74.8705240 | 70.0466341 | 67.7953076 | 65.6437859 | 61.6201193 |
| 84 | 75.6813207 | 70.7518348 | 68.4530424 | 66.2572851 | 62.1539646 |
| **85** | 76.4900955 | 71.4541094 | 69.1075049 | 66.8672262 | 62.6838358 |
| 86 | 77.2968533 | 72.1534699 | 69.7587114 | 67.4736301 | 63.2097626 |
| 87 | 78.1015993 | 72.8499285 | 70.4066780 | 68.0765171 | 63.7317743 |
| 88 | 78.9043385 | 73.5434973 | 71.0514209 | 68.6759076 | 64.2499000 |
| 89 | 79.7050758 | 74.2341882 | 71.6929561 | 69.2718220 | 64.7641688 |
| **90** | 80.5038163 | 74.9220131 | 72.3312996 | 69.8642803 | 65.2746092 |
| 91 | 81.3005649 | 75.6069840 | 72.9664672 | 70.4533027 | 65.7812498 |
| 92 | 82.0953265 | 76.2891127 | 73.5984749 | 71.0389091 | 66.2841189 |
| 93 | 82.8881063 | 76.9684110 | 74.2273382 | 71.6211192 | 66.7832446 |
| 94 | 83.6789090 | 77.6448906 | 74.8530728 | 72.1999528 | 67.2786547 |
| **95** | 84.4677397 | 78.3185633 | 75.4756943 | 72.7754295 | 67.7703768 |
| 96 | 85.2546031 | 78.9894406 | 76.0952183 | 73.3475687 | 68.2584386 |
| 97 | 86.0395044 | 79.6575342 | 76.7116600 | 73.9163897 | 68.7428671 |
| 98 | 86.8224483 | 80.3228557 | 77.3250348 | 74.4819119 | 69.2236894 |
| 99 | 87.6034397 | 80.9854164 | 77.9353580 | 75.0441544 | 69.7009324 |
| **100** | 88.3824835 | 81.6452280 | 78.5426448 | 75.6031361 | 70.1746227 |

## PRESENT VALUE OF ANNUITY $[1 - (1 + i)^{-n}]/i$
### (Continued)

| Years n | Rate i | | | | |
|---|---|---|---|---|---|
| n | .01(1 %) | .01125(1⅛ %) | .0125(1¼ %) | .015(1½ %) | .0175(1¾ %) |
| 1 | 0.99009901 | 0.98887515 | 0.98765432 | 0.98522167 | 0.98280098 |
| 2 | 1.97039506 | 1.96674923 | 1.96311538 | 1.95588342 | 1.94869875 |
| 3 | 2.94098521 | 2.93374460 | 2.92653371 | 2.91220042 | 2.89798403 |
| 4 | 3.90196555 | 3.88998230 | 3.87805798 | 3.85438465 | 3.83094254 |
| 5 | 4.85343124 | 4.83558200 | 4.81783504 | 4.78264497 | 4.74785508 |
| 6 | 5.79547647 | 5.77066205 | 5.74600992 | 5.69718717 | 5.64899762 |
| 7 | 6.72819453 | 6.69533948 | 6.66272585 | 6.59821396 | 6.53464139 |
| 8 | 7.65167775 | 7.60973002 | 7.56812429 | 7.48592508 | 7.40505297 |
| 9 | 8.56601758 | 8.51394810 | 8.46234498 | 8.36051732 | 8.26049432 |
| 10 | 9.47130453 | 9.40810690 | 9.34552591 | 9.22218455 | 9.10122291 |
| 11 | 10.3676282 | 10.2923183 | 10.2178034 | 10.0711178 | 9.92749181 |
| 12 | 11.2550775 | 11.1666930 | 11.0793120 | 10.9075052 | 10.7395497 |
| 13 | 12.1337401 | 12.0313404 | 11.9301847 | 11.7315322 | 11.5376410 |
| 14 | 13.0037030 | 12.8863688 | 12.7705527 | 12.5433815 | 12.3220059 |
| 15 | 13.8650525 | 13.7318851 | 13.6005459 | 13.3432330 | 13.0928805 |
| 16 | 14.7178738 | 14.5679951 | 14.4202923 | 14.1312640 | 13.8504968 |
| 17 | 15.5622513 | 15.3948036 | 15.2299183 | 14.9076493 | 14.5950828 |
| 18 | 16.3982686 | 16.2124139 | 16.0295489 | 15.6725609 | 15.3268627 |
| 19 | 17.2260085 | 17.0209285 | 16.8193076 | 16.4261684 | 16.0460567 |
| 20 | 18.0455530 | 17.8204485 | 17.5993161 | 17.1686388 | 16.7528813 |
| 21 | 18.8569831 | 18.6110739 | 18.3696949 | 17.9001367 | 17.4475492 |
| 22 | 19.6603793 | 19.3929037 | 19.1305629 | 18.6208244 | 18.1302695 |
| 23 | 20.4558211 | 20.1660358 | 19.8820374 | 19.3308614 | 18.8012476 |
| 24 | 21.2433873 | 20.9305669 | 20.6242345 | 20.0304054 | 19.4606856 |
| 25 | 22.0231557 | 21.6865928 | 21.3572687 | 20.7196112 | 20.1087820 |
| 26 | 22.7952037 | 22.4342079 | 22.0812530 | 21.3986317 | 20.7457317 |
| 27 | 23.5596076 | 23.1735060 | 22.7962993 | 22.0676175 | 21.3717264 |
| 28 | 24.3164432 | 23.9045795 | 23.5025178 | 22.7267167 | 21.9869547 |
| 29 | 25.0657853 | 24.6275199 | 24.2000176 | 23.3760756 | 22.5916017 |
| 30 | 25.8077082 | 25.3424177 | 24.8889062 | 24.0158380 | 23.1858493 |
| 31 | 26.5422854 | 26.0493623 | 25.5692901 | 24.6461458 | 23.7698765 |
| 32 | 27.2695895 | 26.7484424 | 26.2412742 | 25.2671387 | 24.3438590 |
| 33 | 27.9896925 | 27.4397452 | 26.9049622 | 25.8789544 | 24.9079695 |
| 34 | 28.7026659 | 28.1233575 | 27.5604564 | 26.4817285 | 25.4623779 |
| 35 | 29.4085801 | 28.7993646 | 28.2078582 | 27.0755946 | 26.0072510 |
| 36 | 30.1075050 | 29.4678513 | 28.8472674 | 27.6606843 | 26.5427528 |
| 37 | 30.7995099 | 30.1289011 | 29.4787826 | 28.2371274 | 27.0690445 |
| 38 | 31.4846633 | 30.7825969 | 30.1025013 | 28.8050516 | 27.5862846 |
| 39 | 32.1630330 | 31.4290204 | 30.7185198 | 29.3645829 | 28.0946286 |
| 40 | 32.8346861 | 32.0682526 | 31.3269332 | 29.9158452 | 28.5942295 |
| 41 | 33.4996892 | 32.7003734 | 31.9278352 | 30.4589608 | 29.0852379 |
| 42 | 34.1581081 | 33.3254620 | 32.5213187 | 30.9940500 | 29.5678014 |
| 43 | 34.8100081 | 33.9435965 | 33.1074753 | 31.5212316 | 30.0420652 |
| 44 | 35.4554535 | 34.5548544 | 33.6863954 | 32.0406222 | 30.5081722 |
| 45 | 36.0945084 | 35.1593121 | 34.2581683 | 32.5523372 | 30.9662626 |
| 46 | 36.7272361 | 35.7570454 | 34.8228822 | 33.0564898 | 31.4164743 |
| 47 | 37.3536991 | 36.3481289 | 35.3806244 | 33.5531920 | 31.8589428 |
| 48 | 37.9739595 | 36.9326367 | 35.9314809 | 34.0425536 | 32.2938013 |
| 49 | 38.5880787 | 37.5106420 | 36.4755367 | 34.5246834 | 32.7211806 |
| 50 | 39.1961175 | 38.0822171 | 37.0128758 | 34.9996881 | 33.1412095 |

## PRESENT VALUE OF ANNUITY $[1 - (1 + i)^{-n}]/i$
### (Continued)

| Years $n$ | Rate $i$ | | | | |
|---|---|---|---|---|---|
| | .01(1 %) | .01125(1⅛ %) | .0125(1¼ %) | .015(1½ %) | .0175(1¾ %) |
| 50 | 39.1961175 | 38.0822171 | 37.0128758 | 34.9996881 | 33.1412095 |
| 51 | 39.7981362 | 38.6474335 | 37.5435810 | 35.4676730 | 33.5540142 |
| 52 | 40.3941942 | 39.2063619 | 38.0677343 | 35.9287419 | 33.9597191 |
| 53 | 40.9843507 | 39.7590723 | 38.5854166 | 36.3829969 | 34.3584463 |
| 54 | 41.5686641 | 40.3056339 | 39.0967078 | 36.8305388 | 34.7503158 |
| 55 | 42.1471922 | 40.8461151 | 39.6016867 | 37.2714668 | 35.1354455 |
| 56 | 42.7199922 | 41.3805836 | 40.1004313 | 37.7058786 | 35.5139513 |
| 57 | 43.2871210 | 41.9091061 | 40.5930186 | 38.1338706 | 35.8859473 |
| 58 | 43.8486347 | 42.4317490 | 41.0795245 | 38.5555375 | 36.2515452 |
| 59 | 44.4045888 | 42.9485775 | 41.5600242 | 38.9709729 | 36.6108553 |
| 60 | 44.9550384 | 43.4596563 | 42.0345918 | 39.3802689 | 36.9639855 |
| 61 | 45.5000380 | 43.9650495 | 42.5033005 | 39.7835161 | 37.3110423 |
| 62 | 46.0396416 | 44.4648203 | 42.9662228 | 40.1808041 | 37.6521300 |
| 63 | 46.5739026 | 44.9590312 | 43.4234299 | 40.5722208 | 37.9873514 |
| 64 | 47.1028738 | 45.4477441 | 43.8749925 | 40.9578530 | 38.3168072 |
| 65 | 47.6266078 | 45.9310201 | 44.3209802 | 41.3377862 | 38.6405968 |
| 66 | 48.1451562 | 46.4089197 | 44.7614619 | 41.7121046 | 38.9588175 |
| 67 | 48.6585705 | 46.8815028 | 45.1965056 | 42.0808912 | 39.2715651 |
| 68 | 49.1669015 | 47.3488285 | 45.6261784 | 42.4442278 | 39.5789337 |
| 69 | 49.6701995 | 47.8109553 | 46.0505466 | 42.8021949 | 39.8810160 |
| 70 | 50.1685143 | 48.2679409 | 46.4696756 | 43.1548718 | 40.1779027 |
| 71 | 50.6618954 | 48.7198427 | 46.8836302 | 43.5023368 | 40.4696832 |
| 72 | 51.1503915 | 49.1667171 | 47.2924743 | 43.8446668 | 40.7564454 |
| 73 | 51.6340510 | 49.6086202 | 47.6962709 | 44.1819377 | 41.0382756 |
| 74 | 52.1129218 | 50.0456071 | 48.0950824 | 44.5142243 | 41.3152586 |
| 75 | 52.5870512 | 50.4777326 | 48.4889703 | 44.8416003 | 41.5874777 |
| 76 | 53.0564864 | 50.9050508 | 48.8779953 | 45.1641383 | 41.8550149 |
| 77 | 53.5212736 | 51.3276151 | 49.2622176 | 45.4819096 | 42.1179508 |
| 78 | 53.9814590 | 51.7454785 | 49.6416964 | 45.7949848 | 42.3763644 |
| 79 | 54.4370882 | 52.1586932 | 50.0164903 | 46.1034333 | 42.6303336 |
| 80 | 54.8882061 | 52.5673109 | 50.3866571 | 46.4073235 | 42.8799347 |
| 81 | 55.3348575 | 52.9713829 | 50.7522539 | 46.7067227 | 43.1252430 |
| 82 | 55.7770867 | 53.3709596 | 51.1133372 | 47.0016972 | 43.3663322 |
| 83 | 56.2149373 | 53.7660910 | 51.4699626 | 47.2923125 | 43.6032749 |
| 84 | 56.6484528 | 54.1568267 | 51.8221853 | 47.5786330 | 43.8361424 |
| 85 | 57.0776760 | 54.5432156 | 52.1700596 | 47.8607222 | 44.0650048 |
| 86 | 57.5026495 | 54.9253059 | 52.5136391 | 48.1386425 | 44.2899310 |
| 87 | 57.9234154 | 55.3031455 | 52.8529769 | 48.4124557 | 44.5109887 |
| 88 | 58.3400152 | 55.6767817 | 53.1881253 | 48.6822224 | 44.7282444 |
| 89 | 58.7524903 | 56.0462613 | 53.5191361 | 48.9480023 | 44.9417636 |
| 90 | 59.1608815 | 56.4116304 | 53.8460604 | 49.2098545 | 45.1516104 |
| 91 | 59.5652292 | 56.7729349 | 54.1689485 | 49.4678370 | 45.3578480 |
| 92 | 59.9655735 | 57.1302199 | 54.4878504 | 49.7220069 | 45.5605386 |
| 93 | 60.3619539 | 57.4835302 | 54.8028152 | 49.9724206 | 45.7597431 |
| 94 | 60.7544098 | 57.8329100 | 55.1138915 | 50.2191335 | 45.9555215 |
| 95 | 61.1429800 | 58.1784029 | 55.4211274 | 50.4622005 | 46.1479327 |
| 96 | 61.5277030 | 58.5200523 | 55.7245703 | 50.7016754 | 46.3370345 |
| 97 | 61.9086168 | 58.8579010 | 56.0242670 | 50.9376112 | 46.5228841 |
| 98 | 62.2857592 | 59.1919911 | 56.3202637 | 51.1700603 | 46.7055372 |
| 99 | 62.6591676 | 59.5223645 | 56.6126061 | 51.3990742 | 46.8850488 |
| 100 | 63.0288788 | 59.8490625 | 56.9013394 | 51.6247037 | 47.0614730 |

## PRESENT VALUE OF ANNUITY $[1 - (1 + i)^{-n}]/i$

(Continued)

| Years |  |  | Rate $i$ |  |  |
|---|---|---|---|---|---|
| $n$ | .02(2 %) | .0225(2¼ %) | .025(2½ %) | .0275(2¾ %) | .03(3 %) |
| 1 | 0.98039216 | 0.97799511 | 0.97560976 | 0.97323601 | 0.97087379 |
| 2 | 1.94156094 | 1.93446955 | 1.92742415 | 1.92042434 | 1.91346970 |
| 3 | 2.88388327 | 2.86989687 | 2.85602356 | 2.84226213 | 2.82861135 |
| 4 | 3.80772870 | 3.78474021 | 3.76197421 | 3.73942787 | 3.71709840 |
| 5 | 4.71345951 | 4.67945253 | 4.64582850 | 4.61258186 | 4.57970719 |
| 6 | 5.60143089 | 5.55447680 | 5.50812536 | 5.46236678 | 5.41719144 |
| 7 | 6.47199107 | 6.41024626 | 6.34939060 | 6.28940806 | 6.23028296 |
| 8 | 7.32548144 | 7.24718461 | 7.17013717 | 7.09431441 | 7.01969219 |
| 9 | 8.16223671 | 8.06570622 | 7.97086553 | 7.87767826 | 7.78610892 |
| 10 | 8.98258501 | 8.86621635 | 8.75206393 | 8.64007616 | 8.53020284 |
| 11 | 9.78684805 | 9.64911134 | 9.51420871 | 9.38206926 | 9.25262411 |
| 12 | 10.5753412 | 10.4147788 | 10.2577646 | 10.1042037 | 9.95400399 |
| 13 | 11.3483737 | 11.1635979 | 10.9831850 | 10.8070109 | 10.6349553 |
| 14 | 12.1062488 | 11.8959392 | 11.6909122 | 11.4910081 | 11.2960731 |
| 15 | 12.8492635 | 12.6121655 | 12.3813777 | 12.1566989 | 11.9379351 |
| 16 | 13.5777093 | 13.3126313 | 13.0550027 | 12.8045732 | 12.5611020 |
| 17 | 14.2918719 | 13.9976834 | 13.7121977 | 13.4351077 | 13.1661185 |
| 18 | 14.9920313 | 14.6676611 | 14.3533636 | 14.0487666 | 13.7535131 |
| 19 | 15.6784620 | 15.3228959 | 14.9788913 | 14.6460016 | 14.3237991 |
| 20 | 16.3514333 | 15.9637124 | 15.5891623 | 15.2272521 | 14.8774749 |
| 21 | 17.0112092 | 16.5904277 | 16.1845486 | 15.7929461 | 15.4150241 |
| 22 | 17.6580482 | 17.2033523 | 16.7654132 | 16.3434999 | 15.9369166 |
| 23 | 18.2922041 | 17.8027896 | 17.3321105 | 16.8793186 | 16.4436084 |
| 24 | 18.9139256 | 18.3890362 | 17.8849858 | 17.4007967 | 16.9355421 |
| 25 | 19.5234565 | 18.9623826 | 18.4243764 | 17.9083180 | 17.4131477 |
| 26 | 20.1210358 | 19.5231126 | 18.9506111 | 18.4022559 | 17.8768424 |
| 27 | 20.7068978 | 20.0715038 | 19.4640109 | 18.8829741 | 18.3270315 |
| 28 | 21.2812724 | 20.6078276 | 19.9648887 | 19.3508264 | 18.7641082 |
| 29 | 21.8443847 | 21.1323498 | 20.4535499 | 19.8061571 | 19.1884546 |
| 30 | 22.3964556 | 21.6453298 | 20.9302926 | 20.2493013 | 19.6004413 |
| 31 | 22.9377015 | 22.1470209 | 21.3954074 | 20.6805852 | 20.0004285 |
| 32 | 23.4683348 | 22.6376742 | 21.8491780 | 21.1003262 | 20.3887655 |
| 33 | 23.9885636 | 23.1175298 | 22.2918809 | 21.5088333 | 20.7657918 |
| 34 | 24.4985917 | 23.5868262 | 22.7237863 | 21.9064071 | 21.1318367 |
| 35 | 24.9986193 | 24.0457958 | 23.1451573 | 22.2933403 | 21.4872201 |
| 36 | 25.4888425 | 24.4946658 | 23.5562511 | 22.6699175 | 21.8322525 |
| 37 | 25.9694534 | 24.9336585 | 23.9573181 | 23.0364161 | 22.1672354 |
| 38 | 26.4406406 | 25.3629912 | 24.3486030 | 23.3931057 | 22.4924616 |
| 39 | 26.9025888 | 25.7828765 | 24.7303444 | 23.7402488 | 22.8082151 |
| 40 | 27.3554792 | 26.1935222 | 25.1027751 | 24.0781011 | 23.1147720 |
| 41 | 27.7994895 | 26.5951317 | 25.4661220 | 24.4069110 | 23.4124000 |
| 42 | 28.2347936 | 26.9879039 | 25.8206068 | 24.7269207 | 23.7013592 |
| 43 | 28.6615623 | 27.3720332 | 26.1664457 | 25.0383656 | 23.9819021 |
| 44 | 29.0799631 | 27.7477097 | 26.5038495 | 25.3414751 | 24.2542739 |
| 45 | 29.4901599 | 28.1151195 | 26.8330239 | 25.6364721 | 24.5187125 |
| 46 | 29.8923136 | 28.4744445 | 27.1541696 | 25.9235738 | 24.7754491 |
| 47 | 30.2865820 | 28.8258626 | 27.4674826 | 26.2029915 | 25.0247078 |
| 48 | 30.6731196 | 29.1695478 | 27.7731537 | 26.4749309 | 25.2667066 |
| 49 | 31.0520780 | 29.5056702 | 28.0713695 | 26.7395922 | 25.5016569 |
| 50 | 31.4236059 | 29.8343963 | 28.3623117 | 26.9971700 | 25.7297640 |

## PRESENT VALUE OF ANNUITY $[1 - (1 + i)^{-n}]/i$
### (Continued)

| Years $n$ | .02(2 %) | .0225(2¼ %) | .025(2½ %) | .0275(2¾ %) | .03(3 %) |
|---|---|---|---|---|---|
| | | | Rate $i$ | | |
| 50 | 31.4236059 | 29.8343963 | 28.3623117 | 26.9971700 | 25.7297640 |
| 51 | 31.7878489 | 30.1558888 | 28.6461577 | 27.2478540 | 25.9512272 |
| 52 | 32.1449499 | 30.4703069 | 28.9230807 | 27.4918287 | 26.1662400 |
| 53 | 32.4950489 | 30.7778062 | 29.1932495 | 27.7292737 | 26.3749903 |
| 54 | 32.8382833 | 31.0785391 | 29.4568288 | 27.9603637 | 26.5776605 |
| 55 | 33.1747875 | 31.3726544 | 29.7139793 | 28.1852688 | 26.7744276 |
| 56 | 33.5046936 | 31.6602977 | 29.9648578 | 28.4041545 | 26.9654637 |
| 57 | 33.8281310 | 31.9416114 | 30.2096174 | 28.6171820 | 27.1509357 |
| 58 | 34.1452265 | 32.2167349 | 30.4484072 | 28.8245081 | 27.3310055 |
| 59 | 34.4561044 | 32.4858043 | 30.6813729 | 29.0262852 | 27.5058306 |
| 60 | 34.7608867 | 32.7489529 | 30.9086565 | 29.2226620 | 27.6755637 |
| 61 | 35.0596928 | 33.0063109 | 31.1303966 | 29.4137830 | 27.8403531 |
| 62 | 35.3526400 | 33.2580057 | 31.3467284 | 29.5997888 | 28.0003428 |
| 63 | 35.6398432 | 33.5041621 | 31.5577838 | 29.7808163 | 28.1556726 |
| 64 | 35.9214149 | 33.7449018 | 31.7636915 | 29.9569989 | 28.3064783 |
| 65 | 36.1974655 | 33.9803440 | 31.9645771 | 30.1284661 | 28.4528915 |
| 66 | 36.4681035 | 34.2106054 | 32.1605630 | 30.2953441 | 28.5950403 |
| 67 | 36.7334348 | 34.4357999 | 32.3517688 | 30.4577558 | 28.7330488 |
| 68 | 36.9935635 | 34.6560391 | 32.5383110 | 30.6158207 | 28.8670377 |
| 69 | 37.2485917 | 34.8714318 | 32.7203034 | 30.7696552 | 28.9971240 |
| 70 | 37.4986193 | 35.0820849 | 32.8978570 | 30.9193725 | 29.1234214 |
| 71 | 37.7437444 | 35.2881026 | 33.0710800 | 31.0650827 | 29.2460401 |
| 72 | 37.9840631 | 35.4895869 | 33.2400780 | 31.2068931 | 29.3650875 |
| 73 | 38.2196697 | 35.6866376 | 33.4049542 | 31.3449082 | 29.4806675 |
| 74 | 38.4506566 | 35.8793521 | 33.5658089 | 31.4792294 | 29.5928811 |
| 75 | 38.6771143 | 36.0678261 | 33.7227404 | 31.6099556 | 29.7018263 |
| 76 | 38.8991317 | 36.2521526 | 33.8758443 | 31.7371830 | 29.8075983 |
| 77 | 39.1167958 | 36.4324231 | 34.0252140 | 31.8610054 | 29.9102896 |
| 78 | 39.3301919 | 36.6087267 | 34.1709405 | 31.9815138 | 30.0099899 |
| 79 | 39.5394039 | 36.7811509 | 34.3131127 | 32.0987969 | 30.1067863 |
| 80 | 39.7445136 | 36.9497808 | 34.4518172 | 32.2129410 | 30.2007634 |
| 81 | 39.9456016 | 37.1147000 | 34.5871388 | 32.3240301 | 30.2920033 |
| 82 | 40.1427466 | 37.2759903 | 34.7191598 | 32.4321461 | 30.3805858 |
| 83 | 40.3360261 | 37.4337313 | 34.8479607 | 32.5373685 | 30.4665881 |
| 84 | 40.5255158 | 37.5880013 | 34.9736202 | 32.6397747 | 30.5500856 |
| 85 | 40.7112900 | 37.7388765 | 35.0962149 | 32.7394401 | 30.6311510 |
| 86 | 40.8934216 | 37.8864318 | 35.2158194 | 32.8364380 | 30.7098554 |
| 87 | 41.0719819 | 38.0307402 | 35.3325067 | 32.9308399 | 30.7862673 |
| 88 | 41.2470411 | 38.1718730 | 35.4463480 | 33.0227153 | 30.8604537 |
| 89 | 41.4186677 | 38.3099003 | 35.5574127 | 33.1121317 | 30.9324794 |
| 90 | 41.5869292 | 38.4448902 | 35.6657685 | 33.1991549 | 31.0024071 |
| 91 | 41.7518913 | 38.5769098 | 35.7714814 | 33.2838490 | 31.0702982 |
| 92 | 41.9136190 | 38.7060242 | 35.8746160 | 33.3662764 | 31.1362118 |
| 93 | 42.0721754 | 38.8322975 | 35.9752352 | 33.4464978 | 31.2002057 |
| 94 | 42.2276230 | 38.9557922 | 36.0734002 | 33.5245720 | 31.2623356 |
| 95 | 42.3800225 | 39.0765694 | 36.1691709 | 33.6005567 | 31.3226559 |
| 96 | 42.5294339 | 39.1946889 | 36.2626057 | 33.6745078 | 31.3812193 |
| 97 | 42.6759155 | 39.3102092 | 36.3537617 | 33.7464796 | 31.4380770 |
| 98 | 42.8195250 | 39.4231875 | 36.4426943 | 33.8165251 | 31.4932787 |
| 99 | 42.9603187 | 39.5336797 | 36.5294559 | 33.8846960 | 31.5468725 |
| 100 | 43.0983516 | 39.6417405 | 36.6141053 | 33.9510423 | 31.5989053 |

## PRESENT VALUE OF ANNUITY $[1 - (1 + i)^{-n}]/i$ (Continued)

| Years | Rate $i$ | | | | |
|---|---|---|---|---|---|
| $n$ | .035(3½%) | .04(4%) | .045(4½%) | .05(5%) | .055(5½%) |
| 1 | 0.96618357 | 0.96153846 | 0.95693780 | 0.95238095 | 0.94786730 |
| 2 | 1.89969428 | 1.88609467 | 1.87266775 | 1.85941043 | 1.84631971 |
| 3 | 2.80163698 | 2.77509103 | 2.74896435 | 2.72324803 | 2.69793338 |
| 4 | 3.67307921 | 3.62989522 | 3.58752570 | 3.54595050 | 3.50515012 |
| 5 | 4.51505238 | 4.45182233 | 4.38997674 | 4.32947667 | 4.27028448 |
| 6 | 5.32855302 | 5.24213686 | 5.15787248 | 5.07569207 | 4.99553031 |
| 7 | 6.11454398 | 6.00205467 | 5.89270094 | 5.78637340 | 5.68296712 |
| 8 | 6.87395554 | 6.73274487 | 6.59588607 | 6.46321276 | 6.33456599 |
| 9 | 7.60768651 | 7.43533161 | 7.26879050 | 7.10782168 | 6.95219525 |
| 10 | 8.31660532 | 8.11089578 | 7.91271818 | 7.72173493 | 7.53762583 |
| 11 | 9.00155104 | 8.76047671 | 8.52891692 | 8.30641422 | 8.09253633 |
| 12 | 9.66333433 | 9.38507376 | 9.11858078 | 8.86325164 | 8.61851785 |
| 13 | 10.3027385 | 9.98564785 | 9.68285242 | 9.39357299 | 9.11707853 |
| 14 | 10.9205203 | 10.5631229 | 10.2228253 | 9.89864094 | 9.58964790 |
| 15 | 11.5174109 | 11.1183874 | 10.7395457 | 10.3796580 | 10.0375809 |
| 16 | 12.0941168 | 11.6522956 | 11.2340150 | 10.8377696 | 10.4621620 |
| 17 | 12.6513206 | 12.1656689 | 11.7071914 | 11.2740662 | 10.8646086 |
| 18 | 13.1896817 | 12.6592970 | 12.1599918 | 11.6895869 | 11.2460745 |
| 19 | 13.7098374 | 13.1339394 | 12.5932936 | 12.0853209 | 11.6076535 |
| 20 | 14.2124033 | 13.5903263 | 13.0079365 | 12.4622103 | 11.9503825 |
| 21 | 14.6979742 | 14.0291599 | 13.4047239 | 12.8211527 | 12.2752441 |
| 22 | 15.1671248 | 14.4511153 | 13.7844248 | 13.1630026 | 12.5831697 |
| 23 | 15.6204105 | 14.8568417 | 14.1477749 | 13.4885739 | 12.8750424 |
| 24 | 16.0583676 | 15.2469631 | 14.4954784 | 13.7986418 | 13.1516990 |
| 25 | 16.4815146 | 15.6220799 | 14.8282090 | 14.0939446 | 13.4139327 |
| 26 | 16.8903523 | 15.9827692 | 15.1466114 | 14.3751853 | 13.6624954 |
| 27 | 17.2853645 | 16.3295857 | 15.4513028 | 14.6430336 | 13.8980999 |
| 28 | 17.6670188 | 16.6630632 | 15.7428735 | 14.8981273 | 14.1214217 |
| 29 | 18.0357670 | 16.9837146 | 16.0218885 | 15.1410736 | 14.3331012 |
| 30 | 18.3920454 | 17.2920333 | 16.2888885 | 15.3724510 | 14.5337452 |
| 31 | 18.7362758 | 17.5884936 | 16.5443910 | 15.5928105 | 14.7239291 |
| 32 | 19.0688655 | 17.8735515 | 16.7888909 | 15.8026767 | 14.9041982 |
| 33 | 19.3902082 | 18.1476457 | 17.0228621 | 16.0025492 | 15.0750694 |
| 34 | 19.7006842 | 18.4111978 | 17.2467580 | 16.1929040 | 15.2370326 |
| 35 | 20.0006611 | 18.6646132 | 17.4610124 | 16.3741943 | 15.3905522 |
| 36 | 20.2904938 | 18.9082820 | 17.6660406 | 16.5468517 | 15.5360684 |
| 37 | 20.5705254 | 19.1425788 | 17.8622398 | 16.7112873 | 15.6739985 |
| 38 | 20.8410874 | 19.3678642 | 18.0499902 | 16.8678927 | 15.8047379 |
| 39 | 21.1024999 | 19.5844848 | 18.2296557 | 17.0170407 | 15.9286615 |
| 40 | 21.3550723 | 19.7927739 | 18.4015844 | 17.1590864 | 16.0461247 |
| 41 | 21.5991037 | 19.9930518 | 18.5661095 | 17.2943680 | 16.1574642 |
| 42 | 21.8348828 | 20.1856267 | 18.7235498 | 17.4232076 | 16.2629992 |
| 43 | 22.0626887 | 20.3707949 | 18.8742103 | 17.5459120 | 16.3630324 |
| 44 | 22.2827910 | 20.5488413 | 19.0183831 | 17.6627733 | 16.4578506 |
| 45 | 22.4954503 | 20.7200397 | 19.1563474 | 17.7740698 | 16.5477257 |
| 46 | 22.7009181 | 20.8846536 | 19.2883707 | 17.8800665 | 16.6329154 |
| 47 | 22.8994378 | 21.0429361 | 19.4147088 | 17.9810157 | 16.7136639 |
| 48 | 23.0912443 | 21.1951309 | 19.5356065 | 18.0771578 | 16.7902027 |
| 49 | 23.2765645 | 21.3414720 | 19.6512981 | 18.1687217 | 16.8627514 |
| 50 | 23.4556179 | 21.4821846 | 19.7620078 | 18.2559255 | 16.9315179 |

## PRESENT VALUE OF ANNUITY $[1 - (1 + i)^{-n}]/i$
### (Continued)

| Years n | .06(6 %) | .065(6½ %) | .07(7 %) | .075(7½ %) | .08(8 %) |
|---|---|---|---|---|---|
| | | | Rate $i$ | | |
| 1 | 0.94339623 | 0.93896714 | 0.93457944 | 0.93023256 | 0.92592593 |
| 2 | 1.83339267 | 1.82062642 | 1.80801817 | 1.79556517 | 1.78326475 |
| 3 | 2.67301195 | 2.64847551 | 2.62431604 | 2.60052574 | 2.57709699 |
| 4 | 3.46510561 | 3.42579860 | 3.38721126 | 3.34932627 | 3.31212684 |
| 5 | 4.21236379 | 4.15567944 | 4.10019744 | 4.04588490 | 3.99271004 |
| 6 | 4.91732433 | 4.84101356 | 4.76653966 | 4.69384642 | 4.62287966 |
| 7 | 5.58238144 | 5.48451977 | 5.38928940 | 5.29660132 | 5.20637006 |
| 8 | 6.20979381 | 6.08875096 | 5.97129851 | 5.85730355 | 5.74663894 |
| 9 | 6.80169227 | 6.65610419 | 6.51523225 | 6.37888703 | 6.24688791 |
| 10 | 7.36008705 | 7.18883022 | 7.02358154 | 6.86408096 | 6.71008140 |
| 11 | 7.88687458 | 7.68904246 | 7.49867434 | 7.31542415 | 7.13896426 |
| 12 | 8.38384394 | 8.15872532 | 7.94268630 | 7.73527827 | 7.53607802 |
| 13 | 8.85268296 | 8.59974208 | 8.35765074 | 8.12584026 | 7.90377594 |
| 14 | 9.29498393 | 9.01384233 | 8.74546799 | 8.48915373 | 8.24423698 |
| 15 | 9.71224899 | 9.40266885 | 9.10791401 | 8.82711975 | 8.55947869 |
| 16 | 10.1058953 | 9.76776418 | 9.44664860 | 9.14150674 | 8.85136916 |
| 17 | 10.4772597 | 10.1105767 | 9.76322209 | 9.43395976 | 9.12163811 |
| 18 | 10.8276035 | 10.4324664 | 10.0590869 | 9.70600908 | 9.37188714 |
| 19 | 11.1581165 | 10.7347102 | 10.3355952 | 9.95907821 | 9.60359920 |
| 20 | 11.4699212 | 11.0185072 | 10.5940142 | 10.1944914 | 9.81814741 |
| 21 | 11.7640766 | 11.2849833 | 10.8355273 | 10.4134803 | 10.0168032 |
| 22 | 12.0415817 | 11.5351956 | 11.0612405 | 10.6171910 | 10.2007437 |
| 23 | 12.3033790 | 11.7701367 | 11.2721874 | 10.8066893 | 10.3710589 |
| 24 | 12.5503575 | 11.9907387 | 11.4693340 | 10.9829668 | 10.5287583 |
| 25 | 12.7833562 | 12.1978767 | 11.6535832 | 11.1469459 | 10.6747762 |
| 26 | 13.0031662 | 12.3923725 | 11.8257787 | 11.2994845 | 10.8099780 |
| 27 | 13.2105341 | 12.5749977 | 11.9867090 | 11.4413810 | 10.9351648 |
| 28 | 13.4061643 | 12.7464767 | 12.1371113 | 11.5733776 | 11.0510785 |
| 29 | 13.5907210 | 12.9074898 | 12.2776741 | 11.6961652 | 11.1584060 |
| 30 | 13.7648312 | 13.0586759 | 12.4090412 | 11.8103863 | 11.2577833 |
| 31 | 13.9290860 | 13.2006347 | 12.5318142 | 11.9166384 | 11.3497994 |
| 32 | 14.0840434 | 13.3339293 | 12.6465553 | 12.0154776 | 11.4349994 |
| 33 | 14.2302296 | 13.4590885 | 12.7537900 | 12.1074210 | 11.5138884 |
| 34 | 14.3681411 | 13.5766089 | 12.8540094 | 12.1929498 | 11.5869337 |
| 35 | 14.4982464 | 13.6869567 | 12.9476723 | 12.2725114 | 11.6545682 |
| 36 | 14.6209871 | 13.7905697 | 13.0352078 | 12.3465222 | 11.7171928 |
| 37 | 14.7367803 | 13.8878589 | 13.1170166 | 12.4153695 | 11.7751785 |
| 38 | 14.8460192 | 13.9792102 | 13.1934735 | 12.4794135 | 11.8288690 |
| 39 | 14.9490747 | 14.0649861 | 13.2649285 | 12.5389893 | 11.8785824 |
| 40 | 15.0462969 | 14.1455269 | 13.3317088 | 12.5944087 | 11.9246133 |
| 41 | 15.1380159 | 14.2211520 | 13.3941204 | 12.6459615 | 11.9672346 |
| 42 | 15.2245433 | 14.2921615 | 13.4524490 | 12.6939177 | 12.0066987 |
| 43 | 15.3061729 | 14.3588371 | 13.5069617 | 12.7385281 | 12.0432395 |
| 44 | 15.3831820 | 14.4214433 | 13.5579081 | 12.7800261 | 12.0770736 |
| 45 | 15.4558321 | 14.4802284 | 13.6055216 | 12.8186290 | 12.1084015 |
| 46 | 15.5243699 | 14.5354257 | 13.6500202 | 12.8545386 | 12.1374088 |
| 47 | 15.5890282 | 14.5872542 | 13.6916076 | 12.8879429 | 12.1642674 |
| 48 | 15.6500266 | 14.6359195 | 13.7304744 | 12.9190166 | 12.1891365 |
| 49 | 15.7075723 | 14.6816145 | 13.7667985 | 12.9479224 | 12.2121634 |
| 50 | 15.7618606 | 14.7245207 | 13.8007463 | 12.9748116 | 12.2334846 |

## ANNUITY WHOSE PRESENT VALUE IS 1

$$\frac{1}{a_{\overline{n}|}} = a_{\overline{n}|}^{-1} = \frac{i}{1 - (1 + i)^{-n}} = \frac{i}{1 - v^n} = s_{\overline{n}|}^{-1} + i$$

| Years |  |  | Rate $i$ |  |  |
|---|---|---|---|---|---|
| $n$ | .0025($\frac{1}{4}$%) | .004167($\frac{1}{3}\frac{5}{2}$%) | .005($\frac{1}{2}$%) | .005833($\frac{7}{12}$%) | .0075($\frac{3}{4}$%) |
| 1 | 1.00250000 | 1.00416667 | 1.00500000 | 1.00583333 | 1.00750000 |
| 2 | 0.50187578 | 0.50312717 | 0.50375312 | 0.50437924 | 0.50563200 |
| 3 | .33500139 | .33611496 | .33667221 | .33722976 | .33834579 |
| 4 | .25156445 | .25260958 | .25313279 | .25365644 | .25470501 |
| 5 | .20150250 | .20250693 | .20300997 | .20351357 | .20452242 |
| 6 | .16812803 | .16910564 | .16959546 | .17008594 | .17106891 |
| 7 | .14428928 | .14524800 | .14572854 | .14620986 | .14717488 |
| 8 | .12641035 | .12735512 | .12782886 | .12830352 | .12925552 |
| 9 | .11250462 | .11343876 | .11390736 | .11437698 | .11531929 |
| 10 | .10138015 | .10230596 | .10277057 | .19323632 | .10417123 |
| 11 | .09227840 | .09319757 | .09365903 | .09412175 | .09505094 |
| 12 | .08469370 | .08560748 | .08606643 | .08652675 | .08745148 |
| 13 | .07827595 | .07918532 | .07964224 | .08010064 | .08102188 |
| 14 | .07277510 | .07368082 | .07413609 | .07459295 | .07551146 |
| 15 | .06800777 | .06891045 | .06936436 | .06982000 | .07073639 |
| 16 | .06383642 | .06473655 | .06518937 | .06564401 | .06655879 |
| 17 | .06015887 | .06105387 | .06150579 | .06195966 | .06287321 |
| 18 | .05688433 | .05778053 | .05823173 | .05868499 | .05959766 |
| 19 | .05395722 | .05485191 | .05530253 | .05575532 | .05666740 |
| 20 | .05132288 | .05221630 | .05266645 | .05311889 | .05403063 |
| 21 | .04893947 | .04983183 | .05028163 | .05073383 | .05164543 |
| 22 | .04677278 | .04766427 | .04811380 | .04856585 | .04947748 |
| 23 | .04479455 | .04568531 | .04613465 | .04658663 | .04749846 |
| 24 | .04298121 | .04387139 | .04432061 | .04477258 | .04568474 |
| 25 | .04131298 | .04220270 | .04265186 | .04310388 | .04401650 |
| 26 | .03977312 | .04066247 | .04111163 | .04156376 | .04247693 |
| 27 | .03834736 | .03923645 | .03968565 | .04013793 | .04105176 |
| 28 | .03702347 | .03791239 | .03836167 | .03881415 | .03972871 |
| 29 | .03579093 | .03667974 | .03712914 | .03758186 | .03849723 |
| 30 | .03464059 | .03552936 | .03597892 | .03643191 | .03734816 |
| 31 | .03356449 | .03445330 | .03490304 | .03535633 | .03627352 |
| 32 | .03255569 | .03344458 | .03389452 | .03434815 | .03526634 |
| 33 | .03160806 | .03249708 | .03294727 | .03340124 | .03432048 |
| 34 | .03071620 | .03160540 | .03205586 | .03251020 | .03343053 |
| 35 | .02987533 | .03076476 | .03121550 | .03167024 | .03259170 |
| 36 | .02908121 | .02997090 | .03042194 | .03087710 | .03179973 |
| 37 | .02833004 | .02922003 | .02967139 | .03012698 | .03105082 |
| 38 | .02761843 | .02850875 | .02896045 | .02941649 | .03034157 |
| 39 | .02694335 | .02783402 | .02828607 | .02874258 | .02966893 |
| 40 | .02630204 | .02719310 | .02764552 | .02810251 | .02903016 |
| 41 | .02569204 | .02658352 | .02703631 | .02749379 | .02842276 |
| 42 | .02511112 | .02600303 | .02645622 | .02691420 | .02784452 |
| 43 | .02455724 | .02544961 | .02590320 | .02636170 | .02729338 |
| 44 | .02402855 | .02492141 | .02537541 | .02583443 | .02676751 |
| 45 | .02352339 | .02441675 | .02487117 | .02533073 | .02626521 |
| 46 | .02304022 | .02393409 | .02438894 | .02484905 | .02578495 |
| 47 | .02257762 | .02347204 | .02392733 | .02438798 | .02532532 |
| 48 | .02213433 | .02302929 | .02348503 | .02394624 | .02488504 |
| 49 | .02170915 | .02260468 | .02306087 | .02352265 | .02446292 |
| 50 | .02130099 | .02219711 | .02265376 | .02311612 | .02405787 |

### ANNUITY WHOSE PRESENT VALUE IS 1
$$a_{\overline{n}|}^{-1} = i/(1 - v^n) = s_{\overline{n}|}^{-1} + i \text{ (Continued)}$$

| Years | Rate $i$ | | | | |
|---|---|---|---|---|---|
| $n$ | .0025($\frac{1}{4}$%) | .004167($\frac{5}{12}$%) | .005($\frac{1}{2}$%) | .005833($\frac{7}{12}$%) | .0075($\frac{3}{4}$%) |
| 50 | .02130099 | .02219711 | .02265376 | .02311612 | .02405787 |
| 51 | .02090886 | .02180557 | .02226269 | .02272563 | .02366888 |
| 52 | .02053184 | .02142916 | .02188675 | .02235027 | .02329503 |
| 53 | .02016906 | .02106700 | .02152507 | .02198919 | .02293546 |
| 54 | .01981974 | .02071830 | .02117686 | .02164157 | .02258938 |
| 55 | .01948314 | .02038234 | .02084139 | .02130671 | .02225605 |
| 56 | .01915858 | .02005843 | .02051797 | .02098390 | .02193478 |
| 57 | .01884542 | .01974593 | .02020598 | .02067251 | .02162496 |
| 58 | .01854308 | .01944426 | .01990481 | .02037196 | .02132597 |
| 59 | .01825101 | .01915287 | .01961392 | .02008170 | .02103727 |
| 60 | .01796869 | .01887123 | .01933280 | .01980120 | .02075836 |
| 61 | .01769564 | .01859888 | .01906096 | .01952999 | .02048873 |
| 62 | .01743142 | .01833536 | .01879796 | .01926762 | .02022795 |
| 63 | .01717561 | .01808025 | .01854337 | .01901366 | .01997560 |
| 64 | .01692780 | .01783315 | .01829681 | .01876773 | .01973127 |
| 65 | .01668764 | .01759371 | .01805789 | .01852946 | .01949460 |
| 66 | .01645476 | .01736156 | .01782627 | .01829848 | .01926524 |
| 67 | .01622886 | .01713639 | .01760163 | .01807449 | .01904286 |
| 68 | .01600961 | .01691788 | .01738366 | .01785716 | .01882716 |
| 69 | .01579674 | .01670574 | .01717206 | .01764622 | .01861785 |
| 70 | .01558996 | .01649971 | .01696657 | .01744138 | .01841464 |
| 71 | .01538902 | .01629952 | .01676693 | .01724239 | .01821728 |
| 72 | .01519368 | .01610493 | .01657289 | .01704901 | .01802554 |
| 73 | .01500370 | .01591572 | .01638422 | .01686100 | .01783917 |
| 74 | .01481887 | .01573165 | .01620070 | .01667814 | .01765796 |
| 75 | .01463898 | .01555253 | .01602214 | .01650024 | .01748170 |
| 76 | .01446385 | .01537816 | .01584832 | .01632709 | .01731020 |
| 77 | .01429327 | .01520836 | .01567908 | .01615851 | .01714328 |
| 78 | .01412708 | .01504295 | .01551423 | .01599432 | .01698074 |
| 79 | .01396511 | .01488177 | .01535360 | .01583436 | .01682244 |
| 80 | .01380721 | .01472464 | .01519704 | .01567847 | .01666821 |
| 81 | .01365321 | .01457144 | .01504439 | .01552650 | .01651790 |
| 82 | .01350298 | .01442200 | .01489552 | .01537830 | .01637136 |
| 83 | .01335639 | .01427620 | .01475028 | .01523373 | .01622847 |
| 84 | .01321330 | .01413391 | .01460855 | .01509268 | .01608908 |
| 85 | .01307359 | .01399500 | .01447021 | .01495501 | .01595308 |
| 86 | .01293714 | .01385935 | .01433513 | .01482060 | .01582034 |
| 87 | .01280384 | .01372685 | .01420320 | .01468935 | .01569076 |
| 88 | .01267357 | .01359740 | .01407431 | .01456115 | .01556423 |
| 89 | .01254625 | .01347088 | .01394837 | .01443588 | .01544064 |
| 90 | .01242177 | .01334721 | .01382527 | .01431347 | .01531989 |
| 91 | .01230004 | .01322629 | .01370493 | .01419380 | .01520190 |
| 92 | .01218096 | .01310803 | .01358724 | .01407679 | .01508657 |
| 93 | .01206446 | .01299234 | .01347213 | .01396236 | .01497382 |
| 94 | .01195044 | .01287915 | .01335950 | .01385042 | .01486356 |
| 95 | .01183884 | .01276836 | .01324930 | .01374090 | .01475571 |
| 96 | .01172957 | .01265992 | .01314143 | .01363372 | .01465020 |
| 97 | .01162257 | .01255374 | .01303583 | .01352880 | .01454696 |
| 98 | .01151776 | .01244976 | .01293242 | .01342608 | .01444592 |
| 99 | .01141508 | .01234790 | .01283115 | .01332549 | .01434701 |
| 100 | .01131446 | .01224811 | .01273194 | .01322696 | .01425017 |

**ANNUITY WHOSE PRESENT VALUE IS 1**

$$a_{\overline{n}|}^{-1} = i/(1 - v^n) = s_{\overline{n}|}^{-1} + i \text{ (Continued)}$$

| Years | Rate $i$ | | | | |
|---|---|---|---|---|---|
| $n$ | .01(1%) | .01125(1⅛%) | .0125(1¼%) | .015(1½%) | .0175(1¾%) |
| 1 | 1.01000000 | 1.01125000 | 1.01250000 | 1.01500000 | 1.01750000 |
| 2 | 0.50751244 | 0.50845323 | 0.50939441 | 0.51127792 | 0.51316295 |
| 3 | .34002211 | .34086130 | .34170117 | .34338296 | .34506746 |
| 4 | .25628109 | .25707058 | .25786102 | .25944479 | .26103237 |
| 5 | .20603980 | .20680034 | .20756211 | .20908932 | .21062142 |
| 6 | .17254837 | .17329034 | .17403381 | .17552521 | .17702256 |
| 7 | .14862828 | .14935762 | .15008872 | .15155616 | .15303059 |
| 8 | .13069029 | .13141071 | .13213314 | .13358402 | .13504292 |
| 9 | .11674036 | .11745432 | .11817055 | .11960982 | .12105813 |
| 10 | .10558208 | .10629131 | .10700307 | .10843418 | .10987534 |
| 11 | .09645408 | .09715984 | .09786839 | .09929384 | .10073033 |
| 12 | .08884879 | .08955203 | .09025831 | .09167999 | .09311377 |
| 13 | .08241482 | .08311626 | .08382100 | .08524036 | .08667283 |
| 14 | .07690117 | .07760138 | .07830515 | .07972332 | .08115562 |
| 15 | .07212378 | .07282321 | .07352646 | .07494436 | .07637739 |
| 16 | .06794460 | .06864363 | .06934672 | .07076508 | .07219958 |
| 17 | .06425806 | .06495698 | .06566023 | .06707966 | .06851623 |
| 18 | .06098205 | .06168113 | .06238479 | .06380578 | .06524492 |
| 19 | .05805175 | .05875120 | .05945548 | .06087847 | .06232061 |
| 20 | .05541531 | .05611531 | .05682039 | .05824574 | .05969122 |
| 21 | .05303075 | .05373145 | .05443749 | .05586550 | .05731464 |
| 22 | .05086372 | .05156525 | .05227238 | .05370332 | .05515638 |
| 23 | .04888584 | .04958833 | .05029666 | .05173075 | .05318796 |
| 24 | .04707347 | .04777701 | .04848665 | .04992410 | .05138565 |
| 25 | .04540675 | .04611144 | .04682247 | .04826345 | .04972952 |
| 26 | .04386888 | .04457479 | .04528729 | .04673196 | .04820269 |
| 27 | .04244553 | .04315273 | .04386677 | .04531527 | .04679079 |
| 28 | .04112444 | .04183299 | .04254862 | .04400108 | .04548151 |
| 29 | .03989502 | .04060498 | .04132228 | .04277878 | .04426424 |
| 30 | .03874811 | .03945953 | .04017854 | .04163919 | .04312975 |
| 31 | .03767573 | .03838866 | .03910942 | .04057430 | .04207005 |
| 32 | .03667089 | .03738535 | .03810791 | .03957710 | .04107812 |
| 33 | .03572744 | .03644349 | .03716786 | .03864144 | .04014779 |
| 34 | .03483997 | .03555763 | .03628387 | .03776189 | .03927363 |
| 35 | .03400368 | .03472299 | .03545111 | .03693363 | .03845082 |
| 36 | .03321431 | .03393529 | .03466533 | .03615240 | .03767507 |
| 37 | .03246805 | .03319072 | .03392270 | .03541437 | .03694257 |
| 38 | .03176150 | .03248589 | .03321983 | .03471613 | .03624990 |
| 39 | .03109160 | .03181773 | .03255365 | .03405463 | .03559399 |
| 40 | .03045560 | .03118349 | .03192141 | .03342710 | .03497209 |
| 41 | .02985102 | .03058069 | .03132063 | .03283106 | .03438170 |
| 42 | .02927563 | .03000709 | .03074906 | .03226426 | .03382057 |
| 43 | .02872737 | .02946064 | .03020466 | .03172465 | .03328666 |
| 44 | .02820441 | .02893949 | .02968557 | .03121038 | .03277810 |
| 45 | .02770505 | .02844197 | .02919012 | .03071976 | .03229321 |
| 46 | .02722775 | .02796652 | .02871675 | .03025125 | .03183043 |
| 47 | .02677111 | .02751173 | .02826406 | .02980342 | .03138836 |
| 48 | .02633384 | .02707632 | .02783075 | .02937500 | .03096569 |
| 49 | .02591474 | .02665910 | .02741563 | .02896478 | .03056124 |
| 50 | .02551273 | .02625898 | .02701763 | .02857168 | .03017391 |

$$a_{\overline{n}|}^{-1} = i/(1 - v^n) = s_{\overline{n}|}^{-1} + i \text{ (Continued)}$$

| Years $n$ | .01(1 %) | .01125(1⅛ %) | .0125(1¼ %) | .015(1½ %) | .0175(1¾ %) |
|---|---|---|---|---|---|
| | | | Rate $i$ | | |
| 50 | .02551273 | .02625898 | .02701763 | .02857168 | .03017391 |
| 51 | .02512680 | .02587494 | .02663571 | .02819469 | .02980269 |
| 52 | .02475603 | .02550606 | .02626897 | .02783287 | .02944665 |
| 53 | .02439956 | .02515149 | .02591653 | .02748537 | .02910492 |
| 54 | .02405658 | .02481043 | .02557760 | .02715138 | .02877672 |
| 55 | .02372637 | .02448213 | .02525145 | .02683018 | .02846129 |
| 56 | .02340824 | .02416592 | .02493739 | .02652106 | .02815795 |
| 57 | .02310156 | .02386116 | .02463478 | .02622341 | .02786606 |
| 58 | .02280573 | .02356726 | .02434303 | .02593661 | .02758503 |
| 59 | .02252020 | .02328366 | .02406158 | .02566012 | .02731430 |
| 60 | .02224445 | .02300985 | .02378993 | .02539343 | .02705336 |
| 61 | .02197800 | .02274534 | .02352758 | .02513604 | .02680172 |
| 62 | .02172041 | .02248969 | .02327410 | .02488751 | .02655892 |
| 63 | .02147125 | .02224247 | .02302904 | .02464741 | .02632455 |
| 64 | .02123013 | .02200329 | .02279203 | .02441534 | .02609821 |
| 65 | .02099667 | .02177178 | .02256268 | .02419094 | .02587952 |
| 66 | .02077052 | .02154758 | .02234065 | .02397386 | .02566813 |
| 67 | .02055136 | .02133037 | .02212560 | .02376376 | .02546372 |
| 68 | .02033889 | .02111985 | .02191724 | .02356033 | .02526597 |
| 69 | .02013280 | .02091571 | .02171527 | .02336329 | .02507459 |
| 70 | .01993282 | .02071769 | .02151941 | .02317235 | .02488930 |
| 71 | .01973870 | .02052552 | .02132941 | .02298727 | .02470985 |
| 72 | .01955019 | .02033896 | .02114501 | .02280779 | .02453600 |
| 73 | .01936706 | .02015779 | .02096600 | .02263368 | .02436750 |
| 74 | .01918910 | .01998177 | .02079215 | .02246473 | .02420413 |
| 75 | .01901609 | .01981072 | .02062325 | .02230072 | .02404570 |
| 76 | .01884784 | .01964442 | .02045910 | .02214146 | .02389200 |
| 77 | .01868416 | .01948269 | .02029953 | .02198676 | .02374285 |
| 78 | .01852488 | .01932536 | .02014436 | .02183645 | .02359806 |
| 79 | .01836983 | .01917226 | .01999341 | .02169036 | .02345748 |
| 80 | .01821885 | .01902323 | .01984652 | .02154832 | .02332093 |
| 81 | .01807179 | .01887812 | .01970356 | .02141019 | .02318828 |
| 82 | .01792851 | .01873678 | .01956437 | .02127583 | .02305936 |
| 83 | .01778887 | .01859908 | .01942881 | .02114509 | .02293406 |
| 84 | .01765273 | .01846489 | .01929675 | .02101784 | .02281223 |
| 85 | .01751998 | .01833409 | .01916808 | .02089396 | .02269375 |
| 86 | .01739050 | .01820654 | .01904267 | .02077333 | .02257850 |
| 87 | .01726418 | .01808215 | .01892041 | .02065584 | .02246636 |
| 88 | .01714089 | .01796081 | .01880119 | .02054138 | .02235724 |
| 89 | .01702056 | .01784240 | .01868491 | .02042984 | .02225102 |
| 90 | .01690306 | .01772684 | .01857146 | .02032113 | .02214760 |
| 91 | .01678832 | .01761403 | .01846076 | .02021516 | .02204690 |
| 92 | .01667624 | .01750387 | .01835272 | .02011182 | .02194882 |
| 93 | .01656673 | .01739629 | .01824724 | .02001104 | .02185327 |
| 94 | .01645971 | .01729119 | .01814425 | .01991273 | .02176017 |
| 95 | .01635511 | .01718851 | .01804366 | .01981681 | .02166944 |
| 96 | .01625284 | .01708816 | .01794541 | .01972321 | .02158101 |
| 97 | .01615284 | .01699007 | .01784941 | .01963186 | .02149480 |
| 98 | .01605503 | .01689418 | .01775560 | .01954268 | .02141074 |
| 99 | .01595936 | .01680041 | .01766391 | .01945560 | .02132876 |
| 100 | .01586574 | .01670870 | .01757428 | .01937057 | .02124880 |

### ANNUITY WHOSE PRESENT VALUE IS 1

$$a_{\overline{n}|}^{-1} = i/(1 - v^n) = s_{\overline{n}|}^{-1} + i \text{ (Continued)}$$

| Years | Rate $i$ | | | | |
|---|---|---|---|---|---|
| $n$ | .02(2 %) | .0225(2¼ %) | .025(2½ %) | .0275(2¾ %) | .03(3 %) |
| 1 | 1.02000000 | 1.02250000 | 1.02500000 | 1.02750000 | 1.03000000 |
| 2 | 0.51504950 | 0.51693758 | 0.51882716 | 0.52071825 | 0.52261084 |
| 3 | .34675467 | .34844458 | .35013717 | .35183243 | .35353036 |
| 4 | .26262375 | .26421893 | .26581788 | .26742059 | .26902705 |
| 5 | .21215839 | .21370021 | .21524686 | .21679832 | .21835457 |
| 6 | .17852581 | .18003496 | .18154997 | .18307083 | .18459750 |
| 7 | .15451196 | .15600025 | .15749543 | .15899747 | .16050635 |
| 8 | .13650980 | .13798462 | .13946735 | .14095795 | .14245639 |
| 9 | .12251544 | .12398170 | .12545899 | .12694095 | .12843386 |
| 10 | .11132653 | .11278768 | .11425876 | .11573972 | .11723051 |
| 11 | .10217794 | .10363649 | .10510596 | .10658629 | .10807745 |
| 12 | .09455960 | .09601740 | .09748713 | .09896871 | .10046209 |
| 13 | .08811835 | .08957686 | .09104827 | .09253252 | .09402954 |
| 14 | .08260197 | .08406230 | .08553652 | .08702457 | .08852634 |
| 15 | .07782547 | .07928852 | .08076646 | .08225917 | .08376658 |
| 16 | .07365013 | .07511663 | .07659899 | .07809710 | .07961085 |
| 17 | .06996984 | .07144039 | .07292777 | .07443186 | .07595253 |
| 18 | .06670210 | .06817720 | .06967008 | .07118063 | .07270870 |
| 19 | .06378177 | .06526182 | .06676062 | .06827802 | .06981388 |
| 20 | .06115672 | .06264207 | .06414713 | .06567173 | .06721571 |
| 21 | .05878477 | .06027572 | .06178733 | .06331941 | .06487178 |
| 22 | .05663140 | .05812821 | .05964661 | .06118640 | .06274739 |
| 23 | .05466810 | .05617097 | .05769638 | .05924410 | .06081390 |
| 24 | .05287110 | .05438023 | .05591282 | .05746863 | .05904742 |
| 25 | .05122044 | .05273599 | .05427592 | .05583997 | .05742787 |
| 26 | .04969923 | .05122134 | .05276875 | .05434116 | .05593829 |
| 27 | .04829309 | .04982188 | .05137687 | .05295776 | .05456421 |
| 28 | .04698967 | .04852525 | .05008793 | .05167738 | .05329323 |
| 29 | .04577836 | .04732081 | .04889127 | .05048935 | .05211467 |
| 30 | .04464992 | .04619934 | .04777764 | .04938442 | .05101926 |
| 31 | .04359635 | .04515280 | .04673900 | .04835453 | .04999893 |
| 32 | .04261061 | 04417415 | .04576831 | .04739263 | .04904662 |
| 33 | .04168653 | 04325722 | .04485938 | .04649253 | .04815612 |
| 34 | .04081867 | .04239655 | .04400675 | .04564875 | .04732196 |
| 35 | .04000221 | .04158731 | .04320558 | .04485645 | .04653929 |
| 36 | .03923285 | .04082522 | .04245158 | .04411132 | .04580379 |
| 37 | .03850678 | .04010643 | .04174090 | .04340953 | .04511162 |
| 38 | .03782057 | .03942753 | .04107012 | .04274764 | .04445934 |
| 39 | .03717114 | .03878543 | .04043615 | .04212256 | .04384385 |
| 40 | .03655575 | .03817738 | .03983623 | .04153151 | .04326238 |
| 41 | .03597188 | .03760087 | .03926786 | .04097200 | .04271241 |
| 42 | .03541729 | .03705364 | .03872876 | .04044175 | .04219167 |
| 43 | .03488993 | .03653364 | .03821688 | .03993871 | .04169811 |
| 44 | .03438794 | .03603901 | .03773037 | .03946100 | .04122985 |
| 45 | .03390962 | .03556805 | .03726751 | .03900693 | .04078518 |
| 46 | .03345342 | .03511921 | .03682676 | .03857493 | .04036254 |
| 47 | .03301792 | .03469107 | .03640669 | .03816358 | .03996050 |
| 48 | .03260184 | .03428233 | .03600599 | .03777158 | .03957777 |
| 49 | .03220396 | .03389179 | .03562348 | .03739773 | .03921314 |
| 50 | .03182321 | .03351836 | .03525806 | .03704092 | .03886549 |

## ANNUITY WHOSE PRESENT VALUE IS 1
$$a_{\overline{n}|}^{-1} = i/(1 - v^n) = s_{\overline{n}|}^{-1} + i \text{ (Continued)}$$

| Years | Rate $i$ | | | | |
|---|---|---|---|---|---|
| $n$ | .02(2%) | .0225(2¼%) | .025(2½%) | .0275(2¾%) | .03(3%) |
| 50 | .03182321 | .03351836 | .03525806 | .03704092 | .03886549 |
| 51 | .03145856 | .03316102 | .03490870 | .03670014 | .03853382 |
| 52 | .03110909 | .03281884 | .03457446 | .03637444 | .03821718 |
| 53 | .03077392 | .03249094 | .03425449 | .03606297 | .03791471 |
| 54 | .03045226 | .03217654 | .03394799 | .03576491 | .03762558 |
| 55 | .03014337 | .03187489 | .03365419 | .03547953 | .03734907 |
| 56 | .02984656 | .03158530 | .03337243 | .03520612 | .03708447 |
| 57 | .02956120 | .03130712 | .03310204 | .03494404 | .03683114 |
| 58 | .02928667 | .03103977 | .03284244 | .03469270 | .03658848 |
| 59 | .02902243 | .03078268 | .03259307 | .03445153 | .03635593 |
| 60 | .02876797 | .03053533 | .03235340 | .03422002 | .03613296 |
| 61 | .02852278 | .03029724 | .03212294 | .03399767 | .03591908 |
| 62 | .02828643 | .03006795 | .03190126 | .03378402 | .03571385 |
| 63 | .02805848 | .02984704 | .03168790 | .03357866 | .03551682 |
| 64 | .02783855 | .02963411 | .03148249 | .03338118 | .03532760 |
| 65 | .02762624 | .02942878 | .03128463 | .03319120 | .03514581 |
| 66 | .02742122 | .02923070 | .03109398 | .03300837 | .03497110 |
| 67 | .02722316 | .02903955 | .03091021 | .03283236 | .03480313 |
| 68 | .02703173 | .02885500 | .03073300 | .03266285 | .03464159 |
| 69 | .02684665 | .02867677 | .03056206 | .03249955 | .03448618 |
| 70 | .02666765 | .02850458 | .03039712 | .03234218 | .03433663 |
| 71 | .02649446 | .02833816 | .03023790 | .03219048 | .03419266 |
| 72 | .02632683 | .02817728 | .03008417 | .03204420 | .03405404 |
| 73 | .02616454 | .02802169 | .02993568 | .03190311 | .03392053 |
| 74 | .02600736 | .02787118 | .02979222 | .03176698 | .03379191 |
| 75 | .02585508 | .02772554 | .02965358 | .03163560 | .03366796 |
| 76 | .02570751 | .02758457 | .02951956 | .03150878 | .03354849 |
| 77 | .02556447 | .02744808 | .02938997 | .03138633 | .03343331 |
| 78 | .02542576 | .02731589 | .02926463 | .03126806 | .03332224 |
| 79 | .02529123 | .02718784 | .02914338 | .03115382 | .03321510 |
| 80 | .02516071 | .02706376 | .02902605 | .03104342 | .03311175 |
| 81 | .02503405 | .02694350 | .02891248 | .03093674 | .03301201 |
| 82 | .02491110 | .02682692 | .02880254 | .03083361 | .03291576 |
| 83 | .02479173 | .02671387 | .02869608 | .03073389 | .03282284 |
| 84 | .02467581 | .02660423 | .02859298 | .03063747 | .03273313 |
| 85 | .02456321 | .02649787 | .02849310 | .03054420 | .03264650 |
| 86 | .02445381 | .02639467 | .02839633 | .03045397 | .03256284 |
| 87 | .02434750 | .02629452 | .02830255 | .03036667 | .03248202 |
| 88 | .02424416 | .02619730 | .02821165 | .03028219 | .03240393 |
| 89 | .02414370 | .02610291 | .02812353 | .03020041 | .03232848 |
| 90 | .02404602 | .02601126 | .02803809 | .03012125 | .03225556 |
| 91 | .02395101 | .02592224 | .02795523 | .03004460 | .03218508 |
| 92 | .02385859 | .02583577 | .02787486 | .02997038 | .03211694 |
| 93 | .02376868 | .02575176 | .02779690 | .02989850 | .03205107 |
| 94 | .02368118 | .02567012 | .02772126 | .02982887 | .03198737 |
| 95 | .02359602 | .02559078 | .02764786 | .02976141 | .03192577 |
| 96 | .02351313 | .02551366 | .02757662 | .02969605 | .03186619 |
| 97 | .02343242 | .02543868 | .02750747 | .02963272 | .03180856 |
| 98 | .02335383 | .02536578 | .02744034 | .02957134 | .03175281 |
| 99 | .02327729 | .02529489 | .02737517 | .02951185 | .03169886 |
| 100 | .02320274 | .02522594 | .02731188 | .02945418 | .03164667 |

**ANNUITY WHOSE PRESENT VALUE IS 1**

$$a_{\overline{n}|}^{-1} = i/(1 - v^n) = s_{\overline{n}|}^{-1} + i \text{ (Continued)}$$

| Years | Rate $i$ | | | | |
|---|---|---|---|---|---|
| $n$ | .035(3½ %) | .04(4 %) | .045(4½ %) | .05(5 %) | .055(5½ %) |
| 1 | 1.03500000 | 1.04000000 | 1.04500000 | 1.05000000 | 1.05500000 |
| 2 | 0.52640049 | 0.53019608 | 0.53399756 | 0.53780488 | 0.54161800 |
| 3 | .35693418 | .36034854 | .36377336 | .36720856 | .37065407 |
| 4 | .27225114 | .27549005 | .27874365 | .28201183 | .28529449 |
| 5 | .22148137 | .22462711 | .22779164 | .23097480 | .23417644 |
| 6 | .18766821 | .19076190 | .19387839 | .19701747 | .20017895 |
| 7 | .16354449 | .16660961 | .16970147 | .17281982 | .17596442 |
| 8 | .14547665 | .14852783 | .15160965 | .15472181 | .15786401 |
| 9 | .13144601 | .13449299 | .13757447 | .14069008 | .14383946 |
| 10 | .12024137 | .12329094 | .12637882 | .12950457 | .13266777 |
| 11 | .11109197 | .11414904 | .11724818 | .12038889 | .12357065 |
| 12 | .10348395 | .10655217 | .10966619 | .11282541 | .11602923 |
| 13 | .09706157 | .10014373 | .10327535 | .10645577 | .10968426 |
| 14 | .09157073 | .09466897 | .09782032 | .10102397 | .10427912 |
| 15 | .08682507 | .08994110 | .09311381 | .09634229 | .09962560 |
| 16 | .08268483 | .08582000 | .08901537 | .09226991 | .09558254 |
| 17 | .07904313 | .08219852 | .08541758 | .08869914 | .09204197 |
| 18 | .07581684 | .07899333 | .08223690 | .08554622 | .08891992 |
| 19 | .07294033 | .07613862 | .07940734 | .08274501 | .08615006 |
| 20 | .07036108 | .07358175 | .07687614 | .08024259 | .08367933 |
| 21 | .06803659 | .07128011 | .07460057 | .07799611 | .08146478 |
| 22 | .06593207 | .06919881 | .07254565 | .07597051 | .07947123 |
| 23 | .06401880 | .06730906 | .07068249 | .07413682 | .07766965 |
| 24 | .06227283 | .06558683 | .06898703 | .07247090 | .07603580 |
| 25 | .06067404 | .06401196 | .06743903 | .07095246 | .07454935 |
| 26 | .05920540 | .06256738 | .06602137 | .06956432 | .07319307 |
| 27 | .05785241 | .06123854 | .06471946 | .06829186 | .07195228 |
| 28 | .05660265 | .06001298 | .06352081 | .06712253 | .07081440 |
| 29 | .05544538 | .05887993 | .06241461 | .06604551 | .06976857 |
| 30 | .05437133 | .05783010 | .06139154 | .06505144 | .06880539 |
| 31 | .05337240 | .05685535 | .06044345 | .06413212 | .06791665 |
| 32 | .05244150 | .05594859 | .05956320 | .06328042 | .06709519 |
| 33 | .05157242 | .05510357 | .05874453 | .06249004 | .06633469 |
| 34 | .05075966 | .05431477 | .05798191 | .06175545 | .06562958 |
| 35 | .04999835 | .05357732 | .05727045 | .06107171 | .06497493 |
| 36 | .04928416 | .05288688 | .05660578 | .06043446 | .06436635 |
| 37 | .04861325 | .05223957 | .05598402 | .05983979 | .06379993 |
| 38 | .04798214 | .05163192 | .05540169 | .05928423 | .06327217 |
| 39 | .04738775 | .05106083 | .05485567 | .05876462 | .06277991 |
| 40 | .04682728 | .05052349 | .05434315 | .05827816 | .06232034 |
| 41 | .04629822 | .05001738 | .05386158 | .05782229 | .06189090 |
| 42 | .04579828 | .04954020 | .05340868 | .05739471 | .06148927 |
| 43 | .04532539 | .04908989 | .05298235 | .05699333 | .06111337 |
| 44 | .04487768 | .04866454 | .05258071 | .05661625 | .06076128 |
| 45 | .04445343 | .04826246 | .05220202 | .05626173 | .06043127 |
| 46 | .04405108 | .04788205 | .05184471 | .05592820 | .06012175 |
| 47 | .04366919 | .04752189 | .05150734 | .05561421 | .05983129 |
| 48 | .04330646 | .04718065 | .05118858 | .05531843 | .05955854 |
| 49 | .04296167 | .04685712 | .05088722 | .05503965 | .05930230 |
| 50 | .04263371 | .04655020 | .05060215 | .05477674 | .05906145 |

## ANNUITY WHOSE PRESENT VALUE IS 1

$$a_{\overline{n}|}^{-1} = i/(1 - v^n) = s_{\overline{n}|}^{-1} + i \text{ (Continued)}$$

| Years $n$ | .06(6 %) | .065(6½ %) | .07(7 %) | .075(7½ %) | .08(8 %) |
|---|---|---|---|---|---|
| | | | Rate $i$ | | |
| 1 | 1.06000000 | 1.06500000 | 1.07000000 | 1.07500000 | 1.08000000 |
| 2 | 0.54543689 | 0.54926150 | 0.55309179 | 0.55692771 | 0.56076923 |
| 3 | .37410981 | .37757570 | .38105167 | .38453763 | .38803351 |
| 4 | .28859149 | .29190274 | .29522812 | .29856751 | .30192080 |
| 5 | .23739640 | .24063454 | .24389069 | .24716472 | .25045645 |
| 6 | .20336263 | .20656831 | .20979580 | .21304489 | .21631539 |
| 7 | .17913502 | .18233137 | .18555322 | .18880032 | .19207240 |
| 8 | .16103594 | .16423730 | .16746776 | .17072702 | .17401476 |
| 9 | .14702224 | .15023803 | .15348647 | .15676716 | .16007971 |
| 10 | .13586796 | .13910469 | .14237750 | .14568593 | .14902949 |
| 11 | .12679294 | .13005521 | .13335690 | .13669747 | .14007634 |
| 12 | .11927703 | .12256817 | .12590199 | .12927783 | .13269502 |
| 13 | .11296011 | .11628256 | .11965085 | .12306420 | .12652181 |
| 14 | .10758491 | .11094048 | .11434494 | .11779737 | .12129685 |
| 15 | .10296276 | .10635278 | .10979462 | .11328724 | .11682954 |
| 16 | .09895214 | .10237757 | .10585765 | .10939116 | .11297687 |
| 17 | .09544480 | .09890633 | .10242519 | .10600003 | .10962943 |
| 18 | .09235654 | .09585461 | .09941260 | .10302896 | .10670210 |
| 19 | .08962086 | .09315575 | .09675301 | .10041090 | .10412763 |
| 20 | .08718456 | .09075640 | .09439293 | .09809219 | .10185221 |
| 21 | .08500455 | .08861333 | .09228900 | .09602937 | .09983225 |
| 22 | .08304557 | .08669120 | .09040577 | .09418687 | .09803207 |
| 23 | .08127848 | .08496078 | .08871393 | .09253528 | .09642217 |
| 24 | .07967900 | .08339770 | .08718902 | .09105008 | .09497796 |
| 25 | .07822672 | .08198148 | .08581052 | .08971067 | .09367878 |
| 26 | .07690435 | .08069480 | .08456103 | .08849961 | .09250713 |
| 27 | .07569717 | .07952288 | .08342573 | .08740204 | .09144810 |
| 28 | .07459255 | .07845305 | .08239193 | .08640520 | .09048891 |
| 29 | .07357961 | .07747440 | .08144865 | .08549811 | .08961854 |
| 30 | .07264891 | .07657744 | .08058640 | .08467124 | .08882743 |
| 31 | .07179222 | .07575393 | .07979691 | .08391628 | .08810728 |
| 32 | .07100234 | .07499665 | .07907292 | .08322599 | .08745081 |
| 33 | .07027293 | .07429924 | .07840807 | .08259397 | .08685163 |
| 34 | .06959843 | .07365610 | .07779674 | .08201461 | .08630411 |
| 35 | .06897386 | .07306226 | .07723396 | .08148291 | .08580326 |
| 36 | .06839483 | .07251332 | .07671531 | .08099447 | .08534467 |
| 37 | .06785743 | .07200534 | .07623685 | .08054533 | .08492440 |
| 38 | .06735812 | .07153480 | .07579505 | .08013197 | .08453894 |
| 39 | .06689377 | .07109854 | .07538676 | .07975124 | .08418513 |
| 40 | .06646154 | .07069373 | .07500914 | .07940031 | .08386016 |
| 41 | .06605886 | .07031779 | .07465962 | .07907663 | .08356149 |
| 42 | .06568342 | .06996842 | .07433591 | .07877789 | .08328684 |
| 43 | .06533312 | .06964352 | .07403590 | .07850201 | .08303414 |
| 44 | .06500606 | .06934119 | .07375769 | .07824710 | .08280152 |
| 45 | .06470050 | .06905968 | .07349957 | .07801146 | .08258728 |
| 46 | .06441485 | .06879743 | .07325996 | .07779354 | .08238991 |
| 47 | .06414768 | .06855300 | .07303744 | .07759190 | .08220799 |
| 48 | .06389765 | .06832505 | .07283070 | .07740527 | .08204027 |
| 49 | .06366356 | .06811240 | .07263853 | .07723247 | .08188557 |
| 50 | .06344429 | .06791393 | .07245985 | .07707241 | .08174286 |

## COMPOUND AMOUNT OF 1 FOR FRACTIONAL
### PERIODS $(1+i)^{\frac{1}{p}}$

| p | ¼% | 1/12% | ½% | 7/12% | ¾% |
|---|---|---|---|---|---|
| 2 | 1.0012 492 | 1.0020 812 | 1.0024 969 | 1.0029 124 | 1.0037 430 |
| 3 | 1.0008 326 | 1.0013 870 | 1.0016 639 | 1.0019 407 | 1.0024 938 |
| 4 | 1.0006 244 | 1.0010 400 | 1.0012 477 | 1.0014 552 | 1.0018 697 |
| 6 | 1.0004 162 | 1.0006 932 | 1.0008 316 | 1.0009 699 | 1.0012 461 |
| 12 | 1.0002 089 | 1.0003 466 | 1.0004 157 | 1.0004 848 | 1.0006 229 |
| 13 | 1.0001 921 | 1.0003 199 | 1.0003 837 | 1.0004 475 | 1.0005 749 |
| 26 | 1.0000 960 | 1.0001 599 | 1.0001 919 | 1.0002 237 | 1.0002 874 |
| 52 | 1.0000 480 | 1.0000 800 | 1.0000 959 | 1.0001 119 | 1.0001 437 |
| 365 | 1.0000 068 | 1.0000 114 | 1.0000 137 | 1.0000 159 | 1.0000 205 |

| p | 1% | 1⅛% | 1¼% | 1½% | 1¾% |
|---|---|---|---|---|---|
| 2 | 1.0049 876 | 1.0056 093 | 1.0062 306 | 1.0074 721 | 1.0087 121 |
| 3 | 1.0033 223 | 1.0037 360 | 1.0041 494 | 1.0049 752 | 1.0057 996 |
| 4 | 1.0024 907 | 1.0028 008 | 1.0031 105 | 1.0037 291 | 1.0043 466 |
| 6 | 1.0016 598 | 1.0018 663 | 1.0020 726 | 1.0024 845 | 1.0028 956 |
| 12 | 1.0008 295 | 1.0009 327 | 1.0010 357 | 1.0012 415 | 1.0014 468 |
| 13 | 1.0007 657 | 1.0008 609 | 1.0009 560 | 1.0011 459 | 1.0013 354 |
| 26 | 1.0003 828 | 1.0004 304 | 1.0004 779 | 1.0005 728 | 1.0006 675 |
| 52 | 1.0001 914 | 1.0002 152 | 1.0002 389 | 1.0002 864 | 1.0003 337 |
| 365 | 1.0000 273 | 1.0000 307 | 1.0000 340 | 1.0000 408 | 1.0000 475 |

| p | 2% | 2¼% | 2½% | 2¾% | 3% |
|---|---|---|---|---|---|
| 2 | 1.0099 505 | 1.0111 874 | 1.0124 228 | 1.0136 568 | 1.0148 892 |
| 3 | 1.0066 227 | 1.0074 444 | 1.0082 648 | 1.0090 839 | 1.0099 016 |
| 4 | 1.0049 629 | 1.0055 782 | 1.0061 922 | 1.0068 052 | 1.0074 171 |
| 6 | 1.0033 059 | 1.0037 153 | 1.0041 239 | 1.0045 317 | 1.0049 386 |
| 12 | 1.0016 516 | 1.0018 559 | 1.0020 598 | 1.0022 633 | 1.0024 663 |
| 13 | 1.0015 244 | 1.0017 130 | 1.0019 012 | 1.0020 890 | 1.0022 763 |
| 26 | 1.0007 619 | 1.0008 562 | 1.0009 502 | 1.0010 440 | 1.0011 375 |
| 52 | 1.0003 809 | 1.0004 280 | 1.0004 750 | 1.0005 218 | 1.0005 686 |
| 365 | 1.0000 543 | 1.0000 610 | 1.0000 676 | 1.0000 743 | 1.0000 810 |

| p | 3½% | 4% | 4½% | 5% | 5½% |
|---|---|---|---|---|---|
| 2 | 1.0173 495 | 1.0198 039 | 1.0222 524 | 1.0246 951 | 1.0271 319 |
| 3 | 1.0115 331 | 1.0131 594 | 1.0147 805 | 1.0163 964 | 1.0180 071 |
| 4 | 1.0086 374 | 1.0098 534 | 1.0110 650 | 1.0122 722 | 1.0134 752 |
| 6 | 1.0057 500 | 1.0065 582 | 1.0073 631 | 1.0081 649 | 1.0089 634 |
| 12 | 1.0028 709 | 1.0032 737 | 1.0036 748 | 1.0040 741 | 1.0044 717 |
| 13 | 1.0026 498 | 1.0030 215 | 1.0033 916 | 1.0037 601 | 1.0041 270 |
| 26 | 1.0013 240 | 1.0015 096 | 1.0016 944 | 1.0018 783 | 1.0020 614 |
| 52 | 1.0006 618 | 1.0007 545 | 1.0008 468 | 1.0009 387 | 1.0010 302 |
| 365 | 1.0000 942 | 1.0001 075 | 1.0001 206 | 1.0001 337 | 1.0001 467 |

| p | 6% | 6½% | 7% | 7½% | 8% |
|---|---|---|---|---|---|
| 2 | 1.0295 630 | 1.0319 884 | 1.0344 080 | 1.0368 221 | 1.0392 305 |
| 3 | 1.0196 128 | 1.0212 135 | 1.0228 091 | 1.0243 998 | 1.0259 856 |
| 4 | 1.0146 738 | 1.0158 683 | 1.0170 585 | 1.0182 446 | 1.0194 265 |
| 6 | 1.0097 588 | 1.0105 511 | 1.0113 403 | 1.0121 264 | 1.0129 095 |
| 12 | 1.0048 676 | 1.0052 617 | 1.0056 541 | 1.0060 449 | 1.0064 340 |
| 13 | 1.0044 923 | 1.0048 560 | 1.0052 181 | 1.0055 786 | 1.0059 376 |
| 26 | 1.0022 436 | 1.0024 250 | 1.0026 056 | 1.0027 854 | 1.0029 644 |
| 52 | 1.0011 212 | 1.0012 118 | 1.0013 020 | 1.0013 918 | 1.0014 811 |
| 365 | 1.0001 596 | 1.0001 726 | 1.0001 854 | 1.0001 982 | 1.0002 109 |

# NOMINAL RATES CONVERTIBLE $p$ TIMES PER YEAR EQUIVALENT TO EFFECTIVE RATE $i$ GIVEN IN HEADING, $j_p = p[(1 + i)^{\frac{1}{p}} - 1]$

| $p$ | $\frac{1}{4}\%$ | $\frac{5}{12}\%$ | $\frac{1}{2}\%$ | $\frac{7}{12}\%$ | $\frac{3}{4}\%$ |
|---|---|---|---|---|---|
| $\frac{1}{4}$ | .0025 094 | .0041 928 | .0050 376 | .0058 846 | .0075 848 |
| $\frac{1}{2}$ | .0025 032 | .0041 754 | .0050 125 | .0058 504 | .0075 281 |
| 2 | .0024 984 | .0041 623 | .0049 938 | .0058 249 | .0074 860 |
| 4 | .0024 977 | .0041 602 | .0049 907 | .0058 206 | .0074 790 |
| 6 | .0024 974 | .0041 595 | .0049 896 | .0058 192 | .0074 767 |
| 12 | .0024 971 | .0041 587 | .0049 886 | .0058 178 | .0074 743 |
| 13 | .0024 971 | .0041 587 | .0049 885 | .0058 177 | .0074 742 |
| 52 | .0024 969 | .0041 582 | .0049 878 | .0058 167 | .0074 725 |
| 365 | .0024 969 | .0041 580 | .0049 876 | .0058 164 | .0074 721 |
| ∞ | .0024 969 | .0041 580 | .0049 875 | .0058 164 | .0074 720 |

| $p$ | $1\%$ | $1\frac{1}{8}\%$ | $1\frac{1}{4}\%$ | $1\frac{1}{2}\%$ | $1\frac{3}{4}\%$ |
|---|---|---|---|---|---|
| $\frac{1}{4}$ | .0101 510 | .0114 413 | .0127 363 | .0153 409 | .0179 648 |
| $\frac{1}{2}$ | .0100 500 | .0113 133 | .0125 781 | .0151 125 | .0176 531 |
| 2 | .0099 751 | .0112 185 | .0124 612 | .0149 442 | .0174 241 |
| 4 | .0099 627 | .0112 029 | .0124 418 | .0149 164 | .0173 863 |
| 6 | .0099 586 | .0111 976 | .0124 354 | .0149 071 | .0173 737 |
| 12 | .0099 545 | .0111 924 | .0124 290 | .0148 979 | .0173 612 |
| 13 | .0099 541 | .0111 920 | .0124 285 | .0148 971 | .0173 602 |
| 52 | .0099 513 | .0111 884 | .0124 240 | .0148 907 | .0173 515 |
| 365 | .0099 505 | .0111 874 | .0124 227 | .0148 889 | .0173 490 |
| ∞ | .0099 503 | .0111 872 | .0124 225 | .0148 886 | .0173 486 |

| $p$ | $2\%$ | $2\frac{1}{4}\%$ | $2\frac{1}{2}\%$ | $2\frac{3}{4}\%$ | $3\%$ |
|---|---|---|---|---|---|
| $\frac{1}{4}$ | .0206 080 | .0232 708 | .0259 532 | .0286 553 | .0313 772 |
| $\frac{1}{2}$ | .0202 000 | .0227 531 | .0253 125 | .0278 781 | .0304 500 |
| 2 | .0199 010 | .0223 748 | .0248 457 | .0273 135 | .0297 783 |
| 4 | .0198 517 | .0223 126 | .0247 690 | .0272 209 | .0296 683 |
| 6 | .0198 353 | .0222 919 | .0247 435 | .0271 901 | .0296 317 |
| 12 | .0198 190 | .0222 713 | .0247 180 | .0271 594 | .0295 952 |
| 13 | .0198 177 | .0222 697 | .0247 161 | .0271 570 | .0295 924 |
| 52 | .0198 064 | .0222 554 | .0246 985 | .0271 358 | .0295 672 |
| 365 | .0198 032 | .0222 513 | .0246 934 | .0271 297 | .0295 600 |
| ∞ | .0198 026 | .0222 506 | .0246 926 | .0271 287 | .0295 588 |

| $p$ | $3\frac{1}{2}\%$ | $4\%$ | $4\frac{1}{2}\%$ | $5\%$ | $5\frac{1}{2}\%$ |
|---|---|---|---|---|---|
| $\frac{1}{4}$ | .0368 808 | .0424 647 | .0481 297 | .0538 766 | .0597 062 |
| $\frac{1}{2}$ | .0356 125 | .0408 000 | .0460 125 | .0512 500 | .0565 125 |
| 2 | .0346 990 | .0396 078 | .0445 048 | .0493 902 | .0542 639 |
| 4 | .0345 498 | .0394 136 | .0442 600 | .0490 889 | .0539 007 |
| 6 | .0345 002 | .0393 492 | .0441 787 | .0489 891 | .0537 804 |
| 12 | .0344 508 | .0392 849 | .0440 977 | .0488 895 | .0536 604 |
| 13 | .0344 470 | .0392 799 | .0440 915 | .0488 818 | .0536 512 |
| 52 | .0344 128 | .0392 355 | .0440 355 | .0488 131 | .0535 683 |
| 365 | .0344 030 | .0392 228 | .0440 195 | .0487 934 | .0535 447 |
| ∞ | .0344 014 | .0392 207 | .0440 169 | .0487 902 | .0535 408 |

| $p$ | $6\%$ | $6\frac{1}{2}\%$ | $7\%$ | $7\frac{1}{2}\%$ | $8\%$ |
|---|---|---|---|---|---|
| $\frac{1}{4}$ | .0656 193 | .0716 166 | .0776 990 | .0838 673 | .0901 223 |
| $\frac{1}{2}$ | .0618 000 | .0671 125 | .0724 500 | .0778 125 | .0832 000 |
| 2 | .0591 260 | .0639 767 | .0688 161 | .0736 441 | .0784 610 |
| 4 | .0586 954 | .0634 731 | .0682 341 | .0729 784 | .0777 062 |
| 6 | .0585 528 | .0633 064 | .0680 416 | .0727 583 | .0774 567 |
| 12 | .0584 106 | .0631 403 | .0678 497 | .0725 390 | .0772 084 |
| 13 | .0583 997 | .0631 276 | .0678 350 | .0725 222 | .0771 893 |
| 52 | .0583 016 | .0630 129 | .0677 027 | .0723 710 | .0770 180 |
| 365 | .0582 736 | .0629 802 | .0676 649 | .0723 278 | .0769 692 |
| ∞ | .0582 689 | .0629 748 | .0676 586 | .0723 207 | .0769 610 |

## AMOUNT FOR YEAR OF *p* DEPOSITS OF 1/*p*, *p* TIMES PER YEAR, $i/j_p$

| p | ¼% | ⅜% | ½% | ⅝% | ¾% |
|---|---|---|---|---|---|
| ¼ | 0.9962 5 | 0.9937 717 | 0.9925 312 | 0.9912 924 | 0.9888 201 |
| ½ | 0.9974 8 | 0.9979 210 | 0.9975 062 | 0.9970 918 | 0.9962 640 |
| 2 | 1.0006 246 | 1.0010 406 | 1.0012 484 | 1.0014 562 | 1.0018 715 |
| 4 | 1.0009 370 | 1.0015 611 | 1.0018 730 | 1.0021 848 | 1.0028 081 |
| 6 | 1.0010 412 | 1.0017 347 | 1.0020 813 | 1.0024 278 | 1.0031 205 |
| 12 | 1.0011 453 | 1.0019 083 | 1.0022 896 | 1.0026 708 | 1.0034 329 |
| 13 | 1.0011 533 | 1.0019 216 | 1.0023 056 | 1.0026 895 | 1.0034 569 |
| 52 | 1.0012 254 | 1.0020 418 | 1.0024 498 | 1.0028 577 | 1.0036 732 |
| 365 | 1.0012 461 | 1.0020 762 | 1.0024 911 | 1.0029 058 | 1.0037 351 |
| ∞ | 1.0012 495 | 1.0020 819 | 1.0024 979 | 1.0029 138 | 1.0037 453 |

| p | 1% | 1⅛% | 1¼% | 1½% | 1¾% |
|---|---|---|---|---|---|
| ¼ | 0.9851 244 | 0.9832 823 | 0.9814 441 | 0.9777 791 | 0.9741 295 |
| ½ | 0.9950 249 | 0.9944 065 | 0.9937 888 | 0.9925 558 | 0.9913 259 |
| 2 | 1.0024 938 | 1.0028 046 | 1.0031 153 | 1.0037 360 | 1.0043 618 |
| 4 | 1.0037 422 | 1.0042 089 | 1.0046 754 | 1.0056 076 | 1.0065 388 |
| 6 | 1.0041 586 | 1.0046 773 | 1.0051 958 | 1.0062 319 | 1.0072 671 |
| 12 | 1.0045 751 | 1.0051 458 | 1.0057 163 | 1.0068 565 | 1.0079 957 |
| 13 | 1.0046 071 | 1.0051 819 | 1.0057 564 | 1.0069 046 | 1.0080 518 |
| 52 | 1.0048 956 | 1.0055 063 | 1.0061 169 | 1.0073 372 | 1.0085 564 |
| 365 | 1.0049 780 | 1.0055 991 | 1.0062 199 | 1.0074 608 | 1.0087 007 |
| ∞ | 1.0049 917 | 1.0056 145 | 1.0062 371 | 1.0074 814 | 1.0087 247 |

| p | 2% | 2¼% | 2½% | 2¾% | 3% |
|---|---|---|---|---|---|
| ¼ | 0.9704 950 | 0.9668 757 | 0.9632 715 | 0.9596 824 | 0.9561 082 |
| ½ | 0.9900 990 | 0.9888 752 | 0.9876 543 | 0.9864 365 | 0.9852 217 |
| 2 | 1.0049 752 | 1.0055 937 | 1.0062 114 | 1.0068 284 | 1.0074 446 |
| 4 | 1.0074 686 | 1.0083 984 | 1.0093 268 | 1.0102 542 | 1.0111 807 |
| 6 | 1.0083 013 | 1.0093 344 | 1.0103 667 | 1.0113 979 | 1.0124 282 |
| 12 | 1.0091 339 | 1.0102 711 | 1.0114 072 | 1.0125 424 | 1.0136 766 |
| 13 | 1.0091 980 | 1.0103 431 | 1.0114 873 | 1.0126 305 | 1.0137 727 |
| 52 | 1.0097 747 | 1.0109 919 | 1.0122 082 | 1.0134 234 | 1.0146 376 |
| 365 | 1.0099 396 | 1.0111 775 | 1.0124 143 | 1.0136 502 | 1.0148 850 |
| ∞ | 1.0099 670 | 1.0112 083 | 1.0124 486 | 1.0136 878 | 1.0149 261 |

| p | 3½% | 4% | 4½% | 5% | 5½% |
|---|---|---|---|---|---|
| ¼ | 0.9490 046 | 0.9419 6 | 0.9349 7 | 0.9280 5 | 0.9211 8 |
| ½ | 0.9828 010 | 0.9803 922 | 0.9779 951 | 0.9756 098 | 0.9732 360 |
| 2 | 1.0086 748 | 1.0099 020 | 1.0111 262 | 1.0123 475 | 1.0135 660 |
| 4 | 1.0130 309 | 1.0148 774 | 1.0167 203 | 1.0185 594 | 1.0203 950 |
| 6 | 1.0144 858 | 1.0165 396 | 1.0185 895 | 1.0206 357 | 1.0226 781 |
| 12 | 1.0159 420 | 1.0182 035 | 1.0204 611 | 1.0227 148 | 1.0249 647 |
| 13 | 1.0160 541 | 1.0183 316 | 1.0206 051 | 1.0228 748 | 1.0251 407 |
| 52 | 1.0170 632 | 1.0194 847 | 1.0219 623 | 1.0243 160 | 1.0267 259 |
| 365 | 1.0173 517 | 1.0198 145 | 1.0222 733 | 1.0247 282 | 1.0271 793 |
| ∞ | 1.0173 997 | 1.0198 693 | 1.0223 349 | 1.0247 967 | 1.0272 546 |

| p | 6% | 6½% | 7% | 7½% | 8% |
|---|---|---|---|---|---|
| ¼ | 0.9143 7 | 0.9076 1 | 0.9009 1 | 0.8942 7 | 0.8876 8 |
| ½ | 0.9708 738 | 0.9685 230 | 0.9661 836 | 0.9638 554 | 0.9615 385 |
| 2 | 1.0147 815 | 1.0159 942 | 1.0172 040 | 1.0184 110 | 1.0196 152 |
| 4 | 1.0222 269 | 1.0240 552 | 1.0258 800 | 1.0277 013 | 1.0295 190 |
| 6 | 1.0247 168 | 1.0267 517 | 1.0287 830 | 1.0308 106 | 1.0328 346 |
| 12 | 1.0272 107 | 1.0294 529 | 1.0316 914 | 1.0339 262 | 1.0361 572 |
| 13 | 1.0274 027 | 1.0296 609 | 1.0319 154 | 1.0341 661 | 1.0364 131 |
| 52 | 1.0291 319 | 1.0315 340 | 1.0339 324 | 1.0363 270 | 1.0387 179 |
| 365 | 1.0296 265 | 1.0320 699 | 1.0345 095 | 1.0369 453 | 1.0393 774 |
| ∞ | 1.0297 087 | 1.0321 589 | 1.0346 053 | 1.0370 480 | 1.0394 870 |

# AMERICAN EXPERIENCE MORTALITY TABLE

Based on 100,000 living at age 10, giving: $l_x$, number of living; $d_x$, number of deaths; $p_x$, probability of living; $q_x$, probability of dying for age $x$ from 10 to 95.

| $x$ | $l_x$ | $d_x$ | $p_x$ | $q_x$ | $x$ | $l_x$ | $d_x$ | $p_x$ | $q_x$ |
|---|---|---|---|---|---|---|---|---|---|
| 10 | 100000 | 749 | .992510 | .007490 | 55 | 64563 | 1199 | .981429 | .018571 |
| 11 | 99251 | 746 | .992484 | .007516 | 56 | 63364 | 1260 | .980115 | .019885 |
| 12 | 98505 | 743 | .992457 | .007543 | 57 | 62104 | 1325 | .978665 | .021335 |
| 13 | 97762 | 740 | .992431 | .007569 | 58 | 60779 | 1394 | .977064 | .022936 |
| 14 | 97022 | 737 | .992404 | .007596 | 59 | 59385 | 1468 | .975280 | .024720 |
| 15 | 96285 | 735 | .992366 | .007634 | 60 | 57917 | 1546 | .973307 | .026693 |
| 16 | 95550 | 732 | .992339 | .007661 | 61 | 56371 | 1628 | .971120 | .028880 |
| 17 | 94818 | 729 | .992312 | .007688 | 62 | 54743 | 1713 | .968708 | .031292 |
| 18 | 94089 | 727 | .992273 | .007727 | 63 | 53030 | 1800 | .966057 | .033943 |
| 19 | 93362 | 725 | .992235 | .007765 | 64 | 51230 | 1889 | .963127 | .036873 |
| 20 | 92637 | 723 | .992195 | .007805 | 65 | 49341 | 1980 | .959871 | .040129 |
| 21 | 91914 | 722 | .992145 | .007855 | 66 | 47361 | 2070 | .956293 | .043707 |
| 22 | 91192 | 721 | .992094 | .007906 | 67 | 45291 | 2158 | .952353 | .047647 |
| 23 | 90471 | 720 | .992042 | .007958 | 68 | 43133 | 2243 | .947998 | .052002 |
| 24 | 89751 | 719 | .991989 | .008011 | 69 | 40890 | 2321 | .943238 | .056762 |
| 25 | 89032 | 718 | .991935 | .008065 | 70 | 38569 | 2391 | .938007 | .061993 |
| 26 | 88314 | 718 | .991870 | .008130 | 71 | 36178 | 2448 | .932335 | .067665 |
| 27 | 87596 | 718 | .991803 | .008197 | 72 | 33730 | 2487 | .926267 | .073733 |
| 28 | 86878 | 718 | .991736 | .008264 | 73 | 31243 | 2505 | .919822 | .080178 |
| 29 | 86160 | 719 | .991655 | .008345 | 74 | 28738 | 2501 | .912972 | .087028 |
| 30 | 85441 | 720 | .991573 | .008427 | 75 | 26237 | 2476 | .905629 | .094371 |
| 31 | 84721 | 721 | .991490 | .008510 | 76 | 23761 | 2431 | .897689 | .102311 |
| 32 | 84000 | 723 | .991393 | .008607 | 77 | 21330 | 2369 | .888936 | .111064 |
| 33 | 83277 | 726 | .991282 | .008718 | 78 | 18961 | 2291 | .879173 | .120827 |
| 34 | 82551 | 729 | .991169 | .008831 | 79 | 16670 | 2196 | .868266 | .131734 |
| 35 | 81822 | 732 | .991054 | .008946 | 80 | 14474 | 2091 | .855534 | .144466 |
| 36 | 81090 | 737 | .990911 | .009089 | 81 | 12383 | 1964 | .841395 | .158605 |
| 37 | 80353 | 742 | .990766 | .009234 | 82 | 10419 | 1816 | .825703 | .174297 |
| 38 | 79611 | 749 | .990592 | .009408 | 83 | 8603 | 1648 | .808439 | .191561 |
| 39 | 78862 | 756 | .990414 | .009586 | 84 | 6955 | 1470 | .788641 | .211359 |
| 40 | 78106 | 765 | .990206 | .009794 | 85 | 5485 | 1292 | .764448 | .235552 |
| 41 | 77341 | 774 | .989992 | .010008 | 86 | 4193 | 1114 | .734319 | .265681 |
| 42 | 76567 | 785 | .989748 | .010252 | 87 | 3079 | 933 | .696980 | .303020 |
| 43 | 75782 | 797 | .989483 | .010517 | 88 | 2146 | 744 | .653308 | .346692 |
| 44 | 74985 | 812 | .989171 | .010829 | 89 | 1402 | 555 | .604137 | .395863 |
| 45 | 74173 | 828 | .988837 | .011163 | 90 | 847 | 385 | .545455 | .454545 |
| 46 | 73345 | 848 | .988438 | .011562 | 91 | 462 | 246 | .467532 | .532468 |
| 47 | 72497 | 870 | .988000 | .012000 | 92 | 216 | 137 | .365741 | .634259 |
| 48 | 71627 | 896 | .987491 | .012509 | 93 | 79 | 58 | .265823 | .734177 |
| 49 | 70731 | 927 | .986894 | .013106 | 94 | 21 | 18 | .142857 | .857143 |
| 50 | 69804 | 962 | .986219 | .013781 | 95 | 3 | 3 | .000000 | 1.000000 |
| 51 | 68842 | 1001 | .985459 | .014541 | | | | | |
| 52 | 67841 | 1044 | .984611 | .015389 | | | | | |
| 53 | 66797 | 1091 | .983667 | .016333 | | | | | |
| 54 | 65706 | 1143 | .982604 | .017396 | | | | | |

## COMMISSIONERS 1941 STANDARD ORDINARY MORTALITY TABLE*

| $x$ | $l_x$ | $d_x$ | $p_x$ | $\overset{\circ}{e}_x$ | $x$ | $l_x$ | $d_x$ | $p_x$ | $\overset{\circ}{e}_x$ |
|---|---|---|---|---|---|---|---|---|---|
| **0** | 1 023 102 | 23 102 | .977 42 | 62.33 | **50** | 810 900 | 9 990 | .987 68 | 21.37 |
| 1 | 1 000 000 | 5 770 | .994 23 | 62.76 | 51 | 800 910 | 10 628 | .986 73 | 20.64 |
| 2 | 994 230 | 4 116 | .995 86 | 62.12 | 52 | 790 282 | 11 301 | .985 70 | 19.91 |
| 3 | 990 114 | 3 347 | .996 62 | 61.37 | 53 | 778 981 | 12 020 | .984 57 | 19.19 |
| 4 | 986 767 | 2 950 | .997 01 | 60.58 | 54 | 766 961 | 12 770 | .983 35 | 18.48 |
| **5** | 983 817 | 2 715 | .997 24 | 59.76 | **55** | 754 191 | 13 560 | .982 02 | 17.78 |
| 6 | 981 102 | 2 561 | .997 39 | 58.92 | 56 | 740 631 | 14 390 | .980 57 | 17.10 |
| 7 | 978 541 | 2 417 | .997 53 | 58.08 | 57 | 726 241 | 15 251 | .979 00 | 16.43 |
| 8 | 976 124 | 2 255 | .997 69 | 57.22 | 58 | 710 990 | 16 147 | .977 29 | 15.77 |
| 9 | 973 869 | 2 065 | .997 88 | 56.35 | 59 | 694 843 | 17 072 | .975 43 | 15.13 |
| **10** | 971 804 | 1 914 | .998 03 | 55.47 | **60** | 677 771 | 18 022 | .973 41 | 14.50 |
| 11 | 969 890 | 1 852 | .998 09 | 54.58 | 61 | 659 749 | 18 988 | .971 22 | 13.88 |
| 12 | 968 038 | 1 859 | .998 08 | 53.68 | 62 | 640 761 | 19 979 | .968 82 | 13.27 |
| 13 | 966 179 | 1 913 | .998 02 | 52.78 | 63 | 620 782 | 20 958 | .966 24 | 12.69 |
| 14 | 964 266 | 1 996 | .997 93 | 51.89 | 64 | 599 824 | 21 942 | .963 42 | 12.11 |
| **15** | 962 270 | 2 069 | .997 85 | 50.99 | **65** | 577 882 | 22 907 | .960 36 | 11.55 |
| 16 | 960 201 | 2 103 | .997 81 | 50.10 | 66 | 554 975 | 23 842 | .957 04 | 11.01 |
| 17 | 958 098 | 2 156 | .997 75 | 49.21 | 67 | 531 133 | 24 730 | .953 44 | 10.48 |
| 18 | 955 942 | 2 199 | .997 70 | 48.32 | 68 | 506 403 | 25 553 | .949 54 | 9.97 |
| 19 | 953 743 | 2 260 | .997 63 | 47.43 | 69 | 480 850 | 26 302 | .945 30 | 9.47 |
| **20** | 951 483 | 2 312 | .997 57 | 46.54 | **70** | 454 548 | 26 955 | .940 70 | 8.99 |
| 21 | 949 171 | 2 382 | .997 49 | 45.66 | 71 | 427 593 | 27 481 | .935 73 | 8.52 |
| 22 | 946 789 | 2 452 | .997 41 | 44.77 | 72 | 400 112 | 27 872 | .930 34 | 8.08 |
| 23 | 944 337 | 2 531 | .997 32 | 43.88 | 73 | 372 240 | 28 104 | .924 50 | 7.64 |
| 24 | 941 806 | 2 609 | .997 23 | 43.00 | 74 | 344 136 | 28 154 | .918 19 | 7.23 |
| **25** | 939 197 | 2 705 | .997 12 | 42.12 | **75** | 315 982 | 28 009 | .911 36 | 6.82 |
| 26 | 936 492 | 2 800 | .997 01 | 41.24 | 76 | 287 973 | 27 651 | .903 98 | 6.44 |
| 27 | 933 692 | 2 904 | .996 89 | 40.36 | 77 | 260 322 | 27 071 | .896 01 | 6.07 |
| 28 | 930 788 | 3 025 | .996 75 | 39.49 | 78 | 233 251 | 26 262 | .887 41 | 5.72 |
| 29 | 927 763 | 3 154 | .996 60 | 38.61 | 79 | 206 989 | 25 224 | .878 14 | 5.38 |
| **30** | 924 609 | 3 292 | .996 44 | 37.74 | **80** | 181 765 | 23 966 | .868 15 | 5.06 |
| 31 | 921 317 | 3 437 | .996 27 | 36.88 | 81 | 157 799 | 22 502 | .857 40 | 4.75 |
| 32 | 917 880 | 3 598 | .996 08 | 36.01 | 82 | 135 297 | 20 857 | .845 84 | 4.46 |
| 33 | 914 282 | 3 767 | .995 88 | 35.15 | 83 | 114 440 | 19 062 | .833 43 | 4.18 |
| 34 | 910 515 | 3 961 | .995 65 | 34.29 | 84 | 95 378 | 17 157 | .820 12 | 3.91 |
| **35** | 906 554 | 4 161 | .995 41 | 33 44 | **85** | 78 221 | 15 185 | .805 87 | 3.66 |
| 36 | 902 393 | 4 386 | .995 14 | 32.59 | 86 | 63 036 | 13 198 | .790 63 | 3.42 |
| 37 | 898 007 | 4 625 | .994 85 | 31.75 | 87 | 49 838 | 11 245 | .774 37 | 3.19 |
| 38 | 893 382 | 4 878 | .994 54 | 30.91 | 88 | 38 593 | 9 378 | .757 00 | 2.98 |
| 39 | 888 504 | 5 162 | .994 19 | 30.08 | 89 | 29 215 | 7 638 | .738 56 | 2.77 |
| **40** | 883 342 | 5 459 | .993 82 | 29.25 | **90** | 21 577 | 6 063 | .719 01 | 2.58 |
| 41 | 877 883 | 5 785 | .993 41 | 28.43 | 91 | 15 514 | 4 681 | .698 27 | 2.39 |
| 42 | 872 098 | 6 131 | .992 97 | 27.62 | 92 | 10 833 | 3 506 | .676 36 | 2.21 |
| 43 | 865 967 | 6 503 | .992 49 | 26.81 | 93 | 7 327 | 2 540 | .653 34 | 2.03 |
| 44 | 859 464 | 6 910 | .991 96 | 26.01 | 94 | 4 787 | 1 776 | .629 00 | 1.84 |
| **45** | 852 554 | 7 340 | .991 39 | 25.21 | **95** | 3 011 | 1 193 | .603 79 | 1.63 |
| 46 | 845 214 | 7 801 | .990 77 | 24.43 | 96 | 1 818 | 813 | .552 81 | 1.37 |
| 47 | 837 413 | 8 299 | .990 09 | 23.65 | 97 | 1 005 | 551 | .451 74 | 1.08 |
| 48 | 829 114 | 8 822 | .989 36 | 22.88 | 98 | 454 | 329 | .275 33 | .78 |
| 49 | 820 292 | 9 392 | .988 55 | 22.12 | 99 | 125 | 125 | .000 00 | .50 |

* Reproduced by permission of the Actuarial Society of America.

# COMMUTATION COLUMNS $2\frac{1}{2}\%$*

## Commissioners 1941 Standard Ordinary Mortality Table

| $x$ | $D_x$ | $N_x$ | $C_x$ | $M_x$ | $1 + a_x$ | $A_x$ |
|---|---|---|---|---|---|---|
| 0 | 1 023 102.00 | 31 374 230 | 22 538.536 6 | 257 876.88 | 30.665 8 | 0.252 054 |
| 1 | 975 609.76 | 30 351 128 | 5 491.969 1 | 235 338.35 | 31.109 9 | .241 222 |
| 2 | 946 322.43 | 29 375 518 | 3 822.115 2 | 229 846.38 | 31.041 8 | .242 884 |
| 3 | 919 419.28 | 28 429 196 | 3 032.216 8 | 226 024.26 | 30.920 8 | 245 834 |
| 4 | 893 962.20 | 27 509 776 | 2 607 370 2 | 222 992.05 | 30.772 9 | .249 442 |
| 5 | 869 550.88 | 26 615 814 | 2 341.136 0 | 220 384.68 | 30.608 7 | .253 447 |
| 6 | 846 001.18 | 25 746 263 | 2 154.480 3 | 218 043.54 | 30.432 9 | .257 734 |
| 7 | 823 212.53 | 24 900 262 | 1 983.744 5 | 215 889.06 | 30.247 7 | .262 252 |
| 8 | 801 150.42 | 24 077 050 | 1 805.642 5 | 213 905.32 | 30.053 1 | .266 998 |
| 9 | 779 804.53 | 23 275 899 | 1 613.174 7 | 212 099.67 | 29.848 4 | .271 991 |
| 10 | 759 171.73 | 22 496 095 | 1 458.745 1 | 210 486.50 | 29.632 4 | .277 258 |
| 11 | 739 196.60 | 21 736 923 | 1 377.065 5 | 209 027.75 | 29.406 1 | .282 777 |
| 12 | 719 790.36 | 20 997 726 | 1 348.556 5 | 207 650.69 | 29.172 0 | .288 488 |
| 13 | 700 885.94 | 20 277 936 | 1 353.882 1 | 206 302.13 | 28.931 9 | .294 345 |
| 14 | 682 437.28 | 19 577 050 | 1 378.169 3 | 204 948.25 | 28.687 0 | .300 318 |
| 15 | 664 414.29 | 18 894 613 | 1 393.730 0 | 203 570.08 | 28.438 0 | .306 390 |
| 16 | 646 815.33 | 18 230 198 | 1 382.081 2 | 202 176.35 | 28.184 5 | .312 572 |
| 17 | 629 657.27 | 17 583 383 | 1 382.353 7 | 200 794.27 | 27.925 3 | .318 895 |
| 18 | 612 917.42 | 16 953 726 | 1 375.535 5 | 199 411.91 | 27.660 7 | .325 349 |
| 19 | 596 592.68 | 16 340 808 | 1 379.212 5 | 198 036.38 | 27.390 2 | .331 946 |
| 20 | 580 662.42 | 15 744 216 | 1 376.533 1 | 196 657.17 | 27.114 2 | .338 677 |
| 21 | 565 123.40 | 15 163 553 | 1 383.619 6 | 195 280.63 | 26.832 3 | .345 554 |
| 22 | 549 956.28 | 14 598 430 | 1 389.541 6 | 193 897.01 | 26.544 7 | .352 568 |
| 23 | 535 153.17 | 14 048 474 | 1 399.327 5 | 192 507.47 | 26.251 3 | .359 724 |
| 24 | 520 701.32 | 13 513 320 | 1 407.270 0 | 191 108.14 | 25.952 2 | .367 021 |
| 25 | 506 594.02 | 12 992 619 | 1 423.464 9 | 189 700.88 | 25.647 0 | .374 463 |
| 26 | 492 814.61 | 12 486 025 | 1 437.519 2 | 188 277.41 | 25.336 2 | .382 045 |
| 27 | 479 357.22 | 11 993 210 | 1 454.549 1 | 186 839.89 | 25.019 4 | .389 772 |
| 28 | 466 211.03 | 11 513 853 | 1 478.200 3 | 185 385.34 | 24.696 7 | .397 643 |
| 29 | 453 361.83 | 11 047 642 | 1 503.646 4 | 183 907.14 | 24.368 3 | .405 652 |
| 30 | 440 800.58 | 10 594 280 | 1 531.158 0 | 182 403.50 | 24.034 2 | .413 800 |
| 31 | 428 518.18 | 10 153 480 | 1 559.609 4 | 180 872.34 | 23.694 4 | .422 088 |
| 32 | 416 506.91 | 9 724 962 | 1 592.845 3 | 179 312.73 | 23.348 9 | .430 516 |
| 33 | 404 755.37 | 9 308 455 | 1 626.987 4 | 177 719.88 | 22.997 7 | .439 080 |
| 34 | 393 256.29 | 8 903 699 | 1 669.050 8 | 176 092.90 | 22.641 0 | .447 781 |
| 35 | 381 995.63 | 8 510 443 | 1 710.561 0 | 174 423.84 | 22.278 9 | .456 612 |
| 36 | 370 968.10 | 8 128 447 | 1 759 080 1 | 172 713.28 | 21.911 4 | .465 574 |
| 37 | 360 161.02 | 7 757 479 | 1 809.692 8 | 170 954.20 | 21.538 9 | .474 660 |
| 38 | 349 566.90 | 7 397 318 | 1 862.134 5 | 169 144.51 | 21.161 4 | .483 869 |
| 39 | 339 178.75 | 7 047 751 | 1 922.486 9 | 167 282.38 | 20.778 9 | .493 198 |
| 40 | 328 983.61 | 6 708 573 | 1 983.511 0 | 165 359.89 | 20.391 8 | .502 639 |
| 41 | 318 976.11 | 6 379 589 | 2 050.694 7 | 163 376.38 | 20.000 2 | .512 190 |
| 42 | 309 145.51 | 6 060 613 | 2 120.338 1 | 161 325.68 | 19.604 4 | .521 844 |
| 43 | 299 485.04 | 5 751 467 | 2 194.136 7 | 159 205.35 | 19.204 5 | .531 597 |
| 44 | 289 986.39 | 5 451 982 | 2 274.595 1 | 157 011.21 | 18.800 8 | .541 443 |
| 45 | 280 638.95 | 5 161 996 | 2 357 209 0 | 154 736 61 | 18.393 7 | .551 373 |
| 46 | 271 436.89 | 4 881 357 | 2 444.154 2 | 152 379.40 | 17.983 4 | .561 381 |
| 47 | 262 372.33 | 4 609 920 | 2 536.765 0 | 149 935.25 | 17.570 1 | .571 460 |
| 48 | 253 436.24 | 4 347 548 | 2 630.859 4 | 147 398.48 | 17.154 4 | .581 600 |
| 49 | 244 624.00 | 4 094 112 | 2 732.529 2 | 144 767.62 | 16.736 3 | .591 796 |
| 50 | 235 925.04 | 3 849 488 | 2 835.622 1 | 142 035.10 | 16.316 6 | .602 035 |

* Reproduced by permission of the Actuarial Society of America.

# COMMUTATION COLUMNS $2\frac{1}{2}\%$* (Continued)

## Commissioners 1941 Standard Ordinary Mortality Table

| $x$ | $D_x$ | $N_x$ | $C_x$ | $M_x$ | $a_x$ | $A_x$ |
|---|---|---|---|---|---|---|
| 51 | 227 335.15 | 3 613 563 | 2 943.137 4 | 139 199.47 | 15.895 3 | .612 310 |
| 52 | 218 847.25 | 3 386 227 | 3 053.177 2 | 136 256.34 | 15.473 0 | .622 609 |
| 53 | 210 456.33 | 3 167 380 | 3 168.222 9 | 133 203.16 | 15.050 1 | .632 925 |
| 54 | 202 155.03 | 2 956 924 | 3 283.812 1 | 130 034.94 | 14.627 0 | .643 244 |
| 55 | 193 940.61 | 2 754 769 | 3 401.913 1 | 126 751.12 | 14.204 2 | .653 556 |
| 56 | 185 808.43 | 2 560 828 | 3 522.090 1 | 123 349.21 | 13.782 1 | .663 852 |
| 57 | 177 754.43 | 2 375 020 | 3 641.783 5 | 119 827.12 | 13.361 2 | .674 116 |
| 58 | 169 777.17 | 2 197 265 | 3 761.696 8 | 116 185.34 | 12.942 1 | .684 340 |
| 59 | 161 874.57 | 2 027 488 | 3 880.185 4 | 112 423.64 | 12.525 1 | .694 511 |
| 60 | 154 046.23 | 1 865 614 | 3 996.199 9 | 108 543.46 | 12.110 7 | .704 616 |
| 61 | 146 292.80 | 1 711 567 | 4 107.708 0 | 104 547.26 | 11.699 6 | .714 644 |
| 62 | 138 616.97 | 1 565 275 | 4 216.676 0 | 100 439.55 | 11.292 1 | .724 583 |
| 63 | 131 019.40 | 1 426 658 | 4 315.413 8 | 96 222.87 | 10.888 9 | .734 417 |
| 64 | 123 508.39 | 1 295 638 | 4 407.831 2 | 91 907.46 | 10.490 3 | .744 139 |
| 65 | 116 088.15 | 1 172 130 | 4 489.449 7 | 87 499.63 | 10.096 9 | .753 734 |
| 66 | 108 767.29 | 1 056 042 | 4 558.728 2 | 83 010.18 | 9.709 2 | .763 191 |
| 67 | 101 555.70 | 947 274.4 | 4 613.189 3 | 78 451.45 | 9.327 6 | .772 497 |
| 68 | 94 465.545 | 845 718.7 | 4 650.452 1 | 73 838.26 | 8.952 7 | .781 642 |
| 69 | 87 511.050 | 751 253.1 | 4 670.014 3 | 69 187.81 | 8.584 7 | .790 618 |
| 70 | 80 706.625 | 663 742.1 | 4 669.226 0 | 64 517.79 | 8.224 1 | .799 411 |
| 71 | 74 068.942 | 583 035.4 | 4 644.235 4 | 59 848.57 | 7.871 5 | .808 012 |
| 72 | 67 618.148 | 508 966.5 | 4 595.428 1 | 55 204.33 | 7.527 1 | .816 413 |
| 73 | 61 373.498 | 441 348.3 | 4 520.662 7 | 50 608.90 | 7.191 2 | .824 605 |
| 74 | 55 355.921 | 379 974.8 | 4 418.249 2 | 46 088.24 | 6.864 2 | .832 580 |
| 75 | 49 587.526 | 324 618.9 | 4 288.286 9 | 41 669.99 | 6.546 4 | .840 332 |
| 76 | 44 089.787 | 275 031.4 | 4 130.220 2 | 37 381.70 | 6.238 0 | .847 854 |
| 77 | 38 884.206 | 230 941.6 | 3 944.961 8 | 33 251.48 | 5.939 2 | .855 141 |
| 78 | 33 990.850 | 192 057.4 | 3 733.725 8 | 29 306.52 | 5.650 3 | .862 189 |
| 79 | 29 428.077 | 158 066.6 | 3 498.684 1 | 25 572.80 | 5.371 3 | .868 993 |
| 80 | 25 211.636 | 128 638.5 | 3 243.115 8 | 22 074.11 | 5.102 3 | .875 553 |
| 81 | 21 353.602 | 103 426.8 | 2 970.736 8 | 18 831.00 | 4.843 5 | .881 865 |
| 82 | 17 862.047 | 82 073.24 | 2 686.402 0 | 15 860.26 | 4.594 8 | .887 931 |
| 83 | 14 739.984 | 64 211.19 | 2 395.321 2 | 13 173.86 | 4.356 3 | .893 750 |
| 84 | 11 985.151 | 49 471.21 | 2 103.356 1 | 10 778.54 | 4.127 7 | .899 324 |
| 85 | 9 589.474 6 | 37 486.06 | 1 816.194 6 | 8 675.180 | 3.909 1 | .904 656 |
| 86 | 7 539.390 5 | 27 896.58 | 1 540.039 4 | 6 858.986 | 3.700 1 | .909 753 |
| 87 | 5 815.463 2 | 20 357.19 | 1 280.145 4 | 5 318.946 | 3.500 5 | .914 621 |
| 88 | 4 393.477 3 | 14 541.73 | 1 041.564 6 | 4 038.801 | 3.309 8 | .919 272 |
| 89 | 3 244.754 6 | 10 148.25 | 827.621 52 | 2 997.236 | 3.127 6 | .923 717 |
| 90 | 2 337.992 9 | 6 903.496 | 640.937 68 | 2 169.615 | 2.952 7 | .927 982 |
| 91 | 1 640.030 9 | 4 565.503 | 482.773 06 | 1 528.677 | 2.783 8 | .932 103 |
| 92 | 1 117.257 1 | 2 925.472 | 352.770 63 | 1 045.904 | 2.618 4 | .936 136 |
| 93 | 737.236 29 | 1 808.215 | 249.339 10 | 693.133 5 | 2.452 7 | .940 178 |
| 94 | 469.915 86 | 1 070.979 | 170.088 82 | 443.794 4 | 2.279 1 | .944 413 |
| 95 | 288.365 67 | 601.062 8 | 111.467 79 | 273.705 6 | 2.084 4 | .949 162 |
| 96 | 169.864 58 | 312.697 2 | 74.109 795 | 162.237 8 | 1.840 9 | .955 101 |
| 97 | 91.611 740 | 142.832 6 | 49.001 885 | 88.128 0 | 1.559 1 | .961 973 |
| 98 | 40.375 419 | 51.220 9 | 28.545 208 | 39.126 1 | 1.268 6 | .969 058 |
| 99 | 10.845 444 | 10.845 4 | 10.580 921 | 10.580 9 | 1.000 0 | .975 610 |

* Reproduced by permission of the Actuarial Society of America.

# MOMENT OF INERTIA FOR VARIOUS BODIES
The mass of the body is indicated by $m$.

| Body | Axis | Moment of inertia |
|---|---|---|
| Uniform thin rod, length $l$ | Normal to the length, at one end | $m\dfrac{l^2}{3}$ |
| Uniform thin rod, length $l$ | Normal to the length, at the center | $m\dfrac{l^2}{12}$ |
| Thin rectangular sheet, sides $a$ and $b$ | Through the center parallel to $b$ | $m\dfrac{a^2}{12}$ |
| Thin rectangular sheet, sides $a$ and $b$ | Through the center perpendicular to the sheet | $m\dfrac{a^2 + b^2}{12}$ |
| Thin circular sheet of radius $r$ | Normal to the plate through the center | $m\dfrac{r^2}{2}$ |
| Thin circular sheet of radius $r$ | Along any diameter | $m\dfrac{r^2}{4}$ |
| Thin circular ring. Radii $r_1$ and $r_2$ | Through center normal to plane of ring | $m\dfrac{r_1^2 + r_2^2}{2}$ |
| Thin circular ring. Radii $r_1$ and $r_2$ | Any diameter | $m\dfrac{r_1^2 + r_2^2}{4}$ |
| Rectangular parallelopiped, edges $a$, $b$, and $c$ | Through center perpendicular to face $ab$, (parallel to edge $c$) | $m\dfrac{a^2 + b^2}{12}$ |
| Sphere, radius $r$ | Any diameter | $m\dfrac{2}{5}r^2$ |
| Spherical shell, external radius $r_1$, internal radius $r_2$ | Any diameter | $m\dfrac{2}{5}\dfrac{(r_1^5 - r_2^5)}{(r_1^3 - r_2^3)}$ |
| Spherical shell, very thin, mean radius $r$ | Any diameter | $m\dfrac{2}{3}r^2$ |
| Right circular cylinder of radius $r$, length $l$ | The longitudinal axis of the solid | $m\dfrac{r^2}{2}$ |
| Right circular cylinder of radius $r$, length $l$ | Transverse diameter | $m\left(\dfrac{r^2}{4} + \dfrac{l^2}{12}\right)$ |
| Hollow circular cylinder, length $l$, radii $r_1$ and $r_2$ | The longitudinal axis of the figure | $m\dfrac{(r_1^2 + r_2^2)}{2}$ |
| Thin cylindrical shell, length $l$, mean radius $r$ | The longitudinal axis of the figure | $mr^2$ |
| Hollow circular cylinder, length $l$, radii $r_1$ and $r_2$ | Transverse diameter | $m\left[\dfrac{r_1^2 + r_2^2}{4} + \dfrac{l^2}{12}\right]$ |
| Hollow circular cylinder, length $l$, very thin, mean radius $r$ | Transverse diameter | $m\left(\dfrac{r^2}{2} + \dfrac{l^2}{12}\right)$ |
| Elliptic cylinder, length $l$, transverse semiaxes $a$ and $b$ | Longitudinal axis | $m\left(\dfrac{a^2 + b^2}{4}\right)$ |
| Right cone, altitude $h$, radius of base $r$ | Axis of the figure | $m\dfrac{3}{10}r^2$ |
| Spheroid of revolution, equatorial radius $r$ | Polar axis | $m\dfrac{2}{5}r^2$ |
| Ellipsoid, axes $2a$, $2b$, $2c$ | Axis $2a$ | $m\dfrac{b^2 + c^2}{5}$ |

| | | | | | |
|---|---|---|---|---|---|
| ⌗ | Number (if written before a numeral); pounds (weight), lb. (if written after a numeral.) | Apr. | April | Dr. | Debit, debtor, doctor |
| | | a/s | Account sales | | |
| | | Aug. | August | ea. | Each |
| | | av. | Average | e.g. | (exempli gratia) for example |
| | | avoir. | Avoirdupois | | |
| | | bal. | Balance | etc. | And so forth |
| | | bbl. or | Barrel | ex. | Example, exercise, express |
| @ | At, as "@ 5¢ per C," for "at 5 cents per hundred." | brl. | | | |
| | | bk. | Bank, book | exch. | Exchange |
| | | bl. | Bale | exp. | Expense |
| | | B/L | Bill of lading | F | Fahrenheit |
| % | Per cent; per hundred. | bu. | Bushel | Feb. | February |
| | | bx. | Box | f.o.b. | Free on board |
| ¢ | Cents (placed after figures) | C | (centum) hundred | Fri. | Friday |
| | | | | frt. | Freight |
| $ | Dollars, (prefixed before figures). | cd. | Cord | ft. or f. | Foot |
| | | cg. | Centigram | gal. | Gallon |
| | | ch. | Chain | gi. | Gill |
| √ | Check mark | chg. | Charge | gr. | Grain |
| & | And, as in "Smith, Jones & Co." | c.i.f. | Carriage and insurance free. | gro. | Gross |
| | | | | gr. gro. | Great gross |
| | | ck. | Check | guar. | Guarantee |
| c/o | Care of | cm. | Centimeter | hf. | Half |
| A | Acre | cml. | Commercial | hhd. | Hogshead |
| a/c | Account | Co. | Company, county | hr. | Hour |
| acct. | Account | | | i.e. | (id est) that is |
| ad val | (ad valorem), according to value | c.o.d. | Cash on delivery | in. | Inch, inches |
| | | coll. | Collection | ins. | Insurance |
| | | com. | Commission | inst. | (instant) the present month |
| A.M. or a.m. | (ante meridiem) in the morning, between midnight and the following noon. 12:00 A.M. is noon, better 12:00 M, 12:01 A.M. is one minute after midnight. | cr. | Credit, creditor, crate | | |
| | | | | int. | Interest |
| | | cs. | Case | inv. | Invoice |
| | | c. or | Cent | inv'y | Inventory |
| | | ct. | | Jan. | January |
| | | cu. | Cubic | kg. | Keg, kilogram |
| | | cwt. | Hundredweight | km. | Kilometer |
| | | da. | Day | lb., lbs. | Pound, pounds |
| | | Dec. | December | lp | List price |
| | | dept. | Department | ltd. | Limited |
| | | dft. | Draft | L.S. | (locus sigillis) place for the seal |
| amt. | Amount | disc. | Discount | | |
| ans. | Answer | dm. | Decimeter | M | (mille) thousand; meridiem as in 12:00 M |
| ap. | Apothecaries' weight or measure | do. | Ditto | | |
| | | doz. | Dozen | | |
| | | dr. | Dram | | |

## Symbols and Abbreviations of Commercial Arithmetic (Continued)

| | | | | | |
|---|---|---|---|---|---|
| m. | Mill, meter | P.M. | (post meridiem) | etc. | west, etc. |
| Mar. | March | *or* | in the after- | Sat. | Saturday |
| mdse. | Merchandise | p.m. | noon, between | sec. | Second |
| mi. | Mile | | noon and the | sec'y | Secretary |
| min. | Minute | | following mid- | Sept. | September |
| mm. | Millimeter | | night. 12:00 | set. | Settlement |
| mo. | Month | | P.M. is mid- | sig. | Signed, signa- |
| Mon. | Monday | | night, 12:01 | | ture. |
| mortg. | Mortgage | | P.M. is one | sq. | Square |
| N, NE, | North, North- | | minute after | stk. | Stock |
| NW, | east, North- | | noon. | Sun. | Sunday |
| etc. | west, etc. | pp. | Pages | T. | Ton. |
| no. *or* | Number | pr. | Pair | temp. | Temperature |
| numb. | | *prox.* | (proximo) in the | Thu. | Thursday |
| Nov. | November | | following | treas. | Treasurer, |
| Oct. | October | | month | | treasury |
| O.K. | Correct | pt. | Pint, point | Tues. | Tuesday |
| oz. | Ounce | pwt. | Pennyweight | *ult.* | (ultimo) in the |
| p. | Page | (*or* | | | last month |
| par. | Paragraph | dwt.) | | *via* | By way of |
| pay't | Payment | qr. | Quire | viz. | (videlicet) |
| pc. | Piece | qt. | Quart | | namely |
| pd. | Paid | rd. | Rod, road | vol. | Volume |
| per | By, by the, as in | rec'd | Received | Wed. | Wednesday |
| | "per C," "per | rec't | Receipt | wk. | Week |
| | M," "per doz." | rm. | Ream | wt. | Weight |
| pfd. | Preferred | S, SE, | South, South- | yd. | Yard |
| pk. | Peck, pecks | SW, | east, South- | yr. | Year |
| pkg. | Package | | | | |

---

## Symbols Belonging to Plane Geometry

| | | | |
|---|---|---|---|
| ∠ | Angle. Use "rt ∠" not "∟" for "right angle." Write out the word "arc" rather than using "⌒." On ∠ABC, B is the vertex, A, C, points on the sides of the angle. | △ | Triangle |
| | | □ | Square. Use "rect." not ▭ for "rectangle," and use "trap." not △ for trapezoid. |
| ⊥, ⊥s | Perpendicular, perpendiculars. | ⊙, ⊙s | Circle, circles. ⊙ A(B) designates the circle with center at A and passing through the point B. ⊙ (ABC), designates the circle passing through given distinct points, A, B, C. |
| ∥, ∥s | Parallel (to), parallel lines. | | |
| ▱ | Parallelogram (vertices are named in counter-clockwise order, starting at any vertex). | | |
| | | ≅ | (is) congruent (to). |
| | | ∼ | (is) similar (to). |

## Symbols Belonging to Plane Geometry (Continued)

| | | | |
|---|---|---|---|
| ≈ | (is) homothetic (to); (is) similar (to) and similarly placed (with). | $\overrightarrow{AB}$ | Directed segment, A to B. |
| | | \|(AB) | Line (of infinite length) containing points A and B. |
| # | (is) homothetically congruent (to); or otherwise stated, (is) congruent (to) and similarly placed (with). In case of line segments, this becomes, (is) parallel (with) and congruent (to). | ↑(AB) | Directed line (of infinite length) containing points A and B, and in the direction from A to B. |
| | | $R\!\!\!/$ | cross-ratio, anharmonic ratio. |
| ⇌ | (is) equivalent (to), (in area or volume). | $\overline{\overline{\wedge}}, \overset{P}{\overline{\overline{\wedge}}}$ | (is) perspective with, (is) perspective with, from center P. |
| $\overline{AB}$ | Length of line segment between A and B. | $\overline{\wedge}$ | (is) projective with. |

## General Mathematical Symbols and Abbreviations

"Bold-face" type—To indicate vectors. In manuscript and at the blackboard, bold-faced type is variously indicated by wavy underscoring, or enclosure in a circle, or even by wavy overscoring. Some persons use German type.

Half-spaces—In writing numbers with many recorded digits, half-spaces (rather than commas or other marks) may well be used to separate convenient groups of digits. Thus $\pi = 3.14159\ 26536-$.

Superscripts—To indicate: **1.** powers, as in $x^2$, $(a-x)^n$, etc. In modern practice $a^0 = 1$ always by definition (even for $a = 0$). Also in $\infty'$, $\infty^2$, etc., indicating number of degrees of freedom. Wherever the context restricts the value of $a$ to non-negative (real) values and $n$ to positive integers, $a^{1/n}$ means the non-negative (real) $n$th root of $a$. For complex numbers, $x^y$ is defined as $e^{y\ (\log x)}$, where the principal value of $\log x$ is to be taken. In tables $0.0^5314$ may be used to indicate $0.00000314$. Note special use of $\sin^n x$ for $(\sin x)^n$ except for $n = -1$, also for $\cos^n x$, etc. **2.** symbolic powers, or order of iteration, as in $T^n$ or in $D^n$ $(= d^n/dx^n)$, or in inverse functions as in $\sin^{-1}$, $\cos^{-1}$, $\sinh^{-1}$, etc. **3.** order of differentiation, as in $y'$ ("y prime"), $y''$ ("y second," or "y double prime"), $\cdots$, $y^{(N)}$, $\cdots$. **4.** feet and inches, as in $3'4''$. **5.** degrees, minutes, seconds, as in $34°5'17''$. Do not omit ° for common angles. Write 0°, 30°, 45°, 60°, etc., not 0, 30, 45, 60, etc. Do not use superscript, $^r$, for radians. Write $180° = \pi$ rad, but write $\cos (\pi/3)$ for $\cos 60°$. **6.** days, hours, minutes, seconds, as in $10^d3^h27^m5.3^s$. **7.** degrees of temperature as in $104°$. Where C (for Centigrade) or F (for Fahrenheit) is given, recent usage approves the omission of the °,. thus $100C = 212F$, and $-40C = -40F$. **8.** For use with integral sign $\int$, and with vertical bar $|$, see these symbols.

Dot-accents—To indicate derivatives with respect to time, (Newton's notation), as in $\dot{x}$ for $x$-component of velocity, and $\ddot{x}$ for $x$-component of acceleration.

Subscripts—To indicate: **1.** position in a sequence, set, or matrix, as in $a_1$, $a_2$, $a_3$, $\cdots a_n$, $\cdots$, or $a_0x^n + a_1x^{n-1} + \cdots + a_rx^{n-r} + \cdots a_n$ or in

$\begin{pmatrix} a_{11}a_{12}a_{13} \\ a_{21}a_{22}a_{23} \end{pmatrix}$. **2.** general distinguishing mark. Two subscripts may be written adjacently without commas as $a_{11}$ and to be read "$a$ sub one one," not "$a$ sub eleven." A subscript is sometimes enclosed in parentheses as in $F_{(0)1}$ where such distinction seems demanded. For special uses see associated symbols.

Juxtaposition—To indicate: **1.** the algebraic product, as in $2bxy$. **2.** the logical product as in $AB$ where $A$ and $B$ are given classes, and in symbolic logic. Also written with centrally placed dot as $A \cdot B$. **3.** the group product, as in $ST$ (the result of performing first $S$, then $T$, or in $aH$, the co-set consisting for given $a$ of all operations $ah$, where $h$ is in $H$. **4.** general operational or functional combination as in $dy/dx$, $\sin x$, $\log x$, $\max y$, $\lim x_n$, etc. **5.** sequence of points or other elements determining a geometric figure, as line $AB$, parallelogram $ABCD$, $\angle ABC$, etc. **6.** sum of products (in tensor notation) when index appears as subscript for one factor and superscript for another. Thus $a_i x^i$ means $\Sigma a_i x^i$, in tensor notation.

( )—Parentheses ("round brackets") to indicate: **1.** aggregation, as in $(a + b) \cdot (a - b) = a^2 - b^2$. **2.** argument of function, as in $f(x)$, $g(x,y)$, etc. **3.** sequence or set, as in $a = (a_i)$, $x = (x_{ij})$, $(x,y,z)$, etc. **4.** matrix, as in $\begin{pmatrix} a_{11}a_{12}a_{13} \\ a_{21}a_{22}a_{23} \end{pmatrix}$ also written as $\begin{Vmatrix} a_{11}a_{12}a_{13} \\ a_{21}a_{22}a_{23} \end{Vmatrix}$. **5.** permutation (or substitution) in group theory as in $\begin{pmatrix} a_1 a_2 a_3 \\ b_1 b_2 b_3 \end{pmatrix}$ where $a_i$ is replaced by $b_i (i = 1,2,3)$. **6.** binomial coefficient, as in $\binom{n}{r} = n!/[r!(n - r)!]$. This is also designated by $C_{n,r}$ or $_nC_r$. For $n,r$, positive integers, $\binom{-n}{r} = (-1)^r \binom{n + r - 1}{r}$, $\binom{n}{-r} = 0$, by definition. **7.** cycle or cylic permutation (in group theory) as in $(a_1, a_2, a_3)$ for $\begin{pmatrix} a_1 a_2 a_3 \\ a_2 a_3 a_1 \end{pmatrix}$. **8.** greatest common divisor, as in $(30,42) = 6$, $(7,5) = 1$. **9.** inner product as in $(ab)$, $= \Sigma_i a_i b_i$. **10.** segment or open interval, as in $(a,b)$, for system of values of $x$, where $a < x < b$.

Superscript ( )—To indicate: **1.** general index as distinguished from exponent. **2.** index of order of derivative as in $y, y', \cdots, y^{(n)}, \cdots$. **3.** "factorial," as in $x^{(r)} = x(x - 1) \cdots (x - r + 1)$. By definition $x^{(-r)} = 1/[(x + 1) \cdot (x + 2) \cdots (x + r)]$.

[ ]—Brackets ("square brackets"), to indicate: **1.** aggregation. **2.** argument of function as with ( ). **3.** greatest integer in, as $[2] = 2$, $[-7/3] = -3$. **4.** inner product (for coefficients in normal equations in the method of least squares), as in $[aa]$, $[XY]$, etc. **5.** outer product of vectors. Other notations are $V\,ab$ and $a \times b$. **6.** divided difference (in formal interpolation). $[x_i] = y_i$, $[x_i, x_{i+1}] = (y_{i+1} - y_i)/(x_{i+1} - x_i)$, $\cdots [x_i, x_{i+1}, \cdots, x_{i+r}] = ([x_{i+1}, \cdots, x_{i+r}] - [x_i, \cdots, x_{i+r-1}])/(x_{i+r} - x_i)$. **7.** range of points (in projective geometry) as in $[P]$. **8.** base (basis) of Abelian group, as in $[a,b, \cdots, k]$. **9.** module or ideal, as $[2] = [0, \pm 2, \pm 4, \cdots, \pm 2n, \cdots]$. **10.** Christoffel symbol, as in $\begin{bmatrix} mn \\ p \end{bmatrix} = \frac{1}{2}\left( \frac{\partial g_{pm}}{\partial x^n} + \frac{\partial g_{pn}}{\partial x^m} = \frac{\partial g_{mn}}{\partial x^p} \right)$. **11.** closed interval, as in $[a,b]$ for system of values of $x$ where $a \leqq x \leqq b$.

Subscript—Note. The use of adjacent subscripts, rather than of indices placed directly below is recommended on account of its availability for running text, and its economy of space and of expense in type setting. Thus use

$$\sum_{i} \text{ rather than } \sum_{i}, \quad \int_{a}^{b} \text{ rather than } \int_{a}^{b}, \text{ etc.}$$

{ }—Braces ("curly brackets") to indicate: **1.** aggregation, as in $\{(x - a)(x - b)\}^2$. **2.** class of (in theory of aggregates), where the general element only is mentioned, as in $\{a_i\} = [a_1, a_2, a_3]$, $(i = 1,2,3)$. **3.** Christoffel symbol, as in $\begin{Bmatrix} m & n \\ p \end{Bmatrix} = g^{rp} \begin{bmatrix} m & n \\ p \end{bmatrix}$.

< >—Angle brackets to indicate: **1.** aggregation. **2.** closed interval as with { }.

| |—Vertical bars, to indicate: **1.** absolute value (modulus of complex number), as $|a + ib|^2 = a^2 + b^2$. **2.** magnitude of (for vectors) as $a = |a|$. **3.** determinant, as in $\begin{vmatrix} a & b \\ c & d \end{vmatrix} = ad - bc$. The use of the notation $|a_{ij}|$ for the determinant of the matrix $(a_{ij})$, is common but is ambiguous. The notation $\det (a_{ij})$ may be used for this determinant.

‖ ‖—Double bars, to indicate: **1.** matrix as in $\begin{Vmatrix} a_{11}a_{12}a_{13} \\ a_{21}a_{22}a_{23} \end{Vmatrix}$ or in $\|a_{ij}\|$. **2.** generalized length (for metrical spaces), as in $\|f\|^2 = \int f^2(x)dx$.

(], [).—For intervals, as $(a,b]$, for system of values of $x$ for which $a < x \leq b$, and $[a,b)$, for system of values of $x$ for which $a \leq x < b$. Similarly $(a,b >$, and $< a,b)$ are sometimes used for these respectively.

⊃—**1.** contains (or containing) as proper sub-class. **2.** implies (or implying).

⊇—contains (or containing) as sub-class. (Some writers use, ⊃, for this.)

⊂—(is) contained as proper sub-class within.

⊆—(is) contained as sub-class within. (Some writers use, ⊂, for this.)

≡—**1.** (is) identical with. $\equiv_x$ indicates (is) identical with for all values of $x$ for which both members are defined. **2.** (is) congruent to (with respect to indicated modulus) as in $a \equiv b \pmod{m}$. **3.** (is) equivalent to (in formal logic).

=—(is) equal (to).

<—(is) less than.

>—(is) greater than.

≦ or ≤—(is) less than or equal to. Sometimes read (in the case of real numbers) as "(is) not greater than."

≧ or ≥—(is) greater than or equal to. Sometimes read (in the case of real numbers) as "(is) not less than.".

≢—**1.** (is) not identically equal (to). (Not "identically unequal to"), is unequal to for at least one value. **2.** (is) not congruent (to).

≠—(is) not equal (to).

≶—**1.** (is) not equal (to), (or real quantities). **2.** (Sometimes when explained by context) less than or greater than respectively.

∼—**1.** (is) formally, asymptotically, or approximately equal to. (The context should make the meaning specific.) Do not use $\doteq$ for "approximately equal to." **2.** (is) similar (to). **3.** not (in some works on formal logic).

422

→—**1.** approaches (as a limit), as in $\lim_{x\to a} f(x) = b$, $f(x) \to b$, as $x \to a$, etc. (Do not use $\doteq$). Not usually employed with long expressions. **2.** leads to, validates, implies (in logic). **3.** corresponds to.

↔—**1.** mutually implies (in logic). **2.** in one-to-one correspondence with, corresponds reciprocally to.

Superscript →—directed line as $\overrightarrow{AB}$.

|—Vertical bar, to indicate: **1.** value at, as in $f(x)|_a = f(a)$, or $f(x)|_{x=a} = f(a)$. **2.** value between as in $f(x)|_a^b = f(b) - f(a)$. **3.** is a divisor of, divides (in number theory) as $3|6$, or $(x-a)|(x^2-a^2)$. **4.** inner product (with parentheses) as $(a|b) = \sum_i a_i b_i$.

\ or /—Stroke, mark of cancellation as in $\not{3}x = \overset{2}{\not{6}}$, $x + \not{3} = \overset{4}{\not{7}}$.

/—Solidus, or oblique rule, to indicate: **1.** actual or symbolic division, as in $3/7$, $(x-a)/(x-b)$, $d/dx$, $dy/dx$, $d^2y/dx^2$. Do not write ambiguously $a - b/c - d$, but $(a-b)/(c-d)$ or $a - (b/c) - d$, as may be intended. Do not write $a/bc$ but $(a/b)c$ or $a/(bc)$ as intended. Write a proportion as $a/b = c/d$ not $a{:}b{:}{:}c{:}d$. Where $A$, $B$, $C$, $D$ designate displayed expressions, write the proportion as $\frac{A}{B} = \frac{C}{D}$. In commercial typing in place of $8\tfrac{5}{12}$, it is usual to write 8-5/12. The solidus form $a/b$, adapted to running text should be used where conveniently possible, rather than the displayed form $\frac{a}{b}$. **2.** quotient or factor group (in group theory) as $G/H$, (where $H$ is a normal subgroup of $G$). **3.** per, as in ft/sec. **4.** discount symbol, as in Cash 6, 4/5, 2/30, n/90 indicating 6 % discount for immediate payment, 4 % discount if paid within 5 days, 2 % discount if paid within 30 days, no discount thereafter, but face amount of bill is due (net) not later than the 90th day. **5.** shilling, (in British currency) as in 3/6d, or 10/ —.

Superscript ‾—Vinculum. This may be regarded as obsolescent for general use as a mark of aggregation due to its unsuitability for monotype setting. In conjunction with the radical sign it is widely used, but may often be avoided. There is little logical or historical basis for using $\sqrt{2}$ rather than $\sqrt{2}$. For a longer expression, one may write $\sqrt{(x^2 + a^2)}$ rather than $\sqrt{x^2 + a^2}$. Instead of $\sqrt{x-a}\,(x-b)$, one might write $(x-b)\sqrt{(x-a)}$. In geometry, the vinculum may be used for line segments as in $\overline{AB}$.

Superscript ‾—Bar. To indicate: **1.** complex conjugate of, as $\bar{z}$. This is somewhat inconvenient for "upper extended" letters and capitals as, $\bar{b}$, $\bar{h}$, $\bar{X}$, etc. Also indicated by *conj*, as $conj\,(x + iy) = x - iy$ or by use of a "star" as in $z^*$. · **2.** arithmetic mean value of, as in $\bar{x}$, $= \sum_i x_i/n$. **3.** closure of (in topology), as in $\bar{E}$ (the closure of $E$). **4.** "least upper," as in $\overline{\lim}$, and $B$ for least upper limit and least upper bound, respectively. See "sup."

Subscript ___—To indicate: **1.** italics (in manuscript). **2.** "greatest lower," as in $\underline{\lim}$, and B, for greatest lower limit, and greatest lower bound respectively. See "inf."

——— —horizontal rule, sign of division, as in $\frac{x-a}{x+a}$. Ordinarily the solidus form, adapted to running text, is preferred, as in $(x-a)/(x+a)$. When numerator and denominator are both complicated, the displayed form using horizontal rule may be avoided by writing "$A/B$, where $A = \cdots$, and $B = \cdots$."

**—** (centrally placed)—Minus sign. To indicate: **1.** subtraction as in $7 - 2 = 5$, $a^2 - b^2 = (a - b)(a + b)$. **2.** overestimate, as in $3.5-$. **3.** approach through negative values as in $-\infty$ and $-0$. **4.** region where variable indicated by context is negative (in graphs). **5.** logical difference (in theory of classes). **6.** in $(-)^n$, the sign expressed by $(-1)^n$.

**.** (on line)—**1.** decimal point. In the decimal representation of a number between 0 and 1, the cipher, 0, should (except in tables) appear before the decimal point. Thus 0.314 not .314. Notation by powers of 10, ("scientific notation") is recommended, especially when recording approximate values; thus to four significant figures, $3.140 \times 10^9$ and $3.140 \times 10^{-6}$. **2.** (sometimes used in quoting bond prices) as in 95.17 for $95\frac{17}{32}$. **3.** (sometimes used in recording mental age) as in 12.3 for 12 yr. 3 mo. **4.** (in symbolic logic) as mark of punctuation separating terms, also as, "and."

**:—**Colon. To indicate: **1.** hours, in recording time, as in 4:10 p.m. **2.** ratio (an obsolescent form) as in $a:b$. The form $a/b$ is preferred. **3.** (in symbolic logic) as mark of punctuation separating groups of terms, as in $p \cdot p \supset q : \supset : q$.

**·** (centrally placed)—**1.** mark of algebraic multiplication, particularly where mere juxtaposition would be ambiguous, as in $\overline{AB} \cdot \overline{CD}$. **2.** (for vectors), the mark of inner or dot multiplication as in $a \cdot b = ab \cos < ab$. Other notations are $(ab)$ and $S\ ab$.

**· · ·** (preferably centrally placed)—"three dots" meaning "and so forth," or "and so forth up to." Particularly in relation to the sequence of natural numbers, as in $1, 2 \cdots, n, \cdots$; or $a_0, a_1, \cdots, a_n, \cdots$, or $1, \cdots, m$.

**∴**—hence, therefore.

**∴, ∷, ⦂⦂,** etc.—(in symbolic logic), marks of punctuation stronger than **·** and **:**

**″**— ditto.

**+** plus sign. To indicate: **1.** addition, as in $2 + 3$, $a + b$, $10^{a+1}$. **2.** underestimate, as in $3.5+$. **3.** continued fraction as in $a_0 + \dfrac{1}{a_1+}\ \dfrac{1}{a_2+} \cdots$ for

$$a_0 + \cfrac{1}{a_1 + \cfrac{1}{a_2+}}.$$ **4.** approach through positive values as in $+\infty$, and in $+0$.

**5.** region where variable indicated by the context is positive, (in graphs). **6.** logical addition (in theory of classes). **7.** " .. or .. or both," (in formal logic). . Note: In writing series indicate sign before and after dots of omission, as $a_0 + a_1 + \cdots + a_n$, or $1 - \dfrac{1}{2} + \dfrac{1}{3} + \cdots + (-1)^{n-1}\dfrac{1}{n}$. **8.** in abstract group theory a group or co-set may be expressed as the sum of its elements.

**±**—**1.** "plus or minus." The repeated appearance of $\pm$ as in $\pm a \pm b \pm c$ is ambiguous. In many cases the sign $\pm$ before a term which appears repeatedly is intended to indicate the systematic use of the positive determination or of the negative determination throughout. Thus one may write $(a \pm b)^3 = a^3 \pm 3a^2b + 3ab^2 \pm b^3$. Where the context restricts the value of $a$ to non-negative (real) values, $\sqrt{a}$ means the non-negative (real) square root of $a$. Hence when both signs are desired, write $\pm$ before the radical. For roots of a quadratic equation $ax^2 + bx + c = 0$, use $\pm$ as in $(-b \pm \sqrt{b^2 - 4ac})/(2a)$. **2.** (in theory of observation), "with a probable error of." As in $17.2 \pm 0.5$ cm.

$\mp$—"minus or plus respectively." Used in context where $\pm$ has appeared previously, as in $(a \pm b)(a^2 \mp ab + b^2) = a^3 \pm b^3$. Here upper signs are to be taken throughout, or else lower signs. The notation $\pm a \mp b \pm c$ is ambiguous, meaning perhaps one of the four values $\pm(a - b) \pm c$, or one of the two values $\pm(a - b + c)$.

$\times$—**1.** times, (sign of algebraic multiplication). Used chiefly in arithmetic, as in $2 \times 2 = 4$, $7.3 \times 10^4$. **2.** (for vectors) the sign of outer or cross multiplication. **3.** (for classes) the Cartesian product. Thus $A \times B$ is the class of all ordered pairs $(a,b)$ where $a$ is an element of $A$, and $b$ of $B$.

$\div$—sign of division. Used chiefly in arithmetic. Should be replaced by solidus, $/$, where convenient.

$\sqrt{\ }$ $\sqrt[n]{\ }$—square root of, $n$th root of. (See discussion under "superscript," and under "vinculum"). By custom, for $a$ positive, $\sqrt{(-a)}$ means usually $i\sqrt{a}$, rather than $-i\sqrt{a}$, but the latter unambiguous forms are preferred.

$!$—"factorial," as in $3! = 1 \cdot 2 \cdot 3 = 6$. $0! = 1$, (by definition). The elementary arithmetic definition of factorial $n$, may be replaced in favor of the definition as a special case of the Gamma function $\Gamma(x)$. For $n$ a natural number, $n! = \Gamma(n + 1)$, $= \int_0^\infty x^n e^{-x} dx$. For $n$ a large natural number, Stirling's asymptotic formula (extended) yields $n! \sim \sqrt{2n\pi}(n/e)^n\left(1 + \dfrac{1}{12n} + \dfrac{1}{288n^2} - \dfrac{139}{51840n^3} - \cdots\right)$. Note: Do not use the obsolescent form $\lfloor n$ for $n!$

$\int$, $\int_a^b$, $\int_a^x$, $\iint$, $\int_c$—Integral signs. (use preferably bold-face type)

$\int_a^b \int_c^d f(x,y)dxdy$ denotes $\int_a^b\left(\int_c^d f(x,y)dx\right)dy$, $= \int_a^b dy \int_c^d dxf(x,y)$.

$\mathscr{S}$—curvilinear integral over closed path free from singularities. (Use preferably bold-face type.)

§—section, or article.

⁋ or ¶—paragraph.

$\propto$ — varies as. Instead of $y \propto x$ one may write $y = kx$, $k$ being the constant factor of proportionality.

$\nabla$—nabla—To indicate: **1.** linear vector operator $\left(\dfrac{\partial}{\partial x}, \dfrac{\partial}{\partial y}, \dfrac{\partial}{\partial z}\right)$ as used also in divergence, gradient, and curl (or rotation). **2.** backward difference (in interpolation theory) $\nabla a_n = a_n - a_{n-1}$.

$\nabla^2$—Laplace operator.

$\square$—D'Alembertian operator.

$°$, $'$, $''$, $'''$, $\cdots$, $(N) \cdots$, (superscript)—superscript numbers. See "superscripts."

$\infty$—infinity. Use $+\infty$ or $-\infty$ respectively, where direction of approach along real numbers is to be indicated. Otherwise use $\infty$ rather than $\pm\infty$. Note: "$n \to \infty$," may be read "as $n$ increases without bound."

ℵ—Aleph (initial Hebrew letter) transfinite cardinal number, in particular that of all real numbers. $ℵ_0$ (aleph null) first transfinite cardinal.

α—Alpha. To indicate: **1.** (in analytic geometry of 3 dimensions), direction angle with $X$-axis. **2.** angular acceleration. **3.** (in statistics) $\alpha_0 = 1$, $\alpha_1 = 0$, $\alpha_2 = 1$, $\alpha_3 = \mu_3/\sigma^3$, $\alpha_4 = \mu_4/\sigma^4 = \mu_4/\mu_2^2$. **4.** (in mathematical astronomy), right ascension (also indicated by R.A.) **5.** angle of triangle at $A$, opposite side $a$. **6.** root of algebraic equation as in $a(x - \alpha)(x - \beta)(x - \gamma) = 0$.

B—(Greek Beta)—$B(m,n) = \Gamma(m)\Gamma(n)/\Gamma(m + n)$, (Eulerian Beta-function).

β—Beta. To indicate: **1.** (in analytic geometry of 3 dimensions), direction angle with $Y$-axis. **2.** (in statistics), $\beta_1 = \alpha_3^2 = \mu_3^2/\mu_2^3$, $\beta_2 = \alpha_4 = \mu_4/\mu_2^2$. **3.** angle of triangle at $B$, opposite side $b$. **4.** root of algebraic equation. See α.

Γ—$\Gamma(x)$ Gamma-function. See "!" Among numerous definitions equivalent for positive real values of $x$, are the two following: (i) $\Gamma(x) = \lim\limits_{n \to \infty} \dfrac{1 \cdot 2 \cdots n}{x(x + 1) \cdots (x + n - 1)} n^{x-1}$, $x > 0$. (ii) $\Gamma(x) = \displaystyle\int_0^\infty e^{-t} t^{x-1} dt$, $R(x) > 0$.

γ—Gamma. To indicate: **1.** (in analytic geometry of 3 dimensions) direction angle with $Z$-axis. **2.** Euler or Mascheroni constant. (Also indicated by $C$.) $\gamma = \lim\limits_{n \to \infty} \left( \dfrac{1}{1} + \dfrac{1}{2} + \cdots + \dfrac{1}{n} - \log n \right) = 0.57721\ 56649\ 01532\ 86060\ 65120 \cdots$ **3.** angle of triangle at $C$, opposite side $c$. **4.** radius of geodesic curvative. **5.** universal constant of gravitation $= 6.670 \times 10^{-8}$ cm³/(gm. sec²). **6.** root of algebraic equation, see α.

Δ—Delta. To indicate: **1.** triangle (in plane geometry). (For right triangle, write rt△, not $\varDelta$). Also area of triangle. **2.** increment, as in $\Delta x$, $\Delta f$, $f(x + \Delta x)$, etc. **3.** forward difference (interpolation theory). $\Delta a_n = a_{n+1} - a_n$. **4.** Laplacian operator $\dfrac{\partial^2}{\partial x^2} + \dfrac{\partial^2}{\partial y^2}$, or $\dfrac{\partial^2}{\partial x^2} + \dfrac{\partial^2}{\partial y^2} + \dfrac{\partial^2}{\partial z^2}$ also designated by $\nabla^2$. **5.** selected square root of the discriminant of a given polynomial, as in $\Delta^2 = b^2 - 4ac$ for the polynomial $ax^2 + bx + c$. **6.** triangular number, (of form $(n^2 - n)/2$). **7.** Legendre's radical, $\Delta(\varphi)^2 = 1 - k^2 \sin^2 \varphi$.

δ—Delta. To indicate: **1.** positive constant dependent upon $\epsilon$ that may be chosen initially as near to zero as desired. (In theory of limits, of continuity, etc.) **2.** variation of. **3.** (in interpolational theory) central difference $\delta y_{c+i+\frac{1}{2}} = y_{c+i+1} - y_{c+i}$ **4.** (in mathematical astronomy) apparent declination. **5.** number of double points, or nodes (Plücker number). **6.** (in statistics) deviation. **7.** force of interest, $e^\delta = 1 + i$, (in mathematics of finance). **8.** Kronecker Delta, $\delta_{ij} = 0$ for $i \neq j$, $= 1$ for $i = j$. In tensor notation, also $\delta_i{}^j$. One has $\delta_{ij} = \begin{pmatrix} o \\ i - j \end{pmatrix}$ or $C_{0,i-j}$. **9.** unit elongation (in strength of materials).

∂—curly d. To indicate: **1.** partial differentiation as in $\partial f(x,y)/\partial x$. **2.** The Jacobian operator, as in $\partial(u,v,w)/\partial(x,y,z)$. This is variously represented, sometimes as $J\left(\dfrac{u,v,w}{x,y,z}\right)$ etc. **3.** a specified square root of the discriminant $D$. (also sometimes as Δ.)

$\epsilon$—Epsilon. To indicate: **1.** positive constant, that may be chosen initially independently as near to zero as desired. (In theory of limits, of continuity, etc.) **2.** primitive root of unity. **3.** (is) member of, (relation of element to containing class). **4.** eccentricity of conic section, usually better designated by $e$. **5.** (in mathematical astronomy) obliquity of ecliptic. **6.** an $\epsilon$-number is a transfinite ordinal of a certain limiting type. Note: Do not use $\epsilon$ or $\varepsilon$ for Napierian base except in engineering. See $e$.

$\not\in$—(is not a member of.)

$\zeta$—Zeta. To indicate: **1.** Riemann Zeta-function $\zeta(s) = \sum_{n=1}^{\infty} n^{-s}$ (for $s > 1$). **2.** (in statistics) a test of linearity. $\zeta = \eta^2 - r^2$.

$\eta$—Eta. To indicate: **1.** general variable or unknown constant, analogous to $y$ as in case of moving system of coordinates, etc. Used in ordered set $(\xi, \eta, \zeta)$. **2.** a confocal coordinate. See $\xi$. **3.** (in statistics), correlation ratio. **4.** order-type of the aggregate of all rational numbers.

$\Theta$—Theta. To indicate: **1.** Theta-function. See $\vartheta$. **2.** absolute temperature (where $t$ is used for time).

$\theta$—Theta. To indicate: **1.** general angular displacement, (in trigonometry and analytic geometry). **2.** (in plane polar coordinates $(r,\theta)$) angle from initial ray to radius vector, $x = r \cos\theta$, $y = r \sin\theta$. **3.** (in cylindrical coordinates $(r,\theta,z)$) angle from initial radial half-plane to radial half-plane containing radius vector. **4.** (in spherical coordinates $(r,\theta,\varphi)$) co-latitude (measured from zenith) and (in astronomy) zenith distance. This notation is traditional in mathematical physics. In texts on analytic geometry, usage varies, $\theta$ being employed frequently for the longitude. See $\varphi$. **5.** Theta-function. See $\vartheta$. **6.** (in formal theory of operations), a displacement operator. **7.** ordinary temperature (when $t$ is used for time).

$\vartheta$—Theta-function. Definitions and notations vary widely. For elliptic Theta-functions the notation here given is that followed by Whittaker and Watson. Here $\theta_i$ designates the value of $\vartheta_i(o,q)$, $\vartheta_i'$, the value of $d\vartheta_i(z,q)/dz$. ($i = 1,2,3,4$). These are defined by $\vartheta_1(z,q) = 2q^{\frac{1}{4}} \sin Z - 2q^{\frac{9}{4}} \sin 3z + 2q^{\frac{25}{4}}$ $\sin 5z - \cdots \vartheta_2(z,q) = 2q^{\frac{1}{4}} \sin z + 2q^{\frac{9}{4}} \sin 3z + 2q^{\frac{25}{4}} \sin 5z + \cdots \vartheta_3(z,q)$ $= 1 + 2q \cos 2z + 2q^4 \cos 4z + 2q^9 \cos 6z + \cdots \vartheta_4(z,q) = 1 - 2q \cos$ $2z + 2q^4 \cos 4z - 2q^9 \cos 6z + \cdots$.

$\iota$—Iota, number of inflexions (a Plücker number).

$\imath$—inverted Iota, (in formal logic) the unique element fulfilling description stated.

$\kappa$—Kappa, number of cusps. (A Plücker number).

$\Lambda$—Lambda, sometimes used for null-class.

$\lambda$—Lambda. To indicate: **1.** general linear parameter (e.g., in a pencil), as in $F + \lambda G$. **2.** running index, as in $x_\lambda (\lambda = 1, 2, \cdots )$. **3.** longitude (in mathematical astronomy). **4.** characteristic value (as in $\lambda_i$) in theory of linear differential equations of second order, linear integral equations, etc. **5.** order-type of the aggregate of all real numbers.

$\mu$—Mu. To indicate: **1.** running index, usually used with $\lambda$, as in $x_\lambda y_\mu$. **2.** general linear parameter, when used with $\lambda$, as in $\lambda F + \mu G$. **3.** (in statistics) moment, about the arithmetic mean, as in $\mu_k = \Sigma_i f_i (x_i - \bar{x})^k$, $\mu_2 = \varsigma^2 =$ variance. **4.** $\mu_x$, force of mortality $= -d (\log_e l_x)/dx$. **5.** (in number theory) inversion function of Moebius and Mertens.

$\nu$—Nu. To indicate: **1.** running index, usually with $\lambda$ and $\mu$. **2.** (in statistics) moment about arbitrary origin $A$ (in "short method") as in $\nu_k = \Sigma_i f_i (x_i - A)^k$.

$\xi$—Xi. To indicate: **1.** general variable, or unknown constant analogous to $x$, as in moving systems of coordinates, etc. **2.** a confocal coordinate as in

(i) confocal ellipses and hyperbolas, $\dfrac{x^2}{a^2 - \lambda} + \dfrac{y^2}{b^2 - \lambda} = 1$, $-\infty < \xi < b^2 <$

$\eta < a^2$. (ii) confocal ellipsoids and hyperboloids of revolution, $\dfrac{x^2}{a^2 - \lambda} +$

$\dfrac{y^2 + z^2}{b^2 - \lambda} = 1$, $-\infty < \xi < b^2 < \eta < a^2$. (iii) confocal parabolas, $y^2 + 2\lambda \cdot$

$(x - \lambda) = 0$, $-\infty < \xi < 0 < \eta < +\infty$. (iv) confocal paraboloids of revolution, $y^2 + z^2 + 2\lambda(x - \lambda) = 0$, $-\infty < \xi < 0 < \eta < +\infty$. (v) confocal ellipsoids and hyperboloids, $\dfrac{x^2}{a^2 - \lambda} + \dfrac{y^2}{b^2 - \lambda} + \dfrac{z^2}{c^2 - \lambda} = 1$, $-\infty <$

$\xi < c^2 < \eta < b^2 < \zeta < a^2$. (vi) confocal paraboloids, $\dfrac{x^2}{a^2 - \lambda} + \dfrac{y^2}{b^2 - \lambda} =$

$2z - \lambda$, $-\infty < \xi < b^2 < \eta < a^2 < \zeta < +\infty$.

$\Pi$, $\Pi_i \Pi_{i=m}^{n}$, $\Pi_{(R)}$ or $\Pi$—**1.** product of terms with index $i$, or $j$, etc. ranging from $m$ to $n$, or over $R$. Do not use $\Pi_i$, $\overset{n}{\underset{i=m}{\Pi}}$, etc. (Bold-faced type preferred.) **2.** (in some formal logical treatments) "for every."

$\Pi_{ij}$, $\Pi_{ijk}$, $\cdots$ —$\Pi_i \Pi_j$, $\Pi_i \Pi_j \Pi_k$, etc.

$\pi$—Pi. **1.** the ratio of the length of circumference of a circle, to the diameter. $\pi = 3.14159$ $26535$ $89793$ $23846$ $\cdots$ **2.** general notation for plane, projectivity, projective, period, etc.

$\rho$—Rho. **1.** radius of geodesic curvature. **2.** proportionality factor, as in $\rho X_i = \Sigma_j a_{ij} x_j$.

$\sum$, $\sum_{i}$, $\sum_{i=m}^{n}$, $\sum_{(R)}$ or $\underset{(R)}{\sum}$—Sigma. **1.** summation, sum of terms of index $i$, or $j$, etc., ranging from $m$ to $n$, or over range $R$. Do not use $\sum_i$, $\overset{n}{\underset{i=m}{\sum}}$, etc.

(bold-faced type preferred). **2.** (on some formal logical treatments) "for at least one." **3.** (in number theory) $\Sigma_{d/n}$ summation extended over all divisors of $n$. **4.** (in mathematical astronomy) $\Sigma$-pt is the intersection of the meridian with the equator.

$\Sigma_{ij}$, $\Sigma_{ijk}$ $\cdots$ —$\Sigma_i \Sigma_j$, $\Sigma_i \Sigma_j \Sigma_k$, etc.

$\sigma$—Sigma. To indicate: **1.** radius of torsion. **2.** (in statistics) standard deviation $\sigma^2 N = \Sigma_i (x_i - \bar{x})^2 f_i$. **3.** (in number theory), $\sigma_k(n) =$ sum of $k$th powers of divisors of $n$. **4.** any one of several analogous Sigma-functions. The simplest elliptic Sigma-function $\sigma(x)$ is related to the Weierstrassian $\wp$ function by $\wp u = -d^2 \log \sigma u / du^2$. One has $\sigma u = u \left\{ 1 - \dfrac{g_2}{2} \dfrac{u^4}{5!} - \right.$

$6 g_3 \dfrac{u^6}{7!} - \dfrac{9}{4} g_2^2 \dfrac{u^8}{9!} - 18 g_2 g_3 \dfrac{u^{10}}{11!} - \cdots \left. \right\}$ **5.** proportionality factor, usually used with $\rho$.

$\tau$—Tau. To indicate: **1.** number of bitangents (a Plücker number). **2.** time (when $t$ is used for temperature). **3.** torsion (of curve in space).

ϒ—Upsilon. (In mathematical astronomy) vernal equinox.

φ—Phi. To indicate: **1.** general functional symbol, especially for polynomials. **2.** (in spherical coordinates, $(r,\theta,\varphi)$, longitude from $x$ to $y$ in right-handed system. In some astronomical work the $z$-axis points to the zenith, $\theta$ is the zenith-distance, and $\varphi$ is the west azimuth. In some works on analytic geometry the roles of $\theta$ and $\varphi$ are interchanged, although the system given is traditional mathematical physics. $x = r \sin\theta \cos\varphi$, $y = r \sin\theta \sin\varphi$, $z = r \cos\theta$. **3.** (in geocentric coordinates, $(r,\varphi,\lambda)\varphi$ = latitude (not co-latitude as with spherical coordinates). **4.** (in plane polar coordinates $(r,\varphi)$.) Used chiefly as specialized case of spherical coordinates $(r,\pi/2,\varphi)$. See $\theta$. **5.** inclination of plane curve, $\tan\varphi = dy/dx = m$. **6.** (in number theory.) Euler's function or indicatrix. $\varphi(n)$ is the number of positive integers not exceeding $n$ and prime to $n$. **7.** $\varphi_i(x)$, characteristic function, see $\lambda_i$. **8.** argument in Legendre's elliptic integrals. $E(\varphi,k) = \int_0^\varphi \Delta(\varphi)d\varphi$, $F(\varphi_1 k) = \int_0^\varphi d\varphi/\Delta(\varphi)$. **9.** the normal probability function of Laplace and Gauss in the form $\varphi(t) = \dfrac{1}{\sqrt{2\pi}}e^{-t^2}$. **10.** $\varphi_n(x)$, sometimes used for Bernoulli polynomial. See $B_n(x)$.

χ—Chi. (In statistical theory) $\chi^2$ is a measure of goodness of fit, devised by Karl Pearson. $\chi^2 = \Sigma(f_i - Np_i)^2/(Np_i)$ for $N$ items, with $p_i$ the probability of appearances and $f_i$ the frequency for items in an $i$th class.

ψ—Psi. To indicate: **1.** general functional symbol (usually with $\varphi$). **2.** angle from radius vector to tangent of plane curve. **3.** (with geocentric coordinates in mathematical astronomy), co-latitude. See $\varphi$.

Ω—Omega. To indicate: **1.** a certain annihilator in the theory of binary concomitants. **2.** (with subscript) transfinite ordinals of certain minimal type. **3.** (in geometry of the triangle) $\Omega, \Omega'$, the Brocard points.

ω—Omega. To indicate: **1.** angular velocity. **2.** first transfinite ordinal, order-type of the aggregate of all natural numbers. **3.** imaginary cube root of unity, related to $i$, by $\omega = (-1 + i\sqrt{3})/2$. **4.** $\omega_1$, $\omega_2$, $\omega_3$, half-periods of Weierstrassian $\wp$-function.

A—**1.** A vertex, and the associated angle of $\triangle ABC$. See $\alpha$. **2.** $A_{ij}$, algebraic complement of $a_{ij}$ in determinant, $D$. $A_{ij} = dD/da_{ij}$. **3.** (in astronomy) azimuth. **4.** (in astronomy) astronomical unit, mean geocentric distance to the sun. **5.** acres. **6.** area.

AM—arithmetic mean. See also superscript ⁻.

Ans.—answer.

AP—arithmetic progression.

Ax—axiom.

a—**1.** (in elementray algebra) initial term in arithmetic or geometric progression. **2.** (with subscript) coefficient in Fourier series, $(a_0/2) + \Sigma_{n=1}^\infty(a_n \cos nx + b_n \sin nx)$. **3.** (with two indices) element in matrix or determinant, as in $\begin{pmatrix} a_{11}\,a_{12}\,a_{13} \\ a_{21}\,a_{22}\,a_{23} \end{pmatrix}$ or $\begin{vmatrix} a_{11}\,a_{12} \\ a_{21}\,a_{22} \end{vmatrix}$. **4.** (in elementary geometry) apothegm. **5.** (in geometry of triangle) first side-line, also length of first side of the triangle. **6.** (in elementary analytic geometry) $x$-intercept. **7.** (in elementary analytic geometry) semi-major axis of ellipse or semi-transverse axis of hyperbola.

etc. (When equations are in normal form.) For central conics and quadrics the $a$ is usually associated with $x$, as in $(x^2/a^2) + (y^2/b^2) = 1$, even when $a$ may be less than $b$, or as in $-(x^2/a^2) + (y^2/b^2) = 1$, where $a$ is the semi-conjugate axis.

abs—absolute value of.

acc—acceleration.

am—amplitude function. $\varphi = \operatorname{am} u$, where $u = F = \int_0^{\varphi} d\varphi/\Delta(\varphi)$.

amp—amplitude of vibration.

approx—approximate(ly).

arc (in "arc sin" etc.)—inverse. Also written $\sin^{-1}$ etc. Do not use "arc" for inverse of hyperbolic functions. Write $\sinh^{-1}$, etc.

arg—argument. For $r$ and $\theta$ real, $\theta$ is the argument of $re^{i\theta}$.

av—average.

$B$—1. (With subscripts) Bernoulli numbers and polynomials. To indicate what usage among many is being followed in any given case, authors would do well to list the values of the first few Bernoulli numbers as for example, $B_1 = \frac{1}{2}$, $B_2 = \frac{1}{6}$, $B_3 = 0$, $B_4 = -\frac{1}{30}$, etc. The Bernoulli polynomials, are defined as $B_n(x) = \Sigma_{r=0}^n \binom{n}{r} B_r x^{n-r}$, and satisfy $B_n(x+1) - B_n(x) = nx^{n-1}$ with the choice of notation for Bernoulli numbers given above. (Also designated by $\varphi_n(x)$.) 2. bound (general symbol). $\bar{B}$, $\underline{B}$ designate least upper, and greatest lower bound respectively. Preferred notations are "sup" and "inf" respectively. 3. a vertex and the associated angle of $\triangle ABC$. See $\beta$. 4. (in elementary solid geometry), area of base of a solid.

$b$—1. (in elementary geometry) length of base of plane figure. $b, b'$, parallel bases of trapezoid. 2. (in elementary analytic geometry) $y$-intercept. 3. (in elementary analytic geometry) semi-axis. See $a$. 4. (in geometry of the triangle) second side-line, also length of second side of the triangle.

bei(z)—Thomson-Bessel function, $\operatorname{bei}(z) = \dfrac{(\frac{1}{2}z)^2}{(2!)^2} = \dfrac{(\frac{1}{2}z)^6}{(6!)^2} + \dfrac{(\frac{1}{2}z)^{10}}{(10!)^2} = \cdots$ $\operatorname{ber}(z) \pm i\operatorname{bei}(z) = J_0(zi\sqrt{} \pm i) = I_0(z\sqrt{} \pm i)$.

ber(z)—Thomson-Bessel function. (See bei(z).) $\operatorname{ber}(z) = 1 - \dfrac{(\frac{1}{2}z)^4}{(4!)^2} + \dfrac{(\frac{1}{2}z)^8}{(8!)^2} - \cdots$.

$C$—1. arbitrary constant of integration. 2. (in elementary geometry) circumference of circle; also, circle. 3. general symbol for curve. 4. (with subscripts) combination, as in $C_{n.r}$ or $_nC_r$, the number of combinations of $n$ things taken $r$ at a time (without repetitions). The form $_nC_r$ or even $^nC_r$ is widely used but the notation $C_{n.r}$ or $C(n,r)$ or $\binom{n}{r}$ is to be preferred. 5. Roman numeral for "hundred." 6. Euler or Mascheroni constant. Also designated by $\gamma$. (See $\gamma$.) 7. (chiefly as subscript) contour of integration. 8. Centigrade, degree Centigrade, as $-52C$.

Ci—cosine integral function, $Ci(x) = \int_\infty^x (\cos u/u)du$.

CF—(in elementary differential equations) complementary function.

$c$—**1.** (in geometry of triangle) third side-line, also length of third side of triangle. **2.** (in elementary analytic geometry), $z$-intercept. **3.** (in elementary analytic geometry) semi-axis. (See $a$.)

cis—cis $\theta = \cos \theta + i \sin \theta = e^{i\theta}. = exp(i\theta)$. The latter forms preferred.

cls—class, set, or aggregate.

cn—cosine amplitude function. (Jacobian elliptic function.)

colog—cologarithm (of).

conj—(complex) conjugate (of). See superscript ‾.

cos—cosine (of).

$\cos^{-1}$—inverse cosine (of). Also written arc cos.

cosh—hyperbolic cosine (of). Do not write Cos nor $\mathfrak{Cof}$ (in German letters).

$\cosh^{-1}$—inverse hyperbolic cosine of. Do not write arc cosh.

csc—cosecant (of).

$\csc^{-1}$—inverse cosecant (of). Also written arc csc.

ctn—cotangent (of).

$\text{ctn}^{-1}$—inverse cotangent (of). Also written arc ctn.

ctnh—hyperbolic cotangent (of). Do not write Ctn, nor $\mathfrak{Ctn}$ (in German letters).

$\text{ctnh}^{-1}$—inverse hyperbolic cotangent of. Do not write arc ctnh.

cu—cubic.

cum—cumulative

cvrs—coversed sine (of) cvrs $x = 1 - \sin x$.

$D$—**1.** differential operator, as in $Dy = y'$, $d_x f(x,y) = \partial f/\partial x$. **2.** Roman numeral for "five hundred." **3.** general symbol for denominator, or for determinant. **4.** discriminant of binary form, or of polynomial. **5.** (in statistical theory), (with subscripts 0, 1, $\cdots$, 10), decile marks. **6.** $D(a_1, a_2, \cdots, a_n)$ sometimes designates the Vandermonde determinant

$$\begin{vmatrix} 1a_1 & \cdots & a_1^{n-1} \\ \cdots & \cdots & \cdots \\ 1a_n & \cdots & a_n^{n-1} \end{vmatrix}$$

Def—definition.

Dem—demonstration, proof.

$d$—**1.** (in elementary algebra), common difference in arithmetic progression. **2.** differential operator, as in $d^2y/dx^2$. **3.** (in elementary geometry) diameter. **4.** (as superscript) days, as in $2^d 3^h 17^m$. **5.** (British currency) pence.

deg—degree, degrees.

det—determinant of, as in det $(a_{ij})$.

div—divergence of, also indicated by $\nabla$.

dn—dn$(z)$, a Jacobian elliptic function.

$\exists$—(there) exists.

$\exists|$—there exist uniquely.

$E$—**1.** $E,F,G$ fundamental differential quantities of first order for surfaces. **2.** $E(\varphi,k)$, Legendre's normal elliptic integral, of the second kind, $E = \int_0^\varphi \Delta(\varphi)d\varphi$. **3.** east. **4.** (in Euler's polyhedral formula) number of edges of polyhedron. **5.** displacement operator, $E(f(x)) = f(x + 1)$. **6.** (in mathematical astronomy) equation of time.

Ei—exponential integral function $Ei(x) = \int_x^\infty du/(ue^u)$.

Eq—equation.

Ex—exercise.

$e$—1. base of natural (or Napierian) logarithms. In place of $e^A$ one may write exp $A$. $e = 2.71828\ 18284\ 59045\ 23536\ \cdots \log_{10} e = M = 0.43429\ 44819$ $03251\ 82765\ \cdots \log_e 10 = 1/M = 2.30258\ 50929\ 94045\ 68402$. In some engineering work, where $e$ is used otherwise, the base of natural logarithms is designated by $\epsilon$. 2. eccentricity of a conic. 3. $e_1 = \wp(\omega_1)$, $e_2 = \wp(\omega_2)$, $e_3 = \wp(\omega_3)$, for Weierstrassian elliptic functions. 4. (in mathematical astronomy) eccentricity of earth's orbit. 5. (in elementary solid geometry) length of lateral edge (of right pyramid, prism, etc.).

erf—error function, $\operatorname{erf}(x) = (\sqrt{2/\pi})\int_x^\infty e^{-\frac{1}{2}t^2}dt$.

exp—exponential function of, as in $\exp(a^2 + b^2)$ for $e^{a^2+b^2}$. One could also write this "$e^u$ where $u = a^2 + b^2$."

exsec—exsecant function, exsec $\theta = \sec \theta - 1$.

F—Force.

$F$—1. general symbol for function or functional. 2. the second fundamental differential quantity of first order for surfaces. See $E$. 3. (in Euler's polyhedral formula) number of faces of polyhedron. 4. $F(\varphi, k)$, Legendre's normal elliptic integral of the first kind, $F = \int_0^\varphi d\varphi/\Delta(\varphi)$. See $\Delta$ and $E$. $\varphi$ is here the amplitude of $F$, $\varphi = \operatorname{am} F$. 5. $F(a, b; c: x)$, hypergeometric function. 6. Fahrenheit, degree Fahrenheit, as in 70F.

FS—Fourier series.

Fig.—figure.

Fr—frontier set of.

$f$—1. general symbol for function or functional. 2. $f_i$, frequency of $X_i$ in univariate table. 3. frequency of vibration. 4. feet as in $f/s$, feet per second. Preferable ft/sec.

ft—feet. See also $f$ and $'$.

$G$—1. general symbol for group. 2. the third fundamental differential quantity of first order for surfaces. 3. $G(x_1, \cdots, x_n; \xi_1, \cdots, \xi_n)$ Green's function for two points in $n$-space. 4. (constant) linear group of points on an algebraic curve. See $g$. 5. gravitational constant.

G.C.T.—Greenwich civil time.

GCD—greatest common divisor.

GCS—greatest common subgroup.

GF—Galois field, as in GF$(p^n)$.

GM—geometric mean.

GP—geometric progression.

$g$—1. general function symbol, used with $f$. 2. (terrestrial) gravitational attraction. 3. (variable) linear group of points on an algebraic curve. See $G$. 4. $g_i$, frequency of $y_i$ in bivariate table. 5. general coefficient in tensor, as in $g_{ij}^k x^i y^i z_k$.

gd—Gudermannian. $e^u = \tan\left(\dfrac{\pi}{4} + \dfrac{1}{2}\operatorname{gd} u\right)$.

grad—gradient of. Also written $\nabla$.

**$H$—1.** general symbol for subgroup, as in $G/H$, particularly for normal (or self-conjugate) subgroup. **2.** Hessian, as $H(f) = \det\dfrac{\partial^2 f}{\partial x_i \partial x_j}$. **3.** $H_n(x)$, $n$th Hermite polynomial, $H_n(x)e^{-x^2/2} = (-1)^n D^n e^{-x^2/2}$. **4.** $H(P_1, P_3; P_2, P_4)$ is the proposition that $P_1$ and $P_3$ separate harmonically $P_2$ and $P_4$. **5.** ortho-center of triangle. **6.** $H(q_1, \cdots, q_n, t, p_1, \cdots, p_n)$ Hamiltonian function (in mathematical physics). **7.** mean curvature of surface, $H = EG - F^2$. **8.** (in mathematical astronomy) hour-angle. Also designated by $t$.

HCF—highest common factor.

HM—harmonic mean.

HP—(in elementary algebra) harmonic progression.

Hyp.—hypothesis.

**$h$—1.** (in interpolation theory), distance, between uniformly spaced ordinates. **2.** class interval, in $x$. **3.** increment of $x$. Also $\Delta x$. **4.** (as superscript) hours, as in $8^h 15^m$. **5.** (terminal) hyperbolic, as in $\sinh$, $\tanh^{-1}$, etc. **6.** altitude ("height").

hav—haversine (of). hav $x = (\text{vers } x)/2$.

**$I$—1.** general symbol for interval, and for definite integral. **2.** Roman numeral for "one." Write IV not IIII, IX not VIIII. **3.** $I(\ )$, imaginary part of, also designated by $\mathfrak{F}(\ )$, or Im( ). **4.** $I_n(z)$, the Bessel function "of imaginary argument," $I_n(z) = \sum_{m=0}^{\infty} \dfrac{(\frac{1}{2})z^{n+2m}}{m!\,\Gamma(n+m+1)}$. **5.** (in geometry of triangle) in center. **6.** sometimes used for the identity as an operation in a group.

$\mathfrak{F}$—(Black letter) imaginary part of. See $I$.

Im—imaginary part of. See $I$.

**$i$—1.** running index, as in $a_i$, $i = 1, \cdots, n$. **2.** one of the two imaginary square roots of $-1$. (In electrical engineering, when it is used for the current, $j$ is used for this imaginary unit.)

**$i$—$i$, $j$, $k$,** unit vectors in a right-handed rectangular system. $i \times j = k$, $j \times k = i$, $k \times i = j$.

inf.—("infimum") greatest lower bound.

**$J$—1.** Jacobian as in $J\left(\dfrac{u,v,w}{x,y,z,}\right)$, also designated by $\partial(u,v,w)/\partial(x,y,z)$. **2.** $J_n(z)$, Bessel coefficient of order $n$. **3.** Jacobian curve. **4.** Jacobian group of points in a linear series of groups of points on an algebraic curve.

**$j$—1.** running index, with $i$. **2.** (sometimes in electrical engineering) $\sqrt{(-1)}$. See $i$.

**$j$—**a unit vector. See $i$.

**$K$—1.** specific curvature of surface. **2.** kernel of integral equation, as in $u(x) = f(x) + \lambda \displaystyle\int_a^b \bar{K}(x,t)u(t)dt$. $K_n$, the $n$th iterated kernel is then defined recursively by $K_1 \equiv K$, $K_n(x,y) = \displaystyle\int_a^b K_{n-1}(x,t)K(t,y)dt$. Also designated by $K^{(n)}$. **3.** $K$, $iK'$, periods for Jacobian elliptic functions. **4.** Symmedian (Lemoine) center of triangle. **5.** $K_n(z)$, the Bessel function ("second solution") $\displaystyle\lim_{\nu \to n} \dfrac{(-1)^n}{2}\left[\dfrac{I_{-\nu}(z) - I_\nu(z)}{\nu - n}\right]$

433

# MATHEMATICAL SYMBOLS AND ABBREVIATIONS

*k*—**1.** proportionality factor for variation. Do not use $y \propto x$. **2.** running index, used with $h$. **3.** $k, k'$, modulus and complementary modulus respectively of Jacobian elliptic functions. **4.** class interval, in $y$. **5.** increment in $y$. Also $\Delta y$.

*k*—a unit vector. See $i$.

kei, ker—Bessel functions defined as real for real $z$ and satisfying, $\ker(z) + i \, \mathrm{kei}(z) = K_0(z\sqrt{\ } \pm i)$.

*L*—**1.** general symbol for linear function. **2.** general symbol for linear system, or linear space. **3.** limit, as in $\displaystyle\lim_{n \to \infty} L \; e^{-n} = 0$. See "lim." **4.** Roman numeral for "fifty." **5.** length. Also designated by $l$. **6.** first fundamental differential quantity of second order for surfaces. **7.** Lexis ratio, $\sigma/\sqrt{pq/s}$, for sets of $s$ objects each. **8.** $L_n(x)$, $n$th Laguerre polynomial, $L_n(x)e^{-z}n! = D^n(e^{-x}x^n)$.

LCD—lowest common denominator.

LCM—lowest (or least) common multiple.

*l*—**1.** running index. **2.** (in elementary algebra) last term (of arithmetic or geometric progression). **3.** $l = \cos \alpha$, directional cosine, (with $x$-axis). **4.** length. Also designated by $L$.

lat.—latitude.

li—logarithmic integral or integral logarithm function, $li(x) = \displaystyle\int_0^x du/\log u$.

lim—limit ( ), $\overline{\lim}$, least upper limit, $\underline{\lim}$, greatest lower limit.

ln—(Sometimes) natural logarithm of.

log—logarithm (of). In theoretical work, the natural base, $e$, is understood; in numerical computation with tables, the base 10 is understood unless otherwise specified. Some writers use "ln" for natural logarithm of. Where ambiguity is otherwise likely, indicate the base, thus $\log_b x$, $\log_{10} x$, $\log_e x$.

long—longitude.

*M*—**1.** Roman numeral, thousand. **2.** arithmetic mean. Also designated by superscript bar, as $\bar{X}$, or by AM. **3.** centroid (in geometry of triangle). **4.** second fundamental differential quantity of second order for surfaces.

M.D.—mean deviation.

Md—median.

Mm—mid-mean, arithmetic mean of data in range $Q_1$ to $Q_3$.

Mo—mode.

*m*—**1.** general symbol for natural number, or integer, usually used with $n$. **2.** slope of line, $dy/dx$. **3.** $m = \cos \beta$, directional cosine (with $y$-axis). **4.** $m_a$, $m_b$, $m_c$, median lines, lengths of medians of triangle. **5.** (as subscript) meridian measurement. **6.** class of an algebraic plane curve (a Plücker number). **7.** (superscript) minutes, as in $10^d13^h5^m$. **8.** meters.

max—maximum (of).

meas—measure (of).

mi—miles.

min—**1.** minimum (of). **2.** minutes

mod—**1.** modulus (of), as in $\mathrm{mod}(re^{i\theta}) = r$. **2.** modulo as in $7 \equiv -3 \pmod{5}$.

*N*—**1.** third fundamental differential quantity of second order for surfaces. **2.** north. **3.** total frequency in a statistical distribution.

$n$—**1.** general symbol for natural number or integer. **2.** $n = \cos \gamma$, directional cosine (with $z$-axis). **3.** order or degree of plane algebraic curve (a Plücker number). **4.** (in elementary algebra) number of terms in finite progression. **5.** (sometimes) total frequency. See $N$. **6.** outward normal to surface, as in $\cos (\theta, n)$.

$O$—**1.** origin of coordinates. **2.** circumcenter of triangle. **3.** of comparable order with, as $\Sigma_{n=0}^{N} n = O(N^2)$.

$o$—of inferior order to, as $\log n = o(n)$.

ord—order.

$P$—**1.** general symbol for polynomial, in particular the interpolational polynomial. **2.** product moment. Also expressed by $p$. **3.** general symbol for point. The common notation indicating the coordinate system used as $P(x,y,z)$, $P(r,\theta,\varphi)$, etc., is not recommended. **4.** general probability distribution function, in particular any one of Pearson's standard types, or Poisson's forms. **5.** $P_n(x)$, Legendre polynomial, $2^n n! P_n(x) = D^n(x^2 - 1)^n$. **6.** total force due to pressure. **7.** function, as in $P dx + Q dy$, and in $y' + P(x)y = Q(x)$. **8.** $P_{n,r}$ or $_nP_r$, or $P(n,r)$, number of permutations of $n$ distinct things taken $r$ at a time (without repetitions), $= n!/r!$. **9.** general potential due to finite number of particles. In Newtonian case $P = \Sigma_i m_i / r_i$. See $U$ and $W$. **10.** horizontal parallax. **11.** north celestial pole.

PE—probable error. See $\pm$.

Post.—postulate.

Prob.—**1.** problem. **2.** probability.

Prop.—proposition.

PS—power series.

Pt.—point.

$\wp$—Weierstrassian elliptic function.

$p$—**1.** general symbol for prime number. **2.** semi-latus rectum. **3.** probability ratio. **4.** genus (or deficiency) or plane algebraic curve (a Plücker number). **5.** perpendicular distance from origin to given line or plane.

**6.** $p_n$, numerator of $n$th convergent of continued fraction $a_0 + \dfrac{1}{a_1+} \dfrac{1}{a_2+}$ $\cdots$ $(p_{-1} = 0,\ p_0 = 1)$, $p_1 = a_0$, $p_{n+1} = a_n p_n + p_{n-1}$. **7.** $p_{12}$, $p_{13}$, $p_{14}$, $p_{23}$, $p_{24}$, $p_{34}$, line coordinates (point system). **8.** sometimes "per," as in "$rpm$," revolutions per second. This use is not recommended. **9.** perimeter. **10.** $p(n)$, total number of partitions of $n$. **11.** $p_i$, impulse component.

p.—page.

pos.—positive.

$Q$—**1.** general symbol for quadratic form or quadratic manifold. **2.** $Q_1$, $Q_3$ first and third quartile marks. ($Q_2$ is the median, Md.) **3.** function, as in $P dx + Q dy$, and in $y' + P(x)y = Q(x)$. **4.** $Q(P_1, P_2, P_3; P_4, P_5, P_6)$, quadrangular set of six points.

QD—quartile deviation.

Q.E.D.—("Quod erat demonstrandum") which was to be proved.

Q.E.F.—("Quod erat faciendum") which was to be constructed.

$q$—**1.** complementary probability, $q = 1 - p$. **2.** $q_n$, denominator of $n$th convergent of continued fraction, $a_0 + \dfrac{1}{a_1+} \dfrac{1}{a_2+} \cdots (q_0 = 0)$, $q_1 = 1$,

$q_{n+1} = a_n q_n + q_{n-1}$. . **3.** $q_{12}, q_{13}, q_{14}, q_{23}, q_{24}, q_{34}$, line coordinates (plane system). **4.** $q_1, q_2$, quartile distances from the median. **5.** $q_i$, force component.

$R$—**1.** general symbol for remainder. $R_n(x)$, remainder after $n$ turns in power-series in $x$. **2.** radius, in particular circumradius of triangle. **3.** real part of. Also indicated by $\mathfrak{R}$ (Black letter), and Re. **4.** general symbol for range of variable, as in $\int_{(R)}$.

$\mathfrak{R}$—(Black letter) real value of. See $R$.

R. A.—right ascension. Also designated by $\alpha$.

Re—real value of. See $R$.

RMS—root-mean-square. $\sqrt{(\Sigma_{i=1}^n x^2/n)}$.

$r$—**1.** general running index, as in $r$th term. **2.** radius (see $R$), in particular in radius of triangle. **3.** coefficient of linear correlation, correlation coefficient. **4.** (in elementary algebra) common ratio between successive terms in a geometric progression. **5.** distance, in polar and in spherical coordinates; projected distances in cylindrical coordinates. **6.** (sometimes) revolutions, as in $r.p.m.$ (revolutions per minute). **7.** (sometimes) (superscript) radians, as in $2\pi^{(r)}$. (This usage is not recommended.)

rad—**1.** radius. **2.** radians. Where no units are indicated angles are measured in radians, sin 30 means "sine of 30 radians," not sin 30°. Do not write sin $a^r$ or sin $a^{(r)}$ for sin $a$ (where $a$ is measured in radians), since superscript $r$ is sometimes interpreted as "revolutions."

rot—rotation or curl of vector. Also designated by $\nabla \times$.

$S$—**1.** general symbol for space, as $S_n$, space of $n$ dimension. See $L$. **2.** general symbol for sum, as in $S_n$, sum of first $n$ terms of given sequence or series. See $s$. **3.** south. **4.** standard error of estimate. **5.** radius of spherical curvature of curve.

Si—1st sine-integral function $\mathrm{Si}(x) = \int_0^x (\sin u/u)du$. See si.

S.T.—siderial time.

$s$.—**1.** general running index. Used with $r$. **2.** general symbol for sum, as in $s_n$ sum of first $n$ terms of sequence or series. See $S$. **3.** (in elementary algebra), sum of arithmetic or of geometric progression. **4.** $s_k(n)$, sum of $k$th powers of first $n$ natural numbers. **5.** $s_k$, sum of the $k$th powers of the roots of an algebraic equation. **6.** arc length. **7.** slant height. **8.** (usually as superscript) seconds. **9.** semi-interquartile range. **10.** semi-perimeter of triangle, $s = (a + b + c)/2$. **11.** (sometimes) number of individuals in sample. **12.** root-mean-square deviation about arbitrarily assumed origin, (in "short method").

sec—secant (of).

sec$^{-1}$—inverse secant (of). Also designated by arc sec.

sech—hyperbolic secant (of). Do not use Sec or $\mathfrak{Sec}$ (in German letters).

sech$^{-1}$—inverse hyperbolic secant of. Do not use arc sech.

si—2nd sine-integral function, $\beta_i(x) = \int_\infty^x (\sin u/u)du$. See Si.

sgn—(signum) sign (of), more generally for $z$ complex, sgn $z = z/|z|$

sin—sine (of). Do not use Sin.

sin$^{-1}$—inverse sine (of). Also designated by arc sin.

sinh—hyperbolic sine (of). Do not use Sin, or $\mathfrak{Sin}$ (in German letters).

$\sinh^{-1}$—inverse hyperbolic sine of. Do not use "arc sinh."

sk—skewness of frequency distribution.

sn—(Jacobian elliptic function), sine amplitude.

sq—square.

sup—(supremum) least upper bound. Sometimes designated by L.U.B., or l.u.b.

$T$—1. total time, (as in time of flight of projectile). 2. clock time. 3. general symbol for transformation, $T^n$, $n$th iterate of $T$. 4. tons. 5. (in logic), true or truth. 6. absolute temperature.

Th—theorem.

$t$—1. general variable or parameter. 2. time. See $\tau$. See "dot accent." 3. ordinary temperature. See $T$, $\tau$, $\theta$.

tan—tangent (of).

$\tan^{-1}$—inverse tangent (of). Also designated by arc tan.

tanh—hyperbolic tangent (of). Do not use Tan or $\mathfrak{Tan}$ (in German letters).

$\tanh^{-1}$—inverse hyperbolic tangent (of). Do not use arc tanh.

$U$—general (line surface or volume) potential. In Newtonian case, $U = \int_{(L)} \frac{\mu dL}{r}$ or $\int_{(S)} \frac{\mu dS}{r}$, or $\int_{(V)} \frac{\mu dV}{r}$. See $P$ and $W$.

$u$—1. general variable, especially dependent variable or real part thereof. See $w$. 2. $u_n$, Lucas' function $u_n = (\alpha^n - \beta^n)/(\alpha - \beta)$, $\alpha$, $\beta$, roots of given quadratic.

$V$—1. Roman numeral, five. 2. (in Euler's polyhedral formula) number of vertices. 3. general harmonic function. 4. volume.

$v$—(linear) velocity.

$v$—1. general variable, especial dependent variable, used with $u$, or coefficient of pure imaginary part thereof. See $w$. 2. $v_n$, Lucas' function $\alpha^n + \beta^n$, $\alpha$, $\beta$, roots of given quadratic. See $u_n$. 3. speed.

$W$—1. west. 2. general potential of double layer. In Newtonian case, $W = \int_{(S)} v \frac{\partial}{\partial n}\left(\frac{1}{r}\right) dS, = -\int_{(S)} \frac{v}{r^2} \cos (r,n) \, dS$. See $P$ and $U$. 3. Wronskian,

$$W = \begin{vmatrix} y_1 \; y_1' \; \cdots \; y_1^{(n-1)} \\ \cdots\cdots\cdots\cdots \\ y_n \; y_n' \; \cdots \; y_n^{(n-1)} \end{vmatrix}.$$

4. total weight. Also designated by Wt. 5. work (or energy). Also designated by Wk.

Wt.—weight. See $W$.

$w$—1. general symbol for variable, particularly dependent variable. Used with $u$ and $v$ as in $J\left(\frac{u,v,w}{x,y,z}\right)$, etc. 2. dependent complex variable, $w = u + iv$, or $w(z) = u(x,y) + iv(x,y)$ where $z = x + iy$, $x,y,u,v$, real.

$X$—1. Roman numeral, ten; as in XCIII, etc. 2. $X_i$, original numerical data for $x$-variates, (previous to change of origin or scale). 3. general symbol for variable point, particularly on $x$-axis 4. function, as in $Xdx + Ydy + Zdz$ or $\frac{dx}{X} = \frac{dy}{Y} = \frac{dz}{Z}$.

$x$—**1.** general symbol for independent variable or unknown. **2.** first rectangular coordinate. In space a right-handed coordinate system such as indicated

by $\Big/\!\!\begin{smallmatrix}Z\\O\end{smallmatrix}\!-Y$ or $\Big/\!\!\begin{smallmatrix}Y\\O\end{smallmatrix}\!-X$ is recommended. The former with $OZ$

directed to the zenith is more common. **3.** real part of independent complex variable $z = x + iy$.

$Y$—**1.** $Y_i$, original numerical data for $y$-variates (previous to change of origin or scale). **2.** function as in $X\,dx + Y\,dy + Z\,dz$, or $\dfrac{dx}{X} = \dfrac{dy}{Y} = \dfrac{dz}{Z}$.

$y$—**1.** general symbol for dependent (real) variable. **2.** general symbol for second independent variable, $r$ unknown. **3.** second rectangular coordinate. See $x$. **4.** pure imaginary coefficient, in independent complex variable, $z = x + iy$.

$Z$—zenith.

Z.T.—zone time.

$z$—**1.** independent complex variable, $z = x + iy$. **2.** general symbol for third independent variable or unknown. **3.** third rectangular coordinate. See $x$. **4.** axial coordinate in cylindrical coordinates $(r, \theta, z)$. **5.** zenith distance, $(90^\circ - h)$.

### Selected Symbols Used in Financial and Actuarial Theory

$\alpha$—net premium in first policy year.

$\beta$—net premium in each policy year after the first.

$\delta$—force of interest (and of discount) $e^\delta = 1 + i$.

$\omega$—terminal recorded age in mortality table, "limiting" age.

$A_x$—commutation symbol, present value of net single premium for whole life policy on $(x)$, $= M_x/D_x$.

$a_{\overline{n}|i}$—present value of annuity for unit periodic payment, $= (1 - v^n)/i$.

$a_{\overline{n}|i}^{(p)}$—present value of an annuity of 1 per annum at interest rate $i$, payable $p$ times a year (in installments of $1/p$ each).

$a_x$—commutation symbol, present value of (ordinary) whole life annuity on $(x)$ of unit annual payment.

$a_x^{(m)}$—present value of whole life annuity on $(x)$, of unit annual payment, payable $m$ times a year.

$n|a_x$—present value of whole life annuity, on $(x)$, deferred $n$ years for unit annual payment.

$a_{\overline{x}n|}$—present value of temporary life annuity, on $(x)$, for $n$ years, for unit annual payment.

$a_{\infty i}$—present value of perpetuity at rate of interest, $i$.

$a_{\infty i}$—present value of perpetuity due at rate of interest, $i$.

$a_x$—commutation symbol present value of whole life annuity due, on $(x)$, of unit annual payment.

$a_{\overline{n}|i}$—present value of an annuity due, for unit periodic payments at interest rate $i$.

# MATHEMATICAL SYMBOLS AND ABBREVIATIONS

$B$—book value.

$B_k$—book value, after $k$ years.

$C$—**1.** original cost. **2.** capitalized cost.

$C_x$—commutation symbol, $= v^{x+1}d_x$.

$c_x$—natural premium at age $x$, $= C_x/D_x$.

$D$—total simple discount.

$D_b$—total bank discount.

$D_c$—cash discount, where for example, "terms 4/10, 2/30, n/90" designates $4\%$ discount for payment within 10 days, $2\%$ thereafter but within 30 days, payable net in 90 days.

$D_t$—trade discount.

$D_x$—commutation symbol, $= v^x l_x$.

$d$—rate of simple discount, $= 1 - v = 1 - (1 + i)^{-1} = i/(1 + i)$.

$d_x$—number dying between ages $x$ and $x + 1$, according to mortality table (for 100,000 alive at age 10).

$E$—present value of expectation.

$_nE_x$—present value of an $n$-year pure endowment to $(x)$, $= v^n l_{x+n}/l_x$.

$e_x$—curtate expectation of life for $(x)$, $= (l_x + \cdots + l_\omega)/l_x$.

$\overset{\circ}{e}_x$—complete expectation of life, for $(x)$, $= e_x + \frac{1}{2}$.

$F$—**1.** net-cost-rate factor. **2.** face value of bond.

$I$—total interest (ordinary simple).

$I'$—total interest (exact, simple).

$i$—rate of interest (effective).

$j_{(p)}$—nominal rate of interest convertible $p$ times a year corresponding to effective annual rate $i$, $= p[(1 + i)^{1/p} - 1]$.

$k_x$—valuation symbol, $= C_x/D_{x+1}$.

$_nk_x$—valuation symbol, $= (M_x - M_{x+n})/D_{x+n}$, $[_1k_x = k_x]$, accumulated cost of insurance.

$L$—**1.** list price (for trade discount). **2.** salvage value.

$l_x$—number living at age $x$ according to mortality table (for 100,000 alive at age 10).

$N_x$—("open bar $N$"), commutation symbol, $= D_x + D_{x+1} + \cdots + D\omega$.

$n$—number of conversion periods (for compound interest).

$P$—principal.

$P_b$—bank proceeds.

$P_x$—net annual premium for ordinary whole life policy, on $(x)$, for unit annual payment $= A_x/(1 + a_x)$.

$_rP_x$—net annual premium for $r$-payment life policy, $= M_x/(N_x - N_{x+r})$.

$p$—**1.** probability of success. **2.** interest period/payment interval.

$p_x$—probability of living for another year for a person of age $x$ (according to mortality table).

$_np_x$—probability that a person aged $x$ will live $n$ years, $= l_{x+n}/l_x$.

$p_{xy}$—the probability that $(x)$ and $(y)$ will survive jointly for one year.

$_np_{xy}$—the probability that $(x)$ and $(y)$ will survive jointly for $n$ years.

$q$—probability of failure, $= 1 - p$.

$q_x$—probability of dying within a year for a person of age $x$ (according to mortality table).

$_nq_x$—probability that $(x)$ will die within $n$ years.

# MATHEMATICAL SYMBOLS AND ABBREVIATIONS

$_n|q_x$—the probability that $(x)$ will die between ages $x + n$ and $x + n + 1$.

$R$—**1.** periodic payment or "rent." **2.** replacement cost. **3.** repair charge (annual).

$S$—amount.

$S$—**1.** scrap value. **2.** amount of sinking fund. **3.** subscription price. **4.** amount (at simple interest).

$s$—amount (at compound interest) for unit principal $= (1 + i)^n$.

$s_{\overline{n}|i}$—amount of annuity for unit periodic payment, $= [(1 + i)^n - 1]/i$.

$s_{\infty i}$—amount of perpetuity at interest rate $i$.

$s_{\infty}$—amount of perpetuity due.

$s_{\overline{n}|i}$—amount of an annuity due, for unit periodic payments.

$s_{\overline{n}|i}^{(p)}$—amount at end of $n$ years of annuity of 1 per annum at interest rate $i$, payable $p$ times a year (in installments of $1/p$ each).

$u_x$—valuation symbol, $= D_x/D_{x+1}$.

$_nu_x$—valuation symbol, $(N_x - N_{x+n})/D_{x+n}$, $[_1u_x = u_x]$, accumulated value of individual survivors payments.

$V$—purchase price (of bond).

$_tV_x$—terminal reserve of $t^{th}$ policy year on policy on $(x)$ of unit annual payment.

$v$—present value (at compound interest) for unit principal, $= (1 + i)^{-1}$.

$W$—wearing value, $=$ original cost minus scrap value.

$x$—age of insured (to nearest year).

$(x)$—a person aged $x$ (for use with mortality table).

$x]$—where $[x] + t$ indicates a life, now aged $x + t$, who was accepted for insurance $t$ years ago at age $x$.

1 inch = 2.54 centimeters

1 meter = 39.37 inches

1 pound = 453.6 grams

1 liter = 1.06 quarts

1 kilogram = 2.2 pounds

$M \quad \frac{1000}{1}$
$C \quad \frac{1}{100}$
$D \quad \frac{1}{10}$
$K \quad 1000$

$F = \frac{9}{5}C + 32$

$C = \frac{5}{9}(F-32)$

$D = \frac{M}{U}$

equiv. wt = $\frac{\text{atomic wt.}}{\text{disp. cap. } (v)}$ — formula from valen

440

$\frac{\text{atomic wt.}}{\text{equiv. wt.}}$  atomic wt (approx) = 6.4 spec. heat

$Va =$

Percent Composition   $Al_2(SO_4)_3$

$2 \times 27 = 54$    $\frac{54}{342} \times 100 = 15.8$

$3 \times 32 = 96$    $\frac{96}{342} \times 100 = 28.1$

$12 \times 16 = 192$    $\frac{192}{342} \times 100 = 56.1$

$342$

# INDEX

441

0-2
Cl -1
H +1
K 2
L 8
M 18
N 32
S 2
P 6
d 10
f 14

One gram mole, wt. of any gas at STD occupies 22.4L

Atomic wt. = Equiv. wt × valence

$$DE = \frac{HD \times Abney}{100}$$

$$HD_{(in\ links)} = \frac{DE \times 100}{abney}$$

$$error = \pm \frac{error \times station}{24.00}$$

80 chains = 1 mile

43560 sq. ft. / acre

1 chain = 66' = 100 links

Rod — 16½' = 25 links

4 chain — 1 pole

1 tally — 5 chains — 330 ft

vers = 1 - cos

sin θ = tan θ if θ ≤ 5.7

Elevation Corrections

$$Correction = \frac{Error \times Elapse\ time}{total\ time}$$

log 14.8 = 1.17

log $\sqrt[8]{14.8}$ = 0.1462

$\sqrt[8]{14.8}$ = antilog 0.1462

= 1.4

640 acres = 1 section

160 acres = $\frac{1}{4}$ section

$\frac{4.20}{6.00} \times 5 = 3.5$

Correct elevation = 501.5

$\frac{HD}{55} = \frac{3.5}{4.5}$

= 43 links

Topographic = $\frac{2}{3}$ %

% = $\frac{3}{2}$ topographic

Abney % = $\frac{DE}{HD}$

DE = HD (chains) × Abney

$L = \frac{\text{True length } (99.95)}{\text{Standard length } (100)} \times \text{Measure length}$ (706.5)

Township = 6 × 6 miles

Section = 1 × 1 mile

% = $\frac{DE}{HD} \times 100$

- elevation = 526 ft

26 = abney reading

$\frac{5}{26} = \frac{HD}{100}$

HD = $\frac{522 - 20}{22} = \frac{2}{22} = \frac{1}{11}$ or 9 links

$$\log a \ N^p = p \cdot \log a \ N$$

$$x = \frac{-b \pm \sqrt{b^2 - 4ac}}{2a}$$

if $y = \log a \ N$ then $a^y = N$

$$\log_a N = \frac{\log_b N}{\log_b b}$$